INVENTORY AND MONITORING OF WILDLIFE HABITAT

This report should be cited as:

Cooperrider, A. Y., R. J. Boyd, and H. R. Stuart, eds. 1986. Inventory and monitoring of wildlife habitat. U.S. Dept. Inter., Bur. Land Manage. Service Center. Denver, Co. xviii, 858 pp.

BLM/YA/PT-87/001 + 6600

Lead Editor:
    Janet Poorman
Copy Editor:
    Margaret McGinnis
Contract Editor:
    William Dryer
Section paintings, chapter and cartoon illustrations:
    Peter Doran and Shirley McCulloch
Technical illustrations and cover:
    Peter Doran
Graphs:
    Geri McBeth and Laura Cuplin
Computer graphics:
    Rose Maruska
Chapter paste-ups and chapter illustrations:
    Laura Cuplin
Drawings for Amphibians and Reptiles chapter:
    Lauren Porzer Kepner
Graphics assistance:
    Keith Francis and Herman Weiss
Editorial assistance and word processing:
    Marilyn Chatterton, June Johnson, Geri McBeth, and Margaret Trujillo
Computer assistance:
    Phyllis Elliott and Norma Reitsma

INVENTORY AND MONITORING OF WILDLIFE HABITAT

Compiled and Edited by

Allen Y. Cooperrider, Raymond J. Boyd, and Hanson R. Stuart

Design by

Shirley L. McCulloch

U.S. Department of the Interior   •   Bureau of Land Management   •   September 1986

TABLE OF CONTENTS

PREFACE

This book is intended to guide field biologists and managers in planning, organizing, and administering wildlife inventory and monitoring projects. Although primarily designed for the professional wildlife biologists working for the U.S. Bureau of Land Management, we believe much of the material will interest those working in other agencies and institutions as well.

The book reviews current general procedures and specific techniques. It is not a "cookbook," however, nor an attempt to standardize techniques among biologists. We believe that providing a set of rigid rules for inventorying and monitoring wildlife habitat would be presumptuous since nature itself is complex, diverse, and dynamic. We firmly believe the professional judgment of trained biologists is critical in land management. Their expertise cannot be replaced by modern technology. Although modern technology can make some of their work easier, only the biologist can—

- identify biological problems;
- ensure the correct problem has been identified;
- collect the information needed to address a problem; and
- analyze, interpret, evaluate, and effectively present information to influence management decisions.

Management biologists have demanding, complex, and challenging tasks; few have the luxury of specializing. Each must be knowledgeable of many diverse wildlife groups, other natural resources, and resource conflicts. Management biologists also need good communication skills to effectively deal with concerned citizens, ranchers, miners, administrators, and scientists. This book is therefore intended to help these biologists become more knowledgeable of all facets of wildlife habitat management.

An overriding concern in designing this book was to cover the process of inventory and monitoring in its entirety, i.e., from initial problem identification through presentation of results. We have observed that many biologists do not allocate their time and energy well among the various tasks necessary to complete or conduct an inventory or monitoring project. Good data are often collected to solve problems that are trivial compared to the real priority concerns. Similarly, data are sometimes collected at great expense but are not analyzed, or the

sampling design is so poor that the data cannot be used. Another common problem is that good data are collected and analyzed, but the results are never effectively communicated to the public and the decisionmakers. Therefore, the entire process of conducting an inventory or monitoring a project is presented. Data collection and analysis are obviously important and central tasks of such projects, but they tend to be tasks that biologists perform well. Other aspects such as design, planning, and communication, are included to help biologists improve their skills in these areas.

The book is modular; chapters can be read either alone or in combination for general guidance or as a reference source. As a reference source, a chapter may contain a detailed description of a technique or refer the reader to another source containing a description. This depends on the amount of work available on the subject, the detail involved, and the availability of good descriptions in readily accessible publications. For instance, field techniques for lizard inventory are described in detail since few good references are available on the subject. However, a subject such as mark-recapture methods, to which biostatisticians have devoted whole careers and about which numerous books have been written, has brief coverage supplemented by relevant references.

The book is divided into six major sections. Section I covers general procedures for planning, designing, and organizing wildlife habitat inventory and monitoring programs. These chapters cover such topics as determining objectives; design; use of existing literature; habitat mapping; and choice of areas, measurements, and techniques.

Section II provides guidelines for inventorying and monitoring particular habitats. Each chapter includes classification systems, species groups and habitat features that are particularly important, major impacts on such habitats, particular problems of inventory or monitoring, and habitat analysis systems. The chapters in this section are designed for biologists who are planning inventory or monitoring studies in habitats they have not worked in previously.

Section III provides guidance on inventorying and monitoring habitat for particular animal groups. The coverage of species groups is not organized along taxonomic lines, but rather taxa for which similar techniques are used are lumped together. For each species group, the chapter includes a description of (1) habitat components, e.g., vegetation structure, physical features, that correlate with species in this group and (2) current techniques for population inventories and monitoring.

Section IV describes techniques for measuring habitat variables. These chapters include detailed descriptions of actual measurement techniques and identify advantages and limitations.

Section V covers special monitoring studies. These include methods of food habits determination, climatological studies, and studies of movement and habitat use. Such information is generally used with other habitat or population measurements to determine the cause of observed changes.

The final section, Section VI, covers techniques and procedures for analysis, evaluation, interpretation, and presentation of data and results.

To try to obtain a publication that is as readable and accessible as possible, we have at times edited or rewritten chapter material. In some cases, in the interest of time, we have not been able to return materials to authors for review. We have made every effort not to alter meaning or emphasis; nevertheless some errors may have occurred. For these we apologize to authors and readers and hope that such cases are few.

ACKNOWLEDGMENTS

A work such as this could not be completed without the assistance and support of many individuals too numerous to mention. In addition to the staff members listed and the authors themselves, other reviewers have contributed substantially to the publication. We sincerely appreciate their efforts to help make the publication more complete, accurate, and readable. They are listed separately in the following section.

Certain other individuals deserve particular recognition. Mayo Call, formerly of the U.S. Bureau of Land Management (BLM), originally recognized the need for such a publication and, before he retired, convinced BLM management to support this effort. The editors left with the task have alternately cursed and thanked him for this effort. In the long run, he deserves the credit for the idea, but in the short run, we have often wished that he was here to share the frustrations.

John Crawford, Chief of Wildlife for the BLM from 1974 to 1985, was largely responsible for providing the moral and financial support for this effort. During his tenure as Chief of Wildlife, the BLM wildlife program developed from infancy to a substantial force in multiple-use management. John's commitment and effort was largely responsible for this development. He recognized the need for sound inventory and monitoring of wildlife habitat on public lands and for providing technical support to field biologists through publications of this sort.

The original format for the publication was designed with the assistance of Paul Cuplin, Kniffy Hamilton, Bruce Jones, Richard Kerr, and Chris Maser.

The continued support of members of the BLM wildlife staff in Washington, David Almand, Nancy Green, Kniffy Hamilton, Alan Kesterke, Neal Middlebrook, and William Radtkey, is greatly appreciated. The ongoing support of members of the Denver Service Center—Directors Delmar Vail, Neil Morck, and Robert Moore, and Chief of the Office of Technology Transfer, Mary Gaylord—is appreciated. The senior editors (Cooperrider and Boyd) would like to express particular appreciation to their supervisors, John Baker and Allan Strobel, for their consistent support and encouragement throughout the entire project, and also extend a special thank you to Robert Ader, who delayed several major projects so some of his staff could help with this book.

Faye Leonard assisted with the contracting efforts competently and cheerfully. Carl Anderson provided much assistance with the typesetting and printing. His knowledge of the technical aspects of printing was invaluable and is much appreciated.

Finally, the editors gratefully acknowledge the assistance and contributions of the staff of the BLM library, particularly Sandra Bowers, Teresa Day, and Judy Moisey.

All scientific and common names of animals and plants used in this publication were verified according to the following authorities:

Plants—Checklist of North American Plants for Wildlife Biologists. Prepared by T.G. Scott and C.H. Wasser. 1980. The Wildlife Society, Washington, DC.

Macroinvertebrates—Fresh-water Invertebrates of the United States. Prepared by R.W. Pennak. 1953. The Ronald Press Company, New York, NY.

Fish—A List of Common and Scientific Names of Fishes from the United States and Canada. Prepared by C.R. Robbins, R.M. Bailey, C.E. Bond, J.R. Brooker, E.A. Lachner, R.N. Lea, and W.B. Scott. Special Publication 12, 4th edition. 1980. American Fisheries Society, Bethesda, MD.

Amphibians and Reptiles—Standard Common and Current Scientific Names for North American Amphibians and Reptiles. Prepared by J.T. Collins, R. Conant, J.E. Huheey, J.L. Knight, E.M. Rundquist, and H.M. Smith. Herpetological Circular 12, 2nd edition. 1982. Society for the Study of Amphibians and Reptiles, Ohio University, Athens.

Birds—Checklist of North American Birds. Prepared by The Committee on Classification and Nomenclature of the American Ornithologists' Union. 6th edition. 1983. Allen Press, Inc., Lawrence, KS.

Mammals—Revised Checklist of North American Mammals North of Mexico. 1982. Prepared by J.K. Jones, Jr., D.C. Carter, H.H. Genoways, R.S. Hoffman, and D.W. Rice. Occasional Papers, the Museum, Texas Tech University. 80. Texas Tech Press, Lubbock.

Unless otherwise credited, all photographs were obtained from BLM photo libraries.

REVIEWERS

The accuracy, thoroughness, and readability of the entire book has been enhanced greatly by the following reviewers who have read and critiqued one or more chapters. Their assistance is greatly appreciated.

Bruce B. Ackerman
Idaho Cooperative Wildlife Research Unit
University of Idaho
Moscow, ID 83843

Layne Adams, Wildlife Biologist
U.S. Bureau of Land Management
Fairbanks District Office
Fairbanks, AK 99797

William F. Andelt, Wildlife Extension Agent
Kansas State University
Cooperative Extension Service
Garden City, KS 67846

Stanley Anderson, Wildlife Biologist
U.S. Fish and Wildlife Service
Wyoming Cooperative Fish and Wildlife Research Unit
Laramie, WY 82071

Gary N. Back, Research Associate
University of Nevada—Reno
Range, Wildlife, and Forestry
Reno, NV 89512

James A. Bailey, Professor of Wildlife Biology
Colorado State University
Department of Fishery and Wildlife Biology
Fort Collins, CO 80523

Robert G. Bailey, Geographer
U.S. Forest Service
Land Management Planning Systems
Fort Collins, CO 80524

Gary Bateman
Northern Arizona University
Department of Biological Sciences
Flagstaff, AZ 86011

Fred T. Batson, Natural Resource Specialist
U.S. Bureau of Land Management
Service Center
Denver, CO 80225-0047

Richard G. Beidleman, Professor of Biology
The Colorado College
Department of Biology
Colorado Springs, CO 80903

John Bosworth, Environmental Coordinator
U.S. Bureau of Land Management
Susanville District Office
Susanville, CA 96130-3730

Sandra L. Bowers, Librarian
U.S. Bureau of Land Management
Service Center Library
Denver, CO 80225-0047

R. Bruce Bury, Zoologist
U.S. Fish and Wildlife Service
Denver Wildlife Research Center
Fort Collins, CO 80524

Jack Chugg, Soil Scientist
U.S. Bureau of Land Management
Washington Office Range Staff
Washington, DC 20240

Lewis M. Cowardin, Wildlife Biologist
U.S. Fish and Wildlife Service
Northern Prairie Wildlife Research Center
Jamestown, ND 58401

Paul E. Cuplin, Fishery Biologist
U.S. Bureau of Land Management
Service Center
Denver, CO 80225-0047

Robert K. Davis, Wildlife Economist
U.S. Bureau of Land Management
Washington Office Wildlife Staff
Washington, DC 20006

Russell Davis
The University of Arizona
Department of Ecology and Evolutionary Biology
Tucson, AZ 85721

Stephen Destefano
Idaho Cooperative Wildlife Research Unit
University of Idaho
Moscow, ID 83843

Richard W. Dierking, Soil Scientist
U.S. Soil Conservation Service
West National Technical Center
Portland, OR 97209

Mark A. Dimmitt, Curator of Plants
The Arizona-Sonora Desert Museum
Tucson, AZ 85704

R. Michael Erwin, Wildlife Biologist
U.S. Fish and Wildlife Service
Patuxent Wildlife Research Center
Laurel, MD 20811

Claire Farrell
Southern Oregon State College
Department of Biology
Ashland, OR 97520

Stephen A. Flickinger, Professor of Fishery Biology
Colorado State University
Department of Fishery and Wildlife Biology
Fort Collins, CO 80523

Michael Garratt, Statistician
U.S. Bureau of Land Management
Service Center
Denver, CO 80225

Kenneth M. Giesen, Wildlife Researcher
Colorado Division of Wildlife
Wildlife Research Center
Fort Collins, CO 80526

Nancy F. Green, Wildlife Biologist
U.S. Bureau of Land Management
Washington Office Wildlife Staff
Washington, DC 20006

Carole K. Hamilton, Wildlife Biologist
U.S. Bureau of Land Management
Washington Office Wildlife Staff
Washington, DC 20006

John Haugh, Vertebrate Ecologist
U.S. Bureau of Land Management
Washington Office Resource Sciences Staff
Washington, DC 20006

Steve Hawks, Wildlife Biologist
U.S. Bureau of Land Management
Susanville District Office
Susanville, CA 96130-3730

Dale Hein, Professor of Wildlife Biology
Colorado State University
Department of Fishery and Wildlife Biology
Fort Collins, CO 80523

Marian Hershcopf, Librarian
Colorado Division of Wildlife
Research Center Library
Fort Collins, CO 80526

Dale Hoffman, Limnologist
U.S. Fish and Wildlife Service
Region 6
Denver, CO 80525

Rick Hoffman, Wildlife Researcher
Colorado Division of Wildlife
Wildlife Research Center
Fort Collins, CO 80526

Jon K. Hooper, Coordinator, Parks and Natural Resources
  Management Option
California State University, Chico
Department of Recreation and Parks Management
Chico, CA 95929-0560

Marshall A. Howe, Section Leader, Migratory Nongame
  Birds
U.S. Fish and Wildlife Service
Patuxent Wildlife Research Center
Laurel, MD 20811

Jack D. Jones, Wildlife Biologist
U.S. Bureau of Land Management
Butte District Office
Butte, MT 59702-3388

K. Bruce Jones, Wildlife Biologist
U.S. Bureau of Land Management
Phoenix Training Center
Phoenix, AZ 85016

William Kepner, Fishery Biologist
U.S. Bureau of Land Management
Phoenix District Office
Phoenix, AZ 85017

William L. Kirk, Habitat Specialist
U.S. Fish and Wildlife Service
Anchorage, AK 99503

James F. LaBounty, Fishery Biologist
U.S. Bureau of Reclamation
Denver, CO 80225

Joe Lint, Wildlife Biologist
U.S. Bureau of Land Management
Roseburg District Office
Roseburg, OR 97470

C.D. Littlefield
Malheur Field Station
Princeton, OR 97721

Larry S. Mangan, Wildlife Biologist
U.S. Bureau of Land Management
Shoshone District Office
Shoshone, ID 83352

Chris Maser, Research Wildlife Biologist
U.S. Bureau of Land Management
Corvallis, OR 97331

Ken McGinty, Technical Editor
U.S. Bureau of Land Management
Service Center
Denver, CO 80225-0047

Gary McVicker, Natural Resource Specialist
U.S. Bureau of Land Management
Washington Office Renewable Resources Staff
Washington, DC 20240

Brian A. Millsap, Raptor Biologist
National Wildlife Federation
Raptor Information Center
Washington, DC 20036

Sam Montgomery, Wildlife Biologist
U.S. Bureau of Land Management
Colorado State Office
Denver, CO 80205

James A. Mosher, Consultant
Savage River Consulting
Frostburg, MD 21532

Lewis Nelson, Jr., Professor
University of Idaho
College of Forestry, Wildlife, and Range Sciences
Moscow, ID 83843

Nick Nydegger, Wildlife Biologist
U.S. Bureau of Land Management
Boise District Office
Boise, ID 83705

Richard R. Olendorff, Wildlife Biologist
U.S. Bureau of Land Management
California State Office
Sacramento, CA 85825

Lewis W. Oring, Professor
The University of North Dakota
Department of Biology
Grand Forks, ND 58202

Ed Parsons, Natural Resource Specialist
U.S. Bureau of Land Management
Washington Office Range Staff
Washington, DC 20006

Howard Quigley
Idaho Cooperative Wildlife Research Unit
University of Idaho
Moscow, ID 83843

William Radtkey, Wildlife Biologist
U.S. Bureau of Land Management
Washington Office Wildlife Staff
Washington, DC 20006

Harry V. Reynolds, Game Biologist
Alaska Department of Fish and Game
Division of Game
Fairbanks, AK 99701

Richard T. Reynolds, Research Wildlife Biologist
U.S. Forest Service
Rocky Mountain Forest and Range Experiment Station
Fort Collins, CO 80526-2098

Chandler S. Robbins, Research Biologist
U.S. Fish and Wildlife Service
Patuxent Wildlife Research Center
Laurel, MD 20708

John T. Rotenberry, Assistant Professor
Bowling Green State University
Department of Biological Sciences
Bowling Green, OH 43403

Robert Roudabush, Soil Scientist
U.S. Bureau of Land Management
Arizona State Office
Phoenix, AZ 85011

Hal Salwasser, National Wildlife Ecologist
U.S. Forest Service

Wildlife and Fish Ecology Unit
Fort Collins, CO 80524

Henry L. Short, Terrestrial Ecologist
U.S. Fish and Wildlife Service
Western Energy and Land Use Team
Fort Collins, CO 80526-2899

Ronnie Sidner
The University of Arizona
Department of Ecology and Evolutionary Biology
Tucson, AZ 85721

Karen Steenhof, Wildlife Biologist
U.S. Bureau of Land Management
Boise District Office
Boise, ID 83705

George A. Swanson, Wildlife Biologist
U.S. Fish and Wildlife Service
Northern Prairie Wildlife Research Center
Jamestown, ND 58401

Charlene Swibas, Technical Information Specialist
U.S. Environmental Protection Agency
National Enforcement Investigations Center
Denver, CO 80225

Michael Tewes
Idaho Cooperative Wildlife Research Unit
University of Idaho
Moscow, ID 83843

S.P. Thompson
U.S. Fish and Wildlife Service
Stillwater Habitat Management Area
Fallon, NV 89406

Roy E. Tomlinson, Southwest Dove Coordinator
U.S. Fish and Wildlife Service
Office of Migratory Bird Management
Albuquerque, NM 87103

Jared Verner, Research Ecologist
U.S. Forest Service
Forestry Sciences Laboratory
Fresno, CA 93710

Lee F. Werth, Natural Resource Specialist
U.S. Bureau of Land Management
Service Center
Denver, CO 80225-0047

U.W. Wilson
U.S. Fish and Wildlife Service
Olympia, WA 98504

Jerry O. Wolff, Assistant Professor of Biology
University of Virginia
Department of Biology
Charlottesville VA 22901

Leonard S. Young, Wildlife Biologist
U.S. Bureau of Land Management
Boise District Office
Boise, ID 83705

INTRODUCTION

Inventory and monitoring of wildlife and wild-life habitat is often considered mundane and uninteresting work, yet many great discoveries in both general biology and more specifically wildlife biology were made while biologists and naturalists performed these "mundane" tasks. Charles Darwin and Alfred Wallace were both conducting "inventories" when they developed their concepts of evolution and natural selection. In more recent times, members of the U.S. Biological Survey, the forerunner of the U.S. Fish and Wildlife Service, inventoried wildlife and wildlife habitat of western North America, contributing significantly to our understanding of the ecology and zoogeography of these regions. Although much of their work involved collecting and documenting evidence of fauna in various regions, their contributions went far beyond merely listing the animals present.

Consider the contributions of C. Hart Merriam (**Merriam's Life Zones**), Olaus Murie (**The Elk of North America** and **Alaska-Yukon Caribou**), or Aldo Leopold, who developed many revolutionary ideas about such subjects as predation and wildlife habitat management while performing duties as a forester for the U.S. Forest Service in the Southwest and later directing game surveys in the Midwest. One can, of course, argue that these men were doing work more akin to research, particularly later in their careers. This may be partly true, but the distinction between research and the activities of inventory and monitoring can be nebulous. In any case, the skills required for successfully conducting an inventory or monitoring study are similar to those needed for successful research. Both require an ability to systematically make and record observations, conceptually and quantitatively synthesize large amounts of data, and effectively communicate, both verbally and in writing.

Inventory and monitoring of wildlife habitat is a statutory responsibility of many land management agencies including the U.S. Bureau of Land Management and the U.S. Forest Service.

Inventory and monitoring of wildlife habitat is based on the assumption that measurements of a set of habitat attributes can be used to predict presence or abundance of wildlife species. The same relationship between habitat variables and wildlife populations is used for both habitat inventory and monitoring. This relationship has long been recognized by naturalists and is the basis of several recent habitat evaluation systems. Habitat variables may consist of vegetative structure, plant species composition, presence of physical features, or other factors. Predictions resulting from such measurements need to be verified by observing presence or measuring relative abundance of the wildlife species of interest. In some cases these measurements need to be taken concurrently to determine the most relevant habitat variables. Thus species or population measurements are a necessary part of development and use of any system for inventory and monitoring of wildlife habitat.

Wildlife habitat inventory consists of measuring selected habitat variables on a piece of land to infer presence or abundance of wildlife species. The purpose is to determine the wildlife resources currently supported by the area.

Wildlife habitat monitoring consists of repeatedly measuring habitat or population variables to infer changes in the capability of the land to support wildlife. The purpose is usually issue-oriented, i.e., it determines how some activity such as mining, livestock grazing, or recreational activity is affecting wildlife habitat and ultimately wildlife populations. Monitoring is also used to determine the effectiveness of habitat management practices such as seeding, burning, or water development. Although monitoring is designed to detect changes from human activities, it may also detect changes caused by climatic conditions or other factors not under human control. Therefore, the purpose of monitoring is not only to measure change but also to determine the cause(s) of change. In particular, programs for monitoring wildlife habitat must be designed to separate the effects of human activity from those caused by variations in weather.

Typically, a monitoring program consists of measuring habitat variables that are required by key wildlife species or correlate with presence or abundance of key wildlife species. For example, the number of pileated woodpeckers highly correlates with the number of suitable nesting snags. A reduction in the number of such snags can thus be assumed to cause a reduction in the number of breeding woodpeckers.

Habitat monitoring, like inventory, may be accompanied by population measurements to confirm the habitat relationships. If the purpose is to measure the effectiveness of a habitat management practice, then species or population measurements must be taken. For example, if water is being developed to improve habitat for Gambel's quail, then monitoring should be designed to measure changes in the number of quail, not changes in the number of "guzzlers."

Over 50 years ago, Aldo Leopold, in a chapter on "Game Range" in his classic volume on **Game Management** wrote:

"What is Game Range? When the game manager asks himself whether a given piece of land is suitable for a given species of game, he must realize that he is asking no simple question, but rather he is facing one of the great enigmas of animate nature. An answer good enough for practical purposes is usually easy to get by the simple process of noting whether the species is there and ready, or whether it occurs on 'similar' range nearby. But let him not be cocksure about what is 'similar,' for this involves the deeper question of why a species occurs in one place and not in another, which is probably the same as why it persists at all. No living man can answer that question fully in even one single instance."

When Leopold referred to a biologist determining "similar" ranges, he introduced the concept of a "habitat model" and described the reasons monitoring is necessary.

Habitat models can of course be of many types. Hunters often use conceptual models for determining, for example, high density autumn pheasant habitat when passing some fields and hunting in others. Hunter perceptions of good habitat may be accurate even though they are unable to describe specific qualities when choosing sites. After a day in the field, a hunter may reflect on the day afield and suggest that "millet fields adjacent to uncultivated swales and breaks are the best places to hunt." This is a verbal model. A biologist may go further and describe optimum habitat as "grain fields of 40 acres or more within ½ mile of water and within ¼ mile of uncultivated areas, having brushy cover at least 4 feet high." This is a quantitative model which can be systematically tested and evaluated.

Two points deserve noting about habitat models and their use by biologists and others. First, we all use models in our everyday life, including habitat models. Many are good, although based only on "professional judgment," i.e., conceptual models. Second, with the controversy surrounding many current biological assessments, biologists are being asked, encouraged, or even required to make their models more explicit by various parties, interest groups, publics, and agencies involved with or affected by project decisions. Explicit and quantitative models not only provide a mechanism for improving predictions, but also provide an important communication tool by taking some of the mystery out of "professional judgment."

But models have their limits. Models are approximations at best. As Aldo Leopold suggested, no living person can develop a "perfect" habitat model. However, monitoring can allow us to test and refine our models in addition to minimizing the risk of resource damage from poor predictions. We can thus have a cycle of prediction, decision, action, and monitoring.

This approach to natural resource problems has received a lot of attention in the last 10 years and has been variously described as adaptive environmental assessment, cyclic-incrementalism, "muddling through," or even "common-sense management," as discussed in several chapters in this book. It seems to be a logical and common-sense approach to solving a wide variety of natural resource problems. With such an approach, the separate but interrelated tasks of problem identification, data collection, prediction, decision, and monitoring can also be linked in a cyclical process. This process can result in better management of wildlife resources and also development of better tools (models) for understanding wildlife habitat relationships. Although many of the following chapters describe isolated parts of this process, they should be viewed in context, not as ends in themselves, but as necessary steps in a continuing process toward better management of our natural resources.

Allen Y. Cooperrider

I PLANNING

1

THE INVENTORY AND MONITORING PROCESS

K. Bruce Jones[1]

U.S. Bureau of Land Management
Phoenix Training Center
Phoenix, AZ 85015

"The amount of time spent in solving a problem is inversely proportional to the amount of time spent in characterizing the problem."

— Alan Speigel, *Speigel's Laws of Management*

"Planning without action is futile. Action without planning is fatal."

— K. Hamilton and E.P. Bergersen, *Methods to Estimate Aquatic Habitat Variables*

Editor's Note: This chapter provides an overview of the entire inventory and monitoring process, with emphasis on the planning stage. Biologists in their hurry to get to the field to gather the all-important data often neglect to spend the necessary time in planning their work. They may also neglect to allow time for the necessary follow-up procedures, such as data analysis. Such actions result in much wasted time and money. This chapter not only provides an overview of the entire process, but also directs the reader to other sections and chapters in the book that cover specific topics in more depth.

INTRODUCTION

The most critical stage of implementing and completing an inventory or monitoring study is not data collection, presentation, or interpretation, but rather design. Years of data can be useless if a study is poorly designed. This chapter outlines a procedure for any inventory or monitoring project. By following these steps, biologists will establish a flexible, systematic, and logical approach toward solving wildlife habitat management problems. Use of this procedure should also increase the effectiveness of inventory and monitoring studies, reduce costs, and decrease failures caused by poor design or implementation. The process will also lead to improved interpretation and presentation of results. By focusing inventories and monitoring studies on specific issues, wildlife resources should receive greater consideration in the decisionmaking process and realize greater benefits. Therefore, issue-driven inventories and studies, such as resolving conflicting land-use opportunities, are emphasized.

The inventory and monitoring process consists of a series of events:

(1) Problem definition (scoping)—

- identifying issues, concerns, or opportunities;
- reducing general problems to specific ones;
- predicting and analyzing extent of potential problems;
- identifying specific inventory and monitoring study objectives;
- prioritizing objectives; and
- deciding types and levels of data needed.

[1]Current address: Office of Endangered Species, U.S. Fish and Wildlife Service, Washington, DC. 20240.

(2) Data collection (inventory, studies);

(3) Data analysis, interpretation, evaluation, presentation, and storage;

(4) Management decision;

(5) Monitoring studies; and

(6) Management review.

Although the stages may be called different names in different organizations, this approach to problem solving is quite basic. This chapter covers this process with emphasis on steps 1, 2, 3, and 5 which are major concerns of staff biologists and specialists.

PROBLEM DEFINITION (SCOPING)

Problem definition, often termed scoping, determines the detail of inventory or monitoring studies and is critical in conducting these efforts successfully. It is the process of determining specific problems and issues that need to be addressed, data needed to address these issues, and priority issues and data needs. It consists of six sequential steps as listed in the Introduction and described here.

Identifying Issues, Concerns, or Opportunities

Wildlife- and habitat-related problems originate from the following six general sources:

(1) Need for baseline data for land-use planning;

(2) Proposals from wildlife biologists;

(3) Management proposals from persons outside the wildlife resource;

(4) Major land-use planning guidance;

(5) Ongoing impacts from resource development, originating within the agency; and

(6) Ongoing impacts from resource development, originating outside the agency.

Baseline data for land-use planning are the basic driving force of wildlife inventories because they show conditions as they currently exist. Baseline data are useful in determining potential impacts and in comparing actual impacts after development.

Proposals from wildlife biologists to improve habitat for one species may also produce potential problems for other species. Consider, for example, a habitat management plan that proposes to convert pinyon-juniper (*Pinus-Juniperus* sp.) and chaparral habitats into grassland for enhancing pronghorn (*Antilocapra americana*) populations. Although this proposal would benefit pronghorn, it would also decrease habitat available to raptors, upland game, and nongame species.

Proposals by managers outside the wildlife resource could cause many potential impacts. These impacts are identified by biologists, other resource specialists, and managers. For example, a biologist identifies a general problem between a mining plan and wildlife habitat; a proposed open-pit mineral operation would greatly reduce the amount and quality of wildlife habitat in the area.

Some of the more general, broad-scale problems that require inventories and monitoring studies are identified through land-use planning. For example, an areawide grazing proposal, if implemented, could negatively affect several million acres of wildlife habitat. This type of problem could be identified by a wide variety of resource specialists within an agency during the scoping process. Ongoing impacts or problems warranting inventories and monitoring can also be identified by resource specialists inside an agency (e.g., range conservationists) or outside. For example, biologists within an agency could identify that current livestock grazing practices are reducing the quality and quantity of forage available to big game. Similarly, these kinds of problems can be identified by sources outside an agency, including other federal agencies, state game and fish departments, private wildlife organizations (e.g., The Wildlife Society), and local citizens.

Reducing General Problems to Specific Ones

After general issues have been identified, the next step is to break down general problems (as previously discussed) into specific ones. For example, a biologist finds a correlation between reduced wildlife habitat and habitat quality and increased livestock grazing. The next step is to identify, more specifically, factors that might account for relationships between grazing pressure and loss of wildlife habitat and quality. In this example, the agency biologist might identify three specific problems:

(1) Increased stocking of livestock may reduce the amount and number of perennial plant species.

(2) Long-term overstocking of livestock may reduce the quality of the "A horizon" in the soil, resulting in large-scale erosion and a drop in vegetation productivity.

Perennial plant species may be reduced by increased livestock grazing.

(3) Overstocking and poor livestock distribution may eliminate cover around waterfowl nesting ponds.

Sections II and III of this book can provide assistance in identifying habitat and species problems. For example, a new biologist initiating an inventory in a grassland area with known populations of prairie chickens (*Tympanuchus cupido*) may wish to consult Chapter 6, Rangelands, and Chapter 20, Upland Game Birds, for guidance on habitat and featured species.

In identifying specific problems from general ones, biologists should seek expertise from other resource specialists. In the example given above, the soil scientist or soil conservationist plays a major role in making general problems specific. In this example, range conservationists, hydrologists, and surface protection specialists would also play major roles in identifying specific problems.

Predicting and Analyzing Extent of Potential Problems

After specific problems have been identified, the biologist should attempt to make some preliminary predictions as to the extent of these specific problems. General predictions can be formulated from a large variety of information sources:

(1) Existing agency data (e.g., range survey files);

(2) Agency expertise in resources other than wildlife (e.g., soil sciences);

(3) Review of literature containing data and results on similar problems (e.g., manuscripts

on impacts to wetland vegetation from livestock grazing);

(4) Public input (e.g., observations of citizens familiar with the problem and area);

(5) Interest group input (e.g., local wildlife advocacy groups familiar with the area and/or problem);

(6) Experts on the habitat or species in question.

The biologist should make sure he or she has gathered available information before collecting additional data. Chapter 3, Literature Review, provides guidance on searching existing data sources. In addition to sources listed above, some recently described procedures may allow biologists to predict specific problems that could exist between resources and the extent. Thomas (1979) developed life-form tables that group species according to components of habitat used for feeding and breeding. Similarly, Short (1982) developed a procedure that groups species into guilds based on habitat layers used for feeding and breeding. Both procedures allow biologists to use varying degrees of existing information to assess the complexity of wildlife species arranged in habitat space. Biologists can then predict the extent of impacts to potential species that would occur if certain habitat components were lost. Although these procedures neither predict species occurrence in an area nor generate species-specific data, they do provide an excellent preliminary analysis of potential impacts to most wildlife species within a given area.

The U.S. Fish and Wildlife Service and U.S. Forest Service have developed models that can be used for analyzing potential impacts to wildlife. Generally, these models provide an index of habitat quality for various vertebrates. By knowing the amount and quality of habitat that may be affected by a proposed action, the biologist can use these models to determine corresponding impacts on specific vertebrates. The use of these models are discussed in greater detail in Chapter 2, Data Types, and Chapter 38, Habitat Evaluation Systems.

After compiling information from existing data sources and making some preliminary predictions, the biologist will know whether an on-the-ground inventory or study is needed to adequately assess or rectify specific problems. Existing data and preliminary analyses may be enough that a biologist needs only to collect data on one or a few specific problems.

Based on existing data and preliminary predictions, the agency biologist can provide decision-makers with information that may affect a proposed action. The impact of the biologist's recommendations on the proposed action will depend on the adequacy of existing biological data and economical and political factors. Preliminary predictions influence managers to make the following decisions relative to the proposal:

(1) Drop the proposal entirely;

(2) Leave the proposal as is; or

(3) Modify the proposal so adverse impacts are reduced or eliminated.

Providing good information to managers at an early stage can be quite effective in mitigating impacts. Proposals can be dropped or modified before a project has progressed too far in planning.

Modifying a proposed action often involves proposing new alternatives to mitigate predicted adverse impacts. The degree of mitigation will depend on the accuracy of existing data and techniques used to make preliminary predictions. Broad, incomplete wildlife data used to predict impacts of a site-specific proposal would not produce accurate assessments.

Identifying Specific Inventory and Monitoring Study Objectives

At this stage in the process, the agency biologist has identified specific problems, determined the adequacy of existing data, and made some preliminary predictions. The biologist will, therefore, have a list of specific problems requiring on-the-ground data.

To develop a series of procedures and analyses needed to address the identified problems, the biologist should transform each specific problem into specific objectives. For example, a specific problem was identified when the biologist suspected increased livestock grazing was reducing habitat structure. He or she must then ask the following types of questions:

(1) Is livestock grazing reducing habitat structure?

(2) If so—

- Are stocking rates related to reduced habitat structure?

- How much livestock grazing causes losses in habitat structure?

- Which plants are structurally affected by livestock?

These are examples of a few specific questions that can be asked about a specific problem. The questions then should be transformed into specific objectives. For example, determine the plant species that are structurally reduced by livestock. This information can then be used for prioritizing objectives.

Agency biologists must follow this logical procedure in formulating specific objectives, because the effectiveness of the inventory or study will only be as good as the biologist's understanding of the problem(s) and his or her ability to formulate specific objectives that will answer specific questions.

Prioritizing Objectives

Typically, funding and personnel are inadequate to collect on-the-ground data for all identified objectives. Therefore, the agency biologist needs to prioritize. In many instances, agencies have identified priority species and habitat; however, the biologist may need to consider other factors, such as—

- policies, laws, and regulations;

- agency priorities;

- potential degree of impact;

- feasibility (i.e., whether the problem can be logically, biologically, or economically resolved in the time given);

- public interests.

Deciding Types and Levels of Data Needed

Once a decision is made to collect data on priority objectives, the biologist must decide the types and levels of data needed. Chapter 2, Data Types, provides guidance on types and levels of data needed for inventory and monitoring studies.

DATA COLLECTION (INVENTORY, STUDIES)

After all objectives and methods for an inventory or study are determined, the biologist should develop a schedule. This schedule should allot time for—

- hiring or contracting;

- obtaining necessary equipment;

- holding personnel meetings;

- doing preliminary field work;

- selecting specific methods;

- habitat mapping and field sampling; and

- analyzing data and interpreting, evaluating, and presenting results.

Although data analysis, interpretation, evaluation, and presentation are covered separately, any schedule should include enough time for these critical tasks. Some efforts require more than one person, but even a single biologist should follow the same sequence of events when conducting an inventory or monitoring study. Section IV in this book, Habitat Measurements, provides guidance on field data collection methods.

Hiring or Contracting

Competent field personnel are essential in obtaining inventory and monitoring study objectives. The degree of expertise needed will vary greatly, depending on the type of animals and habitats to be sampled. Vegetation and topography can be sampled by a general biologist having a few days of training. Animal population sampling, however, is specialized and usually requires someone with formal education and field experience with the taxa to be sampled. Contracting may be a way of obtaining the expertise needed to conduct a highly specialized inventory or monitoring study. However, contractors generally cost more than in-house personnel.

Whether an inventory or monitoring study is conducted in-house or by contract, a biologist must plan specific hiring needs at least 3 months before starting. The best possible study design and funding level could fail if a hiring or contracting plan was late or poorly organized.

Obtaining Necessary Equipment

The biologist must determine the types of equipment needed to meet inventory or monitoring study objectives. The biologist must order any expensive or hard-to-get equipment at least 3 months before the inventory or monitoring study.

Holding Personnel Meetings

Preliminary meetings of all involved personnel are perhaps the most important and essential part of a successful inventory or monitoring study. At the first meeting, the lead biologist should introduce everyone, assure objectives are clear, and outline agency procedures. The lead biologist should then request the specialists to review existing data and literature pertinent to their respective inventory or monitoring study objectives. For example, a raptor specialist could gather locality records from all museums that have made collections in the study area. He or she should then contact regional and national experts who have worked with the species in question. Literature specific to the species and habitats should also be reviewed. Team members can learn a great deal about the general ecology, habitat requirements, and population dynamics of species through

literature reviews. This knowledge will also aid them in selecting the best sampling methods and analyses for the study.

Doing Preliminary Field Work

While team members are accomplishing all the tasks outlined in the first meeting, a field trip into the study area should be conducted to familiarize all personnel with habitat diversity and size, overall topography, soil types, elevations and, most importantly, access. Maps should be supplied to all personnel before this initial field trip. Biologists should also meet with appropriate supervisors and land users during this period to avoid complications during active sampling.

Selecting Specific Methods

After all literature and museum reviews have been completed, a series of meetings should be conducted to determine the methods that should be used, the time the monitoring study or inventory will begin, and the length of the study. At this point, the team leader should make sure that all team members know funding and schedule limitations and reiterate the objectives. The following are the types of questions that should be addressed during this type of meeting:

(1) What methods will be used for each habitat and animal type?

(2) What sample size will be needed to meet each objective?

(3) Which groups of animals and habitats will be sampled during each season?

(4) What additional equipment is needed (e.g., aircraft or four-wheel drive vehicles)?

(5) Can all habitat data be collected by using one or two methods; will these data be sufficient for all wildlife groups?

(6) Can all wildlife groups be sampled at the same location for all habitat types?

(7) What are the major sampling deficiencies?

(8) Is access to sample sites a problem?

(9) Has everyone contacted the appropriate specialists in other federal and state agencies?

(10) Can other ecological questions be answered without increasing funding or time?

(11) How will the data be analyzed using the chosen sampling methods?

(12) How will the data be interpreted and presented?

(13) How and where will raw data, summary analyses, and interpretations be stored?

(14) How much preliminary sampling is needed?

All of these are extremely important questions that must be answered before an inventory or monitoring study is conducted. Once these questions are answered, the biologist or team leader should write an inventory or monitoring plan covering objectives, methods, data analysis, and storage.

Habitat Mapping and Field Sampling

Habitat Mapping. Following this meeting, a field trip should be conducted to map habitat types and locate sample sites. Sample sites should be randomly located within the area in question. If an inventory or study is conducted by habitat type, the entire sample area should be stratified into subareas. Each subarea would represent a habitat type, and the number of samples in each would be proportional to the amount occupied by that habitat type in the sample area. Subareas may also represent controls and different intensities of land use. For example, a biologist may want to develop a study to determine the effects of fire on vegetation and vertebrate species. The biologist would randomly sample vegetation and wildlife within stratified subgroups such as unburned, burned, and partially burned areas. Chapter 4, Habitat Mapping, provides guidance on this important step.

Field Sampling. Once sample sites are located, the biologist should develop a sampling schedule with deadlines for completing each sample. At this point, preliminary samples should be taken. This allows each biologist to test the methods he or she has selected and to fine-tune, method-specific skills (e.g., bird transects).

During field work, the lead biologist should conduct weekly meetings to identify problems and ensure quality control over the specific, planned objectives.

DATA ANALYSIS, INTERPRETATION, EVALUATION, PRESENTATION, AND STORAGE

Once data have been collected, they need to be analyzed and prepared in a way that provides useful information to a decisionmaker. These tasks are just as important as collecting data; unfortunately, many biologists do not allow or spend enough time on this follow-up. Section VI in this book provides guidance on these efforts.

Data Analysis, Interpretation, and Evaluation

When field work is completed, the team should meet to analyze the data. The type of analyses used should have been decided when specific methods were selected, before the inventory or study.

Once analyzed, the data should be interpreted and evaluated. The opinions of those biologists who conducted the inventory or study should be preserved because the biologists are most familiar with the data and circumstances of collection. Chapter 37, Statistical Analysis, provides guidance on using statistics; Chapter 38, Habitat Evaluation Systems, provides guidance on systems developed especially for evaluating habitat; Chapter 39, Evaluation and Interpretation, provides guidance on the more subjective analysis procedures; and Chapter 40, Economic Analysis, describes how changes in wildlife productivity can be used to predict changes in economic value.

Presentation

A biologist must effectively communicate results to managers and others. For example, detailed statistical analyses and complicated tables and figures should not be used to convey information to managers. These types of data analyses and displays are best suited to a specialized technical audience. Simple, easily accessible tables, figures, and interpretations should be used for more general audiences.

Generally, documents or manuscripts containing inventory or study data and interpretations should be structured in the following format:

(1) **Introduction,** describing the problem and the reasons the biologist conducted the inventory or study;

(2) **Methods Section,** describing procedures used to collect data; and

(3) **Results/Discussion/Summary,** describing results of the inventory or study and an interpretation of those results, followed by a summary of the results and conclusions (one to three sections).

A complete manuscript contains all these components. This is the best way to ensure all elements of the inventory or study are preserved for future considerations, especially the biologist's interpretations of the data. Chapter 41, Written Communications, provides guidance on preparing written material.

In addition to writing a separate manuscript, the biologist may be required to orally present results to managers, the public, and others in briefings, staff meetings, public forums, and other gatherings. Personal communications are often the most effective, and the biologist should not overlook their importance. Chapter 42, Verbal Presentations, provides guidance on oral presentations.

Data Storage

Data stored in files and on computers preserve results of inventories and studies. Computers also allow biologists to continually add information to a file in a standard format and retrieve it easily. This is especially important in monitoring studies where data were collected infrequently or over several years. Chapter 36, Data Management, provides guidance on managing and storing data.

MONITORING STUDIES

After an inventory or study has been conducted and the results presented to a manager, a decision will be made on some action. Such a decision should be based on particular objectives for wildlife and other resources, and on the predicted effects of the chosen wildlife resource alternative. Predicted effects are normally based on limited data; thus, the biologist needs to monitor the wildlife resources to determine if the objectives are being met. This requires additional data collection and may result in changes in management. Hence, monitoring is a cyclic phenomena (Figure 1) in which periodic data collection is followed by re-evaluation of earlier management decisions.

The design and implementation of monitoring studies follow the procedure listed earlier in this chapter. In general, monitoring studies are more site- and problem-specific than inventories. Inventories usually involve determining the species and habitats in an area and, less frequently, habitats used by certain species. The accuracy of wildlife uses of habitats, taken on a one-time basis, is usually low because of limited sample periods. Longer term monitoring studies better estimate fluctuations in wildlife uses of habitat. To determine how certain land-use practices affect wildlife and habitat, the biologist should conduct a long-term monitoring study rather than a one-time inventory. Several inventories should be conducted to better understand the wildlife species and habitats occurring in an area.

Although monitoring may occur independently of an inventory (e.g., bald eagle nesting success related to dewatering of an aquatic habitat), many monitoring studies resulting from land-use plans will be based on inventory results. Therefore, biologists may need to sample after an inventory has been conducted in an area.

Generally, monitoring studies involve collecting wildlife and habitat information over time to determine—

(1) Wildlife use of habitat components (e.g., preferred height of sagebrush for sage grouse nesting);

(2) Effects of certain land uses on certain wildlife and habitats:

- individual wildlife species (e.g., how off-road vehicle [ORV] use affects desert tortoise [*Gopherus agassizi*] density);

- individual plant species (e.g., how intensive livestock grazing affects key mule deer browse);

- individual habitat components (e.g., how a mining operation increases the sediment load in a trout stream);

- portions of the wildlife community (e.g., how a powerline affects migratory raptors);

- entire wildlife communities (e.g., how water impoundment affects vertebrates in a riparian community).

(3) Species or habitat changes caused by certain natural environmental conditions (e.g., effects of flooding on desert fishes);

(4) Accuracy of predictive models (e.g., comparison of white-winged dove [*Zenaida asiatica*] responses to habitat changes with those predicted by a U.S. Fish and Wildlife Service Habitat Suitability Index [HSI] model);

Off-road vehicle use can damage wildlife habitats.

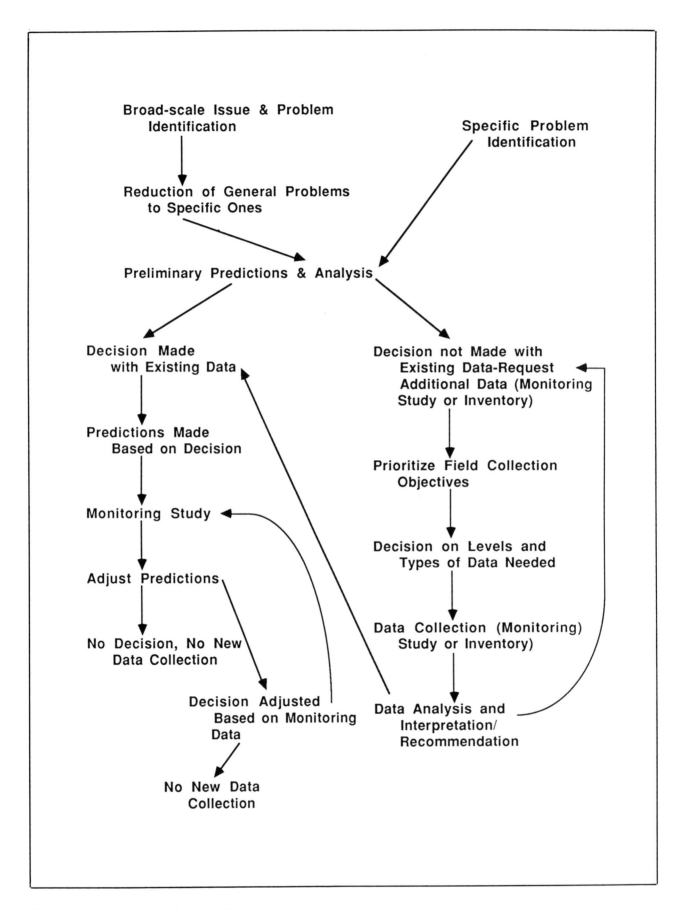

Figure 1. Inventory and monitoring process.

(5) Improving the accuracy of predictive models (e.g., possibly modifying the HSI model for white-winged dove, by using on-the-ground data collection);

(6) Additional mitigation to protect wildlife and habitat in an area (e.g., monitoring data may have indicated a mitigation plan was not protecting nesting habitat for black hawks [*Buteogallus anthracinus*]. From new data, new stipulations may be recommended to protect the raptor's nesting habitat.);

(7) Additional habitat improvement to benefit a species or habitat of concern (e.g., a water development program may not be increasing pronghorn herds in an area as predicted. From the new monitoring data, the plan will probably need to be modified.).

Some of the above objectives related to improving a biologist's predictive ability or the models used. Thus, monitoring can serve dual purposes: (1)

determining whether management objectives are being met and (2) improving a biologist's predictive capabilities. This approach to management and monitoring is variously termed "cyclic-incrementalism" (Bailey 1982), "adaptive-environmental assessment" (Holling 1978), "adaptive-management" (Barrett and Salwasser 1982) or, more simply, "common-sense management" (Barrett and Salwasser 1982) or "muddling through" (Bailey 1982). These approaches are fundamental to monitoring and are discussed in more detail in many chapters throughout this book.

SUMMARY

In summary, biologists are strongly advised to follow the logical thought processes developed in this chapter. Successful inventories and monitoring studies do not come easily. Only through careful planning, precise problem and objective identification, and complete compilation of results, will an inventory or monitoring study be successful.

LITERATURE CITED

BAILEY, J.A. 1982. Implications of "muddling through" for wildlife management. Wildl. Soc. Bull. 10:363-369.

BARRETT, R.H. and H. SALWASSER. 1982. Adaptive management of timber and wildlife habitat using dynast and wildlife-habitat relationship models. Western Assoc. of Fish and Wildl. Agencies, Proc. 62:350-365.

HOLLING, C.S., ed. 1978. Adaptive environmental assessment and management. Vol. 3, International Series on Applied Systems Analysis. John Wiley and Sons, New York, NY. 377pp.

SHORT, H.L. 1982. Techniques for structuring wildlife guilds to evaluate impacts on wildlife communities. U.S. Dep. Inter., Fish and Wildl. Serv., Spec. Rep. 244. 34pp.

THOMAS, J.W., ed. 1979. Wildlife habitats in managed forests—the Blue Mountains of Oregon and Washington. U.S. Dep. Agric., For. Serv. Agric. Handbook 553. 512pp.

2

DATA TYPES

K. Bruce Jones[1]

U.S. Bureau of Land Management
Phoenix Training Center
Phoenix, AZ 85015

Editor's Note: A good, well-planned and organized inventory or monitoring program cannot be based on cookbook methodology. The biologist must use considerable judgment in identifying problems, specifying objectives, setting priorities, and choosing methodology. The choice of data to be collected is critical. Yet the biologist can collect an almost unlimited number of types of data. This chapter provides an overview of data types and appropriate situations for collecting a particular type.

INTRODUCTION

After identifying specific objectives and questions for an inventory or monitoring study, a biologist must decide on the types and levels of data needed. This decision is often a confusing part of the inventory and monitoring process. Many different types of data can be collected to answer specific questions. In addition, the intensity of data collection must be determined. For example, an objective is established to determine the influence of a new water development on an area's pronghorn (*Antilocarpa americana*) population. Do we need to determine the density of pronghorns in the area before and after the development? Do we need a control? Would relative abundance rather than density answer the question? Decisions made on sampling design and data types are extremely important. In the previous example, why spend a great deal of time and money collecting density data when abundance information will suffice? If a control was not used, how will we know if the observed changes in pronghorn abundance result from our habitat improvement?

This chapter discusses different types of data and sampling considerations, and provides some basic guidelines for making decisions on types of data and intensity of data collection to use. It also discusses some procedures that are used to analyze existing data.

SAMPLING CONSIDERATIONS

Throughout this chapter, I highlight some basic data types and sampling intensities. Some basic factors related to sampling design and intensity apply to all types of data collection.

Before a biologist starts collecting data, a decision must be made on sampling intensity. The number of samples required will depend on the variability of animals and habitats to be measured and limitations of sampling techniques used. For

---

[1]Current Address: Office of Endangered Species, U.S. Fish and Wildlife Service, Washington, DC 20240

example, homogeneous habitats require fewer samples because they are less variable. Conversely, heterogeneous habitats require more samples because they are more variable. Sampling techniques and habits of animals also affect sample size. For example, bird transects detect far fewer birds in closed habitats than in open ones. Therefore, to make the probability of detection equal in the two habitats, sample size must be increased. Also, certain bird species are secretive, requiring more intensive sampling to adequately cover such species.

A number of minimum sample size equations have been developed for various vertebrates. Most of these are based on population variability and animal detectability. Seber (1973), Smith et al. (1975), and Gysel and Lyon (1980) provide formulas and discuss how minimum sample size is determined.

Because most inventories and monitoring studies are restricted by funds and personnel, biologists are often confronted with deciding on where to place samples. Generally, samples should be placed randomly within habitats or areas. Cause-and-effect studies require biologists to place samples within preselected areas (stratified sampling). However, biologists should select random sites within these preselected areas, assuring that area-related variability is considered. Random sites can be selected by assigning numbers to grids placed over a map of the area in question. Numbers can be selected from random numbers tables. In monitoring studies where the biologist wants to determine animal or habitat changes before, during, and after a specific land use (e.g., prescribed burn), controls should be established. Without control, there is no way to determine whether specific land use has affected habitat structure. For example, improvements in vegetation structure on an allotment with a three-pasture, rest-rotation system may result from higher-than-normal precipitation over the past 5 years rather than from the system. In this example, control samples taken outside the grazing system but where similar physical conditions (vegetation, soils, to name two) exist would allow the biologist to account for other possible causes of observed vegetation structure changes.

In cases where money and access restrict sampling, biologists may have to cluster samples rather than spread them over the entire habitat. This will reduce the probability that habitat variability was adequately sampled. For example, a biologist wants to compare vegetation structure between pinyon-juniper (*Pinus-Juniperus* sp.) and chaparral, but is limited to two samples in each habitat type and one habitat is five times larger than the other. Because habitat size is not considered in allocating samples, the biologist may not be able to determine which habitat has greater vegetation structure, even if the data suggest large differences. If samples of habitat and animal variables are taken from the same site,

then the biologist can determine relationships between animals and their habitats.

The types and numbers of animals and habitat characteristics sampled directly depend on objectives established for an inventory or study. This will determine the complexity and intensity of sampling. Intensity can range from simple verification of one animal in one habitat to large-scale vertebrate samples taken in many habitats over several years. (Table 1) provides some examples of different sampling intensities, given some specific objectives. In addition, Green (1979) provides an excellent discussion of sampling design and data intensity.

Generally, biologists are confronted with three types of data: animal, habitat, and animal/habitat.

ANIMAL DATA COLLECTION

Animal data are characterized by two basic types: (1) individual species and (2) groups of species. Each of these are detailed below.

Individual Species Measurements

There are many types of individual species data, which are summarized in (Table 2). Although biologists will not likely collect all these types of data, they will need some knowledge of them to interpret results of contracts and other existing studies.

Presence. The simplest measurement of individual species populations is presence/absence. In many cases, the only objective is to verify use of a habitat or site-specific area by a species (e.g., bald eagles [*Haliaeetus leucocephalus*] along a riparian stretch). These types of data help determine potential impacts to a species and its habitat from development or natural factors such as fire. These data also help focus the biologist's efforts on site-specific areas, especially those of threatened or endangered species.

One-time verification of a species in an area may only be accurate for a short time, especially when a species uses specific habitats only during certain seasons. For example, black hawks (*Buteogallus anthracinus*) may nest in a riparian area during a wet year when aquatic prey is abundant, but fail to nest in the same area in the following year because of drought-reduced prey abundance. Another concern in using presence/absence data involves one-time failure to identify a species in an area. Several factors may account for species not being verified in an area: unskilled observers, poor sampling techniques, weather conditions during sampling, and absence of that species in the area during the sampling period. The biologist should be very cautious in using one-time, presence/absence data to assess an area's fauna. Multiple-year verification of species in habitats is preferred.

Table 1. Examples of specific objectives carried through the design process.

Specific Objective/Question	Sampling Questions	Solution
Determine how a new water development will affect mule deer use of key browse in the area.	What are the key browse in the area? How does water development affect use? How did mule deer use in the area compare before installing the new development versus after? Did other changes occur that might account for differences before and after development?	Since I did not know the size of the area (several thousand acres of continuous sagebrush-grass), I systematically located my sample points along four lines, out from the water development at right angles (cross shaped). Samples were located at 100 m (300 ft) intervals along these lines (10 samples/line). Angle of the first line was randomly selected. At each point, I measured key browse by a modified Cole technique. Since cows graze the area year-round, I could not determine whether browse were being used by livestock or deer. To assess relative food consumption, I took deer and cow fecal samples at each point. To detemine deer use, I established 20 points along each line (50 m [165 ft] apart, every other point at a browse utilization station), where I read 0.025 ha (0.01 a.) deer pellet plots. I sampled both deer and browse utilization twice before construction of the development, 30 days after development, and then once each session for 3 years.
Determine if a riparian improvement plan will increase the number of nesting black hawks and nesting success on Yankee Creek.	What was the black hawk nesting density like before implementing the plan? What was the average number of young produced at nests before implementing the plan? What was the black hawk nesting density 1, 3, 5, 10, and 15 years after implementation of the plan? How many new nests were built 1, 3, 5, 10, and 15 years after implementation of the plan? What was the impact of the plan on primary black hawk prey? Did factors other than those provided by the plan affect the results?	In order to determine the number of black hawk nests before and after implementation of the plan, I counted all nests within cottonwood-willow stands along the creek. To estimate increases in the amount of tree canopy in periods after implementation, I obtained infrared, low-level photos of the area every other year for 15 years. To determine the effects of the plan on the fish prey base, I established permanent sampling stations where I sampled fish before and 1, 3, 5, 10, and 15 years after the plan was implemented. This included sampling riffles, runs and pools, and sites near known nests. Samples were taken in the spring. Since there were over 15 nests, nest success at all of them could not be monitored. I, therefore, randomly selected three nests to monitor at 1, 3, 5, 10, and 15 years after implementation to determine nest success and habitat uses. New nests were plotted against changes in vegetation. Before and 1, 3, 5, 10, and 15 years after implementation, I determined the total number of active nests in the creek. I also monitored weather and flow conditions in the creek for years previously listed via a hygrothermograph and a U.S. Geological Survey gauging station, respectively.

Table 2. Summary of data types, some procedures and limitations.

Data Type	Method/Expression	Application/Limitation
I. *Individual Species*		
A. Presence/absence		
1. Searches (visual)	List of species in an area or habitat.	Used to verify key species in certain areas or habitats. Multi-year samples needed for species that migrate or use habitats seasonally. To compare two or more areas, sampling intensity must be equal. Random or systematic sampling.
2. Capture and harvest	Same as above.	As above, along with sampling techniques; must be similar to compare two or more areas or habitats (e.g., similar depth traps). Indirect sampling methods.
3. Sign	Same as above.	Feces, nests, and other physical evidence that a species occupies an area or habitat. Indirect method. Sampling limitations as above.
4. Auditory	Same as above.	Direct and indirect methods of verifying species in a habitat or area via sound. Sampling limitations as above.
5. Museum or other existing records	Animal and plant records by county, township and range, sections, and habitat type with general notes. From museums, literature, and individual records. Data same as above.	Indirect method of verifying species in habitats or areas. Data highly variable. Many records only at county level. Some animals/plants misidentified.
B. Abundance (indexes of population size)		
1. Counts/searches	Number of animals/unit effort (usually time).	Direct method of determining abundance of animals in certain areas or habitats. Some methods such as road riding are inexpensive. Data good for comparing different sites and impacts of land use on wildlife and habitats if controls are used. Good techniques for monitoring if permanent sites are established. Subject to observer biases, and good only for readily observable species.
2. Capture/trapping	Number of animals caught/unit time.	A series of individual methods for determining species abundance. Methods usually specific to certain species groups (e.g., pit-fall traps and lizards). Less observer bias than direct searches. Some procedures excel in verifying secretive species. Relatively cost-effective. Excellent procedures for monitoring, provided sampling is systematic.

Table 2. Summary of data types, some procedures and limitations (continued).

Data Type	Method/Expression	Application/Limitation
3. Line searches	Similar to searches within an area or habitat, but generally expressed as number of animals seen/line distance (e.g., birds per mile).	Direct methods of determining abundance of animals in certain habitats or an area as a function of distance and time spent searching. When lines are permanently located, these methods are excellent for long-term monitoring. Similar to searches, these have observer-associated biases.
4. Sign	Includes scent stations, nests, number of tracks or pellet groups. Data are expressed in number of sign/unit area or effort.	Commonly used as indexes of certain big game abundance. Also used for lizards, snakes, tortoises, and small mammals. Most of these indexes produce highly variable data. Recommend these procedures only when techniques cannot be used.
5. Auditory	Generally the recording of different animal calls/unit time.	Commonly used for small birds, raptors, frogs, toads, and predators. Often difficult to count or estimate the number of different individuals. Generally used for verifying a species in an area.
C. Density/spatial		
1. Counts/searches	Number of animals/unit area.	Common procedure used for key species including big game and threatened or endangered species. Labor-intensive and effective only on easily verified species. If combined with point procedure (e.g., variable circle used for birds), procedure is less labor-intensive.
2. Line searches	Animals/unit area as a function of expected versus observed (Chi-squared test).	Includes methods with horizontal belts along a line (e.g., Emlen's bird transects). Used for birds and other species easily observed. Generally inexpensive to run, but procedures require expert observers. Not effective in small discontinuous habitats (e.g., riparian).
3. Mark and recapture	Population size/area as a function of marked versus unmarked animals.	Several different procedures. Some one-time sampling; others multiple samples. Commonly used to monitor terrestrial and aquatic populations. Procedure allows monitoring of individual animals. Generally labor-intensive.
4. Depletion	As above, marked animals are considered removed.	Similar to above. Some procedures involve physical removal of animals. Removal usually on small, easily captured animals (e.g., fish). Generally labor-intensive. Best results with closed populations.
5. Capture/trapping	Number of animals/unit area.	Live and kill traps. Used in intensive studies where population size is needed. Most effective on readily trapped animals. Also used in conjunction with mark-and-recapture procedures. Time- and labor-intensive.

Table 2. Summary of data types, some procedures and limitations (continued).

Data Type	Method/Expression	Application/Limitation
6. Telemetry	Animal movement/unit time or percentage of time spent in an area or habitat, performing certain behaviors.	Effective method for determining behavior and movement patterns. Initially labor-intensive. Generally limited to priority species.
D. Population structure		
1. Sex ratios	Ratio males to females.	Some animals have a sex ratio range that represents a fit population. Numbers outside these ranges can indicate a stressed population. Generally used for big game. Less accurate for lower vertebrates because their sex ratios vary with different, natural environmental conditions.
2. Age ratios	Ratio of animals in certain age groups.	Similar to sex ratios. Other-than-normal ratios of animals in certain age groups can indicate a stressed population. Generally used for animals whose age structure does not vary with environmental fluctuations. Be cautious in using these in lower vertebrates for reasons listed for sex ratios.
E. Productivity (recruitment rates)	Generally, reproductive effort (number of recruits).	Commonly used for big game and other species whose birth or recruitment rates can be measured. Generally, labor-intensive. Many populations cyclic.
F. Population condition	Generally, percentage of animals in certain condition classes (e.g., rankings of fat storage).	Animals conditions used as indicators of population fitness and stress. Limited to priority species. Labor-intensive.
II. *Wildlife Communities*		
A. Species richness		
1. Presence/absence (habitat type)	List of species in a habitat type or total number species/habitat type.	Lists complied from on-site data collection and existing information. Can be used to compare habitat species richness. Commonly used for land-use planning, with limited utility on site-specific assessments.
2. Presence/absence (habitat components)	Similar to above but expressed by habitat component (e.g., number of species using rock for feeding substrate).	Used to identify critical components of habitat based on species' uses. Also used to assess impact of habitat component loss on groups of wildlife. Guilding is a process for grouping animals (see text). Use for land-use planning, but cautiously for site-specific analysis.
B. Community abundance	Overall abundance of a taxonomic group (e.g., small mammals) in habitats. Data expression varies with sampling methods (see Individual Species section).	Used to assess value of habitats (e.g., pinyon-juniper versus chaparral) for certain groups of wildlife. More time- and labor-intensive than presence/absence. Problems similar to those for sampling individual species abundance (see Individual Species section).

Table 2. Summary of data types, some procedures and limitations (continued).

Data Type	Method/Expression	Application/Limitation
C. Community density	As above but expressed as animals/unit area.	As above. Subject to problems associated with individual species densities.
D. Biomass	Weight or mass (gms) a species contributes to the overall community. Often expressed in ratios.	Used to estimate species contributions to a community based on mass. Also estimates trophic levels and food available to certain predators. Limited utility in most management-related studies.
E. Species similarities (similarity coefficients)	Index generally between 0 (no similarity) and 1 (identical). Single value.	Used to compare species assemblages on two different sites. Calculations are simple and do not require abundance (presence/absence only). Some formulas emphasize similarity; others, differences. Excellent for comparing wildlife communities.
F. Species diversity and habitat use diversity	Index generally ranging from 0 (no diversity) to 10 (high diversity). Certain formulas emphasize evenness of abundance shared by species on a site ($\log_{10}$); others, richness of species ($\log_e$).	Commonly used to compare species diversity between sites or the diversity of habitats used by species (habitat use diversity or niche breadth). Abundance or density data needed for calculations. Subject to biases associated with abundance and density. When sampling is conducted over long periods, data provide insight into changes in species dominance relative to a management prescription.
G. Species overlap	Like similarity coefficients, but value range of 0 to 1 is based on shared species abundance versus total abundance. Horn—Overlap is the most commonly used procedure.	Used to assess differences in animal community structure between habitats. Abundance or density data required. Also assesses species contributions on one site versus those on other sites. Biases similar to those of abundance and density sampling.
III. *Habitat* (characteristics, composition, and structural conditions)		
A. Point	Percentage of plant cover, substrate type, plant frequency, plant and other horizontal and vertical attributes of habitat.	Used for gross characterizations of habitats and areas. When points are permanently located, changes in habitat can be determined. Often combined with a line to determine percentages. Generally poor for grasses and forbs.
B. Line	As above, but as a function of distance along a line.	Extremely useful for characterizing plant composition and frequency and habitat components for a habitat or area. Generally quick and easy to read. Excellent for monitoring changes if permanently marked. Most effective on habitats dominated by shrubs.
C. Plot	Number of a habitat component/unit area. Also, weight contributed by a plant species/unit area.	Commonly used for grass and forb density, composition, and biomass on an area or in a habitat. Labor-intensive. Not generally effective for woodland and forest habitats. Good for monitoring rangeland if permanently located.

Table 2. Summary of data types, some procedures and limitations (concluded).

Data Type	Method/Expression	Application/Limitation
D. Plotless	Number of plants or a certain habitat component/unit area as a function of distance from a center point.	Fast and effective way of determining absolute densities of trees, shrubs, and other habitat components such as snags. Structural characteristics of habitat components are also usually measured. Point-center-quarter method is a commonly used plotless method. Excellent for monitoring if points are permanently located.
IV. *Animal/Habitat*		
A. Animal/habitat indexes	Usually expressed as a quality index value ranging from 0 (poor quality habitat) to 1 (best possible habitat). Data also expressed as quality (suitability) index × the area = habitat value.	Indexes are suited for broad-scale land-use planning, especially when using a generic model. Can be used for more site-specific application if area-specific data are used to develop the model. Habitat Suitability Index models use a series of ecological relationships to develop models for individual species. Habitat Relation models rank seral stages of habitats for individual species relative to performing important ecological functions.
B. Animal/habitat correlations	Data expression varies with procedures (see below).	Procedures that use empirical data to determine relationships between animals and habitats.
1. Correlation and regression	Data expressed as a linear or nonlinear (e.g., polynomial) relationship, usually between animal population and one or several habitat variables.	If animal and habitat data are collected on similar sites, these equations are ideal for area-specific monitoring and development of predictive equations for management assessment. SPSS and BMDP software provide these types of analysis. With practice, these are easily developed.
2. Principle components	Data generally expressed as location along axes (e.g., X,Y,Z). Locations on axes represent combined habitat variables.	Valuable tool for illustrating differences in animal uses of habitat. Allows the biologists to compress several habitat variables into two or three axes which then are easily illustrated.

Abundance and Density. Abundance and density measurements have been widely used in wildlife inventories and monitoring studies. Generally, there are three types of abundance measurements: total number of animals in a population; number of animals per unit area (density); and abundance and density of one population relative to another (Caughley 1977). Rarely will biologists measure the absolute number of animals in a population or area and need actual numbers or density. Therefore, most wildlife inventories and monitoring studies use estimates of population size and density. Estimates are usually accomplished by indexes that are correlated with population size and density (Caughley 1977; Eberhardt 1978).

Estimates of population size or absolute abundance are commonly used in wildlife inventories. Because these estimates are indexes of populations and not ascribed to units of areas, they are usually termed abundance. Abundances include animal numbers obtained from direct observation, sign (tracks, etc.), and captures. Certain biases are associated with each of these methods. Caughley (1977) and Eberhardt (1978) provide excellent summaries of these biases; biologists should consult these and other sources before deciding a method. Estimates of abundance include, but are not limited to—

- number of animals seen per hour of observation (also termed time-restraint);
- number of animals seen per linear distance (e.g., raptors seen per mile of powerline);
- number of animals trapped per 24 hours;
- number of tracks counted per hour of observation;
- number of calls heard per hour (e.g., frogs and owls).

All these can be measured without regard to area. Therefore, they are estimates that presumably are correlated with population size.

Relative abundance generally refers to the contribution a species makes to the total abundance of that wildlife community. For example, if three observations of species A and one observation of species B were made, then species A makes up 75% of the abundance and species B, 25%. These relative abundances are expressed as 0.75 and 0.25, respectively (see Hendrickson et al. 1980 for excellent fish examples).

Density refers to animal numbers per unit area (Caughley 1977). Estimates of density are obtained in ways similar to those acquired for abundance estimates, but they are applied to a naturally or artificially ascribed area (e.g., habitat boundary or marked hectare or acre plot, respectively). For example, a biologist estimates lizard density by searching a premarked area and counting all lizards seen (Bury 1982). Similarly, bird density can be estimated by using a variable plot method where the number of birds are counted within 1/100 ha (0.025 a.) circular plots (see Ralph and Scott 1981, for examples).

Estimates of density are also obtained by counting the number of animals seen within prescribed belts established along a fixed line. By using probability statistics, animal densities can be predicted in prescribed belts outside areas adjacent to the transect line. Perhaps the most commonly used line/area transect is that developed by Emlen (1971) for birds. Emlen's bird transect has been modified to reduce sampling biases, including statistical applications available on computer software. Ralph and Scott (1981) provide a series of papers about bird sampling.

When comparing estimates of population abundance and density, the biologist should consider the number of samples to be allocated to each area. This is especially important when comparing densities. To compare two sites, biologists should compensate for area-related variability by allocating sample size relative to proportions of area. For example, if area A is 1,000 ha (2,500 a.); area B is 5,000 ha (2,500 a.); and area C is 10,000 ha (250,000 a.), then area A would have 1/10 the number of samples of area C, and area B, 1/2 the number of area C.

Depletion sampling and mark-and-recapture are other methods commonly used to estimate population size and density. Generally, removal methods involve removing animals during two or more sample periods, where only two factors are used: population size N and capture probability. Population data are obtained by comparing expected captures to actual captures, generally by a goodness-of-fit test (Chi-squared test). One problem with this method is that it assumes all animals have an equal probability of capture. In many cases, this is not true. For example, the probability of capturing large fish is greater than small fish when electroshocking is used. Otis et al. (1978) and White et al. (1982) have developed more generalized removal models that can account for unequal capture probability. Removal procedures are common in estimating the number of fish in a stream, primarily because the biologist is sampling a relatively closed system. White et al. (1982) provide a good review of a number of removal methods.

Mark-and-recapture techniques involve marking animals and then sampling at a later date to determine the ratio of marked to unmarked animals. Population size is determined from the ratio of marked to unmarked animals in one or more successive samples. The Petersen-Lincoln estimator is perhaps the most commonly used mark-and-recapture method.

Mark-and-recapture methods require several assumptions: (1) no loss or gain of marked animals, (2) no recruitment, (3) equal catchability in marked and unmarked animals, and (4) equal mortality rates in marked versus unmarked animals (Tipton 1980). These criteria are more easily met in samples taken within short periods (e.g., consecutive days) than over longer periods (e.g., several months). Data obtained by these methods often vary (Tipton 1980), primarily because multiple samples have been taken under different climatic conditions, affecting animal activity and behavior. Otis et al. (1978) and White et al. (1982) provide detailed discussions of these biases.

Spatial Arrangement and Movement. In addition to estimating abundance and density, determining spatial arrangement and movement of individual species in habitat types may be important. For species that require different habitats for different functions, such as breeding or feeding, biologists should collect data on species movements and different uses of habitats. Individual movements can be obtained from direct observations of marked or unmarked animals or from radiotelemetry. Chapter 33, Radiotelemetry, provides guidance on such efforts. These types of data help biologists determine habitat needs of individual species, which aid in various types of environmental assessment. Limitations of mark-and-recapture (resighting) animals (see previous section) and of radiotelemetry are generally related to cost, the former being labor-intensive and the latter requiring expensive equipment.

Population Structure. Sex and age ratios are used to determine conditions of natural populations, especially big game. Sex ratios of healthy populations are compared with those of populations being studied, thus giving the biologist an indicator of population health. Although sex ratios may indicate population problems, biologists should take other population data to support conclusions derived from sex ratios.

Generally, age ratios also reflect population condition. Lack of certain age classes such as juveniles and breeding adults can indicate a stressed population. For example, biologists are concerned about large numbers of old desert tortoises (*Gopherus agassizii*) and lack of young in Arizona populations. As with sex ratios, corroborative data such as abundance, density, and productivity should be collected along with age ratios.

Biologists should be cautious when using and interpreting population structure data. Many species' age and sex ratios fluctuate naturally with changes in environmental conditions. Therefore, it is important to obtain multiple-year samples with controls to determine human changes in population structure.

Productivity. Like population structure, productivity can indicate population fitness. Productivity is usually considered the number of young (as defined) recruited into the population per adults, adult females or adult pairs. Examples are the number of young fledged per nest and fawns per doe. Although often a better indicator of species' fitness than population structure, this measurement may be hard to obtain with some species.

Condition. Condition of individual animals can indicate fitness of a population, especially population stress. For example, if 90% of the animals in a bighorn sheep (*Ovis canadensis*) population are in poor condition (e.g., emaciated, having thin coats or high incidences of sinusitus), then a biologist might predict that this population is in trouble. Although often good indicators of population condition, these measurements are generally hard to obtain, expensive, and labor-intensive.

General Considerations. Biologists should be careful in selecting, making, and interpreting population measurements, particularly estimates of abundance, density, population structure, or productivity. Population numbers, sex and age ratios, and productivity all vary naturally. If a biologist needs to collect such data on a species whose abundance fluctuates naturally (e.g., rabbit populations), then samples should be taken over several years.

Knowledge of natural population fluctuations is extremely important in interpreting data from cause-and-effect studies. For example, observed declines in a population on a mined area may result from low precipitation during sampling rather than from mine-caused habitat alteration.

Community Measurements

Community measurements are data collected on species groups. The species groups may be taxonomic (e.g., songbirds) groups that use habitat in similar ways (guilds) or other logical groupings. For example, a biologist may want to compare species richness (total number of species) between two habitat types to help decide where to place a powerline.

Community data may also involve only a specific taxonomic group. For example, because of limited funding, a biologist may only assess species diversity of bird communities on habitat types. Data collection limited to a taxonomic group or community may also be caused by objectives established during preplanning. For example, data may be collected only on raptors because of priorities established during preliminary planning. Community measurements are summarized in (Table 2).

The simplest and most widely used community measurement is the presence/absence of the wildlife groups. Presence/absence data allow biologists to determine wildlife community composition in different habitat types. These data also allow biologists to compare faunal richness of habitat types. These comparisons may be useful in land-use planning. For example, an inventory might show that pinyon-juniper habitats are more faunally rich than adjacent desert grassland habitats and possess a greater number of threatened or endangered species. These data are then used to support a management alternative of placing a mining road through desert grassland habitat rather than through pinyon-juniper.

While primarily used at a habitat level (e.g., pinyon-juniper), presence/absence data can also be used to determine species groups that depend on certain habitat components or spatial arrangement (e.g., vertical vegetation arrangement). For example, bird species can be verified in predetermined increments of vertical vegetation layers, thus indicating bird species arrangements within a habitat type. This type of data can also be useful in land-use planning. A biologist may find that shrub and old growth components of pinyon-juniper contain the greatest variety of birds. These data are then used to support a management alternative that would limit wood cutting to middle-aged trees.

Presence/absence data collection is far less expensive than abundance or density data collection, especially when censusing an entire wildlife community. Collecting presence data for wildlife groups is similar to that for single species; however, the analysis, interpretation, and use of such data are often quite different.

Several types of statistical procedures have been used to analyze presence/absence data of wildlife communities. Similarity coefficients are the simplest of these analyses. A summary of these coefficients is listed in (Table 2). Generally, similarity coefficients compare the number of species common to two habitats with the total number of species. Generally, these values range between 0 (no similarity) and 1 (identical communities). Some similarity coefficients such as Simpson's emphasize similarities between two sites, and others such as Jaccard's emphasize differences between sites. See Pimentel (1979) for a full discussion of these methods.

In interpreting presence/absence data, biologists should consider the intensity of the sample. In short-term inventories, a biologist would not likely observe all species in a given area, especially rare species and those with restricted activity. The methods used to verify species in an area may also be incomplete, and this will affect the total number of species observed.

Cluster analysis is another method to group species that use similar habitat or habitat components. Cluster analysis also provides a visual perspective of degrees of similarity between groups and variability within a cluster of species. Clusters are depicted in two-dimensional graphs along X and Y axes or in histograms based on separation between groups. Separation or distance between clustered species groups is determined several ways depending on the cluster statistic used. For example, one clustering statistic determines group distances by calculating a central location in the X and Y axes of each group. Pimentel (1979) provides a detailed explanation of this application of cluster analysis, and Short and Burnham (1982) provide an example of this analysis, demonstrating how bird species cluster in terms of habitat uses.

Another approach to determining groupings of species is to determine guilds, which are groups of species that use similar habitat components. Short (1983, 1984) also describes a simple procedure for determining species guilds based on where they breed and feed. For example, one guild breeds in vegetation canopy (above 4.5 m [15 ft]) and feeds on the surface, whereas another guild could feed in the same location but also in the canopy. These groups are different in their use of habitat for feeding and breeding. Other important ecological functions can be used to group species into guilds, although these are not described by Short. For example, thermoregulation is important in reptile communities; therefore, for this community, it is important to describe where and how they thermoregulate in addition to where they breed and feed.

By grouping species that use habitats in similar ways (guilds), the biologist can predict the species groups that will be affected when a habitat component is altered or lost. The detail or breakdown of habitat components with which species are associated can vary. For example, whereas one biologist identifies 3 vertical layers of vegetation, another may identify 10. The biologist who identifies three layers may be more concerned with horizontal arrangement of vegetation for determining habitat requirements of small mammals and, therefore, will only use three vertical layers, whereas another biologist, studying bird communities, may need greater delineation of vertical space.

Simply stated, guilding is a method of sorting wildlife into groupings based on the use of habitat components for important ecological functions. The primary function of placing species into guilds is to provide a way of looking at how species groups might be affected by changes in habitat structure, rather than determining requirements of each species and then projecting how each might be affected by a proposed action. For example, a group of species dependent on downed logs for breeding, feeding, and thermal cover, would be negatively affected by removal of downed and dead material from the area.

Guild data can be effectively used during early land management planning stages, especially to determine potential conflicts with land-use proposals. Guilding also helps focus attention on heavily used components of habitat. Biologists, however, should be cautious when using guild data. For example, guild data do not account for the ability of a species to shift to secondary habitat structures when preferred habitat is lost. In addition, guilds are artificially defined groups described by biologists. Mannin et al. (1984) found that 67% of birds within guilds in Oregon forest habitats responded differently to habitat changes than predicted. Some biologists argued that each species occupies a separate guild and, therefore, reacts differently to habitat changes (see discussions of Mannin et al. 1984). Biologists should not attempt to use guilding data to determine precise, site-specific changes in species abundance and composition. Again, these data are best used to focus attention on important habitat components, rather than as precise predictive models.

Another related procedure is use of indicator species. One use of this procedure involves selecting a species termed an indicator species, which represents a group of species or guild. This species is then sampled to determine how it is affected by land-use practices. Data obtained for this species are then applied to the entire group of species in the guild. For example, alligator lizards (*Gerrhonotus* sp.) represent a guild of species that require downed leaf litter within habitats they occupy. Therefore, in theory, if we know how alligator lizard populations will change with changes in leaf litter composition, we know how all other members of that guild will respond. Like guilding, this procedure assumes that all species in a guild use habitat in an identical manner and all have the same ability to use secondary habitat. As mentioned earlier, Mannin et al. (1984) found that species within guilds did not react similarly to habitat changes. From a management perspective, the indicator species process saves time and money since it allows the biologist to sample only a few species and yet determine how the entire wildlife community responds to habitat changes. Biologically, however, this concept does not consistently hold up. While I recommend using guilding procedures to focus on important habitat components, biologists should be cautious in using indicator species to represent species guilds, especially when accurate, site-specific predictions are needed.

The U.S. Forest Service, Region 6 (Albuquerque, NM), uses indicator species in a different way. Instead of representing a group or guild of species, an indicator species is used to indicate quality of a certain habitat component on a site. A group of indicator species is selected so that all important habitat components on a site are covered. Then, when a certain site is altered by a land-use practice, the biologist can look at changes in indicator species to determine effects on important habitat components. Perhaps an easier way to determine the same effects would be to measure changes in important habitat components. The biologist identifies these important components from existing studies and literature.

When it is possible to collect data on abundance or density of a wildlife or taxonomic community (e.g., raptors), species diversity and overlap indexes can be calculated. Of the several types of diversity indexes, the most commonly used is the Shannon-Weaver index (Hair 1980). This index provides a single value for a wildlife community based both on the total number of species and the evenness of abundance among the species. All the indexes allow biologists to assess relative values of habitats based on species diversity. Since the indexes are based partially on relative abundance or density, they can only be used within groups having abundance measured in similar ways. For example, a single diversity index cannot be computed for big game and lizards, because relative abundance or density is determined in different ways.

Whereas similarity coefficients compare species similarities between habitats, overlap indexes compare proportions of species and their abundance between habitats. Perhaps the most commonly used overlap index is that described by Horn (1966). Routledge (1980) and Ricklefs and Lau (1980) discuss limitations and bias associated with these types of indexes. Biologists should consult these and other sources before using diversity or overlap indexes.

Another type of data used to assess and compare species composition and influence is biomass. In many wildlife studies, where the biologist is trying to determine how species contribute to trophic levels, biomass is measured. For example, it may be important to know how the loss or reduction of a certain species will affect food available to other species in the community. In trophic level and food niche studies, biomass information is generally preferred over abundance data; two species may provide similar energy to a system even though one is small and abundant and the other is common and rare.

HABITAT DATA

In most cases, biologists collect habitat data to make some type of prediction about animal populations. Many of the same kinds of measurements discussed for animals and animal communities can also be applied to plant communities (habitat types) and individual plant species. In addition, habitat measurements include abiotic physical features such as rock and soils. I discuss measurements and data collection in two general areas: (1) habitat area or type and (2) habitat component.

Habitat Area or Type Data

These types of data apply to a habitat type or area as a whole. Generally, a habitat type is an area, delineated by a biologist, that has certain consistent abiotic and biotic attributes such as dominant and subdominant vegetation. The U.S. Bureau of Land Management (BLM) terms these "habitat sites" (Kerr and Brown 1977). Groups of habitat areas with similar attributes that support similar groupings of species are termed "habitat types" or in BLM, "standard habitat sites."

Similar to animal community measurements, the simplest measurement of habitat type is presence/absence. In most cases, this involves identifying and mapping habitat sites within an area.

The following spatial measurements of habitat types are commonly used to assess habitat availability:

- size of habitat sites (area);
- location and position of habitat sites, including distance between habitat sites and heterogeneity within an area;
- edge influences created by habitat site interfaces and ecotones;
- temporal availability of habitat sites (e.g., temporary lentic habitat sites).

All these data help biologists assess availability of certain habitats and the potential for an area to support various types of wildlife.

Indexes have been used to quantify potential influences of edges on wildlife habitat. Patton (1975) provides a simple index of edge.

Plant species richness, diversity, similarity, and overlap can be computed for habitat sites or types in ways similar to animal species composition in animal communities. Plant species richness is the total number of species present within a habitat type. Similarity coefficients can be computed by comparing shared plant species richness between habitats. Plant species diversity and overlap between habitat types are computed from diversity indexes identical to those previously discussed for animals. Often, these data help assess forage quantity and quality between habitat sites or types.

Habitat Component Data

Habitat component data refer to information taken on abiotic and biotic attributes of habitat. Generally, data collection is limited to those components known to affect wildlife distribution and population fitness. Data can include spatial arrangement of these components at a single point in time or over several years, or physical characteristics of components such as average height and width. Habitat component data can represent an entire habitat type or a specific area occupied by species. Table 2 provides a summary of these data. Examples of abiotic data include—

- average surface rock cover,
- average size of surface rocks,
- tallus and rock outcrop abundance and size,
- soil depth,
- vertical and horizontal heterogeneity of soils and rock.

Measurement and classification of terrestrial and aquatic physical features are covered in Chapters 27 and 28 in this book. Examples of biotic data include—

- average litter depth;
- average litter cover per unit area;
- snag density and size;
- average height of different vegetation life-forms (grasses, shrubs, and trees);
- vertical and horizontal heterogeneity of litter, snags, and live vegetation.

Other data often collected include attributes such as elevation, latitude and longitude, slope, and aspect.

Many sampling methods can be used to obtain presence/absence, abundance, density, size, spatial arrangement, and habitat and habitat component availability data. These methods fall into four general categories:

(1) Point (e.g., point intercept);

(2) Line (e.g., line intercept);

(3) Area or plot;

(4) Plotless (e.g., point-center-quarter).

Generally, point data can be obtained quickly, depending on the number of points needed. The number of samples taken will depend on variability of the habitat component to be measured. For example, a biologist can use several point samples to determine leaf litter depth. These points can be systematically (e.g., on a line) or randomly located. One of the most widely used of these methods is the toe-pace transect (Hays et al. 1981). Point methods can also be used to determine frequency and relative abundance of certain components. For example, a toe-pace transect can be used to determine percentages of certain substrate on habitat surfaces. This type of procedure does not identify the density or arrangement of habitat components on the surface but rather frequency and relative abundance of these components (expressed as a percentage). These types of data are best used as a rough indicator of component composition and frequency on a site.

Line transect methods also generate data on habitat component composition, frequency, and abundance. In addition, they provide data on horizontal arrangement of habitat components (a function of distance between components). Similar to point transects, these data are expressed as percentages and can be used to characterize habitat components on a site. The most common line transect method is the line-intercept (see Hays et al. 1981).

Plot sampling techniques are frequently used to describe habitat component arrangement, density, and composition within an area. The area in which habitat components are measured is usually predefined, and area size can vary greatly. Methods used to generate these data are usually time- and labor-intensive, providing relatively accurate data but only for a small area. They are most commonly used when grass and forb composition and density data are needed. Several plot or area methods have been developed. See Hays et al. (1981) for greater detail. Data generated from plot methods are usually expressed as the number of plants per unit area. In many forage studies, data are expressed in weight by plant species per unit area.

Plotless sampling techniques produce density estimates for habitat components, but as a function of distance rather than density in a predetermined area. One of the more commonly used plotless techniques is the point-center-quarter method (Phillips 1959), which allows many samples to be collected in less time than a plot method.

When set up as permanent samples and read over several years, line, plot, and plotless methods yield valuable information on changes in habitat components on a site. Nonetheless, these habitat measurement techniques have many biases and eliminations. Chapters 26 through 32 discuss habitat component sampling methods in greater detail.

In all these methods, characteristics of individual habitat components can be measured. For example, tree density determined from a point-center-quarter method (plotless) is based on distances of trees from the point. Each tree sampled for distance can also be measured for physical characteristics such as height and diameter. In some cases, habitat components cannot be measured randomly or systematically. For example, a biologist might need to determine physical characteristics of snags used by nesting spotted owls (*Strix occidentalis*) so that adequate habitat is provided in the area's snag management plan. In this case, the biologist would measure only those snags with known spotted owl nests.

Heterogeneity of both abiotic and biotic habitat components can be computed from diversity indexes. Foliage height diversity and patchiness indexes are two of the more commonly used (see Ralph and Scott 1981; Hays et al. 1981; Chapter 31 in this book). Foliage height diversity data give the biologist an indication of how evenly vegetation is distributed in vertical space. Patchiness diversity indexes provide data on how evenly vegetation is spread on horizontal space. Vertical spatial data are extremely helpful in determining a site's ability to support certain birds, while horizontal spatial data help determine which small mammals and lizards occupy a site.

In addition to other types of habitat data discussed, population structure (e.g., age ratios), productivity, and condition (e.g., degree of hedging) measurements can be taken on certain plant species. These types of measurements are similar to those taken on individual animal species, but are generally easier to obtain because plants are stationary. These measurements help biologists determine the condition and fitness of certain types of plants such as key riparian tree species or important big game browse.

ANIMAL/HABITAT CORRELATIONS

Perhaps the most important consideration in designing and conducting a habitat inventory or monitoring project is ensuring that animal and habitat data can be compared. By doing so, biologists can then predict how habitat alterations will affect animal populations.

Two factors are extremely important if animal and habitat data are to be compared. First, animal and habitat data should be collected on the same site. As samples accumulate, the biologist can determine how animal populations fluctuate with differences in physical and spatial arrangement of habitats. If a biologist samples habitats and animals at different sites, habitat and animal data cannot be compared.

Second, the level of sampling needed to compare animal and habitat data should be carefully determined. In most cases, animal and habitat sampling levels do not need to be similar. For example, most inventories of wildlife communities in habitat types require only presence and absence data for animals. However, habitat measurements are generally more specific than simple presence or absence of habitat components; these tell little about habitat quality and condition. More often, habitat measurements include spatial arrangement and abundance of habitat components.

Conversely, sometimes biologists may need more detailed data on animals than habitat. For example, a biologist who is monitoring the effect of new water developments on a pronghorn population in an area would require detailed information on movement, abundance or density, spatial arrangement, and reproduction of pronghorns. Habitat data collection would probably be limited to habitat mapping and presence or absence of water. In both cases, the level or complexity of animal versus habitat sampling depend on specific inventory and monitoring objectives. However, habitat data are usually less costly and time-consuming to collect and more accurate than animal data; plants are easier to locate and are somewhat stationary. Therefore, most inventories and studies generally have more detailed habitat data. (Table 2) provides a summary of these data.

Many statistical procedures compare animal and habitat data. Perhaps the simplest of these procedures is to compile a list of species observed or collected in a habitat component or habitat type. This allows biologists to weigh relative wildlife values of certain habitat components and habitat types, which can then be used in evaluating proposed land management.

Multivariate analyses, such as correlation, regression, and principal component analyses, can be used to compare animal and habitat data. For example, a biologist may want to determine which physical attributes of habitat affect species richness. Jones et al. (1985) used a step-wise, multiple regression to determine how reptile species richness on habitat islands was affected by habitat size and habitat component structure. In this study, animal data consisted of only presence and absence of species on sites, while habitat data were more detailed and included size, elevation, and detailed horizontal and vertical habitat structures. Pimentel (1979) and Green (1979) discuss these statistical procedures and provide examples. In addition, Jones and Glinski (1983), discussing lizards; Rotenberry and Wiens (1980), discussing birds; and Matthews and Hill (1981), discussing fish, provide examples of multivariate analyses of animal/habitat data.

The U.S. Fish and Wildlife Service and U.S. Forest Service have developed models that assess habitat capability or suitability for certain species. The former has developed the Habitat Evaluation Proce-

dures (HEP) system, consisting of a series of habitat suitability index (HSI) models developed for individual animals (Schamberger et al. 1982).

The HEP process and HSI models have some drawbacks. First, habitat ratings are indexes, and are normally derived from expert opinion and literature review rather than from empirical data. Testing these models is difficult, since the index cannot be verified in the field.

Another type of habitat evaluation model was developed by Williams et al. (1977). These are known as Pattern Recognition (PATREC) models, which, unlike HEP models, are based on statistical inference. Data used in these models are often empirical (e.g., population data). Models result in probability statements on an area's suitability to support a certain species (e.g., an area in question has a 75% probability of supporting dinosaurs). Because PATREC models are developed from empirical data (generally a population factor such as presence or density), they are easier than HSI models to test.

The U.S. Forest Service has developed a series of models (habitat capability relation models) that correlate species with habitat components. The U.S. Forest Service has also developed simulation models that simulate changes in vegetation over time as a result of plant succession and land-use practices on an area. By combining these two types of models, biologists can predict how wildlife habitat quality and, thus, wildlife populations will change over time given a certain land use.

This approach is limited in that habitat quality is evaluated only by seral stages of cover types (habitat types). The procedure does not account for relationships between site-specific habitat components and wildlife, and it is based on models developed for individual species. Currently, only a few species have been modeled. Therefore, I recommend caution when using this system, especially when assessing management alternatives on a site-specific basis. As with guilding, I believe such models are most valuable during major land-use planning, especially to focus attention on major issues.

The area of animal/habitat correlations is covered in more detail in Chapter 38, Habitat Evaluation Systems.

DISCUSSION

Generally, there are two approaches to data collection and their use in recommending wildlife and habitat alternatives. These two approaches have been described by Bailey (1982) and are termed "Linear-Comprehensive Management" and "Cyclic-Incrementalism."

Linear-comprehensive management is the accumulation of data on all habitat components and wildlife populations in all ecosystems (Figure 1). This includes detailed, intensive data on population sizes and productivities, seasonal distributions of animals, forage productivity, cover availability, precipitation, and all other ecological factors affecting biological systems. This management philosophy also assumes clear definitions of publicly agreed-upon management goals; the biologist will have specific data that support public opinions on issues. It also assumes that all population and habitat treatment methods are clearly understood and that the biologist has a comprehensive knowledge of how each treatment will affect the ecosystem and animals in question.

In general, linear-comprehensive management generates large amounts of site-specific data without regard to how the resulting data will be used in management decisions. In some cases, models are developed and used in planning without local testing. Linear-comprehensive management does not work in most wildlife management situations for several reasons. First, wildlife is diverse in most ecosystems. Simply stated, the biologist cannot collect data on all population and habitat factors, nor can a biologist determine how each species will be affected by every treatment. Some of the most comprehensive studies have only censused a tiny fraction of the animal population in an ecosystem. In addition, the relationships between animals and ecosystems are very complex. Most animals have several habitat requirements, and these requirements are often interrelated in complex ways. Therefore, predicting how any particular animal will react to habitat changes is difficult. As mentioned earlier, Mannan et al. (1984) found that bird species within well-defined guilds responded differently to certain management prescriptions. Finally, wildlife budgets prohibit collection of large amounts of wildlife data. Because knowledge and budgets are limited, most wildlife management programs are extensive, rather than intensive.

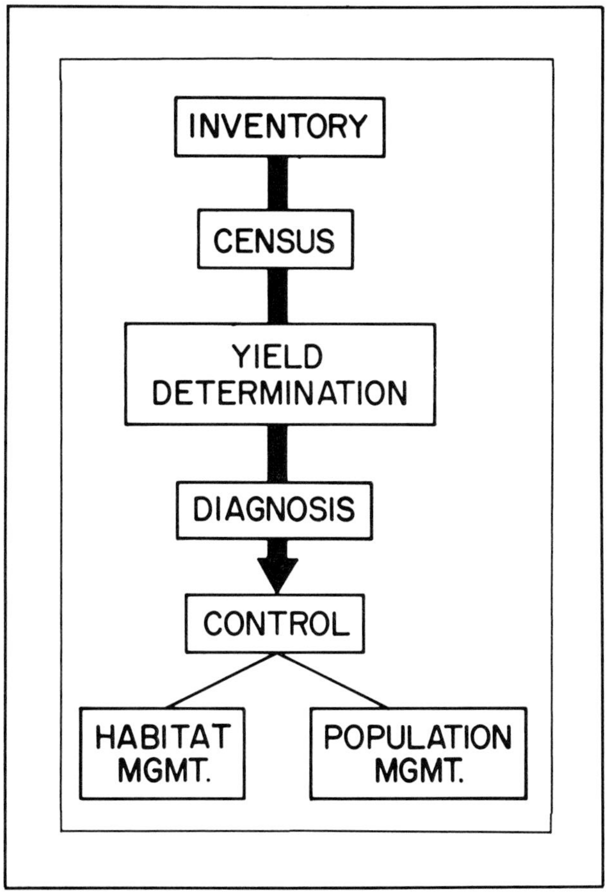

Cyclic-incrementalism is defined as a slow, subjective process of collecting data and knowledge on how certain management prescriptions affect wildlife (Figure 2). This process also allows for continuous adjustment of treatments and management based on monitoring data. In this process, the biologist identifies a series of achievable goals (e.g., 30% more browse in an area). These goals are measured in units that relate directly to management objectives. The biologist then selects a series of methods that are believed to achieve the management objective (e.g., prescribed burn). Since the biologist is not 100% confident that the prescription will have the desired result, it is applied on a limited (incremental) basis, and then the result is monitored. From the

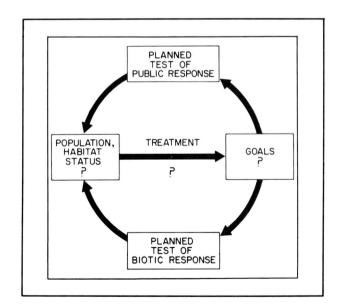

Figure 1. The linear-comprehensive approach to wildlife management (after Bailey 1982).

Figure 2. The cyclic-incremental approach to wildlife management (after Bailey 1982).

monitoring data, the biologist can determine if the habitat management prescription or land use needs to be modified.

In this process, the biologist determines the concerns and needs of the public in formulating management objectives. It is also extremely important to inform the public about any findings made during the monitoring of a management prescription. This will help the biologist reinforce or modify management objectives. Because prescriptions are conducted and monitored on a site-specific basis, the biologist has a better understanding of the local situation. This type of procedure is more likely to gain public support, as opposed to use of rigid procedures developed for large regions.

In his description of these concepts, Bailey (1982) points out that wildlife management is an art, not a science. Wildlife managers apply the science of biology, but the application of this science is an art. The process of cyclic-incrementalism allows the biologist to accumulate site-specific data relative to publicly-accepted wildlife management objectives, and slowly build a basis for management decisions. Because this process does not require large-scale data collection, it can be scaled to available budget.

The key to successful inventories and monitoring studies is in establishing achievable and management-related objectives, and in orienting the type and level of data collected to these objectives. It serves no purpose to determine the distribution of all wildlife in several habitat types if the objective is to determine how grazing practices affect certain key wildlife species. Data should be collected to solve specific management problems.

Throughout the chapter, I have highlighted different types and levels of data. This information should be used in making decisions on the type of data needed to answer specific management questions. I do not recommend using a standard set of methods and data, but rather an assortment of techniques and information, depending on individual objectives, goals, priorities, and budget.

LITERATURE CITED

BAILEY, J.A. 1982. Implications of "muddling through" for wildlife management. Wildl. Soc. Bull. 10(4):363-369.

BROWN, D.E., C.H. LOWE, and C. PASE. 1979. A digitized classification system for the biotic communities of North America, with community (series) and association examples for the Southwest. J. Arizona—Nevada, Acad. Sci. 14, Supplement 1.

BURY, R.B. 1982. Structure and composition of Mojave Desert reptile communities determined with a removal method. Herpetological Communities, U.S. Dep. Inter., Fish and Wildl. Serv., Wildl. Res. Rep. 13.

CAUGHLEY, G. 1977. Analysis of vertebrate populations. John Wiley and Sons, London. 234pp.

EBERHARDT, L.L. 1978. Appraising variability in population studies. J. Wildl. Manage. 42(2):207-238.

EMLEN, J.T. 1971. Population densities of birds derived from transect counts. Auk 88:323-342.

GREEN, R.H. 1979. Sampling design and statistical methods for environmental biologists. John Wiley and Sons, New York, NY.

GYSEL, L.W. and L.J. LYON. 1980. Habitat analysis and evaluation. Pages 305-327 in Schemnitz, S.D., ed. Wildlife Management Techniques Manual. The Wildl. Soc., Washington, DC.

HAIR, J.D. 1980. Measurements of ecological diversity. Pages 269-275 in Schemnitz, S.D., ed. Wildlife Management Techniques Manual. The Wildl. Soc., Washington, DC.

HAYS, R.L., C. SUMMERS, and W. SEITZ. 1981. Estimating wildlife habitat variables. U.S. Dep. Inter., Fish and Wildl. Serv. FWS/OBS-81/47. 111pp.

HENDRICKSON, D.A., W.L. MINCKLEY, R.R. MILLER, D.J. SIEBERT, and P.H. MINCKLEY. 1980. Fishes of the Rio Yaqui Basin, Mexico and United States. J. Arizona, Acad. Sci. 15(3):65-106.

HORN, H.S. 1966. Measurements of overlap in comparative ecological studies. Am. Nat. 100:419-424.

JONES, K.B. and C. GLINSKI. 1983. Microhabitats of lizards and southwestern riparian community. Pages 342-346 in Johnson, R.R., C.D. Ziebell, D.R. Patton, P.F. Ffolliott, and R.H. Hamre, tech. coords. Riparian Ecosystems and their Management: Reconciling Conflicting Uses. U.S. Dep. Agric., Forest Serv., Gen. Tech. Rep. RM-120.

———, L.P. KEPNER, and T.E. MARTIN. 1985. Species of reptiles occupying habitat islands in western Arizona: A deterministic assemblage. Oecologia. In press.

KERR, R.M. and K. BROWN. 1977. Data requirements for terrestrial wildlife habitat inventory in Classification, Inventory, and Analysis of Fish and Wildlife Habitat. Proc. Natl. Symp. Phoenix, AZ, January 1977. U.S. Govt. Printing Office, Washington, DC.

KUCHLER, A.W. 1964. Map of potential natural vegetation of the conterminous United States. Am. Geophysical Soc., Spec. Publ. 36.

MANNAN, R.W., M.L. MORRISON, and E.C. MESLOW. 1984. Comment: The use of guilds in forest bird management. Wildl. Soc. Bull. 12(4):426-430.

MATTHEWS, W.J. and L.G. HILL. 1980. Habitat partitioning in the fish community of a southwestern USA river. Southwestern Nat. 25(1): 51-66.

OTIS, D.L., K.P. BURNHAM, G.C. WHITE, and D.R. ANDERSON. 1978. Statistical inference from capture data on closed animal populations. Wildl. Monogr. 62:1-135.

PATTON, D.R. 1975. A diversity index for quantifying habitat "edge." Wild. Soc. Bull. 3(4):171-173.

PHILLIPS, E.A. 1959. Methods of vegetation study. Henry Holt and Company, Inc. 107pp.

PIMENTEL, R.A. 1979. Morphometrics: The multivariate analysis of biological data. Kendall/Hunt Publ. Co., Dubuque, IA.

RALPH, C.J. and J.M. SCOTT, eds. 1981. Estimating numbers of terrestrial birds. Allen Press, Inc., Lawrence, KS.

RICKLEFS, R.E. and M. LAU. 1980. Bias and dispersion of overlap indices: Results of some Monte Carlo simulations. Ecology 61(5):1019-1024.

ROTENBERRY, J.T. and J.A. WIENS. 1980. Habitat structure, patchiness, and avian communities in North America steppe vegetation: A multivariate analysis. Ecology 61:1228-1250.

ROUTLEDGE, R.D. 1980. Bias in estimating the diversity of large, uncensused communities. Ecology 61(2):276-281.

SCHAMBERGER, M.A., A.H. FARMER, and J.W. TERRELL. 1982. Habitat suitability index models: Introduction. U.S. Dep. Inter., Fish and Wildl. Serv. FWS/OBS-82/10.

SEBER, G.A.F. 1973. Estimation of animal abundance and related parameters. Griffin, London. 506pp.

SHORT, H.L. 1983. Wildlife guilds in Arizona desert habitats. U.S. Dep. Inter., Bur. Land Manage., Tech. Note 362. 258pp.

———. 1984. Habitat suitability index models: The Arizona guild and layers of habitat models. U.S. Dep. Inter., Fish and Wildlife Serv. FWS/OBS-82/10.70. 37pp.

——— and K.P. BURNHAM. 1982. Technique for structuring wildlife guilds to evaluate impacts on wildlife communities. U.S. Dep. Inter., Fish and Wildl. Serv., Special Sci. Rep. 244. Washington, DC.

SMITH, M.H., R.H. GARDNER, J.B. GENTRY, D.W. KAUFMAN, and M.J. O'FARRELL. 1975. Density estimation of small animal populations. Pages 25-53 in Golley, F.B., K. Petrusewicz, and L. Ruszkowski, eds. Small Mammals: Their Production and Population Dynamics. Int. Biol. Prog. 5, Cambridge Univ. Press, London.

THOMAS, J.W. 1979. Wildlife habitats in managed forests: The Blue Mountains of Oregon and Washington. U.S. Dep. Agric., For. Serv., Agric. Handbook 553.

TIPTON, A.R. 1980. Mathematical modeling in wildlife management. Pages 211-220 in Schemnitz, S.D., ed. Wildlife Management Techniques Manual. The Wildl. Soc. Washington, DC.

WHITE, G.C., D.R. ANDERSON, K.P. BURNHAM, and D.L. OTIS. 1982. Capture-recapture and removal methods for sampling closed populations. Los Alamos Natl. Laboratory LA-8787-NERP.

WILLIAMS, G.L., K.R. RUSSELL, and W.K. SEITZ. 1977. Pattern recognition as a tool in the ecological analysis of habitat in Marmelstein, A., ed. Classification, Inventory, and Analysis of Fish and Wildlife Habitat. U.S. Dep. Inter., Fish and Wildl. Serv. FWS/OBS-78/76. 604pp.

3

LITERATURE REVIEW

Ora Wagoner[1]

Bureau of Land Management
Service Center
Denver, CO 80225-0047

"Immediately after characterizing a problem, and immediately before initiating any action, find out who might already know the answer. Remember to ask the librarian."

———Alan Speigel

Editor's Note: Too many biologists duplicate work done by others. Libraries can help you determine what's already been accomplished in your field.

Consulting existing information is a mandatory step in preparing for an inventory or monitoring study. This involves more than a literature review. Today's libraries search literature and other information sources with electronic data bases, and they pool their resources by operating in networks. They can also provide you with unpublished data and referrals to current researchers or other information sources, such as museum records.

INTRODUCTION

Wildlife inventories and monitoring studies should begin with searches of existing literature to determine past research and current studies. The tremendous growth in stores of knowledge has made searching the literature a complicated procedure requiring differing techniques and special tools.

A librarian's approach to literature searching is systematic, to investigate all possible sources of information. This chapter provides biologists with guidance on how scientific literature and other information are accessed, and introduces BLM employees to the services provided by the BLM Library (see Appendix I).

Wildlife biologists need to use libraries and their resources to ensure that they perform thorough literature searches and that they access other sources of information essential to wildlife inventories and monitoring studies. Library users must allot time for literature searches to be performed, as materials must often be obtained from distant sources.

The processes used to get information depend on the nature and amount of data requested. In a typical search, an information specialist first checks printed sources available at the library; if not successful, he or she then uses computer networks to inquire about information from other locations. The delivery of documents from other locations can take 4 to 6 weeks, so biologists should plan on this amount of time to conduct their searches.

This chapter covers published materials including serials, reports, books, and other documents, and specialized systems of organized data such as computer data bases and museums. It also provides suggestions on accessing unpublished data.

[1] Present Address: Dudley Knox Library, Naval Postgraduate School, Monterey, CA 93943-5002.

PRINTED MATERIALS

Printed materials include published and unpublished documents. Information about published materials is found in many different forms. Announcements of new books or reviews provide the best method for keeping abreast of newly published material in a specific subject area. These can be found in many journals. Information from book publishers, societies, and universities that publish in particular areas of interest can also be invaluable for learning of new publications. A review of **Subject Guide to Books in Print** (published by R. R. Bowker Company, 205 E. 42nd St., New York, NY 10017) will reveal most new books in all subject areas as well as older books that are still available from the publishers. Appropriate subject headings to use in searching Books in Print are wildlife management and animal populations.

Because book material becomes quickly outdated, the most current printed information is found in serials or periodicals. The process of finding appropriate information begins with locating the appropriate periodicals.

There are various processes available for identifying desired periodicals. Most libraries have access to current subscriptions for the major serial publications in a given subject area. A look at the Table of Contents in each of the appropriate periodicals will identify new articles covering selected areas of interest. For assistance in selecting periodical titles for any subject area, as well as obtaining subscription information, **Ulrich's International Periodicals Directory** is a valuable source to use. Suggested subject headings to check in Ulrich's Directory are Biology-Zoology, Environmental Studies, and Conservation.

If you are not fortunate enough to have easy access to a library that subscribes to the desired journals, personal subscriptions must be considered. They can be expensive, however, and can require time and space for maintenance.

You will probably want to consider some other alternatives. One is to access **Current Contents.** There are several subject-specific versions of Current Contents, each of which is issued monthly. Each issue reprints the Table of Contents from selected journals within its specialty area.

Current Contents/Agriculture, Biology, and Environmental Sciences, in particular, covers over 1,000 periodicals and 300 books of interest in wildlife inventory and monitoring.

Another alternative is to access periodicals through abstracting and indexing services. These are subscription services, usually appearing monthly;

they provide an index to articles, reports, books, and other documents related to specific subject areas. Separate services exist for most subject areas, such as Engineering Index for engineers, or Chemical Abstracts for chemists.

Indexes reference citations under subject headings and authors, giving full citations. For periodical articles, a typical reference will list author, article title, title of the periodical in which it was printed, volume number, issue number, page numbers, and date published.

Abstracting services provide brief summaries about items in addition to information about how they can be located. (Indexing services include only title and bibliographic information.) Some of the more useful abstracting and indexing services to consult for a literature search covering wildlife are

1. Agricultural Index
2. Bibliography of Agriculture
3. Bio Research Index (supplements Biological Abstracts)
4. Biological Abstracts
5. Biological and Agricultural Index
6. Chemical Abstracts
7. Ecology Abstracts
8. Science Citation Index
9. Wildlife Abstracts (Cumulations of Wildlife Review)
10. Wildlife Review
11. Zoological Record.

Other indexing and abstracting services that can be invaluable in a literature search are

1. Cumulative Subject Index to the Monthly Catalog of U.S. Government Publications 1900–1971
2. Supplementary Index to U.S. Publications
3. Masters Abstracts
4. Dissertation Abstracts.

These services cover government documents and doctorate and masters theses. The indexed publications may be published or unpublished documents. A biologist should not overlook the usefulness of these types of publications and other unpublished materials that may be identified through other sources, such as peer contacts.

Each of these services covers a different selection of publications that deal with the subject of wildlife, including inventory and monitoring. The BLM Library, any large public library, or a technical research library can help you access these sources. (See Appendix I for more detailed information on these services.)

Bibliographies

Bibliographies covering specific subject areas cannot be overlooked as sources of information. Depending upon the date of compilation, a bibliography may be excellent for background information if the subject in question must include older, but still applicable, materials. Some useful bibliographies for wildlife subject areas are

1. U.S.—Canadian Range Management, 1935–1977: A Selected Bibliography on Ranges, Pastures, Wildlife, Livestock, and Ranching;
2. U.S.—Canadian Range Management, 1978–1980: A Selected Bibliography on Ranges, Pastures, Wildlife, Livestock, and Ranching; and
3. Wildlife Abstracts—the entire series, from 1935 through 1980.

Other, more subject-specific bibliographies (example, a bibliography on the pronghorn antelope) are valuable resources. They can be found in a variety of places within library collections.

Another often-overlooked source of bibliographies is the references listed at the end of the article or report the biologist already has on an individual topic.

Once an article is identified, a biologist can request a copy of the article from the author, library, or other appropriate organization. Preprinted reprint request cards are useful for this purpose.

Some of the major journals published in wildlife research are outlined in Appendix II. Not listed because of their number are journals that are specific to a State; examples are California Fish and Game and Wyoming Wildlife. These journals are highly useful even for areas outside of the specified State. They can be identified through the use of indexes at the BLM Library or other large library facility.

COMPUTER SYSTEMS

After a researcher has reviewed the appropriate manually-searchable sources, the next step is to consult computer data bases. These data bases generally fall into two major categories—bibliographic and nonbibliographic.

Bibliographic data bases produce results similar to searching the indexing and abstracting services previously mentioned. These data bases contain citations to specific articles, books, and reports, and can be searched by keywords, title words, authors, or other appropriate identifiers. Nonbibliographic data bases differ in that they contain actual data and usually do not refer the user to a printed source.

The use of bibliographic computer data bases is the most efficient method to develop current bibliographies on any topic. Online data bases have existed since the mid 1960s, but they were primarily private files accessible only to special groups. In the early 1970s, online literature searching data bases were made available to the general public, thus limiting the time-consuming step of manually searching tables of contents, indexes, and abstracts. With a few exceptions, coverage of data bases is generally limited to literature from the 1970s to the present. Therefore, any researching into literature published before 1970 must be done manually.

To access the hundreds of data bases available requires the use of a vendor with a software system which provides the commands for searching. The three most frequently used vendors for literature searching are

DIALOG—operated by the Lockheed Corporation,

ORBIT—operated by SDC Search Service, and

BRS—operated by the Bibliographic Retrieval Services Company.

Since knowledge of software is necessary to search efficiently, most researchers access these systems through trained librarians. For example, the computer version of Biological Abstracts on DIALOG goes back to 1969, whereas the printed version began publication in 1927. Experience has shown that researchers sometimes become so impressed with the computer that they tend to forget that not all the published literature is contained within its files. If you desire a comprehensive search, be sure to use both manual and computer searches. Computer searches may be adequate if only recent data are desired.

BLM librarian performing online computer search.

For interactive searching, librarians use terminals and communicate directly with computers to get the desired citations. Searches for wildlife information will most frequently be performed in the data bases AGRICOLA, BIOSIS, CAB, and CRIS, expanding to other sources depending upon the topic.

Commercial sources represent only a portion of the many computer sources which provide information on wildlife inventory and monitoring. Other sources of interest may or may not be bibliographic, and there may be special requirements for access. Noncommercial bibliographic files are basically structured the same as the commercial sources discussed above. Data bases are often maintained and updated by the originating organizations, and access to the data bases is made available only through their approval.

Several noncommercial data bases have been developed by Federal agencies to assist in meeting their missions. Information on specific noncommercial information systems can be found in DuBrock et al. (1981). Three data bases of primary interest for inventory and monitoring of wildlife habitat are the Fish and Wildlife Reference Service, RUNWILD, and the Procedures System. Other data bases pertaining to wildlife-related subjects are summarized in Appendix III.

Fish and Wildlife Reference Service (FWRS)

FWRS is a computer index of documents from the Federal Aid in Fish and Wildlife Restoration Program (Pittman-Robertson and Dingell-Johnson Acts), the Anadromous Fish Conservation Program, the Endangered Species Grant Program, the Cooperative Fishery and Wildlife Research Units, and State game and fish agencies. The data base does not include most routine publications of the U.S. Fish and Wildlife Service.

The system allows access to research information from the State level by providing an index to selected State agency technical reports. Knowledge of indexed publications can be gained from the FWRS quarterly newsletter, which lists new publications, or by obtaining a computer search that will also include older publications. A computer search can be ordered directly from FWRS; there is a charge unless the requester is employed by the U.S. Fish and Wildlife Service or a cooperating agency. This data base is available as a private file on the DIALOG System. The BLM Library has received permission to access it through DIALOG and can accomplish searches for BLM employees.

RUNWILD

RUNWILD is a storage and retrieval system containing wildlife information that can be accessed from three levels: inventory, species-habitat associations, and management data. Developed in 1973 by the USDA Forest Service, it is stored on a computer in Fort Collins, Colorado. RUNWILD can be used for 875 vertebrate species and subspecies in the Southwest, but its format is applicable to any geographical area. Casner et al. 1978, Lehmkuhl and Patton 1982, and Patton 1978, 1979a,b provide details of the system.

Access to RUNWILD is available to any Federal employee and can be obtained by contacting the USDA, Fort Collins Computer Center (FCCC) to establish an account. They will supply a form that requires the requester to provide information necessary for computer access codes and passwords. Accounting and use information is periodically issued to the user from the FCCC. Each account number is billed for use charges as necessary. The data base manager, located in the Region 3 Forest Service in Albuquerque, New Mexico, is the contact person for questions about the system and for obtaining a data base password. Because this is a nonbibliographic data base and the user is usually searching for specific raw data, the BLM Library does not perform these searches for users. I recommend that one account be opened for use by interested personnel at a specific office.

New additions and updates are being made to the file on a continuing basis. RUNWILD II was made available in November 1978 and RUNWILD III in 1982. The data base contents have been made available on microfiche through the National Technical Information Service (NTIS). Information on the use of the microfiche is given in Patton (1979a).

Procedures

"A Procedure for Describing Fish and Wildlife" (nicknamed Procedures) was developed by the U.S. Fish and Wildlife Service for uniformly describing characteristics of fish and wildlife populations (Cushwa et al. 1980; Mason et al. 1979). The system outlines procedures for collecting ecological facts concerning species of vertebrates and selected invertebrates and can be applied to information gathering for species in any area. The Procedures system has been used in data collection in several States, including Pennsylvania, Colorado, Wyoming, Missouri, Illinois, Virginia, Kentucky, and Tennessee. The data bases are administered by the game and fish agency for the State involved, and access is obtained by contacting the data base manager at that organization to set up an account for interactive searching or for requesting a batch search.

The Procedures system provides a useful and valuable methodology for maintaining fish and wildlife species data regardless of the geographic area being considered. The system summarizes information on wildlife habitat use and species distribution, status, and life history. Workbooks that provide specific coding descriptions are used when preparing data for input into the data bases. The standard classifications required for coding the information are widely accepted, recognized standards that are easily understood and applied. For categories in which there were no accepted classification standards already in use, standards were developed and applied.

ACCESSING BIBLIOGRAPHIC COMPUTER DATA BASES

Data bases may be accessed by anyone who has a terminal and has made the necessary financial arrangements. I recommend, however, that biologists obtain bibliographic information through the services of a librarian or information specialist. These professionals are trained in techniques necessary for efficiently and effectively using the variety of subject data bases available. They also keep current on data base changes by reading literature and attending updated training sessions for experienced searchers. Biologists can best use their time reviewing the subject bibliographies that librarians provide for publications of interest.

Many organizations perform literature searches upon request. Most large public libraries and academic libraries offer the service. In most large cities, there are commercial organizations that advertise this kind of service. These sources usually charge actual costs for communications and offline prints and add a percentage as a service charge. Some private individuals also provide computer literature searching for a fee. Consequently, anyone can have access to bibliographic data bases and thus to current research data. The key is knowing where to find the organizations or individuals that will perform the searching.

Within BLM, access to computer literature searching services is available through the BLM Library. The Library maintains contracts with DIALOG, SDC, and BRS, enabling access to more than 250 data bases. The requester simply telephones the BLM Library with details of the request or sends a completed Library Search Request Form to the Library (Figure 1).

To conduct an effective search, a librarian must obtain specific information from the requester concerning the data needed. In addition to a general statement of the overall objective of the search request, the requester must provide key words. Key words are any meaningful words that are important

to the topic being researched. They are terms or phrases that must be present in the citations for the resultant bibliography to be pertinent to the search request. Names of authors and organizations may also serve as specific keys upon which a search can be based.

Librarians develop search strategies from the relationships that exist among key words, grouping like concepts. Search strategies are executed in various data bases that cover subjects of interest, and bibliographies are returned to requesters. Employees then have the opportunity to review the listings, mark those items of interest, and return the lists to the Library. The BLM Library then obtains copies or loans of the desired items. (Appendix I describes some of the data bases available through the BLM Library that contain wildlife information.)

OTHER INFORMATION SOURCES

Information from other than published and electronic information sources can be used to great advantage in research for wildlife inventory and monitoring studies. Two major areas to be considered will be discussed in the remainder of this chapter.

Museums

Museum data can be a useful source of information for the wildlife biologist (See Figure 2). Several museums have important systematic biological research resources that can be used for natural history information on specimens. Of special interest in the consideration of this data source is information on species location. Information such as place of collection, date of collection, specific locality, and county are required in the records for a species.

Museum collections that would be useful for wildlife inventory research are found in many different institutions (see Appendix IV). These organizations produce many publications that contain information about their collections. Information regarding what they publish can be obtained from a variety of sources, mentioned by Moore (1980). Assistance in obtaining any of the references mentioned can be obtained from a large public or a technical library. BLM personnel should seek help from the BLM Library at the Service Center.

Once a museum source is identified, it is possible to locate catalogs of that museum's holdings or specimen listings. One can then access the museum's records covering the species or geographical areas of interest. The searcher should be aware of a major problem that sometimes exists with museum data. If only general localities are recorded for an observation, the usefulness of the record for studies of distribution and habitat may be lost. Accurate association

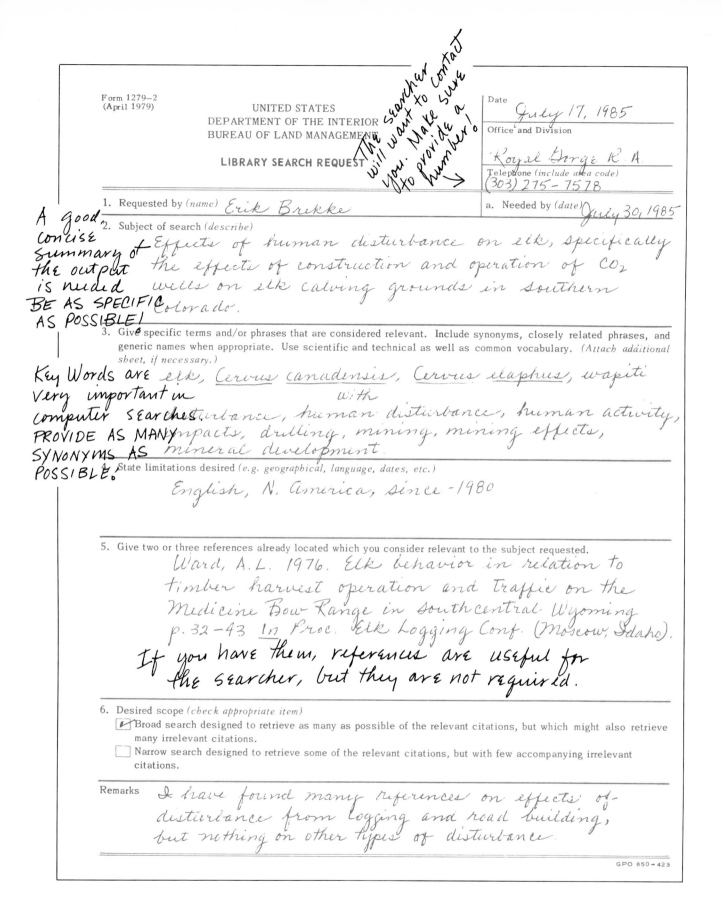

Form 1279-2
(April 1979)

UNITED STATES
DEPARTMENT OF THE INTERIOR
BUREAU OF LAND MANAGEMENT

LIBRARY SEARCH REQUEST

The searcher will want to contact you. Make sure to provide a number! →

Date
July 17, 1985

Office and Division
Royal Gorge R. A.

Telephone *(include area code)*
(303) 275-7578

1. Requested by *(name)* *Erik Brikke*

a. Needed by *(date)* *July 30, 1985*

2. Subject of search *(describe)*

A good concise summary of the output is needed. BE AS SPECIFIC AS POSSIBLE!

Effects of human disturbance on elk, specifically the effects of construction and operation of CO_2 wells on elk calving grounds in southern Colorado.

3. Give specific terms and/or phrases that are considered relevant. Include synonyms, closely related phrases, and generic names when appropriate. Use scientific and technical as well as common vocabulary. *(Attach additional sheet, if necessary.)*

Key Words are very important in computer searches. PROVIDE AS MANY SYNONYMS AS POSSIBLE!

elk, Cervus canadensis, Cervus elaphus, wapiti with disturbance, human disturbance, human activity, impacts, drilling, mining, mining effects, mineral development.

4. State limitations desired *(e.g. geographical, language, dates, etc.)*

English, N. America, since -1980

5. Give two or three references already located which you consider relevant to the subject requested.

Ward, A.L. 1976. Elk behavior in relation to timber harvest operation and Traffic on the Medicine Bow Range in south central Wyoming p. 32-43 In Proc. Elk Logging Conf. (Moscow, Idaho).

If you have them, references are useful for the searcher, but they are not required.

6. Desired scope *(check appropriate item)*

[✓] Broad search designed to retrieve as many as possible of the relevant citations, but which might also retrieve many irrelevant citations.

[ ] Narrow search designed to retrieve some of the relevant citations, but with few accompanying irrelevant citations.

Remarks *I have found many references on effects of disturbance from logging and road building, but nothing on other types of disturbance.*

GPO 850-423

Figure 1. A completed BLM Library Search Request Form.

MUSEUM OF VERTEBRATE ZOOLOGY DATA FOR BIRDS COLLECTED IN COLORADO   06/07/85   PAGE 1

NO. OF ITEMS IN QUERY RESPONSE: 7
NO. OF ITEMS IN DATA BANK: 27438
PERCENTAGE OF RESPONSE/TOTAL DATA BANK: 0.03%

Locality data may be very general or absent

PARULINAE
DENDROICA   CORONATA   MEMORABILIS
          MVZ CAT.NO.: 37399 SKIN: STUDY   SKEL.: NONE
     SEX: M   AGE : JUV.   COLLECTOR: DILLE FRED M.   COLL.NO.:   144
     COUNTRY: COLORADO   STATE/CO./PROV.: LARIMER CO.
      ELEV: --- --; LOCALITY: ESTES PARK
        DATE: 4 AUGUST   1902 WT.: ---   REPRO.: ---
        FAT: ---   MOLT:YES STOM.CONT.:NO   COLORS:NO
        REMARKS: ED:MOLT-SEE SPECIMEN.
DENDROICA   CORONATA   MEMORABILIS
          MVZ CAT.NO.: 44533 SKIN: STUDY   SKEL.: NONE
     SEX: M   AGE : U AD.   COLLECTOR: DILLE FRED M.   COLL.NO.:   205
     COUNTRY: COLORADO   STATE/CO./PROV.: LARIMER CO.
      ELEV: --- --; LOCALITY: ESTES PARK
        DATE: 6 JULY   1904 WT.: ---   REPRO.: ---
        FAT: ---   MOLT:NO   STOM.CONT.:NO   COLORS:NO
        REMARKS: ED:MST.
DENDROICA   CORONATA   MEMORABILIS
          MVZ CAT.NO.: 78903 SKIN: STUDY   SKEL.: NONE
     SEX: F   AGE : U AD.   COLLECTOR: FOWLER F.H.   COLL.NO.:   252
     COUNTRY: COLORADO   STATE/CO./PROV.: LARIMER CO.
      ELEV: --- --; LOCALITY: BERTHOUD PASS
        DATE: 18 AUGUST 1897 WT.: ---   REPRO.: ---
        FAT: ---   MOLT:YES STOM.CONT.:NO   COLORS:NO
        REMARKS: ED:MOLT-SEE SPECIMEN.
WILSONIA   PUSILLA   PILEOLATA
          MVZ CAT.NO.: 78915 SKIN: STUDY   SKEL.: NONE
     SEX: U   AGE : U   COLLECTOR: FOWLER F.H.   COLL.NO.:   318
     COUNTRY: COLORADO   STATE/CO./PROV.: LARIMER CO.
      ELEV: --- --; LOCALITY: LONG'S PEAK; ROCKY MOUNTAIN NAT. PARK
        DATE: 9 JULY   1899 WT.: ---   REPRO.: ---
        FAT: ---   MOLT:NO   STOM.CONT.:NO   COLORS:NO
        REMARKS: BASIN ABOVE TIMBERLINE
WILSONIA   PUSILLA   PILEOLATA
          MVZ CAT.NO.: 78916 SKIN: STUDY   SKEL.: NONE
     SEX: M   AGE : U   COLLECTOR: FOWLER F.H.   COLL.NO.:   319
     COUNTRY: COLORADO   STATE/CO./PROV.: LARIMER CO.
      ELEV: --- --; LOCALITY: LONG'S PEAK; ROCKY MOUNTAIN NAT. PARK
        DATE: 10 JULY   1899 WT.: ---   REPRO.: ---
        FAT: ---   MOLT:NO   STOM.CONT.:NO   COLORS:NO
        REMARKS: BASIN ABOVE TIMBERLINE
TURDINAE
MYADESTES   TOWNSENDI   TOWNSENDI
          MVZ CAT.NO.: 107381 SKIN: STUDY   SKEL.: NONE
     SEX: M   AGE : U   COLLECTOR: ---   COLL.NO.:   ---
     COUNTRY: COLORADO   STATE/CO./PROV.: LARIMER CO.
      ELEV: --- --; LOCALITY: LOVELAND
        DATE: -- MAY   1904 WT.: ---   REPRO.: ---
        FAT: ---   MOLT:NO   STOM.CONT.:NO   COLORS:NO
        REMARKS: ---

Records often date back many years providing valuable historical information

Habitat data may be very general or absent

MUSEUM OF VERTEBRATE ZOOLOGY DATA FOR BIRDS COLLECTED IN COLORADO   06/07/85   PAGE 2

TURDINAE
SIALIA   CURRUCOIDES   ---
          MVZ CAT.NO.: 39662 SKIN: STUDY   SKEL.: NONE
     SEX: F   AGE : U   COLLECTOR: DILLE F.M.   COLL.NO.:   15
     COUNTRY: COLORADO   STATE/CO./PROV.: LARIMER CO.
      ELEV: --- --; LOCALITY: FT.COLLINS
        DATE: 1 APRIL   1900 WT.: ---   REPRO.: ---
        FAT: ---   MOLT:NO   STOM.CONT.:NO   COLORS:NO
        REMARKS: ---

Figure 2. Major scientific museums have computer bases on their collections that contain valuable information on species distribution; an example from the Museum of Vertebrate Zoology at the University of California, Berkeley is shown here.

of the specimen with a particular habitat type may be impossible. The site named may be some distance from the actual collection or observation point, or, in some instances, more than one point in the general area might have the same name. Care should also be exercised in checking the records to be sure they correctly represent the specimen being reported.

Personal Contacts

The value of knowing who is prominent in a specific area of research cannot be overlooked as a potential source for valuable information. Generally these specialists are willing and anxious to tell anyone about their research or send copies of their publications upon request. A way to identify specialists is to make note of recurrent names in subject bibliographies. Libraries can conduct author searches using the data bases discussed earlier; thus, a bibliography of writings done by a specific person can be generated. In addition, the CRIS Data Base and the Federal Research in Progress Data Base, which are available through DIALOG, are data bases that cover current research information. To learn more about the research project listed there, the specialist can contact the researcher whose name is given.

The key step in using this method is locating the specialist. Some useful non-computer tools in your library that can correctly identify and locate an individual are – –

- directories of organizations
- information in proceedings of meetings, symposia, and conferences
- subject matter directories such as the Conservation Directory
- who's who-type publications
- introductory remarks, short biographical information, and title page information in some publications
- inquiries to people who have already been identified.

In many instances, conversation with a colleague can lead to information sources that would be impossible to otherwise identify.

The telephone becomes an important research tool.

SUMMARY

The importance of thorough literature searches cannot be overemphasized. When biologists have conducted studies that are similar to yours, you can realize considerable savings in time and resources. In some instances there may be little or no information available in response to an inquiry, but that in itself is useful to know. If no previous studies exist, the results of your study may be invaluable.

One of the major focuses of libraries today is interlibrary cooperation and shared resources. Even if one has no idea where to begin to look for some person, publication, or resource, a check with your library or information center is a good way to begin.

Most large libraries and many technical libraries have computer services that enable them to identify book and periodical holdings of other libraries throughout the Nation. These services will save time and increase the thoroughness of literature reviews. At the BLM Library, the needs of field employees are given highest priority. For library and information needs, it is the place to begin.

LITERATURE CITED

CASNER, W.B., B. KULONGOWSKI, D.R. PATTON, and S.J. PINKERTON. 1978. RUNWILD—For the UNIVAC 1100 Series: implementation and maintenance. U.S. Dep. Agric., For. Serv. Gen. Tech. Rep. RM-51A. 31pp.

CUSHWA, C.T., C.W. DUBROCK, N.D. GLADWIN, G.R. GRAVATT, R.C. PLANTICO, R.N. ROWSE, and L.J. SLASKI. 1980. A procedure for describing fish and wildlife for Pennsylvania: summary evaluation report. U.S. Dep. Inter., Fish and Wildl. Serv. FWS/OBS-79/19A. 15pp.

DUBROCK, C.W., D.N. GLADWIN, W.T. MASON, Jr., and C.T. CUSHWA. 1981. State-of-the-art of fish and wildlife species information systems in the United States. Trans. North Am. Wildl. Nat. Resour. Conf. 46:156-170.

LEHMKUHL, J.F. and D.R. PATTON. 1982. RUNWILD Wildlife/habitat relationships: user's manual for the RUNWILD III data storage and retrieval system. U.S. Dep. Agric., For. Serv. Southwestern Region. Wildl. Unit Tech. Rep. 68pp.

MASON, W.T. Jr., C.T. CUSHWA, L.J. SLASHI, and D.N. GLADWIN. 1979. A procedure for describing fish and wildlife: coding instructions for Pennsylvania. U.S. Dep. Inter., Fish and Wildl. Serv. FWS/OBS-79/19. 21pp.

MOORE, J.L. 1980. Wildlife management literature. Pages 7.38 in S.D. SCHEMNITZ, ed. Wildlife management techniques manual. 4th ed. Wildl. Soc. Washington, DC. 686pp.

————. 1978. RUNWILD: a storage and retrieval system for wildlife habitat information. U.S. Dep. Agric., For. Serv. Gen. Tech. Rep. RM-51. 8pp

PATTON, D.R. 1978. RUNWILD: a storage and retrieval system for wildlife habitat information. U.S. Dep. Agric., For. Serv. Gen. Tech. Rep. RM-51. 8pp.

————. 1979a. How to use RUNWILD data files stored on microfiche. U.S. Dep. Agric., For. Serv. Res. Note RM-377. 2pp.

————. 1979b. RUNWILD II: a storage and retrieval system for wildlife data. Trans. North Am. Wildl. Nat. Resour. Conf. 44:425–430.

APPENDIX I. <u>BLM Library</u>

History

The BLM Library was established as part of the BLM Service Center in 1970. The Library's services continue to grow with advances in library technology and information management. Today the BLM Library offers a full range of library services, including reference, circulation, aid in acquisition/purchasing, cataloging, interlibrary loan, plus automated and manual literature searching.

Library Collection

The BLM Library contains more than 30,000 volumes and subscribes to over 200 periodicals. This collection covers a wide range of subjects covering all aspects of land management, research and development, computer science, and administration. The library's collection is arranged according to the Library of Congress Classification System and is cataloged through the online shared cataloging system of Online Computer Library Center (OCLC) Inc., a sophisticated online computer network that links over 2000 participating libraries.

Loans

The BLM Library can deliver any published material to field offices. Field personnel are encouraged to use their local resources first; if a publication is not easily identified or obtained, they should contact the BLM Library for assistance.

Most materials in the Library's collection can be loaned for 4 weeks. If the item is small, a photocopy may be made and sent to the requester for retention.

If the publication you need is not owned by the Library, it will be located at another library and borrowed on interlibrary loan. If the publication is available free of charge, you may be provided with the information necessary to obtain your own copy.

Literature Searching

The BLM Library has literature searching capabilities that enable the staff to access over 250 data bases and quickly prepare bibliographies on almost any subject. This service is available to all BLM personnel and may be requested by filling out a "Library Search Request" Form (BLM Form No. 1279-2), or by calling the Library.

The requester provides the librarian with a general statement of the information needed and with key words that can be used in building a search strategy for entering data bases. The key words provided are important in that they determine how suc-

cessful the search will be. Terms must be pertinent to the subject area to locate citations on the desired request.

Reference

A full range of reference services is provided by the Library staff. Requests involve short, specific information questions that may be answered by phone or general reference questions that require more extensive searching. Comprehensive information requests require identification and location of materials; response time will vary from several hours to many days.

Referral

Often the most current or relevant information you seek may not yet be published and may be available only from a specialist. The Library's staff can locate researchers or organizations that specialize in your subject area. The staff has a good knowledge of potential referrals from the personal contacts they make, and from the computerized networks they access.

Current Awareness

The Library's current awareness services are an extension of literature searching. Users can be kept current in selected subject areas through computer based services called Selective Dissemination of Information (SDI). Search strategies are stored and saved as SDIs in selected data bases. As updated materials are added to these data bases, the SDI programs are executed and the Library is provided with offline printouts that are forwarded to the requester.

Special Collections

Presidential Executive Orders (Numbered) June 1985–Present

Federal Register–All volumes available— 1936–Present

Code of Federal Regulations (All titles)

Memoranda—Instruction and Information— Washington Office: 1964–Present

BLM Service Center: 1965–Present

Wildlife information data bases available through the BLM Library.

Data Base	Description	Coverage Dates	Producer	Update Frequency	Comments
AGRICOLA	The cataloging and indexing data base of the National Agricultural Library; contains publications of the USDA Forest Service. Covers worldwide journal and monographic literature in agriculture and related subjects, including animal science, forest and plant-related areas, entomology, and agricultural engineering.	1970–Present	National Agriculture Library	Monthly	Records are citations only.
BIOSIS Previews	Covers all aspects of the life sciences, drawing on all forms of original published literature for citations. Corresponds to the printed publications Biological Abstracts and Biological Abstracts/RRM (formerly entitled Bioresearch Index).	1969–Present	Bioscience Information Service	Semimonthly	Records primarily citation only; but abstracts given for the Biological Abstracts records from July 1976 to the present.
CAB Abstracts	A comprehensive file of agricultural and biological information containing all records in the 26 main abstract journals published by the Commonwealth Agricultural Bureau. Other publications, including books and journals, are scanned. In some instances, less accessible literature is abstracted by scientists working in other countries. Included in this data base are Forestry Abstracts.	1972–Present	Commonwealth Agricultural Bureau	Monthly	Significant papers abstracted; less important works reported as citations only.

Wildlife information data bases available through the BLM Library (continued).

Data Base	Description	Coverage Dates	Producer	Update Frequency	Comments
Comprehensive Dissertation Index (CDI)	Provides access to records of more than 1,000 scientific and technical papers presented at over 1,000 major regional, national, and international meetings each year. Primary subject areas covered include life sciences and chemistry.	1973–Present	Cambridge Scientific Abstracts	Monthly	Records are citations only, but availability and ordering information also given.
Current Research Information Service (CRIS)	A current awareness data base for agriculturally-related research sponsored or conducted by U.S. Department of Agriculture research agencies, State forestry schools, and other cooperating State institutions. Currently active and recently completed projects (within the last 2 years) are in the file. Included among the subjects reported are biological sciences, natural resource conservation and management, and environmental protection.	Last two years	U.S. Department of Agriculture, Washington, DC	Quarterly	Abstracts included with the records.
ENVIROLINE	Covers more than 5,000 international primary and secondary source publications reporting on all aspects of the environment. Has a section on wildlife publications, as well as many other subject overages.	1971–Present	Environment Information Center, Inc.	Monthly	Records contain abstracts.

Wildlife information data bases available through the BLM Library (continued).

Data Base	Description	Coverage Dates	Producer	Update Frequency	Comments
Federal Research in Progress	Provides access to information about ongoing Federally-funded research projects in physical sciences, engineering, and life sciences. Project descriptions include: project title, keywords, start date, estimated completion date, principal investigator, performing and sponsoring organizations, summary, and progress report.	Current reserch	National Technical Information Service	Semiannual (reload)	Abstracts included with the records.
Fish and Wildlife Reference Service	Includes indexed documents from the Federal Aid in Fish and Wildlife Restoration Program (Pittman-Robertson and Dingell-Johnson Acts), the Anadromous Fish Conservation Program, the Endangered Species Grants program, Cooperative Fishery and Wildlife Research Units, and State fish and wildlife agencies. Documents include reports, published papers, technical publications, theses, and special materials, such as endangered species recovery plans.	1950s–Present	U.S. Fish and Wildl. Serv., Division of Federal Aid	Quarterly	
GPO Monthly Catalog	The machine-readable equivalent of the printed Monthly Catalog of United States Government Publications. Contains records of reports, studies, fact sheets, maps, handbooks, conference proceedings, etc., issued by all U.S. Government agencies, including the U.S. Congress.	1976–Present	U.S. Government Printing Office	Monthly	Records contain abstracts.

Wildlife information data bases available through the BLM Library (concluded).

Data Base	Description	Coverage Dates	Producer	Update Frequency	Comments
Life Sciences Collection	Gives worldwide coverage of journal articles, books, conference proceedings, and report literature. Contains information in the fields of animal behavior, biochemistry, ecology, entomology, genetics, immunology, microbiology, toxicology, and virology, among others.	1978–Present	Cambridge Scientific Abstracts	Monthly	Records contain abstracts.
SCISEARCH	A multidisciplinary index to the literature of science and technology that contains all the records published in Science Citation Index and additional records from the Current Contents series of publications that are not included in the printed version of Science Citation Index.	1974-Present	Institute for Scientific Information	Biweekly	Records are citations only.
Water Resources Abstracts	Prepared from materials collected by over 50 water research centers and institutes in the United States. Covers a wide range of water resource topics including water resource economics, ground and surface water hydrology, metropolitan water resources planning and management, and water-related aspects of nuclear radiation and safety.	1968–Present	U.S. Department of the Interior	Monthly	Citations contain abstracts.
Zoological Records	Provides extensive coverage of the world's zoological literature with particular emphasis on systematic/taxonomic information.	1978–Present	Biosciences Information	Bimonthly	Records are citations and contain systematic classification of up to six levels for the organism cited.

APPENDIX II. Publications useful for wildlife studies.

Title	Frequency	Source	Publications in which Indexed	Comments
American Birds	Bimonthly	National Audubon Society 950 Third Avenue New York, NY 10022	Biological Abstracts	Major areas of interest are the changing distribution, population, migration, and rare occurrences of birds throughout the Americas. Formerly issued as Audubon Magazine, Section 2; Audubon Field Notes.
American Fisheries Society Transactions	Bimonthly	American Fisheries Society 5410 Grosvenor Lane Suite 110 Bethesda, MD 20814	Biological Abstracts Chemical Abstracts Current Contents Excerpta Medica Oceanic Abstracts Pollution Abstracts	Objectives of the Society are conservation, development, and wise utilization of recreational and commercial fisheries, promotion of all branches of fisheries science and practice, and exchange and dissemination of knowledge about fish, fisheries, and related subjects.
Auk	Quarterly	American Ornithologists' Union %University of Illinois at the Medical Center Department of Anatomy Box 6998 Chicago, IL 60680	Biological Abstracts Chemical Abstracts Current Contents	Scholarly articles on various topics concerning birds basic to the study of animal or bird behavior. Covers studies throughout the world, but articles are all in English.
Condor	Quarterly	Cooper Ornithological Society, Inc. Meriden Rd. Lebanon, NH 03766	Biological Abstracts Chemical Abstracts Current Contents Zoological Record	A scholarly journal devoted to the biology and behavior of birds in the wild.
Copeia	Quarterly	American Society of Ichthyologists and Herpetologists Department of Ichthyology American Museum of Natural History New York, NY 10024	Biological Abstracts Chemical Abstracts Current Contents Oceanic Abstracts	Concerned with fishes, amphibians, and reptiles.
Fisheries	Bimonthly	American Fisheries Society 5410 Grosvenor Lane Bethesda, MD 20814	Current Contents	Articles are aimed toward scientific research and enlightened management of aquatic resources.
Herpetologics	Quarterly	The Herpetologists' League, Inc. Department of Biology University of Southwestern Louisiana Lafayette, LA 70504	Biological Abstracts Chemical Abstracts Current Contents Zoological Record	The journal is dedicated to furthering knowledge of the biology of amphibians and reptiles.
Journal of Herpetology	Quarterly	Society for the Study of Amphibians and Reptiles Ohio University Dept. of Zoology Athens, OH 45701	Biological Abstracts Current Contents Zoological Record	Contains original research articles and comprehensive reviews on amphibians and reptiles.

Title	Frequency	Source	Publications in which Indexed	Comments
Journal of Mammology	Quarterly	American Society of Mammologists Vertebrate Museum Shippensburg State College Shippensburg, PA 17257	Biological Abstracts Biological and Agricultural Index Current Contents Index Medicus Oceanic Abstracts Pollution Abstracts Selected Water Resources Abstracts	Covers the entire field of mammalian biology, including marine mammals. Papers on each issue may involve taxonomy, ecology, genetics, behavior, physiology, or distribution of species.
Journal of Wildlife Management	Quarterly	The Wildlife Society 5410 Grosvenor Lane Bethesda, MD 20814	Biological Abstracts Biological and Agricultural Index Chemical Abstracts Science Citation Index	Topics ranging from habitat management to the effect of toxic agents on animals and plants and other wildlife management issues.
North American Journal of Fisheries Management	Quarterly	American Fisheries Society 5410 Grosvenor Lane Suite 110 Bethesda, MD 20814		The society promotes the development of all branches of fishery science and practice, and the conservation, development, and wise utilization of fisheries, both recreational and commercial. Journal reports and papers reflect these objectives.
North American Wildlife and Natural Resources Conference Transactions	Annually	Wildlife Management Institute 709 Wire Bldg. Washington, DC 20005		The institute promotes the better management and wise use of all renewable natural resources in the public interest.
Raptor Research	Quarterly	Raptor Research Foundation, Inc. Dept. of Zoology 161 WIDB Brigham Young University Provo, UT 84602		Focuses on predatory birds. Covers all aspects of general ecology, natural history, management, and conservation of diurnal and nocturnal predatory birds.

APPENDIX II. <u>Publications useful for wildlife studies (concluded).</u>

Title	Frequency	Source	Publications in which Indexed	Comments
Wildlife Monographs	Irregular	The Wildlife Society 5410 Grosvenor Lane Bethesda, MD 20814	Current Contents	Each Monograph covers an individual subject relating to resource conservation and wildlife management.
Wildlife Review	Quarterly	Editorial Office U.S. Fish and Wildlife Service Aylesworth Hall Colorado State University Fort Collins, CO 80523		Alerts wildlife biologists of current worldwide literature of wildlife management and conservation. The individual issues of the Wildlife Review are accumulated into Wildlife Abstracts.
Wildlife Society Bulletin	Quarterly	The Wildlife Society 5410 Grosvenor Lane Bethesda, MD 20814	Biological Abstracts	Covers all aspects of management, law enforcement, education, economics, administration, philosophy, contemporary problems, and other topics related to wildlife.
Wilson Bulletin	Quarterly	Wilson Ornithological Society Department of Ornithology Royal Ontario Museum 1000 Queen's Park Toronto, Ont. M552C6	Biological Abstracts Current Contents Science Citation Index Zoological Record	Articles based on research or field observations throughout the world.

APPENDIX III. <u>Other data bases useful for wildlife research.</u>

Title	Source	Emphases
BIO-STORET	Environmental Protection Agency	Zooplankton, macroinvertebrates, some vertebrates.
Data base of animal and plant species of concern to Office of Endangered Species	Brookhaven National Laboratory	Review and candidate species for endangered list and those listed as proposed threatened or endangered.
Information system for regional energy-related assessment and planning (GEOECOLOGY)	Environmental Sciences Division Oak Ridge National Laboratory	Wildlife data—includes breeding bird information, endangered and mammal range maps and distribution data.
Integrated Habitat Inventory and Classification System (IHICS)	Bureau of Land Management	Site-specific wildlife species information—amphibians, birds, reptiles, mammals.
National Data Base (RPA)	Forest Service	Birds, mammals, reptiles, amphibians, fish, invertebrates
Raptor Management Information System (RMIS)	Bureau of Land Management	Management and impact information on all nocturnal and diurnal raptors worldwide. Provides for retrieval of annotated bibliographies of published and unpublished information concerning raptors.
Sensitive Wildlife Information System (SWIS)	U.S. Army Corps of Engineers	Biology and distribution of approximately 100 selected mammal, bird, reptile, amphibian, fish, and invertebrate species. Emphasizes Federal "endangered" or "threatened" species.
Species Data Bases	Migratory Bird and Habitat Research Laboratory (MBHRL)	Avian Information
Species Data Bases	National Coastal Ecosystems Team	Aquatic species—fish, molluscs, aquatic crustaceans
Species Data Bases	Office of Migratory Bird Management (MBMO)	Avian Information
Species Systems	Northern California and Pacific Northwest Coastal Characterization species systems	Vertebrate species and selected invertebrates
Terrestrial Species Database	Western Energy Land Use Team (WELUT)	Amphibians, reptiles, birds, mammals
Western Sierra Wildlife/Habitat Relationships Program (WHR)	Forest Service Region 5	Birds, mammals, reptiles, amphibians
WILD RAM	Forest Service Region 4	Birds, mammals, reptiles, amphibians, fish
Wildlife-Habitat Relationships Data Base (WILDHAB)	Forest Service Region 6	Birds, mammals, reptiles, amphibians, fish
Wildlife Management Information System (WMIS)	Forest Service Region 9	Birds, mammals, reptiles, amphibians, fish
WILD01	Forest Service Region 1	Birds, mammals, reptiles, amphibians, fish

APPENDIX IV. <u>Museums useful for wildlife inventory research.</u>

American Museum of Natural History
79th Street and Central Park West
New York, NY 10024
212-873-1300

California Academy of Science
Golden Gate Park
San Francisco, CA 94118
415-221-5100

Carnegie Museum of Natural History
4400 Forbes Avenue
Pittsburgh, PA 15213
412-622-3131

Field Museum of Natural History
Roosevelt Road at Lake Shore Drive
Chicago, IL 60605
312-922-9410

Los Angeles County Museum of Natural History
900 Exposition Boulevard
Los Angeles, CA 90007
213-744-3414

Museum of Vertebrate Zoology
University of California
2593 Life Sciences Building
Berkeley, CA 94720
415-642-3567

Museum of Zoology
University of Michigan
1109 Washtenau
Ann Arbor, MI 48109
313-764-0476

National Museum of Natural Sciences
Victoria Memorial Building
McLeod and Metcalfe Streets
Ottawa, Ontario, K1A OMB
CANADA

U.S. National Museum of Natural History
Smithsonian Institute
10th Street and Constitution Ave. NW
Washington, DC 20560
202-357-2664

4

HABITAT MAPPING

Richard M. Kerr

U.S. Bureau of Land Management
Las Cruces District Office
Las Cruces, NM 88004

"Facts concerning game distribution, behavior, history, and management can often be accumulated on maps or tables to better advantage than in notes."

—Aldo Leopold, *Game Management*

Editor's Note: Mapping and classifying land areas into distinct habitat types is a necessary part of most wildlife activities. This is particularly true of wildlife inventories, but it is also generally necessary for management, monitoring, and research. Although the principles of habitat mapping and classification have not changed since Leopold (1933) wrote about them, many new tools are now available. This chapter covers the principles and provides a guide to the new techniques available.

INTRODUCTION

Aldo Leopold noted that facts necessary for wildlife management can better be recorded as maps and tables rather than notes because notes tend to be unorganized and difficult to analyze. He went further to describe type mapping and the sorts of wildlife information that could be placed on base maps (GLO plats, U.S. Geological Survey quads, or aerial photography; Leopold 1933).

Mapping is done for several purposes or uses in wildlife habitat management:

- to show geographic locations of wildlife habitat types;

- to show relationships of types to other types;

- to show community (types of habitat) interspersion;

- to quantify types of wildlife habitat;

- to overlay wildlife habitat types with other resource inventories; and

- to provide geographic locators in which to record site-specific animal occurrence and use.

Mapping various types of habitat by drawing boundaries around these types not only provides data for inventory and analysis, but also provides the habitat manager with information for monitoring management direction or problems. With habitat maps, the biologist can identify and locate the problem, quantify the size of the problem and provide, in some instances, certain types of baseline data.

Most wildlife data bases or inventory systems used before 1970 described the life history of a species and, as part of that discussion, related the kinds of habitat that the species used. This is an impractical organization of data for a land manager because as many as 400 vertebrate species may occur in a U.S. Bureau of Land Management (BLM) District. Mapping the habitat individually for each one of these species would be an impossible job. Ranges would have to be delineated by observation or capture, and this would be difficult for 1 species and impossible for 400.

A system that delineates, measures, and locates on a map different types of habitat and describes the occurrence of animal species in each type is more useful to the land manager. Such a system can allow sampling of habitats and extrapolation of data to similar habitats.

In addition, land managers must have a system that allows them to record site-specific information (e.g., 200 elk [*Cervus elaphus*] winter in this area). Also, special features in the landscape like cliffs, caves, and springs need to be recorded in the system.

CLASSIFICATION SYSTEMS FOR MAPPING

Mapping from the Top Down: Continental or Regional Classifications

In the late 1890s, Clinton Hart Merriam published "Life Zones of the San Francisco Mountains." This elevational zone classification was one of the first ecosystem classifications to be used by ecologists in North America (see Figure 1) and is still useful in ecological analyses (Brown 1982). The early ideas of Clements (1928) and, later, Kuchler (1964), tended to locate regional ecosystems described by dominant natural potential vegetation.

The recent efforts of Brown et al. (1977), although at a larger scale (1:1,000,000), are still regional, geographic vegetation types based on natural potential vegetation (Figure 2).

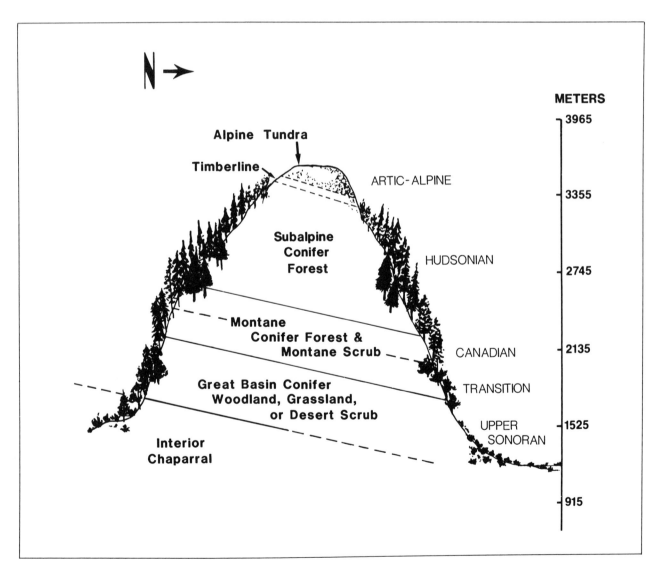

Figure 1. Merriam's Life Zones, although helpful as a general characterization, cannot be used as an inventory because of individual site variations within elevational zones (Merriam 1890).

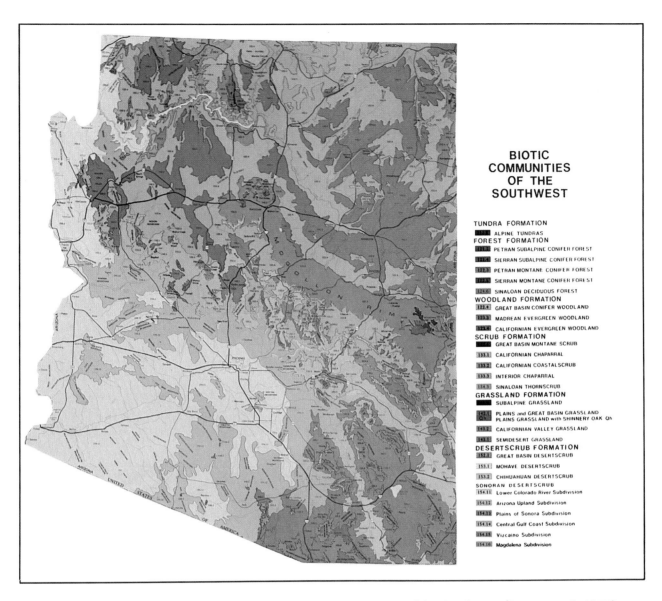

Figure 2. A regional classification map called Biotic Communities of the Southwest (Brown et al. 1977), although at a larger scale than most regional maps, is still too small for field management information. The State of Arizona is shown as an example.

Robert Bailey's "Ecoregions of the United States" (1976) does not predominantly use vegetation data as most do but uses a variety of biotic and abiotic factors to develop a single geographic classification at a scale of 1:7,500,000. This again could be considered a regional ecosystem map or classification (Figure 3).

The BLM has taken A.W. Kuchler's (1975) map of Potential Natural Vegetation (Figure 4) and regionalized it by using physiographic region boundaries based on soils, vegetation, and regional topography. These regionalized potential vegetation types are used as ecosystem boundaries within which to aggregate, analyze, and extrapolate information or data.

The trouble with most of these delineations and classifications that start mapping from the top down (from regional or continental ecosystems) is that the scale is extremely small for use by field biologists, and mapping is based on potential vegetation and not on the existing vegetation. Consequently, accuracy in the field is very limited. The major benefit then of these preclassified geographic systems is to use their boundaries for aggregating data for limiting extrapolation of information.

Mapping from the Ground Up: Integrated and Component Classifications

The classifications of Merriam (1890), Kuchler (1964), Brown et al. (1977), and Bailey (1976)

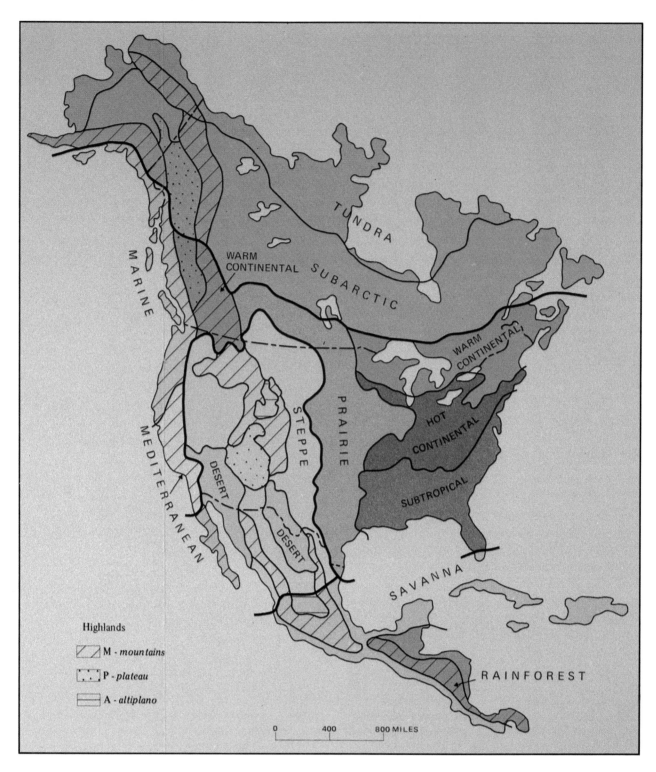

Figure 3. Ecoregions of the United States are a classification that represents a hierarchy of regional ecosystems.

might be considered to be integrated because they are geographically specific, and their boundaries encompass all habitat components within the mapped ecosystem. Field-level classifications that use all habitat components for delineating mapping units are also integrated systems.

Another type of classification system has been constructed where each component (vegetation, landform, soil, climate, etc.) is mapped individually and independently from local to continental levels, but is not "integrated" into one mapping unit to form an ecosystem. This is called a hierarchical com-

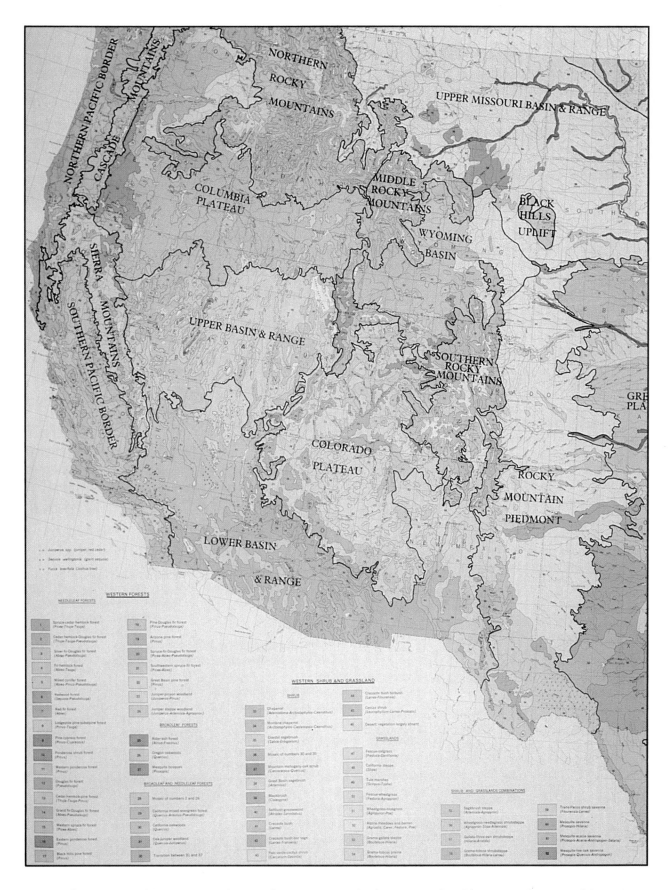

Figure 4. A.W. Kuchler's Potential Natural Vegetation is further regionalized by using physiographic region boundaries.

ponent classification system. Hence there are integrated and component classifications.

Since integrated classifications are maps or depictions of geographically located ecosystems, they are best for wildlife habitat mapping. This is because animals respond to all components within an area, not just one. In addition, they react to the size and location of these small ecosystems.

Within the last decade, integrated concepts have been so mixed with hierarchical component concepts that it is now difficult to determine a partially integrated system from the hierarchical component system. A good example of this is "A Component Land Classification for the United States" (Driscoll et al. 1983). This system, authored by five government agencies, is meant to be a hierarchical component classification system; yet two components, soil and vegetation, are integrated through habitat types and range sites. Other component hierarchies are not yet developed. What is called a component system now appears to be an integrated system.

In the field, less time should be spent on regional classification systems and more time on local inventories, as far as wildlife habitat data are concerned. A classification can be built from a good inventory, but an inventory cannot be built from a classification.

MAPPING TOOLS

To inventory wildlife habitat, a biologist must construct a map to quantify and geographically locate habitat. Describing animal communities found within plant communities by composition is merely a characterization of different kinds of habitat. An inventory of wildlife habitat has not been completed until a reasonably accurate map of the habitat has been constructed. Similarly, monitoring studies initiated must have a map to be of continuing value; anything less is incomplete or unusable.

The map may be an overlay of a base map, a computer graphic printout, delineators of habitat on a U.S. Geological Survey quadrangle map, a typed aerial photo (see Glossary for definitions), a Landsat image, a typed planimetric map, a plane table map, or typed orthophoto maps.

A map scale for inventorying and monitoring should be at the range somewhere between 1/60,000 to 1/2,000, depending on the intensity and purposes of the study. Maps at a smaller scale than 1:60,000 may provide some assistance in planning, but are not large enough to solve actual habitat management problems.

Some maps have been constructed by using a scale of 1/2 inch to equal a mile or 1/100,000. These were commonly used in BLM's Unit Resource Analysis (URA) system. At this scale, these maps can only give spatial relationships of gross kinds of habitat. They are not suitable for recording and analyzing wildlife habitat data.

Aerial Photos

The most commonly used mapping tools are aerial photos from 1/2,000 to 1/63,831, and 7.5- and 15-minute U.S. Geological Survey quadrangles. Obviously, the larger the survey area in acres, the smaller the scale will be to meet economic criteria. The easiest and best photo-map combination for broad inventories over large acreages of land 8,000 to 400,000 ha (20,000 to 1 million or more a.) is the U.S. Geological Survey orthophoto quadrangle (1/24,000) (Figure 5) and the 7.5-minute topographic quadrangle (Figure 6). The orthophoto quad is a corrected copy of an aerial photo at 1:24,000 scale, which allows the habitat typing to be placed directly on a corrected aerial photo which is the same area, scale, and control as the base map. Habitat type lines can be traced or plotted from the orthophoto quadrangle to the topographic quadrangle of the same area.

Orthophoto maps (Figure 7) are corrected aerial photos with topographic map information superimposed. They thus combine all features of both 7.5-minute topographic quadrangles and orthophoto quadrangles. These are ideal for habitat mapping but are only available for a few areas.

If orthophoto quadrangles are not available at 1/24,000, a 7.5-minute U.S. Geological Survey quadrangle map is used; type lines are transferred from aerial photos with a plotter or zoom transfer scope.

A complete description of the principles behind aerial photography can be found in Burr (1976).

The kind of aerial photos used may vary as to the situation and region. The first habitat inventories were completed with black and white aerial photos (Figure 8), and these are still very useful and acceptable. A recent innovation is the use of color-infrared film which is particularly useful if one wants to emphasize riparian vegetation or seasonally dominant vegetation. This film produces a brighter shade of red on the print where more growth is taking place (Figure 9).

In the Southwest, where vegetation is sparse and soil highly visible, the use of true color film is desirable. Color often gives better definition between habitat types than black and white photos give (Figure 10).

Figure 5. Orthophoto quadrangles like these are excellent corrected photos for habitat mapping.

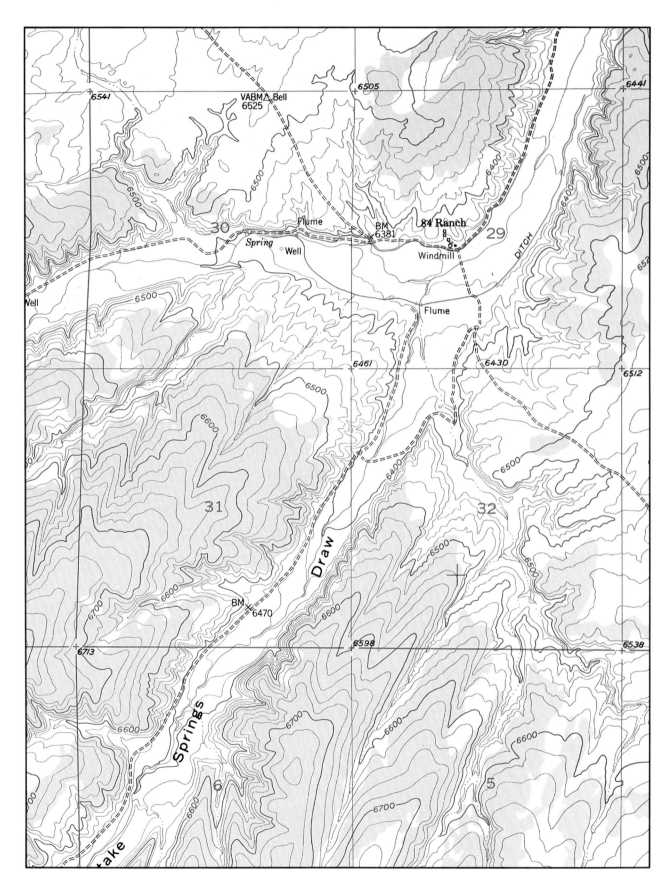

Figure 6. U.S. Geological Survey 7.5-minute topographic quadrangles are the mainstay for base maps for wildlife habitat inventory.

Figure 7. The U.S. Geological Survey 7.5-minute orthophoto map provides a corrected aerial photo with topographic and other map features.

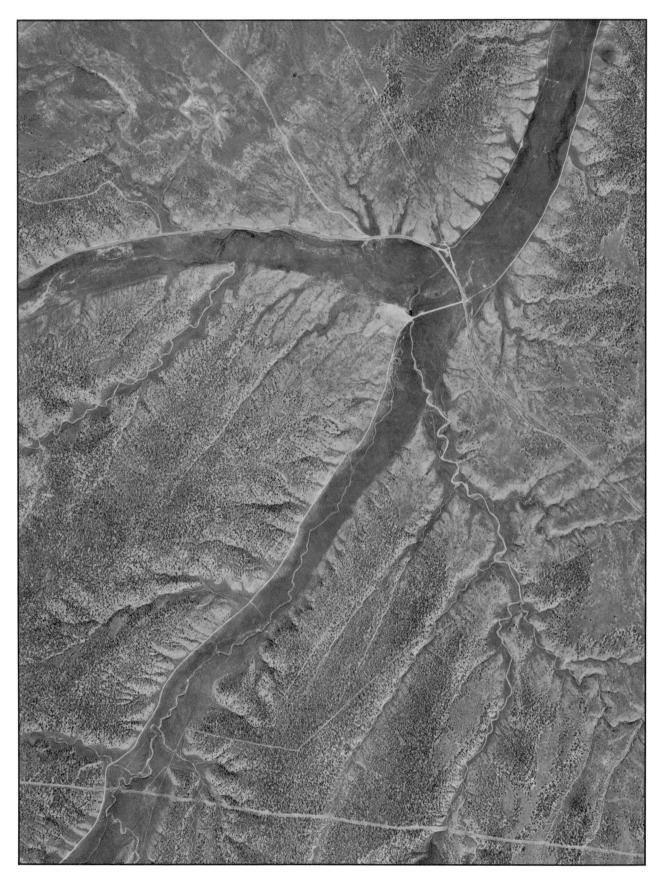

Figure 8. Black and white aerial photo from Piceance Basin, Colorado.

Figure 9. Color infrared aerial photo of same area as Figure 8.

Figure 10. True color aerial photo of same area as Figure 8.

The photo scale recommended for overall inventories on public lands has historically been close to 1/24,000 because this ties in well with the scale of U.S. Geological Survey quads, which make excellent base maps for typing vegetation. This medium-scale photography is normally available from various government agencies (Appendix I).

Larger-scale photos about 1/2,000 to 1/4,000 are beneficially used where typing is necessary on highly valuable habitats such as riparian areas in semiarid regions. Color-infrared aerial photography for these areas may be valuable (Figure 11). This large scale is also extremely useful for habitat monitoring because individual trees and shrubs can easily be seen as well as stream channel changes. This large-scale photography is normally not available from government agencies and must be obtained by contract. In some instances, larger scale photography has been used for monitoring vegetation damage.

Figure 11. Large-scale (1/2,000) color infrared aerial photo of riparian areas along Black Canyon Creek, Arizona.

A complete description of low-level aerial photography for riparian inventory and monitoring was given by Cuplin (1981).

In addition to mapping, aerial, oblique, and ground-based photographs are indispensable as records for baseline data and for composition, density, and structure of habitat. A properly identified photograph may be the best record for a baseline study of a variety of monitoring studies. The use of a cover or profile board can show the decreasing density of perennial grass on a duck-nesting habitat study, whereas a series of yearly photos from a photo hub may show the invasion of grass into a shrub type used for deer winter feeding. "A picture is worth a thousand words."

Landsat Images

Landsat images are sometimes used to delineate gross vegetation cover types. Reflected light is recorded in four bands and can be used to generate Landsat images that can be manually interpreted or the digital reflectance data can be computer-classified. Pixels of about 0.04 ha (1.1 a.) picture reflected light and are density-sliced and artificially classified into false colors for various classifications. Because of the characteristics of the Landsat reflections, these scenes do not provide all the benefits of a photograph at medium scales. They show no texture, shadow, or highlights, but just the color of a particular classification (Figure 12). Also, the discerning abilities of the Landsat scanners are not capable of separating vegetation species or areas that give the same reflectance. Detailed classifications are not possible with Landsat images.

A common standard used to describe levels of classification detail has been a "Land Use and Land Cover Classification System for Use with Remote Sensor Data" (Anderson et al. 1976). (Note: The author gives description titles to only Levels I and II, leaving the development of Levels III and IV to local workers [Table 1].)

Information given in the latest Manual of Remote Sensing (Colwell 1983) states "Efforts to classify Level III categories using Landsat generally result in overall accuracy figures of less than 70%, a figure often considered unacceptable." In actuality, vegetation cover classifications for land management use require more definition than Level III (Anderson et al. 1976). Level IV approaches the level necessary for management use, and it is even less accurate than Level III, perhaps 50 percent or less. If Level II was described as shrubland, then the Level III classification descriptor might be rabbit brush (*Chrysothamnus* sp.) while the Level IV descriptor might be rabbit brush-snakeweed (*Gutierrezia* sp.).

Unlike more easily interpreted photographic scenes, Landsat scenes are highly dependent on ground truthing. The more ground truthing, the more accurate is the final classification scene. The problem of signature extension has not been solved for all areas and vegetation types, hence a poorly ground-truthed scene of vegetation may be highly inaccurate.

Vegetation signatures (reflection shades) many times do not remain accurate even over reasonable distances (3 to 5 mi.); therefore, for accurate classifications, signatures must be classified for small areas by using a great deal of ground truthing and supervised classifications (Short 1982). Because of this, it may be more economical to use aerial photos to lend more accuracy to final products. Also, because definitions on photos exceed those of pixel classifications, ground control (section corners, etc.) is better accomplished with photos than Landsat images.

Although Landsat images may be an efficient advance in providing a mapping base where there are no existing base maps (i.e., Alaska or Africa), most areas in the western U.S. are already accurately mapped with 7.5-minute U.S. Geological Survey topographic quadrangles. These maps, constructed through photo interpretation, in many instances have some vegetation mapped at a level comparable to the Level III mapping used by contemporary Landsat projects. This mapping is much more accurate and at a larger scale than the Landsat images available either by standard order or by computer construction and enhancement. Computer-enhanced Landsat images therefore must be used with discretion because they do not provide mapping at the accuracy and level (or scale) for most BLM management needs. However, they may supplement or provide an additional tool for enhancing management data such as information on snow cover, cloud cover, soils, and repetitive synoptic views. If aerial photos were to be totally replaced by Landsat scenes as a basic habitat inventory tool, the land management profession would have taken a giant step backward.

Sources of Supply

Aerial photos and Landsat images may be obtained from affiliates of the National Cartographic Information Center (Appendix I). Assistance for BLM employees may be obtained from the BLM Service Center. For U.S. Geological Survey maps of all kinds, including orthophoto quads for areas west of the Mississippi, write to the U.S. Geological Survey, Box 25286, Denver Federal Center, Denver, CO 80225.

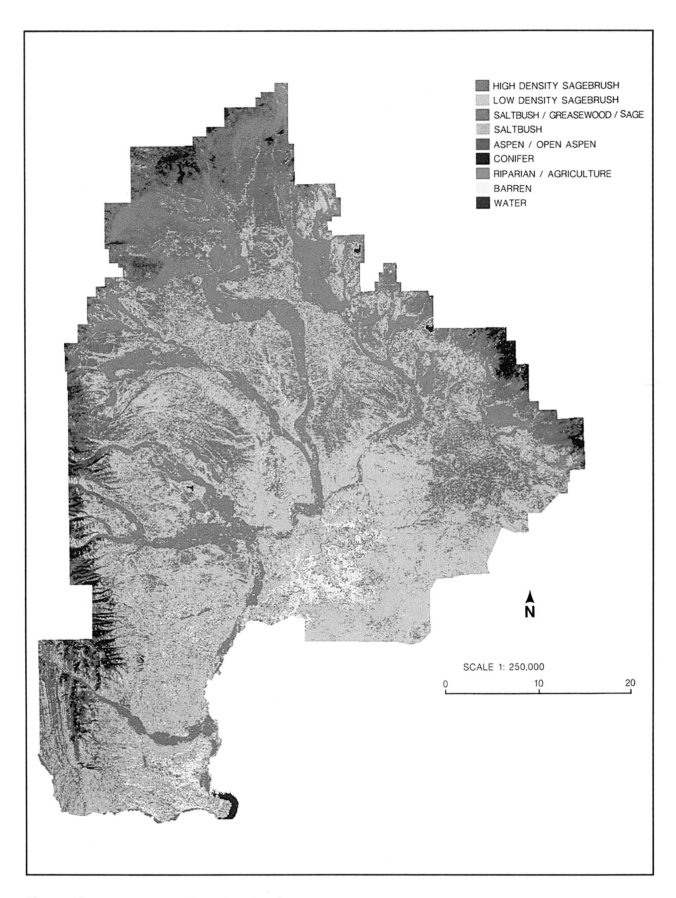

HIGH DENSITY SAGEBRUSH
LOW DENSITY SAGEBRUSH
SALTBUSH / GREASEWOOD / SAGE
SALTBUSH
ASPEN / OPEN ASPEN
CONIFER
RIPARIAN / AGRICULTURE
BARREN
WATER

N

SCALE 1: 250,000

0   10   20

Figure 12. An unsupervised Landsat classification.

Table 1. Land use and land cover classification system for use with remote sensor data (modified from Anderson et al. 1976).

Level I[1]	Level II[2]
Urban or built-up land	11. Residential[3] 12. Commercial and services 13. Industrial 14. Transportation, communications, and utilities 15. Industrial and commercial complexes 16. Mixed urban or built-up land 17. Other urban or built-up land
Agricultural land	21. Cropland and pasture 22. Orchards, groves, vineyards, nurseries, and ornamental horticultural areas 23. Confined feeding operations 24. Other agricultural land
Rangeland	31. Herbaceous rangeland 32. Shrub and brush rangeland 33. Mixed rangeland
Forest land	41. Deciduous forest land 42. Evergreen forest land 43. Mixed forest land
Water	51. Streams and canals 52. Lakes 53. Reservoirs 54. Bays and estuaries
Wetland	61. Forested wetland 62. Nonforested wetland
Barren land	71. Dry salt flats 72. Beaches 73. Sandy areas other than beaches 74. Bare exposed rock 75. Strip mines, quarries, and gravel pits 76. Transitional areas 77. Mixed barren land
Tundra	81. Shrub and brush tundra 82. Herbaceous tundra 83. Bare ground tundra 84. Wet tundra 85. Mixed tundra
Perennial snow or ice	91. Perennial snowfields 92. Glaciers

[1]Level 1 Typical data characteristics at this level would be found on Landsat types of data.
[2]Level 2 Typical data characteristics at this level would be found on high-altitude data at 40,000 ft. (12,400 m) or above (less than 1:80,000 scale).
[3]Numbers and titles refer to standard land use codes and definitions from U.S. Urban Renewal Administration et al. 1965.

THE INTEGRATED MAPPING PROCESS

The traditional integrated mapping approach fits well with the concept of habitat inventory, which has five basic steps:

(1) mapping;
(2) stratification and classification;
(3) inventory of habitat-species relationships;
(4) site-specific inventory; and
(5) data storage, retrieval, and analysis.

Mapping

To provide for the aggregation of wildlife habitat data at local levels and up into higher levels of field classification, a mapping unit is used to collect and quantify data. This mapping unit is delineated on aerial photographs as a homogeneous polygon—homogeneous as to existing vegetation, landform, and soil. Although size of the mapping unit has no required range, it varies between 0.8 ha and perhaps 4,000 ha (2a. and 10,000a.). There may be some misunderstanding of what the mapping unit is called. In BLM's Integrated Habitat Inventory and Classification System (IHICS), it is called a habitat site (Hamilton et al. 1983). In other systems, it is called a mapping unit, whereas in the BLM's vegetation inventory, it is called a site writeup area.

Mapping units are first pretyped on aerial photos (1:24,000) or orthophoto quads. This is done by examining the photos and drawing boundary lines around areas homogeneous in terms of existing vegetation, landform, and soils (if soil inventory overlays or ecological site delineations are available). To reduce displacement caused by relief, the effective area or central portion of a photo pair should be used for interpretation.

Once all areas of the photos are pretyped, the boundaries or delineations that were put on in the office are checked in the field by visual observation. It is also desirable to use some management boundaries to break the mapping unit by forming one of its boundaries (e.g., a grazing allotment boundary should not be crossed when delineating mapping units because many times data need to be accumulated and analyzed according to grazing allotment). Similarly, Resource Area boundaries should not be crossed when delineating mapping units. During a field check, section corners are located and pinpricked through the photograph. Identification is placed on the back of the photo for control. If orthophoto quads are used, this is not necessary; each mapping unit is assigned a unique designation within the inventory area.

Certain habitat data are recorded for each mapping unit while checking boundaries in the field. Landform, site elevation, dominant and subdominant vegetation (by visual observation or vegetation data), aspect (by cardinal direction), and slope data are recorded and entered on the appropriate form. Acreage should be computed and recorded as soon as the unit boundary is mapped and becomes final.

Once mapping units have been checked and are considered final, they are transferred to a 1:24,000 U.S. Geological Survey quadrangle map if they are not already on an orthophoto map. This is done by a zoom transfer scope or other type of plotter and by using the located section corners for control.

Where ecological sites (potential vegetation) have been delineated on the ground and units of existing vegetation have been delineated on maps, the same units and numbers can be used for habitat

inventory data base. If this option is available, the work described in the preceding paragraphs is not necessary except when collecting the described habitat data.

Stratification and Classification

After all mapping units have been given an identification number and initial habitat information has been gathered and recorded, the mapping units are placed in strata which will ultimately be a field level classification. To determine the number and types of strata, the biologist in charge will need to make a field review, noting which types of habitat should be designated as habitat strata. The partially completed habitat information forms can be used for stratifying by reviewing the habitat site information on them, particularly the dominant and subdominant vegetation, landform, or other factors based on the needs of the inventory situation. Once criteria for grouping strata are determined, classifications are made by assigning each mapping unit to the stratum that applies.

The BLM IHICS can take input forms showing habitat data for mapping units and automatically sort strata by selected criteria. For example, if all mapping units located on a mesa where ponderosa pine (*Pinus ponderosa*) is dominant and Columbia needlegrass (*Stipa columbiana*) is subdominant are selected as a stratum, the computer will easily sort and form the stratum. Each classification (stratum) is assigned a number and name. Each mapping unit then has its classification number recorded on the appropriate form. New strata may be devised at any time by using different criteria and reassembling the mapping units.

Although existing vegetation and landform are important, criteria for forming strata may vary. If a particularly important animal is present, a stratum of habitat may be made for it by using an important characteristic of its habitat. For instance, if Gila monsters (*Heloderma suspectum*) are found in a creosote-bursage habitat, but only in areas that contain abundant ground litter, and if abundant litter is used as a criterion within this cover type, a stratum is constructed that will represent potential Gila monster habitat.

Sufficient habitat data (described below) are collected for each map unit. Strata can be constructed by using habitat data in manual or automatic data processing (ADP) operations (i.e., sort all map units that are ponderosa pine and pine needlegrass [*Stipa pinetorum*] at 7,000 to 9,000 ft [2,121 to 2,727 m] elevation). Consequently, biologists have the ability to construct strata for sampling based on a variety of criteria once map units are delineated and initial habitat information is recorded.

The mapping unit is the lowest level of ecosystem classification systems. The stratum level is the aggregation of mapping units having similar vegetation, landform, soil, etc. The two lower levels (map unit, stratum) provide a means of categorizing field inventory data to facilitate data analysis for land-use planning and decisionmaking. They provide a long-term accumulation and aggregation of new data from the mapping unit level to upper levels of continental or regional systems.

Inventory of Habitat-Species Relationships

Once delineation and classification of mapping units have been made, the next step is to collect information that will reveal species-habitat relationships. For each stratum, representative mapping units are selected for sampling vegetation and wildlife.

Vegetation composition and structural data should be sampled in the same habitat sites where the animal sampling occurs. If these data are available from other vegetation inventories, then sampling is not needed.

A hypothetical list prepared through literature review by using upper-level classifications (Kuchler 1964; Brown et al. 1977) can be used as a basis for sampling animal occurrence. A sampling plan is developed that verifies the occurrence of animal species listed hypothetically. If a complete wildlife inventory is conducted, each animal class is inventoried for one or more seasons, depending on its life history. Generally, inventories are conducted for mammals, birds, reptiles, and amphibians. When time and money are limited, only those classes determined important in the management situation are inventoried. Species thought to occur in the selected habitat sites are listed in the data base as hypothetical. Unique or important animals expected to occur in the inventory area should be verified by using appropriate inventory methods.

Sampling of animals in a stratum will relate occurrence of animals to certain canopies or other habitat structure, or other special features within the habitat. One way to do this is to use inferential statistics and compare occurrence of certain animals with occurrence of a particular layer of habitat or special feature. This is accomplished best if the biologist completes the same vegetation (habitat) inventory at each animal sampling location. After sufficient numbers of samples have been taken, a statistical comparison can be made. Vegetation or habitat sampling methods may be developed by region or area of inventory, considering those things in the habitat that appear to be important in that particular region.

A simple list of animals occurring in an area is helpful, but the land manager needs additional infor-

mation. This includes season of use; function of the habitat for a particular species; determination of whether the habitat is crucial for the species; and the relative abundance of the species, compared with other habitats.

If stratification and sampling have revealed that two or more strata have the same animal community and uses, then these may be combined into a single habitat stratum.

If the purpose of mapping is to monitor a wildlife habitat problem, then the same procedures of mapping apply except that vegetation sampling is done by a system that monitors those aspects of the habitat that are being managed or affected.

Because the BLM IHICS uses inventories of existing vegetation, the potential vegetation situation is normally portrayed by using habitat types (plant associations) for forests and range or ecological sites for rangelands. Comparing the existing vegetation with this potential vegetation will give possibilities for vegetation management, which would direct animal use or animal community progression toward a desired level. This potential determination may be available for broad areas or can be determined individually for small management areas (such as deer feeding areas).

Much money and time can be spent acquiring potential information on the total area of rangelands within a BLM administrative unit jurisdictional boundary, when in practice, only a small amount of this information will be used in habitat management decisions. Biologists, therefore, cannot afford to spend their time delineating potential for all areas. Biologists should restrict their efforts toward determining vegetation potential only in areas where information is not available from the U.S. Soil Conservation Service (SCS) range site system or the forest habitat type system, and the information is necessary for specific immediate wildlife habitat management analysis.

It is important to understand that vegetation progression under commercial forest management changes structure rapidly, whereas composition and structural changes under range management situations take long periods and the effects are much more subtle and generally less predictable.

Site-Specific Inventories

Mapping units provide the mechanism for recording site-specific data because each has a unique number which locates it geographically. For those species important to the management of public lands and for which information cannot be safely extrapolated, site-specific data must be collected. These species are generally highly mobile species (such as raptors and wild ungulates) whose presence is not well correlated with just a habitat or vegetation type (e.g., because all ponderosa pine stands do not contain deer, we must find ones that do and record by a mapping unit number).

The form for recording information for mapping units and site-specific data should also allow for continuing entry of animal occurrence data as they are gathered, either in complete inventories or opportune sightings.

Sometimes features of the habitat that are too small to map (springs, walls, power poles, cliffs, etc.) have a major effect on whether certain species of wildlife occur in an area. The effect may be either negative or positive. These are called special habitat features, and a complete habitat inventory should record them. Time and money will not allow a total inventory of all special habitat features. The biologists must choose those features that are important to wildlife in their inventory areas and inventory them. (For instance, all special habitat features that are water-related should be inventoried.) Species that are benefitted or discouraged by the special habitat feature are listed. This gives the biologists the second form of site-specific data for their data bases.

Data Analysis, Storage, and Retrieval

In the next stage, field forms for animal use, occurrence, relative abundance, and crucial habitat are assembled and, depending on the system, summarized on additional forms. At this stage, the biologist may need to modify the original strata designations based on the additional information collected.

At this stage, data is normally entered into some sort of computer system. In the BLM IHICS, the summary forms are entered into a computer data base. Regardless of the system used, forms should be checked carefully prior to key-entry.

In the BLM's IHICS, summary data are edited automatically and then used to create data bases that are available in the field on either a time-sharing computer system or on a field office microcomputer. Separate data bases are maintained for habitat sites (mapping units), standard habitat sites (mapping strata), and special habitat features for each inventory area.

The use of ADP has generally proceeded in two reasonable directions as far as wildlife habitat inventory and monitoring are concerned. Some agencies have emphasized digitized graphic displays (maps) of types of habitat. This was done by using systems such as the Map Overlay and Statistical System (MOSS) to construct polygons (habitat mapping units from digitized data derived from aerial photos). For large study areas, 400,000 ha (1 million a.) or more at 1/24,000 accuracy, digitizing needed for constructing computer-generated maps is expensive and time-consuming, but its use is increasing at the field level.

Other agencies emphasized the measurement of biological components within strata and mapping units. These data are normally input as tables and other narratives whereas the maps that have been used with them have been manually constructed. The BLM IHICS is a good example of a system that sorts several dozen habitat characteristics.

Both types of systems are valuable where large amounts of data are handled, and the automation entices field offices to use the data repeatedly for a variety of uses, thereby obtaining greater benefit.

The present move toward balanced emphasis on computer mapping and definitive biological data will make the data even more usable and valuable. This type of balanced emphasis could provide a very usable Geographic Information System (GIS). Processes such as the digital elevation model (DEM) can be included or used in conjunction with GIS thereby enhancing the utility of both data bases.

DISCUSSION

The overall purpose of mapping is to organize wildlife habitat data to manage wildlife habitat and to mitigate or eliminate impacts of other uses. The habitat map is the basic tool for the land-management biologist. Geographic locations, quantification of habitat, and specific habitat characterization cannot be accomplished without a map. In addition, maps are necessary to compare wildlife habitat with other resources for multiple-use decisions. Even though contemporary map-making methods may change from a manually-constructed paper map to a computer-generated graphic, a map is only as accurate as its human constructor.

LITERATURE CITED

ANDERSON, J.A., E.E. HARDY, J.T. ROACH, and R.E. WIT-MER. 1976. A land use and land cover classification system for use with remote sensor data. U.S. Dep. Inter., Geological Survey, Professional Paper 964. 28pp.

BAILEY, R.G. 1976. Ecoregions of the United States. U.S. Dep. Agric., Forest Service. Ogden, UT 84401. 77pp.

BROWN, D.E., ed. 1982. Desert plants, biotic communities of the American Southwest, United States and Mexico. Vol. 4, Numbers 1-4, Special issue, University of Arizona, Tucson. 342pp.

———, C.H. LOWE, and C.P. PASE. 1977. Biotic communities of the Southwest. U.S. Dep. Agric., Gen. Tech. Rep. RM-41. 342pp.

BURR, R.D. 1976. The use of aerial photographs. Technical Note 287. U.S. Dep. Inter., Bur. Land Manage. BLM Service Center, Denver, CO 80225. 34pp.

CLEMENTS, F.E. 1928. Plant succession and indicators. The H.W. Wilson Co. New York, NY. 453pp.

COLWELL, R.N., ed. 1983. Manual of remote sensing. 2nd Ed., Vol. II. American Society of Photogrammetry. Falls Church, VA. 2440pp.

CUPLIN, P. 1981. The use of large-scale color infrared photography for stream habitat and riparian vegetation inventory. Technical Note 325, U.S. Dep. Inter., Bur. Land Manage. BLM Service Center, Denver, CO 80225. 7pp.

DRISCOLL, R.S., D.L. MERKLE, J.S. HAGIHARA, and D.L. RADLOFF. 1983. A component land classification for the United States: Status report. Technical Note 360. U.S. Dep. Inter., Bur. Land Manage. BLM Service Center, Denver, CO 80225. 30pp.

HAMILTON, C.K., R.M. KERR, and L.A. PETERSON. 1983. IHICS, the Bureau of Land Management's habitat inventory system. Presented at National Workshop on Computer Uses in Fish and Wildlife Programs—A State of the Art Review. Virginia Polytechnic Institute and State University, Blacksburg, VA. 13pp.

KUCHLER, A.W. 1964. Potential natural vegetation of the conterminous United States, map and manual. Special Publication 36, Am. Geographic Soc. New York, NY. 122pp.

———. 1975. Potential natural vegetation of the conterminous United States, revised map. Am. Geographic Soc. New York, NY.

LEOPOLD, A. 1947. Game management. Charles Scribner's Sons. New York, NY. 481pp.

MERRIAM, C.H. 1890. Results of a biological survey of the San Francisco Mountain region and desert of the Little Colorado in Arizona. North Am. Fauna No. 3. U.S. Dep. Agric., Washington, DC (Reprinted in selected works of Clinton Hart Merriam. Natural Sciences in America, K.B. Sterling, ed.) Arno Press. New York, NY 1974.

SHORT, N.M. 1982. The Landsat tutorial workbook, basics of satellite remote sensing. NASA Reference Publication 1078. National Aeronautics and Space Administration. Washington, DC.

U.S. URBAN RENEWAL ADMINISTRATION, HOUSING AND HOME FINANCE AGENCY, and BUREAU OF PUBLIC ROADS. 1965. Standard land use coding manual, a standard system for identifying and coding land use activities. Washington, DC. 111pp.

APPENDIX I. Sources of Supply

National Affiliate Offices

1. National Cartographic Information Center
   U.S. Geological Survey
   507 National Center
   Reston, VA 22092.

2. Eastern Mapping Center
   National Cartographic Information Center
   U.S. Geological Survey
   536 National Center
   Reston, VA 22092.

3. Mid-Continent Mapping Center
   National Cartographic Information Center
   U.S. Geological Survey
   1400 Independence Road
   Rolla, MO 65401

4. Rocky Mountain Mapping Center
   National Cartographic Information Center
   U.S. Geological Survey
   Stop 504, Box 25046, Federal Center
   Denver, CO 80225.

5. Western Mapping Center
   National Cartographic Information Center
   U.S. Geological Survey
   345 Middlefield Road
   Menlo Park, CA 94025.

6. Alaska Office National Cartographic Information Center
   U.S. Geological Survey
   Skyline Building
   218 E Street
   Anchorage, AK 99501.

7. EROS Data Center
   U.S. Geological Survey
   Sioux Falls, SD 57198

State Affiliate Offices

1. *Arizona*
   Arizona State Land Department
   Information Resources Division
   1624 West Adams, Room 302
   Phoenix, AZ 85007

2. *Idaho*
   Idaho State Historical Library
   325 West State
   Boise, ID 83702

State Affiliate Offices (cont.)

3. *Montana*
   Montana Bureau of Mines and Geology
   Montana Tech
   Main Hall, Room 200
   Butte, MT 59701

4. *Nebraska*
   Director and State Geologist
   Conservation and Survey Division
   University of Nebraska
   Lincoln, NE 68508

5. *New Mexico*
   University of New Mexico
   Technology Applications Center
   2500 Central Avenue, S.E.
   Albuquerque, NM 87131

6. *Nevada*
   Nevada Bureau of Mines and Geology
   University of Nevada, Reno
   Reno, NV 89557-0088

7. *Oregon*
   Oregon State Library
   Public Services
   Salem, OR 97310

8. *Utah*
   Utah Geological and Mineral Survey
   606 Black Hawk Way
   Research Park
   Salt Lake City, UT 84108-1280

9. *Washington*
   (User Services)
   Washington State Library
   Information Services Division
   Olympia, WA 98504

   (Data Acquisitions)
   Division of Management Services
   Photos, Maps, and Reports Section
   QW-21, Public Lands Building
   Olympia, WA 98504

10. *Wyoming*
    State Engineer
    Barrett Building
    Cheyenne, WY 82002

II MAJOR HABITATS

Shirley McCulloch 1987

5

FORESTS

Jack Ward Thomas

Pacific Northwest Forest and Range Experiment Station
U.S. Forest Service
LaGrande, OR 97850

Jared Verner

Pacific Southwest Forest and Range Experiment Station
U.S. Forest Service
Fresno, CA 93710

"Forest ecosystems are far too complicated for us to ever fully understand and precisely predict future conditions. Inventories of current conditions, and technologies for analyzing resource potentials and conducting management actions, are often incomplete or less than desired.... None of these are excuses for lack of action. They are simply the circumstances under which resource managers operate."

— Hal Salwasser

Editor's Note: This is the first in a series of chapters dealing with habitats—other upland habitats include deserts, rangelands, and tundra. These are not clearly demarked ecosystems; they are important basic habitat types that overlap geographically and descriptively. As such, they require different emphases when planning inventory or monitoring studies of wildlife resources.

While more emphasis has been placed on inventory and monitoring of forested habitats than on others, there are no generally accepted or standardized techniques. Biologists still need to design studies based on local needs, while taking advantage of the experiences of others.

INTRODUCTION

The question to be answered in this chapter is, what are the important attributes of forest habitat to be measured if inventorying or monitoring of wildlife habitat is the goal? The answer will vary depending on the questioner's interests. For example, if the aim is to obtain a general idea of the habitat and which species groups are (or could be) present, it may be sufficient to determine the extent of each forest type and its attendant successional stages or structural conditions and the presence or absence of animal groups of interest. This could be accomplished either through observation or from information relating vertebrate species to forest plant communities and attendant seres or structural conditions (see Thomas 1979b or Verner and Boss 1980 as examples).

If, however, one desires sufficient information to predict the response of a single species to habitat alterations, more specific habitat attributes must be considered. For example, if Rocky Mountain elk (*Cervus elaphus nelsoni*) in the heavily forested areas of the intermountain West were of particular interest, information should be collected on stand size, stand height, canopy closure, density of roads open to vehicular traffic, cover/forage ratios, distance to edges between cover and forage, and, in some instances, quantity and quality of forage. In short, the more specific the question, the more detailed the habitat information required.

Jenkins (1977:43) quoted Frank Egler as saying, "Ecosystems are not only more complex than we think, they are more complex than we can think." He then said,

"... to deal with this literally incomprehensible complexity, for whatever purpose, none of us have any choice but to take a strenuously reductionist approach.... which means making hard choices about which aspects to emphasize and which to disregard. No single set of choices can ever satisfy everyone or every purpose, so there will never be a single classification system ... it is both necessary and legitimate to tailor our efforts to our own purposes ..."

First, we need a clear idea of what to inventory or monitor and why. There are no pat answers to the questions—what should be monitored? What approach should be used? How should the inventory and monitoring be accomplished? The answers depend on the legal requirements, management needs, objectives of the wildlife management, resources, and skills of persons available to do the work. There is not and should not be a list of species, guilds, or life forms that should be monitored on each forested area. There is not and should not be specification of a vegetative classification system to be used. There is not and should not be a prescribed list of the right techniques to be used to inventory and monitor either habitats or associated wildlife species.

It sounds trite, but the only realistic answer is—it all depends. This entire area of activity is so new and so dynamic, in terms of management need and technology available, that the best any reviewer can do is to array the existing information and let the user choose, considering the particular objectives, needs, and resources available.

One needs to settle on a forest habitat classification system to structure the effort. This is necessary to provide—

- a basis for stratifying forest habitats for sampling;

- a framework for communication among various disciplines and the public;

- a mechanism for aggregating information from local areas into district, regional, and even larger assessments.

These first steps of deciding what and why to inventory and of selecting an appropriate habitat classification system to guide that effort are critical and must be carefully considered. Decisions should be predicated upon these questions:

(1) How much will it cost and can it be afforded?

(2) What steps can be taken to ensure the usefulness of a data base that can be developed at a realistic cost?

Intensive and frequent sampling of forest habitat is expensive. Sampling that includes statistically valid estimates of animal numbers can be prohibitively expensive (Verner 1983). In many situations, then, only relatively simple, nonintensive surveys are affordable.

Further, it is likely that wildlife biologists will continue, at least in the foreseeable future, to occupy a distinctly minority position in the major land management agencies. If they want to be effective, therefore, they will recognize the advantages of making their data bases compatible with those developed by the disciplines that dominate the agency—e.g., foresters and planners. Among the advantages are—

- increased probability that forest wildlife and wildlife habitat can be more readily considered in land-use planning and management decisions;

- better communication among disciplines and with the public;

- possible reduction in the cost of gathering needed information about wildlife habitat.

CLASSIFICATION SYSTEMS

The habitat classification system used in inventory and monitoring of forest wildlife and their habitats is usually selected on the basis of the classification system being used by forest inventory or timber managers, usually both. Forest habitat classification is complex and little agreement exists on a standard approach (Bailey 1977). The confused status of the situation is apparent from a perusal of a 1977 symposium on "Classification, Inventory, and Analysis of Fish and Wildlife Habitat" (Marmelstein 1977).

Several criteria have been used to develop systems of ecosystem classification, including biological (Brown et al. 1980; Garrison et al. 1977) and physical (Godfrey 1977). The most commonly used standard classification system for western forests based primarily on vegetation was developed by Daubenmire (1968). With some modification, Daubenmire's system has been extended to half or more of the forested land of the western U.S. The primary classification systems in use in the 11 western States and Alaska are shown in Table 1.

Bailey (1982:16) noted that—

"Past wildlife studies and inventories have proceeded without the benefit of an integrated system. Biologists often had to depend on any available, sometimes inadequate, information or devise their own classification, usually a map featuring forest cover. Many investigators gathered disconnected bits of descriptive information on habitat without a classification framework to give them meaning. Without such a framework, it was very difficult and sometimes impossible to integrate wildlife information with other information for evaluating trade-offs or interactions within the fish and wildlife resource and between it and other resources. As of 1970, there was no national approach to integrating wildlife information . . ."

What was true in 1970 is still true today. But improvements have been made and efforts are underway to develop an acceptable National approach (Hoekstra et al. 1983).

What can be done when it makes sense to use a finer or coarser breakdown of habitats than fits the

Table 1. Major classification systems for forests of the western States.

System	Description	Source
Habitat types		Daubenmire 1968; Pfister 1977
Land systems	Involves delineation, description, and evaluation of relatively homogeneous units of land at local or regional scale. Hierarchical components exert the most control at the top.	Wertz and Arnold 1972; Bailey 1976, 1978; Crowley 1967
ECOCLASS	A method of integrating several systems to identify homogeneous land units. Developed by the U.S. Forest Service.	Cortiss 1974; Buttery 1978
ECOSYM	Links classification to land management needs.	Henderson et al. 1978
National Site (Land) Classification System	Like ECOCLASS, a component system that involves vegetation, soil, landform, and water. Developed jointly by the U.S. Forest Service, Bureau of Land Management, Fish and Wildlife Service, Geological Survey, and Soil Conservation Service.	Driscoll et al. 1978
Integrated Habitat Inventory Classification System	A six-level system for organizing species occurrence data from plant communities to physiographic regions. Developed by Bureau of Land Management.	U.S. Department of the Interior, Bureau of Land Management 1978
Land resource regions and major land resource areas	Groups organizationally related and geographic factors related to land use, topography, climate, water, and soil. Developed by the Soil Conservation Service.	Austin 1965; Kuchler 1964
Land use and cover mapping program	Broad-based information, i.e., not intended for wildlife. Developed by the U.S. Geological Survey.	Anderson et al. 1976
Forest cover types	Classification based on dominant tree species.	Society of American Foresters 1954

classification system in use by dominant forces in the agency? A mechanism exists to allow data collection at the most meaningful level for specific wildlife purposes. One such mechanism, developed for use in the Blue Mountains of the Pacific Northwest, has proved useful there and elsewhere (Table 2). In such a system, the classifications are "crosswalked" so that information gathered under one system can be appropriately applied to others.

Given such information as that shown in Table 2, data on wildlife habitat can be developed at the most appropriate level for the wildlife resource and then, if appropriate, can be applied to other land

Table 2. Relationships among four plant community classifications in the Blue Mountains of Oregon and Washington (adapted from Thomas et al. 1979a).

Forest and range ecosystems as described by Garrison et al. (1977)	Plant community designations from Thomas et al. (1979a)	Plant community types of the Blue Mountains as described by Hall (1973)	Potential natural vegetation as described by Kuchler (1964)
Pinyon-juniper[1]	Western juniper Juniper/stiff sage scabland Juniper/low sagebrush Juniper/big sagebrush	Juniper/bunchgrass	K24 Juniper steppe woodland
Ponderosa pine	Ponderosa pine Ponderosa pine/fescue Ponderosa pine/bitterbrush/Ross sedge Ponderosa pine/blue wildrye	Ponderosa pine/wheatgrass	K10 Ponderosa shrub forest
Douglas-fir	Mixed conifer	Ponderosa pine/Douglas-fir/elk sedge Ponderosa pine/Douglas-fir/snowberry-oceanspray Ponderosa pine/Douglas-fir/ninebark	K12 Douglas-fir forest (interior)
Larch		Mixed conifer/pinegrass-ash soil Mixed conifer/pinegrass-residual soil	K14 Grand fir/Douglas-fir forest
Spruce-fir	White fir (grand fir)	White fir/twinflower White fir/big huckleberry White fir/grouse huckleberry	
	Subalpine fir/big huckleberry	Subalpine fir/grouse huckleberry Subalpine fir/whitebark pine/sedge	K15 Western spruce-fir forest
Lodgepole	Lodgepole pine	Lodgepole pine/pinegrass-grouse huckleberry Lodgepole pine/big huckleberry Lodgepole/grouse huckleberry	No provision in Kuchler (1964)

[1]See specific reference citations for a listing of scientific names of plants noted in this table.

classification systems. The rule-of-thumb, then, for selecting the appropriate habitat classification system to be used as the basis for inventorying and monitoring has two components:

(1) Select the system in use by the dominant professional group in the agency in order to enhance communication.

(2) If another finer or coarser grained classification is used as the framework for the wildlife-habitat data base (for whatever reason), make sure it can be "crosswalked" with other classification systems (Verner 1984).

The ultimate objective is to present wildlife habitat in such a manner that it will be effectively considered by land-use planners and managers. The selection of a habitat classification system that may be technically superior for wildlife-habitat evaluation purposes is a strategic error if it cannot be easily translated into the system used by the dominant resource.

This requirement for crosswalking is addressed by Bailey (1980:17) in his discussion of the ecosystem concept of classification:

"This concept regards the earth as a series of interrelated systems in which all components are linked, so that a change in any one component may bring about a change in other components and in the operation of the whole. An ecosystem approach to land evaluation stresses the interrelationship among components ... Since ecosystems are spatial systems, they will be consistently inserted, or nested, into each other. Each level subsumes the environment of the system at the level below it. At each level, new processes emerge that were not present or not evident at the next lower level..."

In this example (Table 2), the dominant land management agency (U.S. Forest Service) active in the area used Hall's (1973) description of plant communities as the basic classification system to guide forestry and range management decisions. On the whole, the divisions were too fine to be germane to the classification of information about wildlife-habitat relationships. Therefore, for relating wildlife to habitats, resource professionals developing information on wildlife-habitat relationships (Thomas et al. 1979a) modified the classification system derived by Garrison et al. (1977). They thought that these broader community descriptors were more suitable to the existing state-of-knowledge concerning wildlife-habitat relationships. The biologists involved recognized that the vegetative classification schemes developed by Kuchler (1964 and 1970) were receiving favorable attention by persons dealing with na-

tional assessments, but they thought that such a system was too broad to be meaningful in the context of wildlife-habitat relationships.

The decision about what classification system to use may have already been decided by the existence of a wildlife-habitat data base for the area in question. The development of such data bases was stimulated by requirements of the National Environmental Policy Act of 1969 (which required environmental impact statements for federally funded projects), the Forest and Rangelands Renewable Resource Planning Act of 1974, the National Forest Management Act of 1976, and the Federal Land Policy and Management Act of 1976. The first such data bases for the western States were developed by Patton (1978) for the Southwest and Thomas (1979b) and associates for the Pacific Northwest. These initial publications were quickly followed by similar efforts for the western Sierra Nevada in California (Verner and Boss 1980), the Great Basin of southeastern Oregon (Maser and Thomas 1983), and western Oregon and Washington (Brown, in press). Parallel efforts are underway in several other areas in the western U.S. and Canada. The Fish and Wildlife Habitat Relationships Program of the U.S. Forest Service was established to encourage the development of similar programs throughout the U.S. and to enhance development of additional habitat analysis techniques. Cushwa and DuBrock (1982) detailed various wildlife data bases in existence or being developed by various State and Federal agencies.

Various permutations of this basic approach to wildlife-habitat analysis seem to be most widely used in dealing with analysis and management of forested habitats of the western U.S. The basis of the original system was to consider wildlife habitats at three levels:

(1) The relationship of groups and individual species to major plant communities and their successional stages or structural conditions for activities, including feeding and reproduction;

(2) A description of special habitats that were not adequately considered through plant communities and successional stages;

(3) The habitat requirements of featured species, i.e., the species that receive special management attention.

MAJOR SPECIES GROUPS

The purpose of this section is to review and evaluate the existing approaches to forming groups of species for inventory and monitoring in forests so as to reflect habitat conditions.

When dealing with the vertebrate component of the forest ecosystem, it is necessary to determine which species or group of species need to be inventoried. Obviously, there are insufficient knowledge, skill, and resources to deal with inventory and monitoring of all the species.

When wildlife-habitat data bases are developed, each individual species must be considered. But if the relationships of all vertebrate species within an area to habitat features are considered, the detail and sheer volume of data can be overwhelming. When possible, it would be more convenient and cheaper to use groups of species rather than individuals.

Featured Species

The desirability of the featured species approach (examining the relationship of groups of species to habitat variables) is in keeping with the necessity for the "strenuous reductionist approach" mentioned earlier in relation to habitat classification. A group called the Committee of Scientists, who recommended regulations as required by the National Forest Management Act of 1976, called for use of indicator species in setting up and monitoring forest management plans. These indicators were to serve as surrogates for the welfare of a group of species.

Assume that the spotted owl *(Strix occidentalis)* was chosen as the indicator species for species that thrive in old-growth Douglas-fir *(Pseudotsuga*

menziesii) forests in western Washington. If the spotted owl's habitat requirements were met, according to the indicator species concept, other species that require old-growth Douglas-fir would be provided for simultaneously.

Verner (1984) reviewed the use of the guild concept as applied to management and essentially rejected the indicator species concept on practical and technical grounds. A guild is made of species within an order that jointly exploit the same resource in an ecosystem. He did believe that the use of whole guilds (i.e., each bird of any species within a guild is tallied in sampling) to evaluate habitat conditions might be useful but recommended that (p. 1) "much testing must be done before it is applied." This means that the research community has not yet tested the hypotheses inherent in the indicator species approach. Field biologists who are using the approach should admit that to themselves and to the users of that work.

Guilds. The guild concept assumes that animal species within an order can be grouped by how similarly they use environmental resources (Root 1967). Severinghaus (1981) applied the guild concept to species of vertebrates according to their response to habitat and habitat change, delineating 30 mammal and 31 bird guilds. He said (p. 189), "The usefulness of guilds . . . relies on the principle that . . . actions impacting one member of the guild should impact . . . other members in a similar way."

Short and Burnham (1982) and Short (1983) presented a technique for structuring guilds for use in evaluating impacts of habitat alterations on wildlife communities. Described are mathematical and computer aids to form guilds, as opposed to the more intuitive classifications proposed by Thomas et al. (1979a), Severinghaus (1981), and others.

The Short-Burnham and other mathematically derived techniques, although holding promise, are probably more complex than needed for application by most field biologists. Mathematical sophistication may exceed biological sensibility in this approach (Verner 1984). It might be best to contract for these services if this approach is broadly applied in management.

Thomas et al. (1979a), in an effort to respond to the recommendations of the Committee of Scientists, modified a suggestion of ornithologist Antti Haapanen (1965, 1966) that species of birds could be grouped according to their habitat use into "life forms." They extended the concept to include all vertebrates and grouped the species (379) that occurred in the Blue Mountains of Oregon and Washington into 16 life forms. Life forms include groupings of vertebrates—regardless of order—that require similar habitat attributes.

Oversophisticated mathematics may shed great darkness on the subject.

What those initial life forms were is not as important as the concept; for habitat management, vertebrate species could be grouped by the general type of habitat they used for feeding and reproduction, irrespective of taxonomic considerations. The concept assumes only that each species in a life form will be present in suitable habitat. It does not, however, assume that species within the life form use the habitat similarly or that numbers of the various species will rise and fall simultaneously.

Life forms are constructed to fill a management need, and the number of life forms is limited only by the amount of knowledge available on the relationship of the individual species to habitat. Life forms can be created or eliminated, or species can be moved between life forms to fit the need or to respond to new information. It is also important to understand that in using the life form approach, it is the habitat condition that is inventoried and monitored, not the species in the life form.

The three approaches discussed for grouping species in order to relate them to habitats (indicator species, guilds, and life forms) share the idea that animal species can be grouped according to response to habitat. If so, that grouping can be a real aid in the simplification of habitat analysis across the spectrum of the vertebrate species present in the area to be considered.

Other approaches have included those of Root (1967), MacMahon et al. (1981), and Jaksic (1981). Techniques used to formulate guilds include cluster analysis (Crome 1978), principal components analysis (Holmes et al. 1979; Landres and MacMahon 1980; Short and Burnham 1982), canonical correlation (Folse 1981), discriminant function analysis (DeGraaf and Chadwick 1984; Dueser and Shugart

1979; Lindeman et al. 1980; Nie et al. 1974; Rao 1966; Williams 1980), and polar-ordination (Anderson 1971; Austin and Orloci 1966; Bannister 1968; Bray and Curtis 1957; DeGraaf and Chadwick 1984; Gauch 1982). Note that all these techniques produce investigator-defined guilds, "a fact that introduces circularity into their use for examining ecological questions" (Verner 1984:1). This simply means that there is a danger, if the investigator defines the guild, of altering the expected to fit the observed species-habitat conditions and vice-versa.

It seems inappropriate to present lists of life forms or guilds here. They should be developed by the user from the available wildlife data base on the occurrence of animal species and their relationship to various habitat conditions. The only advantage of dealing with life forms or guilds is the enormous savings that can result from monitoring whole guilds instead of indicator species. Conversely, if the decision is made to monitor indicator species, the species groupings delineate those species that the indicator species represents. We reject the indicator species approach to monitoring as neither reasonable nor practical for the reasons presented by Verner (1984). In practice, most management analysts have fallen back on consideration of individual species—either *en masse* or of a select few of particular interest.

We recommend the following:

(1) Do not use the indicator species approach unless regulations require it. If the indicator species approach is used, recognize that it is merely a hypothesis and that the users must provide the test.

(2) Use the guild approach, as it seems to be the most economical and practical approach to monitoring species as reflective of habitat condition.

(3) Use the life form approach when monitoring is, for financial or other reasons, restricted to vegetative conditions; it is essential to understand that the approach involves a hypothesis that must be tested by the user.

CRITICAL HABITAT FEATURES

Soil

Soil is a primary variable contributing to the development of plant communities. With the exception of fossorial vertebrates, the soil type *per se* does not appear to be a controlling factor in animal habitat. The relationships between soils and wildlife are thoroughly discussed by Robinson and Bolen (1984).

Thomas et al. (1979a:26) suggested that—

"Plant communities and their successional stages have unique environmental conditions that are ecologically important as niches for wildlife species . . . The niches are a product of the plant community, its successional stages, and other environmental factors—including soil type, moisture regime, microclimate, slope, aspect, elevation, and temperature. The complex interactions of site and plant community structure could be dissected and the more precise of each on the animal community determined. If such information existed, it would probably be too complex to use readily. The plant community type, however, can be considered an integrator of the many factors interacting on the site."

The factors that plant communities integrate include soils. We recommend that soils not be a part of monitoring unless there are particular reasons for including them, i.e., the soil texture has particular significance to a wildlife species of sufficient interest that monitoring is deemed appropriate. Even then, it is important to identify what soil attribute is significant to the occurrence of the species in question. This could include such things as texture, size of soil particles, cohesiveness, moisture retention properties, depth, and drainage.

Physical Features

Maser et al. (1979a, b) noted that geomorphic and edaphic habitat features occurred within the general vegetative mosaic and have special values to wildlife. These "unique" or "geomorphic" habitats included cliffs, caves, talus, lava flows, sand dunes, and playas. Each of these habitats supports one or more species not found in the general forest environment.

Talus is the accumulation of rocks at the base of steep slopes.

Verner and Boss (1980:2-3) called such components "special habitat requirements," adding ground burrows, friable soils, moist soil, earthen bank, rock outcrops, limestone outcrops, and crevices. The species to which such features are important were identified. For example, friable soils are important to burrowing animals; dead-and-down woody material is critical to reptiles, amphibians, and small mammals; caves harbor bats; and cliffs provide nest sites and roosts for raptors.

Plant Communities and Successional Stages

The forest habitat types (from whatever classification scheme is chosen for use) are the first vegetative component considered. Forest condition within each habitat type is described by successional stage. Thomas et al. (1979a) identified six such stages:

(1) grass forb
(2) shrub seedling
(3) pole-sapling
(4) young
(5) mature
(6) old-growth

Verner and Boss (1980) suggested four such stages for forest habitats:

(1) grass/forb
(2) shrub/seedling/sapling
(3) pole/medium tree
(4) large tree

Special Habitat Features

According to Thomas et al. (1979a:21), special habitats are "biological in nature, can be manipulated by the forest manager, and play a critical role in the lives of at least some species. These habitats include riparian zones, edges, snags, logs, and other dead woody material on the forest floor." Verner and Boss (1980) added forest openings, elevated perches, nest cavities, hollows, and litter to the list of what they called "vegetation elements." Which of these special habitats should be included in inventories or monitoring operations depends on the wildlife species or groups of species considered important by the responsible land manager. For example, snags would be important if cavity-nesting birds received management emphasis, and logs and other dead woody material would be of interest if reptiles and amphibians were of interest. Of these, we believe that only riparian zones, edges, snags, logs, and forest openings will generally be considered critical inventory elements.

Riparian Zones. Riparian zones are those areas identified by the presence of vegetation that requires free or unbound water. When they occur within forested areas, they generally create well-defined mesic areas within much drier surrounding areas. They make up a minor portion of the area, are more productive of biomass than surrounding forests, and are a dramatic source of diversity. Of the 378 vertebrate species in the Blue Mountains of Oregon, 285 were identified as dependent on riparian zones or as using them more frequently than other habitats (Thomas et al. 1979b).

Edges. Edges are places where different plant communities or successional stages meet and are identified as particularly rich in wildlife. Leopold (1933:131) stated that "game wildlife is a phenomenon of edges... We do not understand the reason for all of these edge effects, but in those cases where we can guess the reason, it usually harks back either to the desirability of simultaneous access to more than one environmental type, or the great richness of border vegetation or both." Patton (1975) suggested that the amount of edge per unit of area might serve as an index to diversity.

Thomas et al. (1979d) divided edges into inherent edges (those resulting from the meeting of two plant communities) and induced edges (those between two successional stages within a plant community). They suggested further that the degree of contrast in height of vegetation along an edge would be correlated with the diversity of animals encountered along the edge and in adjacent stands. Initial testing supports this hypothesis.

Snags. Snags are dead or partly dead trees at least 10.2 cm (4 in.) in diameter at breast height (dbh); snags at least 1.8 m (6 ft) tall are critical to many species of forest wildlife. For example, in the Blue Mountains, 39 bird and 23 mammal species (16% of the 379 species occurring) use snags for nesting or shelter. Snags are now recognized by managers of public forest land as a critical habitat component.

Recommendations on size, species, and numbers of snags required to support various population levels of wildlife dependent on snags are beginning to emerge (Thomas et al. 1979b). The following information on snags should be gathered:

- species
- height
- dbh inside bark
- degree of decay (hard or soft)
- top condition (whole or broken)
- surrounding vegetative structure
- density
- use by wildlife

Logs. Logs (dead-and-down woody material) are dead trees or portions of trees lying on the forest

U.S. Forest Service

Logs partly submerged in water form an important link between terrestrial and aquatic habitats for some species.

U.S Forest Service

Snags are critical habitat components for many species.

floor. Logs are important wildlife habitat components (Maser et al. 1979c). Elton (1966:279) said—

"When one walks through the rather dull and tidy woodlands . . . that result from modern forestry practices, it is difficult to believe that dead wood provides one of the two or three greatest resources for animal species in a natural forest, and that if fallen timber and slightly decayed trees are removed, the whole system is gravely impoverished of perhaps more than a fifth of its fauna."

In the Blue Mountains, for example, 5 amphibians, 9 reptiles, 116 birds, and 49 mammals (47% of the 379 species present) make some use of dead-and-down woody material (Maser et al. 1979c) (Figure 1). This is evidently common because Elton (1966:279), speaking of England, said " . . . indexes of the Geological Survey contain 456 species of animals (including invertebrates) at Wytham living in wood or under bark where decay had begun or already gone far. Another 518 species are known to occur in this habitat elsewhere in Britain." Maser et al. (1979c) presented a state-of-knowledge review about dead-and-down woody material as wildlife habitat. They also presented information about the role of such material in forest ecology.

Forest Openings. Forest opening areas within a forest that do not support trees (for whatever reason) are an important source of diversity within the forest. They frequently support species that do not occupy forested habitats *per se*, and they are important to species associated with their edges. For example, more elk and mule deer *(Odocoileus hemionus)* occur within about 183 m (600 ft) of edges between forest cover and forage areas (Reynolds 1966; Harper 1969; Leckenby 1984). This was a key factor in the development of elk and deer habitat models that are receiving wide application (see Thomas et al. 1979c for an example). The inventory of forest openings can be accounted for under the inventory of plant communities, successional stages, and edges discussed earlier.

Structural Conditions of the Forest

Even greater detail may be required for structural conditions of the forest beyond what can be inferred from knowledge of the successional stage of a given plant community. Included are the following:

- **dbh** of trees, treating conifers and broadleafs separately

- **tree height and height of the base of the crown**

- **canopy volume**—the space occupied by the crowns of trees

- **canopy closure**

- **understory volume**—the space occupied by the leaves and limbs treating shrubs separately from grasses and forbs

- **sight distance**

- **stand size**

Dbh. Dbh can be important in dealing with management of snags and dead-and-down woody material. Living trees are the snags and logs of the future. Division into conifers and broadleaved trees can be important, as many birds and some arboreal mammals are influenced by this variable (Thomas et al. 1977).

Tree Height and Height of Base of Crown. Tree height and the height of the base of the crown must be known if the relationship between vegetative volume and wildlife species is to be considered.

Canopy Volume. The importance of considering canopy volumes, particularly for purposes of explaining bird occurrence, has been emphasized by a number of investigators (reviewed in Larson 1981). MacArthur (1964) believed that variability in bird occurrence due to foliage height diversity could be accounted for by considering three layers of vegetation: 0-60, 60-750, and 750 cm (0-2, 2-25, and 25 ft). Thomas et al. (1977), however, found that considering vegetative volumes in 1.5-m (5-ft) layers

Ron Rohweder

Openings provide diversity in a forest.

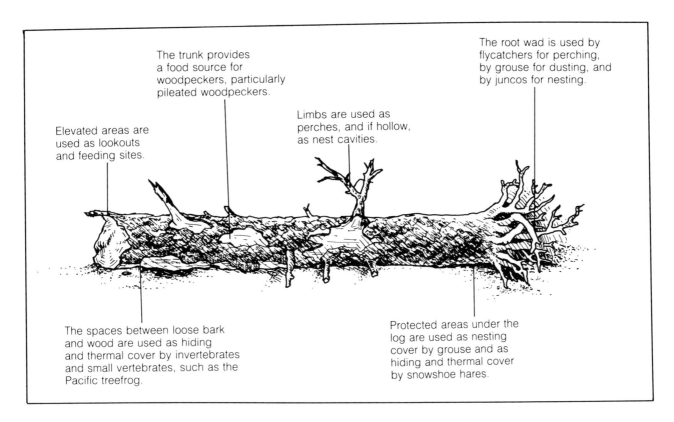

The root wad is used by flycatchers for perching, by grouse for dusting, and by juncos for nesting.

The trunk provides a food source for woodpeckers, particularly pileated woodpeckers.

Limbs are used as perches, and if hollow, as nest cavities.

Elevated areas are used as lookouts and feeding sites.

The spaces between loose bark and wood are used as hiding and thermal cover by invertebrates and small vertebrates, such as the Pacific treefrog.

Protected areas under the log are used as nesting cover by grouse and as hiding and thermal cover by snowshoe hares.

Figure 1. Downed logs furnish many structural features important to wildlife.

The myriad of openings and vegetation types in this area form edges important to wildlife.

markedly increased the variability in bird occurrence explained by vegetative volumes. Mawson et al. (1976) described a technique called HTVOL (height-volume) whereby trees were measured within a plot in a way that vegetative volumes in various "slices" could be determined. Each tree to be sampled was assigned to a geometric form and appropriate measurements taken. The degree of detail needed to determine vegetative volumes depends on the investigator's need.

Canopy Closure. Canopy closure provides information that is useful in describing the stand quality in terms of thermal cover, i.e., cover that is used by ungulates to thermoregulate during extremes of ambient temperature (Thomas et al. 1979e) (Figure 2). Such information can also be useful in predicting the productivity of understory vegetation within such stands.

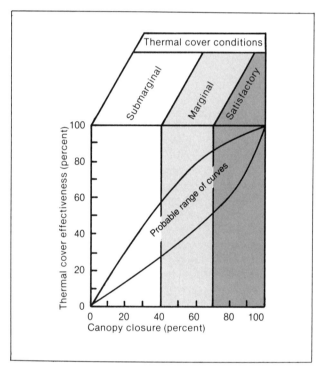

Figure 2. Effectiveness of thermal cover for deer and elk is closely related to canopy cover.

Understory Volume. The volume of understory vegetation (particularly shrubs) is useful in predicting bird occurrence (MacArthur 1964; also see review by Larson 1981) and as a measure of forage available for herbivores. Forage availability can be expressed as kg/ha (lb/a.) of air-dried forage.

Sight Distance. Sight distance is the distance at which 90% or more of a standing deer or elk is hidden from view. Sight distance can be useful in evaluating the effectiveness of hiding cover for deer or elk. Hiding cover has been defined as existing

when an elk or deer is 90% or more hidden at a distance of 61 m (200 ft) or less from an observer (Black et al. 1976).

Stand Size. Stand size is an important habitat variable for several reasons. For example, optimum stand sizes are recommended to ensure use by elk and deer. These sizes usually range from 10 to 16 ha (25 to 40 a.). Some consider stand width to be a more important measure of stand size than area, as this characteristic, because of edge effect, has the most influence (positive and negative) on animal occurrence and density (Leckenby 1984). For example, recommendations for optimum habitat for deer and elk call for stand width to be held at 183-366 m (600-1,200 ft; Thomas et al. 1979c). In addition, stand size is related to the number of species that will be found in the stand and the diversity of species within the stand. The number of species that are found within a stand is positively correlated with the size of the stand up to some size. This relationship is called the species/area curve; see Cain and Castro (1959), Greig-Smith (1964), Galli et al. (1976), and Whitcombe et al. (1981) for reviews of this concept.

Species Composition

It is sometimes desirable to consider the species of plants involved in a habitat. This information is gathered in addition to categorization of the plant community (identified by characteristic dominant vegetation in the climax stage) and the successional stage. The following examples show why data about species composition may be valuable in wildlife habitat assessment:

- variability in palatability and food value in forage plants between consumer species;

- differences in values of various species of trees to cavity nesters;

- indication of range condition.

Remember, however, that collection and analysis of inventory data including species composition increases costs many times. In some instances, such as the classification of plant communities, it may be sufficient to record plant species as present or absent or to deal with estimates of relative abundance.

INVENTORY

Broadscale Systems

The broadscale inventorying and monitoring of wildlife populations and wildlife habitats are mandated by law on National Forest lands but little has been done to date (Salwasser et al. 1983). There are no well developed, well tested systems to accomplish those tasks, although some efforts are underway to produce the tools to accomplish them (Hoekstra et al. 1979, 1983; Verner 1983). The systems that are available have been called "working hypotheses," and their developers advise caution in their application.

The basic system that has received the broadest application on forested land in western North America was initially described by Thomas (1979a) and associates and has become known as the Wildlife and Fish Habitat Relationship (WFHR) approach. The system has been and is being modified in the permutations being developed for other ecosystems in the U.S. and Canada. Examples include the application for the western Sierra Nevada (Verner and Boss 1980), western Oregon and Washington (Brown, in press), and the Oregon portions of the Great Basin (Maser and Thomas 1983). This general approach has been used in many other areas in the West, but the adapted models and data bases have not been formally published. Scientists in British Columbia are working on the system to help describe the ecosystems of British Columbia.

All applications of this general approach attempt to identify habitat needs for feeding and reproduction (some adaptations include other activities such as resting) by each vertebrate species for each plant community, according to successional stage or structural condition. Most approaches use the formation of life forms or guilds to facilitate analysis and monitoring. Expected changes in habitat can be superficially evaluated by comparing the wildlife in the existing habitat to those in the anticipated habitat. Predicted changes in species occurrence are, indeed, the evaluation. Some species will be helped, some will be hurt, and some will not be affected by any major change in a given habitat. The impact on each species, or group of species, can be evaluated at a crude level.

The required habitat inventory for this level of analysis is relatively quick and easy to accomplish by simple delineation of plant communities and their successional stages or structural conditions. Aerial photo-interpretation is easily applied, and imagery from multispectral scans obtained from satellites (LANDSAT) shows promise in this regard and is being effectively applied in the Blue Mountains of Oregon and Washington by the Oregon Department of Fish and Wildlife and the U.S. Forest Service in monitoring big game habitat conditions. It has been particularly useful in deriving forage-cover ratios, sizing and spacing of cover and forage areas, and quantification of cover quality.

Special Habitat Features

This first level of analysis may not be sufficient to deal with special habitat features or with the detailed requirements of individual species of special concern to management. Special and unique habitat features are then considered. These were listed and discussed earlier.

Here we use snags as an example. Standard forest management regimes are unlikely to provide snags in adequate numbers to support viable populations of all members of the life forms that excavate cavities in dead trees for nesting or for those that occupy existing cavities for nesting. Therefore, a snag inventory should be routinely done in managed stands if the welfare of the wildlife species that use snags is of concern. This can be accomplished by regular inventorying by forest crews whose primary job is to provide data to support the timber management program (and who, importantly, are well financed to do that job) or, with less accuracy, by use of aerial photography.

Admittedly, snags are an obvious and relatively easy special habitat feature to inventory and monitor. They are also a feature that has received considerable management attention. Other features, such as dead-and-down woody material, edges, talus, and others have not been routinely inventoried. Whether these features should be inventoried depends on management objectives. If there are wildlife species that depend on such features that are of significant interest to management, the associated habitat feature should be monitored. The relationship of wildlife species to several special habitat features is detailed in such publications as Thomas (1979b). The techniques for inventory, if they exist, have not become standardized. Also, there is no standard list of special habitat features. Whether to inventory and monitor special habitat features, and which ones to address, are determined by the habitat management objectives of the area in question. Prime candidates for inventory and monitoring are those that are critical to featured species, indicator species, or management guilds. Significance and priority for attention are determined by emphasis offered by the management plan.

When the needs of individual species must be considered, additional habitat features germane to management of that species will become important. This is illustrated by the discussion of featured species that follows.

Featured Species

Featured species, or species of special interest to managers, usually require special consideration.

These usually include game species, threatened or endangered species, management indicator species, and ecological indicator species. The National Forest Management Act and the regulations issued pursuant to that Act require the maintenance of viable populations of all native and desirable non-native species in National Forest management. The regulations specify that progress toward achievement of that goal be evaluated by monitoring the occurrence and density of management indicator species. Astute selection of management indicator species and assurance of their subsequent welfare were assumed to be an appropriate mechanism to meet legal requirements for maintenance of viable populations of all wildlife. Included within this group are some rather vaguely defined "ecological indicators" which, by implication, represent a larger group of species. We believe this approach to be impractical and unrealistic for the reasons specified by Verner (1984). It is, however, the law and the U.S. Forest Service must attempt to comply. A rational approach to carrying out such an effort has been spelled out by Verner (1983). Agencies not bound by the National Forest Management Act are advised to use other approaches such as management guilds (discussed later), or stay with individual species monitoring without inference to other species.

No general comprehensive list of habitat attributes for featured species can be listed here. These attributes are unique to the species being considered. The description of the system by Thomas et al. (1979c) used elk and mule deer as examples of featured species. The habitat attributes to be measured, and mentioned throughout this chapter include—

- percentage of the area consisting of thermal cover, hiding cover, and forage areas,
- stand size,
- density of roads open to vehicular traffic,
- cover/forage area ratios.

If, however, the pileated woodpecker (*Dryocopus pileatus*) were chosen as a featured species, other habitat attributes would become important, such as—

- snags greater than 51-cm (20-in.) dbh,
- species of snags,
- height of canopy,
- dead-and-down woody material,
- the presence of carpenter ants (*Camponotus* sp.).

Each featured species will introduce a different set of habitat attributes to be considered.

The U.S. Department of Interior, Fish and Wildlife Service (1980) has developed "Habitat Evaluation Procedures (HEP)" focusing on habitat requirements of fish and wildlife species applicable to project planning and impact evaluation (Schamberger and Farmer 1978). This was the impetus for development of Habitat Suitability Index (HSI) models (Schamberger et al. 1982) for select wildlife species. These models provide a good source of information on habitat variables that one should measure when using one of the particular species as an indicator or featured species. Examples of species for which such habitat models exist include beaver (*Castor canadensis*) (Allen 1982a), marten (*Martes americana*) (Allen 1982b), and black-capped chickadee (*Parus atricapillus*) (Schroeder 1983).

The relationship between these habitat evaluation procedures and the habitat evaluation procedures of Thomas (1979b), Verner and Boss (1980), and others is explored in detail by Thomas (1982).

MONITORING

A wag once said that monitoring was an inventory done over and over. So it is. The National Forest Management Act of 1976, and regulations issued pursuant thereto, contain instructions to monitor indicator species to determine (1) if management objectives are being met, and (2) if the management indicator species are changing in status. The costs of such monitoring of individual wildlife species are likely to be very high in personnel and dollars. Verner (1983) estimated that for the western Sierra Nevada it would take some 300,000 10-minute point counts to detect a 10% change in numbers of such species of special interest such as the pileated woodpecker or willow flycatcher (*Empidonax traillii*). If 20 counts per observer per day were made, 15,000 observer days would be required. Because the suitable counting period within any one season is about 60 days, some 250 temporary employees capable of locating the sample points and capable of recognizing birds by sight and sound would be needed. Salary costs alone are estimated at $825,000 per year. Verner (1983:357) summed up by saying:

"Not only are the costs and personnel needs for such an effort out of reason, but also it is unreasonable to find such a large number of counting points because each must be independent of the others to satisfy assumptions of the statistical models. This fantasy can be extended to include all of the various species we may be concerned about and in all of the various types of habitats where they may occur. Obviously other approaches are required."

Note also that even after a change in the population is detected, this does not assure information about cause and effect. Is the change due to weather, food supply, habitat change, or some other factor or combination of factors? Are such changes indicative of something that requires management action or merely normal perturbations in population numbers?

Toward More Practical Monitoring

Verner (1983) suggested various ways to make monitoring more feasible in terms of costs and management need. These are summarized below:

(1) Separate species into categories of high and low risk to be reduced below acceptable levels in terms of range or density by forest management activities. We believe that the vast majority of species will fall in the low risk category and that habitat monitoring will suffice to monitor trends in their status. High risk species will probably require monitoring of the species itself.

(2) Design monitoring activities to detect only declining trends. Only in rare circumstances, such as with ungulates (which are hunted) or gophers (which cause damage to young trees), would increases be a cause for concern. Besides, data on animal damage are very apt to be available from sources such as forest surveys for the forestry program. The monitoring should be designed to protect against statistical type II errors (concluding that a population is stable when it has really declined).

Costs vary with the power of the test and the magnitude of the decline to be detected. We recommend a power of 0.8 (failure to detect a specified decline 20% of the time) as a good compromise between tolerable costs and management needs. In all situations, the sampling design should be standardized to produce as nearly identical conditions as possible every time the sampling is done (probably annually). The following should be considered:

- sampling intensity
- time of day
- season
- sample sites
- weather
- order of sampling sites
- variability due to observers

(3) Select "high probability" sites for sampling when indicator species are monitored. Management indicator species, with the exception of game species, are apt to be uncommon; in fact, they may have been selected because they were rare, threatened, or endangered.

Therefore, average counts of such species are generally so low in a randomly selected set of sampling points that costs preclude sampling enough points to detect declining trends with statistical confidence (Verner 1984). A pre-monitoring inventory should be used to identify sites where target species occur and monitoring stations should be randomly selected from among those sites.

(4) Monitor "management guilds" rather than individual species. Management guilds are species that respond in a similar way to changes in their environment. Verner (1983:360) said, "The primary use of such management guilds should be to monitor trends in the suitability of various zones of a habitat to support wildlife species. As such, guilds will probably make their greatest contribution to a monitoring system as indicators of the quality and quantity of certain habitats that are most likely to be changed by management activities."

One obvious advantage of monitoring management guilds is that counts of a group of species are higher than counts of any of the component species. Therefore, fewer samples are required. Further, the biologist obtains a more complete listing of the species assemblage than would result if only indicator species were counted. At least for birds, the cost of obtaining the more complete list is no greater than tallying just one or a few species (Verner 1983). This assumes, of course, that personnel are available who can readily identify the species by both sight and sound. This gives managers at least some hint of the changing status of individual species.

(5) Monitor only during a single season. Ideally, managers should have knowledge of the year-round status of habitats and occupying species that would require at least four monitoring efforts per year. Likely, only one effort per year can be afforded. For birds, that effort should correspond with the breeding season (Verner 1983). For game species, particularly big game, monitoring is best done as close to hunting season as feasible to allow time for adjustment in hunting regulations.

For birds, Verner (1983:361) hypothesized that "If transients and winter residents use the same zones of a habitat for feeding and cover in basically the same ways as the breeders do, maintenance of the populations of all breeding species should ensure maintenance of suitable habitat for transients and winter residents."

(6) Monitor trends in habitat. The assumption in such monitoring is that if enough is known about species-habitat relationships, trends in populations (or potential populations) could be inferred from monitoring habitat trends. These systems are probably adequate for low risk species, at least for the time being. Nonetheless they are still in a rudimentary stage. They require testing, verification, and continuous correction.

Ultimately, it may be possible to effectively monitor trends in most wildlife populations almost exclusively through habitats, even for management indicator species. This will be the most cost-effective method because trends in habitats must be monitored for information on timber resources. Thus, the cost of monitoring wildlife trends can be mainly absorbed by monitoring timber resources.

An Example of a Monitoring System

The Sierra National Forest has developed a wildlife monitoring plan that seems well conceived, adequate, realistic, and promising (Verner 1983). The plan calls for 5 years of inventory to precede institution of monitoring efforts. This inventory effort will provide the sampling framework and baseline information on which monitoring plans are based. The plan is in three phases:

(1) Monitoring of management indicator species. This is required by law, and the minimum legal requirement will be met by monitoring seven species, five of which are rare, threatened, or endangered, and two of which are game species.

(2) Monitoring, at 2-year intervals, management guilds of birds in three habitats considered especially vulnerable to alteration by management. These habitats include late-successional mixed-conifer forests, riparian habitats, and meadow edges. Each would include 200 sampling points. It is hypothesized that stability in bird assemblages indicates similar stability in assemblages of other vertebrate groups.

(3) Monitoring of most wildlife species in most habitats by monitoring trends in habitat defined by plant community, successional stage, and special and unique habitat features such as snags and dead-and-down woody material. Such an approach requires the development of data bases of site-specific wildlife-habitat relationships such as those described by Patton (1978), Thomas (1979b), or Verner and Boss (1980).

Monitoring nesting habitats of rare, threatened, or endangered species should be done yearly.

DISCUSSION

The inventorying and monitoring of forest wildlife habitats and forest wildlife (except for game species) are in their infancies. The literature reveals more speculation than action at this point. In fact, most of what has been discussed in this chapter is based on hypothesized wildlife-habitat relationships formulated from the synthesis of ecological theory and some basic data on how different species of wildlife react to their habitats. The result has been called "a working hypothesis, a place to start, and a way to derive tentative answers to questions for which there are no certain answers" (Thomas 1979b:7). But we do have a place to start. We are confident that, as speculation gives way to action, experience will allow improvements in the currently primitive systems, and the art of monitoring will evolve to a science. An overriding consideration in all of this must be its cost, because if economical ways cannot be found to do the job, it will not get done.

LITERATURE CITED

ALLEN, A.W. 1982a. Habitat suitability index models: beaver. FWS/OBS-82/10.30. U.S. Dep. Inter., Fish and Wildl. Serv. Washington, DC. 20pp.

———. 1982b. Habitat suitability index models: marten. FWS/OBS-82/10.11. U.S. Dep. Inter., Fish and Wildl. Serv. Washington, DC. 9pp.

ANDERSON, A.J.B. 1971. Ordination methods in ecology. J. Ecol. 59:713-726.

ANDERSON, J.R., E.E. HARDY, J.T. ROACH, and R.E. WITMER. 1976. A land use and land cover classification system for use with remote sensor data. U.S. Dep. Inter., Geol. Surv. Prof. Pap. 964. Reston, VA. 28pp.

AUSTIN, M.E. 1965. Land resource regions and major land resource areas of the United States (exclusive of Alaska and Hawaii). USDA Soil Conserv. Serv. Agric. Handb. 296. Washington, DC. 82pp.

AUSTIN, M.P. and L. ORLOCI. 1966. Geometric models in ecology. II. An evaluation of some ordination techniques. J. Ecol. 54:217-227.

BAILEY, R.G. 1976. Ecoregions of the United States (map). U.S. Dep. Agric. For. Serv., Intermountain Region. Ogden, UT.

———. 1977. A new map of the ecosystem regions of the United States. Pages 121-128 in Classification, Inventory, and Analysis of Fish and Wildlife Habitat—the Proceedings of a National Symposium. FWS/OBS-78/76. U.S. Dep. Inter., Fish and Wildl. Serv. Washington, DC.

———. 1978. Description of the ecoregions of the United States. U.S. Dep. Agric., Forest Service, Intermountain Region. Ogden, UT. 77pp.

———. 1980. Integrated approaches to classifying land as ecosystems, in Proc. IUFRO/ISS workshop on land evaluation for forestry. Wageningen, The Netherlands.

———. 1982. Classification systems for habitat and ecosystems. Pages 16-26 in Mason, W.T. ed. Research on Fish and Wildlife Habitat. Office of Research and Development, U.S. Environmental Protection Agency. Washington, DC.

BANNISTER, P. 1968. An evaluation of some procedures used in simple ordinations. J. Ecol. 56:27-34.

BLACK, H. Jr., R. SCHERZINGER, and J.W. THOMAS. 1976. Relationships of Rocky Mountain elk and Rocky Mountain mule deer habitat to timber harvest in the Blue Mountains of Oregon and Washington. Pages 105-118 in Proceedings of the Elk-Logging-Roads Symposium. Univ. Idaho, Moscow.

BRAY, J.R. and J.T. CURTIS. 1957. An ordination of the upland forest communities of southern Wisconsin. Ecol. Monogr. 27:325-349.

BROWN, D.E., C.H. LOWE, and C.P. PASE. 1980. A digitized systematic classification for ecosystems with an illustrated summary of the natural vegetation of North America. U.S. Dep. Agric., For. Serv. Gen. Tech. Rep. RM-73. 93pp.

BROWN, H.R., ed. In Press. Wildlife habitats in managed forests—western Oregon and Washington. U.S. Dep. Agric., For. Serv., Pacific Northwest Region. Portland, OR.

BUTTERY, R.F. 1978. Modified ECOCLASS—A Forest Service method for classifying ecosystems. Pages 157-168 in Integrated Inventories of Renewable Natural Resources. Tucson, AZ. U.S. Dep. Agric., For. Serv. Gen. Tech. Rep. RM-55.

CAIN, S.A. and G.M. DE OLIVERIA CASTRO. 1959. Manual of vegetation analysis. Harper and Brothers. New York, NY. 325pp.

CORTISS, J.C. 1974. ECOCLASS—a method for classifying ecosystems. Pages 264-271 in Foresters in Land-Use Planning. Proc. of the 1973 Natl Conv., Soc. Am. For. Washington, DC.

CROME, F.H.J. 1978. Foraging ecology of an assemblage of birds in lowland rainforest in northern Queensland. Aust. J. Ecol. 3:195-212.

CROWLEY, J.M. 1967. Biogeography. Can. Geogr. 11:312-326.

CUSHWA, C.T. and C.W. DUBROCK. 1982. Design of computerized fish and wildlife species data bases by state and federal agencies. Pages 37-46 in Mason, W.T. ed. Research on Wildlife Habitat. EPA-600/8-82-022. U.S. Environmental Protection Agency. Washington, DC.

DAUBENMIRE, R. 1968. Plant communities: a textbook of plant synecology. Harper and Row. New York, NY. 300pp.

DEGRAAF, R.M. and N.L. CHADWICK. 1984. Habitat classification: a comparison using avian species and guilds. Environ. Manage. 8(6):511-518.

DRISCOLL, R.S., J.W. RUSSELL, and M.C. MEIER. 1978. Recommended national land classification system for renewable resource assessments. U.S. Dep. Agric., For. Serv. Rocky Mtn. For. and Range Exp. Sta. Fort Collins, CO (unpublished manuscript). 44pp.

DUESER, R.D. and H.H. SHUGART, Jr. 1979. Niche pattern in a forest-floor small-mammal fauna. Ecology 60:108-118.

ELTON, C.S. 1966. Dying and dead wood. Pages 279-305 in The Pattern of Animal Communities. John Wiley and Sons, Inc. New York, NY.

FOLSE, L.J. Jr. 1981. Ecological relationships of grassland birds to habitat and food supply in east Africa. Pages 160-166 in Capen, D.E. ed. The Use of Multivariate Statistics in Studies of Wildlife Habitat. U.S. Dep. Agric., For. Serv. Gen. Tech. Rep. RM-87.

GALLI, A.E., C.F. LECK, and R.T.T. FORMAN. 1976. Avian distribution patterns in forest islands of different sizes in central New Jersey. Auk 93(2):356-364.

GARRISON, G.A., J.J. BJUGSTAD, D.A. DUNCAN, M.E. LEWIS, and D.R. SMITH. 1977. Vegetation and environmental features of forest and range ecosystems. U.S. Dep. Agric., For. Serv. Agric. Handb. 475. U.S. Govt. Print. Off. Washington, DC. 68pp.

GAUCH, H.G. Jr. 1982. Multivariate analysis in community ecology. Cambridge Univ. Press, Cambridge. 298pp.

GODFREY, A.E. 1977. A physiographic approach to land use planning. Environ. Geol. 2:43-50.

GREIG-SMITH, P. 1964. Quantitative plant ecology. 2nd ed. Butterworths, London. 256pp.

HAAPANEN, A. 1965. Bird fauna of the Finnish forests in relation to forest succession. I. Ann. Zool. Fenn. 2(3):153-196.

———. 1966. Bird fauna of the Finnish forests in relation to forest succession. II. Ann. Zool. Fenn. 3(3):176-200.

HALL, F.C. 1973. Plant communities of the Blue Mountains in eastern Oregon and southeastern Washington. U.S. Dep. Agric., For. Serv. Reg. 6 Area Guide 3-1. 62pp.

HARPER, JAMES A. 1969. Relationship of elk to reforestation in the Pacific Northwest. Pages 67-71 in Black, H.C. ed. Wildlife and Reforestation in the Pacific Northwest. School of Forestry, Oreg. State Univ. Corvallis.

HENDERSON, J.A., L.S. DAVIS, and E.M. RYBERG. 1978. ECOSYM: a classification and information system for wildland resource management. Utah State Univ. Logan. 30pp.

HOEKSTRA, T.W., D.E. CHALK, C.L. HAWKES, and S.A. MILLER. 1983. Monitoring regional wildlife and fish habitats and populations for national assessments and appraisals. Pages 308-314 in Trans. 48th North Am. Wildl. and Nat. Resour. Conf.

————, D.L. SCHWEITZER, C.T. CUSHWA, S.H. ANDERSON, and R.B. BARNES. 1979. Preliminary evaluation of a national wildlife and fish data base. Pages 308-314 in Trans. 44th North Am. Wildl. and Nat. Resour. Conf.

HOLMES, R.T., R.E. BONNEY, Jr., and S.W. PACALA. 1979. Guild structure of the Hubbard Brook bird community: a multivariate approach. Ecology 60:512-520.

JAKSIC, F.M. 1981. Abuse and misuse of the term "guild" in ecological studies. Oikos 37:397-400.

JENKINS, R.E. 1977. Classification and inventory for the perpetuation of ecological diversity. Pages 41-51 in Classification, Inventory, and Analysis of Fish and Wildlife—the Proceedings of a National Symposium, U.S. Dep. Inter., Fish and Wildl. Serv. Washington, DC.

KUCHLER, A.W. 1964. Potential natural vegetation of the conterminous United States (map and manual). Am. Geogr. Spec. Publ. 36. 116pp.

————. 1970. Potential natural vegetation. (Map, 1966.) Pages 90-91 in The National Atlas of the United States of America. U.S. Dep. Inter., Geological Survey. Washington, DC.

LANDRES, P.B. and J.A. MACMAHON. 1980. Guilds and community organization: analysis of an oak woodland avifauna in Sonora, Mexico. Auk 97:351-365.

LARSON, T.A. 1981. Ecological correlates of avian community structure in mixed-conifer habitat: an experimental approach. Ph.D. Dissertation. Illinois State Univ. Normal.

LECKENBY, D.A. 1984. Elk use and availability of cover and forage habitat components in the Blue Mountains, Northeast Oregon, 1976-1982. Wildl. Res. Rep. 14. Oregon Dep. of Fish and Wildl. Portland. 40pp.

LEOPOLD, A. 1933. Game management. Charles Scribner Sons. New York, NY. 481pp.

LINDEMAN, R.H., P.F. MERENDA, and R.F. GOLD. 1980. Introduction to bivariate and multivariate analysis. Scott, Foresman and Co. Glenview, IL. 444pp.

MACARTHUR, R.H. 1964. Environmental factors affecting bird species diversity. Am. Nat. 98:387-397.

MACMAHON, J.A., D.J. SCHIMPF, D.C. ANDERSON, K.G. SMITH, and R.L. BAYN Jr. 1981. An organism-centered approach to some community and ecosystem concepts. J. Theor. Biol. 88:287-307.

MARMELSTEIN, A. 1977. Classification, inventory, and analysis of fish and wildlife habitat—proceedings of a national symposium. U.S. Dep. Inter., Fish and Wildl. Serv. Washington, DC. 604pp.

MASER, C., J.M. GEIST, D.M. CONCANNON, R. ANDERSON, and B. LOVELL. 1979a. Wildlife habitats in managed rangelands—the Great Basin of southeastern Oregon: geomorphic and edaphic habitats. U.S. Dep. Agric., For. Serv. Gen. Tech. Rep. PNW-99. 84pp.

————, J.E. RODIEK and J.W. THOMAS. 1979b. Cliffs, talus, and caves. Pages 96-103 in Wildlife Habitats in Managed Forests—the Blue Mountains of Oregon and Washington. U.S. Dep. Agric., Agric. Handb. 553. U.S. Govt. Print. Off. Washington, DC.

————, R.G. ANDERSON, K. CROMACK Jr., J.T. WILLIAMS, and R.E. MARTIN. 1979c. Dead and down woody material. Pages 78-95 in Wildlife Habitats in Managed Forests—the Blue Mountains of Oregon and Washington. U.S. Dep. Agric., Agric. Handb. 553. U.S. Govt. Print. Off. Washington, DC.

———— and J.W. THOMAS. 1983. Wildlife habitats in managed rangelands—the Great Basin of southeastern Oregon: Introduction. U.S. Dep. Agric., For. Serv. Gen. Tech. Rep. PNW-160. 15pp.

MAWSON, J.C., J.W. THOMAS, and R.M. DEGRAAF. 1976. Program HTVOL—the determination of crown volume by layers. U.S. Dep. Agric., For. Serv. Res. Pap. NE-354. 9pp.

NIE, N.H., C.H. HULL, J.G. JENKINS, K. STEINBRENNER, and D.H. BENT. 1974. SPSS statistical package for the social sciences. 2nd ed. McGraw-Hill. New York, NY. 675pp.

PATTON, D.R. 1975. A diversity index for quantifying habitat "edge." Wildl. Soc. Bull. 3(4):171-173.

————. 1978. RUNWILD: a storage and retrieval system for wildlife habitat information. U.S. Dep. Agric., For. Serv. Gen. Tech. Rep. RM-51. 8pp.

PFISTER, R.D. 1977. Ecological classification of forest land in Idaho and Montana. Pages 329-358 in Ecological Classification of Forest Land in Canada and Northwestern USA. Univ. British Columbia. Vancouver, Canada.

RAO, C.R. 1966. Influence on discriminant function coefficients. Pages 587-602 in R.C. Rose, I.M. Chakrovarti, P.C. Mahalanobis, C.R. Rao, and K.J.C. Smith eds. Essays in Probability and Statistics. Univ. North Carolina Press, Chapel Hill.

REYNOLDS, H.G. 1966. Use of openings in spruce-fir forests of Arizona by deer, elk and cattle. U.S. Dep. Agric., For. Serv. Res. Note 78, 4pp.

ROBINSON, W.L. and E.B. BOLEN. 1984. Wildlife ecology and management. MacMillan Publ. Co. New York, NY. 478 pp.

ROOT, R.B. 1967. The niche exploitation pattern of the blue-gray gnatcatcher. Ecol. Monogr. 37:317-350.

SALWASSER, HAL, C.K. HAMILTON, W.B. KROHN, J. LIPSCOMB, and C.H. THOMAS. 1983. Monitoring wildlife and fish: mandates and their implications. Pages 297-306 in Trans. 48th North Am. Wildl. and Nat. Resour. Conf.

SCHAMBERGER, M. and A. FARMER. 1978. The habitat evaluation procedures: their application in project planning and impact evaluation. Pages 274-283 in Trans. 43rd North Am. Wildl. and Nat. Resour. Conf.

————, ————, and J.W. TERRELL. 1982. Habitat suitability index models: introduction. FWS/OBS-82/10. U.S. Dep. Inter., Fish and Wildl. Serv. Washington, DC. 2pp.

SCHROEDER, R.L. 1983. Habitat suitability index models: black-capped chickadee. FWS/OBS-82/10.37. U.S. Dep. Inter., Fish and Wildl. Serv. Washington, DC. 12pp.

SEVERINGHAUS, W.D. 1981. Guild theory development as a mechanism for assessing environmental impact. Environ. Manage. 5:187-190.

SHORT, H.L. 1983. Wildlife guilds in Arizona desert habitats. U.S. Dep. Inter., Bur. Land Manage. Serv. Cen. Tech. Note 362. 258pp.

———— and K.P. BURNHAM. 1982. Technique for structuring wildlife guilds to evaluate impacts on wildlife communities. U.S. Dep. Inter., Fish and Wildl. Serv. Spec. Sci. Rep. 244. Washington, DC. 34pp.

SOCIETY OF AMERICAN FORESTERS. 1954. Forest cover types of North America. Society of American Foresters. Washington, DC. 67pp.

THOMAS, J.W. 1979a. Introduction. Pages 10-21 *in* Wildlife Habitats in Managed Forests—the Blue Mountains of Oregon and Washington. U.S. Dep. Agric., Agric. Handb. 553. U.S. Govt. Print. Off. Washington, DC.

————— ed. 1979b. Wildlife habitats in managed forests—the Blue Mountains of Oregon and Washington. U.S. Dep. Agric., Agric. Handb. 553. U.S. Govt. Print. Off. Washington, DC. 510pp.

—————. 1982. Species/habitat relationships—a key to considering wildlife in planning and land management decisions. Pages 27-36 *in* Mason, W.T. ed. Research on Wildlife Habitat. EPA-600/8-82-022. U.S. Environmental Protection Agency. Washington, DC.

—————, R.M. DEGRAAF, and J.C. MAWSON. 1977. Determination of habitat requirements for birds in suburban areas. U.S. Dep. Agric., For. Serv. Res. Pap. NE-357. 15pp.

—————, R.J. MILLER, C. MASER, R.G. ANDERSON, and B.E. CARTER. 1979a. Plant communities and successional stages. Pages 22-39 *in* Wildlife Habitats in Managed Forests—the Blue Mountains of Oregon and Washington. U.S. Dep. Agric., Agric. Handb. 553. U.S. Govt. Print. Off. Washington, DC.

—————, R.G. ANDERSON, C. MASER, and E.L. BULL. 1979b. Snags. Pages 60-77 *in* Wildlife Habitats in Managed Forests—the Blue Mountains of Oregon and Washington. U.S. Dep. Agric., Agric. Handb. 553. U.S. Govt. Print. Off. Washington, DC.

—————, H. BLACK Jr., R.J. SCHERZINGER, and R.J. PEDERSEN. 1979c. Deer and elk. Pages 104-127 *in* Wildlife Habitats in Managed Forests—the Blue Mountains of Oregon and Washington. U.S. Dep. Agric., Agric. Handb. 553. U.S. Govt. Print. Off. Washington, DC.

—————, C. MASER, and J. RODIEK. 1979d. Edges. Pages 48-59 *in* Wildlife Habitats in Managed Forests—the Blue Mountains of Oregon and Washington. U.S. Dep.

Agric., Agric. Handb. 553. U.S. Govt. Print. Off. Washington, DC.

—————, —————, and —————. 1979e. Riparian zones. Pages 40-47 *in* Wildlife Habitats in Managed Forests—the Blue Mountains of Oregon and Washington. U.S. Dep. Agric., Agric. Handb. 553. U.S. Govt. Print. Off. Washington, DC.

U.S. DEPARTMENT OF INTERIOR, BUREAU OF LAND MANAGEMENT. 1978. Integrated habitat inventory and classification system, BLM Manual Section 6602. Washington, DC. 37pp.

U.S. DEPARTMENT OF INTERIOR, FISH AND WILDLIFE SERVICE. 1980. Habitat evaluation procedures (HEP). ESM 121. U.S. Dep. Inter., Fish and Wildl. Serv. Washington, DC.

VERNER, J. 1983. An integrated system for monitoring wildlife on the Sierra National Forest. Pages 355-366. *in* Trans. 48th North Am. Wildlife. and Nat. Resour. Conf.

—————. 1984. The guild concept applied to management of bird populations. Environ. Manage. 8(1):1-14.

————— and A.S. BOSS. 1980. California wildlife and their habitats: western Sierra Nevada. U.S. Dep. Agric., For. Serv. Gen. Tech. Rep. PSW-37. 439pp.

WERTZ, W.A. and J.F. ARNOLD. 1972. Land systems inventory. U.S. Dep. Agric., For. Serv., Intermountain Region. Ogden, UT. 12pp.

WHITCOMB, R.F., C.S. ROBBINS, J.F. LYNCH, B.L. WHITCOMB, M.K. KLIMBIEWICZ, and D. BYSTRAK. 1981. Effects of forest fragmentation on avifauna of the eastern deciduous forest. Pages 125-205 *in* Burgess, R.L. and D.M. Sharpe eds. Forest Island Dynamics in Man-Dominated Landscapes. Springer-Verlag. New York, NY.

WILLIAMS, B.K. 1980. Discriminant analysis in wildlife research: theory and applications. Pages 59-71 *in* Capen, D.E. ed. The Use of Multivariate Statistics in Studies of Wildlife Habitat. U.S. Dep. Agric., For. Serv. Tech. Rep. RM-87.

6

RANGELANDS

Henry L. Short

U.S. Fish and Wildlife Service
Western Energy and Land Use Team
Ft. Collins, CO 80526

"As demands have grown for the products of range-lands, it has become obvious that such cliches as 'good range management is good wildlife management' will no longer suffice."

—Chris Maser and Jack W. Thomas from *Wild-life Habitats in Managed Rangelands—The Great Basin of Southeastern Oregon*

Editor's Note: Most range studies have focused on problems of livestock management. Most wildlife-oriented efforts have concentrated on alleviating impacts from grazing and have focused on problems such as forage allocation between livestock and wild ungulates.

This chapter provides techniques to inventory and monitor habitat structure. Because structure (trees, shrubs, etc.) on rangelands is very limited, it is extremely important to wildlife. Areas with structure are where biologists should concentrate their efforts. Systems based on structural diversity will be the most useful on rangelands.

INTRODUCTION

Rangelands, as discussed in this chapter, are considered to be lands—

- where the potential natural vegetation is mostly grass, grasslike plants, forbs, or shrubs;

- where grazing and browsing were important influences during prehistoric times; and

- that are more suitable for management by ecological than by agronomic principles (after Schwarz et al. 1976).

Western range and Great Plains ecosystems total over 258 million ha (646 million a.) (Table 1) in 17 western and Great Plains States. Eighty-six percent is grazed by domestic livestock. More than 136 million kg (300 million t) of herbage and browse are produced annually on these rangelands, providing nearly 149 million Animal Unit Months (AUMs) of domestic livestock use (Table 1). The approximate location of the potential natural vegetation types that comprise rangelands is illustrated in Figure 1.

About 65% of the rangeland area listed in Table 1 occurs in 11 western states where shrublands, mountain grassland, and desert grasslands predominate. These 167 million ha (418 million a.) provide only about 48% of the herbage and browse and 38% of the AUMs produced in the western range and Great Plains ecosystems (Table 1). The Bureau of Land Management administers about 68.4 million ha (171 million a.) within 11 western states and authorizes the use of about 12 million AUMs of forage for 3.5 million cattle and 4.9 million sheep (U.S. Department of Interior, Bureau of Land Management 1975).

Rangelands are vast areas that provide great diversity and present significant problems to managers. Many of the western rangelands are fragile, occurring on poorly developed, shallow, and highly alkaline soils in arid or semiarid climates with a

Table 1. Production of forage and Animal Unit Months (AUMs) in 1970 by ecosystem type (after U.S. Forest Service 1972).

Ecosystems	Total land area by ecosystem (thousands of acres)	Herbage and browse production by ecosystem (thousands of tons per year)	Total land area grazed (thousands of acres)	Animal Unit Month production by ecosystem (thousands of AUMs)
Sagebrush	94,219	35,840	90,453	10,850
Desert shrub	86,043	9,491	58,762	1,742
Southwestern shrub-steppe	38,601	3,526	35,382	1,958
Chaparral-mountain shrub	32,801	11,559	30,118	1,957
Pinyon-juniper	42,677	4,934	34,163	1,715
Mountain grasslands	79,839	60,858	75,206	21,441
Mountain meadows	4,045	5,482	3,785	4,309
Desert grasslands	26,098	6,481	26,098	5,073
Annual grasslands	6,700	6,886	6,696	7,003
Alpine	8,322	97	162	33
Shinnery	2,004	927	1,982	456
Texas savanna	15,221	8,352	14,870	5,042
Plains grasslands	173,260	91,408	163,709	50,454
Prairie	37,533	54,252	36,539	36,814
Total	646,643	300,092	557,925	148,848

short growing season. Only 18% of the western range acreages are considered in good condition, whereas 50% are rated fair and 32% are rated poor (U.S. Forest Service 1972). The U.S. Bureau of Land Management considers 17% of its land in satisfactory or better condition; 83% produces vegetation at a rate less than its potential (U.S. Bureau of Land Management 1975). Forty-eight percent of the ranges in the more mesic Great Plains are considered in good condition, 45% in fair condition, and only 7% in poor condition (U.S. Forest Service 1972). Rangelands in the 11 western states provide a variety of products in addition to forage. Rangeland surveys evaluate—

- the current year's production of herbage and browse;

- the yield of water in acre-feet per acre per year;

- the quantity of sediments deposited in stream channels per year;

- changes in the fertility, structure, or drainage of soils;

- carbon and particulate content in the atmosphere, as measures of air quality;

- aesthetic quality;

- changes in populations of rare and endangered wildlife species;

- diversity of habitat for nongame birds;

- resident big game populations;

- outdoor recreation use; and

- cultural values.

Results of these surveys indicate that western rangelands have poor soil stability; poor to fair non-hunting recreation opportunities; fair soil quality; fair to good air quality; fair to good habitat for carnivores, raptors, and rare and endangered species of wildlife and nongame birds; and fair to good hunting and scenic and cultural values (U.S. Forest Service 1972).

Rangeland habitats are immense and complex. Some sort of common denominator for rangelands seems necessary so that range surveys can provide results that are comparable and interpretable between areas. The concept of layers of habitat appears to be a useful denominator for comparing rangelands.

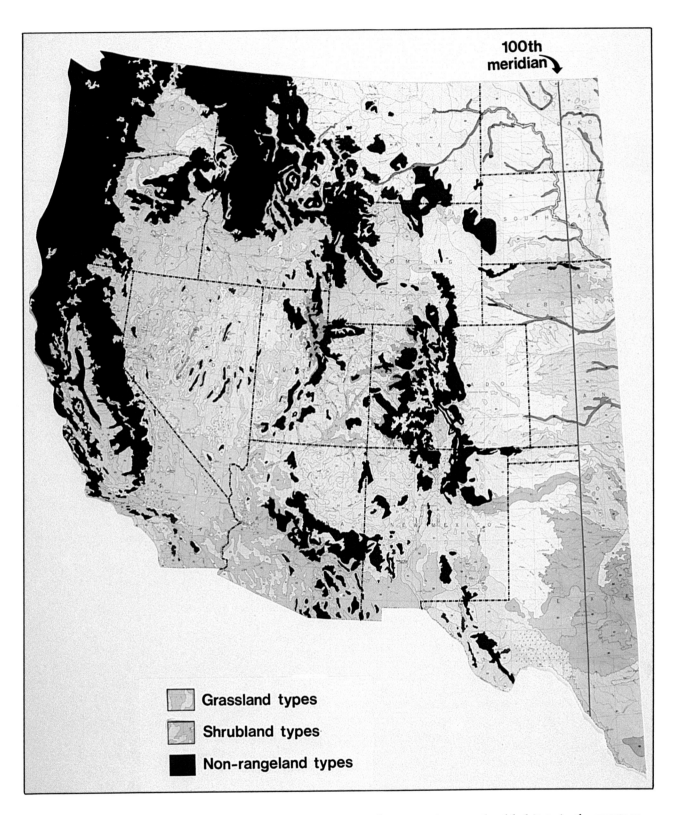

Figure 1. Occurrence of potential natural vegetation types that comprise rangeland habitats in the western U.S. (after Kuchler 1964).

The processes described in this chapter are based on the assumption that the niches of individual wildlife species can be positioned within the vertical structure of habitats. This vertical structure can be represented in terms of habitat layers. The abstraction of representing cover types as habitat layers provides a means for performing a variety of quantitative assessments of habitat. For example, the structure of several land units can be compared by measuring the areas of the different layers of habitat present on those land units. Monitoring the area of habitat layers will describe the general direction of change over time in the quantity of habitat available for the wildlife community.

The layers of habitat present on a land unit can be mapped and measured. Wildlife species can be associated with particular layers of habitat through application of the species-habitat matrix, where groups or guilds of wildlife species that share dependencies on the same general structure of habitat are formed. Maps of layers of habitat and the guilds associated with those layers of habitat are distribution maps for wildlife guilds and species. The areas in the distribution maps can be monitored over time to describe trends in the quantity of habitat available for particular wildlife guilds and their component wildlife species. Land-use changes often can be considered in terms of impact to layers of habitat. The impacts of those land use changes on wildlife species can be predicted because wildlife species have been associated with habitat layers through the wildlife guilding process.

A layer of habitat can be thought of as providing a large array of habitat conditions. Guilds of wildlife species that have a dependency on a habitat layer can be disaggregated to describe the dependency of individual species on specific conditions along this array or habitat gradient. This disaggregation is done with species-habitat models (or HSI models) developed for individual wildlife species. These models emphasize features that seem important to individual wildlife species. These features can be measured during inventories to predict whether or not a habitat apparently is suitable for an individual species.

The absence of a wildlife species in a planning unit during a wildlife inventory frequently can be attributed to either the absence of a habitat layer or inadequate habitat conditions within that layer of habitat. It is possible, in this way, to predict why a species is present or absent within a habitat and, presumably, to develop remedial management practices to make that habitat more suitable.

CLASSIFICATION SYSTEMS

The vegetation in western rangelands has been extensively studied. Sagebrush and pinyon-juniper ecosystems make up about one-third of the area of western rangelands (Table 1); each has been the subject of recent technical symposia (Utah State University 1975, 1979). These symposia emphasized the distribution of these major vegetational cover types in the western U.S., results of autoecological and synecological studies of the ecosystems, faunal communities, processes (e.g., fire, mechanical, and herbicidal techniques) for modifying the structure of the ecosystems, impacts of ecosystem modification on other land uses, and procedures for increasing herbage production in modified habitats. The distribution of shrubs within the U.S., uses of shrub tissues, physiology and nutritive quality of shrubs, techniques for regenerating shrubs, and the future of shrubs in arid lands have been emphasized in other studies (McKell et al. 1972). Additional publications about rangelands have emphasized floral and faunal relationships in Great Basin habitats (Harper and Reveal 1978) and topics such as seedbed preparation and planting and the management of seeded ranges (Plummer et al. 1955, 1968), impacts of fire on shrubs (Wright 1972; Wright et al. 1979), and impacts of drought on grasslands (Albertson and Weaver 1946).

Studies of rangelands that describe the structure, composition, distribution, and ecological relationships among vegetative components have been done on a State (Nichol 1937; Costello 1944) and a regional basis (Weaver 1954; Weaver and Albertson 1956). A map of the natural vegetation in the U.S. and a description of associated cover types was published in the Atlas of American Agriculture (U.S. Department of Agriculture 1936). The presumed distribution of potential range vegetation types in the U.S. was published in map form by Kuchler (1964; see Figure 1). Kuchler (1964) also provided a photographic description of different potential rangeland types. A more intensive mapping of range cover types in the southwestern U.S. was done by Brown and Lowe (1980), and a text description of range types was provided by Brown (1982).

Many other authors have provided specialized descriptions of rangeland vegetation. These descriptions vary from statewide assessments to intensive treatments of small range areas. Several range vegetation classification systems are summarized in Table 2 by area of application, general type of rangeland vegetation considered, a brief description of the vegetative classification system, and the apparent utility of the system in inventories and assessments of wildlife habitat.

The references in Table 2 will be especially helpful to persons working in unfamiliar range habitats. The publications listed frequently provide maps of the distribution of range vegetation, descriptions of vegetation communities, and lists of wildlife species that use different range cover types.

Table 2. Range vegetation classification systems developed for grassland, shrubland, and woodland cover types in the western U.S. and their utility in inventories and assessments of wildlife habitat quality.

Area of application	Type of vegetation	Classification system	Utility in inventorying and monitoring	Reference
Grasslands				
1. Southeastern Washington, northeastern Oregon, west-central Idaho	Fescue-wheatgrass	Descriptions of vegetative associations	Describes a variety of climax communities in Pacific Northwest bunch-grass types	Tisdale (1983)
2. Idaho	Fescue-wheatgrass	Description of vegetative associations similar to those of Tisdale (1983)	Provides map of potential vegetation types in Idaho	Sharp and Sanders (1978)
3. Snake River Canyon, Idaho	Fescue-wheatgrass	Dichotomous key to grasslands in the Snake River Canyon	Lists specific habitat criteria for vegetative association	Tisdale (1979)
4. Southwestern U.S.	Alpine and subalpine grasslands	Description of vegetative associations	Text, in conjunction with map (Brown and Lowe 1980), provides a description of the location and structure of this vegetative community in the Southwest	Brown (1982)
5. Southwestern U.S.	Plains and Great Basin grasslands	Same as above	Same as above	Brown (1982)
6. Southwestern U.S.	Semidesert grassland	Same as above	Same as above	Brown (1982)
7. Southwestern U.S.	California valley grassland	Same as above	Same as above	Brown (1982)
8. Southwestern U.S.	Sonoran savanna grassland	Same as above	Same as above	Brown (1982)
9. California	Grasslands	Dichotomous key to grasses; illustrations of common species	Describes appearance, distribution and use of individual species	Sampson et al. (1951)
Shrublands				
1. Southern California	Chamise chaparral and mixed chaparral	Lists of plant components of different vegetative types	Describes some vegetative associations along moisture and temperature gradients	Mooney and Parsons (1973)
2. Southwestern U.S.	Oak brush (*Quercus* sp.)	Description of vegetative associations	Text, in conjunction with map (Brown and Lowe 1980), provides a description of the location and structure of this community in the Southwest	Brown (1982)
3. Southwestern U.S.	California coastal scrub	Same as above	Same as above	Brown (1982)
4. Southwestern U.S.	California coastal chaparral	Same as above	Same as above	Brown (1982)
5. Southwestern U.S.	Interior chaparral	Same as above	Same as above	Brown (1982)
6. New Mexico	Saltbush (*Atriplex* sp.)	Dichotomous key, photographs, species descriptions, range maps	Describes species of *Atriplex* and identifies their range	Wagner and Aldon (1978)

Table 2. Range vegetation classification systems developed for grassland, shrubland, and woodland cover types in the western U.S. and their utility in inventories and assessments of wildlife habitat quality (continued).

Area of application	Type of vegetation	Classification system	Utility in inventorying and monitoring	Reference
Shrublands (continued)				
7. Intermountain area	Sagebrush (*Artemisia* sp.), rabbitbrush (*Chrysothamnus* sp.), horsebrush (*Tetradymia* sp.), and matchbrush or snakewood (*Xanthocephalum* sp.)	Description and dichotomous key for species of the four shrubs	Describes appearance, distribution, and use of individual species; provides illustrations that may be helpful in species identification	McArthur et al. (1979)
8. Western Montana	Sagebrush-grasslands	Key based on understory and mid-story components	Describes distribution and vegetative composition of cover types, impacts of grazing on cover types, and response of cover types to range management	Mueggler and Stewart (1980)
9. Intermountain region	Sagebrush-grasslands	Variety of taxonomic keys based on vegetative characteristics	Describes species of sagebrush; management of sagebrush for livestock; and the presumed impacts of sagebrush management on livestock	Blaisdell et al. (1982)
10. Columbia River Basin-Idaho, Oregon, Washington	Sagebrush-grasslands	Lists of midstory-understory components	Association of sagebrush-grassland complexes with edaphic and climatic factors	Hironaka (1979)
11. Northern Great Plains	Sagebrush species	Lists ecological relationships of some common sagebrush species and associates	Describes factors contributing to the distribution of sagebrush species in Montana, Wyoming, and the Dakotas	Johnson (1979)
12. Blue Mountains in eastern Oregon and southeastern Washington	Sagebrush-dominated rangelands	Describes environmental and edaphic conditions characteristic of range type	Lists species components, range appearance, and criteria for describing range condition	Hall (1973)
13. Western U.S.	Sagebrush	Dichotomous key	Photographs of herbarium types and distribution maps of 12 sagebrush taxa	Beetle (1960)
14. Southern Idaho	Sagebrush-grasslands	Dichotomous key	Describes wildlife use of habitat types and provides suggestion for management of habitats	Hironaka et al. (1983)
15. Oregon	Sagebrush	Diagrammatic key	Describes habitats where different sagebrush species occur	Winward (1980)

Table 2. Range vegetation classification systems developed for grassland, shrubland, and woodland cover types in the western U.S. and their utility in inventories and assessments of wildlife habitat quality (concluded).

Area of application	Type of vegetation	Classification system	Utility in inventorying and monitoring	Reference
Woodlands 1. Southwestern U.S.	Pinyon-juniper	Descriptions of vegetative associations	Text, in conjunction with map (Brown and Lowe 1980), provides a description of the location and structure of the pinyon-juniper community in the Southwest	Brown (1982)
2. Southwestern U.S.	Oak-woodlands	Same as above	Same as above	Brown (1982)

MAJOR SPECIES GROUPS

Western range ecosystems provide habitat for at least 10 rare and endangered terrestrial vertebrate wildlife species (U.S. Forest Service 1972):

- Utah prairie dog (*Cynomys parvidens*)
- Grizzly bear (*Ursus arctos horribilis*)
- Yuma clapper rail (*Rallus longirostris yumanensis*)
- Light-footed clapper rail (*R. l. levipes*)
- Masked bobwhite (*Colinus virginianus ridgwayi*)
- California condor (*Gymnogyps californianus*)
- Sonoran pronghorn (*Antilocapra americana sonoriensis*)
- San Joaquin kit fox (*Vulpes macrotis mutica*)
- Black-footed ferret (*Mustela nigripes*)
- Whooping crane (*Grus americana*)

The use of rangeland habitats by terrestrial vertebrate wildlife species is probably mostly dependent on the structure of the rangeland vegetative cover. For example, treeland habitats generally support a more diverse wildlife community than do shrubland or grassland habitats, and shrubland habitats frequently support a more diverse wildlife community than do grassland habitats. Other factors influencing the diversity of the wildlife community on a rangeland include—

- latitude;
- climate;
- topography;
- distance to water;
- distance to cliff faces, caves, or other features;
- density, height, and vigor of range vegetation; and
- presence or absence of particular plant species.

Many of these factors are described in greater detail in the following section.

CRITICAL HABITAT FEATURES

Range surveys are often conducted to describe soil profiles and to estimate (1) the potential natural vegetation that can occur on a range habitat, (2) the condition of range vegetation, and (3) the wildlife community that is present.

Range surveys, until World War II, usually were conducted entirely by ground methods, such as traversing compass lines across landscapes and sketching in planimetric and vegetation details (Poulton 1970). Cost effectiveness and usefulness of range surveys were enhanced by the widespread acceptance of interpretive aerial photography. Interpretation of aerial photographs, combined with field surveys, offers an increased capability to evaluate large land areas to—

(1) identify many plant species and soil surface features;

(2) classify surface features into specific habitat types;

(3) measure vegetation characteristics such as cover, density, height, and spatial distribution; and

(4) monitor changes in vegetation and soil surface conditions over time.

Samples of current annual growth collected during range surveys frequently are subjected to chemical, calorimetric, and digestive analyses to develop estimates of range carrying capacity for domestic livestock and selected wildlife species. Range conditions often are evaluated by determining if the plants that characteristically should grow in the area are present and in good vigor (Stoddard et al. 1975). Surveys to determine the presence of wildlife in range cover types usually involve on-site assessments with standardized trapping techniques, especially for small mammals and reptiles, and census lines for avian surveys or for locating pellet group plots for large mammals. Animal survey techniques sometimes are supplemented with interpreted aerial photographs that show, for example, waterfowl on lakes, deer and elk against snowfield, and domestic livestock on range.

Rangelands are complex ecosystems that can be studied at many levels of detail. Inventories can be very intensive and applicable to small areas or be extremely general, providing limited information to managers. It seems desirable, in this chapter, to provide a general framework for conducting surveys to inventory rangelands and monitor their wildlife values. This framework is a conceptual representation of the structure of rangeland within which general survey information applicable to large land areas can be gathered and analyzed in a timely manner and within which very specific information also can be gathered. I have not included extensive lists of range variables and techniques for their measurement; this information is available elsewhere. Instead, I have provided a general inventory process that—

- is universally applicable to a wide variety of terrestrial rangeland types;

- considers all the vertebrate wildlife species that might occur on a rangeland;

- allows a manager to predict the impacts that land use change might have on wildlife species; and

- uses state-of-the-art technologies to provide quantitative appraisals of rangelands so that rangeland resources can be monitored through time.

This inventory process includes a way to abstractly represent the structure of range vegetation, associate wildlife species with the structure of range vegetation, and relate some types of inventory information to range management.

It is unrealistic to consider the total wildlife community in inventories and assessments of rangelands, unless some general criteria can be identified that determine how wildlife species use habitats and are easily measured. Layers of habitat, discussed below, is an easily-measured criterion that is a critical habitat feature for terrestrial vertebrate species.

Any terrestrial habitat, including a rangeland, can be considered a volume of space that contains structure, such as vegetation which may be useful to wildlife species. The volume of space in a mixed rangeland habitat containing shrubland, grassland, and treeland components is represented in Part A of Figure 2. The structure of this rangeland habitat also can be considered in terms of habitat layers, as in Part B of Figure 2, which can be used to inventory and evaluate rangeland habitats. The different habitat layers are defined in Short and Burnham (1982) and in Table 3.

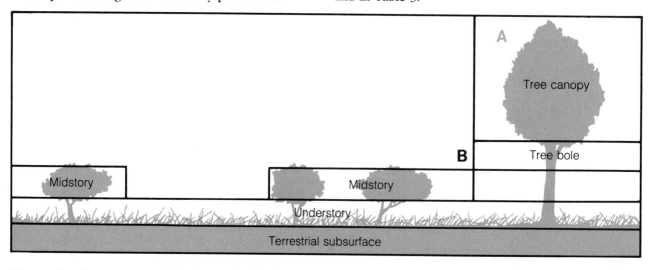

Figure 2. Cover types within a rangeland habitat can be considered in terms of layers of habitat.

Table 3. Suggested criteria for determining the presence of different layers of habitat.

Layer	Criteria
Tree canopy or overstory	Vegetation structure is 8 m (25 ft) or more above the terrestrial or aquatic surface and provides at least 5% cover when projected to the surface (500 m²/ha or 2,200 ft²/a.).
Tree bole	Tree trunks have a dbh 20 cm (8 in.) and occur at a density 12/ha (5/a.).
Shrub midstory	Vegetation height from 50 cm (20 in.) up to 8 m (25 ft), which provides at least 5% cover when projected to the surface (500 m²/ha or 2,200 ft²/a.).
Understory	Layer extends from 10 cm (4 in.) below the apparent surface up to, but not including, 50 cm (20 in.) above the apparent surface and provides at least 5% cover when projected to the surface (500 m²/ha or 2,200 ft²/a.).
Terrestrial subsurface	Extends from more than 10 cm (4 in.) below the apparent surface down.
Surface water layer	Land surface-water interface and shallow water up to 25 cm (10 in.) deep.

The surface water layer includes the shoreline and shallow water (< 25cm [10 in.] deep) areas and the terrestrial substrate that is under the shallow water. Vegetation that emerges through shallow water and is less than 0.5 m (1.6 ft) high is considered a product of the surface water layer, as is floating vegetation in shallow water.

The terrestrial subsurface layer extends upward to within 10 cm (4 in.) of the apparent surface and includes caves and deep crevices that are critical habitat features for some wildlife species and a soil substrate suitable for the construction of burrows and dens.

The terrestrial surface layer extends from 10 cm (4 in.) below to 0.5 m (1.6 ft) above the apparent surface. This layer includes bare ground, talus, cliff faces, litter, herbaceous vegetation, and dwarf or supine woody vegetation as habitat features.

The shrub or midstory layer extends from 0.5 to 8.0 m (1.6 to 26.4 ft) above the apparent surface and includes the canopies of shrubs and dwarf trees, as well as other vegetative plant parts that extend into this strata.

The tree bole layer consists of live and dead tree trunks that provide both a foraging substrate and a variety of nest substrates, including bark and cavities. Tree boles comprise a vertical feature that extends through horizontal layers. Snags are specialized tree boles.

The tree canopy extends above 8.0 m (26.4 ft) and provides large and small branches of living and dead trees as nest substrates and includes leaves, buds, and fruit as food for wildlife species.

Considering habitat in terms of layers has several advantages. The concept seems intuitively correct, insofar as the presence of layers is readily perceivable, even though attempts to define the layers may seem arbitrary (Table 3). Layers of habitat can be mapped, wildlife species can be identified with particular habitat layers, and many management actions impact habitat layers, which can be used to predict the impacts of land use change on wildlife.

Wildlife species can be associated with layers of habitat because the niche of an individual species occurs within one or more habitat strata. Grasslands contain only the terrestrial subsurface and terrestrial surface layers, defined above. Shrublands provide terrestrial subsurface, terrestrial surface, and midstory layers; woodland habitats may also provide tree boles for cavity makers and users and a tree canopy layer. Rangeland habitats that provide only a few layers of habitat have a limited volume of space within which wildlife species can find niches. More niches are potentially available as more layers of habitat occur in cover types, so more wildlife species potentially are supported by more structurally complex habitats.

Rangelands can be described in terms of habitat layers. For example, Kuchler (1964) listed 27 potential natural vegetation types in the western U.S. that can be considered rangelands. These types are arrayed in Figure 3 according to the number of habitat layers that each type provides for the wildlife community. Considerable similarity exists in the structure of the wildlife communities that occur in the 14 grassland-dwarf shrub cover types, which contain terrestrial subsurface and terrestrial surface layers of habitat. Great similarity also is evident in the structure of the wildlife communities that occur in the seven shrubland cover types, which contain terrestrial subsurface, terrestrial surface, and midstory layers of habitat. The similarities in the wildlife communities within grasslands and the communities within shrublands occur even when the vegetation

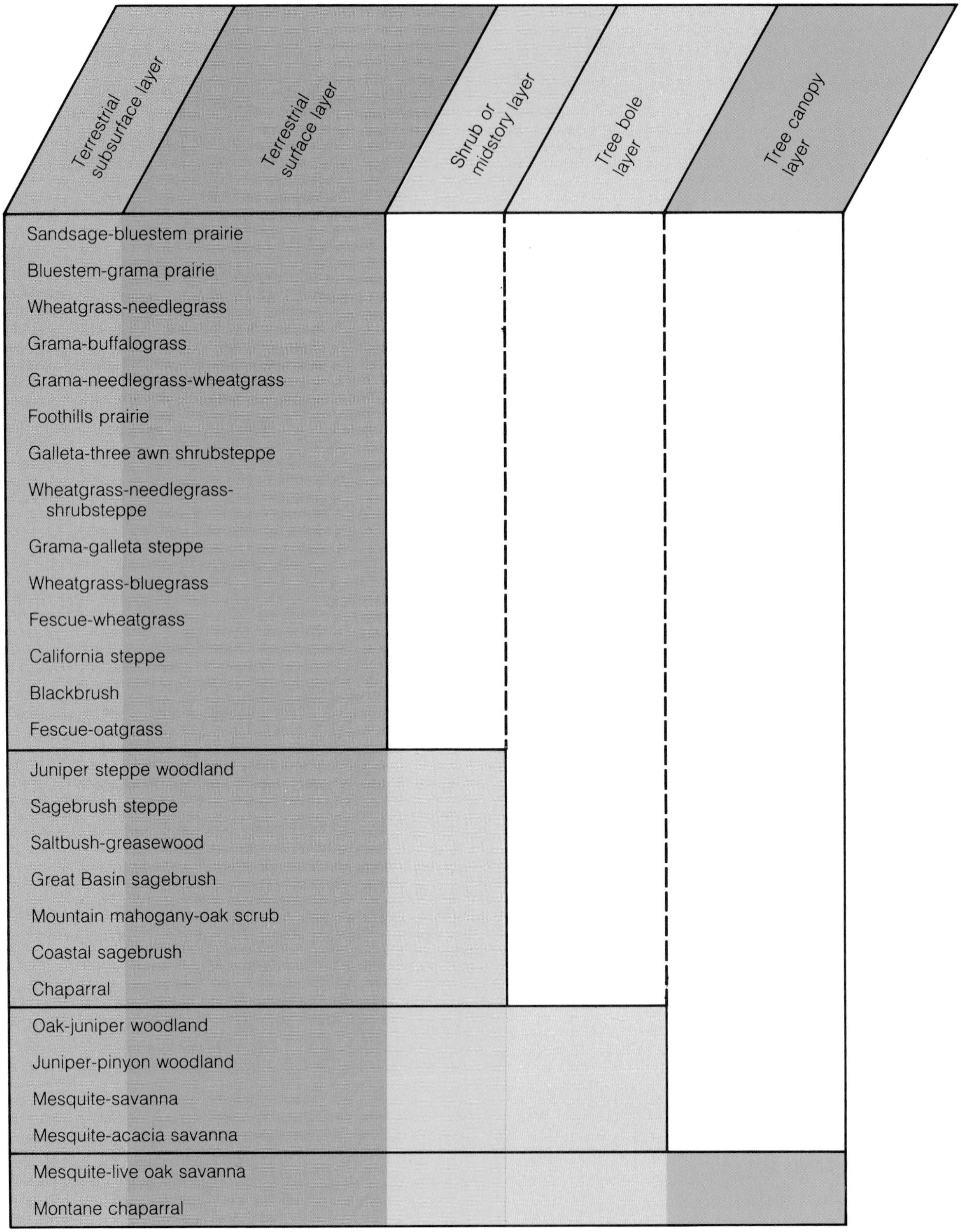

Figure 3. Rangeland cover types provide different habitat layers for the wildlife community.

species differ among grasslands or among shrublands. Certain broad habitat changes within grasslands or within shrublands are expected to affect similar functional segments of the wildlife community in a predictable manner. The capability to predict impacts on the wildlife community resulting from changes in a cover type is important to resource managers.

Layers of habitat can be mapped and used to describe potential wildlife habitat values in a planning unit. As the quantity of a habitat layer changes, the quantity of habitat available for species dependent on that habitat layer also changes. Thus, a measure of the structure of a rangeland provides a first estimate of the utility of that rangeland as habitat for wildlife species.

Habitat Layer Index (HLI)

The interpretation of aerial photography has become an important tool in range surveys because it is the best way to represent the physical relationships between surface cover features. For example, aerial photographs have often been used to describe where shrubland, grassland, and treeland cover types, depicted in Figure 2A, occur within a study area. An aerial photograph that has been interpreted to describe cover types is provided in Figure 4, which indicates the location and identification of surface cover types on a selected land area within the Piceance Basin of northwestern Colorado. The photograph has been interpreted according to the

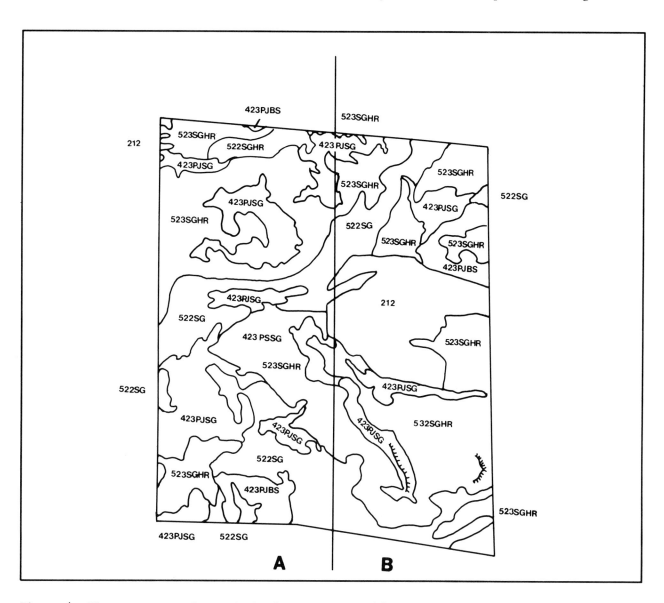

Figure 4. The cover type polygons in this figure were traced from an interpreted aerial photograph of a small portion of the Piceance Basin in northwestern Colorado. Identification of the vegetation within individual polygons can be made from vegetation classes listed in Table 5. Segments A and B are described in detail in the text.

hierarchical classification system listed in Table 4, coupled with ground truthing, which is the on-site examination of photo points to correlate images on the photograph with cover features on the ground.

Maps of cover types, like that in Figure 4, can provide useful information to persons trying to inventory and assess wildlife habitat on rangelands because some wildlife species, within their distribution range, are closely associated with the habitat structure provided by specific cover types. For example, species like sage grouse (*Centrocercus urophasianus*), Brewer's sparrows (*Spizella breweri*), sage sparrows (*Amphispiza belli*), and sagebrush voles (*Lagurus curtatus*) may be dependent on the presence of sagebrush (*Artemesia* sp.) habitat, whereas bushtits (*Psaltriparus minimus*), ash-throated flycatchers (*Myiarchus cinerascens*), gray vireos (*Vireo vicinior*), black-throated gray warblers (*Dendroica nigrescens*), and pinyon mice (*Peromyscus truei*) may be dependent on the presence of pinyon-juniper (*Pinus-Juniperus* sp.) and oak brush (*Quercus* sp.). Lark buntings (*Calamospiza melanocorys*), horned larks (*Eremophila alpestris*), chestnut-collared longspurs (*Calcarius ornatus*), McCown's longspurs (*Calcarius mccownii*), western meadowlarks (*Sturnella neglecta*), Baird's sparrows (*Ammodramus bairdii*), swift foxes (*Vulpes velox*), northern grasshopper mice (*Onchomys leucogaster*), plains harvest mice (*Reithrodontomys montanus*), Ord's kangaroo rats (*Dipodomys ordii*), thirteen-lined ground squirrels (*Spermophilus tridecemlineatus*), and pronghorns (*Antilocapra americana*), may be dependent on the presence of prairie grasses.

Interpreted aerial photographs can be used to determine the presence of other important habitat features like high cliffs and cliff faces, which may be habitat for peregrine falcons (*Falco peregrinus*), prairie falcons (*Falco mexicanus*), black swifts (*Cypseloides niger*), white-throated swifts (*Aeronautes saxatalis*), cliff swallows (*Hirundo pyrrhonota*), and canyon wrens (*Catherpes mexicanus*); boulder fields, talus slopes, and rock slides in mountainous areas, which may be habitat for pikas (*Ochotona princeps*); caves, which may be habitat for a variety of bats; and prairie dog towns, which may be habitat for black-tailed prairie dogs (*Cynomys ludovicianus*), black-footed ferrets, and burrowing owls (*Athene cunicularia*); and water sources essential to the reproduction of amphibians and a life requisite for numerous other species. The absence of these

Table 4. Hierarchical classification system for interpreting aerial photographs, developed for the Piceance Basin of Northeastern Colorado.

Level 1	Level 2	Level 3	Level 4	Level 5
1. Urban or built-up land	1. Commercial 2. Residential	1. Transportation (update of USGS maps only)		
2. Agricultural/ reclaimed land	1. Agricultural	1. Irrigated crops 2. Nonirrigated crops 3. Orchards, groves, nurseries 4. Other		
	2. Reclaimed land	1. Reclaimed mine land 2. Other reclaimed land 3. Chained land 4. Other		
3. Wetlands (interpreted according to National Wetland Inventory Standards)		Percent cover of dominant cover type	Dominant cover	Subdominant cover

Table 4. Hierarchical classification system for interpreting aerial photographs, developed for the Piceance Basin of Northeastern Colorado (continued).

Level 1	Level 2	Level 3	Level 4	Level 5
4. Forest (>20% trees)	1. Deciduous	1. Closed 80 + % 2. Open 50 to 80% 3. Sparse 20 to 50%	AS Aspen UD Upland deciduous OT Other	BS Bare soil BR Bare rock HR Herbaceous SG Sagebrush OB Oakbrush US Upland shrub HA Halophytic shrub OT Other
	2. Evergreen	1. Closed 80 + % 2. Open 50 to 80% 3. Sparse 20 to 50%	PD Ponderosa pine JN Juniper PY Pinyon pine DF Douglas fir SP Spruce sp. SA Subalpine fir LP Lodgepole pine PJ Pinyon pine/ juniper assn. SF Spruce/fir assn. CN Coniferous OT Other	BS Bare soil BR Bare rock HR Herbaceous SG Sagebrush OB Oakbrush US Upland shrub HA Halophytic shrub OT Other
	3. Mixed deciduous/ evergreen (>33% deciduous and >33% evergreen)	1. Closed 80 + % 2. Open 50 to 80% 3. Sparse 20 to 50%	AS Aspen PD Ponderosa pine JN Juniper PY Pinyon pine DF Douglas fir SP Spruce sp. SA Subalpine fir LP Lodgepole pine PJ Pinyon pine/ juniper assn. SF Spruce/fir assn. UD Upland deciduous CN Coniferous OT Other	BS Bare soil BR Bare rock HR Herbaceous SG Sagebrush OB Oakbrush US Upland shrub HA Halophytic shrub OT Other
5. Shrubland (>20% shrubs and <20% trees)	1. Deciduous	1. Closed 80 + % 2. Open 50 to 80% 3. Sparse 20 to 50%	OB Oakbrush US Upland shrub OT Other	BS Bare soil BR Bare rock HR Herbaceous OT Other
	2. Evergreen	1. Closed 80 + % 2. Open 50 to 80% 3. Sparse 20 to 50%	SG Sagebrush SL Saltbrush GR Greasewood HA Halophytic shrub OT Other	BS Bare soil BR Bare rock HR Herbaceous OT Other
	3. Mixed deciduous/ evergreen (>33% deciduous and >33% evergreen)	1. Closed 80 + % 2. Open 50 to 80% 3. Sparse 20 to 50%	SG Sagebrush OB Oakbrush SL Saltbrush GR Greasewood US Upland shrub HA Halophytic shrub OT Other	BS Bare soil BR Bare rock HR Herbaceous OT Other

Table 4. Hierarchical classification system for interpreting aerial photographs, developed for the Piceance Basin of Northeastern Colorado (concluded).

Level 1	Level 2	Level 3	Level 4	Level 5
6. Grassland (>20% grass and <20% trees and <20% shrubs)	1. Plains grassland	1. Closed 80% 2. Open 50 to 80% 3. Sparse 20 to 50%	TL Tallgrass SH Shortgrass BN Bunchgrass DS Desert grass AN Annual grass OT Other	BS Bare soil BR Bare rock OT Other
	2. Mountain grassland	1. Closed 80+% 2. Open 50 to 80% 3. Sparse 20 to 50%	TL Tallgrass SH Shortgrass BN Bunchgrass DS Desert grass AN Annual grass OT Other	BS Bare Soil BR Bare rock OT Other
7. Barren land (>40% bare ground and <20% trees and <20% shrubs and <20% grasses)	1. Natural	1. Bare exposed rock 2. Bare exposed soil 3. Spires/cliffs	HR Herbaceous SG Sagebrush US Upland shrub HA Halophytic shrub PJ Pinyon pine/ juniper assn. SF Spruce/fir assn. AS Aspen CN Coniferous OT Other	
	2. Man-made	1. Quarries 2. Strip mine 3. Gravel pit 4. Mine spoils 5. Nonvegetated		
8. Tundra	1. Shrub and brush tundra 2. Herbaceous tundra 3. Bare ground tundra 4. Wet tundra 5. Mixed tundra			
9. Perennial snow or ice	1. Perennial snowfield 2. Glacier			

important habitat features in a planning unit or study site suggests that wildlife species dependent on the structure of these physical features will be uncommon or absent.

Many wildlife species seem to utilize a habitat structure more general than that provided by a single plant species. Consequently, it may be easier to produce maps like that in Figure 4 than to determine what the maps really mean in terms of species presence. For example, it is difficult to list the wildlife species expected to use each of the polygons in Figure 4 or to compare the structure of the habitats in segments A and B. However, the concept of habitat layers provides a framework for interpreting the usefulness of the structure of such habitats to the wildlife community.

HLI provides a way to quantitatively describe the relative structural complexity of the vegetative cover occurring in a study area. It provides a number between 0.0 (no structural diversity) and 1.0 (high structural diversity) that can be used to characterize vegetative diversity on a parcel of land, compare vegetative diversity on several parcels of land, or provide a basis for statistical assessments that show direction and rate of change in habitat structure over time. The index does not predict the suitability of habitats for individual wildlife species, although wildlife species that tend to occur in structurally complex habitats may occur where HLIs are high, whereas other wildlife species requiring simple habitats may occur where HLIs are low. High HLIs should not be equated to "good" habitat and low HLIs to "poor." A grassland, for example, might provide excellent habitat for grassland wildlife species and still receive a low HLI because of its limited structural diversity. Disturbance to a grassland could result in the invasion of shrub species, which might produce increased structural diversity and a high HLI, but result in a poor quality habitat for grassland wildlife species. The HLI would be considered simply as a way to numerically represent change in structure in order to enhance habitat assessments.

The cover types depicted in Figure 2A were represented in terms of layers of habitat in Figure 2B. Likewise, the aerial photograph of the land area within the Piceance Basin can be represented in terms of cover types (Figure 4) or in terms of layers of habitat. This interpretation (Figure 5) is based

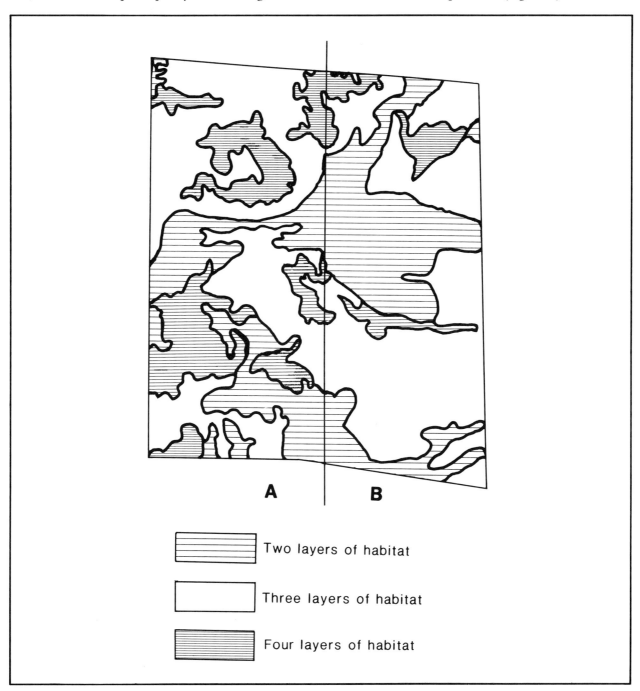

A **B**

Two layers of habitat

Three layers of habitat

Four layers of habitat

Figure 5. Aerial photograph of the land area represented in Figure 4 has been reinterpreted to indicate the number of layers of habitat present in different polygons.

on the assumption that the niche of a wildlife species can be associated with the structure of habitat, represented in terms of layers of habitat. Figure 5 identifies the number of habitat layers present in each polygon, but not the identity of the individual layers. This information is sufficient to calculate the HLI.

The determination of the areas of the tree canopy, tree bole, shrub midstory, understory, subsurface layer suitable for the establishment of burrows, and the water surface (if it exists) on a study area constitutes an inventory of habitat resources on that study area. Results of such an inventory can be expressed in terms of hectares (acres) of each habitat layer within the study area.

Results of this type of inventory for segments A and B of the habitat illustrated in Figure 5 are presented in Table 5. The inventory summarized in Table 5 was accomplished by determining the layers of habitat present in the different cover types.

The formula for calculating the HLI for a study area is—

$$\text{HLI} = \frac{X \sum\limits_{i=1}^{n} A_i}{(6)(5) \sum\limits_{j=1}^{n} A_j}$$

where:

X = the number of layers of habitat present within some bounded area,

Ai = the area of layer of habitat i within the bounded area,

Aj = the surface area of cover type j within the bounded area,

n = the number of different cover types present within the bounded area,

6 = the maximum number of habitat layers that could occur in a unit of structurally complex terrestrial habitat, and

5 = the maximum number of units of area of habitat layers that could occur within a unit of structurally complex terrestrial habitat.

The calculation of HLIs for segments A and B of Figure 5 is presented below. There are four layers of habitat present in segment A (terrestrial subsurface, understory, midstory, and tree bole); the sum of the area of the layers of habitat equals 836.7 ha (2091.8 a.) (Table 5). The denominator equals six layers of habitat and 5 × 281.1 ha (702.8 a.) of habitat layers.

$$\text{HLI} = \frac{\text{number of actual layers actually present} \times \text{actual area of those habitat layers}}{\text{number of habitat layers potentially present} \times \text{potential area of those habitat layers}}$$

$$= \frac{4 \times 2091.8}{6 \times 5 \times 702.8} = 0.397 \text{ or } 39.7\%$$

Segment A contains a structural diversity measure of 39.7%. This HLI can be compared with that of other land units to compare the structural diversity of different study areas.

The HLI for segment B in Figure 5 is calculated in a similar manner. The same four layers of habitat are present in B as in A; the area of the habitat layers in B equals 732.7 ha (1831.7 a.) (Table 5). The denominator equals six layers of habitat and 5 × 269.4 ha (673.6 a.).

$$\text{HLI} = \frac{4 \times 1831.7}{6 \times 5 \times 673.6} = 0.362 \text{ or } 36.2\%$$

The HLI for segment B is reduced because a substantial block of sagebrush habitat was cleared to produce a dry land pasture (polygon 212 in section B of Figure 4). The loss of sagebrush, which provided a midstory layer on this land unit, made this polygon unsuitable for species with obligate ties to sagebrush and for species requiring a midstory structure.

Habitat Layers—Wildlife Guilds

The inventory and assessment of the structure of habitat is one level of range analysis; the determination of the quantity of particular habitats suitable for particular wildlife guilds is a second range evaluation process. The map in Figure 5 shows where two, three, or four habitat layers occur on the study area in the Piceance Basin, although the particular habitat layers present in any one polygon are not identified. Five combinations of habitat layers actually occur in the mapped area. Polygons identified as 212 in Figure 4 provide subsurface and understory layers of habitat (Table 5). Polygons identified as 522 SG provide subsurface and midstory layers; polygons identified as 523 SGHR and 522 SGHR provide subsurface, understory, and midstory layers. Polygons identified as 423 PJBS provide subsurface, midstory, and tree bole layers; and polygons identified as 423 PJSG provide subsurface, understory, and midstory, and tree bole layers of habitat. These different habitat structures may vary in their suitability for wildlife species.

The location of each of the different habitat structures can be represented on a map. Data for drawing such maps can be obtained from terrestrial

Table 5. Areas (acres) of each cover type and individual layers of habitat present in habitat segments A and B of Figure 5.

Segment	Cover type (Figure 4)	Individual layers of habitat present					
		Total	Sub-surface	Under-story	Mid-story	Tree bole	Total area of layers
A	212	5.3	5.3	5.3	—	—	10.6
	523 SGHR	352.9	352.9	352.9	352.9	—	1058.7
	423 PJSG	144.9	144.9	144.9	144.9	144.9	579.7
	522 SGHR	22.0	22.0	22.0	22.0	—	66.0
	522 SG	156.2	156.2	—	156.2	—	312.4
	423 PJBS	21.5	21.5	—	21.5	21.5	64.5
	Total	702.8	702.8	525.1	697.5	166.4	2091.8
B	212	139.6	139.6	139.6	—	—	279.2
	523 SGHR	328.9	328.9	328.9	328.9	—	986.7
	423 PJSG	48.5	48.5	48.5	48.5	48.5	194.0
	522 SGHR	0.0	—	—	—	—	0.0
	522 SG	98.0	98.0	—	98.0	—	196.0
	423 PJBS	58.6	58.6	—	58.6	58.6	175.8
	Total	673.6	673.6	517.0	534.0	107.1	1831.7

The numerator of the Habitat Layer Index is calculated by determining the product of the number of habitat layers actually present in a study area, like that in Figure 5, and the area of the individual habitat layers present on that area. The denominator is the hypothetical value that would be realized if all six layers of habitat (water surface, terrestrial subsurface, terrestrial surface, midstory, tree bole, and tree canopy) occurred on the study area and five of these layers extended throughout the study area.

surveys of the structure of cover types or from interpretive aerial photography with ground truthing. Each polygon in the map of habitat structure within the Piceance Basin study area (Figure 6) provides subsurface, surface, midstory, and tree bole layers of habitat. Wildlife species can be associated with the structure of habitats like that represented in Figure 6 through the formation of wildlife guilds (described below). Maps of habitat structure and lists of wildlife guilds dependent on that habitat structure will show, for example, that the notated polygons in Figure 6 constitute a distribution map of suitable habitat for cavity-using species of wildlife in this study area. The habitat layer-wildlife guild maps help explain the distribution of wildlife species throughout the rangeland and provide a rationale for inventorying habitat conditions suitable for groups of wildlife species.

The association of wildlife species with polygons of habitat can be accomplished with the guilding procedure designed by Short and Burnham (1982), as modified by Short (1983). The vertical layers of habitat are represented in that procedure as axes of a two-dimensional matrix. The x-axis of the matrix represents layers of habitat where nesting, birthing, or hatching occur; the y-axis of the matrix represents habitat layers where wildlife species forage for food. This type of "species-habitat" matrix is illustrated in Figure 7. The y-axis of the matrix is divided so that layers where primary consumption (plant materials) occurs can be differentiated from habitat

layers where secondary consumption (animal materials) occurs. The process described below produces both guilds of primary consumers and guilds of secondary consumers. Omnivorous species occupy two guilds, one as a primary consumer and one as a secondary consumer.

The blocks formed by the intersection of the lines that differentiate the layers of habitat on the x- and y-axes of the matrix are called "guild blocks." The species-habitat matrices for the variety of rangeland habitats are different because the number of guild blocks actually available for use by members of the wildlife community varies among range cover types. The guild blocks available to wildlife in the three basic range cover types are indicated in Figure 7 for grassland, shrubland, and woodland habitats. Woodland habitats obviously provide more guild blocks than a shrubland habitat which, in turn, provides more guild blocks than a grassland habitat.

Guild blocks represent the different ways in which wildlife species utilize the resources of habitats. For example, wildlife species in grassland habitats (Figure 7) can breed in the terrestrial subsurface layer and forage in the subsurface layer, on the terrestrial surface, or in the air. Or they can breed on the terrestrial surface and feed underground, on the terrestrial surface, or in the air. Wildlife species can breed in other habitats and forage in the subsurface layer, on the terrestrial surface, or in the air above

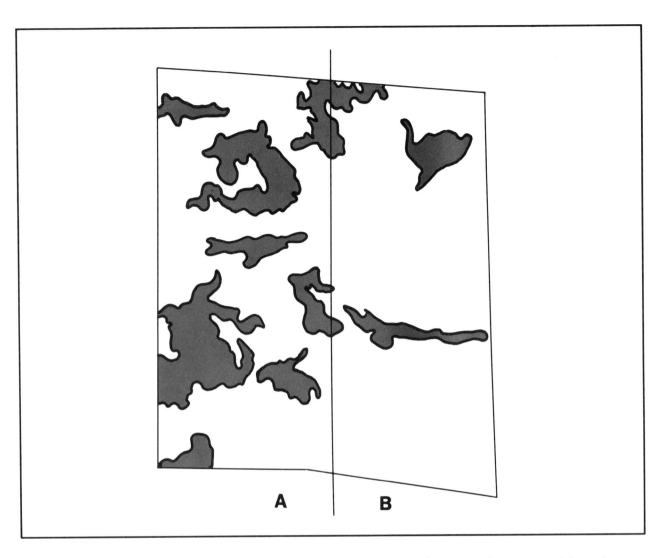

Figure 6. Map of segments A and B of the Piceance Basin study area showing polygons containing subsurface, surface, midstory, and tree bole layers of habitat.

the grassland. Shrubland and woodland communities are more complex because more layers of habitat are available for the location of niche spaces for wildlife species.

Groups or guilds of wildlife species are developed from a species-habitat data base. The data base describes the layers of habitat where breeding (nesting, birthing, or hatching) occurs, as well as the layers of habitat where foraging occurs, for each wildlife species potentially occurring in a study area. The information within the wildlife species data base is processed (Short 1983) as follows: the numerical codes that indicate the layers of habitat used for breeding and for feeding (listed along the x- and y-axes of Figure 7) are entered into a computer for each vertebrate wildlife species inhabiting a cover type. These coded data are subjected to standard "merge-sort" routines that produce lists of species with dependencies on the same guild block or the

same group of guild blocks. An example of the wildlife guilds produced with this technique is provided in Table 6, which lists the guilds of primary consumers occupying chaparral rangelands habitats in the Hualapai-Aquarius Planning Units in west-central Arizona. This list indicates the dependency of the wildlife community on the structure of the chaparral habitat in this study area.

Wildlife guilds occurring in pinyon-juniper habitats in the Piceance Basin could be developed in the same way that guilds were developed in Table 6 and associated with a map of specific layers of habitat like that in Figure 6. Wildlife species requiring understory and midstory vegetation could occur in the polygons in Figure 6, as well as in the polygons with understory and midstory vegetation. The polygons listed in Figure 6, however, would be the only habitat suitable for cavity-making and cavity-using

Feeding loci

Secondary consumers

	1. Temporary water sources	2. Bottom of water column	3. Water column	4. Water surface	5. Terrestrial subsurface	6. Terrestrial surface	7. Shrub layer	8. Tree bole	9. Tree canopy	10. Breeds elsewhere
10. Feeds elsewhere										
9. Air					G W S	G W S	W S	W		G W S
8. Tree canopy										
7. Tree bole					W	W	W	W		W
6. Shrub layer					W S	W S	W S	W		W S
5. Terr. surface					G W S	G W S	W S	W		G W S
4. Terr. subsurface					G W S	G W S				G S
3. Water surface										
2. Water column										
1. Bottom water column										

Primary consumers

	1. Temporary water sources	2. Bottom of water column	3. Water column	4. Water surface	5. Terrestrial subsurface	6. Terrestrial surface	7. Shrub layer	8. Tree bole	9. Tree canopy	10. Breeds elsewhere
8. Tree canopy										
7. Tree bole					W	W	W	W		W
6. Shrub layer					W S	W S	W S	W		W S
5. Terr. surface					G W S	G W S	W S	W		G W S
4. Terr. subsurface					G W S	G W S				G S
3. Water surface										
2. Water column										
1. Bottom water column										

Breeding loci (1. Temporary water sources, 2. Bottom of water column, 3. Water column, 4. Water surface, 5. Terrestrial subsurface, 6. Terrestrial surface, 7. Shrub layer, 8. Tree bole, 9. Tree canopy, 10. Breeds elsewhere)

Figure 7. Form of the species-habitat matrix used in the development of wildlife guilds, and use of guild blocks by wildlife species in grassland (G), shrubland (S), and woodland (W) habitats.

Table 6. Wildlife guilds of primary consumers in chaparral habitats of west-central Arizona (from Short 1983).

Guild No.	Guild members	Feeding loci						Breeding loci					
		Terrestrial subsurface	Terrestrial surface	Shrub or midstory layer	Tree bole	Tree canopy	Air	Breeds elsewhere	Terrestrial subsurface	Terrestrial surface	Shrub or midstory layer	Tree bole	Tree canopy
1	Black bear	•	•	•					•	•			
	Collared peccary	•	•	•					•	•			
	Deer mouse	•	•	•					•	•			
	Cactus mouse	•	•	•					•	•			
	Coyote	•	•	•					•	•			
2	Striped skunk	•	•						•	•			
	Hog-nosed skunk	•	•						•	•			
3	Botta's pocket gopher	•	•						•				
4	White-throated woodrat		•	•					•	•	•		
5	Bighorn sheep		•	•					•	•			
	Gray fox		•	•					•	•			
	Stephen's woodrat		•	•					•	•			
	Ringtail		•	•					•	•			
	Brush mouse		•	•					•	•			
6	Harris' antelope squirrel		•	•					•	•			
7	Brown-headed cowbird		•	•								•	•	
	House finch		•	•								•	•	
	Mockingbird		•	•								•	•	
	Cactus wren		•	•								•	•	
	Costa's hummingbird		•	•								•	•	
	Western harvest mouse		•	•								•	•	
	Crissal thrasher		•	•								•	•	
8	Mule deer		•	•								•		
	Rock squirrel		•	•								•		
	Cattle		•	•								•		
9	Scrub jay		•	•									•	
	Bushtit		•	•									•	
10	Scott's oriole		•	•								•		
	American robin		•	•				•					
	Lesser goldfinch		•	•				•					
	Townsend's solitaire		•	•				•					
	Anna's hummingbird		•	•				•					
	Lewis' woodpecker		•	•				•					
	Blue grosbeak		•	•				•					
	Black-chinned hummingbird		•	•				•					
	Acorn woodpecker		•	•				•					

Table 6. Wildlife guilds of primary consumers in chaparral habitats of west-central Arizona (from Short 1983) (continued).

Guild No.	Guild members	Feeding loci						Breeding loci					
		Terrestrial subsurface	Terrestrial surface	Shrub or midstory layer	Tree bole	Tree canopy	Air	Breeds elsewhere	Terrestrial subsurface	Terrestrial surface	Shrub or midstory layer	Tree bole	Tree canopy
10 (cont.)	Broad-tailed hummingbird		●	●				●					
	Cassin's kingbird		●	●				●					
	Mountain bluebird		●	●				●					
	Rufous hummingbird		●	●				●					
	Starling		●	●				●					
	Pinyon jay		●	●				●					
	Calliope hummingbird		●	●				●					
	Green-tailed towhee		●	●				●					
	Black-headed grosbeak		●	●				●					
	American goldfinch		●	●				●					
	Common flicker		●	●				●					
	Steller's jay		●	●				●					
	Ladder-backed woodpecker		●	●				●					
	Lazuli bunting		●	●				●					
	Yellow-rumped warbler		●	●				●					
	Western kingbird		●	●				●					
	Swainson's thrush		●	●				●					
	Elk		●	●				●					
	Hermit thrush		●	●				●					
	White-winged dove		●	●				●					
	Western bluebird		●	●				●					
11	Desert spiny lizard		●						●	●			
	Canyon mouse		●						●	●			
	Western spotted skunk		●						●	●			
	Cliff chipmunk		●						●	●			
	Arizona woodrat		●						●	●			
12	Southern grass-hopper mouse		●						●				
	Ord's kangaroo rat		●						●				
	Northern grass-hopper mouse		●						●				
	Desert tortoise		●						●				
13	Mourning dove		●							●	●		
14	Rufous-sided towhee		●							●			
	Eastern cottontail		●							●			
	Black-tailed jack-rabbit		●							●			
	Common raven		●							●			
	Rock dove		●							●			
	Gambel's quail		●							●			
	House mouse		●							●			

Table 6. Wildlife guilds of primary consumers in chaparral habitats of west-central Arizona (from Short 1983) (concluded).

Guild No.	Guild members	Feeding loci						Breeding loci					
		Terrestrial subsurface	Terrestrial surface	Shrub or midstory layer	Tree bole	Tree canopy	Air	Breeds elsewhere	Terrestrial subsurface	Terrestrial surface	Shrub or midstory layer	Tree bole	Tree canopy
14 (cont.)	Desert cottontail		●							●			
	Rofous-crowned sparrow		●							●			
15	Brown towhee		●								●		
	Black-chinned sparrow		●								●		
	Black-throated sparrow		●								●		
16	Western meadowlark		●					●					
	Lark sparrow		●					●					
	Chipping sparrow		●					●					
	Fox sparrow		●					●					
	Purple finch		●					●					
	Brewer's sparrow		●					●					
	Dark-eyed junco		●					●					
	White-crowned sparrow		●					●					
	Water pipit		●					●					
17	Say's phoebe			●					●	●			
18	Verdin			●							●		
19	Hooded oriole			●				●					
	Warbling vireo			●				●					
	Phainopepla			●				●					
	Ruby-crowned kinglet			●				●					
	Plain titmouse			●				●					
	Ash-throated flycatcher			●				●					
	Wied's crested flycatcher			●				●					
	Northern oriole			●				●					
	Yellow-bellied sapsucker			●				●					
	Hermit warbler			●				●					

species that require the tree bole layer habitat. The map in Figure 6 would identify the distribution of habitat favorable to this group of species. The land units containing particular layers of habitat can be surveyed to determine the quantity of habitat that exists for specialized wildlife species or groups of wildlife species. For example, 66.6 ha (166.4 a.) of habitat containing tree boles suitable for cavity nesting species occurred in Segment A, and 42.8 ha (107.1 a.) of this habitat occurred in Segment B of Figure 6 (Table 5). The chaining of pinyon-juniper on Segments A or B would reduce the quantity of the tree bole layer and adversely affect wildlife guilds having a dependency on the tree bole layer.

Use of Habitat Layers by Individual Species

Maps of habitat layers, coupled with lists of the wildlife guilds that use those habitat layers, provide one way to evaluate a habitat cover type. Approximating where a niche space of a species occurs in a layer of habitat is a second appraisal technique, although a more arduous one. This technique, however, yields an estimate of the utility of a range habitat for a particular wildlife species.

A layer of habitat can vary greatly in its composition and utility to wildlife. For example, the terrestrial surface layer can provide a variety of structural features for wildlife (listed under code 6 in Table 7). The understory can (1) be devoid of cover on salt playas and some beaches, (2) have the appearance of desert pavement, (3) contain rocks or be a rock surface in talus fields and on cliffs, (4) be covered with tree litter under a forest overstory, and (5) be covered with grasses, forbs, and dwarf shrubs of different densities and heights. The large array of structured conditions along the terrestrial surface layer can be considered as constituting a gradient of conditions for wildlife species having a dependency on this layer of habitat. Range surveys that describe

surface cover, plant cover type, and plant vigor provide information that helps position a study area along such a terrestrial surface gradient.

The terrestrial surface layer in the native grasslands of North America provides a variety of structures corresponding to those listed in subunits 6.14 to 6.19 of Table 7. The grasslands might vary from bunchgrasses, providing low, scattered herbaceous cover, to sod grasses, providing a tall, dense herbaceous cover. Wildlife species may generally select a particular habitat layer (e.g., terrestrial surface layer) and a particular structure of that habitat layer (e.g., shortgrass prairie with sparse cover) and then fine tune their habitat selection on criteria like percentage bare ground or density and height of particular plant species.

Thus, the greatest abundance of wildlife species A may occur at point X along the terrestrial surface habitat gradient, whereas the greatest abundance of wildlife species B may occur at point Y along the gradient.

A hypothetical habitat layer gradient for grasslands is presented in Figure 8. Horned larks (*Eremophila alpestris*) occupy a position along the habitat gradient characterized as open shortgrass prairie; western meadowlarks occupy a position characterized by medium-dense mid to tall grasses; and bobolinks (*Dolichonyx oryzivorus*) occupy a position characterized by dense, tall stands of grasses, weeds, or alfalfa. These three species might belong to the same grassland wildlife guild, even though their individual presence in a survey would be dependent on the nature of the herbaceous cover in the grassland being inventoried.

Individual wildlife species can be approximately positioned within a gradient developed for a layer of habitat, if simple word models or HSI models (U.S. Fish and Wildlife Service 1980) are constructed.

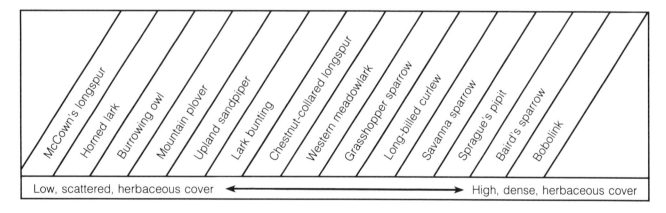

Figure 8. Hypothetical habitat gradient that illustrates how a variety of birds select grasslands with slightly different structures.

Table 7. Habitat conditions that help describe gradients for the terrestrial subsurface, terrestrial surface, midstory, tree bole, and tree canopy layers of habitat. The codes 5–9 cross-reference to the identification of habitat layers listed along the x-axes of the species-habitat matrices in Figure 7.

---

5. Terrestrial subsurface (to 10 cm [4 in.] below apparent surface)

5.01 Rocky substrate unsuitable for burrow or tunnel construction
5.02 Hydric or heavy soils unsuitable for burrow or tunnel construction
5.03 Powdery soils unsuitable for burrow or tunnel construction
5.04 Soils suitable for burrow or tunnel construction
5.05 Cave and deep crevice
5.06 Artificial (man-made) structures, such as mine shafts and out buildings, where interior use is similar to that of burrows or caves

---

6. Terrestrial surface—Understory layer (from 10 cm [4 in.] below to 0.15 m [6 in.] above apparent surface)

6.01 Salt playas or flats with hydric soils
6.02 Beaches (mud, sand, or rock) without hydrophytes
6.03 Marshy areas with hydrophytes but not hydric soils
6.04 Bare ground (sand to rubble, up to 305 mm [12 in.] particles)
6.05 Boulder (> 305 mm [12 in.])—covered surface
6.06 Talus—unvegetated
6.07 Talus—vegetated
6.08 Cliff—on ledge near valley floor
6.09 Cliff—in cavity near valley floor
6.10 Cliff—on ledge near mesa or mountaintop
6.11 Cliff—in cavity near mesa or mountaintop
6.12 Herbaceous litter
6.13 Woody litter (includes shrub branches, tree branches, and stumps)
6.14 Shortgrass prairie vegetation with sparse (< 50%) cover
6.15 Shortgrass prairie vegetation with open or closed (> 50%) cover
6.16 Midgrass prairie vegetation with sparse (< 50%) cover
6.17 Midgrass prairie vegatation with open or closed (> 50%) cover
6.18 Tallgrass prairie vegetation with sparse (< 50%) cover
6.19 Tallgrass prairie vegetation with open or closed (> 50%) cover
6.20 Supine or dwarf woody vegetation or woody vegetation within 0.5 m (19 in.) of apparent surface
6.21 Cactus stems and pads
6.22 Artificial (man-made) structures—ground debris and artifacts, bridges, trestles, and rooftops where external use is analogous to that of the horizontal and vertical surface of natural objects

---

7. Midstory layer (from 0.5 to 8.0 m [19 to 26 ft] above apparent surface)

7.01 Canopy of deciduous shrubs or small trees (< 50% cover)
7.02 Canopy of deciduous shrubs or small trees (> 50% cover)
7.03 Canopy of evergreen shrubs or small trees (< 50% cover)
7.04 Canopy of evergreen shrubs or small trees (> 50% cover)
7.05 Grass and grasslike vegetation (includes bamboo) extending into midstory layer
7.06 Forb vegetation extending into midstory layer
7.07 Cactus stems and pads extending into midstory layer
7.08 Artificial (man-made) structures extending into midstory layer and used in a manner analogous to that of natural vegetation

---

8. Tree bole layer

8.01 Snag—trunk of dead deciduous tree
8.02 Snag—trunk of dead evergreen tree
8.03 Trunk—living deciduous tree
8.04 Trunk—living evergreen tree
8.05 Cactus bole or stem
8.06 Artificial (man-made) structure—telephone and power poles, chimneys, nest boxes

---

9. Tree canopy

9.01 Small branches—live deciduous trees (< 50% cover)
9.02 Small branches—live deciduous trees (> 50% cover)
9.03 Small branches—live evergreen trees (< 50% cover)
9.04 Small branches—live evergreen trees (> 50% cover)
9.05 Large branches—live deciduous trees (< 50% cover)
9.06 Large branches—live deciduous trees (> 50% cover)
9.07 Large branches—live evergreen trees (< 50% cover)
9.08 Large branches—live evergreen trees (> 50% cover)
9.09 Large branches—dead deciduous trees
9.10 Large branches—dead evergreen trees

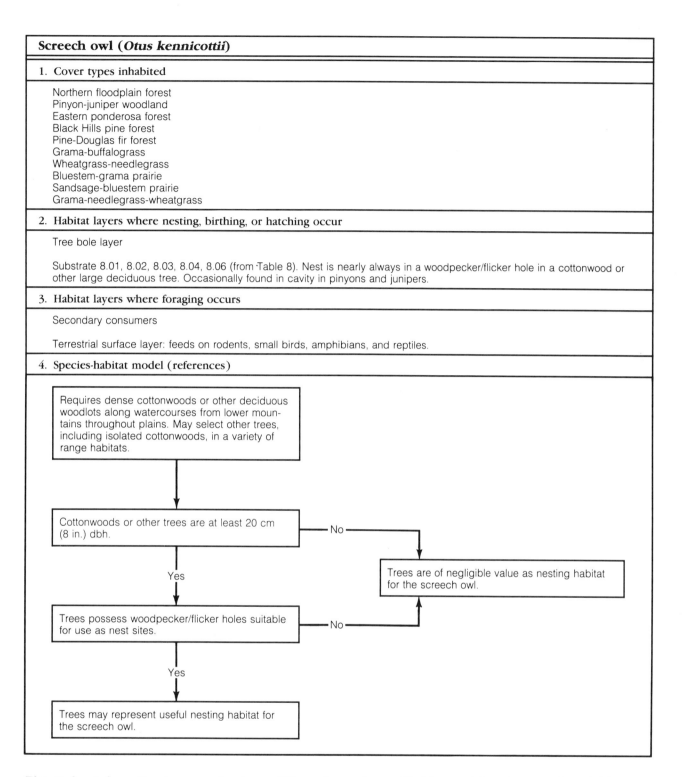

Screech owl (*Otus kennicottii*)

1. Cover types inhabited

Northern floodplain forest
Pinyon-juniper woodland
Eastern ponderosa forest
Black Hills pine forest
Pine-Douglas fir forest
Grama-buffalograss
Wheatgrass-needlegrass
Bluestem-grama prairie
Sandsage-bluestem prairie
Grama-needlegrass-wheatgrass

2. Habitat layers where nesting, birthing, or hatching occur

Tree bole layer

Substrate 8.01, 8.02, 8.03, 8.04, 8.06 (from Table 8). Nest is nearly always in a woodpecker/flicker hole in a cottonwood or other large deciduous tree. Occasionally found in cavity in pinyons and junipers.

3. Habitat layers where foraging occurs

Secondary consumers

Terrestrial surface layer: feeds on rodents, small birds, amphibians, and reptiles.

4. Species-habitat model (references)

Requires dense cottonwoods or other deciduous woodlots along watercourses from lower mountains throughout plains. May select other trees, including isolated cottonwoods, in a variety of range habitats.

↓

Cottonwoods or other trees are at least 20 cm (8 in.) dbh. ——No——→

Yes ↓

Trees possess woodpecker/flicker holes suitable for use as nest sites. ——No——→

Trees are of negligible value as nesting habitat for the screech owl.

Yes ↓

Trees may represent useful nesting habitat for the screech owl.

Figure 9. Information to approximate conditions along a layer of habitat useful to the screech owl (*Otus kennicottii*) in Wyoming and Colorado (after U.S. Forest Service 1981).

Least chipmunk (*Tamias minimus*)

1. Cover types inhabited

Mountain mahogany-oak scrub
Sagebrush steppe
Eastern ponderosa pine
Black Hill pine forest
Pine-Douglas fir forest
Pinyon-juniper woodland
Great Basin sagebrush
Douglas fir forest
Saltbush-greasewood

2. Habitat layers where nesting, birthing, or hatching occur

Terrestrial subsurface layer—Substrate 5.04
Terrestrial surface layer—Substrate 6.06, 6.07, 6.13, 6.22 (from Table 8). Nests are found under stumps, logs, or rocks.

3. Habitat layers where foraging occurs

Primary consumer
Terrestrial surface layer: consumes fruit, nuts, seeds, berries, mushrooms, leaves, stems.

Secondary consumer
Terrestrial surface layer: consumes invertebrates, especially insects.

4. Species-habitat model

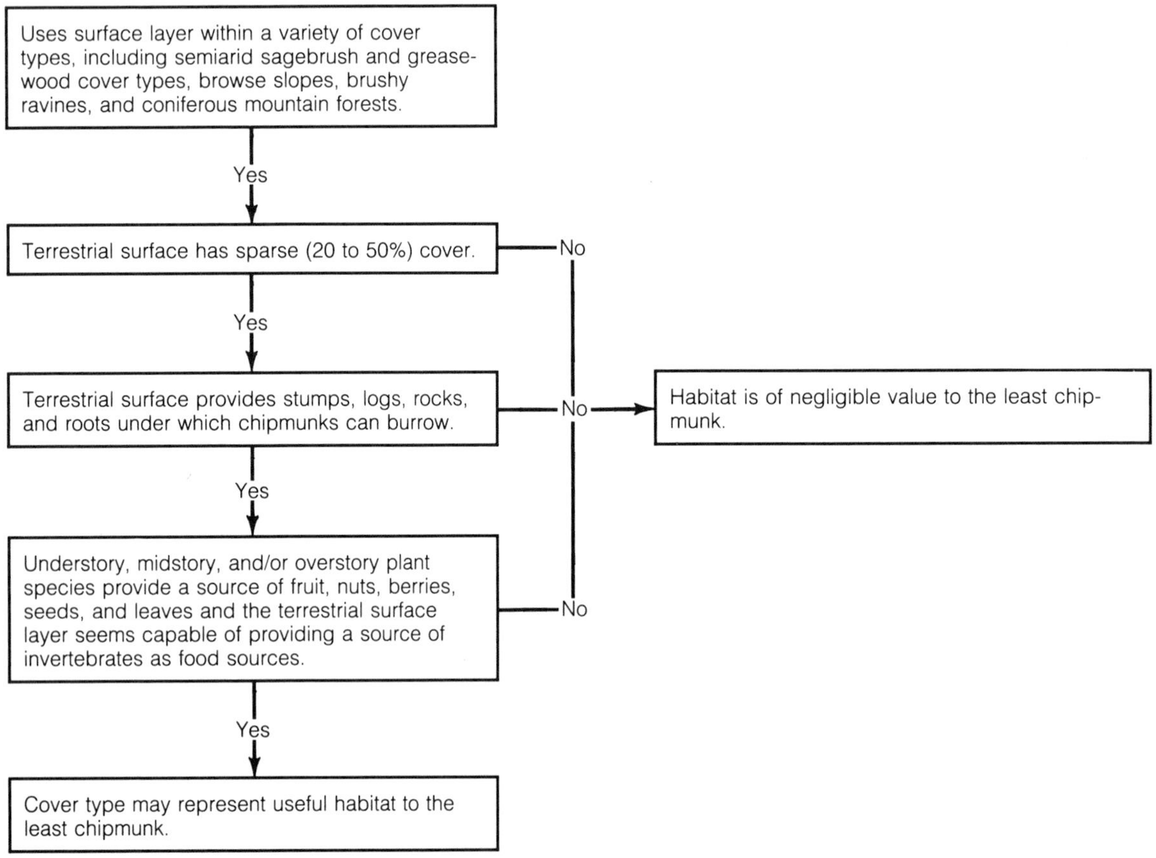

Uses surface layer within a variety of cover types, including semiarid sagebrush and greasewood cover types, browse slopes, brushy ravines, and coniferous mountain forests.

→ Yes

Terrestrial surface has sparse (20 to 50%) cover. — No

→ Yes

Terrestrial surface provides stumps, logs, rocks, and roots under which chipmunks can burrow. — No

Understory, midstory, and/or overstory plant species provide a source of fruit, nuts, berries, seeds, and leaves and the terrestrial surface layer seems capable of providing a source of invertebrates as food sources. — No

Habitat is of negligible value to the least chipmunk.

→ Yes

Cover type may represent useful habitat to the least chipmunk.

Figure 10. Information to approximate conditions along a layer of habitat useful to the least chipmunk (*Tamias minimus*) in Wyoming and Colorado (after U.S. Forest Service 1981).

Brewer's sparrow (*Spizella breweri*)

1. Cover types inhabited

Grama-buffalo grass
Sandsage-bluestem prairie
Mountain mahogany-oak scrub
Great Basin sagebrush
Wheatgrass-needlegrass shrub steppe
Wheatgrass-needlegrass
Grama-needlegrass-wheatgrass
Saltbush-greasewood
Sagebrush steppe

2. Habitat layers where nesting, birthing, or hatching occur

Terrestrial surface layers

Substrate 6.20, 7.01, 7.02, 7.03, 7.04 (from Table 8). Brewer's sparrows frequently construct their nest about 15 to 25 cm (6 to 10 in.) above ground in dense woody shrubs, especially sagebrush.

3. Habitat layers where foraging occurs

Primary consumer: terrestrial surface layer. The Brewer's sparrow feeds on grass and seeds on the ground.

Secondary consumer: terrestrial surface layer. The Brewer's sparrow gleans insects from the ground and from low shrubs. Midstory layer: the Brewer's sparrow gleans insects from large shrubs.

4. Species-habitat model (references)

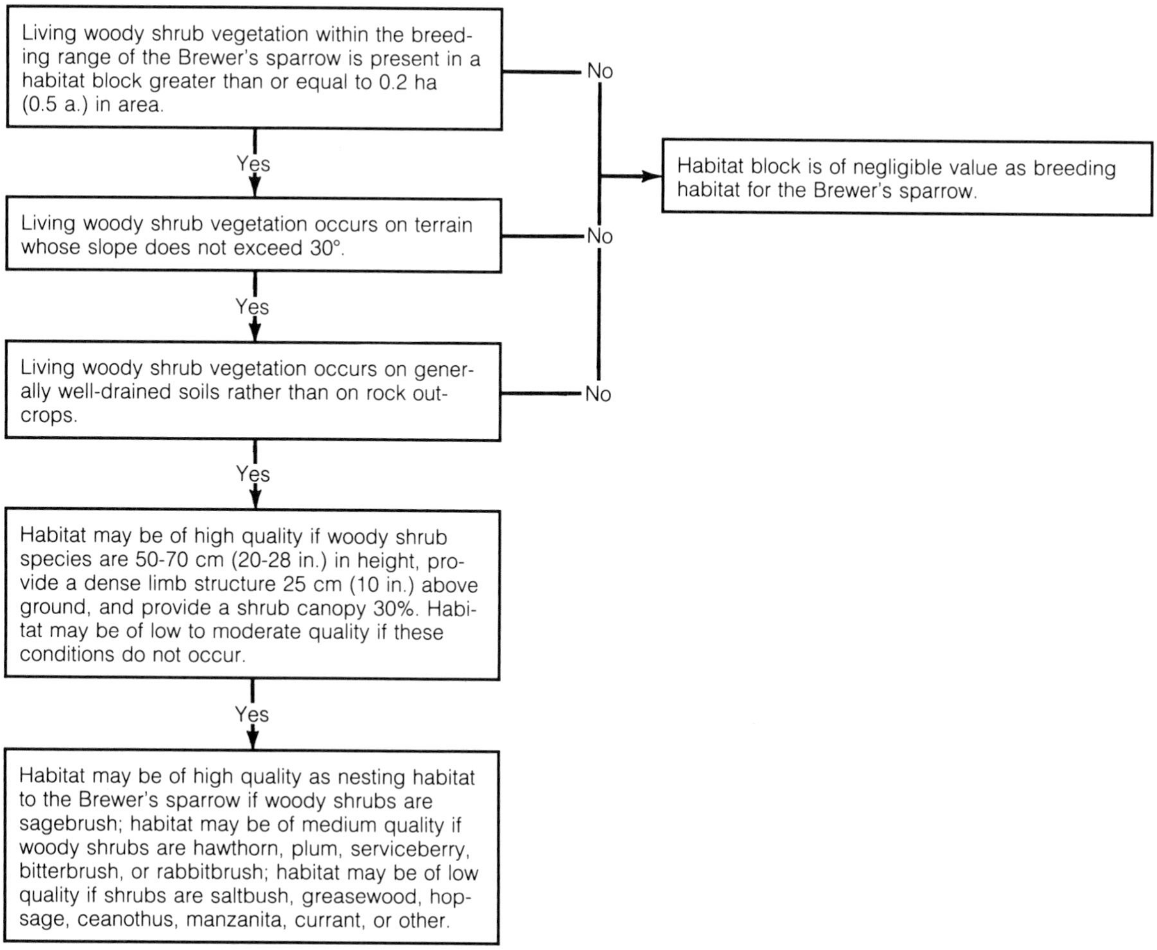

Figure 11. Information to approximate conditions along a layer of habitat useful to the Brewer's sparrow in (*Spizella breweri*) Wyoming and Colorado (after U.S. Forest Service 1981).

The intent of either model is to describe habitat conditions favorable to the species. Word models are listed in Figures 9 through 11 for the screech owl (*Otis kennicottii*), least chipmunk (*Tamias minimus*), and Brewer's sparrow, respectively. The models describe the cover types inhabited by the species. This information can be compiled from many sources, including field guides, range maps, museum records, and other published literature. The best situation is where such a list already exists. For example, U.S. Forest Service personnel already have associated wildlife species with range cover types in Colorado, Wyoming, Kansas, Nebraska, and South Dakota (U.S. Forest Service 1981); for Arizona and New Mexico on the computerized RUNWILD format (Patton 1978); and for the western Sierra Nevadas (Verner and Boss 1980).

The models also identify the layers of habitat where nesting, hatching, or birthing of the species occur and where foraging takes place and special structural features or plant species apparently selected by the species within a habitat layer. The numerical designation of the major structural features within layers of habitat corresponds to the coded subunits in Table 8. Sound, professional judgment is needed when developing word models for placing wildlife species along habitat gradients because species-habitat information usually is not well-synthesized in the literature.

Models like those in Figures 9 to 11 try to define the niche space of a species in sufficient detail so that the usefulness of habitat for particular species can be qualitatively estimated in inventories. Field surveys can be used to estimate the relative quantity of habitat for particular species. It may also be possible to determine, from the word model, those life-requisite needs of the species that need to be provided or modified by remedial management actions.

A typical sagebrush rangeland in the western United States.

LITERATURE CITED

ALBERTSON, F.W. and J.E. WEAVER. 1946. Reduction of ungrazed mixed prairie to short grass as a result of drought and dust. Ecol. Monogr. 16(4):449-463.

BEETLE, A.A. 1960. A study of sagebrush. The section tridentatae of Artemisia. Wyoming Agric. Exp. Sta. Bull. 368. Laramie. 83pp.

BLAISDELL, J.P., R.B. MURRAY, and E.D. MCARTHUR. 1982. Managing intermountain rangelands—sagebrush-grass ranges. U.S. Dep. Agric., For. Serv. Gen. Tech. Rep. INT-134. 41pp.

BROWN, D.E. 1982. Biotic communities of the American Southwest—United States and Mexico. Boyce Thompson Southwestern Arboretum. Superior, AZ. 342pp.

———— and C.H. LOWE. 1980. Biotic communities of the Southwest. U.S. Dep. Agric., For. Serv. Gen. Tech. Rep. RM-78. 1pp. (map).

COSTELLO, D.F. 1944. Important species of the major forage types in Colorado and Wyoming. Ecol. Monogr. 14(1):107-134.

HALL, F.C. 1973. Plant communities of the Blue Mountains in eastern Oregon and southwestern Washington. U.S. Dep. Agric., For. Serv. PNW-R6 Area Guide 3-1. 62pp.

HARPER, K.T. and J.L. REVEAL (symp. organizers). 1978. Intermountain biography: a symposium. Great Basin Naturalist Memoirs. 2. Brigham Young Univ. Provo, UT. 268pp.

HIRONAKA, M. 1979. Basic synecological relationships of the Columbia River sagebrush type. Pages 27-32 in The Sagebrush Ecosystem—A Symposium. Utah State Univ., College of Natural Resources. Logan. 251pp.

————, M.A. FOSBERG, and A.H. WINWARD. 1983. Sagebrush-grass habitat types of southern Idaho. Forest, Wildlife, and Range Exp. Sta. Bull. 35. Univ. of Idaho, Moscow. 44pp.

JOHNSON, K.L. 1979. Basic synecological relationships of the sagebrush types on the high plains of Montana, Wyoming, and the Dakotas. Pages 42-49 in the Sagebrush Ecosystem—A Symposium. Utah State Univ., College of Natural Resources. Logan. 251pp.

KUCHLER, A.W. 1964. Manual to accompany the map. Potential natural vegetation of the conterminous United States. Am. Geogr. Soc. Spec. Publ. 36. 39pp. + 116 plates. (map).

MCARTHUR, E.D., A.C. BLAUER, A.P. PLUMMER, and R. STEVENS. 1979. Characteristics and hybridization of important intermountain shrubs. III. Sunflower family. U.S. Dep. Agric., For. Serv. Res. Pap. INT-220. 82pp.

MCKELL, C.M., J.P. BLAISDELL, and J.R. GOODIN, tech. eds. 1972. Wildland shrubs—their biology and utilization. U.S. Dep. Agric., For. Serv. Gen. Tech. Rep. INT-1. 494pp.

MOONEY, H.A. and D.J. PARSONS. 1973. Structure and function of the California chaparral—an example from San Dimas. Pages 83-112 in di Castra, F. and H.A. Mooney, eds. Mediterranean Type Ecosystems: Origin and Structure. Springer-Verlag. New York, NY.

MUEGGLER, W.F. and W.L. STEWART. 1980. Grassland and shrubland habitat types of western Montana. U.S. Dep. Agric., For. Serv. Gen. Tech. Rep. INT-66. 154pp.

NICHOL, A.A. 1937. The natural vegetation of Arizona. Ariz. Agric. Exp. Sta. College of Agric., Univ. Ariz. Tucson. Tech. Bull. 68:181-222.

PATTON, D.R. 1978. RUNWILD: A storage and retrieval system for wildlife habitat information. U.S. Dep. Agric., For. Serv. Gen. Tech. Rep. RM-51. 8pp.

PLUMMER, A.P., D.R. CHRISTENSEN, and S.B. MONSEN. 1968. Restoring big-game range in Utah. Publ. No. 68-3. Utah Div. Fish and Game. Salt Lake City. 183pp.

————, A.C. HULL, Jr., G. STEWART, and J.H. ROBERTSON. 1955. Seeding rangelands in Utah, Nevada, southern Idaho, and western Wyoming. U.S. Dep. Agric., For. Serv. Agric. Handb. 71. 73pp.

POULTON, C.E. 1970. Practical applications of remote sensing in range resources development and management. Pages 179-189 in Range and Wildlife Habitat Evaluation—A Research Symposium. U.S. Dep. Agric., For. Serv. Misc. Publ. 1147. Washington, DC.

SAMPSON, A.W., A. CHASE, and D.W. HEDRICK. 1951. California grasslands and range forage grasses. Calif. Agric. Exp. Sta., College of Agric. Univ. Calif. Bull. 724. 130pp.

SCHWARZ, C.F., C.E. THOR, and G.H. ELSNER. 1976. Wildlife planning glossary. U.S. Dep. Agric., For. Serv. Gen. Tech. Rep. PSW-13. 252pp.

SHARP, L.A. and K.D. SANDERS. 1978. Rangeland resources of Idaho: A basis for development and improvement. Idaho Rangeland Comm. and College of FWR. FWR Exp. Sta. Misc. Publ. 6. Moscow, ID. 74pp.

SHORT, H.L. 1983. Wildlife guilds in Arizona desert habitats. U.S. Dep. Inter., Bur. Land Manage. Tech. Note 362. 258pp.

———— and K.P. BURNHAM. 1982. Technique for structuring wildlife guilds to evaluate impacts on wildlife communities. U.S. Dep. Inter., Fish and Wildl. Serv. Spec. Sci. Rep. - Wildl. 244. 34pp.

STODDARD, L.A., A.D. SMITH, and T.W. BOX. 1975. Range management. Third ed. McGraw-Hill Book Co. New York, NY. 532pp.

TISDALE, E.W. 1979. A preliminary classification of Snake River Canyon grasslands in Idaho. Univ. Idaho FWR Exp. Sta. Note. 32. Moscow.

————. 1983. Grasslands of western North America: The Pacific Northwest bunchgrass type. Pages 223-245 in Nicholson, A.C., A. McLean, and T.E. Baker, eds. Grassland Ecology and Classification Symposium Proceedings. B.C. Min. For. Victoria, B.C.

U.S. DEPARTMENT OF AGRICULTURE. 1936. Atlas of American agriculture. U.S. Govt. Printing Office. Washington, DC.

U.S. DEPARTMENT OF INTERIOR, BUREAU OF LAND MANAGEMENT. 1975. Range condition report prepared for the Senate Committee on appropriations. U.S. Dep. Inter., Bur. Land Manage. Washington, DC. (unpubl.).

U.S. FISH AND WILDLIFE SERVICE. 1980. Habitat Evaluation Procedures (HEP), ESM 102. U.S. Dep. Inter., Fish and Wildl. Serv. Div. of Ecological Services. Washington, DC.

U.S. FOREST SERVICE. 1972. The Nation's range resources—a forest-range environmental study. For. Resour. Rep. 19. U.S. Dep. Agric., For. Serv. Washington, DC. 147pp.

————. 1981. Wildlife and fish habitat relationships. Vol. I Narratives. Vol. II Matrices. U.S. Dep. Agric., For. Serv. Rocky Mtn. Region. Denver, CO.

UTAH STATE UNIVERSITY. 1975. The pinyon-juniper ecosystem: a symposium. Utah State Univ., College of Natural Resources, Utah Agric. Exp. Sta., Logan. 194pp.

————.1979. The sagebrush ecosystem: a symposium. Utah State Univ., College of Natural Resources, Logan. 251pp.

VERNER, J. and A.S. BOSS. 1980. California wildlife and their habitats: Western Sierra Nevada. U.S. Dep. Agric., For. Serv. Gen. Tech. Rep. PSW-37. 439pp.

WAGNER, W.L. and E.F. ALDON. 1978. Manual of the saltbushes (*Atriplex* sp.) in New Mexico. U.S. Dep. Agric., For. Serv. Gen. Tech. Rep. RM-57. 50pp.

WEAVER, J.E. 1954. North American prairie. Johnson Publ. Co. Lincoln, NE. 348pp.

———— and F.W. ALBERTSON. 1956. Grasslands of the Great Plains. Johnson Publ. Co. Lincoln, NE. 395pp.

WINWARD, A.H. 1980. Taxonomy and ecology of sagebrush in Oregon. Agric. Exp. Sta. Bull. 642. Oregon State Univ., Corvallis. 15pp.

WRIGHT, H.A. 1972. Shrub response to fire. Pages 204-217 *in* McKell, C.M., J.P. Blaisdell, and J.R. Goodin, tech eds. Wildland Shrubs—Their Biology and Utilization. U.S. Dep. Agric., For. Serv. Gen. Tech. Rep. INT-1. 494pp.

————, L.F. NEUENSCHWANDER, and C.M. BRITTON. 1979. The role and use of fire in sagebrush-grass and pinyon-juniper plant communities. A state-of-the-art review. U.S. Dep. Agric., For. Serv. Gen. Tech. Rep. INT-58. 48pp.

7

DESERTS

K. Bruce Jones[1]

U.S. Bureau of Land Management
Phoenix Training Center
Phoenix, AZ 85015

"But the desert is much more than merely warm. It is a consistent world with a special landscape, a special geography, and to go with them, a special flora and fauna adapted to that geography and that climate."

—Joseph Wood Krutch, from *The Voice of the Desert*

Editor's Note: Deserts compose a large portion of the western U.S. Wildlife are one of their most important resources. Animals of the desert have unique adaptations to the extremes of heat and precipitation that characterize such regions. As the author emphasizes, effective inventory and monitoring studies must take into account these extremes and desert animals' adaptations to them.

INTRODUCTION

Deserts are characterized by low, erratic precipitation and highly variable temperatures, and extend from southeastern Oregon and southern Idaho through Nevada and Utah, except at higher elevations, continuing south through southern California and Arizona, and eastward through central and southern New Mexico (Oosting 1956). Desert habitats range from homogeneous stands of sagebrush (*Artemisia* sp.) in the Great Basin Desert to highly diverse, structurally rich vegetation of the Sonoran Desert. To a large degree, vegetation structure within deserts reflects the areas' precipitation pattern and temperature regimes. For example, structural simplicity within the Great Basin Desert reflects the area's short growing season, low precipitation, and precipitation pattern (60% of the precipitation is in the form of snow). Conversely, parts of the Sonoran Desert are structurally rich because of a year-round growing season (few freezing temperatures), biannual precipitation patterns, and precipitation in the form of rain.

Northern, cooler desert regions, such as the Great Basin Desert, support far fewer wildlife species than more southern, warmer regions such as the Sonoran Desert (Bender 1982; Brown 1982b). Certain groups of wildlife, such as large herbivores, are generally more numerous in northern deserts. Similar to their effect on vegetation, shorter growing seasons affect the diversity of wildlife, especially small birds, mammals, reptiles, and amphibians by reducing the diversity and availability of insect prey. Thermal regimes in northern deserts limit ectothermic (cold-blooded) and small homeothermic (warm-blooded) wildlife activity to short periods (generally May to early September).

Desert habitats possess some of the most unusual wildlife in North America. Many desert animals are physiologically and morphologically adapted to survive under extreme environmental conditions (low, erratic rainfall and highly variable temperatures). Many small mammals require no free water; these animals survive on their own metabolic water and through water conservation strategies such as

---

[1]Current Address: U.S. Fish and Wildlife Service, Office of Endangered Species, Washington, DC 20240.

nocturnal activity patterns (Golley et al. 1975). Many desert animals such as lizards conserve water by excreting uric acid rather than urea (Porter 1972).

Perhaps the single most important adaptation employed by desert wildlife is behavior. Many small mammals and snakes are entirely nocturnal and fossorial. They avoid high temperatures by remaining inactive in burrows, under rock, or in caves (e.g., bats) during the day, and perform feeding and reproductive activities at night. Even diurnal animals such as some birds, big game, and lizards are inactive during hot parts of the day.

In desert regions, most animals hibernate or remain inactive during cold winter months. This is especially true in northern sections of the Great Basin Desert where winter temperatures drop below 0° F. In the Sonoran Desert, where temperatures rarely reach the freezing point, many small mammals and small lizards remain active year-round.

Great Basin Desert in the winter.

Although many desert wildlife require no free-standing water (see Golley et al. 1975 for examples), permanent and temporary water sources are critical to certain wildlife. For example, big game species such as bighorn sheep (*Ovis canadensis*) occupy areas with scattered, but reliable free-standing water (Wilson et al. 1980). Many habitat management strategies are developed around this concept; bighorn sheep populations can be increased by increasing the distribution and reliability of free-standing water. Small streams transecting through desert habitats are inhabited by several small fish and amphibians. These animals are entirely dependent on permanent, running (lotic) water within these regions.

Because of extreme environmental conditions, desert wildlife are highly dependent on microhabitats, especially those that provide thermal cover such

as vegetation patches, rock, soil, and surface debris (e.g., logs). The arrangement and abundance of these microhabitats determine the diversity and abundance of desert wildlife; small changes in these microhabitats can alter species abundance and diversity (see Heatwole 1982 and Short 1983 for examples). Because animals are closely associated with microhabitats, man can easily affect the composition and abundance of wildlife in deserts.

With rapid expansion of man into desert habitats, many habitat components crucial to species existence are being altered, especially those important to both man and wildlife. For example, dewatering of perennial streams and springs for domestic and livestock water has drastic effects on wildlife, especially aquatic organisms. Recreation activities have become very popular in deserts near metropolitan areas, and these activities have both direct and indirect effects on wildlife and their habitats (physical disturbance and habitat alteration, respectively). In addition, many regions, especially within the Great Basin Desert, have large coal, oil, and gas deposits. The development of these resources can have significant effects on desert habitats and their faunas.

Response (return to original state) of desert habitats after man-caused physical changes is slow, and in severe instances, where soils are lost, habitats may never return to their original state.

Inventories and monitoring studies of wildlife communities in desert habitats help biologists and managers understand the sensitive and complex interrelationships between wildlife species and communities, and resources of desert habitats. With these data, one can protect, and in some situations, enhance the integrity of our deserts. This chapter describes desert habitats, including habitat components, and provides general guidance for conducting inventories and monitoring studies in deserts.

Desert bighorn sheep at man-made water supply.

CLASSIFICATION AND DESCRIPTIONS OF MAJOR DESERTS

Although deserts cover large sections of western North America, they possess certain similar environmental characteristics throughout (Oosting 1956). All deserts share the following general characteristics:

1. low, erratic precipitation, generally less than 300 mm (12 in.) per year
2. high, daily air and soil temperatures that drop rapidly at night
3. highly variable, seasonal temperatures
4. low atmospheric moisture throughout most of the year
5. few overcast or cloudy days

Shreve (1942) and Oosting (1956) characterized deserts into two general groups based on climate: cold formation and warm formation. Lowe and Brown (1982) further subdivided warm formation deserts into warm-temperate and tropical-subtropical based on climate and plant species affinities and origin:

1. Cold-temperate Deserts
   a. Great Basin Desert
2. Warm-temperate Deserts
   a. Mojave Desert
   b. Chihuahuan Desert
3. Tropical-subtropical Deserts
   a. Sonoran Desert

Because most authors agree on the four major deserts listed above, I will base my discussions around this classification. Finer delineation of these four major deserts is available. Perhaps the most ex-tensive delineation of North America's four major deserts is that of Brown (1982b). In his publication, deserts are broken down to association and community (series) levels, following the digitized format of Brown et al. (1979). Other delineations of deserts include Province and Region descriptions by Bailey (1978), and potential natural vegetation descriptions to the association level by Kuchler (1964).

The following are brief descriptions of each desert (see Figure 1 for locations).

Great Basin Desert

The Great Basin Desert is the most extensive desert in the U.S., stretching from southeastern Oregon and Wyoming, south to northern Arizona and New Mexico, east to northern New Mexico, and west into extreme eastern California. Topography of the Great Basin Desert varies, but generally consists of wide valley floors between 1,200 and 1,800 m (4,000 and 6,000 ft), interrupted by mountains. Temperatures drop much lower than any other U.S. desert, with a short frost-free season and very cold winters (Oosting 1956), and precipitation ranges from 76 to 300 mm (4 to 12 in.). Two major vegetation communities occur within this desert, both of which are structurally and floristically simple: sagebrush associations dominated by sagebrush, *Artemisia* sp., and shadscale or saltbush associations dominated by saltbushes, *Atriplex* sp. (Oosting 1956; Turner 1982). Species with evolutionary affinities to warmer climates such as rabbitbush (*Chrysothamnus* sp.) and blackbrush (*Coleogyne* sp.) are also present in the Great Basin Desert (Turner 1982a).

H. L. Shantz

Great Basin Desert in Utah, dominated by sand sagebrush.

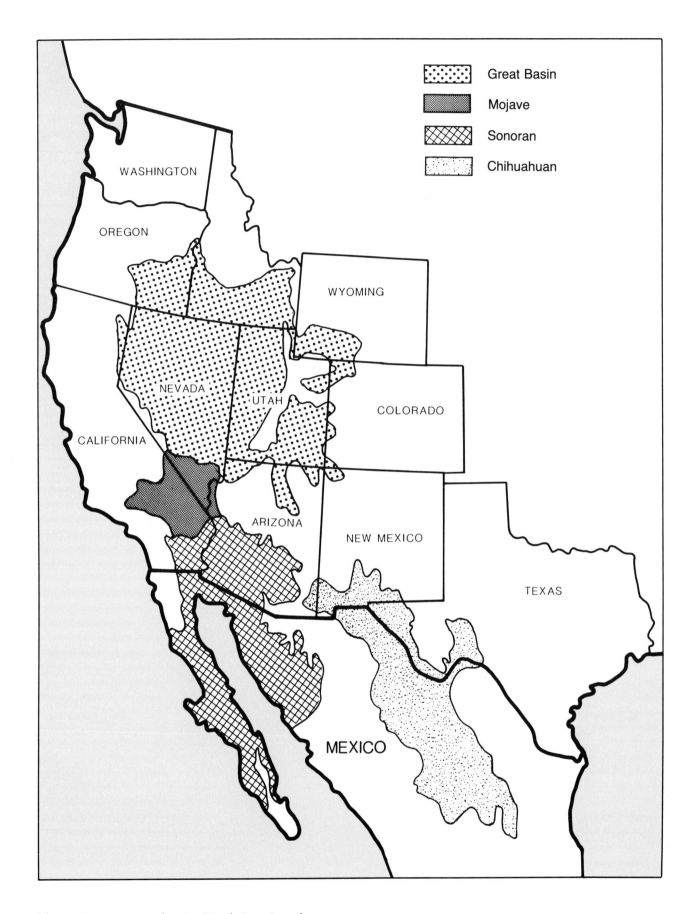

Figure 1. Locations of major North American deserts.

Mojave (Mohave) Desert

The Mojave Desert is the smallest of the desert formations, occurring in southeastern California, southern Nevada, northwestern Arizona, and extreme southwestern Utah at elevations of 300-1,200 m (1,000-4,000 ft; Oosting 1956). Summers are hot and dry; precipitation throughout this desert is generally meager (less than 120 mm [5 in.] per year) although some areas receive up to 22.5 cm (9 in.) per year (Thorne et al. 1981). Floristically, faunally, and geographically, the Mojave Desert is an intermediate between Great Basin and Sonoran Deserts, although its fauna more closely resembles that of the Sonoran Desert (Turner 1982b). The Mojave Desert is perhaps the most structurally and floristically variable of all the deserts although most regions consist of low-height (<1.5 m [5 ft]) shrubs consisting of homogeneous stands of creosotebush (*Larrea* sp.) and blackbrush; other regions include structurally-diverse flora such as the Joshua tree (*Yucca brevifolia*; Turner 1982a). There are few Mojave Desert endemics (plant species) that distinguish this desert from others (with the exception of the Joshua tree). Classification of the Mojave Desert as a distinct desert is primarily based on geographic position and climate rather than plant or animal associates (Turner 1982b).

Yucca in bloom.

A Mojave Desert Joshua tree "woodland" community in Arizona.

Chihuahuan Desert, with mesquite (New Mexico).

Chihuahuan Desert

The Chihuahuan Desert is floristically and structurally variable and has great regional differences in plant species composition (Brown 1982a). Most of this desert occurs in Mexico (80%) with northern boundaries extending into southeastern Arizona, southern and central New Mexico, and western Texas at elevations of 900-1,800 m (3,000-6,000 ft; Brown 1982a). Similar to the Great Basin Desert, this desert is interrupted by high mountains (Oosting 1956). Precipitation is variable and ranges from 76–300 mm (4-12 in.) per year. The Chihuahuan Desert has expanded in the past 200 years at the expense of semidesert grassland, primarily due to man's activities (York and Dick-Peddie 1969; Brown 1982a). Although present in the Mojave and Sonoran Deserts, mesquite (*Prosopis* sp.) and creosotebush dominate most sites within the U.S. Chihuahuan Desert. Whereas most areas are structurally homogeneous and simple, whitethorn acacia (*Acacia constricta*), ocotillo (*Fouquieria splendens*), yuccas (*Yucca* sp.), agaves (*Agave* sp.), and cactus (*Opuntia* sp.) add to structural diversity in mountainous areas and canyons (Brown 1982a). Solid mesquite dune stands are common in southern New Mexico, primarily on sites previously occupied by semidesert grassland (Brown 1982a).

Sonoran Desert

The Sonoran Desert, occupying areas in southern Arizona, southeastern California, and northwestern Mexico, is perhaps the most structurally and floristically diverse desert in the world. It is also the only U.S. desert with most of its flora derived from tropical climatic zones, and appears to have formed less than 10,000 years ago (Turner and Brown 1982). There are two major subdivisions of the Sonoran Desert within the U.S.: Lower Colorado River Valley and Arizona Upland (Turner and Brown 1982). The Lower Colorado subdivision occurs primarily in southwestern Arizona and southeastern California at elevations of 0–600 m (0-2,000 ft). Precipitation is low (less than 175 mm, 7 in. per year) and temperatures moderate (mostly frost-free). Creosotebush and bursage (*Franseria* sp.) dominate most of this subdivision. Structural and floristic diversity is achieved in these areas along intermittent washes consisting of ironwood (*Olneya tesota*), blue palo verde (*Cercidium floridum*), and mesquite (Turner and Brown 1982).

The Arizona Upland subdivision of the Sonoran Desert is the most structurally diverse of all U.S. deserts. It occurs in southern Arizona and northern Sonora at elevations of 300-1,200 m (1,000-4,000 ft). Similar to the Lower Colorado subdivision, this subdivision receives rain biannually (summer and winter), but unlike its other Sonoran counterpart, has greater moisture (due to higher elevations and rugged, broken terrain; Turner and Brown 1982). Turner and Brown (1982) attributed dominance of arboreal and succulent vegetation within this region to available moisture. Overstory structure is provided by ironwoods, foothill palo verde (*Cercidium microphyllum*), saguaro cactus (*Carnegiea gigantea*), and mesquite. A wide variety of understory components may also be present: cactus (*Opuntia* sp.), bursage, ratany (*Krameria* sp.), buckwheat (*Eriogonum* sp.), brittlebush (*Encelia* sp.), and jojoba (*Simmondsia chinensis;* Turner and Brown 1982).

Sonoran Desert in Arizona.

MAJOR WILDLIFE SPECIES GROUPS

Wildlife species assemblages of North American deserts range from relatively undiverse in homogeneous, northern sections of the Great Basin Desert to highly diverse (Table 1) in the Arizona Upland subdivision of the Sonoran Desert (see Bender 1982 and Brown 1982b). Great differences in faunas of northern portions of the Great Basin Desert and southern deserts such as the Sonoran Desert primarily result from differences in temperature, moisture, and structural characteristics associated with each. As discussed in the previous section, the Great Basin Desert is extremely homogeneous, structurally simple, cold, and precipitation falls primarily in the winter (60%) when plants are dormant. Conversely, the Sonoran Desert is structurally diverse, warm, and receives precipitation during both winter and summer. Moderate temperatures allow plants to use winter and summer precipitation for growth (Oosting 1956; Daubenmire 1974). Lack of available moisture and short growing seasons may preclude existence of many arboreal plants from the Great Basin Desert, common in southern deserts.

The Great Basin Desert has fewer wildlife species than any of the other deserts. However, this desert supports larger populations of pronghorn (*Antilocapra americana*), mule deer (*Odocoileus hemionus*), and elk (*Cervus elaphus*) than other deserts (see

Table 1. Qualitative assessment of species diversity for the four major U.S. deserts.
● = highly diverse, ◐ = moderately diverse, ○ = low diversity.

Desert	Total Diversity	Raptor	Fish	Amphibians	Reptiles	Small Birds	Mammals (Non-game)	Upland Game	Water-fowl	Big Game
Great Basin	○	◐	○	○	○	○	◐	◐	◐	●
Mojave	◐	◐	○	◐	◐	◐	◐	◐	○	○
Chihuahuan	◐	◐	○	●	●	◐	◐	◐	○	◐*
Sonoran	●	●	◐	●	●	●	●	◐	○	◐

*Moderate diversity results primarily from introduced species.

Schmidt and Gilbert 1978). It also supports large upland game populations (Johnsgard l973) such as chukars (*Alectoris chukar*) and sage grouse (*Centrocercus urophasianus*). Several bird species move into the Great Basin Desert during spring and summer to breed, although breeding bird diversity and abundance is generally less than any of the other three deserts (see Brown and Gibson 1983). Breeding and resident raptor and bird species are greatest within the Great Basin Desert in areas adjacent to more structurally diverse habitats, such as riparian areas and cliffs. For example, riparian sites provide structural diversity necessary for nesting, whereas the adjacent Great Basin Desert provides feeding grounds. Areas with cliffs increase diversity in this desert by increasing structural habitat diversity.

Reptile, amphibian, and small mammal diversity is relatively low in the Great Basin Desert when compared with the three other deserts (see Brown and Gibson 1983). As previously discussed, low diversity of small nongame wildlife results primarily from a short growing season and low environmental temperatures.

The Mojave Desert supports an array of wildlife. Whereas this desert's big and upland game diversity and abundance is not as great as the Great Basin Desert, it does support a diverse small mammal and reptile fauna. Similar to the Great Basin Desert, small bird and raptor diversity and abundance are greatly enhanced in areas with added structural diversity (cliffs, riparian habitats, canyons, and Joshua trees).

The Chihuahuan and Sonoran Deserts have highly diverse faunas, including large numbers of amphibians, reptiles, small birds, mammals, and raptors. High species diversity results from topographical and vegetational structural diversity, a long growing season, and influence of Mexican and southcentral U.S.

Siberian ibex in southern New Mexico habitat. Released in 1975 in the Canadian River Canyon.

faunas. In southern New Mexico, Ibex (*Capra aegagrus*) and Oryx (*Oryx gazella*) have been introduced into parts of the Chihuahuan Desert. Javelina (*Tayassu tajacu*) have also been introduced into several parts of both the Chihuahuan and Sonoran Deserts. These introductions, combined with native big game and upland game species, give these deserts relatively diverse game faunas.

Oryx, commonly called Gemsbok, in southern New Mexico habitat. Released in 1969 on White Sands Missile Range.

The Sonoran Desert has the highest wildlife diversity of any North American desert (see Brown and Gibson 1983), primarily resulting from a year-round growing season and great vegetation structural diversity.

Bender (1982) and Brown (1982b) provided lists of wildlife and plants associated with North American deserts. Table 1 provides a general assessment of species richness in the four major U.S. deserts.

CRITICAL HABITAT FEATURES

Deserts consist of several physical habitat components that contribute to wildlife species diversity. These components are used by wildlife to perform a number of ecological functions such as mating, feeding, nesting, and thermoregulation, and they also provide resting substrate and escape cover. Habitat components or resources are partitioned in time and space by desert wildlife (Creusere and Whitford 1982). Because deserts are environmentally extreme, many wildlife species use specific habitat components, especially those components that provide greater moisture and lower temperatures. For example, the desert night lizard (*Xantusia vigilis*) is restricted to desert regions with downed litter of yucca and agave plants (Zweifel and Lowe 1966; Jones 1981a).

Several other factors determine wildlife community composition and affect availability of habitat components. These include slope, aspect, precipitation, ecotones, geographic, and man-caused factors.

Microhabitat components, such as soil, rock, vegetation, and water, vary greatly between and within our four U.S. deserts. The following discusses each habitat component with examples of their relations to various wildlife. This will help determine which microhabitats should be sampled when surveying and monitoring certain desert wildlife. Tables 2 through 4 summarize important habitat components in deserts.

Table 2. Important habitat components of desert habitats.

Microhabitat Components	Description	Variables/Factors		Defense	Escape Cover	Food or Prey	Feeding Substrate	Nest or Birthing Substrate	Physiological	Reproduction	Resting Substrate	Thermoregulatory Substrate
Water (Lotic)	Rivers and streams, flowing springs	Riffle/run/pool water temperature, turbidity, DO, organic content, siltation, pollutants, interface with other habitats, substrate	FI		•	•	•	•	•	•		•
			RE		•	•	•	•	•	•		•
			BG						•			
			RA			•						
Water (Permanent Lentic)	Ponds, marshes, lakes, potholes, bogs, seeps, springs, agricultural runoff, natural and man-made catchments	Water temperature, DO, organic content, siltation, pollutants, interface with other habitats (e.g., nesting islands), emergent vegetation, shoreline vegetation, substrate, water distributors	FI		•	•	•	•	•			•
			AM		•	•	•	•	•	•		
			RE		•	•	•	•	•			•
			RA			•						
			WA			•			•		•	
			BA			•	•					
			BG						•			
Water (Temporary Lentic)	Temporary rain pools, irrigation ditches	Water temperatures, duration, frequency, siltation, pollutants, DO, emergent vegetation, substrate interface with other habitats, organic content, water distribution	AM		•	•	•	•	•	•		•
			RE		•	•	•		•			•
			WA			•					•	
			BG						•			
Rock	Talus slopes, caves, cliffs, boulders, substrate, outcorps, instream structure	Rock size, heterogeneity, interfaces with other habitats, origin, vertical and horizontal structure	FI		•	•	•	•		•		
			AM		•	•	•	•		•		
			RE	•	•			•	•			•
			SM		•			•	•		•	
			BA		•			•	•		•	•
			BG	•	•			•	•		•	•
			RA	•	•	•		•	•			
			SB	•	•	•		•	•		•	•
Soil	Surface and subsurface soil types	Soil types, depth, heterogeneity, horizontal and vertical structure, interfaces with other habitats	AM		•	•	•	•	•			•
			RE		•	•	•	•				•
			SB			•	•	•				
			RA		•	•	•	•				•
			SM		•	•	•	•				•
Vegetation-Litter/Debris	Leaves, logs, limbs and other persistent and non-persistent litter/debris	Litter size, depth, heterogeneity, horizontal and vertical structure, type, moisture retention, temperature.	FI		•	•	•				•	•
			AM		•	•	•			•	•	•
			RE		•	•	•				•	
			SB		•	•		•			•	
			SM			•	•	•			•	•
			UG		•	•	•	•			•	

Major Vertebrate Associations and Relationship of Species' Ecology to Components

Table 2. Important habitat components of desert habitats (concluded).

Microhabitat Components	Description	Variables/Factors	Code	Defense	Escape Cover	Food or Prey	Feeding Substrate	Nest or Birthing Substrate	Physiological	Reproduction	Resting Substrate	Thermoregulatory Substrate
Vegetation-Dead	Standing vegetation, roots	Size, interface with other habitats, heterogeneity, vertical and horizontal structure, soils (roots only).	FI		•	•	•					
			AM		•	•	•	•			•	•
			BA		•	•	•	•			•	•
			UG		•	•	•	•			•	•
			RE	•	•	•	•	•			•	•
			SB	•	•	•	•	•			•	•
			RA	•	•	•	•	•			•	•
			SM	•	•	•	•	•			•	•
			A			•	•				•	
Vegetation-Live	All vegetation including roots	Horizontal and vertical structure, interfaces with abiotic habitats, heterogeneity	AL	•	•	•	•	•		•	•	•
Vegetation-Plant Species	Individual plant species associations	Individual plant species occurrence and abundance	RE			•	•	•				•
			SB		•			•				
			RA					•				
			UG					•				
Animal-Created	Burrows and other cover sites	Cover site size, shape, animal species activity patterns, animal species size	AM		•			•			•	•
			RE		•			•			•	•
			RA		•			•			•	•
			SM		•			•			•	•
			CA					•			•	
Man-made Structures (Other than water and agricultural)	Bridges, towers, electrical lines, buildings, mine shafts, posts, fences	Size, type, frequency.	AL	•	•	•	•	•		•	•	•

Codes for major vertebrate associations:

AL — all wildlife
AM— amphibians
BA — bats
BG — big game
CA — carnivores
FI — fish
RA — raptors
RE — reptiles
SB — small birds
SM— small mammals
UG — upland game
WA— waterfowl

Table 3. Important macrohabitat components/factors in deserts.

Macrohabitat Components/Factors	Description	Variables/Factors	Microhabitats Affected
Slope	% angle of area from horizontal	% slope, moisture avail., thermal regimes, vegetation structure	Water, soils, vegetation debris, vegetation (live and dead)
Aspect	South, north, east, and west facing	Direction, moisture avail., temperature regimes, vegetation structure	Water, soils, vegetation debris, vegetation (live and dead)
Elevation	Vertical above or below sea level	Vertical distance, moisture avail., thermal regimes, vegetation structure	Water, vegetation debris, vegetation (live and dead)
Precipitation	All forms	Quantity, type, duration, frequency, moisture avail., thermal regimes, vegetation structure	Water, soils, vegetation debris, vegetation (live and dead)
Ecotones/Habitat Juxtaposition	Habitat interfaces and locations	Heterogeneity, interface size, quantity, position	Vegetation debris and vegetation (live and dead)
Geographic Location	Major geographic boundaries and barriers, habitat location	Size, location, and frequency, habitat size, disjunction, influence of major faunal groups in adjacent areas	Direct effect on species reproductive capabilities
Human Influences	Disturbance and alterations of habitat due to man	Habitat loss and structural change	Loss of habitat necessary to meet ecological needs. Less diverse structure associated with habitat alterations

Table 4. Abundance and diversity of habitat components in four deserts.
Code for abundance and diversity: ● = high, ◐ = moderate, ○ = low

Habitat Component	Great Basin abundance	Great Basin diversity	Mojave abundance	Mojave diversity	Chihuahuan abundance	Chihuahuan diversity	Sonoran abundance	Sonoran diversity
WATER								
Lotic	○	○	○	○	○	○	●	◐
Permanent Lentic	○	○	○	○	○	◐	●	●
Temporary Lentic	◐	◐	○	○	○	◐	◐	◐
ROCK	◐	◐	●	●	◐	●	●	●
SOIL	●	◐	●	◐	●	●	●	●
VEGETATION								
Litter/Debris	○	○	○	◐	○	◐	◐	●
Dead	○	○	◐	◐	◐	◐	●	●
Live	○	○	◐	◐	◐	◐	●	●
Plant Species	○	○	○	○	○	○	○	○
ANIMAL-CREATED	◐	◐	◐	◐	◐	◐	◐	◐

Water (Lotic)

Running, permanent water (lotic water) is an extremely important component in desert ecosystems (Naiman and Soltz 1981). Several species, especially aquatic wildlife such as fish, amphibians, and some reptiles, are physically dependent on lotic water sources (Jones 1981a; Lowe 1964; Minckley 1973; Naiman and Soltz 1981). Without this component, these types of wildlife cannot exist within deserts. Aquatic amphibians, turtles, and snakes require running water for physiological functions such as thermoregulation, water balance, escape cover, and food (Stebbins 1966).

Lotic (running-water) habitat.

Substrate of running streams often determine the presence and abundance of certain fish species. For example, the desert sucker (*Catostomus clarki*) feeds on rock-bound algae that is present only in streams and rivers with cobble bottoms (Minckley 1973).

Aquatic sites and riparian areas also provide an abundant food source. For example, certain raptor species such as black hawks (*Buteogallus anthracinus*) and bald eagles (*Haliaeetus leucocephalus*) frequent deserts only where aquatic food is available (see Bent 1961 and Millsap 1981). Generally, these raptors require large fish such as desert suckers, and these types of prey are restricted to permanent streams, rivers, and lakes. For these raptors to successfully capture prey and nest along streams, rivers, and lakes, vertical structures such as snags, cliffs, and trees must be present. This is an example of more than one habitat component that must be available for a species to use an area. It also demonstrates importance of habitat edges and land/water ecotones (see Thomas et al. 1979).

Running streams also provide drinking water for many species. Many big game species inhabiting deserts are dependent on flowing streams for physiological water, although lentic (still) water distribution is usually more important. Yoakum (1980) and Kindschy et al. (1982) stated that American pronghorns, within the Great Basin Desert, require permanent water at less than 8-km (5-mi.) intervals.

The quality of water in desert streams also limits species' occurrence and abundance. Naiman and Soltz (1981) discussed the importance of physiochemical, heavy metal, stream structure, and macroinvertebrate (benthic) characteristics in determining fish diversity and abundance. Ratios of riffles, runs, pools, and backwater subhabitats also determine fish occurrence in streams much like vertical and horizontal structures in terrestrial habitats (see discussions in Naiman and Soltz 1981).

Water (Permanent Lentic)

Permanent, lentic habitats are important to large numbers of desert-dwelling wildlife. Lentic dwelling fish, including introduced fishes such as bass (*Per-

Lentic (still-water) habitat.

cichthyidae sp.), catfish (*Ictaluridae* sp.), and sunfish (*Centrarchidae* sp.), are totally restricted to and are dependent on lakes, stock ponds, and natural ponds such as cienegas within deserts (Minckley 1973; Naiman and Soltz 1981). Cienegas, springs, bogs, and potholes provide the only habitat within deserts for fish such as desert pupfish (*Cyprinodon macularius*) and Gila top minnows (*Poeciliopsis occidentalis*).

Aquatic amphibians (e.g., Rio Grande leopard frogs, *Rana berlanderi*), turtles (e.g., mud turtles, *Kinosternon* sp.), and snakes (e.g., checkered garter snake, *Thamnophis marcianus*) are totally dependent on lentic waters within deserts (when lotic habitats are not present) for reproduction, food, escape cover, physiological processes such as thermoregulation and water regulation, and egg and tadpole development (frogs and toads).

Lentic waters, like running streams, also provide an abundant and diverse prey base. For example, certain bats (Chiroptera) require large amounts of insect prey, which in many desert regions are provided directly above lentic water sources such as reservoirs and lakes (see Barbour and Davis 1969 for Chiroptera requirements). Raptors such as ospreys (*Pandion haliaetus*) and bald eagles are highly dependent on fish (Bent 1961; Millsap 1981), and lakes are often the only source of these prey in desert regions.

Most waterfowl are limited to permanent, lentic habitats within deserts (see Fleming 1959 for examples). Lentic habitats provide waterfowl with food, escape cover, and resting sites.

Interfaces of lentic habitat with adjacent habitat, especially shoreline and emergent vegetation, enhance and increase use of lentic habitats by fish, frogs, toads, snakes, waterfowl, and small birds. Emergent and shoreline vegetation increase nesting opportunities for frogs, toads, and waterfowl, and provide excellent escape cover and feeding substrate for all wildlife. Floating logs and islands also provide excellent in-water structures for basking turtles (thermoregulation and escape cover) and waterfowl (nesting substrate and isolation from predators), respectively.

Permanent natural or man-made lentic habitats (e.g., stock tanks and rainwater catchments) are extremely important drinking waters for big game species inhabiting deserts. Although relatively drought tolerant, most desert bighorn sheep and pronghorn require free-standing water, especially during the breeding season (Wilson et al. 1980; Yoakum 1980).

Water quality, as discussed for lotic habitat, is equally important in lentic habitats. Dissolved oxygen, temperature, pollutant concentrations, habitat structure (water depth and horizontal arrangement),

and water availability and distribution determine success of many wildlife species in desert habitats (see Naiman and Soltz 1981 for examples).

Turtle basking on log.

Man-made water catchment.

Water (Temporary Lentic)

Temporary surface water accumulation is common throughout U.S. deserts, especially on clay soils (slow percolation) during summer convectional storms. In particular, the Chihuahuan Desert is dominated by clay soils, providing large areas of temporary surface water. Large amounts of surface water are reflected in this desert's abundant and diverse amphibian fauna (see Conant 1978). Toad and salamander (e.g., tiger salamander, *Ambystoma tigrinum*) breeding is tied to summer rain and agricultural pools. Water is necessary for embryonic development of these animals (see Stebbins 1966 for species' examples). These waters also provide escape cover and food for many forms of wildlife. For example, yellow mud turtles (*Kinosternon flavescens*) and waterfowl use temporary pools created by summer rains or agricultural runoff for escape and resting cover, and for food (see Fleming 1959 and Stebbins 1966).

Rocky and boulder-strewn canyons also retain intermittent surface water. Red-spotted toads (*Bufo punctatus*) use these canyon pools for breeding (see Jones 1981a). These natural temporary catchments are also important physiological water sources for big game such as bighorn sheep, especially during warm summer months (Wilson et al. 1980).

Temporary lentic habitat.

Rock

Rock arrangement, heterogeneity, and proximity to other habitat components affect nearly every species of wildlife in deserts (see discussions of Thomas et al. 1979 and Maser et al. 1979a).

Talus slopes, cliffs, and rock outcrops provide nesting and feeding substrate, thermal and escape cover, and resting sites for many forms of wildlife including small birds, lizards, snakes, small mammals, big game, bats, predatory mammals, and raptors. Rock structure is an extremely important component for desert bighorn sheep. Deep, rugged cliffs are necessary for lambing, escape, and thermal cover (Wilson et al. 1980). Raptors also use these sites as perches for locating and capturing prey (Call 1978; Bent 1961). Caves provide excellent resting sites for bats. Several million bats have been documented in a single large cave (Connor, personal comm.) because caves provide stable, moderate temperatures throughout the year (see Barbour and Davis 1969).

Type and origin of rock also determine species' use of rock structures (Maser et al. 1979a). For example, chuckwallas (*Sauromalus obesus*) use rock

structures that flake and crack (mostly granitic and volcanic rock) as escape cover, bloating themselves between cracked walls making it extremely hard for predators to remove them (Stebbins 1966).

Arrangement of different size rock and depth below the surface affect wildlife use in deserts. Burrowing wildlife are especially affected by these factors. Generally, small burrowing mammals such as kangaroo rats (*Dipodomys* sp.) inhabit only areas where surface and subsurface rock is broken or soils are deep. Other small mammals such as pocket mice (*Perognathus* sp.) and certain ground squirrels (*Citellus* sp.) exploit rocky hills and mountain slopes because rocks are broken (e.g., volcanic soils), providing excellent escape, resting, and nesting cover (see Burt and Grossenheider 1976 and Golley et al. 1975).

Boulder-strewn surfaces (large boulders) provide excellent feeding, nesting, and resting sites for

Color variations in collared lizards can be linked to different habitats.

Another color variation of collared lizard.

many wildlife. Desert tortoises (*Gopherus agassizii*) are common in boulder-strewn areas of west-central Arizona (Burge 1979). Boulders seem to provide tortoises with excellent cover sites (located below rocks) and a cryptic substrate. Large boulders also provide small birds and predatory lizards (e.g., collared lizards, *Crotaphytus collaris*) with perching sites for obtaining food.

Rocks are also extremely important for thermoregulation in reptiles, especially lizards. Simon and Middendorf (1976) showed that Yarrow's spiny lizards (*Sceloporus jarrovi*) were able to attain core temperatures necessary for activity during winter months because rocky, south-facing slopes acted as heat sinks. Rocky hillsides also provide caverns in which rattlesnakes (*Crotalus* sp.) and other snakes hibernate (see Hirth et al. 1969).

Rocky slopes and hillsides also contain many small, moist microhabitats created by water buildup and shading. Cumulatively, this phenomenon creates a high degree of heterogeneity in vegetation structure and composition which in turn increases invertebrate production and diversity (see Maser et al. 1979a).

Soil

The number of subsurface (fossorial) niches in deserts is largely dependent on soil characteristics. Lack of vegetation structure in deserts is often offset by subsurface space created by deep and diverse soils, especially in warm deserts (see discussions of Bender 1982, Brown 1982b, and Attenborough 1976). Creosotebush stands of the Chihuahuan and Sonoran Deserts have little vegetation structure, but have a rich fauna, especially amphibians, lizards, snakes, and small birds and mammals (Bender 1982; Brown 1982b), primarily because of soil diversity and access to subsurface space.

Badger at burrow.

Soil depth, type, heterogeneity, and interface with other habitat components such as rock and vegetation, determine subsurface space for wildlife. Some soils such as clay, and in areas with bedrock, are impenetrable to certain burrowing wildlife (e.g., green toad, *Bufo debilis*). On these sites, roots of vegetation are important in breaking up rock and soil. In parts of the Chihuahuan and Sonoran Deserts, creosotebush breaks up clay soils and bedrock, providing wildlife access to otherwise unavailable space (Mares and Hulse 1977; Barbour et al. 1977).

Similar to surface and arboreal edges created by landform and vegetation, greater soil heterogeneity and interfaces with other habitat components (e.g., rock) provide greater numbers of spatial niches, resulting in higher wildlife biomass and diversity, especially amphibians, reptiles, and small mammals (see Thomas et al. 1979 for surface and arboreal examples).

Wildlife use subsurface niches for a wide variety of ecological functions, and several species depend on soil characteristics for exploitation of desert regions. For example, spadefoot toads (*Scaphiopus* sp.) are dependent on deep, loose soils to burrow and estivate (McClanahan 1967). Spadefoot toads remain

Spadefoot toad.

burrowed in these soils for the entire year, except during warm-season convectional storms when they surface to feed and breed. Similarly, small mammals are affected by soil type, depth, and heterogeneity (Golley et al. 1975). For example, many kangaroo rats are generally incapable of burrowing into hard, coarse, shallow soil, except along deeply rooted plants (see Burt and Grossenheider 1976 for examples), and are limited to deserts with deep, loose, and gravel substrate.

In addition to providing resting sites, certain soils provide nesting, thermoregulatory substrate, and escape cover. For example, fringe-toed lizards (*Uma* sp.) exploit deserts with fine sandy soils. Besides supplying nesting substrate, fine textured sand provides fringe-toed lizards cryptic background and warm thermal regimes necessary for activity (see Norris 1958).

Water movement through different soils (percolation) also affects species' existence in deserts. Jones et al. (1983) and Conant (1978) showed that deserts with clay soils accumulated more surface water than areas with loose, gravelly, and rocky soils, resulting in larger desert amphibian faunas.

Soil depth, origin (e.g., volcanic), and heterogeneity also affect vegetation composition and structure within deserts (Davis 1976). Vegetation composition and structure are discussed later in this chapter.

Vegetation—Litter/Debris

Ground debris or litter provides excellent feeding, thermoregulatory, nesting substrate, and escape cover for wildlife inhabiting desert regions. Vegetation debris consists of dead plant material (e.g., tree limbs and leaves) that accumulate on the surface, and it is generally correlated with vegetation composition and abundance (Daubenmire 1974). Litter abundance and diversity are probably highest in the Sonoran Desert and least in sections of the Great Basin Desert.

In deserts, large numbers of invertebrate species inhabit ground litter, providing abundant prey for ground-foraging amphibians, lizards, and small birds (see Pianka 1970 and Tomoff 1974 for examples).

Downed limbs and logs are important nest substrate for many lizards, snakes, and small mammals, providing cool, moist, well-concealed sites within hot deserts. Certain species such as Gilbert's skink (*Eumeces gilberti*) are highly dependent on these microhabitats for maintaining relatively low preferred body temperatures within deserts (Jones and Glinski 1985). Pack rats (*Neotoma* sp.) require various forms of litter to build nests, and their occurrence within desert regions seems to be related to occurrence of vegetation debris (Burt and Grossenheider 1976).

Vegetation debris is extremely important in aquatic desert habitats. Downed logs, limbs, and other litter provide excellent thermal and resting cover for amphibians, turtles, snakes and fishes, and contribute organic nutrients to aquatic systems (Naiman and Soltz 1981).

Because wildlife respond to several physical

K. Bruce Jones

Pack rat nest.

attributes of litter in deserts, it is important to record the type of litter, depth, width, and frequency.

Vegetation—Standing—Dead

Standing, dead vegetation or snags provide excellent vertical structure for nesting, feeding, resting, thermoregulatory substrate, and escape cover within deserts. Many cavity nesting birds (e.g., Gila woodpeckers, *Melanerpes uropygialis*) and raptors (e.g., screech owl, *Otus asio*) use standing, dead vegetation for nest substrate, roosting, and resting sites (see Knopf 1977 for examples). Small lizards such as tree lizards (*Urosaurus ornatus*) use standing, dead vegetation for foraging, defense, and thermoregulation substrate (Vitt et al. 1981).

Similar to downed litter, standing, dead vegetation abundance and diversity are positively associated with vegetation composition and structure (see Daubenmire 1974). Therefore, Sonoran Desert regions, especially the Arizona Upland subdivision, probably possess the highest abundance and diversity of snags among major U.S. deserts.

Vegetation—Live

Live vegetation structure is perhaps the most important habitat component in desert regions, although soils and rock may be more significant where vegetation is low and homogeneous. A number of vegetation variables should be sampled when conducting inventories and monitoring in deserts.

Arrangement of vertical and horizontal vegetation structure in deserts, and its relations to wildlife, has been thoroughly studied (see Rottenberry and Wiens 1980 for an example). Most authors agree that high wildlife abundance and diversity accompany deserts with high horizontal and vertical vegetation structure, especially birds. Tomoff (1974) correlated avian species diversity increases to increases in vegetation structure within the Sonoran Desert. Greater vertical structure increases the number of avian nesting, feeding, and breeding niches within these habitats. Conversely, deserts with little vertical vegetation structure provide few spatial niches. Raptors are also positively associated with vegetation structure (Millsap 1981).

Certain lizards and bats also benefit from vertical vegetation structure (Pianka 1966; Barbour and Davis 1969). Vitt et al. (1981) demonstrated that woody vegetation was important reproductive and feeding substrate for arboreal lizards (tree lizard, long-tailed brush lizard [*Urosaurus graciosus*], and the desert spiny lizard [*Sceloporus magister*]). Vertical vegetation structure provides bats with greater amounts of roosting and resting space (Barbour and Davis 1969), and it also increases abundance of prey (flying insects) for insectivorous lizards, small birds, and bats. Vertical vegetation structure is also used by lizards for thermoregulation. Norris (1953) described climbing behavior of desert iguanas (*Dipsosaurus dorsalis*) into creosote to escape rapidly increasing surface temperatures; temperatures 1-2 m (3-6 ft) above the surface are considerably lower.

Horizontal vegetation structure, in conjunction with vertical structure, also affects species abundance and diversity (Rottenberry and Wiens 1980). Generally, greater varieties of horizontal patchiness are associated with greater wildlife diversity. Rottenberry and Wiens (1980) suggested that certain birds prefer either open or closed habitats. By providing highly variable horizontal structure, desert habitats support species that prefer both open and closed habitats. Deserts possessing homogeneous, horizontal arrangement, and horizontal structure that is extremely opened or closed probably have lower avian diversity than those that are structurally variable.

Similarly, lizards and snakes respond to horizontal patchiness, although their relationship to patchiness is related to foraging and thermoregulatory requirements. Certain lizard species require alternating open and closed habitat configurations (Pianka 1966). These lizards forage in open spaces and retreat to large, dense bushes between foraging bouts to lower their body temperatures. Deserts transected by intermittent washes provide these alternative structures.

Horizontal patchiness also conceals nests of upland game such as Gambel's quail (*Lophortyx gambelli*) and sage grouse, and provides escape cover for individual birds (see Goodwin and Hungerford 1977 for Gambel's quail and Eng and Schladweiler 1972 for sage grouse).

Composition and availability of vegetation in deserts affects species' distribution and diversity. Presence and abundance of certain plant species affect horizontal and vertical structure (as previously discussed), and also provide food for commercially important species such as bighorn sheep, Gambel's quail, herbivorous lizards, birds, and mammals.

Availability of perennial and annual vegetation affects bird species abundance and diversity in desert regions (Serventy 1971; Tomoff 1974). Generally, bird species' diversity increases with greater mixtures of annual and perennial vegetation because of great variety in avian food preferences (Martin et al. 1951). Similarly, abundance, type, and diversity of vegetation affects food available to herbivorous, desert rodents; greatest herbivorous rodent diversity exists on sites with high annual and perennial diversity and mixture (Black 1968; Brown 1973).

Big game use of desert regions are affected by plant species composition and abundance. For example, desert bighorn sheep require a high diversity of forbs, perennial grass, and shrubs in desert habitats to meet basic metabolic needs (Wilson et al. 1980).

Desert sheep select areas near rocky escape cover.

Although wildlife diversity generally increases with increases in plant species diversity, increased plant diversity may reduce numbers of important game species. For example, Eng and Schladweiler (1972) found that sage grouse preferred closed stands of sagebrush.

Extensive root systems of certain plants, such as creosotebush, provide access to subsurface space for toads, salamanders, lizards, snakes, and small mammals. Species diversity is often increased in areas with extensive plant root systems.

Vegetation—Plant Species Associations

Certain wildlife species have evolved morphological, physiological, and behavioral characteristics that are adaptive to certain plant species attributes. These should be carefully considered when sampling desert wildlife. There are several good examples of these relationships in deserts. Desert iguanas forage heavily on creosotebush buds, especially in the spring, and their distribution is closely tied to occurrence of creosotebush (Norris 1953). Sage grouse rely heavily on sagebrush buds, especially in the spring, and this species is highly associated with dense stands of sagebrush throughout its range (Eng and Schladweiler 1972). Although both the desert iguana and sage grouse are dependent on these plant species for food, they also benefit from escape and thermoregulatory cover provided by these plants.

Colorado Division of Wildlife

Wintering sage grouse feed extensively on sagebrush buds and seedheads.

K. Bruce Jones

Cactus wren nest in cholla cactus.

Certain plant species also provide nesting structure for desert wildlife. Occurrence of elf owls (*Micrathene whitneyi*) in the Sonoran Desert is associated with nesting cavities presence in saguaro cactus (Knopf 1977; Bent 1961). Similarly, cactus wrens (*Campylorhynchus brunneicapillus*) are associated with cactus and yuccas, primarily because these plants provide nesting structure (Knopf 1977).

Animal-Created Structures

Structures created by certain wildlife provide other desert animals with habitat necessary for breeding, feeding, escape, resting and thermoregulatory substrate, and escape cover.

Fossorial mammals construct vast networks of subsurface burrows that provide resting and nesting habitat structure for a number of desert dwelling wildlife such as toads, lizards, snakes, and raptors (burrowing owl [*Athene cunicularia*]). Subsurface space contributes greatly to species diversity in deserts with little vegetation structure.

Primary cavity nesting species such as woodpeckers provide nesting habitat in cactus and woody vegetation (e.g., mesquite) for a number of secondary cavity nesting birds such as elf owls (see Knopf 1977 for examples).

Beavers modify flow of desert streams, providing pool and backwater habitat, and enhance populations of fish, toads, frogs, aquatic turtles, shorebirds, and waterfowl (Burt and Grossenheider 1976). It is important to consider animal-created structures when attempting to sample and predict wildlife occurrence within deserts.

Man-Made Structures

Man-made structures have both positive and negative effects on wildlife in desert environments. Although power lines provide nesting, resting, and roosting structure for birds and raptors (e.g., red-tailed hawk, *Buteo jamaicensis*), they also cause mortality due to electrocution and obstruction (see Olendorff et al. 1981).

Man-made structures such as buildings, barns, mine shafts, and fences provide a wide range of nesting, feeding and thermoregulatory substrate, and escape cover for wildlife such as barn owls (*Tyto alba*), fence lizards (*Sceloporus* sp.), bats, mourning doves (*Zenaida macroura*), and house mice (*Mus musculus*). Vertical mine shafts and fences have some negative effects on desert wildlife. Many small wildlife species are trapped in shafts, and fences present physical hazards and movement restriction to big game species (see Yoakum 1980 for pronghorn examples).

A number of man-made structures such as water catchments and nesting platforms have been used in desert regions to enhance wildlife. Maser et al. (1979b) provided an excellent synopsis of man-made habitats and their effect on wildlife. All man-made habitats should be considered when sampling deserts. They often affect the presence or absence of certain species within deserts.

Slope

Because of diverse topography, slopes vary greatly within desert habitats. Slope variability and mixture in deserts contribute greatly to overall habitat variability and diversity of wildlife faunas (see Maser et al. 1979a for examples). Wind currents, direct and indirect heating of substrate, and moisture retention associated with different slope angles directly (animal heat and water exchange, and ease of movement) and indirectly (vegetation differences) affect wildlife (see Maser et al. 1979a). The interrelationship between slope and soils, vegetation, aspect, and elevation determines the physical structure of desert ecosystems. Therefore, effects of slope on physical structures in deserts will vary, depending on interfaces with these other habitat components. Differences in slopes often contribute to presence, absence, and abundance of certain wildlife species. Whereas steep, rugged slopes are generally a requirement of bighorn sheep (Wilson et al. 1980), they preclude occurrence of many other species such as horned lizards (*Phrynosoma* sp.). Slopes should be measured and described when conducting inventories and monitoring in deserts.

Aspect

Aspect involves the compass direction of landscape. Similar to slope, aspect affects moisture availability, air and soil temperatures, which in turn affect vegetation composition and structure, and wildlife thermal and moisture regimes (see previous discussions on these microhabitat components for effects on desert wildlife). Effects of aspect on desert environments also depend on interfaces with microhabitat components, especially soil and vegetation, and macrohabitat factors such as slope, precipitation, and elevation. Generally, vegetation structure is greatest along north- and east-facing slopes because of lower temperatures and higher moisture regimes. However, soil type, rock, and elevation may produce contrary results. Aspect should be considered when selecting sample locations within deserts.

Elevation

Elevation affects moisture availability and temperatures that in turn affect vegetation structure and composition (see Lowe 1964 for examples). It also affects thermal and moisture regimes of air, soil, and litter, which can affect wildlife (see earlier discussions).

The Sonoran Desert exhibits many diverse habitat features.

Generally, higher elevations have cool weather, greater soil and litter moisture, and more precipitation. Increased vegetation structure resulting from greater moisture and cooler weather can be offset by low temperatures associated with higher elevations. For example, high desert regions of Wyoming have very few species of amphibians, reptiles, and small mammals because environmental temperatures are too low for species' thermal maintenance. Food necessary for birds and other herbivorous and insectivorous wildlife are too infrequent (short growing season) for physiological maintenance in these cold desert regions.

Similar to slope and aspect, elevational attributes are affected by association with soil, vegetation, slope, aspect, and degree of mountain rain shadow.

Precipitation

Precipitation varies greatly within deserts (see Bender 1982), and this directly affects vegetation structure and moisture available to wildlife in air, soils, and litter (see previous discussions on these microhabitat components; Oosting 1956). Precipitation within deserts is primarily affected by mountain rain shadow and elevation (see Bender 1982).

Frequency and type of precipitation also affect vegetation structure and moisture available to wildlife. Northern deserts (Great Basin) receive large amounts of snow (Bender 1982). Moisture is generally not available during warm spring and summer months for plant growth and wildlife consumption. Conversely, southern deserts that receive large proportions of their precipitation as rain (e.g. Chihuahuan and Sonoran Deserts) in summer months (see Bender 1982), provide water for plant growth, insect production, amphibian breeding, and wildlife consumption. Large snow packs at higher elevations in the Great Basin Desert (e.g., Wyoming) also reduce plant food available to wildlife, except on south-facing winter ranges (see Skovlin 1982 for an example).

Because precipitation quantity type and frequency can radically affect wildlife activity, year-to-year fluctuations in precipitation are important when interpreting inventory and monitoring results.

Ecotones/Habitat Juxtaposition

Throughout, I have mentioned how edges and position of habitats affect habitat structure and wildlife diversity. Generally, wildlife diversity is highest in deserts with high mixtures of different microhabitat components, and favorable thermal and moisture regimes (warm and moist). The Sonoran Desert fully demonstrates this relationship. Great mixtures of topography, soils, rock and vegetation structure, warm thermal regimes, and moisture provide many different spatial and temporal niches to wildlife (reflected in one of the world's most diverse wildlife faunas).

Ecotones consisting of habitat elements from deserts and adjacent habitats (e.g., pinyon-juniper) create distinct physical elements (e.g., structure) that enhance species diversity (Thomas et al. 1979). For example, breeding bird diversity is increased in ecotones between sagebrush and pinyon-juniper habitats because of greater habitat structural diversity (both tree and shrub life forms).

Geographic Location

Geographic location and past geological history account for present species distribution and diversity of some wildlife within desert regions. For example, species diversity in the Sonoran Desert is greatly enhanced by contributions of adjacent subtropical and tropical avifauna (Brown 1982b; Bender 1982). The evolution of the Sonoran Desert from mostly subtropical vegetation also accounts for occurrence of other wildlife with more southerly ties. Similarly, Great Basin wildlife diversity is increased by species from adjacent pinyon-juniper and grassland communities.

Geographic boundaries associated with deserts are also responsible for present distributions. Abrupt mountain ranges and canyons (e.g., Grand Canyon) have isolated certain desert wildlife (Golley et al. 1975). Current scattered fish distributions within many desert regions reflect a drying trend since the last ice age (10,000 years ago; Naiman and Soltz 1981). Many streams have dried up, leaving disjunct fish populations.

Past and present weather and associated vegetation patterns have also affected species' occurrences throughout deserts. Van Devender and Spaulding (1979) demonstrated recent drying trends in the West (past 10,000 years), resulting from recession of the last ice age. This drying trend left relict and disjunct woodland on mountains throughout southwestern deserts. Several woodland vertebrates remain on these relict sites, with diversity dependent on habitat size and distance from major stands (see Martin 1980, 1981; Jones et al. 1985).

Human Influences

Man has drastically affected plant and animal composition and diversity throughout U.S. deserts. Irrigation, urbanization, and other developments have severely reduced natural desert habitats. Artificial, urban, and agricultural habitats support fewer species than do native surrounding deserts (Davis 1973; Landcaster and Rees 1979). Other land uses have also reduced quality of desert habitats such as off-road vehicles, livestock grazing, and mineral development (Webb and Wilshire 1983; Jones 1981b; and Dunaway 1971). Fire prevention and channelization of desert streams and rivers have also reduced natural characteristics in desert ecosystems. See the following section for greater detail on impacts to desert habitats.

MAJOR IMPACTS ON DESERT HABITATS

There are two major types of impacts on desert habitats, natural and man-caused. I have already discussed, with the exception of fire and flooding, how natural factors affect wildlife distributions and composition in deserts.

Fire affects wildlife within deserts by altering habitat structure (Wright and Bailey 1982). Generally, vegetation on a site is limited to annual grasses and sprouts from perennial shrubs and grasses up to 4 years after a fire. This favors species that prefer open sites and areas with annual grasses and forbs, and is less favorable to species requiring shrubs and trees. However, fires in deserts do not generally carry over large areas; burns are usually patchy (Wright and Bailey 1982). This result tends to increase species diversity in an area due to increased horizontal and vertical vegetation structural diversity. For example, in deserts such as the sagebrush communities of the Great Basin Desert, fire opens up homogenous vegetation stands.

Fire does not seem to result in high direct mortality to wildlife (Vogl 1977). Most animals are able to escape rapidly burning, low intensity desert fires. In summer months following a wet winter or spring, annual grasses are more abundant, resulting in larger and more frequent fires. However, since fuels in deserts are mostly annual grass, fires burn very quickly over a site, with little direct wildlife mortality.

Flooding is another natural phenomena that affects wildlife habitat, especially in desert riparian systems. For the most part, flooding is beneficial to wildlife habitat. In cottonwood-willow (*Populus-Salix* sp.) communities of the Southwest, flooding is required for establishment of deciduous tree seedlings. When flooding is reduced or eliminated by instream structures such as dams, reproduction of these important tree species are reduced or eliminated. Reduction or loss of trees will reduce wildlife diversity on the site.

K. Bruce Jones

Flooding occurs as a result of short, intense summer thunderstorms. Most of this precipitation runs off without penetrating the soil.

Similar to fire, species that occupy riparian habitats evolved with these natural perturbations. There is probably little direct mortality of wildlife during most floods, although 100- and 500-year floods may affect sedentary wildlife such as small mammals and reptiles.

Like natural perturbations of desert habitats, man-caused alterations affect wildlife both directly and indirectly. Noise and activity from off-road vehicle use and mining activity such as drilling have been shown to affect reproductive success of wildlife within an area. For example, drilling activities conducted in a bighorn sheep lambing ground may

cause ewes to abort their young (Wilson et al. 1980). Similarly, Bury and Luckenbach (1983) found that continual off-road vehicle use in an area reduces the number of breeding birds.

Fences and roads also have a direct effect on wildlife within desert habitats. Both types of development reduce or eliminate wildlife movement within an area. For example, the fitness of a pronghorn population in a desert area can be reduced by cutting off natural migrational routes by fencing (Yoakum 1980).

The most extensive and severe impacts to wildlife are those that occur from loss of habitat and habitat quality. Of all habitats, deserts are probably the most severely affected by domestic livestock grazing. Low, erratic precipitation and extreme environmental temperatures reduce the ability of most desert plants to handle persistent livestock grazing, especially around water developments where livestock tend to congregate. In addition, the Mojave, Sonoran, and Chihuahuan Deserts historically had sparse wild ungulate populations (Schmidt and Gilbert 1978). Therefore, most desert plants have not evolved with grazing pressures. An indicator of excessive livestock use in most deserts is reduced amounts of forbs and perennial grasses. In some parts of the Sonoran Desert, perennial grasses are absent, primarily due to long-term, year-round livestock use. Other conditions such as reduced shrub and tree cover (Sonoran Desert) and plant species diversity can indicate excessive livestock use.

The direct impact of livestock on desert vegetation results in reduced wildlife diversity primarily due to habitat structural losses. Excessive livestock grazing also reduces food available to herbivorous wildlife, often resulting in reduced wildlife abundance and diversity.

Other impacts that indirectly affect wildlife through habitat disturbance or loss include mining, road construction, off-road vehicle use, and other activities that cause surface disturbance.

In addition to the type of land use, the severity of the impact depends on the size of the development relative to the total area of habitat and the duration of the project. Generally, a short-duration project that disturbs only a small portion of the total habitat does not significantly reduce the area's overall species diversity. However, even the smallest development can significantly reduce or eliminate a species that historically depends on a specific area (e.g., bighorn sheep lambing ground within the Sonoran Desert or elk winter range on a south slope within the Great Basin Desert).

When a land use modifies or eliminates a large portion of a habitat, even for a short period of time, species diversity can be drastically reduced. Recent studies in animal biogeography indicate that species require some minimum habitat size (see Martin 1980, 1981; Jones et al. 1985).

When a large portion of a habitat is lost, certain species are extirpated because habitat size is reduced below that required to maintain minimal viable populations. This type of impact is most acute in small, isolated habitats where loss of only a few hundred acres represents a significant portion of the

Off-road vehicle damage to wildlife habitats.

total habitat. For example, disturbance and loss of sand dune habitat in the Algodones dunes of southeastern California from intensive off-road vehicle use has significantly reduced fringe-toed lizard populations (Bury and Luckenbach 1983). Other small, isolated habitats within North American deserts whose faunas can be drastically reduced by small man-caused perturbations include woodland on top of mountains and riparian sites. Jones et al. (1985) found that reptile diversity on island woodlands of the Sonoran and Mojave Deserts were highly dependent on the size of the island.

In summary, impacts of land use on desert habitats are generally longer-lived than in other ecosystems, primarily because low, erratic precipitation precludes rapid recovery.

SUMMARY OF FACTORS AFFECTING SAMPLING IN DESERTS

Several factors affect sampling of desert wildlife faunas and their habitats. First and most important, biologists must be aware that most desert wildlife respond quickly to environmental changes, especially amphibians, reptiles, and small mammals. The life-history strategies of most of these animals are "boom

and bust," taking advantage of favorable environmental conditions (Attenborough 1976). Because of these strategies, results of surveys and studies may vary directly with seasonal and yearly climatic conditions under which samples were taken. Therefore, biologists should be cautious in interpreting inventory and monitoring studies in deserts. A one-time inventory of an area, preceded by a dry year, may fail to verify several species. Similarly, results of a monitoring study may be affected by fluctuations in precipitation. For example, a biologist attributes reduced abundance of small mammals on a site to increases in off-road vehicle use, when in fact, reduction in small mammal numbers is caused by a previously dry year. It is very important for one to consider responses of animals to environmental fluctuations when designing wildlife studies in deserts.

In collecting data on distribution and habitat associations of desert wildlife, biologists must be aware of the diverse ways in which these animals use desert resources, especially when deciding which habitat components to measure. For example, soil types, vegetation debris, and water availability play large roles in desert species diversities.

Microhabitat components should be considered when selecting sample site location. For example, the Arizona Upland subdivision of the Sonoran Desert has animals arranged in several microhabitats. Therefore, to adequately sample the faunas of this area, the biologist should select sample sites so that all microhabitats are represented (see earlier discussion for important components).

Because animal abundance and diversity also vary with aspect and slope within deserts, it is important to select sample sites that will represent variation in these factors.

Sample size for inventories and monitoring studies within deserts vary with habitat size and heterogeneity. For example, fewer samples are needed to represent large, homogeneous stands of sagebrush in the Great Basin Desert or creosote in the Chihuahuan Desert, than in relatively diverse stands of the Sonoran Desert. Generally, larger areas require more samples than smaller areas to compensate for area-related sample variability.

Temporal (time) partitioning of desert resources also plays a large role in the composition of desert wildlife (see Creusere and Whitford 1982). There are many different activity phases of desert wildlife, especially nocturnal ones. One must become familiar with different activity periods to obtain complete lists of desert wildlife, or to study responses of certain species to land management.

Certain sampling techniques are more effective in deserts than others. Because many reptiles, amphibians, and small mammals are nocturnal, these animals are most effectively sampled by live and kill trapping, although roadriding is also a popular way of sampling these animals. Trapping also allows the biologist to capture secretive, burrowing forms.

Although effective in woodland and grassland habitats with large big game herds, pellet group transects are not effective for sampling the smaller herds of desert big game species. For example, in an area with 10-15 deer per section, several hundred 1/100-acre circular plots would be needed to adequately sample pellet groups. Aerial count methods may provide a better estimate of big game density.

Because most deserts are dominated by shrubs, and to a lesser extent trees and grasses, I recommend using a line-intercept transect method, or point-intercept method along a line to sample wildlife habitat variables within deserts. This will give a good estimate of habitat frequency, abundance, and horizontal and vertical cover. When monitoring, sample points should be permanently marked. If grass and forb estimates are needed, a combination of a point-intercept along a line and plots is useful. If shrub density is desired (e.g., for sage grouse), a point-center quarter method is recommended. See Chapter 5 for greater detail of habitat measurement techniques.

Great Basin Desert inventories and monitoring should be conducted between May and September, except when working with wintering big game populations. In the Mojave, Chihuahuan, and Sonoran Deserts, sampling is most effective between April and June, and again in September and October, although certain raptors nest in the late winter and early spring within these deserts. Summer months are generally too warm to sample within southern U.S. deserts.

Summer rains within deserts also provide an excellent opportunity to sample many small nongame wildlife. For example, many burrowing snakes and toads are active immediately after rain. Toads commonly breed in temporary rainwater within deserts. Temporary rainwater pools should be checked at night to verify certain toad species.

Deserts are extremely warm during summer months and can be bitter cold during winter, especially in the Great Basin Desert. Generally, most wildlife greatly reduce their activity during these periods. Surveys and studies should be scheduled around extreme environmental conditions.

Most desert regions are remote with limited access and few towns. A wide variety of transportation and sampling schemes may be necessary to counteract limited access. For example, helicopters provide rapid and efficient means of mapping desert habitats. One might also consider placing several samples closely together rather than spreading them out, provided random sampling criteria are considered.

Rattlesnakes are very common within deserts, especially in southern deserts during the spring. Care should be taken when moving through densely vegetated areas while walking bird transects in the early morning or while setting small mammal trap lines in the early evening.

As in other habitats, inventories and monitoring studies of deserts are affected by objectives. Chapter 1 provides a discussion of how survey and study objectives affect sampling. Objectives developed for studies and surveys will also affect species and habitats to be sampled.

In summary, deserts provide tremendous opportunities to study relationships between animals and their environment. But careful consideration must be given if inventories and monitoring are to answer specific management questions.

LITERATURE CITED

ATTENBOROUGH, D., ed. 1976. Deserts and Grasslands. Doubleday and Company, Inc. New York, NY.

BAILEY, R.G. 1978. Description of ecoregions of the United States. U.S. Dep. Agric., For. Serv. Ogden, UT. 77pp.

BARBOUR, M.G., J.A. MAC MAHON, S.A. BAMBERG, and J.A. LUDWIG. 1977. The structure and distribution of *Larrea* communities. Pages 227-251 *in* Mabry, T.J., J.H. Hunziker, and D.R. DiFreo, Jr., eds. Creosote Bush. U.S./IBP Synthesis Series 6. Dowden, Hutchison and Ross, Inc. Stroudsburg.

BARBOUR, R.W. and W.H. DAVIS. 1969. Bats of America. Univ. Kentucky Press. Lexington. 286pp.

BENDER, G.L., ed. 1982. Reference handbook on the deserts of North America. Greenwood Press. Westport, CT. 594pp.

BENT, A.C. 1961. Life histories of North American birds of prey. Vol. 1 398pp. Vol. 2 466pp. Dover Publ., Inc. New York, NY.

BLACK, H.L. 1968. Populations of small rodents in relation to grazing by cattle on foothill rangeland. Masters Thesis, Univ. of Utah. Provo.

BROWN, D.E. 1982. Introduction. Pages 8-16 *in* Brown, D.E., ed. Desert Plants: Biotic Communities of the American Southwest—United States and Mexico. Univ. of Arizona Press. Tucson.

———. 1982a. Chihuahuan desert scrub. Pages 169-179 *in* Brown, D.E., ed. Desert Plants: Biotic Communities of the American Southwest—United States and Mexico. Univ. of Arizona Press. Tucson.

———. 1982b. Desert plants: biotic communities of the American Southwest—United States and Mexico. Univ. of Arizona Press. Tucson. 342pp.

———, C.H. LOWE, and C.P. PASE. 1979. A digitized classification system for the biotic communities of North America, with community (series) and association examples for the Southwest. J. Arizona Acad. Sci. 14 (Suppl):1-16.

BROWN, J.A. 1973. Species diversity of seed-eating desert rodents in sand dune habitats. Ecology 54:775-787.

BROWN, J.H. and A.C. GIBSON. 1983. Biogeography. C.V. Mosby Co. St. Louis, MO 492-523pp.

BURGE, B.L. 1979. Survey of the present distribution of the desert tortoise, *Gopherus agassizii,* in Arizona. U.S. Dep. Inter., Bur. Land Manage. Contract YA-512-CT8-108. Denver, CO.

BURT, W.H. and R.P. GROSSENHEIDER. 1976. A field guide to the mammals. Houghton-Mifflin. Boston, MA. 289pp.

BURY, R.B. and R.A. LUCKENBACH. 1983. Vehicular recreation in arid land drives: biotic responses and management alternatives. Pages 217-221 *in* Webb, R.H. and H.G. Wilshire, eds. Environmental Effects of Off-Road Vehicles. Impacts and Management in Arid Regions. Springer-Verlag. New York, NY.

CALL, M.W. 1978. Nesting habitats and surveying techniques for common western raptors. Tech. Note 316. U.S. Dep. Inter., Bur. Land Manage. BLM Service Center. Denver, CO.

CONANT, R. 1978. Semiaquatic reptiles and amphibians of the Chihuahuan Desert and their relationships to drainage patterns of the region. Pages 445-491 *in* Waver, R.H. and D.W. Riskind, eds. Trans. Symp. Biol. Resour. Chihuahuan Desert Region, U.S. and Mexico. U.S. Dep. Inter., Nat. Park Serv. Proc. Trans. Ser. 3.

CREUSERE, F.M. and W.G. WHITFORD. 1982. Use of time and space by lizards. *in* Scott, N., ed. Herpetological communities, U.S. Dep. Inter., Fish and Wildl. Serv. Wildl. Res. Rep. 13.

DAUBENMIRE, R.F. 1974. Plants and environment: a textbook of autecology. Wiley and Sons, Inc. New York, NY.

DAVIS, G.P. Jr. 1973. Man and wildlife in Arizona: the presettlement era, 1823-1864. MS Thesis. Univ. of Arizona. Tucson.

DAVIS, R.M., ed. 1976. National range handbook. U.S. Dep. Agric., Soil Cons. Serv. Washington, DC.

DUNAWAY, D. 1971. Human disturbances as a limiting factor of Sierra Nevada bighorn sheep. N. A. Wild. Sheep Conf. Trans. 1:165-173.

ENG, R.L. and P. SCHLADWEILER. 1972. Sage grouse winter movements and habitat use in central Montana. J. Wildl. Manage. 36(1):141-146.

FLEMING, W.B. 1959. Migratory waterfowl in Arizona. Ariz. Game and Fish Dep. Wildl. Bull. 5. Phoenix.

GOLLEY, F.B., K. PETRUSEWICZ, and L. RYSZKOWSKI. 1975. Small mammals: their productivity and population dynamics. Cambridge Univ. Press. Cambridge.

GOODWIN, J.G. Jr. and C.R. HUNGERFORD. 1977. Habitat use by native Gambels and scaled quail and released masked bobwhite quail in southern Arizona. U.S. Dep. Agric. For. Serv. Res. Paper RM-197.

HEATWOLE, H. 1982. A review of structuring in herpetological assemblages. Pages 1-19 *in* Scott, N., ed. Herpetological Communities. U.S. Dep. Inter., Fish and Wildl. Serv. Wildl. Res. Rep. 13.

HIRTH, H.F., R.C. PENDLETON, A.C. KING, and T.R. DOWNARD. 1969. Dispersal of snakes from a hibernaculum in northwestern Utah. Ecology 50(2):332-339.

JOHNSGARD, P.A. 1973. Grouse and quails of North America. Univ. of Nebraska Press. Lincoln. 553pp.

JONES, K.B. 1981a. Distribution, ecology, and habitat management of the reptiles and amphibians of the Hualapai Aquarius planning area, Mojave and Yavapai Counties, Arizona. U.S. Dep. Inter., Bur. Land Manage. Tech. Note 353. Denver, CO.

———. 1981b. Effects of grazing on lizard abundance and diversity in western Arizona. Southwest Nat. 26(2): 107-115.

——— and P.C. GLINSKI. 1985. Microhabitats of lizards in a Southwestern riparian community *in* North American Riparian Communities: Resolving Conflicting Uses. U.S. Dep. Agric., For. Serv. Gen. Tech. Note. *In press.*

———, L.M. KEPNER, and W.G. KEPNER. 1983. Anurans of Vekol Valley, Arizona. Southwest Nat. 28(4):469-470.

———, L.P. KEPNER, and T.E. MARTIN. 1985. Species of reptiles occupying habitat islands in western Arizona: a deterministic assemblage. Oecologia *In press.*

KINDSCHY, R.R., C. SUNDSTROM, and J.D. YOAKUM. 1982. Wildlife habitats in managed rangelands—the Great Basin of southeastern Oregon. Pronghorns. U.S. Dep. Agric., For. Serv. Gen. Tech. Report PNW-145.

KNOPF, A.A. 1977. The Audubon Society field guide to North American birds—western region. Alfred A. Knopf, Inc. New York, NY.

KUCHLER, A.W. 1964. The potential natural vegetation of the conterminous United States. American Geographic Society. Special Publ. 361. 116 pp. map.

LANDCASTER, R.K. and W.E. REES. 1979. Bird communities and the structure of urban habitat. Can. J. Zool. 57:2358-2368.

LOWE, C.H., ed. 1964. The vertebrates of Arizona. Univ. of Arizona Press. Tucson. 342pp.

MARES, M.A. and A.C. HULSE. 1977. Patterns of some vertebrate communities in creosote bush deserts. Pages 209-226 *in* Mabry, T.J., J.H. Hunziker, and D.R. DiFreo Jr., eds. Creosote Bush. U.S./IBP Synthesis Series 6, Dowden, Hutchison and Ross, Inc. Stroudsburg.

MARTIN, A.C., H.S. ZIM, and A.L. NELSON. 1951. American wildlife and plants: a guide to wildlife food habits. Dover Publ., Inc. New York, NY. 500pp.

MARTIN, T.E. 1980. Diversity and abundance of spring migratory birds using habitat islands on the Great Plains. Condor 82:430-439.

———. 1981. Limitation in small habitat islands: chance or competition? Auk 98:715-734.

MASER, C., J.M. GEIST, D.M. CONCANNON, R. ANDERSON, and B. LOVELL. 1979a. Wildlife habitats in managed rangelands—the Great Basin of southeastern Oregon—geomorphic and edaphic habitats. U.S. Dep. Agric., For. Serv. Gen. Tech. Report PNW-99.

———, J.W. THOMAS, I.D. LUMAN, and R. ANDERSON. 1979b. Wildlife habitats in managed rangelands—the Great Basin of southeastern Oregon—man-made habitats. U.S. Dep. Agric., For. Serv. Gen. Tech. Report PNW-86.

MC CLANAHAN, L. 1967. Adaptations of the spadefoot toad, *Scaphiopus couchi,* to desert environments. Comp. Bio. Chem. Physiol. 20:73-99.

MILLSAP, B.A. 1981. Distributional status of Falconiformes in west- central Arizona: with notes on ecology, reproductive success, and management. U.S. Dep. Inter., Bur. Land Manage. Tech. Note 355. Denver, CO.

MINCKLEY, W.L. 1973. Fishes of Arizona. Ariz. Game and Fish Dept. Phoenix. 293pp.

NAIMAN, R.J. and D.L. SOLTZ, eds. 1981. Fishes in North American deserts. Wiley and Sons, Inc. New York, NY. 552pp.

NORRIS, K.S. 1953. The ecology of the desert iguana, *Dipsosaurus dorsalis.* Ecology 34:265-287.

———. 1958. The evolution and systematics of the iguanid genus *Uma* and its relation to the evolution of other North American desert reptiles. Bull. Am. Mus. Nat. Hist. 114(3):247-326.

OLENDORFF, R.R., A.D. MILLER, and R.N. LEHMAN. 1981. Suggested practices for raptor protection on power lines: the state of the art in 1981. Raptor Res. Rep. 4, Raptor Research Foundation. Dep. Vet. Biol., Univ. of Minnesota, St. Paul.

OOSTING, H.J. 1956. The study of plant communities. W. H. Freeman and Company. San Francisco, CA. 440pp.

PIANKA, E.R. 1966. Convexity, desert lizards, and spatial heterogeneity. Ecology 47(6):1055-1059.

———. 1970. Comparative autecology of the lizard *Cnemidophorus tigris* in different parts of its geographic range. Ecology 51:703-720.

PORTER, K.R. 1972. Herpetology. W. B. Saunders Co. Philadelphia, PA. 281pp.

ROTTENBERRY, J.T. and J.A. WIENS. 1980. Habitat structure, patchiness, and avian communities in North American steppe vegetation: a multivariate analysis. Ecology 61:1228-1250.

SCHMIDT, J.L. and D.L. GILBERT, eds. 1978. Big game of North America: ecology and management. Stackpole Books. Harrisburg, PA. 512pp.

SERVENTY, D.L. 1971. Biology of desert birds. Pages 287-339 *in* Farmer, D.S., and J.R. King, eds. Avian Biology: Vol. I Academic Press. New York, NY.

SHORT, H.L. 1983. Wildlife guilds in Arizona desert habitats. BLM Tech Note 362. Denver, CO. 258pp.

SHREVE, F. 1942. The desert vegetation of North America. Bot. Rev. 8:195-246.

SIMON, C.A. and G.A. MIDDENDORF. 1976. Resource partitioning by an iguanid lizard: temporal and microhabitat aspects. Ecology 57(6):1317-1320.

SKOVLIN, J.M. 1982. Habitat requirements and evaluations. Pages 369-413 *in* Thomas, J.W. and D.E. Toweill, eds. Elk of North America: Ecology and Management. Stackpole Books, Harrisburg, PA.

STEBBINS, R.C. 1966. A field guide to western reptiles and amphibians. Houghton-Mifflin Co. Boston, MA. 279pp.

THOMAS, J.W., C. MASER, and J.E. RODIEK. 1979. Wildlife habitats in managed rangelands—the Great Basin of southeastern Oregon—edges. U.S. Dep. Agric., For. Serv. Gen. Tech. Rep. PNW-85. 17pp.

THORNE, R.F., B.A. PRIGGE, and J. HENDRICKSON. 1981. A flora of the higher ranges and the Kelso Dunes of the eastern Mohave Desert in California. Aliso 10:F-1-186.

TOMOFF, C.S. 1974. Avian species diversity in desert scrub. Ecology 55(2):396-403.

TURNER, R.M. 1982a. Great Basin desert scrub. Pages 145-155 *in* Brown, D.E., ed. Desert Plants: Biotic Communities of the American Southwest—United States and Mexico. Univ. of Arizona Press. Tucson.

———. 1982b. Mohave desert scrub. Pages 157-168 *in* Brown, D.E., ed. Desert Plants: Biotic Communities of the American Southwest—United States and Mexico. Univ. of Arizona Press. Tucson.

——— and D.E. BROWN. 1982. Sonoran desert scrub. *in* Brown, D.E., ed. Desert Plants: Biotic Communities of the American Southwest—United States and Mexico. Univ. of Arizona Press. Tucson. 342pp.

VAN DEVENDER, T.R. and W.G. SPAULDING. 1979. Development of vegetation and climate in the southwestern United States. Science 204:701-710.

VITT, L.J., R.C. VAN LOBEN SELS, and R.D. OHMART. 1981. Ecological relationships among arboreal desert lizards. Ecology 62(2):398-410.

VOGL, R.J. 1977. Fire: A destructive menace or a natural process? Pages 261-289 *in* Cairns, J. Jr., K.L. Dickson, and E.E. Herricks, eds. Recovery and Restoration of Damaged Ecosystems. Univ. Press of Virginia. Charlottesville.

WEBB, R.H. and H.G. WILSHIRE, eds. 1983. Environmental effects of off-road vehicles: impacts and management in arid regions. Springer-Verlag. New York, NY. 534pp.

WILSON, L.O., J. BLAISDELL, G. WELSH, R. WEAVER, R. BRIGHAM, W. KELLY, J. YOAKUM, M. HINKES, J. TURNER, and J. DE FORGE. 1980. Desert bighorn habitat requirements and management recommendations. Pages 1-7 *in* Des. Bighorn Coun. Trans. 24.

WRIGHT, H.A. and A.W. BAILEY. 1982. Fire ecology. Wiley-Interscience, New York, NY. 501pp.

YOAKUM, J. 1980. Habitat management guides for the American pronghorn antelope. U.S. Dep. Inter., Bur. Land Manage. Tech. Note 347. Denver, CO.

YORK J.C. and W.A. DICK-PEDDIE. 1969. Vegetation changes in southern New Mexico during the past hundred years. Pages 157-166 *in* McGinnies, W.G. and B.J. Goldman, eds. Arid Lands in Perspective. Univ. of Arizona Press, Tucson.

ZWEIFEL, R.G. and C.H. LOWE. 1966. The ecology of a population of *Xantusia vigilis,* the desert night lizard. Am. Mus. Novit. 2247:1-57.

8

TUNDRA

Peter C. Lent

Bureau of Land Management
920 Valley Road
Reno, NV 89512

"When we reach the Arctic regions, or snow-capped summits, the struggle for life is almost exclusively with the elements."

—Charles Darwin, from *On the Origin of Species*

Editor's Note: Animals of tundra habitat must struggle for life. Because of the harsh working conditions and inaccessibility of many tundra areas, few biologists have conducted systematic habitat inventories or surveys of general vertebrate habitat relationships in these severe environments. Most of the work in such areas has concentrated on a few large, economically important wildlife species. Nevertheless, the conditions are so different from those in more temperate areas that the subject deserves a separate chapter. This chapter describes the state-of-the-art for both arctic and alpine tundra; the biologist working in such areas will find much room for innovation and development of new systems.

INTRODUCTION

The origin of the English word "tundra" is said to come from the Finnish "tunturi" then from the Russian "tundra," meaning a marshy, treeless plain. In a general sense the term refers to any cold climate landscape having vegetation without trees. Such landscapes occur predominantly in the northern hemisphere north of the tree line (arctic tundra) and in mountainous areas of both hemispheres above the tree line (alpine tundra). The vegetation communities are characterized by short-stemmed perennial herbaceous plants, stunted or prostrate shrubs, lichens, and mosses. Similar vegetation, where trees are absent due to low-growing season temperatures, also occurs in mid- to high-latitude maritime environments such as the Aleutian Islands and on certain islands in the southern hemisphere, such as South Georgia and the Macquaries (Jenkins and Ashton 1970).

Tundra areas constitute slightly over 8% of the total U.S. land area and about 5% of the earth's land surface. Of the U.S. total, about 74 million ha (183 million a.) are in Alaska and 3 million ha (7.5 million a.) of alpine tundra are in the contiguous 48 states (Figure 1a). Of the Alaskan tundra area, Brown et al. (1978) estimated that 52% is arctic and 48% is alpine tundra (Figure 1b).

The manager or biologist new to arctic ecosystems will find a detailed and comprehensive body of literature available. The purpose of this chapter is to help the manager get started but is by no means exhaustive. In contrast, the managers concerned with alpine areas will find a more scattered body of literature and will need to make a greater effort to seek out material specific to their area. Two general treatments of North American alpine areas are worth noting: Zwinger and Willard (1972) and Price (1981). A glossary of terms broadly relevant to arctic and alpine environments has been prepared by Gabriel and Talbot (1984). The biologist or manager working with alpine areas will find some useful material in

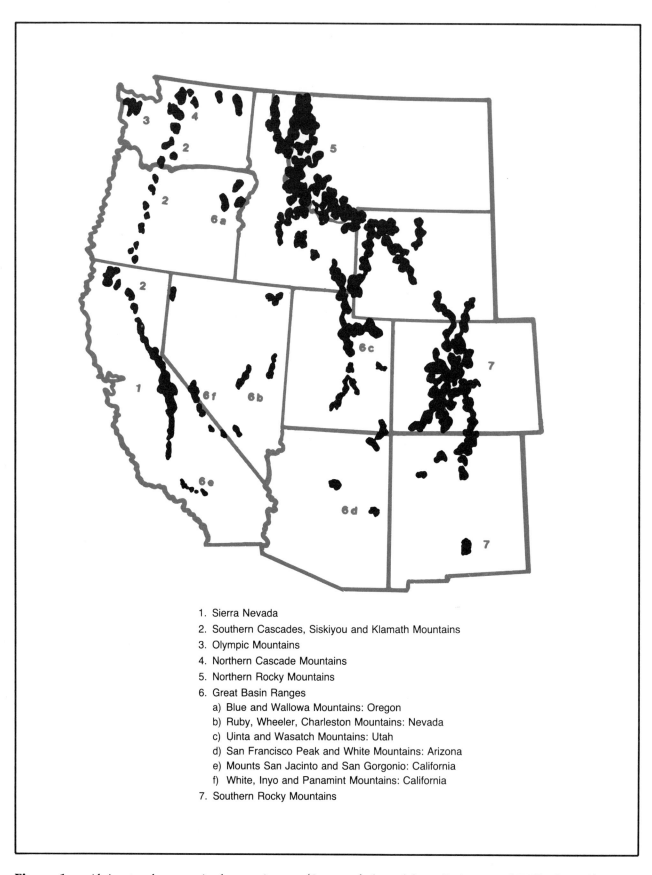

1. Sierra Nevada
2. Southern Cascades, Siskiyou and Klamath Mountains
3. Olympic Mountains
4. Northern Cascade Mountains
5. Northern Rocky Mountains
6. Great Basin Ranges
   a) Blue and Wallowa Mountains: Oregon
   b) Ruby, Wheeler, Charleston Mountains: Nevada
   c) Uinta and Wasatch Mountains: Utah
   d) San Francisco Peak and White Mountains: Arizona
   e) Mounts San Jacinto and San Gorgonio: California
   f) White, Inyo and Panamint Mountains: California
7. Southern Rocky Mountains

Figure 1a. Alpine tundra areas in the contiguous 48 states (adapted from Zwinger and Willard 1972).

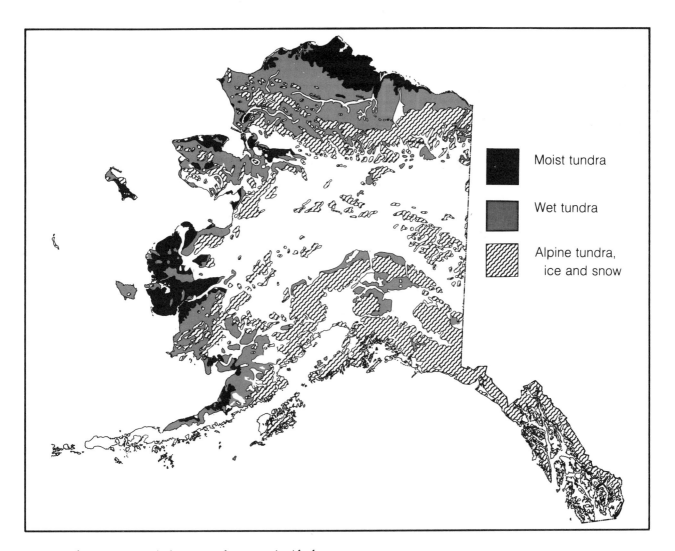

Figure 1b. Arctic and alpine tundra areas in Alaska.

the arctic literature, but must use caution in its application; there are some fundamental differences between arctic and alpine ecologies.

All tundra areas are characterized by short growing seasons, usually fewer than 100 days, and low summer temperatures. In extreme situations the daily temperature may average only 2° to 5° C (36° to 41° F). Although all share this characteristic of "cold-dominated," the vegetation types encompassed by tundra are exceptionally diverse. At one extreme is the high arctic polar desert, where vegetative cover may be less than 10%, composed primarily of cushion plant forms and mosses with a few other annuals scattered sporadically. Polar desert and semi-desert are rare within the U.S. They are best represented in the arctic-alpine environment of the Brooks Range in northern Alaska. At the other end of the spectrum, over most of North America, the tundra grades into forest in a forest-tundra ecotone. Here vegetative biomass can be relatively high with several well-developed canopy layers.

Discussion in this chapter will encompass these transition zones because of the unique qualities they have in common with tundra, such as prevalence and importance of lichens and potential presence of permafrost, and because important migratory species, such as elk (*Cervus elaphus*) and caribou (*Rangifer tarandus*), depend on a single system composed of both tundra and forest-tundra zones.

Some writers have contended that it is better to reserve the term "tundra" to refer to areas with permafrost, either continuous or discontinuous. Billings (1973), for example, preferred the use of the terms "meadow" and "fell-field" for the mesic and xeric alpine equivalents of tundra, respectively. As he noted, important differences exist, such as the more intense solar radiation in alpine environments coupled with extreme diurnal temperature fluctuations, as opposed to the continuous summer daylight in the high latitude tundra environment. But Billings' own work revealed that 50% of the vascular plant species in the alpine zone of the Beartooth Plateau of Montana were species also present in arctic tundra. A similar large overlap of species does not occur between arctic and alpine faunas, however (Hoffmann 1974, 1984).

Aside from the similarities in low growth forms, which suggest that similar vegetation sampling techniques are applicable in alpine and arctic situations, there are some basic similarities arising from the cold-dominated environment of both, such as low primary productivity, low decomposition rates, low stress tolerance, and high susceptibility to physical disturbance—even where permafrost is not present. The complex spatial heterogeneity of arctic and alpine vegetation, a "patchiness" that is based on responses to microrelief features, also dictates that similar problems are to be encountered in inventory and monitoring of arctic and alpine habitats.

The presence of permafrost is certainly characteristic of most arctic tundra areas. Discontinuous permafrost is also found in about 100,000 km^2 (40,000 mi.^{2}) of alpine areas in the western U.S. exclusive of Alaska (Pewe 1983). However, permafrost is not universally present in tundra nor does the presence of permafrost, if it is at sufficient depth, necessarily preclude tree growth. Furthermore, even in the absence of permafrost, *per se*, cryopedogenic

forces (frost action) play a significant ecological role in arctic and alpine habitats. Thus the position taken by Bliss (1981) and the one taken in this chapter is that the presence, absence, and the characteristics of the permafrost layer are among the major influences on the nature of a given tundra area and are major considerations in inventory and management. They are not, however, decisive in determining whether an area is considered to be tundra.

A current tendency exists to shift tundra to lower levels in hierarchical vegetation classification systems. For example, Viereck and Dyrness (1980) distinguished between tundra and grass/herbaceous formations in the first dichotomy (Level I) of their hierarchical system. However, in a later version of their classification system (Viereck et al. 1982), all tundra types were reduced to subcategories under two of their Level I classes (herbaceous and shrub). They classified communities of the Aleutian Islands and other maritime environments that are dominated by *Calamagrostis canadensis* and *Elymus arenarius* as grasslands and not tundra. They also referred to shrubland's several types that have been included with tundra or shrub-tundra by other workers. Driscoll et al. (1983) also included tundra as a subdivision in their grassland/herbaceous class.

Peter Lent

Caribou on tundra riparian area in July.

GENERAL HABITAT CLASSIFICATION SYSTEMS

Various wildlife habitat classification systems have been employed in both arctic and alpine areas. There are no generally or widely used systems and none of them has been systematically tested as a general system. There is, however, some general correspondence among some of these, particularly for terrestrial birds and small mammals (Table 1). Most of these habitat classes represent various subdivisions of the soil moisture gradient from flooded and saturated through desiccated and rocky (Pruitt 1966; Hoffmann 1974). This reflects the dominant role of soil moisture as a niche variable both directly and indirectly through its interrelations with the permafrost regime and vegetation. Winter habitats of small mammals also reflect similar snow-cover gradients (Pruitt 1966). These general habitat classes and other habitat features and their relationships to one another are illustrated in Figures 2 and 3.

Moitoret et al. (1985) performed the most detailed analysis of arctic tundra habitats to date. Using the clustering and ordination analysis program TWINSPAN, they found flooded and riparian to be the most distinct of their seven coastal tundra terrestrial bird habitats. Drier types, other than riparian, had lower and less diverse bird use. Their analysis suggested that habitat factors relating to microrelief and interspersion characteristics may be important in defining habitats. Thus, habitat classes so defined do not necessarily show one-to-one correspondence with the broad vegetation-based classes ascertained from satellite imagery such as that of Landsat.

Several more specialized tundra habitat classifications have been employed. One relating specifically to wetlands is described in the discussion regarding migratory waterfowl. A system used for impact analysis in arctic and subarctic Alaska is described in the section treating inventory and monitoring for impact assessment.

Table 1. Habitat classes used in some studies of arctic and alpine terrestrial birds and mammals.

Locale	Habitat Classes							Reference
Birds and small mammals, Beartooth Plateau, MT	Moist meadow	Sedge tussock	Willow sedge	Dry meadow[1]	Krummholz[2]	Fellfield	Cliff, talus	Hoffmann (1974)
Breeding habitats of birds, Cape Thompson, Alaska	Moist, wet meadow	Heath tussock	Riparian	Dry meadow Fellfield		Combined with dry meadow	Cliffs, talus	Williamson (1961)
Bird habitats, Upper Sheenjek R. (Subarctic-alpine) Alaska	Sedgegrass marsh	Tussock heath	Tall shrub		Dwarf shrub[2]	Dry tundra		Kessel and Schaller (1960)
Bird habitats, coastal Arctic National Wildlife Refuge, Alaska	5 hydric types[3]	Tussock	Riparian					Moitoret et al. 1985
Selected Characteristic Species	Long-tailed, parasitic jaegers, *Stercorarius* sp. Tundra vole, *Microtus Oeconomus*	Lapland, longspur, *Calcarius lapponicus* Red-backed vole, *Clethrionomys rutilus*	Arctic warblers, *Dendroica* sp. Water shrew, *Sorex palustris* Moose, *Alces alces*	Golden plover, *Pluvialis dominica* Pocket gophers, *Thomomys* sp. Dall's sheep	Willow ptarmigan Chipmunks, *Eutamias* sp.	Horned lark, *Eremophila alpestris* Dall's sheep	Marmots, *Marmota* sp. Mountain goat Golden eagle, *Aquila chrysaetos*	

[1]Hoffmann (1974) also distinguishes rock polygons, these being dry meadow with rock stripes or patterns. Characteristic species are pikas, *Ochotona* sp.
[2]Krummholz is a coniferous ecotone below the alpine tundra. These two are only crudely structural counterparts.
[3]Five hydric types identified: Flooded, Wet sedge, Moist sedge, Mosaic, and Moist-sedge shrub.

MAJOR WILDLIFE GROUPS

It is useful, particularly for wildlife species in arctic tundra habitats, to consider three categories of species: (1) resident species that remain active year-round, (2) resident species hibernating in winter, and (3) migratory species present for only a portion of the year. Tundra areas tend to have a larger proportion of migratory and otherwise highly mobile species than most other broad habitat classes.

Resident arctic mammal species include some medium-sized hibernators, such as the arctic ground squirrel (*Spermophilus parryii*) and hoary marmot (*Marmota caligata*), or large ones, such as grizzly bears (*Ursus arctos*), but include a larger variety of species that remain active year-round.

The smaller species, rodents and shrews primarily, tend to be "chionophiles" (Pruitt 1978), that is, they require snow cover to ameliorate an otherwise unsurvivable winter environment. Others are "chionophobes," such as the musk-ox (*Ovibos moschatus*),

requiring habitats of restricted snow cover for winter survival. The importance of snow in the tundra environment is treated in a separate section of this chapter.

The number of resident arctic bird species is extremely small, but may include ptarmigan (*Lagopus lagopus and L. mutus*), ravens (*Corvus corax*), snowy owls (*Nyctea scandiaca*), and gyrfalcons (*Falco rusticolus*). The great majority of the 97 or so bird species using the northern Alaska tundra are migratory (Pitelka 1979). Their dependency on tundra habitats, however critical, is a brief one and timed precisely according to the adaptations of each species. Thus there is a complex and compressed pattern of arrivals and departures that makes the correct timing of inventories critical to their success. In northern Alaska the peak of arrival dates is in late May; some early breeding species may leave as early as late July.

Waterfowl and shorebirds are almost entirely migratory except for a few species that may associate with open water marine environments in winter

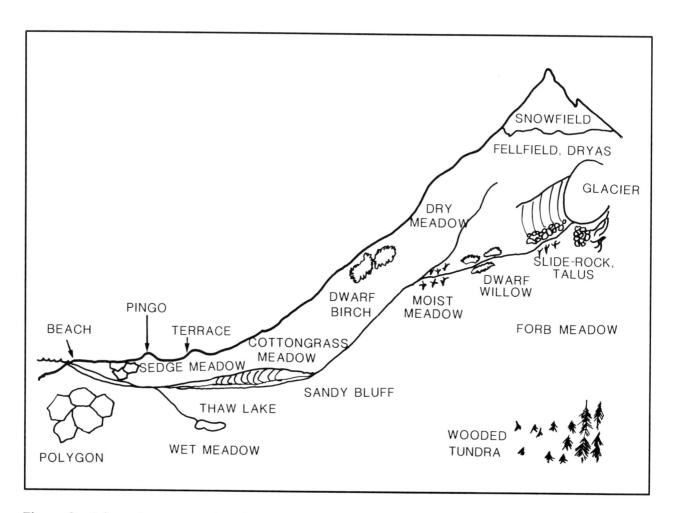

Figure 2. Schematic representation of arctic and arctic-alpine tundra habitat types and features (after Hoffmann 1984).

Musk-ox winter tundra habitat with low snow-cover.

in some arctic areas. Most waterbird species are clearly tied to wet tundra habitats. However, there are some shorebird species clearly associated with dry, upland, or even arctic-alpine habitats (Kessel

and Schaller 1960; King 1979). The arctic-alpine tundra supports a surprisingly diverse array of summer breeding birds, estimated by Pitelka (1979) to be 50 species, of which nearly half are passerines.

Because all migratory species cannot be sampled at an optimal time in a single inventory, it is necessary to have a clear statement of objectives and clear familiarity with the regional literature to strive for the optimal timing for specific needs or specific species. Moulting concentrations are common after breeding in several waterfowl species, and moulting areas may be used only briefly, yet are of critical importance to entire populations (Pitelka 1979; NPR-A Task Force 1978; Derksen et al. 1982).

Systematic surveys of arctic tundra waterfowl with small aircraft began as early as 1948 (Smith and Allen 1948) and have been greatly improved since then (King 1970). Bergman et al. (1977) devised a system for classifying those tundra wetlands that support large breeding bird populations. The system uses data on size of wetland, vegetation, water depth, and water chemistry to identify eight key habitat

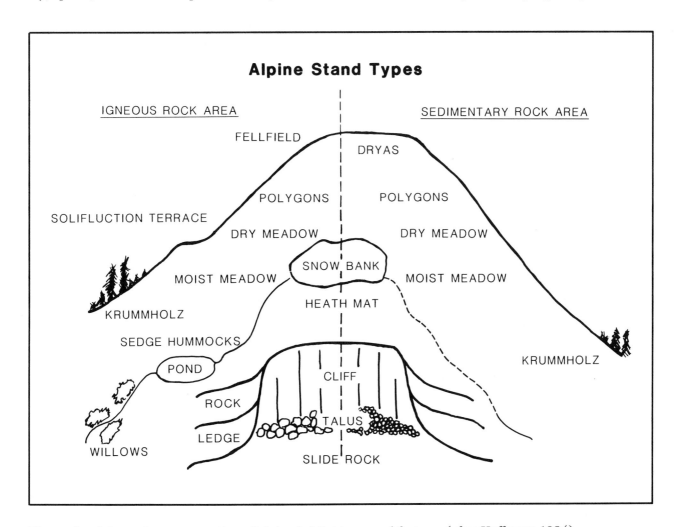

Figure 3. Schematic representation of alpine habitat types and features (after Hoffmann 1984).

classes of importance to waterbirds (Table 2). Preliminary studies suggest that identification of the class of wetland associated with a given tundra area will be an acceptable predictor of the waterbird species, using such an area without a direct survey of the bird populations themselves (U.S. Fish and Wildlife Service 1982).

Some species may have both migratory and resident populations, even within the same general area, i.e., the caribou. In other situations, a population may shift from resident to migratory status depending on certain environmental conditions. In the arctic, the gyrfalcon is one such species in which prey availability can shift behavior.

As with the arctic, alpine tundra areas show low species diversity. A major difference is that, especially with resident species, alpine populations often exist in small islands of habitat. Habitats formerly occupied by extirpated populations will not be quickly recolonized and genetic conservation is more likely to be a management concern. For example, an endemic species of butterfly (*Boloria acronemia*) has been found only in three alpine meadows in the San Juan Mountains of Colorado (Gall 1984).

Thirteen species of herbivorous mammals inhabit the alpine area of the Beartooth Mountains, Montana, and only six species of herbivorous or

Table 2. Wetland classification system of Bergman et al. (1977) with two additional types from Derksen (1979).

Wetland Class	Description
Class I: Flooded tundra	Shallow waters formed during spring thaw when melt water overflows stream basins or is trapped in vegetated tundra depressions. These temporary wetlands form in shallow basins, polygons, or broad meadows.
Class II: Shallow-*Carex*	Shallow ponds with a gently sloping shore zone surrounded by and usually containing emergent *Carex aquatilis* in a central open water zone. These ponds, formed in low centers of polygonal ground, often produce a mosaic pattern of ridges and ponds.
Class III: Shallow-*Arctophila*	Ponds or pools in beaded streams containing *Arctophila fulva* in the central zone and shoreward stands of *A. fulva* or *Carex aquatilis*. Shores are more abrupt than those of Class II ponds. Maximum water depths range from 20 to 50 cm.
Class IV: Deep-*Arctophila*	Wetlands of either large pond or lake size that lack emergents in the central zone and contain stands of *Arctophila fulva* near the shore.
Class V: Deep-open	Large, deep lakes that have abrupt shores, sublittoral shelves, and a deep central zone.
Class VI: Basin-complex	Large, partially drained basins that may contain nearly continuous water in spring due to flooding of the bottom by melt water. A composite of several other classes.
Class VII: Beaded stream	Small, often intermittent, streams consisting of a series of channels formed in ice-wedges and linked to pools that develop at ice-wedge intersections.
Class VIII: Coastal wetlands	Aquatic habitats that occupy low areas within a zone directly influenced by sea water.
Class IX: Upland tundra	Ponds characterized by depressions in upland tussock vegetation (*Eriophorum vaginatum*) that fill with melt water and evolve from ephemeral pools to permanent ponds. When mature, these ponds are typically less than 10 by 3 m with a maximum depth of 1 m.
Class X: Ice-wedge pools	Small (10 m wide) pools formed in ice-wedge troughs in both high and low center polygon areas. Older, enlarged pools resemble Class II ponds and are more diverse than smaller, deep, acidic pools.

Uncompahgre frittilary butterfly.

Pingo and associated tundra ponds.

insectivorous birds regularly breed above timberline. Eight carnivorous mammal species and seven to eight raptor species spend at least part of the year in this alpine environment (Hoffmann 1974; Price 1981). Carnivorous mammals and predatory hawks and owls seem to constitute a relatively greater proportion of the overall species array compared with the proportion in temperate or tropical biomes.

In alpine environments the large mammals, such as grizzly bears, bighorn sheep (*Ovis canadensis*), elk, Dall's sheep (*Ovis dalli*), and mountain goat (*Oreamnos americanus*), generally make altitudinal movements, descending to more wooded habitats in winter. Dall's sheep and mountain goats may on occasion use tundra ranges in winter.

Some bird species also make seasonal altitudinal movements. In the western contiguous states, white-tailed ptarmigan (*Lagopus leucurus*) use a broad array of alpine habitats, moving in winter to lower elevation shrub communities. Farther north, where there are three sympatric ptarmigan species, the white-tailed occupies a narrower niche.

Altitudinal movements may even be on a daily basis (Hoffmann 1974). Many raptors nest at lower elevations, but take advantage of upwelling wind currents to move up to open alpine terrain for foraging during the day.

SPECIAL HABITAT FEATURES

In areas of continuous or near-continuous permafrost, suitable habitat for denning or burrowing species may be very limited. The depth of the active layer (seasonally thawed soil zone) can be an important variable influencing wildlife habitat values. Denning or burrowing species depend upon well-drained or exposed substrates, such as pingos, where the permafrost zone has receded or is ice-free. Pingos are conical-shaped mounds pushed up out of the flat tundra by hydrostatic pressure. These features reach 65 m (213 ft) in height and, because of drainage and aspect, may provide relatively high substrate temperatures as well as lookouts (Hoffmann 1974). Like pingos, coastal bluffs, cut banks, gravel bars, talus slopes, and sand dunes can be important habitat features. Their number and extent may actually be the limiting factor for certain populations. Sandy banks of only 1 m (1 yd) high may be used by arctic foxes (*Alopex lagopus*) for denning (Bee and Hall 1956).

Because of the generally flat, treeless character of the arctic tundra, river and coastal bluffs are often the principal sites for nesting raptors outside of the mountainous zone. Specialized systems have been developed for classifying these raptor habitats (Ritchie 1979) which also include escarpments, rock outcrops, and talus slopes as one moves into the arctic-alpine environment. Any habitat surveys or other intensive activities with aircraft should be conducted so as to have minimal disturbance on nesting raptors, peregrine falcons (*Falco peregrinus*) in particular (Fyfe and Olendorff 1976). Because such sites are frequently also preferred sites for extraction of construction materials (gravel or sand) or sometimes even as camp or construction sites, it is important to inventory these features and assess their value as habitat.

The presence of deep snowdrifts is an important habitat feature for denning wolverines (*Gulo gulo*), polar bears (*Ursus maritimus*), and brown bears (*U. arctos*). The drift itself may form the den or it may form an additional insulative cover over shallow rock or earth dens. On the other hand, Reynolds et al. 1976 suggested that brown bears in the arctic do not den until about the top 10 cm (4 in.) of soil is frozen because otherwise the coarse-textured soils would collapse on the excavation.

Some habitat features may be transient. For example, certain arctic river deltas may provide the only open water for early arriving waterfowl and shorebirds at a time when tundra lakes are still frozen. These critical areas of open water are easily discernible from aerial reconnaissance or from Landsat imagery (NPR-A Task Force 1978; U.S. Fish and Wildlife Service 1982; Lent l985). *Aufeis* or *naled,* the sheets of ice remaining in river and braided streambeds late into summer, are another special habitat feature that provides cool, insect relief areas for caribou, moose (*Alces alces*), and other large mammals.

Thus, the special importance of riparian habitats and riparian-associated habitat features within arctic tundra landscapes cannot be stressed too strongly. Not only do they provide microrelief and thawed soils for burrowers and bluffs and banks for nesting sites, they also provide narrow zones of brushy habitats that are critical to the requirements of other species (NPR-A Task Force 1979; Pamplin 1979; Moitoret et al. 1985).

INVENTORY AND MONITORING SYSTEMS

Range Surveys

Most of the early efforts in the 1920s and 1930s to map, describe, and inventory arctic and subarctic tundra ranges were conducted because of their economic importance for domestic reindeer in the U.S.S.R. and in Alaska (Palmer 1926). With the collapse of the reindeer industry in Alaska and the disruptions resulting from World War II in the Soviet Union, there was a hiatus of scientific effort. In the late 1950s, systematic attention was first turned to the study of caribou and their habitats in Alaska and Canada. This was made possible by improvements in the performance and availability of small aircraft, providing biologists with a mobility and a perspective not previously possible. This work tended to focus on taiga ranges used by wintering caribou.

In the 1950s, scientific studies of Scandinavian domestic reindeer got underway and Soviet work was intensified. Banfield (1954) and Tener (1965) also began their classic studies in the Canadian Arctic. In Alaska, two major reviews of literature and field work relating to caribou range were done by Courtright (1959) and Pegau (1968). Pegau put emphasis on specific comparisons of vegetation inventory techniques suitable for tundra ranges.

Among the pioneer workers in Scandinavia, Skuncke (1969) devised a detailed system for aerial surveys of reindeer pastures to estimate pasture carrying capacities and trends. Much of the system is specialized for the Scandinavian situation, however, and also requires very experienced observers.

Peter Lent

Beaded streams furnish good nesting habitat for white-fronted geese and ducks.

Special inventory techniques are required for tundra areas where lichens are a significant component or likely to be important forage plants. Pegau (1970) used a 9l9-cm^2 (1-ft^2) frame and visually estimated lichen cover based on random throws. Using this simple technique, he was able to assess the damage to lichens caused by holding or herding reindeer on lichen ranges during dry periods. Pegau (1968) also measured growth rates for lichens in Alaska. Although the randomness of random throws has been legitimately criticized, the technique has proven useful (Greig-Smith 1983).

Changes over time in arctic tundra vegetation have been successfully measured in other studies as well. In a study of the effects of grazing by confined musk-oxen on tussock and mat cushion tundra, McKendrick (1981) used the walking point method of Owensby (1973) to measure basal cover and species composition. With these techniques, he was able to demonstrate significant reduction in lichen and shrub-standing crops caused by musk-oxen. Thus the measured difference with regard to musk-oxen influence on shrubs was significantly different from that reported from numerous reindeer studies. Intense grazing pressure by reindeer tends to promote invasion by shrub species. Racine (1979) compared soil condition, permafrost depth, and vegetation on plots before and after tundra fires on the Seward Peninsula. He used simple square meter (square yard) plots, recording stem density and percentage cover to measure significant differences before and after the fires.

Thilenius (1979) presented the best recent discussion of the problems, concepts, and inexact state-of-the-art for assessing and monitoring alpine range communities. He noted that classifying range condition is a great problem in alpine range management. Range condition classes often seem to be confused with site climax classes. For example, cushion plant communities dominated by *Geum rossii* have been treated by range managers as poor condition communities when in fact such forb-dominated communities, common on xeric sites, may represent excellent range condition. He recommended the system of Lewis (1970) who, he stated, properly recognized the unique microclimate and soil features of alpine ranges. Thilenius (1979) also emphasized that alpine range monitoring must be based on annual sampling because of the high degree of year-to-year variability.

As with any class of vegetation or habitat, description and mapping of soils types is an important part of habitat analysis. The characterization, inventory, and mapping of tundra soils has become particularly important in the last two decades because arctic development has required an increased commitment to land planning and engineering skills (Everett 1982).

In arctic soils, the presence of permafrost, its depth and water content, as well as the nature of the overlying vegetation are important considerations.

When permafrost is present, it is frequently associated with areas of relatively little relief. This, plus the generally fine texture of soils and spongy moss cover, limits water movement and results in saturated soils (Figure 4). Gley (wet) soils are indicated by cottonsedge (*Eriophorum* sp.) tussock and dwarf heath communities. Bog soils are characterized as cottongrass sedges (*Carex aquatilis*) and *Dupontia*. Plant communities dominated by lichens, mosses, and dwarf heaths with scattered herbs prevail over shallow dry or rocky soils where the permafrost is also dry and generally 1 m (1 yd) or more deep. Similar vegetation also occurs on dry raised patches of peaty material (Linell and Tedrow 1981).

Remote Sensing Applications

Because of the vast areas involved in arctic tundra management, the lack of access, except by expensive aircraft, and the short field season, there is a strong rationale for the use of remote sensing systems for mapping and inventory of vegetation and

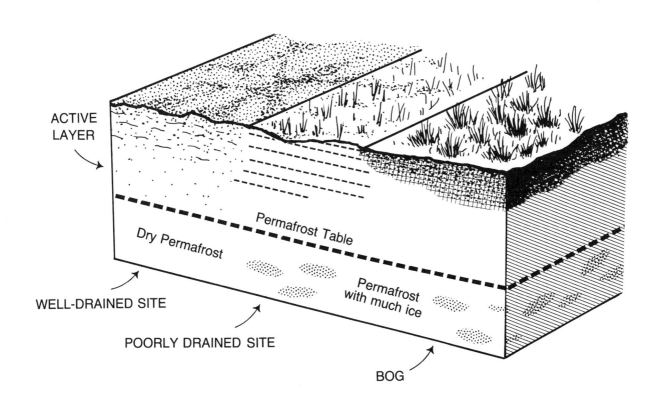

Figure 4. Idealized cross-section of tundra landscape from higher well-drained ground on left to peaty ground on right (after Linell and Tedrow 1981).

wildlife habitats. Several efforts have been directed in recent years toward the use of satellite sensors for that purpose, particularly Landsat. These trial efforts are described by Anderson and Belon (1973), Anderson et al. (1974), LaPerriere (1978), George et al. (1977), and Nodler et al. (1978). Anderson and Belon (1973), Lent and LaPerriere (1974), and Hall et al. (1980) described the use of Landsat imagery to delineate and monitor change in areas that have been subject to recent wildfires. This then provides a useful tool to monitor changes in wildlife habitats due to the wildfires and subsequent recovery of tundra vegetation. Lent (1980) also used Landsat imagery to monitor gross changes in extent of snow cover. More recently, Acevedo et al. (1982) used Landsat for environmental mapping and related baseline studies on a portion of the coastal tundra of the Arctic National Wildlife Refuge. To a certain extent, wildlife biologists have used wildlife habitat inventory and mapping efforts, and use classification schemes that take advantage of the broad land cover types discriminated from Landsat imagery (U.S. Fish and Wildlife Service 1982, 1984). As noted earlier, Moitoret et al. (1985) reported on some of the potential problems with such approaches.

Satellite imagery from Landsat and weather satellites has also been used to assess the snow and ice conditions encountered by nesting geese in the Canadian Arctic. By assessing the year-to-year timing of snow and ice melt on a broad scale, this nesting habitat information has been used to successfully predict productivity of species such as brant (*Branta bernicla*), snow geese (*Chen caerulescens*), arctic-breeding Canada geese (*B. canadensis*), and greater white-fronted geese (*Anser albifrons*) (Reeves et al. 1976).

A major limitation to the use of satellite imagery over much of the arctic is the high frequency of overcast days. The large number of overcast days is partially compensated for by the polar convergence of Landsat orbits, resulting in bursts of imagery on successive days at high latitudes. Because the phenology changes so rapidly and the windows of good weather are frequently so short, it is difficult to obtain comparable imagery in successive years to document long-term trends.

The use of satellite imagery for mapping and monitoring alpine habitats is at present much more difficult because of the problems resulting from topographic complexity, including the effects of shadows on surface albedo. However, Craighead et al. (1982) classified and mapped alpine and subalpine vegetation in western Montana, using Landsat imagery; a computer-assisted, multi-spectral analysis system; and multiple-level, ground-truthing to inventory grizzly bear habitat.

Simple remote sensing techniques involving small aircraft are also useful. For example, good success in mapping tundra-vegetation types has been reported for false-color, infrared photography and simple hand-held, 35 mm cameras in fixed-wing aircraft (Holt 1980). Hesjedal and Larsson (1975) reported color-infrared film to be useful for the detection of eroded and overgrazed areas in Fennoscandian alpine regions, but recommended use of stereo-panchromatic photography as most cost-effective for generalized alpine surveys.

Use of stereoscopic pairs of medium- to large-scale imagery is helpful for raptor nesting habitat surveys. Some habitat features such as pingos are easily mapped from small-scale aerial photographs (Sims 1983).

Sims (1983) used large-scale, color-infrared, 70-mm aerial photography to map lichen types which revealed reindeer winter range types and carrying capacities on the Tuktoyaktuk Peninsula, Canada. Microdensitometric readings on the original film were diagnostic for areas with over 5% lichen cover. About 81% of sample sites were correctly classified.

Inventory and Monitoring for Impact Assessment

The manager of wildlife and wildlife habitat in tundra systems is increasingly involved in issues and decisions involving human uses of these lands. In the arctic, exploration, development, transportation, and production of oil, gas, and mineral ores are prime examples of these land-use problems. In alpine environments, issues are frequently related to intensive recreational use, livestock use, or mineral development. Thus this chapter places considerable emphasis on inventory and monitoring techniques that have had demonstrable applications in such management situations.

Surface disturbance and alteration of permafrost regime have clearly had undesirable aesthetic effects in arctic areas, as well as caused localized erosion problems. The long-term ecological consequences of such changes have been less clear-cut.

Nevertheless, for purposes of planning and inventory before proposed developments in the arctic, mapping of permafrost temperature, depth, moisture content, and protective vegetative cover have received paramount attention (Linell and Tedrow 1981). Similarly, monitoring efforts have often focused on changes in permafrost status and the overlying insulating vegetation (Brown et al. 1978). The fragility or sensitivity to damaged tundra areas is directly proportional to the ice content of the permafrost layer and to the mean annual ground temperature (Ives 1970), as well as to the insulative qualities of the surface cover. The ability to predict such sensitivity is now good. A monitoring program may track the success of stipulations relating to surface disturbance or recovery programs necessitated by unavoidable disturbance (Hok 1969, 1971; van Cleve 1977; Brown and Berg 1980).

During the major monitoring effort associated with construction of the Trans-Alaska Pipeline System, terrain along the corridor was classified into 12 wildlife habitat types. Of these, four (subalpine, alpine tundra, tussock tundra, and wet-meadow tundra) are clearly associated with or are subcategories of tundra. Three others (wetlands, riparian willow, and unvegetated floodplains) frequently occur as islands or narrow strips within tundra habitats. A panel of biologists gave independent ratings for the relative quality of these wildlife habitats, weighing the importance of 24 wildlife groups (mostly taxa at the family level) equally. Based on this relatively crude evaluation process, wet-meadow tundra and wetlands received the highest quality ratings. Riparian willow and tussock tundra were rated high to moderate. The alpine and subalpine types were rated low-moderate. A comparison of preconstruction and post-construction imagery (aerial photography) revealed that 12,709 ha (31,403 a.) of wildlife habitat were altered or destroyed during this major project. Nearly half of these lands were in high quality wetlands and wet-meadow tundra habitats. However, the greatest deviation from impacts predicted in the environmental impact statement (EIS) was in the land altered by construction material sites. The EIS predicted that the disturbance for material (primarily gravel) sites would be about 2,400 ha (6,000 a.) compared with the actual figure of nearly 4,800 ha (12,000 a.), as determined in this monitoring study (Pamplin 1979).

Because of the rapid succession of seasonal changes in tundra areas and the importance of these events to phenology, animal abundance, and sensitivity, it is important that the biologist prepare preliminary charts of these events. Freezing over of lakes, rivers, and coastal lagoons; the timing of critical ice depths; establishment of permanent winter snow cover; and rate of spring ablation are all events critical to planning inventories and environmental assessments. These events also constitute essential information for any environmental impact analysis (U.S. Fish and Wildlife Service 1982; Lent 1985).

In what is certainly the most elaborate mapping project undertaken for a tundra area and perhaps one of the most elaborate done anywhere, Walker et al. (1980) produced a geobotanical atlas of the Prudhoe Bay region in Alaska. Among the many maps are ones showing relative sensitivity of areas to oil spills and sensitivity to damage by vehicles. Also shown are lichen cover, breeding bird density, and the thickness of the active layer (layer subject to seasonal freezing and thawing). One of the more use-

ful maps, an oil spill sensitivity map and the procedures for its production, is described in detail in Walker et al. 1978. They were able to demonstrate great differences in the sensitivity of various plant communities to either diesel or crude oils by measuring live cover on 1-m^2 (10.9-ft^2) quadrats before and 1 year after experimental "spills." These map types are useful to those who must assess and inventory wildlife habitats and who are involved in planning for tundra areas in relation to potential impacts on wildlife.

The production of an atlas like that of Walker et al. (1980) is beyond the budget of most land managers. Furthermore, many of the methodologies used in producing the maps are not described in detail and the reader must refer to the references cited in the atlas.

Sensitivities of alpine tundra areas to human impacts are also well-documented by Willard and Marr (1971). Using sample species cover measures, they monitored the disturbance and recovery of alpine vegetation. In general they reported extremely slow recovery rates; in some instances no recovery had occurred after 4 years of protection, based on total cover and species composition measures. For *Kobresia* sp. meadows it was estimated that damage to the turf caused such severe erosion and loss of the thin humus-enriched horizons that hundreds of years might be necessary to restore the original climax system.

Bell and Bliss (1973) used 10x50 cm (4x20 in.) clipping plots and line intercept sampling of plant cover to measure recovery rates of alpine plant communities after human trampling. Dry tundra and scree slopes were most fragile and slowest to recover. Recovery rates were significantly more rapid in meadows and snowbed communities. They also measured rates of downslope movement as indicators of disturbance.

Snow Cover and Tundra Habitats

Any survey or inventory of winter habitats important to wildlife must include the collection and analysis of information on snow cover if it is to provide the manager with a proper assessment of carrying capacity, relative importance of various subareas, and temporal patterns of use. In their simplest form, inventories of snow cover may be limited only to recording the presence or absence and the timing of accumulation and ablation. Obviously, data on depth or thickness greatly increase the value of a survey. Data on density, hardness, ice, crust layers, and patterns of drifting or distribution in relation to topography are also desirable.

Pruitt (1959) was the first in North America to employ extensive aerial surveys and snow measurements to relate snow-cover characteristics to caribou movements and distribution. The study area for his classic investigation of migratory caribou ecology lay in the taiga, with only a small portion in the tundra zone. Nevertheless, the concepts and techniques he pioneered are applicable to both zones.

Pruitt made snow measurements using a set of standard snow instruments developed and adopted by the National Research Council of Canada (Klein et al. 1950). With these instruments, several measures of snow-cover morphology may be made, of which thickness, density, and hardness are usually considered most pertinent for ecological investigations. Richens and Madden (1973) reported on modifications to these instruments to make them more suitable for wildlife biologists.

Other workers (LaPerriere and Lent 1977; Lent and Knutsen 1971; Skogland 1978; Brooks and Collins 1985) carried out snow surveys using the Ramsonde penetrometer (Figure 5). The penetrometer was developed in the European Alps for avalanche studies and is most suitable for use with dense, windblown snow with complex thin crusts and ice layers, such as is typical of alpine and some tundra environments. It measures the force required to penetrate a given layer from above.

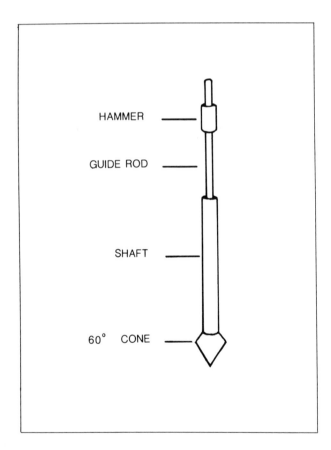

Figure 5. Schematic representation of Ramsonde penetrometer.

Pruitt's studies and those of later investigators working with barren-ground caribou (LaPerriere and Lent 1977) and mountain reindeer (Skogland 1978) have confirmed the preference of winter ranges with relatively low depths, densities, and hardnesses. Musk-oxen have shown even stronger selection for such winter ranges (Lent and Knutsen 1971). For musk-oxen, it has been shown repeatedly that an understanding and knowledge of the prevalence of crusts, ice layers, and groundfast ice on winter ranges is critical to proper habitat evaluation (Vibe 1967; Lent and Knutsen 1971; Thomas et al. 1981).

Miller et al. (1982) combined surveys of caribou winter trails and feeding sites with surveys of snow cover and ice conditions with subsequent vegetation sampling. Vegetation was recorded in summer as percentage frequency of occurrence in quadrats at the feeding sites and at points away from the feeding sites. This investigation showed clearly that several range types with desirable forage species were being underutilized because of difficulty of access. Winter feeding was directed primarily at those poor forage species that were exposed and directly available. Similarly, Gaare and Skogland (1975) concluded that only 25% of the potential winter forage on Norwegian alpine reindeer ranges was actually available for consumption. Thus, summer-only inventories of winter ranges can greatly exaggerate the winter range carrying capacities. Brooks and Collins (1985) reported on snow survey methods to assess forage availability.

Although the presence of a deep, dense snow cover may restrict or prevent winter use of certain tundra ranges by ungulates, it may also restrict use by other species, such as wolves (*Canis lupus*), wolverine, and ptarmigan. The same thick snow cover may provide protection from the abrasive, desiccating actions of winter winds and windblown snow. This "subnivean" environment is relatively warm, moist, and stable and supports small mammals and invertebrates. Special techniques for studying this environment were described by Schmidt (1984).

The best lichen growths on reindeer ranges are associated with moderately deep snow cover because of the protection and the spring moisture provided. Snow accumulations in streambeds and other depressions provide specialized, critical habitats for numerous species by protecting tundra shrubs from winter damage. The vegetative associations of these snowbeds in turn support some specialized wildlife species (for example, the singing vole [*Microtus miurus*]) and provide high quality late summer forage for certain herbivores after other forage plants have gone to senescence. In a detailed study of an alpine area, Thorn (1982) mapped and inventoried the distribution of the pocket gopher (*Thamomys talpoides*) and the distribution of related plant communities. He found that the plant communities were most highly correlated with the mean duration and mean winter depth of the snowpack.

OTHER SPECIAL CONSIDERATIONS FOR WILDLIFE MANAGEMENT IN THE ARCTIC

The low primary production rates for vascular plants in tundra communities cannot be emphasized too strongly. Annual net production estimates between 50 and 500 g/m^2 (2.1 and 21.0 oz/yd^2) are typical. Lichens and mosses may add 200 g/m^2 (8.4 oz/yd^2) to these figures. Furthermore, in both arctic and alpine environments, the ratio of belowground to aboveground biomass for vascular plants is extremely high in comparison with temperate zone communities; values as high as 30:1 have been reported (Wielgolaski 1975).

Not only are animal populations constrained, directly or indirectly, by this low primary production but many wildlife populations in the arctic are particularly difficult to inventory or monitor because their numbers display extreme fluctuations under natural conditions. Population peaks can markedly alter vegetation and other habitat features in some instances, leading to declines and completion of a population cycle.

Willow ptarmingan in dry tundra area.

The brown lemming (*Lemmus sibiricus*) is the classic example of a cyclic species with extreme fluctuations in numbers. In identical trapping efforts for over a decade from less than l/ha (2.5/a.) to highs in 2 years when it reached about 200/ha (500/a.) in the wet tundra of coastal Alaska, density of this species has varied. Even in tussock tundra the cyclic variations can be pronounced. Pruitt (1966) described variation of about 700% in biomass of small mammals trapped on the same plots over 3 years of study.

Certain predatory birds that are closely tied to small mammal numbers, such as pomarine jaegers (*Stercorarius pomarinus*) and snowy owls, may be absent over large areas during years of low numbers of small mammals. The implications of such extreme fluctuations for the design of monitoring systems are obvious: baseline conditions are difficult if not impossible to establish, and relating population change to casual management factors is also an often impossible task.

Clumping phenomena also complicate inventory and monitoring efforts. As noted earlier, even so-called resident species may be highly mobile in arctic tundra regions. Arctic foxes may travel hundreds of miles, deserting previous denning areas (Bannikov 1970). Ptarmigan may coalesce by the thousands in certain favorable river valleys in winter but disperse widely over hundreds of square miles of upland tundra in summer (Irving et al. 1967; NPR-A Task Force 1979). Caribou may go several years without making significant use of certain winter ranges. Then, for reasons yet unknown, they may converge in the thousands on those same wintering areas for several successive years.

Not only does such clumping, erratic distribution patterns and population fluctuations make it difficult to measure natural baselines by which man's influences can be determined, they also make it difficult to apply concepts of sustained yield for either population or habitat management (Beddington and May 1977). Sustained stability is rare and generally unachievable as a management goal in arctic environments.

Dunbar (1973) stated the problem in somewhat different terms by pointing out that arctic systems show great instability on small geographic scales, but overall stability on a large geographic scale. Thus, large expanses are necessary for recovery from either natural or man-made perturbations. Dunbar (1973:180) sums this up succinctly: "Arctic systems must have space. They must also have time." The latter statement is a reference to the slow recovery rates of these systems following stresses. Dunbar considered arctic lakes, because of their slow turnover rates and because they are often isolated (that is, lacking the possibilities for rapid restoration from a broader system), as the most vulnerable parts of arctic systems. Migratory shorebirds and waterfowl are a principal class of consumers dependent in large part on these lakes and ponds and their relatively productive invertebrate populations and emergent vegetation. They are thus vulnerable because of their ties to the aquatic system. This localized vulnerability is usually compensable because of the broad spatial distribution of the populations. Critical vulnerabilities occur whenever major portions of populations exist in concentrations (as with the molting brant in the Teshekpuk Lake area of Alaska) or as isolated clumps with little interchange (as with snow goose colonies). Snow goose nesting colonies represent situations analogous to islands or to isolated lakes. Because of the strong traditions tying each breeding group with a specific location, they function as isolated units not readily restored by inputs from the broader system.

CONCLUSION

Tundra habitats are dominated by low herbaceous growth forms; shrubs are important components in restricted areas, and lichens and mosses are relatively important components in comparison with other major habitat types. These arctic and alpine habitats present many unique ecological attributes for the wildlife manager to consider in inventory, monitoring, and assessment work. These include low productivity, high degree of annual variability, short growing season, and habitat patchiness. Migratory species are relatively large components of the faunas. The short season for conventional field work and the rapid phenological changes during that season present special challenges.

A major limitation to the design of ecologically based monitoring systems in arctic and alpine habitats is the lack of understanding of successional processes and stages.

The distribution, duration, depth, and physical attributes of snow cover are of particular importance in tundra habitats and contiguous boreal and alpine areas. Special techniques are available to describe and measure these elements of wildlife habitats. Distribution and physical attributes of permafrost and frost phenomena are also of special concern in tundra areas.

The immense geographic scale of arctic tundra areas and the unusually great costs in undertaking field work there leads to special emphasis on the use of remote sensing techniques, especially those employing satellite-borne sensors. Such techniques are generally less useful in alpine areas, but small-scale aerial photography has had several applications. Alpine areas present special problems because of the frequent existence of small habitat units and isolated populations.

Peter Lent

Arctic fox.

LITERATURE CITED

ACEVEDO, D., W. WALKER, L. GAYDOS, and J. WRAY. 1982. Vegetation and land cover, Arctic National Wildlife Refuge, Coastal Plain, Alaska. U.S. Geological Survey Map 1-1443. Misc. Investigations Ser. 1 sheet.

ANDERSON, J.G., C.H. RACINE, and H.R. MELCHIOR. 1974. Preliminary vegetation map of the Espenberg Peninsula, Alaska, based on an Earth Resources Technology Satellite image, Pages 290-310 in Melchior, H.R. ed. Final Report. Chukchi-Imuruk Survey. Coop. Park Studies Unit, Univ. of Alaska, Fairbanks. 517pp.

ANDERSON, J.H. and A.E. BELON. 1973. A new vegetation map of the western Seward Peninsula, Alaska, based on ERTS-1 imagery. No. E73-10305. NTIS. Springfield, VA. 20pp.

BANFIELD, A.W.F. 1954. Preliminary investigation of the barren-ground caribou. In two parts. Wildl. Manage. Bull. Ser. 1. 10A and 10B. Can. Dep. of Northern Affairs and Nat. Resour. 79pp. and 112pp.

BANNIKOV, A.G. 1970. Arctic fox in the U.S.S.R. Pages 121-129 in Fuller,W.A. and P.G. Kevan eds. Productivity and Conservation of Northern Circumpolar Lands. IUCN Publ. New Ser. 16. Morges, Switzerland.

BEDDINGTON, J.R. and R.M. MAY. 1977. Harvesting natural populations in a randomly fluctuating environment. Science 197:463-465.

BEE, J.W. and E.R. HALL. 1956. Mammals of northern Alaska on the Arctic Slope. Misc. Publ. 8. Mus. Nat. Hist., Univ. Kansas, Lawrence. 309pp.

BELL, K.L. and L.C. BLISS. 1973. Alpine disturbance studies: Olympic National Park. Biol. Cons. 5:25-32.

BERGMAN, R.D., R.L. HOWARD, K.F. ABRAHAM, and M.W. WELLER. 1977. Water birds and their wetland resources in relation to oil development at Storkerson Point, Alaska. Resource Publ. 129. U.S. Dep. Inter., Fish and Wildl. Serv. Washington, DC. 38pp.

BILLINGS, W.D. 1973. Arctic and alpine vegetations: similarities, differences and susceptibility to disturbance. Bio Science 23:697-704.

BLISS, L.C. 1981. Tundra biome: past and present. Pages 3-24 in Bliss, L.C., O.W. Heal, and J.J. Moore eds. Tundra Ecosystems: A Comparative Analysis. Cambridge Univ. Press, Cambridge.

BROOKS, J. and W. COLLINS. 1985. Snow cover and interpretation of vegetation habitat inventions. Pages 203-210 in LaBau, V.J. and C.L. Kerr eds. Inventorying Forest and Other Vegetation of the High Latitude and High Altitude Regions. Proc. Int. Symp. Am. For. Reg. Conf. Soc. Am. For. Washington, DC.

BROWN, J. and R.L. BERG eds. 1980. Environmental engineering and ecological baseline investigations along the Yukon River—Prudhoe Bay Haul Road. CRREL Report 80-19. Hanover, NH. 187pp.

BROWN, R.W., R.S. JOHNSTON, and K. VAN CLEVE. 1978. Rehabilitation problems in alpine and arctic regions. Pages 23-44 in Reclamation of Drastically Disturbed Land. Soil Sci. Soc. Am. Madison, WI.

COURTRIGHT, A.M. 1959. Range management and the genus Rangifer: A review of selected literature. Unpubl. M.S. Thesis, Univ. Alaska. Fairbanks. 172pp.

CRAIGHEAD, J.J., J.S. SUMNER, and G.B. SCAGGS. 1982. A definitive system for analysis of grizzly bear habitat and other wilderness resources. Wildlife-Wilderness Inst. Monogr. 1, University of Montana, Missoula. 279pp.

DERKSEN, D.V., W.D. ELDRIDGE, and M.W. WELLER. 1982. Habitat ecology of Pacific black brant and other geese moulting near Teshekpuk Lake, Alaska. Wildfowl 33:39-57.

DRISCOLL, R.R., D.L. MERKEL, D.L. RADLOFF, D.E. SNYDER, and J.S. HAGIHARA. 1983. An ecological land classification framework for the United States. U.S. Dep. Agric., For. Serv. Misc. Publ. 1439.

DUNBAR, M. 1973. Stability and fragility in arctic ecosystems. Arctic. 26:179-185.

EVERETT, K.R. 1982. Some recent trends in the physical and chemical characterization and mapping of tundra soils, Arctic Slope of Alaska. Soil Sci. 133:264-280.

FYFE, R. and R. OLENDORFF. 1976. Minimizing the danger of nesting studies to raptors and other sensitive species. Can. Wildl. Serv. Occ. Publ. 23. Ottawa, Canada. 17pp.

GAARE, E. and T. SKOGLAND. 1975. Wild reindeer food habits and range use at Hardangervidda. Pages 196-215 in Wielgolaski, F.G. ed. Fennoscandian Tundra Ecosystems. Part 2. Springer Verlag, Berlin.

GABRIEL, H.W. and S.S. TALBOT. 1984. Glossary of landscape and vegetation ecology for Alaska. BLM-Alaska Tech. Rep. 10. U.S. Dep. Inter., Bur. of Land Manage. Anchorage, AK. 137pp.

GALL, L.J. 1984. Population structure and recommendations for conservation of the narrowly endemic alpine butterfly (Boloria acronemia [Lepidoptira: Nymphalidae]). Biol. Conserv. 28:111-138.

GEORGE, T.H., W.J. STRINGER, J.E. PRESTON, W.R. FIBIEL, and P.C. SCORUP. 1977. Reindeer range inventory in western Alaska from computer-aided digital classification of LANDSAT data. 28th Alaska Science Conf. Anchorage, AK.

GREIG-SMITH, P. 1983. Quantitative plant ecology. 3rd. ed. Univ. Calif., Berkeley. 359pp.

HALL, D.K., J.P. ORMSBY, L. JOHNSON, and J. BROWN. 1980. Landsat digital analysis of the initial recovery of burned tundra at Kokolik River, Alaska. Remote Sensing of Environment 10:263-272.

HESJEDAL O. 1974. Terrestrial vertebrates. Pages 475-570 in Ives, J.D. and R.G. Barry eds. Arctic and Alpine Environments. Methuen, London.

———— and J. LARSSON. 1975. Remote sensing of vegetation in conservation of tundra landscapes. Pages 237-242 in Wielgolaski, F.E. ed. Fennoscandian Tundra Ecosystems; Part 2, Animals and Systems Analysis.

HOFFMANN, R.S. 1974. Terrestrial vertebrates. Pages 475-570 in Ives, J.D. and R.G. Barry, eds. Arctic and Alpine Environments. Methven, London.

———— 1984. Small mammals in winter. The effects of altitude, latitude and geographic history. Pages 9-23 in Merritt, J.E. ed. Winter Ecology of Small Mammals. Carnegie Mus. Spec. Publ. 10.

HOK, J. R. 1969. A reconnaissance of tractor trails and related phenomena on the North Slope of Alaska. Unpubl. U.S. Dep. Inter., Bur. of Land Manage. Anchorage, AK.

HOLT S. 1971. Some effects of vehicle operation on Alaska arctic tundra. M.S. Thesis, Univ. of Alaska, Fairbanks. 85pp.

———— 1980. Vegetation patterns and effects of grazing on caribou ranges in the Sondre Stromfford area, West Greenland. Pages 57-63 in Reimers, E., E. Gaare, S. Skjenneberg eds. Proc. 2nd Int. Reindeer/Caribou Symp. Roros, Norway.

IRVING, L., G.C. WEST, L.J. PEYTON, and S. PANEAK. 1967. Migration of willow ptarmigan in arctic Alaska. Arctic 20:77-85.

IVES, J.D. 1970. Arctic tundra: how fragile? A geomorphologist's point of view. Pages 39-42 in Hare, E.K. ed. The Tundra Environment. Royal Soc. Canada. Univ. Toronto Press, Toronto.

JENKINS, J.F. and D.H. ASHTON. 1970. Productivity studies on Macquarie Island vegetation. Pages 851-863 in Holdgate, M.W. ed. Antarctic Ecol., Vol. 2. Academic Press, London.

KESSEL, B. and G.B. SCHALLER. 1960. Birds of the upper Sheenjek Valley, Northeastern Alaska. Biol. Pap., Univ. Alaska, Fairbanks. 4:1-59.

KING, J.G. 1970. The swans and geese of Alaska's arctic slope. Wildfowl. 21:11-17.

KING, R. 1979. Results of serial surveys of migratory birds on NPR-A in 1977 and 1978. Pages 187-226 in Lent, P.C. ed. Studies of Selected Wildlife and Fish and their Use of Habitats on and Adjacent to the National Petroleum Reserve—Alaska—1977-1978. Field Study Rep. 3. U.S. Dep. Inter., Fish and Wildl. Serv. Anchorage, AK.

KLEIN, G.J., D.C. Pearce, and L.W. Gold. 1950. Method of measuring the significant characteristics of a snow cover. Nat. Res. Coun. Can. Tech. Mem. 18. 56pp.

LaPERRIERE, A.J. 1978. Use of Landsat imagery for wildlife habitat mapping in northeastern and east-central Alaska. Final Report. NASA Contract NAS520915. NTIS. Springfield, VA. 36pp.

——— and P.C. LENT. 1977. Caribou feeding sites in relation to snow characteristics in northeastern Alaska. Arctic. 30:101-108.

LENT, P.C. 1980. Synoptic snowmelt patterns in arctic Alaska in relation to caribou habitat use. Pages 71-76 in Reimers, E., E. Gaare, S. Skjenneberg eds. Proc. Second Int. Reindeer/Caribou Symp. Roros, Norway. Direktoratet for Vilt of Verskvannsfisk, Trondheim.

——— 1985. Cold region vegetation information needs from the perspective of wildlife and fisheries. Pages 20-27 in LaBau, V.J. and C.L. Kerr eds. Inventorying Forest and Other Vegetation of the High Latitude and High Altitude Regions. Proc. Int. Symp. Am. For. Reg. Conf., Soc. Am. For. Washington, DC.

——— and D. KNUTSEN. 1971. Musk-ox and snow cover on Nunivak Island, Alaska. Pages 50-62 in Haugen, A. ed. Proc. Snow and Ice in Relation to Wildlife and Recreation Symp. Iowa State Univ., Ames.

——— and A.J. LaPERRIERE. 1974. Applications of ERTS imagery to the study of caribou movements and winter habitat. Final Rep. NASA Contract NAS521833. NTIS. Springfield, VA. 50pp.

LEWIS, M.E. 1970. Alpine rangelands of the Uinta Mountains, Ashley and Wasatch National Forests. U.S. Dep. Agric., For. Serv., Reg. 4. Ogden, UT. 75pp.

LINELL, K.A. and J.C.F. TEDROW. 1981. Soil and permafrost surveys in the Arctic. Clarendon Press, Oxford. 279pp.

MCKENDRICK, J.D. 1981. Responses of arctic tundra to intensive musk-ox grazing. Agroborealis 13:49-55.

MILLER, F.L., E.J. EDMONDS, and A. GUNN. 1982. Foraging behaviour of Peary caribou in response to springtime snow and ice conditions. Canadian Wildl. Serv. Occ. Pap. 48. 41pp.

MOITORET, C.S., P.A. MILLER, R.M. OATES, and M.A. MASTELLER. 1985. Terrestrial bird populations and habitat use on coastal plain tundra of the Arctic National Wildlife Refuge. Pages 362-446 in 1984 Update Report, Arctic National Wildlife Refuge Coastal Plain Assessment. U.S. Dep. Inter., Fish and Wildl. Serv. Anchorage, AK.

NODLER, F.A., A.J. LaPERRIERE, and D.R. KLEIN. 1978. Vegetation type mapping in northwestern Alaska in relation to caribou and reindeer range potentials. Alaska Coop. Wildlife Research Unit Spec. Rep. 2. Univ. of Alaska, Fairbanks. 33pp.

NPR-A (National Petroleum Reserve—Alaska) Task Force. 1978. Fish and Wildlife resources. Values and Resource Analysis. Section 6, Vol. 3, Study Rep. 2. U.S. Dep. Inter. 224pp.

——— 1979. Ecological Profile. National Petroleum Reserve in Alaska. Study Rep. 4. U.S. Dep. Inter.

OWENSBY, C.E. 1973. Modified step-point system for botanical composition and basal cover estimates. J. Range Manage. 26:302-303.

PALMER, L.J. 1926. Progress of reindeer grazing investigations in Alaska. U.S. Dep. Agric. Bull. 1423. 37pp.

PAMPLIN, W.L. 1979. Construction-related impacts of the Trans-Alaska Pipeline System on terrestrial wildlife habitats. Special Report 24, Joint State Federal Fish and Wildlife Advisory Team. U.S. Dep. Inter., Fish and Wildl. Serv. Anchorage, AK. 132pp.

PEGAU, R.E. 1968. Reindeer range appraisal in Alaska. Arctic 21:255-259.

——— 1970. Effect of reindeer trampling and grazing on lichens. J. Range Manage. 23:95-97.

PEWE, T. 1983. Alpine permafrost in the contiguous United States: A review. Arctic and Alpine Research 15:145-156.

PITELKA, F.A. 1979. An avi-faunal review for the Barrow region and North Slope of Arctic Alaska. Arctic and Alpine Research 6:161-184.

PRICE, L.W. 1981. Mountains and Man. Univ. of Calif. Press, Berkeley. 506pp.

PRUITT, W.O., Jr. 1959. Snow as a factor in the winter ecology of barren-ground caribou. Arctic. 12:159-179.

——— 1966. Ecology of terrestrial mammals. Pages 519-564 in Environment of the Cape Thompson Region, Northwest Alaska. U.S. Atomic Energy Commission. U.S. Govt. Print. Off.

——— 1978. Boreal Ecology. Edward Arnold Publ. Ltd. London. iv + 73pp.

RACINE, C.H. 1979. The 1977 tundra fires in the Seward Peninsula, Alaska: effects and initial revegetation. BLM-Alaska Technical Report 4. U.S. Dep. Inter., Bur. Land Manage. Anchorage, AK. 51pp.

REEVES, H.M., F.G. COACH, AND R.E. MUNRO. 1976. Monitoring arctic habitat and goose production by satellite imagery. J. Wildl. Manage. 40:532-541.

REYNOLDS, H.V., J. CURATOLO, and R. QUIMBY. 1976. Denning ecology of grizzly bears in northeastern Alaska. Pages 403-409 in Pelton, M.J., J.W., Lentfer, and E. Folk eds. Bears - their biology and Management. IUCN New Series 40. Morges, Switzerland.

RICHENS, V.B. and C.G. MADDEN. 1973. An improved snow study kit. J. Wildl. Manage. 37:109-113.

RITCHIE, R. 1979. A survey of cliff-nesting raptors and their habitats. Pages 313-336 in Lent, P.C. ed. Studies of Selected Wildlife and Fish Populations and their Use of Habitats on and Adjacent to NPR-A. 1977-1978. U.S. Dep. Inter., Fish and Wildl. Serv. Anchorage, AK.

SCHMIDT, W.D. 1984. Materials and methods of subnivean sampling. Pages 25-32 in Merritt, J.E. ed. Winter Ecology of Small Mammals. Carnegie Mus. Nat. Hist. Spec. Publ. 10.

SIMS, R.A. l983. Ground-truth and large scale 70 mm aerial photographs in the study of reindeer winter rangeland, Tuktoyaktuk Peninsula area, NWT. PhD. dissertation. Univ. of British Columbia, Vancouver. 178pp.

SKOGLAND, T. 1978. Characteristics of the snow cover and its relationship to wild mountain reindeer (*Rangifer tarandus tarandus L.*) feeding strategies. Arctic and Alpine Research 10:569-580.

SKUNCKE, F. 1969. Reindeer ecology and management in Sweden. Biol. Paper. Univ. Alaska, Fairbanks. 82pp.

SMITH, R.H. AND R.P. ALLEN. 1948. An aerial waterfowl reconnaissance of the far north. U.S. Dep. Inter., Fish and Wildl. Serv. Spec. Rep. 60:5-12.

TENER, J.S. 1965. Musk-oxen in Canada. Can. Wildl. Serv. Monogr. Ser. 2. Dept. of Northern Affairs and Nat. Resources. Ottawa. 166pp.

THILENIUS, J.F. 1979. Range management in the alpine zone. Pages 43-64 *in* Johnson, D.A. ed. Special Management Needs of Alpine Ecosystems. Range Science Serv. Society for Range Management, Denver, CO. 5:43-64.

THOMAS, D.C., F.L. MILLER, R.H. RUSSELL, and G.R. PARKER. 1981. The Bailey Point region and other musk-ox refugia in the Canadian Arctic: A short review. Arctic. 34:34-36.

THORN, C.E. 1982. Gopher disturbance: Its variability by Braun-Blanquet vegetation units in the Niwot Ridge alpine tundra zone, Colorado Front Range, U.S.A. Arctic and Alpine Research 14:45-51.

U.S. FISH AND WILDLIFE SERVICE. 1982. Initial report. Baseline study of the fish, wildlife and their habitats. Arctic National Wildlife Refuge coastal plain resource assessment. U.S. Fish and Wildl. Serv., Anchorage, AK. 507pp.

———. 1983-1984. Update report. Baseline study of the fish, wildlife and their habitats. Arctic National Wildlife Refuge coastal plain resource assessment. U.S. Dep. Inter., Fish and Wildl. Serv. Anchorage, Alaska.

613pp.

VAN CLEVE, K. 1977. Recovery of disturbed tundra and taiga surfaces in Alaska. Pages 422-455 *in* Cairns, J., K.L. Dickson, and E. Herricks eds. Proc. of an Int. Symp. on the Recovery of Damaged Ecosystems. Virginia Polytechnic Inst. and Univ. Blacksburg, VA.

VIBE, C. 1967. Arctic animals in relation to climatic fluctuations. Meddelelser om Gronland 170(5):1-227.

VIERECK, L.A. and C.T. DYRNESS. 1980. A preliminary classification system for vegetation of Alaska. U.S. Dep. of Agric., For. Serv. General Tech. Rep., PNW-106.

———, C.T. DYRNESS, and A.R. BATTEN. 1982. Revision of preliminary classification for vegetation of Alaska. Inst. North. Forestry, Univ. Alaska, Fairbanks. 72pp.

WALKER, D.A., K.R. EVERETT, P.J. WEBBER, and J. BROWN. 1980. Geo-botanical atlas of the Prudhoe Bay Region, Alaska. CRREL Report 80-14. Cold Regions Research and Engineering Laboratory. Hanover, NH. 69pp.

———, P.J. WEBBER, K.R. EVERETT, and J. BROWN. 1978. Effects of crude and diesel oil spills on plant communities at Prudhoe Bay, Alaska, and the derivation of oil spill sensitivity maps. Arctic 31:242-258.

WIELGOLASKI, F.E. 1975. Productivity of tundra ecosystems. Pages 1-12 *in* Productivity of World Ecosystems. Proc. of a Symposium. National Academy of Sciences. Washington, DC.

WILLARD, B.E. and W. MARR. 1971. Recovery of alpine tundra under protection after damage by human activities in the Rocky Mountains of Colorado. Biol. Cons. 3:181-190.

WILLIAMSON, F.S.L., M.C. THOMPSON, and J.Q. HINES. l966. Avi-faunal investigations. Pages 437-480 *in* Wilimovsky, N.J. and J.N. Wolfe eds. Environment of the Cape Thompson Region, Alaska. U.S. Atomic Energy Comm. Washington, DC.

ZWINGER, A.H. and B.E. WILLARD. l972. Land above the trees: a guide to American alpine tundra. Harper and Row, New York, NY. 489pp.

9

RIPARIAN HABITAT

Robert D. Ohmart and Bertin W. Anderson

Center for Environmental Studies
Arizona State University
Phoenix, AZ 85281

Editor's Note: This chapter is the first of two on wetland habitats. These habitats are extremely important, not only because of their high inherent wildlife value, but also because of their effects on the adjacent upland and aquatic areas and their associated biota. This chapter covers wetland areas associated with running water, while the following chapter on marshes covers areas of standing water. These are not universally accepted definitions but provide a convenient breakdown for this book. The length of this chapter reflects the high importance of and current interest in riparian areas. However, much still needs to be learned about these areas, and a critical need exists for better management of them. Inventorying and monitoring riparian habitats will be a central part of such efforts.

INTRODUCTION

One of the most important assignments in the career of a wildlife biologist is to monitor or inventory riparian ecosystems. Only a decade ago few people, including wildlife biologists, had any appreciation or knowledge of these very limited and highly valuable wildlife habitats. Even today, books on wildlife habitats or plant communities seldom separate riparian ecosystems from adjacent upland plant communities. Before undertaking an assignment, we recommend obtaining copies of four riparian symposiums (Johnson and Jones [1977]; Johnson and McCormick [1978]; Warner and Hendrix [1984]; and Johnson et al. [1985]) to use as references.

Riparian as an adjective is defined as "relating to or living or located on the bank of a natural watercourse (as a river) or sometimes of a lake or a tidewater" (Webster's New Collegiate Dictionary 1979:991). To many, riparian is synonymous with wetland, but wetland is often defined as consisting primarily of emergent or marsh communities, which are not discussed in this chapter. (See Chapters 10, 11, and 12 for treatment of marshes, streams, and lakes, respectively.) For this chapter, which addresses only terrestrial riparian ecosystems, we will adhere to the following definition: "A riparian association of any kind [excluding marshes] is one which is in or adjacent to drainageways and/or their floodplains and which is further characterized by species and/or life-forms different than that of the immediately surrounding non-riparian climax" (Lowe 1964:62). This definition includes plant communities along permanently flowing or intermittent drainages. Some of these drainages may not flow for many years or even in our lifetime, but they are riparian communities if the plant species along these drainages are different from those of the adjacent upland.

Obligate or riparian-dependent species such as cottonwoods (*Populus* sp.) and willows (*Salix* sp.)

are frequently referred to in the literature as phreatophytes, referring to vegetation species having their roots in perennial ground water or in the capillary fringe above a water table. Most of these species transpire large quantities of water, and water managers believe that if the streamside vegetation is removed, this water will be saved or remain in the aquifer.

In past water management practices, thousands of acres of riparian vegetation have been removed to prevent this wicking of water into the atmosphere. For example, between 1967 and 1971, about 21,600 ha (54,000 a.) of riparian vegetation was removed along the Pecos River in New Mexico to save water. Although about 18,800 ha (47,000 a.) of the originally cleared area has remained cleared since 1971 (U.S. Department of Interior, Bureau of Reclamation 1979), preliminary results indicate that the amount of water saved is probably insignificant. Riparian ecosystems do not stand alone; they are fed by watersheds, which when destroyed, also destroy the riparian ecosystem.

Nutrients, water, and detrital materials are transported into the riparian system from its watershed.

A healthy watershed generally indicates a healthy riparian system. Degraded watersheds produce high surface runoff carrying valuable soil into the stream, which reduces productivity of both the aquatic and terrestrial portions of the system. As any competent hydrologist knows, to reduce the volume and severity of floods, one must start with the point source— the watersheds; other efforts are "treating symptoms and not the disease."

The importance of western riparian habitats to humans has long been recognized, as indicated by the early settlement patterns of native North Americans and Europeans. During drought periods, settlements that were not near permanent water sources were forced to relocate; many died in the process. Riparian habitats provided and still provide water, rich fertile soils for agriculture, lush forage for domestic livestock, recreation, and home sites. Their importance is amplified in the arid western states, but is also obvious in the East where riparian areas are termed bottomland hardwood habitats.

Riparian habitats in the West are very limited when compared to the amount of acreage they constitute versus upland habitats. Riparian ecosystems

Degraded riparian area.

when compared with upland habitats may total up to 0.5% of the landscape or < 0.1%. Because of the small and finite nature of riparian habitats, their vitalness to human survival in arid environments, their recreational values, and their high fishery and wildlife values, they should receive critical concern in all land-planning and management efforts. For example, Johnson (1978) reported that 64 wildlife species presently listed as endangered, and 47 more species being considered for listing, are dependent on riparian habitats. In the past, riparian habitats have been treated as sewage transport systems and refuse landfill sites and have been subjected to numerous other types of habitat degradation.

The treatment of riparian habitats in the past and their current condition is alarming, which amplifies the need to pay special management concern to these ecosystems. For example, estimates are that 70-90% of the natural riparian ecosystems in the U.S. have been lost to human activities (U.S. Council on Environmental Quality 1978; Warner 1979a). Regional losses in these ecosystems have been estimated to exceed 98% in the Sacramento Valley in California (Smith 1977) and 95% in Arizona (Warner 1979b). Johnson and Carothers (1981) estimated

that in the Rocky Mountains/Great Plains region, 90-95% of the cottonwood-willow riparian ecosystems of the plains and lower foothills have been lost. Possibly as much as 80% of the remaining riparian ecosystems in the U.S. (both privately and publicly owned) are in unsatisfactory condition and are dominated by human activities (Almand and Krohn 1978; Warner 1979b). In the West, these ecosystems support a disproportionately greater number of wildlife species than their upland counterparts.

Public support for wildlife and its habitat needs must be interpreted with caution. Kellert (1980), reporting on a nationwide opinion poll that focused on land-use allocations for wildlife, showed that many Americans were willing to make economic sacrifices in commodity resource production for endangered nongame species and certain featured big game species. Sixty percent agreed that livestock grazing on public lands should be limited if it destroyed vegetation used by wildlife, even if it resulted in higher meat prices; 34% disagreed. Over 75% believed that logging should be done in a manner to enhance wildlife even if lumber and paper prices rose. Conversely, almost 50% believed that natural resources must be developed, even if it

Same riparian area, 10-years later.

meant less wilderness and lowered wildlife populations. These results indicate public awareness for the needs of wildlife and management changes that need to be enacted on public lands to maximize natural resource values. The public at large generally supports the concept of multiple-use management on public lands, but interest groups strongly disagree on specific issues.

Sports enthusiasts in eastern Oregon favorably responded to improved grazing management practices (Megank and Gibbs 1979). Almost 70% of anglers surveyed stated that their recreation experiences would be reduced by management practices that further degraded riparian systems. Their reaction to fences was positive in that it represented better livestock control. Hunters thought that management that improved forage production for livestock would also help deer and elk.

Many values of riparian habitats to our society, seldom considered by terrestrial wildlife biologists, should be factored in as sound arguments toward managing these systems in their natural state. The riparian vegetation adjacent to streams or even large rivers is extremely important as an energy source to the aquatic organisms (see Streams, Chapter 11). In small headwater streams, 99% of the energy for heterotrophic organisms comes from the vegetation along the stream, whereas only 1% comes from photosynthesizing autotrophs (Cummins 1974). In large river systems, such as the Missouri River, as much as 54% of the organic matter consumed by fish is of terrestrial origin (Benner in Kennedy 1977). A factor that has not, to our knowledge, been seriously considered by fishery biologists is the quality of the organic input or species composition of the streamside vegetation. Trees may be desirable as shade to prevent large fluctuations in water temperature, but some tree species will ultimately prove more important as energy input sources than others, e.g., cottonwood and willow leaves and other tree parts are probably of more value to aquatic detritivores than leaves and other parts of the exotic salt cedar (*Tamarix chinensis*). The former would certainly impose less change on total dissolved solids and water chemistry than the latter. Biologists must manage for healthy streamside vegetation and, as knowledge progresses, some efforts should be directed toward encouraging establishment of tree species that have higher nutrient input value to the aquatic fauna. This approach toward managing terrestrial vertebrates is already underway along large river systems.

Streamside vegetation is very important in determining the structure and function of stream ecosystems (Knight and Bottorff 1984). Mahoney and Erman (1984) found that riparian vegetation is an important source of food to stream organisms, provides shade over small-order streams, and serves to stabilize banks in preventing excessive sedimentation and intercepting pollutants. Asmussen et al. (1977) reported that vegetation buffer strips were very effective in reducing pollution from agricultural chemicals. Karr and Schlosser (1977, 1978) reported that proper management of streamside vegetation and the channel may substantially improve water quality in agricultural watersheds. Corbett and Lynch (1985) stressed the importance of streamside zones in water-quality management for municipal water supplies. Haupt (1959) presented guidelines for buffer strip widths in road-building projects, and Benoit (1978) similarly presented guidelines for timber harvest operations in Oregon. Treating water to bring it to potable standards is expensive; stopping pollution at its source and managing for productive riparian vegetation will significantly reduce these costs. Finally, riparian vegetation can be important in flood-control efforts (Chaimson 1984) by reducing water velocity and its erosive energy during flood stage (Li and Shen 1973). The vegetation may also reduce streambank damage from ice, log debris, and animal trampling (Platts 1979; Swanson et al. 1982); armor levees; and prevent channel changes during high flows.

Importance of riparian systems to wildlife has not been quantified or demonstrated to any convincing extent until the past 15 years. The efforts of Carothers et al. (1974) to quantify avian densities in cottonwood habitats along the Verde River in central Arizona and those of Ohmart and Anderson (1974) along the lower Colorado River were beginnings. A riparian symposium (Johnson and Jones 1977; Hehnke and Stone 1978; Thomas et al. 1979) along with others were fruitful in focusing attention on these ecosystems. These studies and subsequent ones indicated that some of the highest densities of breeding birds in North America were found in riparian habitats, and more than 60% of the vertebrates in the arid Southwest were obligate to this ecosystem (see Ohmart and Anderson 1982 for a review). Another 10-20% of the vertebrates were facultative users (present for a portion of the annual cycle but not fully dependent on riparian habitats) of streamside vegetation. Mosconi and Hutto (1982) reported that in western Montana, 59% of the species of land birds use riparian habitats for breeding, and 36% breed only in riparian habitats. Similarly, of the 363 species of land vertebrates in the Great Basin of southeast Oregon, 299 either directly depend on riparian habitats or utilize them more than any other habitat types (Thomas et al. 1979). Therefore, if these ecosystems were totally lost or continued to be reduced to vestiges of their original state, conceivably 60-80% of our native wildlife species could be lost in the western U.S. The Colorado River is a classic example of this, in that at least four species of birds have recently been extirpated and unless some dramatic management changes are made, another six species could be lost in the next 20 years (Hunter et al. unpubl. data).

RIPARIAN HABITAT CLASSIFICATION

Small riparian ecosystems occurring in watersheds at higher elevations eventually connect to form major drainage systems. These major drainages, such as the Green River in Wyoming, connect into larger systems, such as the Colorado River. To aid in understanding these western riparian ecosystems at different elevations, we recommend using the Life Zone concept developed by Merriam (1890), which is widely used in the West for its utilitarian value.

The Brown et al. (1979) concept for naming riparian ecosystems in Merriam's Life Zones is also widely accepted in the West because its hierarchical system for North American biomes has an evolutionary and genetically based approach. It is also digitized, which makes it computer-compatible. Importantly, it is concordant with the Life Zone concept.

Succession

In highly modified or managed rivers, such as the lower Colorado, Pecos, and Rio Grande, there is little evidence of classical succession. If an area is burned or cleared, it tends to return as trees or shrubs and remains in that state. Succession is poorly studied and understood, and it may be that riparian floodplains are so rich in nutrients and water that classical plant succession does not occur. Brady et al. (1985) presented the developmental continuum of a riparian gallery forest ranging from a nursery bar to a mature forest. Bock and Bock (1985) presented data on patterns of reproduction in a species of sycamore (*Platanus wrightii*) in southeastern Arizona.

Communities

Naming individual plant communities varies depending on the biologist mapping and sampling the communities, but is generally based on one or more dominant species (either by density or stature). For example, a cottonwood-willow community may only have 1 cottonwood for every 10 willows in a stand, but because of the size and presence of cottonwoods, it may be called a cottonwood-willow community. In another example, a community may be called honey mesquite (*Prosopis glandulosa*) although it contains mostly shrubs. What a community is called is unimportant as long as the community names and accompanying written descriptions can be interpreted by others. Laurenzi et al. (1983) presented a habitat classification system for mixed broadleaf riparian forests in the Upper Sonoran Life Zone.

Structural Types

Some riparian ecosystems may be extremely dynamic through time whereas others are relatively stable. Recognizing and classifying structural stages (young through mature stages) allows a quick assessment of the riparian ecosystem's health. If no young plant communities develop to replace the old, decadent communities of similar species composition, then animal species dependent on those communities may be lost to the fauna. Also, young plant communities may support a fauna much different from that found in a mature plant community. These structural differences (in plant community age classes and foliage layers) are very important in managing for maximum riparian productivity and vertebrate species richness.

The concept of structural classification of riparian communities is an important one and not difficult to understand if an area is envisioned as going from bare soil to supporting a mature cottonwood-willow forest; all the structural types would then be present over this continuum. Figure 1 shows the structural types in lower elevational systems; Type VI is the young or beginning community, and as it grows it passes to a V, IV, etc., until it becomes a Type I which is a mature cottonwood-willow community. In Type VI, most of the foliage volume is in the grass and shrub layers; as the community matures, a good overstory (Type II) shades out much of the understory. Type I contains overstory, midstory, and understory as some trees die opening the overstory for ingression of shorter trees, shrubs, and annuals. By dividing a continuous process into stages or types, both plant communities and structural types can be assessed together in demonstrating user-oriented impacts. However, structural complexity and mean canopy height are generally reduced where riparian systems are under heavy water management, livestock grazing, pollution, and recreational activities.

In the following example of structural types, a cottonwood-willow community was used to demonstrate Types VI (young) through I (mature). At higher elevations this community could consist of sycamores, narrow-leaf cottonwoods (*Populus angustifolia*), quaking aspen (*P. tremuloides*), or other tree species that have similar vertical and foliage density attributes as cottonwood-willow. Not all tree species form communities that have the same growth pattern as those discussed above, but their community development shows some of the same structural stages. For example, salt cedar communities generally reach maturity as structural Type II,

Figure 1. Vegetation structural types found in lower elevations.

honey mesquite as Type III, and arrowweed (*Tessaria sericea*) and other shrub communities are always Type VI. Managers may find this classification system less confusing than trying to establish a more complex and, hence, more complicated approach to recognizing structural types. Most importantly, the structural types are real to wildlife and its use of the vegetation.

In habitat discussions today of the Colorado River, managers have wanted to know the community and structural type under consideration. They can easily visualize the community and structural types, and we have provided a document that gives species richness, densities, and other wildlife use values seasonally for 3 to 5 years along with mean values. These data are available for only a few riparian ecosystems, and our approach in this chapter is to help managers initiate development in their resource management areas. The system can always be expanded and improved toward better managing these invaluable wildlife habitats.

IMPORTANT HABITAT ATTRIBUTES TO WILDLIFE

Discerning habitat attributes that are most important to wildlife is not an easy task, and reliable identification of those habitat components only comes from long-term, in-depth studies. Seasonal and annual variances of wildlife numbers are generally very high, and until a number of seasons and years have been studied, the habitat components that are truly important to wildlife may not be discernible or fully understood.

Four habitat components, not discussed in depth in this section but important to wildlife, are plant community size (number of acres), continuity of riparian habitat along the streambed, edge or ecotone, and water. The streambed has been widely discussed in island biogeography theory and in terms of habitat fracturing. The more extensive stands of a riparian forest are reduced, the less wildlife value they have for some species. As the tract gets smaller, its wildlife values diminish to the point that the forest contributes little, if any, to overall wildlife values. It probably reaches its zenith of importance in riparian habitats at lower elevations where expansive alluvial floodplains support extensive stands of continuous wildlife habitat. T.E. Martin (Arizona State University, unpubl. ms) identified area size as the primary factor accounting for variation in number of breeding pairs of birds in five of seven of his ecological groups in high-elevation, riparian habitats in central Arizona. As knowledge expands and understanding of the needs of wildlife increases, we observe that continuous areas of some particular riparian community are more than twice the value of that same community in 0.8- to 4-ha (2- to 10-a.) blocks. For example, many bird species have been lost along the Colorado River and others will be lost in the near future as island size stands of cottonwood-willow are reduced. Stands of 28 ha (70 a.) only begin to fill the needs of some bird species, allowing the presence of a few breeding pairs at best. For these reasons, habitat island size is important regardless of whether it is along small streams at high elevations or along rivers in the desert.

An example of continuous riparian habitat.

Continuity of riparian vegetation along the floodplain is extremely important to some species such as small mammals, reptiles, and amphibians. Small, discontinuous blocks may not fulfill the needs of many of these species, causing reductions in numbers and, possibly, extirpation of some populations attempting to use highly fractured riparian habitats as movement corridors. Amphibians and reptiles that need riparian habitats are extremely vulnerable to this fracturing and, as pointed out by Brode and Bury (1984), what were once continuous populations of some species in California are now isolated relict populations. Dispersal routes for pioneering individuals and gene exchange have essentially been halted because once continuous riparian habitats have been disrupted.

The edge or ecotone component may be of less concern because the very nature of riparian ecosystems or ribbons of habitat running through uplands is edge at its maximum. Some believe that riparian ecosystems are all edge, regardless of alluvial floodplain width, because the river constantly meanders across the first terrace, scouring old plant communities and depositing new soils that are revegetated

with early stage plant communities. Continuing this productive, valuable wildlife habitat as edge for wildlife should be the most important factor in good management decisions.

Water may or may not be present aboveground in riparian ecosystems. When present, it is an important component for large mammals and, to a lesser degree, small animals. Most smaller vertebrates gain adequate moisture in their diet but will drink or bathe when the opportunity arises. The primary importance of water to terrestrial wildlife, whether above or below ground, is that it supplies terrestrial vegetation with the quality and quantity needed for health and growth.

Birds

As stated earlier, habitat features most important to wildlife are very difficult to extract from data sets and virtually impossible to extract and confirm from 1- to 2-year studies. What may appear to be an important habitat component one year may not even be a significant component again in a 5- or 10-year study. Bird habitat components were derived from one large river system studied for at least 7 years with intensive monthly sampling over that time span. These data have been tested on other large desert riparian systems, including a revegetation site in which the plant community contained all of the most important habitat components except snags for nest cavities. These were added by erecting nest boxes. The revegetation site is now about 6 years old, the cottonwood trees are more than 15 m (50 ft) high, and the area is replete with the avian species that it was designed to attract. Unfortunately, the area is too small (28 ha [70 a.]) to attract and house many pairs of species that require large areas for breeding territories—again demonstrating the importance of island size effect.

Keep in mind that these habitat components were derived for birds in desert riparian systems. Although similar data in a long-term study are being collected in quaking aspen stands in Colorado (Winternitz 1973, 1976; Winternitz and Cahn 1983), to our knowledge these kinds of data do not exist for birds at higher elevations. Not all of these components may be important at higher elevations and if they are, their order of importance may also differ. These habitat components should be used with caution at higher elevations, and where supporting data are available we have included the references. Again, other and better references may be available and should be used.

Frequently, biologists need bird species lists to illustrate the importance of riparian habitats, to reference particular species, or for other reasons. A list of desert riparian species in each desert and their dependency on riparian revegetation species in each desert is presented by Ohmart and Anderson (1982). Knopf (1985) provided a list of birds observed in a 2-year study along the Front Range in Colorado.

We have found the following habitat components, in the order given, most important for entire avian communities in desert riparian areas:

1. Tree species

   a. Fremont cottonwoods (*Populus fremontii*) and Goodding willows (*Salix gooddingii*)
   b. Honey mesquite

2. Shrubs

   a. Quail bush (*Atriplex lentiformes*)
   b. Iodine bush or inkweed (*Suaeda torreyana*)

3. Mistletoe (*Phoradendron californicum*)

4. Foliage density

5. Foliage height diversity (FHD)

6. Snags

7. Patchiness (PI)

Tree Species.

Cottonwoods and Willows. This tree component was widespread along most permanent streams and rivers at lower elevations in the western U.S. before European settlers. Its widespread distribution and antiquity in western North America (Axelrod 1958) undoubtedly provided many opportunities for an evolving insectivorous avifauna.

A lush canopy provided shade, cover, and a myriad of insects. The rough, ever-sloughing bark attracts wood-boring larvae plus a number of other arthropods, which provide forage for bark-gleaning and trunk-scaling birds. The soft wood is easily excavated by woodpeckers and, when abandoned, secondary cavity-nesting species such as Lucy's warblers (*Vermivora luciae*), brown-crested flycatchers (*Myiarchus tyrannulus*), and elf owls (*Micrathene whitneyi*) have an array of vacant cavities for their nesting activities. Even in winter after leaf drop, the rough, splitting bark provides foraging opportunities for numerous bird species. In early spring the flowers, laden with pollen, are swarmed by arthropods, and wintering and migrant birds consume the pollen and insects attracted to the flowers. As gallery forests of these trees age, some die providing snags and light penetration to the forest floor. Shrubs, other trees, and annuals invade to provide patchiness that attracts other bird species.

These large (18-24 m [60-80 ft] tall and 2-3 m [6-10 ft] DBH), branching trees with their attendant insect fauna, bird life, and proximity to a stream with its aquatic life, also attract a number of wintering and breeding raptors. These birds, at the top of the food chain, find a rich and varied prey base upon which to feed.

Studies of this community type in California (Gaines 1977), Arizona (Carothers et al. 1974; Anderson and Ohmart 1984; Rice et al. 1984), New Mexico (Hubbard 1971; Hink and Ohmart 1984), and in Texas (Wauer 1977; Engel-Wilson and Ohmart 1978) attest to its wildlife value. As this community type becomes extirpated from the West Coast eastward, at least 10 bird species will be lost as well.

Robert D. Ohmart

Cottonwood-willow association.

Woodpeckers can easily excavate cavities in soft-wood trees, such as the cottonwoods.

Deciduous trees at higher elevations may be as important to birds as cottonwoods and willows are in desert riparian systems. Bull and Skovlin (1982), working in Oregon, reported that bird diversity and species composition changed with the amount of deciduous vegetation as it ranged from high (> 40%), to moderate (15-30%), to low (< 1%). Birds using deciduous vegetation in the area sampled were the only group highly dependent on this habitat component. A long-term study in quaking aspen stands in Colorado has documented the value of this deciduous tree to birds (Winternitz 1976).

A 2-year study by Knopf (1985), at elevations ranging between 1,200 and 2,750 m (3,973 and 9,022 ft), indicated that breeding birds in riparian habitats were more simplistically structured to habitat components at higher elevations than at lower elevations. He reported dramatic changes in species richness at intermediate elevations, which could indicate less structuring of avian communities at these elevations or that his study period was too short to fully document what was occurring at these elevations. At elevations above 1,909 m (6,263 ft), the importance of riparian habitat declined; the uplands contained a more diverse avifauna than the riparian areas. Further testing of these correlations are needed, but before wildlife biologists de-emphasize intermediate elevation habitats, we strongly recommend that the manager fully determine whether the wildlife values are indeed low and the potential for maximum riparian productivity on a site has been achieved.

Possibly, the entire western riparian avifauna has evolved more closely with deciduous tree species at various elevations than other habitat components. These trees provide the essentials for life, e.g., food, cover, and space for these insectivorous birds that can also obtain needed water from the riparian system. Box elder (*Acer negundo*), walnut (*Juglans major*), sycamore, narrow-leaf cottonwood, and others may be ecologically equivalent to cottonwood-willow at lower elevations. The importance of these trees to wildlife cannot be overstressed if they are true surrogates; riparian habitats should be managed to ensure healthy communities with young replacement structural types.

Honey Mesquite. This tree is deciduous in desert riparian habitats. It grows slowly and is found primarily on the highest terrace (second terrace) away from the river where channel cutting by the river seldom occurs. Again, the flowers attract wildlife, both by the pollen and the insects feeding on the flowers. The fruits or beans produced by this tree are rich in carbohydrates and are consumed by a wide range of wildlife species.

Robert D. Ohmart

Honey mesquite.

In low areas where floodwaters are trapped, colloidal materials are deposited and form heavier soils that support a mixture of shrub species, primarily quail bush, four-winged saltbush (*Atriplex canescens*), wolfberry (*Lycium* sp.), and inkweed. These shrubs provide important values to a number of wildlife species and enhance the avian productivity of the honey mesquite community.

Honey mesquite communities are also enhanced by numerous annual plants that have high seed production after a wet summer or winter. Seeds produced by these annuals are utilized by a large granivorous guild that includes white-crowned sparrows (*Zonotrichia leucophyrs*), Gambel's quail (*Callipepla gambelii*), and Brewer's sparrows (*Spizella breweri*).

white-crowned sparrow

Shrubs.

Quail Bush. In optimum growing conditions, quail bush reaches heights of 3 to 4 m (10 to 14 ft) and a single plant could cover 13 m² (140 ft²). Although an evergreen, this shrub drops leaves and stems that over the years form a thick layer of composting material. This dense shrub shades the soil to help hold moisture that in turn expedites decomposition of the litter accumulation. Ground-dwelling birds, such as quail, thrashers (*Toxostoma* sp.), and towhees (*Pipilo* sp.), find protection and productive, insect foraging areas in the decomposing litter under this shrub. Small insectivorous birds forage extensively in and among the dense stems and leaves.

When this shrub is mixed with a community of trees, such as honey mesquite or salt cedar, it greatly enhances the wildlife values of the trees. Also, it forms a monoculture where quail and other ground-dwelling bird species can attain high densities. Its seeds are important to these birds as well because the plant is a prolific seed-producing species and the seeds fall to the ground throughout the year.

Iodine Bush or Inkweed. This 0.5- to 1-m (2- to 3-ft) tall shrub is used by numerous ground-dwelling birds, but is most important to sage sparrows (*Amphispiza belli*). Wintering sage sparrows actively select habitats containing this plant or revegetated areas containing inkweed (Meents et al. 1982). Seeds and plant parts of inkweed were found in sage sparrow gizzards, but why they actually select habitats with a preponderance of inkweed is unknown.

Mistletoe.

Mistletoe is a parasite, widespread on trees and shrubs in the pea family (Leguminosae or Fabaceae). Although it can be found on many different host species, it appears to do best on honey mesquite trees. The dense clumps provide shelter for perching birds, nesting cover for breeding species, and berries for a number of frugivorous (fruit-eating) birds, especially Phainopepla (*Phainopepla nitens*; Anderson and Ohmart 1978). Although mistletoe may eventually kill some mesquite trees, its value to wildlife appears to offset its negative effects to mesquite. In healthy riparian systems, life and death are integral parts of a productive community. As mesquite trees die, they produce hardwood snags. The snags attract wood boring insects and can become potential nest sites for the ladder-backed woodpecker (*Picoides scalaris*). These snags also provide perches for hunting raptors.

Foliage Density.

Until recently, the importance of foliage density (surface area of leaves and stems/area³) or foliage height diversity could not be readily separated. In recent strip-clearing studies, foliage density was reduced by 20-40%, whereas foliage height diversity did not change. However, bird life in the area was drastically reduced (Anderson and Ohmart unpubl. ms). This seems to indicate that foliage density is more important in the higher vertical layers than foliage height diversity, as it provides better forage substrate for insect-gleaning birds, concealment from predators, and sites for nesting. Canopy and mid-canopy layers of vegetation are low quality to wildlife unless foliage density is moderate or high. It is generally believed that by increasing foliage density in each layer of vegetation, the carrying capacity of insectivorous birds is increased and new niches are added.

Foliage Height Diversity (FHD).

Foliage height diversity measures how evenly foliage is distributed among the vertical layers. A plant community with little or no foliage density in the tree canopy layer would have a lower FHD value than a similar plant community with dense foliage at the understory, midstory, and canopy levels. Thus, foliage height diversity increases when foliage density values are nearly equal among all vertical layers of vegetation.

Robert D. Ohmart

Salt cedar community.

Figure 2 shows two communities with differing height diversities; the one on the left shows low-, mid-, and upper-canopy volumes while the community on the right shows some midstory volume and a little overstory.

This habitat component is unquestionably valuable to wildlife, but less so than foliage density. Other species of trees can have height density values similar to cottonwood and willow habitat, yet not have similar species richness values and bird densities. Rice et al. (1984) examined the importance of FHD, patchiness (PI), and individual tree species to avian communities. Response of individual bird

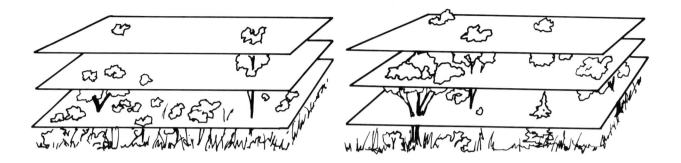

Figure 2. Two plant communities showing different foliage height diversities.

species was significantly higher with greater frequency of individual tree species than with other vegetation variables depicting structure. Although height densities correlated well with other tested habitat components, they were strengthened by adding individual tree species. Generally, it is assumed that as one adds layers of vegetation, these additional layers provide niches for additional species of birds.

Snags. Snags are extremely important to a number of species in riparian ecosystems. Many species use snags for nesting, feeding, roosting, as hunting and loafing perches, for hibernacula while overwintering, and as a moist refuge in dry summer months. Snags can be, and have been reported as, limiting to the presence and abundance of cavity-nesting birds (Haapanen 1965; Balda 1975; Conner et al. 1975; Evans and Conner 1979; Scott 1979; Mannan et al. 1980; Dickson et al. 1983). A wildlife snag symposium (Davis et al. 1983) provided a compilation of papers on this subject and should be referred to for more specific information.

Many of the above studies and others examining the importance of snags to birds have been conducted in upland habitats, but snags in riparian habitats are as limiting, if not more so, than those in upland areas and have the same effect on many primary and secondary cavity-nesting species. T.E. Martin (Arizona State University, unpubl. ms) examined the importance of snags in 13 riparian habitats where the riparian species were primarily big tooth maple (*Acer grandidentatum*), quaking aspen, and New Mexico locust (*Robinia neomexicana*), with an understory of golden pea (*Thermopsis pinetorum*) and raspberry (*Rubus strigosus*). Snags were primarily aspen and were significantly (P < 0.001) more abundant along streams on north-facing slopes than on south-facing slopes. Densities of snag-using species were greatest in snag-rich habitats, and more snag-using species were present.

Brush et al. (1983) found that this habitat component, especially softwood snags, is generally a limiting factor in heavily managed desert riparian systems. Fires, floods, and even removal of snags to protect water skiers has virtually eliminated this important component in the lower Colorado River riparian ecosystem.

Primary and secondary cavity-nesting species are vulnerable unless management is aware of their needs and places high value on ensuring large, quality snags for wildlife. Unfortunately, a prerequisite to snags is living trees; this handicap has been partly overcome and artificial snags are being excavated by some woodpeckers (Grubb et al. 1983; Peterson and Grubb 1983). Presence or absence of snags should be noted as riparian habitats and assessed for wildlife.

Snags provide essential habitat for about 85 bird species (Scott et al. 1977) that use natural cavities, excavate their own, or use holes excavated by other species. Many of these species are obligate riparian forms. In quaking aspen stands in Colorado, almost 40% of the breeding bird species using this type used nest holes, and trees containing these cavities were usually well over 100 years old (Winternitz and Cahn 1983).

Patchiness. Horizontal foliage diversity or intraplant community patchiness on the horizontal scale has long been recognized as valuable to wildlife. Figure 3 attempts to show patchiness in a plant community; the open areas between interlocking trees and some midcanopy vegetation produce a patchy effect in this forested habitat. Patchiness, like foliage height diversity, is thought to create additional niches for birds. Some species are found primarily in continuous riparian forests, whereas others are attracted to openings in the canopy where lesser trees or shrubs provide patches in an otherwise continuous canopy. These patches offer habitat space for new species that would otherwise be absent, because as patchiness increases so does species richness. Anderson et al. (1983) recently developed a method to quantify patchiness.

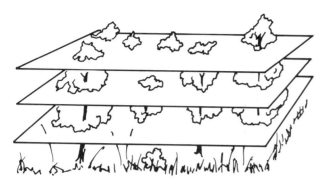

Figure 3. Patchiness in a plant community (diagrammatic).

Mammals

Large Mammals. The total importance of riparian habitats to large mammals is not fully understood, but undoubtedly these ecosystems provide three essential resources to this group: food, water, and cover. Dealy et al. (1981) pointed out that riparian habitats in general, and quaking aspens in particular, provide both thermal cover and forage for ungulates.

In the Modoc National Forest in northern California, Salwasser and Shimamoto (1984) examined animal use of wetlands that have developed since the 1920s behind water storage dams. They examined wetland use for three classes of large mammals: feral horses, domestic cattle, and pronghorn antelope (*Antilocapra americana*). Although these wetlands made up 10% of the available habitats, they were used heavily by all classes from midsummer through fall. Pronghorn antelope use peaked at 80% in August and remained over 40% into October. Feral horse use peaked at 78% in July and remained over 40% into early August. Cattle use peaked at 80% in August and exceeded 50% since late June. Annual use varied by the three classes, but all used the developed wetlands far more extensively than the wetlands that were available among habitats in midsummer to fall.

The extent to which elk (*Cervus elaphus*) use and depend on riparian habitats, other than as travel routes, in the nonsummer months is not well known. However, in summer in western Montana, 80% of elk use in July was within 0.4 km (0.25 mi.) of permanent water (Marcum 1975). Skovlin (1984) reported heavy preference for summer range within 0.8 km (0.5 mi.) from water. Whether the elk are attracted to riparian habitats for the green lush forage, water, or both is unclear; perhaps only lactating cows depend on free water sources at this time (Marcum 1975; Black et al. 1976; Thomas et al. 1976).

Studies examining habitat use by elk in mixed-forest types have shown that of 15 associated habitat types, riparian zones were most heavily used (Pederson et al. 1979). Riparian corridors also served as travel routes between areas.

Although elk will graze areas used by cattle, domestic livestock grazing appears to diminish use of the area by elk (Blood 1966; Nelson and Burnell 1975; Burbridge and Neff 1976; Skovlin et al. 1976). Diminished elk use of areas where cattle have grazed is probably related to season of use and grazing intensity by cattle before or during the time of elk use. Fall and winter use by elk declined significantly following cattle use in late spring and summer on pine-bunchgrass uplands near riparian zones in the Blue Mountains of Oregon (Skovlin 1984).

How much vegetation is removed in riparian habitats by big game is not well studied, but Skovlin (1984) indicated that in northeastern Oregon, deer and elk accounted for about one-third of the total browsing on riparian trees and shrubs. Cattle apparently removed the remaining two-thirds. He also reported that studies conducted near the above sites, where deferred or seasonal livestock grazing has been practiced, showed similar vegetation removal rates for big game and livestock.

Soil compaction from grazing by wild ungulates is normally not a problem in riparian zones in fall and winter, but some compaction damage of saturated or wet soils in the upland range in early spring may occur (Skovlin 1984). He also reported that shrub use by elk in early spring and summer, before grazing by domestic livestock, can significantly affect shrub survival during the ensuing growing season. Cattle browsing on the same shrubs grazed by elk could add to the shrub mortality problem.

Medium-Sized Mammals. Numerous medium-sized species of mammals are either obligate or facultative users of riparian systems at all elevations. For example, in Big Bend National Park in west Texas, 15 medium-sized species were reported using riparian ecosystems and one, the beaver (*Castor canadensis*), was a true obligate (Boeer and Schmidly 1977). Williams and Kilburn (1984) reported that of the 502 recent native species and subspecies of land mammals in California, about 25% (133 taxa) were limited to or largely depended on riparian and other types of wetland communities. They further stated that "No other general type of mammalian habitat in California approaches riparian and other wetland communities in importance to mammals...." Of the 15 species they listed, 5 were in the medium-sized category. Similarly, in Mexico, seven medium-sized mammals, threatened with extinction, are confined to riparian ecosystems (Ceballos 1985).

Lack of any systematic and long-term studies of medium-sized mammals makes it difficult for managers to establish specific habitat management criteria that would ensure these species are not extirpated by water management, timber harvest, or grazing practices. As in most past management decisions, the best approach is to review natural history studies of these species and avoid eliminating habitat components that have been identified as important.

Many of these species are aquatic or semi-aquatic and feed on plant and animal matter in or along the stream. Consequently, instream flows and water quality represent important habitat factors. Streamside vegetation also provides food and cover for these species, so severe vegetation removal by domestic livestock can be important. Therefore, to provide optimum conditions for these species, one must be cognizant of the specific needs for each species found in the area.

In California, five medium-sized mammal species considered obligate to riparian habitats have been recommended for special consideration (Williams and Kilburn 1984). One, the snowshoe hare (*Lepus americanus*), occurs in dense thickets of alders (*Alnus* sp.), willows, and other shrubs in the Sierra Nevada range (Orr 1940). Dense thickets of young conifers also serve as cover for this hare (Williams 1985). This species may not depend on riparian habitat in other portions of its range, which may not be unusual for some high-elevation forms.

The mountain beaver (*Aplodontia rufa*), also found along moist, forested habitats along the Pacific Slope, occurs in small colonies. It favors moist slopes, supporting lush growths of forbs, and often excavates its burrows next to a stream. Its diet includes a variety of forbs and the buds, twigs, and bark of willow and dogwood (*Cornus* sp.). It also cuts forbs to pile as hay (Grinnell and Storer 1924).

A number of medium-sized mammals use riparian ecosystems extensively although they occur in the uplands. Densities are lower in upland habitats than along riparian systems, as noted by studies of the gray fox (*Urocyon cinereoargenteus*) along Putah Creek near Davis, California (Hallbery and Trapp 1984). Two males and females with radio collars spent 76% of their nocturnal and 92% of their diurnal time in riparian habitats and the remainder in agricultural habitats. An example of the latter is exemplified in ringtails (*Bassariscus astutus*), where this species' densities range from 2.5 to 5 times greater in riparian ecosystems as opposed to upland habitats (Belluomini and Trapp 1984). Numerous other facultative riparian species obviously fit into these categories, stressing the importance of these habitats to medium-sized mammals.

The fisher (*Martes pennanti*) is poorly studied especially in the western U.S., but in general, is thought to depend on riparian habitats for travel and escape routes (de Vos 1951, 1952; Kelly 1977; Buck 1982; Mullis 1985). Of the studies conducted thus far, only Kelly (1977) has reported that the long axis of most home ranges in New Hampshire have tended to parallel drainages. Regardless, these riparian habitats are believed to be very important to this species.

In the West, fisher populations have been thought to be declining because of activities such as timber harvesting, road building, and overtrapping. In California the trapping season was closed in 1946, and in recent years these populations appear to have increased (Mullis 1985). Indications are that the marten (*M. americana*) may similarly need riparian habitats.

Beavers, once a dominant aquatic mammal in riparian systems, have virtually been eliminated in western streams through trapping, shooting, instream flow reductions, and other factors. The beaver needs streams 1 m (3 ft) or more deep, and timber for food, lodge, and dam construction. Its propensity to construct dams has frequently made it an undesirable riverine species. Although primarily preferring to live in lodges, the beaver will excavate dens in the riverbank (Nelson and Hooper 1976). Its damming activities frequently have flooded agricultural lands, forest lands, and damaged irrigation systems.

Parker et al. (1985) recently suggested that beavers might have played an important role in resisting minor perturbations in lower-order streams. Their model and arguments are not too difficult to visualize when the impact this species can have on streams and riparian trees is considered. Lang and Weider (1984) suggested that beavers have altered the structure of forests in West Virginia. Platts et al. (1985) supported the beaver model for large storm events. However, the Parker et al. (1985)

model needs further testing before it can be used as a possible management tool in resisting mild perturbations.

Scott (l984) justified the importance of beaver, mink (*Mustela vison*), and muskrat (*Ondatra zibethicus*) by examining the dollar return of these species in California. In some instances, the fur-return value of these species may represent up to 71% of an individual's annual income. In economically depressed communities this could be an important source of income.

Small Mammals. Soil texture, structure, and moisture seem to be important in habitat selection of many small mammals that burrow. Other rodents respond to riparian habitats in varying manners: sciurids respond more to tree species and height of trees; heteromyids, more to soil and open habitats; castorids, to water and forage availability; cricetids, to vegetation density and structure; and zapodidae, possibly to grass height and stem densities in moist soils.

Although identifying habitat components for all small mammals in riparian communities is far from complete, there is good evidence to demonstrate the importance of these habitats to small mammals. Cross (1985) found that riparian habitats in southwestern Oregon, composed of mixed conifer and deciduous broadleaf trees, invariably had greater species richness and total small mammal biomass than upland sites. Studies (Stamp and Ohmart 1979) in riparian habitats in the Sonoran Desert of Arizona show similar results.

Herptofauna

To our knowledge, there are no in-depth, long-term data from a riparian ecosystem at any elevation dealing with habitat factors important to an entire herptofauna. This is a serious omission in riparian studies in that reptiles and amphibians are probably as important, and possibly more so, than birds and mammals in energy flow and nutrient cycling. There are a number of autecological studies on specific species, however, which we used to delineate some of the most important habitat features for amphibians and reptiles. Until in-depth, long-term community ecology studies are conducted, we will be making many assumptions.

In the Hubbard Brook Experimental Forest in New Hampshire, Burton and Likens (1975) estimated salamander densities of 2,950/ha (1,180/a.), which exceeded density estimates of birds and mammals. Salamander biomass exceeded that of birds by 216 times and approximated that of small mammals. Similar densities of Siskiyou Mountain salamanders (*Plethodon stormi*) have been estimated at densities

of 2,700/ha (1,080/a.; Nussbaum 1974) in optimum habitats in Oregon; and Murphy and Hall (1981) reported that in Oregon, the Pacific giant salamander (*Dicamptodon eusatus*) may make up as much as 99% of the total predator biomass in some streams.

Reptile densities are equally high in the West. The western pond turtle (*Clemmys marmorata*) has been reported at densities of 425/ha (170/a.; Bury 1979) and Sonoran mud turtles (*Kinosternon sonoriense*) in Arizona at 825/ha (330/a.; Hulse 1974). Southern ringnecked snakes (*Diadophis punctatus*) have been reported at densities of 1,000-1,500/ha (400-600/a.; Sullivan 1981).

In general, amphibians as a species group are more dependent on riparian ecosystems than are reptiles. Much of this revolves around their evolutionary life-style; they are aquatic or semi-aquatic and lay open eggs (nonshelled) in water or very moist areas. For aquatic species, many of the same needs of fishes would apply to these forms, e.g., shaded stream for cooler water and higher oxygen levels, productive stream bottoms, and escape cover. For more terrestrial forms, such as some salamanders, the presence of rotting logs and dense ground cover (litter or vegetation) is essential.

Because most species in this group are insectivorous and carnivorous, and most spend their active periods in shallow water, on the ground, or in trees, any action that reduces densities of trees, shrubs, or other vegetation and reduces high insect biomass has to be considered negative. On the Colorado River, actions that help birds were also considered to help this group, especially reptiles. This is probably not totally true, but revegetation sites that are primarily designed for birds and small mammals also support high populations of reptiles—higher than those found in most natural communities. Because many biologists believe that birds are nothing more than glorified reptiles, these results should not be surprising.

For some amphibians, the maintenance of backwaters with dense-to-moderate emergent stands of vegetation is essential. There should be stable levels of instream flow with good bank development stabilized with vegetation. Large, decaying logs in the floodplain and in the adjacent uplands are necessary habitat components for numerous amphibians, such as salamanders.

Many herpetile species either overwinter in the soil of the floodplain or in decaying wood under logs. Others overwinter in hibernacula in downed, decaying logs; snags; and even live trees with natural cavities or heart rot. These habitat features are important to amphibians for their overwinter survival. Loss of one or more of these critical habitat features can break the annual life cycle of a species, resulting in its local extirpation.

Another important feature of riparian habitats to amphibians and reptiles, frequently overlooked by managers, is the use of these systems as corridors for dispersal and genetic continuity between populations. Brode and Bury (1984) stressed the importance of continuous riparian ecosystems to help maintain genetic heterogeneity, and noted that habitat disruption has resulted in isolated populations of many species in California riparian habitats.

Although all the habitat components needed for species survival may be present along a stream, a population or species can be extirpated for a number of reasons: (1) their density is so low that an adequate number of matings do not occur to sustain population levels; (2) genetic drift; (3) genetic heterozygosity is not adequate to sustain a healthy population; and (4) some density-independent mortality factor eliminates the population, e.g., severe and prolonged freezing or drought. For this group, habitat continuity and patch size should be considered when making management decisions.

Habitat-Wildlife Correlations

A few years ago, MacArthur and MacArthur (1961) reported a strong correlation between eastern forest birds and FHD. Over the years, ecologists and managers have looked for one or more habitat features that highly correlated with wildlife. Bird species diversity (BSD) is identical in basic concept to FHD, but is based on the number of bird species (species richness) in the plant community and how evenly distributed the density of each species is among the total number of species. An avian community containing 15 species, where 2 or 3 make up 90% of the total birds, would have low BSD values compared with an avian community where the total bird numbers were more evenly distributed among the 15 species.

The BSD and FHD values and their relationships have not been well understood. For a brief period it was thought that the key to good management was to manage for high BSD values. The weakness of this approach becomes fairly obvious in the following example. In most habitat situations the density of rare or federally and state-listed species is low. Consequently, in the earlier example of 15 bird species in a community, the 2 or 3 species in very low density could be lost and hardly change the BSD value. Therefore, one can see the fallacy of trying to manage habitats or ecosystems based on BSD values. Keep in mind that BSD and species richness (number of species present) are very different terms and should not be used interchangeably.

Since high BSD-FHD relationships were reported by MacArthur and MacArthur (1961) in eastern forests, many studies have supported or refuted this relationship throughout North America. Many scientists collecting data have not looked at other habitat components and have been satisfied with relatively good correlations between BSD and FHD. A few other studies looked at important vegetation features, but these research results suffer from one or more of the following: lack of tight experimental design; limited data collection, such as only during the breeding season; and short-term studies, conducted for only 1 or 2 years. These are central criteria in judging the value of field data as applied to management situations. Much money, time, and effort have been and can be lost when management decisions are based on poorly conducted studies.

Many federal and state agencies have tried to reduce ecosystems to one or a few variables for management purposes. Our long-term research, plus that of others, argues persuasively that ecosystems, plant communities, and even small habitats are too complex to reduce to one or a few numbers for management purposes. We know of no shortcut approaches to good wildlife and habitat management and seriously doubt any will be found. Unless managing agencies discover this and proceed with the task at hand, which is the collection of in-depth, long-term changes in plant and animal communities, we as biologists will always be playing "catch-up biology" or patching data together along with our "gut feelings" to make important management decisions and recommendations.

DATA COLLECTION PRIORITIES

Biologists are so frequently enthusiastic about wildlife that when presented with the opportunity to study an area, they immediately begin thinking of ways to census various classes of vertebrates, study life histories of animals, or collect fauna. Although important, highly desirable, and needed, these are probably the last steps that should be undertaken.

We have developed a list of priorities that we believe will help the land manager develop a data base on the riparian ecosystem and also document processes occurring or about to occur in the ecosystem. Since the limiting factor in any study is money, which is people, vehicles, equipment, or some other factors requiring funding, our list assumes that funds will be limited.

Developing Vegetation Maps

Develop a fine-grained map of the riparian vegetation ecosystem(s) under management consideration. By fine-grained, we mean a map depicting and naming the plant communities at a resolution of possibly 0.2 ha (0.5 a.) or less, if necessary, to show discrete plant communities. Common sense must prevail because overzealous type mapping could reduce a community to one tree, then to a limb, and to a leaf. If two tree species occur together along a stream or river, the community might be delineated as a cottonwood-willow association. Or if a tree willow grows in one area and a shrub willow grows in another, you would have Goodding willow (*Salix gooddingii*) as a separate community from coyote willow (*S. exigua*) and so forth. Because riparian systems are linear, and frequently vary in width from a few yards to many miles, maps must be scaled upward to include small communities that may support endangered wildlife species or very highly specialized species.

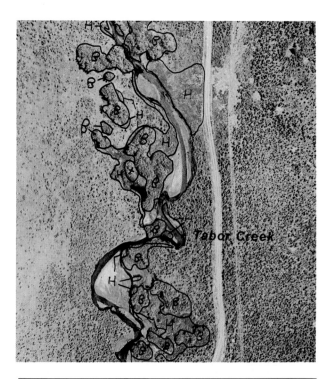

A large scale airphoto (1:2,400) provides a basis for mapping (B) brush, (H) herbaceous vegetation, and (X) bare ground, and (T) trees where present.

If numerous riparian ecosystems are under management consideration and funding only allows half of them to be adequately mapped or all to be superficially mapped, then we recommend prioritizing the streams and intensively mapping only half of them. Otherwise, a poor job on all of them provides little, if any, good information from which to make crucial management decisions and will probably be meaningless to future managers attempting to interpret and use the maps.

Good vegetation type maps should be accompanied by the criteria used in naming each major community. For example, if you elect to name cottonwood-willow associations based on cottonwoods being abundant to scattered in the community, this information should accompany the maps. Or you may elect to name the community as such if about 50% of the trees are cottonwoods and the other half willows. The important point is that good quantitative criteria should be established, adhered to in mapping, and always accompany the maps as legends or as an appendix. These maps will be invaluable to future managers as they attempt to assess and understand habitat changes. The probability is high that you will be transferred in a few years and the person replacing you must be able to interpret the information that you collected while working on riparian systems.

Classifying Plant Community and Structural Types

Quantify vegetation structure and tree species composition in a subset of available plant communities along the stream under management consideration. These data are important in naming communities and assessing structural configurations of vegetation. As riparian ecosystems are perturbed they tend to support less foliage volume at higher layers. For example, fires or floods tend to remove trees, reducing canopy foliage volume. Incoming shrubs or trees increase foliage volume at the herbaceous and shrub layers. Also, as man perturbs these habitats through reduction of instream flow or increased silt concentrations, the perturbations become manifested through vegetation structure as reduced foliage volumes in higher layers of vegetation or the tree canopy.

In our work with community structural types, we have used structural Type I as the mature, most structurally diverse community, and Type VI as the early stage of returning vegetation. A healthy riparian ecosystem will contain mature plant communities and structural types, intermediate types, and Type VI communities that will eventually replace old, decadent stands. In heavily grazed ecosystems, such as those along the Salt and Verde rivers in central Arizona, replacement cottonwood communities have been virtually eliminated and only mature, decadent stands remain. No replacement communities are forthcoming and remedial efforts, such as planting of cuttings, have been attempted to provide replacement cottonwood stands. Although riparian ecosystems can be revegetated more economically through natural flooding, federal agencies are supplementing regrowth through fencing and revegetation efforts to ensure riparian habitats are not lost forever.

Original type maps can be modified to show new plant communities and structural types. Your data on classification and criteria depicting structural types should be archived for subsequent use in the area.

Determining Vertebrate Species Richness and Relative Abundance (Breeding)

Determine vertebrate species richness and species composition for each plant community and structural type during the breeding season, and year-round when possible. Relative densities determined by a gradation of rare-to-common for each bird species is adequate. Small mammals can be assessed through snap trapping for three consecutive nights and expressing each species' relative values as X number of each species caught/number of trap nights (cumulative total). If small mammal trapping is undertaken, voucher specimens must be prepared and housed in a specimen collection where they are properly cared for. If certain community types are important to large mammals for feeding, thermal cover, or breeding grounds, these should be noted.

Attempt to determine relative densities of amphibians and reptiles through trap-and-release with can traps and observations. Values can be based on can-trap days, species and numbers observed per hour, or some other relative index.

Determining Vertebrate Species Richness and Relative Abundance (Winter)

Determine vertebrate species richness and species composition for each plant community and structural type in winter. These values will vary from winter to winter depending on the severity of the winter and the previous breeding success of the overwintering species. Rodents may hibernate and large mammals may move to lower elevations.

Censusing Vertebrates

Establish census lines for birds, snap-trap small mammals (make voucher specimens), and install can-trap grids for reptiles and amphibians. Bird transects must be censused no less than nine times per plant community and structural type per season. Number of census transects for birds should be in about equal proportion to the aerial extent of the community and structural types. Small-mammal trapping and can traps should also follow the same protocol.

Data should be collected for at least 2 years; 3 years is better. Seasonal and annual variation in animal numbers should be determined before realistic densities and habitat affinities can be made.

We believe if managers concentrated on priorities 1 through 3, they would be in a strong position to defend management decisions relating to domestic livestock grazing, presence or absence of endangered species, wildlife values of community and structural types, or wildlife values of areas behind proposed dams. As it is, managers often do not have enough data to demonstrate the high wildlife value of riparian ecosystems that are the most productive wildlife habitats in western North America.

EFFECTS OF LAND MANAGEMENT ACTIVITIES ON RIPARIAN SYSTEMS

Under the multiple-use concept, managers must be aware of impacts or potential impacts of ongoing activities on the riparian resource. Activities of recreationists, once considered harmless, now could be shown to have some profound effects on some vertebrate groups and plant species in the riparian zone. As with other activities, such as domestic livestock grazing and impoundments, we know many impacts can be mitigated to avoid or reduce some of the damage to riparian systems. We hope some of the activities covered in this section will help you avoid some of the major management problems or provide solutions to existing problems.

Domestic Livestock Grazing

Livestock grazing is a historic use on public lands. Overgrazing has been a problem in many areas of the West, however, and overgrazing in upland areas has caused the removal of virtually all nontoxic forage in adjacent floodplains. Reid and Pickford (1946) reported that cattle congregate and utilize riparian forage much more intensively than the vegetation of adjacent ranges. Biologists must be aware that the riparian ecosystem can potentially be much more productive for wildlife under better grazing strategies. Although other land-management activities have imposed losses or serious reductions in productivity of wildlife habitat, livestock grazing may be the major factor negatively affecting wildlife in the 11 western states (Oregon-Washington Interagency Wildlife Council 1978). We agree with Skovlin et al. (1977) that because of the highly limited area of riparian habitats in planning large pasture grazing approaches, riparian systems are sacrificed on areas of domestic livestock grazing on most state and federal land today.

The value of these riparian systems to domestic livestock grazing (essentially the permittee) can only be appreciated through forage production values. Further, the difficulty in bringing about proper stocking levels is deeply embedded in historical and political realms. There are 1.62 million ha (4 million a.) of mountain meadows at elevations between 1,890 and 150 m (6,200 and 6,400 ft) in the 11 western states (U.S. Department of Agriculture, Forest Service 1972). These moist meadows support more beef per acre than any other range type (Skovlin 1984). In northeast Oregon, these meadows are so productive that 1 ha (2.5 a.) is equal in forage production to 10 to 15 ha (25 to 38 a.) of forested rangeland (Reid and Pickford 1946). Although only 1 to 2% of the summer range is meadow in the Pacific Northwest, it potentially produces 20% of the forage (Reid and Pickford 1946; Roath and Krueger 1982). Because of livestock concentrations, topographical constraints on livestock, and distribution of water, the forage in the riparian zone accounted for 81% of that removed by livestock in the Blue Mountain grazing allotment (Roath and Krueger 1982).

Cattle are probably attracted to the riparian ecosystem for the same reasons as other large mammals (Ames 1977; Severson and Boldt 1978). Many riparian plant species remain green and succulent longer than upland vegetation, and sedges (*Carex* sp.) contain higher sustained protein and energy content than important upland plant species (McLean et al. 1963; Skovlin 1967; Paulsen 1969).

Platts (1984) listed eight major approaches managers should consider in managing riparian-stream habitats under multiple-use systems. These range from eliminating grazing permanently or until after recovery to rehabilitating through revegetation and artificial stream structures. Most of these approaches are unacceptable to permittees today but may seem more reasonable with time or as public concern forces political action.

Two alternatives that may hold promise are changing season of forage use and changing kinds and classes of livestock. Siekert et al. (1985) reported that spring grazing showed no significant changes in channel morphology, whereas summer and fall grazing did. The level of grazing (30 cow-calf pairs on 48 ha [120 a.] for 10 days) and duration are probably unrealistic for most permittees. Further, in many riparian ecosystems, most if not all, tree seedlings would be eliminated under this approach. Marlow and Pogacnik (1985) reported that grazing of a riparian system in Montana after the streambanks had dried (< 10% soil moisture) protected the stream channel from damage. They recommended fencing riparian habitat, rest-rotation, light grazing (20% forage removal), and grazing after streambanks have dried to 10% moisture. Fencing has been ruled out by Skovlin (1984) in that it is too expensive regardless of ownership.

Stocking moderately with steers or trying different breeds might reduce damage to riparian ecosystems caused by cow-calf operations. Lactating cows with calves appear to concentrate in areas with green forage and water, whereas steers might range more into the uplands and not concentrate in riparian habitats. Neither of the above approaches will work unless stocking rates are reduced as well. Most examined riparian systems and their watersheds

Cow-and-calf herd in riparian zone.

were unquestionably overgrazed, and use of any management approach without AUM reductions appears to be a waste of time and money. Streams in overgrazed pastures are characterized by being wider and shallower; they contain more fine sediment and have more unstable banks, less bank undercut, and higher summer water temperatures (Marcuson 1977; Van Velson 1979; Platts 1979, 1984).

Large storm events and the response of riparian habitats have been of interest to biologists because of the effects of those events on riparian ecosystems (Gregory and Madew 1982; Lyons and Beschta 1983). An interesting data set has been reported for three streams under study in Nevada and Utah where historically the watersheds of these streams have been heavily grazed (Platts and Nelson 1983; Platts et al. 1983). Peak flows (2-14 times normal) occurred in Gance Creek in 1983 and 1984. Big Creek and Chimney Creek were not grazed, but Big Creek empties into Bear Creek. In 1983, flows of 3,630 cfs exceeded all recorded flows for the past 40-year records (Platts et al. 1985).

Chimney Creek had received heavy grazing until 1981 and showed little bank development. It was rested during 1982 and 1983, and the banks were developing some overhanging vegetation (Platts et al. 1985). Large decomposing aspen logs in the stream and on the banks were evidence of past forests that once lined the banks of Chimney Creek. Aspen forest return has probably been prevented by blowdown, beaver, and heavy grazing of sprouts by livestock (Platts et al. 1985). The severe floods in 1983 and 1984 straightened the meandering channel and widened the streambank, reducing the developing bank overhanging vegetation. The large aspen logs that helped hold the stream previously were decomposed or flushed from the stream by the high discharges.

The riparian vegetation along Gance Creek was dominated by large trees from the floodplain to the streambanks. Flood damage was previously vertical cutting and some lateral movement of the channel (Platts et al. 1985). Damage was minimal and the authors believed that had beavers still controlled the stream as they had done in the 1950s and 1960s, the flood damage would have been lessened.

Changes that occurred on Big Creek were most interesting because a portion of the study stream had been rested for about 10 years and was comparable to two other reaches (one above and one below the rested site) that had received normal grazing pressures. The rested section had dramatically recovered and showed good floodplain vegetation and streambank development. During the flood years, stream width in the grazed portions increased by 40% with extensive lateral stream movement and redeposition

of bedload sediments. The rested section with improved streambanks was able to contain the high flows and showed only a slight increase in channel width (Platts et al. 1985). Floodplain vegetation and soils were altered dramatically in the grazed sections following the storm events, whereas the rested section showed little evidence of vegetation change or newly eroded sediments. Results from this study amplify the admonitions of Heede (1985) that managers should understand the interrelationships between vegetation and hydrologic processes in riparian ecosystems before attempting any type of management change that alters these natural systems.

The economic values of healthy riparian ecosystems and their attendant wildlife are difficult to establish (Everest 1977), but approaches have been made based solely on fisheries. Olson and Armour (1979) suggested that a hypothetical reach of 14,484 km (9,000 mi.) of depleted fishable streams on U.S. Bureau of Land Management land be set aside exclusively for recreation. Based totally on increased fishery visitor days due to restored habitat, they estimated a first-year benefit-cost ratio of 1:1.66. Or, for every $1.00 spent to fence the riparian corridor, there would be $1.66 generated by fishermen. Other values such as backpacking, camping, bird watching, erosion control, and improved water quality were not included in this economic return value.

The above approach needs further study and confirmation because, if true, the cost of fencing could be replaced by the economic return, making it a valid alternative. If fencing is not economical (Skovlin 1984), then it is entirely possible that only light or no livestock grazing of riparian systems is the ultimate answer if maximum wildlife productivity is the management goal. However, Armour (1977) quoted Harmay as stating:

Vegetation in meadows and drainages is closely utilized (by domestic livestock) under any stocking rate or system of grazing. Reducing the livestock or adjusting grazing season usually will not solve the problem . . . .

Findings by Severson and Boldt (1978) support Harmay in that in the northern Great Plains the riparian habitats were excessively used, regardless of stocking rates. In eastern Oregon, Gillen (1981) reported that at a moderate rate, the meadows only produced 3 to 16 times more forage, again supporting the contention that regardless of stocking rate the riparian habitats will receive the greatest grazing pressures. Under continuous grazing (60-100% utilization) in Nevada and Utah, there was no evidence of riparian improvement and under present stocking rates with continuous grazing, the riparian-stream ecosystem continually deteriorated (Platts 1984).

If not limited by factors such as high salinity and no flooding, riparian habitat can recover following heavy grazing (Davis 1977; Glinski 1977; Crouch 1978). Eliminating grazing for 10-12 years may be necessary at higher elevations (2,650 m [4,800 ft]) in willow communities where grazing pressure was heavy and chronic (Knopf and Cannon 1981). Knopf and Cannon (1981) further pointed out that it is more difficult to improve a damaged riparian ecosystem by eliminating grazing than to maintain good conditions in one that is being grazed.

A number of studies have shown a dramatic increase in wildlife values where riparian systems were abused by domestic livestock grazing; the areas were fenced and monitored a number of years after domestic livestock removal. Numbers of small mammals, songbirds, and raptors increased by 350% (Winegar 1977; Duff 1979; Van Velson 1979) in an area fenced for 8 years after grazing. Game animals such as ring-necked pheasants (*Phasianus colchicus*), deer, and waterfowl increased as well (Van Velson 1979). On the South Platte River in Colorado, Crouch (1982) found more ducks, upland game, and twice as many terrestrial birds in areas fenced for 7 years compared with adjacent grazed habitats. Significant differences in bird species richness and foraging guilds have been reported between heavily grazed 2.5 cow-calf units/ha (1/a.) and lightly grazed (0.3 cow-calf units/ha (0.75/a.) riparian habitats. Total density was not significantly different indicating increases in some species that were already present and the extirpation of some species such as flycatchers, ground-foraging thrushes, and foliage-gleaning insectivores.

Small mammals are also adversely affected by domestic livestock grazing in riparian communities. Small mammal densities before and after grazing with a stocking rate of 5 to 6.25 a./AUM (2.0 to 2.5 ha/AUM) declined from 320 to 33/a. (800 to 83/ha) in a Douglas hawthorn (*Crataegus douglasii*)-dominated community, from 180 to 24/a. (450 to 60/ha) in a riparian meadow, and from 52 to 17/a. (129 to 42/ha) in a black cottonwood (*Populus trichocarpa*)-mixed conifer community. Ten months after grazing ceased, no significant difference was found between the small mammal densities in the grazed versus ungrazed plots.

Some grazing investigators have reported increased rodent species richness under moderate or heavy grazing pressures (Moulton 1978). We do not doubt some of these results but point out that small mammal species that are added or increase in numbers are usually habitat generalists whose habitat requirements are broad. Habitat specialists, such as many microtine rodents, are usually reduced or eliminated when grazing pressures are high. Under these grazing conditions, species in the genus *Peromyscus*

and *Perognathus* may increase or be added because the former are generalists and the latter require more open habitat.

Moulton (1978) reported that moderate grazing (2.3 a./AUM [0.9 ha/AUM]) for 6 months in a cottonwood riparian system reduced prairie vole (*Microtus ochrogaster*) numbers and increased deer mouse (*Peromyscus maniculatus*) numbers. Eight species of small mammals were trapped in the grazed plot and four in the ungrazed control. The control site had been ungrazed for 11 + years, and the vegetation had moved toward a uniform, dense grass structure, unsuitable for a number of rodent species. Light or moderate grazing would have altered plant structure and species composition, making the habitat suitable to other rodent species.

Where grazing can be controlled in riparian habitats and seasonally light-to-moderate forage removal is practiced, the impact can be small to riparian vegetation and wildlife. But, as pointed out, by incorporating riparian areas into large pastures, these productive wildlife habitats become sacrifice areas where most, if not all, of the annual plant production is removed. As suggested by May and Davis (1982), riparian habitats should be separated and managed as distinct units.

Preliminary data on riparian populations of the wandering garter snake (*Thamnophis elegans vagrans*) on fenced (1972 and 1975) and unfenced plots on the Rio de los Vacos near Santa Fe, New Mexico, provided some interesting results (Szaro et al. 1985). The fenced plots (only cattle excluded) supported a stand (18%) of trees and shrubs composed of thin-leaf alder (*Alnus tenuifolia*), irrorata willow (*S. irrorata*), Scouler willow (*S. scouleriana*), coyote willow, and Mexican cliff-rose (*Cowania mexicana*). In contrast, 0.1% of the grazed plots supported a mixture of thin-leaf alder and irrorata willow. Herbaceous ground cover (71% versus 88%) and down and dead debris (0.4% versus 5%) was significantly ($P < 0.05$) different in grazed versus ungrazed plots, respectively. Streamside shrubs in the fenced plots filtered out debris during floods to form debris piles up to 4 m (12 ft) in diameter and 2 m (6 ft) high. These decomposing piles supported numerous worms and slugs that made up 62% and 18% of snakes' diet. Snakes were five times more abundant in the ungrazed versus the grazed plots, even though they were more difficult to find in the vegetation and debris. Other species of reptiles are undoubtedly affected by domestic livestock grazing as foliage for insects and cover for the reptiles are reduced or eliminated.

Impacts to wildlife by heavy domestic livestock grazing vary from moderate to extreme depending on whether grazing is seasonal or yearlong. Seasonal grazing may allow limited tree and shrub regeneration that provides some habitat and forage for wildlife, whereas heavy, yearlong grazing eventually leads to removal of most, if not all, of the palatable riparian vegetation. In the latter instance, forage and thermal cover for large mammals are slowly eliminated along with food and habitat for medium-sized and small mammals, birds, and herps. In seasonal heavy grazing, some forage and thermal cover may be left for large mammals, but food and cover for medium-sized and small mammals are generally eliminated. Mid-canopy and understory birds may be affected to the point of exclusion. Yearlong, heavy grazing on the Verde River in central Arizona has resulted in remaining stands of cottonwood-willow communities of structure Type I or mature communities tending toward decadence (Higgins and Ohmart 1981). Although floods produce good seedling development, these seedlings are consumed before they reach 0.6 m (2 ft) in height. Unless corrective measures are taken, in a few years the old decadent communities will expire and there will be no young replacement communities. Crouch (1978) reported a 50% reduction of cottonwoods in a grazed stream in Colorado over an 18-year period.

Birds, for example (Ohmart and Anderson 1982), are associated with four layers of vegetation on the lower Colorado River:

19 species are associated with the 7.6 m (25 ft) or taller layer,

10 species with the 4.6 to 7.6 m (15 to 20 ft) layer,

13 species with the 1.5 to 4.6 m (5 to 15 ft) layer, and

11 species with the 0.15 to 1.5 m (0.5 to 5 ft) layer.

The overstory or canopy group (19 species) are specialists and were absent or poorly represented when this layer was absent or foliage density highly reduced. The 23 species in the two middle layers and some of the 11 species in the understory group were generalists. Some of these species will be present even when their foliage layer is absent or poorly represented. Heavy grazing not only affects the herbaceous and shrub layers, but over time affects the upper canopy layers as riparian tree regeneration is stopped or curtailed.

Domestic livestock grazing in riparian habitats may be used as a management tool to enhance areas for wildlife. This approach has potential, but one would have to know more about the wildlife and its habitat needs than presently known or would have to experiment with different levels of forage removal to bring about the desired wildlife results. Moulton (1978) suggested that grazing in a riparian area in

eastern Colorado may increase rodent species numbers by creating microhabitat diversity. He found eight species of small mammals in a grazed plot (2.3 a./AUM [0.9 ha/AUM]) and four species in the ungrazed plot. The grazed area had been stocked from July through December with spring use deferred for 17 years. This type of seasonal grazing, after maximum spring plant growth, allowed livestock selection of preferred species creating a patchy microhabitat. The ungrazed plot (11 or more years of rest) promoted a uniform vegetation structure without any horizontal patchiness. Prairie vole numbers were higher in the protected site but not excluded in the grazed site.

Colorado Chapter, The Wildlife Society

Prairie vole.

Another possible use of cattle grazing as a management tool has been reported by Krueger and Anderson (1985) in dense shrub-willow communities at high elevations on the North Platte drainage in Wyoming. Apparently, fish populations are not harmed by this activity, at least on the Little Deschutes River in Oregon (Lorz 1974), but this was not examined in the study by Krueger and Anderson (1985). Tunnels created by cattle grazing through the dense shrub-willow altered plant community structure, creating a more diverse set of ecological conditions for birds. Many species respond positively to this treatment except for the green-tailed towee (*Pipilo chlorurus*), which inhabits dense stands of vegetation.

These management tools need to be examined carefully to ensure that wildlife species targeted for enhancement receive the benefits. Domestic livestock grazing is so entrenched on public land that we doubt that use of domestic livestock grazing will become an important management tool in many ecological situations. First, we must reverse the general downward trend in riparian vegetation conditions before cattle are needed as a management tool on a broad basis. Fish habitat appears to be more sensitive to livestock grazing impacts than terrestrial habitats.

Mining

Mining can have profound effects on riparian ecosystems ranging from total sterility of the riparian system to intermittent effects following heavy precipitation. The effects vary in areas in the West and depend on the mineral(s) being mined. In the arid Southwest, the material is frequently sand and gravel; removal of these products has caused extensive channel cutting, reduced water quality, and even flooding and loss of homes. Ruptured holding ponds of leached materials from copper mines has resulted in virtually permanent losses of the flora and fauna in some streams.

Little advice other than extreme caution and a full knowledge of the mining operation, proximity of potential toxins to the stream, safeguards to avoid pollutants, and good common sense must reign in this situation. Also, be aware of potential and real secondary impacts.

An excellent approach is to inventory the resource intensively before any mining disturbance, including seasonal water quality samples (have a control stream if at all possible), and then monitor every 3-5 years thereafter. The control will provide normal variance data and a comparison should litigation ever occur.

Recreational Activities

Recreational activity and its effects on wildlife can range from relatively minor to so severe that virtually all the vegetation is destroyed locally. In many instances, the agency developing the recreational opportunities in riparian habitats builds roads through the habitats allowing vehicles total access to the recreational area. Consequently, users drive off the roads, camp at random, and many assume an attitude of "destroy anything you want, we won't ever return." Wood gathering for firewood consumes down and dead trees, limbs, snags, and many times standing live trees. Many forms of wildlife leave the area and others, such as lizards, snakes, frogs, and salamanders, are destroyed by children and pets.

The impacts of recreational use are poorly documented, but simply by viewing some recreational areas one is left with the impression that only the heartiest and persistent wildlife are left. Aitchison (1977) studied bird densities and species composition in a seasonal-use campground in Oak Creek Canyon in Arizona for 3 years. His control and recreational site primarily supported ponderosa pine (*Pinus ponderosa*), cottonwoods, and Arizona wal-

nut at a 1,646-m (5,400-ft) elevation. The campground was opened from about Memorial Day to Labor Day each year which spans the bird breeding season. In the first year of study (first year the developed campground opened), there was a 40% decrease in bird density on opening day. Agency personnel destroyed 20% of the nests of the Steller's jay (*Cyanocitta stelleri*) by removing and slashing trees. Aitchison (1977:178) reported: "Campers destroyed 30 percent more of the Steller's jay nests and 20 percent of the robin (*Turdus migratorius*) nests by removing branches for firewood, making room for tents, and other reasons." Many species abandoned their nests but foraged in the campground area. Ultimately, bird species remaining in the campground were larger, different, and fewer than on the control site.

In highly stressed riparian systems, trailer park development can be positive to wildlife, especially birds, as was exemplified in one of our studies. Along the Colorado River, the cottonwood-willow association is rapidly disappearing and a wise developer planted native trees in the park for better tree survival and growth, and to attract birds for the enjoyment of the residents. This small oasis supports a few pairs of birds that were once common along the lower river (Grinnell 1914), but are now rapidly approaching extirpation (Anderson and Ohmart 1977). This type of action should be encouraged in developments where trees will be protected, but managers must plan for these developments.

Riparian systems are very attractive to recreationists in that the systems contain water, interesting plants and animals, shade, and numerous other enjoyable features in the otherwise arid and semiarid environments. Hoover et al. (1985) reported in a visitor information study that environmental attributes receiving highest user ratings were primarily ecological features present in healthy riparian ecosystems. Managers should educate the public of the fragile nature and unique values of these systems. This may seem impossible, but there are some guidelines available such as the Recreational Carrying Capacity in the California Desert (U.S. Department of the Interior, Bureau of Land Management 1978) and the California Desert Area Conservation Plan (U.S. Department of the Interior, Bureau of Land Management 1980).

Martin (1984) provided an excellent approach in using recreation planning to restore and protect riparian systems. He recommended ways to control visitor use subtly and directly in an intensively used riparian system replete with wildlife values, water recreation, and large metropolitan areas nearby on the American River in California. Approaches and successes in the California State Park System (Barry 1984) and potential problems and questions in the proposed wildlife enhancement and recreational development at Oristimba Creek in California (Morris 1984) may also be helpful in better planning. If new campgrounds are absolutely necessary, Aitchison's (1977) suggestions may apply: locate new campgrounds in nonsensitive areas, periodically close to the campground to allow revegetation and reduce stress on wildlife; open the campground before or after the height of the breeding season; control visitors and agency habitat destruction; and educate the public through signs showing good camping procedures. We might add to disallow collection of wood for any reason.

Impoundment Construction

Impoundments are constructed for a number of reasons and some are multiple-use structures. Generally, each has regulations that outline its purpose and function such as flood control, hydroelectric power, and water storage for agriculture or municipalities. During construction, roads are built, recreational facilities may be installed, and numerous other secondary impacts to wildlife may occur, along with the eventual inundation of the vegetation in the storage reservoirs. In some instances, the secondary impacts of reservoirs to wildlife can equal or exceed primary impacts.

Reservoirs. Depending on how rapidly water surface levels fluctuate behind reservoirs, there may be a potential for productive wildlife habitats to develop. Rapidly and wildly fluctuating water levels are not conducive to the development of emergent plant communities such as cattails (*Typha* sp.) and bulrushes (*Scirpus* sp.). These types of reservoirs develop a "bathtub ring" for a shoreline where only annual plants grow and perennials are drowned. Reservoirs with slow fluctuating water levels generally develop good emergent plant communities that support animals such as muskrat, beaver, rails, and gallinules. Waterfowl tend to more heavily use reservoirs that have an abundance of emergent vegetation that provides cover and greater foraging opportunities. Reservoirs with rapidly fluctuating shorelines tend to attract only a few diving ducks.

Downstream. The wildlife value of areas below reservoirs tends to degrade slowly over the years. Generally, instream flows are lower than natural flows. Natural floods that provide new soil deposition and enrichment are stopped, and riparian plant health and vigor slowly decline. If controlled releases from the dam or floods do occur, they are generally greater than would have occurred without the dam, and the health of the riparian system may have degraded to a point that is no longer resilient to a heavy flood.

Recreational activities can affect riparian areas.

Another problem tends to occur below dams where instream flows are highly regulated and cessation of natural floods prevent leaching and soil rejuvenation. Total Dissolved Solids (TDS) tend to increase in areas where the water table is near the soil surface. If the stream carries high TDS loads, the process is relatively rapid and the TDS are wicked to the soil surface where they accumulate as the soil moisture evaporates. Sodium or salt levels eventually accumulate to a point that most native species, except halophytes (salt-tolerant plants), cannot germinate or survive. Natural floods generally leached and removed these deposits, and new soils were deposited in low areas.

In some situations below dams the riverbed is essentially dewatered until another major perennial tributary enters. The Salt and Gila rivers in central Arizona and the Rio Grande from about El Paso to Presidio, Texas, are classic examples. Water returning to these dry reaches is in one of two forms: agricultural waste waters high in chemicals and salts or impoundment releases because reservoirs are near or at capacity. Agriculture waste waters generally poison productive riparian vegetation and create conditions that favor growth of less desirable trees or shrubs. These waters seldom flow in the original channel and eventually the channel is obliterated.

During high rainfall years, releases from upstream dams must occur, and the dense, low-growing trees and shrubs that cover the floodplain and block the channel form a living dam that spreads the released water laterally to inundate everything in the floodplain. Floodwaters drain slowly (generally taking months) and frequently relict, productive native plant communities drown.

Logging and Roads

We stated earlier that riparian ecosystems can be and are affected by any major perturbation, whether it be natural (fire, storms) or man-made (logging, roadbuilding, or grazing). Therefore, management must consider all disturbances that could potentially or actually affect riparian ecosystems. Productive fisheries can be lost to high stream sediment loads, to stream channel and streamside vegetation destruction by floods following abuse of watersheds, and to perennial streams becoming intermittent because of continued abuse of watersheds.

Logging and roadbuilding on the watersheds and near riparian systems destroy the natural ground cover and churn and mix the soil to produce transportable sediment. Sediment entering a stream comes from both natural and man-made activities and its rate of passage varies depending on slope, size of area disturbed, severity of disturbance, kind and type of streamside vegetation to stabilize the

transported materials, instream sediment traps, and the periodicity and duration of large streams. Dunn and Leopold (1978) estimated that 5 or more years are needed for a transportable sediment load to totally pass through a stream system. Mahoney and Erman (1984) reported that the sediment load currently moving through any stream is the product of past years' land-use activity and major storms.

Leaving buffer strips near riparian vegetation is apparently successful. Aubertin and Patric (1974) studied a 34-ha (14-a.) clearcut in West Virginia and reported only slight increases in stream turbidity following timber harvest. They attributed the success to leaving a 10 to 20-m (33 to 66-ft) forested strip adjacent to the riparian vegetation. Moring (1975) demonstrated similar results in his 15-year study in Oregon. He showed a 3.8-fold reduction in suspended stream sediments in the clearcut with a buffer strip versus a clearcut without the buffer strip.

A large study on streams in northern California examined macroinvertebrate changes relative to logging with buffered and unbuffered strips (Erman et al. 1977; Ruby et al. 1977; Newbold et al. 1980). Where buffer strips were > 30 m (> 98 ft) on logged sites, there were no differences between invertebrate populations in experimentals and controls. Where buffer strips were less, differences of invertebrate populations were detectable between experimentals and controls.

Buffer strips also reduce pollutants and other chemical substances from surface runoff (Young et al. 1980). Karr and Schlosser (1977) extensively reviewed literature on the value of near-stream vegetation on water quality and stream biology and should be consulted for more in-depth coverage.

Not only are buffer strips effective in reducing physical and, ultimately, biological damage to lower animals, they also protect small mammals from intensive logging operations (Cross 1985). Where buffer or leave strips varying from 12 to 70 m (39 to 230 ft) wide were retained, those remaining habitats supported small mammal communities comparable to undisturbed sites. These studies were conducted in southwestern Oregon in mixed-coniferous riparian vegetation. Harris (1984) suggested maintaining riparian corridors as a means of connecting forest habitat islands in similar stands of old-growth Douglas fir (*Pseudotsuga menziesii*).

Riparian Ground-water Withdrawals

Ground-water pumping may become the most serious threat to North American riparian systems. Water diversions and reduced instream flows can be devastating to riparian habitats, but pumping of riparian ground waters for industrial and municipal development will totally annihilate most, if not all, riparian plant species. Extensive mesquite bosques were killed around Casa Grande Ruins or the Casa Grande National Monument by ground-water pumping in central Arizona (Judd et al. 1971). The water table has receded at 2+ m (7+ ft) per year which, in turn, resulted in the death of this large mesquite forest.

Long-term vegetation changes are well documented by aerial photography for a 3.2-km (2-mi.) reach of the Carmel River near the Monterey Peninsula in California (Groeneveld and Griepentrog 1985). Time-series documentation for a 24-year period (1956-80) conclusively demonstrated a marked decline in riparian trees such as red willow (*S. laevigata*), black cottonwood (*P. trichocarpa*), California sycamore (*Platanus racemosa*), and white alder (*Alnus rhombifolia*). Along with reduced riparian plant cover was an invasion of weedy perennials, annuals, and xerophylic (arid-adapted) shrubs. The riverbanks have become noticeably eroded due to increased channel width.

Groeneveld and Griepentrog (1985) cited other unpublished studies where lowering of the water table by pumping had caused ecological change. This is a real and final threat to many riparian ecosystems in the West. The U.S. Geological Survey is currently studying the effects of ground-water withdrawal on native riparian species along the Owens River south of Bishop, California (Dileanis et al. 1985). Unfortunately, no tree species were involved in the study, but data for Nevada saltbush (*Atriplex torreyi*) and rubber rabbitbush (*Chrysothamnus nauseosus*) may provide insight into how sensitive obligate-riparian species are to gradual and drastic declines of the water table.

LITERATURE CITED

AITCHISON, S.W. 1977. Some effects of a campground on breeding birds in Arizona. Pages 175-182 in Johnson, R.R. and D.A. Jones, tech. coords. Importance, Preservation and Management of Riparian Habitat: A Symposium. U.S. Dep. Agric., For. Serv. Gen. Tech. Rep. RM-43. 217pp.

ALMAND, J.D. and W.B. KROHN. 1978. The position of the Bureau of Land Management on the protection and management of riparian ecosystems. Pages 359-361 in Johnson, R.R. and J.F. McCormick, tech. coords. Strategies for Protection and Management of Floodplain Wetlands and Other Riparian Ecosystems: Proc. of the Symposium. U.S. Dep. Agric., For. Serv. Gen. Tech. Rep. WO-12., Washington, DC. 410pp.

AMES, C.R. 1977. Wildlife conflicts in riparian management: grazing. Pages 49-51 in Johnson, R.R. and D.A. Jones, tech. coords. Importance, Preservation and Management of Riparian Habitat: A Symposium. U.S. Dep. Agric., For. Serv. Gen. Tech. Rep. RM-43. 217pp.

ANDERSON, B.W. and R.D. OHMART. 1977. Breeding bird use of a residential development. Pages 196-201 in Annual Report, submitted to U.S. Dep. Inter., Bureau of Reclamation, Boulder City, NV.

———— and ————, 1978. *Phainopepla* utilization of honey mesquite forests in the Colorado River valley. Condor 80:334-338.

———— and ————, 1984. Vegetation management study for the enhancement of wildlife along the lower Colorado River. U.S. Dep. Inter., Bur. of Rec., Boulder City, NV.

————,————, and W.C. HUNTER. 1983. Quantifying variables for classifying desert riparian vegetation. Pages 32-44 in Moir, W.H. and L. Hendzel, tech. coords., Proc. of the Workshop on Southwestern Habitat Types. U.S. Dep. Agric., For. Serv., Southwest Reg., Albuquerque, NM.

ARMOUR, C.L. 1977. Effects of deteriorated range streams on trout. U.S. Dep. Inter., Bur. Land Manage., Idaho State Off., Boise. 7pp.

ASMUSSEN, L.E., A.W. WHITE, Jr., E.W. HANSON, and J.M. SHERIDAN. 1977. Reduction of 2,4-d load in surface runoff down a grassed waterway. J. Environ. Qual. 6:159-162.

AUBERTIN, G.M. and J.H. PATRIC. 1974. Water quality after clearcutting in a small watershed in West Virginia. J. Environ. Qual. 3:243-249.

AXELROD, D.I. 1958. Evolution of the Madro-Tertiary geoflora. Bot. Rev. 24:433-509.

BALDA, R. 1975. The relationship of secondary cavity nesters to snag densities in western coniferous forests. U.S. Dep. Agric., For. Serv., Southwest Reg., Wildl. Habitat Tech. Bull. 1, Albuquerque, NM. 37pp.

BARRY, W.J. 1984. Management and protection of riparian ecosystems in the state park system. Pages 758-766 in Warner, R.E. and K.M. Hendrix, eds. California Riparian Systems: Ecology, Conservation, and Productive Management. Univ. California Press, Berkeley. 1035pp.

BELLUOMINI, L. and G. TRAPP. 1984. Ringtail distribution and abundance in the Central Valley of California. Pages 906-914 in Warner, R.E. and K.M. Hendrix, eds. California Riparian Systems: Ecology, Conservation, and Productive Management. Univ. California Press, Berkeley. 1035pp.

BENOIT, C. 1978. Fluvial sediment delivery as percent of erosion: The relationship between landslope and effective streamside bufferstrip width. U.S. Dep. Agric., For. Serv., Portland, OR. (typescript)

BLACK, N., R.J. SCHERZINGER, and J.W. THOMAS. 1976. Relationship of Rocky Mountain elk and Rocky Mountain mule deer to timber management in the Blue Mountains of Oregon and Washington. Pages 11-31 in Hieb, S.R., ed. Elk-Logging-Roads Symposium, Univ. Idaho, Moscow. 142pp.

BLOOD, D.A. 1966. Range relationships of elk and cattle in Riding Mountain National Park, Manitoba. Canadian Wildl. Serv., Wildl. Manage. Bull. Ser. 1, 19. 62pp.

BOCK, J.H. and C.E. BOCK. 1985. Patterns of reproduction in Wright's sycamore. Pages 493-494 in Johnson, R.R., C.D. Ziebell, D.R. Patton, P.F. Ffolliott, and R.H. Hamre, tech. coords. Riparian Ecosystems and Their Management: Reconciling Conflicting Uses. Proc. First North Am. Riparian Conf. U.S. Dep. Agric., For. Serv. Gen. Tech. Rep. RM-120. 523pp.

BOEER, W.J. and D.J. SCHMIDLY. 1977. Terrestrial mammals of the riparian corridor in Big Bend National Park. Pages 212-217 in Johnson, R.R and D.A. Jones, eds. Importance, Preservation and Management of Riparian Habitat: A Symposium. U.S. Dep. Agric., For. Serv. Gen. Tech. Rep. RM-43. 217pp.

BRADY, W., D.R. PATTON, and J. PAXSON. 1985. The development of southwestern riparian gallery forests. Pages 39-43 in Johnson, R.R., C.D. Ziebell, D.R. Patton, R.F. Ffolliott, and R.H. Hamre, tech. coords. Riparian Ecosystems and Their Management: Reconciling Conflicting uses. Proc. First North Am. Riparian Conf. U.S. Dep. Agric., For. Serv. Gen. Tech. Rep. RM-120. 523pp.

BRODE, J.M. and R.B. BURY. 1984. The importance of riparian systems to amphibians and reptiles. Pages 30-36 in Warner, R.E. and K.M. Hendrix, eds. California Riparian Systems: Ecology, Conservation, and Productive Management. Univ. California Press, Berkeley. 1035pp.

BROWN, D.E., C.H. LOWE, and C.P. PASE. 1979. A digitized classification system for the biotic communities of North America, with community (series) and association examples for the Southwest. J. Arizona-Nevada Acad. Sci. 14 (Suppl. 1):1-16.

BRUSH, T., B.W. ANDERSON, and R.D. OHMART. 1983. Habitat selection related to resource availability among cavity-nesting birds. Pages 88-89 in Davis, J.W., G.A. Goodwin, and R.A. Ockenfels, tech. coords. Snag Habitat Management: Proc. Symposium. U.S. Dep. Agric., For. Serv. Gen. Tech. Rep. RM-99. 226pp.

BUCK, S.G. 1982. Habitat utilization by fisher near Big Bear, California. M.S. Thesis, Humboldt State Univ., Arcata, CA. 178pp.

BULL, E.L. and J.N. SKOVLEN. 1982. Relationships between anifauna and streamside vegetation. Trans. North. Am. Wildl. Nat. Resour. Conf. 47:496-506.

BURBRIDGE, W.R. and D.J. NEFF. 1976. Coconino National Forest—Arizona Game and Fish Department cooperative roads—wildlife study. Pages 44-57 in Hieb, S.R., ed. Proc. Elk-Logging-Roads Symposium, Univ. Idaho, Moscow.

BURTON, T.M. and G.E. LIKENS. 1975. Salamander population and biomass in the Hubbard Brook experimental forest, New Hampshire. Copeia 1975:541-546.

BURY, R.B. 1979. Population ecology of freshwater turtles in Harless, M. and H. Morlock, eds. Turtles: Prospectives and Research. John Wiley & Sons, Inc., New York, NY. 695pp.

CAROTHERS, S.W., R.R. JOHNSON, and S.W. AITCHISON. 1974. Population structure and social organization of southwestern riparian birds. Am. Zool. 14:97-108.

CEBALLOS, G. 1985. The importance of riparian habitats for the conservation of endangered mammals in Mexico. Pages 96-100 in Johnson, R.R, C.D. Ziebell, D.R. Patton, P.F. Ffolliott, and R.H. Hamre, tech. coords. Riparian Ecosystems and Their Management: Reconciling Conflicting Uses. Proc. First North Am. Riparian Conf. U.S. Dep. Agric., For. Serv. Gen. Tech. Rep. RM-120. 523pp.

CHAIMSON, J.F. 1984. Riparian vegetation planting for flood control. Pages 120-123 in Warner, R.E. and K.M. Hendrix, eds. California Riparian Systems: Ecology, Conservation, and Productive management. Univ. California Press, Berkeley. 1035pp.

CONNOR, R.N., R.G. HOOPER, H.S. CRAWFORD, and H.S. MOSBY. 1975. Woodpecker nesting habitat in cut and uncut woodlands in Virginia. J. Wildl. Manage. 39:144-150.

CORBETT, E.S. and J.A. LYNCH. 1985. Management of streamside zones on municipal watersheds. Pages 187-190 in Johnson, R.R., C.D. Ziebell, D.R. Patton, R.F. Ffolliott, and R.H. Hamre, tech. coords. Riparian Ecosystems and Their Management: Reconciling Conflicting Uses. Proc. First North Am. Riparian Conf. U.S. Dep. Agric., For. Serv. Gen. Tech. Rep. RM-120. 523pp.

CROSS, S.P. 1985. Responses of small mammals to forest riparian perturbations. Pages 269-275 in Johnson, R.R., C.D. Ziebell, D.R. Patton, R.F. Ffolliott, and R.H. Hamre, tech. coords. Riparian Ecosystems and Their Management: Reconciling Conflicting Uses. Proc. First North Am. Riparian Conf. U.S. Dep. Agric., For. Serv. Gen. Tech. Rep. RM-120. 523pp.

CROUCH, G.L. 1978. Effects of protection from livestock grazing on a bottomland wildlife habitat in northeastern Colorado. Pages 118-125 in Graul, W.D. and S.J. Bissell, tech. coords. Lowland River and Stream Habitat in Colorado: A Symposium. Colorado Chap. Wildl. Soc. and Colorado Audubon Council. 195pp.

———. 1982. Wildlife on ungrazed and grazed bottomlands on the South Platte River in northeastern Colorado. Pages 186-197 in Wildlife-Livestock Relationships Symposium. Proc. 10, Univ. Idaho, For. Wildl. Range Exper. Sta., Moscow, ID.

CUMMINS, K.W. 1974. Structure and function of stream ecosystems. BioScience 24:631-641.

DAVIS, G.A. 1977. Management alternatives for the riparian habitat in the Southwest. Pages 59-67 in Johnson, R.R. and D.A. Jones, tech. coords. Importance, Preservation and Management of Riparian Habitat: A Symposium. U.S. Dep. Agric., For. Serv. Gen. Tech. Rep. RM-43. 217pp.

DAVIS, J.W., G.A. GOODWIN, and R.A. OCKENFELS, tech. coords. 1983. Snag habitat management: Proc. of the Symposium. U.S. Dep. Agric., For. Serv. Gen. Tech. Rep. RM-99. 226pp.

DEALY, J.E., D.A. LECKENBY, and D.M. CONCANNON. 1981. Plant communities and their importance to wildlife. Pages 1-66 in Wildlife Habitats in Managed Rangelands—The Great Basin of Southeast Oregon. U.S. Dep. Agric., For. Serv. Gen. Tech. Rep. PNW-120.

DE VOS, A. 1951. Recent findings in fisher and marten ecology and management. Trans. 16th North American Wildl. Conf. 16:498-507.

———. 1952. Ecology and management of fisher and marten in Ontario. Ontario Dep. Lands For. Tech. Bull. 90pp.

DICKSON, J.G., R.N. CONNER, and J.H. WILLIAMSON. 1983. Snag retention increases birds in a clearcut. J. Wildl. Manage. 47:799-809.

DILEANIS, P.D., F.A. BRANSON, and S.K. SORENSON. 1985. Methods for determining effects of controlled dewatering of shallow aquifers on desert phreatophytes in Owens Valley, California. Pages 197-200 in Johnson, R.R., C.D. Ziebell, D.R. Patton, R.F. Ffolliott, and R.H. Hamre, tech. coords. Riparian Ecosystems and Their Management: Reconciling Conflicting Uses. Proc. First North Am. Riparian Conf. U.S. Dep. Agric., For. Serv. Gen. Tech. Rep. RM-120. 523pp.

DUFF, D.A. 1979. Riparian habitat recovery on Big Creek, Rich County, Utah. Pages 91-92 in Proceedings of the Forum—Grazing and Riparian/Stream Ecosystems. Trout Unlimited, Inc. Vienna, VA. 94pp.

DUNN, T. and L.B. LEOPOLD. 1978. Water in environmental planning. W.H. Freeman Co., San Francisco, CA. 818pp.

ENGEL-WILSON, R.W. and R.D. OHMART. 1978. Floral and attendant faunal changes on the lower Rio Grande between Fort Quitman and Presidio, Texas. Pages 139-147 in Johnson, R.R. and J.F. McCormick, tech. coords. Strategies for Protection and Management of Floodplain Wetlands and Other Riparian Ecosystems. Proc. of the Symposium. U.S. Dep. Agric., For. Serv. Gen. Tech. Rep. WO-12. 410pp.

ERMAN, D.C., J.D. NEWBOLD, and K.R. RUBY. 1977. Evaluation of streamside bufferstrips for protecting aquatic organisms. Contr. 165, California Water Resour. Center, Univ. California, Davis. 48pp.

EVANS, K.E. and R.N. CONNOR. 1979. Snag management. Pages 214-225 in DeGraff, R.M. and K.E. Evans, compilers. Management of North-Central and Northeastern Forests for Nongame Birds. U.S. Dep. Agric., For. Serv. Gen. Tech. Rep. NC-51.

EVEREST, F.H. 1977. How to demonstrate the importance of fishery resources to interdisciplinary planning teams. Fisheries 4:15-19.

GAINES, D. 1977. The valley riparian forests of California: Their importance to bird populations. Pages 57-85 in Sands, A., ed. Riparian Forests in California: Their Ecology and Conservation. Inst. Ecology, Univ. California, Davis. 122pp.

GILLEN, R. 1981. 1980 progress report to U.S. Forest Service Pacific Northwest Forest and Range Experiment Station. Under Coop. Aid Program 218, PNW Suppl. 218. Oregon State Univ., Corvallis. 10pp.

GLINSKI, R.L. 1977. Regeneration and distribution of sycamore and cottonwood trees along Sonoita Creek, Santa Cruz County, Arizona. Pages 116-123 in Johnson, R.R. and D.A. Jones, tech. coords. Importance, Preservation and Management of Riparian Habitat: A Symposium. U.S. Dep. Agric., For. Serv. Gen. Tech. Rep. RM-43. 217pp.

GREGORY, K.J. and J.R. MADEW. 1982. Land use changes, flood frequency and channel adjustment. Pages 757-781 in Hey, R.D., J.C. Bathurst, and C.R. Thorne, eds. Gravel-bed. John Wiley & Sons, New York, NY.

GRINNELL, J. 1914. An account of the mammals and birds of the lower Colorado Valley with special reference to the distributional problems presented. Univ. California Publ. Zool. 12:51-294.

———— and T.I. STORER. 1924. Animal life in the Yosemite. Univ. California Press, Berkeley. 952pp.

GROENEVELD, D.P. and T.E. GRIEPENTROG. l985. Interdependence of groundwater, riparian vegetation, and streambank stability: A case study. Pages 44-48 *in* Johnson, R.R., C.D. Ziebell, D.R. Patton, P.F. Ffolliott, and R.H. Hamre, tech. coords. Riparian Ecosystems and Their Management: Reconciling Conflicting Uses. Proc. First North Am. Riparian Conf. U.S. Dep. Agric., For. Serv. Gen. Tech. Rep. RM-l20. 523pp.

GRUBB, T.C., Jr., D.R. PETIT, and D.L. KRUSAC. 1983. Artificial trees for primary cavity nesters. Pages 151-154 *in* Davis, J.W., G.A. Goodwin, and R.A. Ockenfels, tech. coords. Snag Habitat Management: Proceedings of the Symposium. U.S. Dep. Agric., For. Serv. Gen. Tech. Rep. RM-99. 226pp.

HAAPANEN, A. 1965. Bird fauna of the Finnish forests in relation to forest succession. I. Ann. Zool. Fenn. 2:153-196.

HALLBERY, D.L. and G.R. TRAPP. 1984. Gray fox temporal and spatial activity in a riparian/agricultural zone in California's Central Valley. Pages 920-928 *in* Warner, R.E. and K.M. Hendrix, eds. California Riparian Systems: Ecology, Conservation, and Productive Management. Univ. California Press, Berkeley. 1035pp.

HARRIS, L.D. 1984. The fragmented forest—island biogeography theory and the preservation of biotic diversity. Univ. Chicago Press, Chicago, IL. 211pp.

HAUPT, H.F. 1959. A method for controlling sediment from logging roads. U.S. Dep. Agric., For. Serv. Intermountain For. Range Exp. Sta., Misc. Paper 22, Ogden, UT. 22pp.

HEEDE, B. 1985. Interactions between streamside vegetation and stream dynamics. Pages 54-58 *in* Johnson, R.R., C.D. Ziebell, D.R. Patton, R.F. Ffolliott, and R.H. Hamre, tech. coords. Riparian Ecosystems and Their Management: Reconciling Conflicting Uses. Proc. First North Am. Riparian Conf. U.S. Dep. Agric., For. Serv. Gen. Tech. Rep. RM-120. 523pp.

HEHNKE, M. and C.P. STONE. 1978. Value of riparian vegetation to avian populations along the Sacramento River system. Pages 228-235 *in* Johnson, R.R. and J.F. McCormick, tech. coords. Strategies for Protection and Management of Floodplain Wetlands and Other Riparian Ecosystems: Proc. of the Symposium. U.S. Dep. Agric., For. Serv. Gen. Tech. Rep. WO-12., Washington, DC. 410pp.

HIGGINS, A.E. and R.D. OHMART. 1981. Riparian habitat analysis: Tonto National Forest. U.S. Dep. Agric., For. Serv., Tonto Natl. For., Phoenix, AZ.

HINK, V. and R.D. OHMART. 1984. Middle Rio Grande biological survey final report. U.S. Army Corps of Engineers, Albuquerque, NM.

HOOVER, S.L., D.A. KING, and W.J. MATTER. 1985. A wilderness riparian environment: Visitor satisfaction, perceptions, reality, and management. Pages 223-226 *in* Johnson, R.R., C.D. Ziebell, D.R. Patton, P.F. Ffolliott, and R.H. Hamre, tech. coords. Riparian Ecosystems and Their Management: Reconciling Conflicting Uses. Proc. First North Am. Riparian Conf. U.S. Dep. Agric., For. Serv. Gen. Tech. Rep. RM-120. 523pp.

HUBBARD, J.P. 1971. The summer birds of the Gila Valley, New Mexico. Nemouria 2. 35pp.

HULSE, A.C. l974. An autoecological study of *Kinosternon soroniense* LeConte (Chelonia: Kinosternidae). PhD dissertation, Dep. Zool., Arizona State University, Tempe. 105pp.

JOHNSON, R.R. 1978. The lower Colorado River: A western system. Pages 41-55 *in* Johnson, R.R. and J.F. McCormick, tech. coords. Strategies for Protection and Management of Floodplain Wetlands and Other Riparian Ecosystems: Proc. of the Symposium. U.S. Dep. Agric., For. Serv. Gen. Tech. Rep. WO-l2., Washington, DC. 410pp.

———— and S.W. CAROTHERS. 1981. Southwestern riparian habitats and recreation: Interrelationships and impacts in the Rocky Mountain region. Eisenhower Consortium Bulletin. U.S. Dep. Agric., For. Serv. Rocky Mountain For. Range Exp. Sta., Fort Collins, CO.

———— and D.A. JONES, tech. coords. 1977. Importance, preservation and management of riparian habitat: A symposium. U.S. Dep. Agric., For. Serv. Gen. Tech. Rep. RM-43. 217pp.

———— and J.F. MCCORMICK, tech. coords. 1978. Strategies for protection and management of floodplain wetlands and other riparian ecosystems. Proc. Symposium. U.S. Dep. Agric., For. Serv. Gen. Tech. Rep. WO-12. 410pp.

————, C.D. ZIEBELL, D.R. PATTON, P.F. FFOLLIOTT, and R.H. HAMRE, tech. coords. 1985. Riparian ecosystems and their management: reconciling conflicting uses. Proc. First North Am. Riparian Conf. U.S. Dep. Agric., For. Serv. Gen. Tech. Rep. RM-120. 523pp.

JUDD, J.B., J.M. LAUGHLIN, H.R. GUENTHER, and R. HANDERGRADE. 1971. The lethal decline of mesquite on the Casa Grande National Monument. Great Basin Nat. 31:153-159.

KARR, J.R. and I.J. SCHLOSSER. 1977. Impact of near-stream vegetation and stream morphology on water quality and stream biota. Env. Res. Lab. EPA-600/3-77-097, U.S. EPA, Athens, GA. 91pp.

———— and ————. 1978. Water resources and the land-water interface. Science 201:229-234.

KELLERT, S.R. 1980. What do North Americans expect of wildlife management agencies? Proc. 70th Meeting Int. Assoc. Fish. and Wildl. agencies, Washington, DC. 9pp.

KELLY, G.M. 1977. Fisher (*Martes pennanti*) biology in the White Mountains National Forest and adjacent areas. Ph.D. dissertation, Univ. Massachusetts, Amherst. 178pp.

KENNEDY, C.E. 1977. Wildlife conflicts in riparian management: grazing. Pages 49-51 *in* Johnson, R.R. and D.A. Jones, tech. coords. Importance, Preservation and Management of Riparian Habitat: A Symposium. U.S. Dep. Agric., For. Serv. Gen. Tech. Rep. RM-43. 217pp.

KNIGHT, A.W. and R.L. BOTTORFF. 1984. The importance of riparian vegetation to stream ecosystems. Pages 160-167 *in* Warner, R.E. and K.M. Hendrix, eds. California Riparian Systems: Ecology, Conservation, and Productive Management. Univ. California Press, Berkeley. 1035pp.

KNOPF, F.L. 1985. Significance of riparian vegetation to breeding birds across an altitudinal cline. Pages 105-111 *in* Johnson, R.R., C.D. Ziebell, D.R. Patton, P.F. Ffolliott, and R.H. Hamre, tech. coords. Riparian Ecosystems and Their Management: Reconciling Conflicting Uses. Proc. First North Am. Riparian Conf. U.S. Dep. Agric., For. Serv. Gen. Tech. Rep. RM-120. 523pp.

———— and R.W. CANNON. 1981. Structural resilience of a willow riparian community to change in grazing practices *in* Peek, J., ed. Livestock-Wildlife Relationships

Symposium. Univ. Idaho, Moscow.

KRUEGER, H.O. and S.H. ANDERSON. 1985. The use of cattle as a management tool for wildlife in shrub-willow riparian systems. Pages 300-304 *in* Johnson, R.R., C.D. Ziebell, D.R. Patton, P.F. Ffolliott, and R.H. Hamre, tech. coords. Riparian Ecosystems and Their Management: Reconciling Conflicting Uses. Proc. First North Am. Riparian Conf. U.S. Dep. Agric., For. Serv. Gen. Tech. Rep. RM-120. 523pp.

LANG, G.E. and R.K. WEIDER. 1984. The role of beaver in vegetation patterning and development in *Sphagnum*-dominated wetlands in West Virginia. Bull. Ecol. Soc. Am. 65(2):243.

LAURENZI, A.W., R.D. OHMART, and V. HINK. 1983. Classification of mixed broadleaf riparian forest in Tonto National Forest. Pages 72-81 *in* Moir, W.H. and L. Hendzel, tech. coords. Proc. of the Workshop on Southwestern Habitat Types. U.S. Dep. Agric., For. Serv., Southwest Reg., Albuquerque, NM.

LI, R.M. and W.H. SHEN. 1973. Effects of tall vegetation and flow sediment. J. Hydraul. Div., ASCE, Vol. 9, No. HY5, Proc. Paper 9748.

LORZ, H.H. 1974. Ecology and management of brown trout in Little Deschutes River. Oregon Dep. Fish and Wildl. Fish. Res. Rep. 8. 49pp.

LOWE, C.H., ed. 1964. The vertebrates of Arizona. Univ. Arizona Press, Tucson. 270pp.

LYONS, J.K. and R.L. BESCHTA. 1983. Land use, floods, and channel changes, Upper Middle Fork Williamette River, Oregon (1936-1980). Water Resour. Res. 19:436-471.

MACARTHUR, R.H. and J.W. MACARTHUR. 1961. On bird species diversity. Ecology 42:594-598.

MAHONEY, D.L. and D.C. ERMAN. 1984. The role of streamside buffer strips in the ecology of aquatic biota. Pages 168-176 *in* Warner, R.E. and K.M. Hendrix, eds. California Riparian Systems: Ecology, Conservation, and Productive management. Univ. California Press, Berkeley. 1035pp.

MANNAN, R.W., E.C. MESLOW, and H.M WIGHT. 1980. Use of snags by birds in Douglas fir forests, western Oregon. J. Wildl. Manage. 44:787-797.

MARCUM, C.L. 1975. Summer-fall habitat selection and use by a western Montana elk herd. Ph.D. dissertation, Univ. Montana, Missoula. 188pp.

MARCUSON, P.E. 1977. The effects of cattle grazing on brown trout in Rock Creek, Montana. Project F-20-R-21-11-a. Montana Game and Fish, Helena. 28pp.

MARLOW, C.B. and T.M. POGACNIK. 1985. Time of grazing and cattle-induced damage to streambanks. Pages 279-284 *in* Johnson, R.R., C.D. Ziebell, D.R. Patton, P.F. Ffolliott, and R.H. Hamre, tech. coords. Riparian Ecosystems and Their Management: Reconciling Conflicting Uses. Proc. First North Am. Riparian Conf. U.S. Dep. Agric., For. Serv. Gen. Tech. Rep. RM-120. 523pp.

MARTIN, K.E. 1984. Recreation planning as a tool to restore and protect riparian systems. Pages 748-757 *in* Warner, R.E. and K.M. Hendrix, eds. California Riparian Systems: Ecology, Conservation, and Productive Management. Univ. California, Berkeley. 1035pp.

MAY, B. and B. DAVIS. 1982. Practices for livestock grazing and aquatic habitat protection on western rangelands. Pages 271-278 *in* Wildlife-Livestock Relationships Symposium: Proc. 10, Univ. Idaho, Forest, Wildl., Range Exp. Sta., Moscow.

MCLEAN, A., H.H. NICHOLSON, and A.L. VAN RYSWYK.

1963. Growth, productivity and chemical composition of a subalpine meadow in interior British Columbia. J. Range Manage. 16:235-240.

MEENTS, J.K., B.W. ANDERSON, and R.D. OHMART. 1982. Vegetation relationships and food of sage sparrows wintering in honey mesquite habitat. Wilson Bull. 94:129-138.

MEGANK, R.A. and K.C. GIBBS. 1979. A methodology applied to the analysis of selected grazing management strategy and dispersed recreation. Final report to U.S. Dep. Agric., For. Serv., Pacific Northwest For. Range Exp. Sta. under Coop. Aid Prog. PNW-40, Suppl. 57. Oregon State Univ., Corvallis. 67pp.

MERRIAM, C.H. 1890. Results of a biological survey of the San Francisco Mountains region and desert of the Little Colorado in Arizona. U.S. Dep. Agric., North Am. Fauna 3:1-136.

MORING, J.R. 1975. The Alsea watershed study: Effects of logging on the aquatic resources of the headwater streams of the Alsea River, Oregon. Part II. Fishery Res. Rep. 9, Oregon Dep. Fish and Wildlife, Corvallis. 39pp.

MORRIS, R.H. 1984. Planning recreation development and wildlife enhancement in a riparian environment at Oristimba Creek. Pages 767-772 *in* Warner, R.E. and K.M. Hendrix, eds. California Riparian Systems: Ecology, Conservation, and Productive Management. Univ. California, Berkeley. 1035pp.

MOSCONI, S.L. and R.L. HUTTO. 1982. The effects of grazing on land birds of a western Montana riparian habitat. Pages 221-233 *in* Wildlife-Livestock Relationships Symposium: Proc. 10, Univ. Idaho For. Wildl. Range Exp. Sta., Moscow.

MOULTON, M. 1978. Small mammal associations in grazed versus ungrazed cottonwood riparian woodland in eastern Colorado: A symposium. Pages 133-140. Colorado Chap. Wildl. Soc. and Colorado Audubon Council, Greeley. 195pp.

MULLIS, C. 1985. Habitat utilization by fisher (*Martes pennanti*) near Hayfork Bally, California. M.S. Thesis, Humboldt State Univ., Arcata, CA.

MURPHY, M.L. and J.D. HALL. 1981. Varied effects of clearcut logging on predators and their habitat in small streams of the Cascade Mountains, Oregon. Can. J. Fish. Aquat. Sci. 38:137-145.

NELSON, J.R. and D.G. BURNELL. 1975. Elk-cattle competition in central Washington. Pages 71-83 *in* Range Multiple Use Management. Univ. Idaho, Moscow.

NELSON, L., Jr. and J.K. HOOPER. 1976. California fur bearers and their management. Univ. California, Coop. Ext. Serv., Leaflet 2721, Berkeley.

NEWBOLD, J.D., D.C. ERMAN, and K.B. RUBY. 1980. Effects of logging on macroinvertebrates in streams with and without bufferstrips. Can. J. Fish. Aquat. Sci. 37:1076-1085.

NUSSBAUM, R.A. 1974. The distributional ecology and life history of the Siskiyou Mountain salamander (*Plethodon stormi*), in relation to the potential impact of the proposed Applegate Reservoir on this species. Rep. submitted to U.S. Army Corps of Engineers, Portland, OR. 52pp.

OHMART, R.D. and B.W. ANDERSON. 1974. Vegetation management: Annual report. Submitted to U.S. Dep. Inter., Bureau of Reclamation, Boulder City, NV.

——— and ———. 1982. North American desert riparian ecosystems. Pages 433-479 *in* Bender, G.L., ed. Reference Handbook on the Deserts of North America.

Greenwood Press, Westport, CT. 594pp.

OLSON, R.W. and C.L. ARMOUR. 1979. Economic considerations for improved livestock management approaches for fish and wildlife in riparian/stream areas. Pages 67-71 *in* Cope, O.B., ed. Forum—Grazing and Riparian/Stream Ecosystems. Trout Unlimited, Inc. Vienna, VA. 94pp.

OREGON-WASHINGTON INTERAGENCY WILDLIFE COUNCIL. 1978. Managing riparian zones for fish and wildlife in eastern Oregon and eastern Washington. Unpubl. rep.

ORR, R.T. 1940. The rabbits of California. Occ. Papers. California Acad. Sci. 19:1-227.

PARKER, M., F. WOOD, Jr., B.H. SMITH, and R.G. ELDER. 1985. Erosional downcutting in lower order riparian ecosystems: Have historical changes been caused by removal of beaver? Pages 35-38 *in* Johnson, R.R., C.D. Ziebell, D.R. Patton, P.F. Ffolliott, and R. H. Hamre, tech. coords. Riparian Ecosystems and Their Management: Reconciling Conflicting Uses. Proc. First North Am. Riparian Conf. U.S. Dep. Agric., For. Serv. Gen. Tech. Rep. RM-120. 523pp.

PAULSEN, H.A., Jr. 1969. Forage value on a mountain grassland aspen range in western Colorado. J. Range Manage. 22:102-107.

PEDERSON, R.J., A.W. ADAMS, and J. SKOVLIN. 1979. Elk management in Blue Mountain habitats. Oregon Dep. Fish and Wildl., Portland. 27pp.

PETERSON, A.W. and T.C. GRUBB, Jr. 1983. Artificial trees as a cavity substrate for woodpeckers. J. Wildl. Manage. 47:790-798.

PLATTS, W.S. 1979. Livestock grazing and riparian/stream ecosystems—An overview. Pages 39-45 in Cope, O.B., ed. Proc. of the Forum—Grazing and Riparian/Stream Ecosystems. Trout Unlimited, Inc., Vienna, VA. 94pp.

———. 1984. Riparian system/livestock grazing interaction research in the intermountain West. Pages 424-429 *in* Warner, R.E. and K.M. Hendrix, eds. California Riparian Systems: Ecology, Conservation, and Productive Management. Univ. California, Berkeley. 1035pp.

———, K.A. GEBHARDT, and W.L. JACKSON. 1985. The effects of large storm events on basin-range riparian stream habitats. Pages 30-34 *in* Johnson, R.R., C.D. Ziebell, D.R. Patton, P.F. Ffolliott, and R. H. Hamre, tech. coords. Riparian Ecosystems and Their Management: Reconciling Conflicting Uses. Proc. First North Am. Riparian Conf. U.S. Dep. Agric., For. Serv. Gen. Tech. Rep. RM-120. 523pp.

——— and R.L. NELSON. 1983. Population and generic differentiation in the Humboldt cutthroat trout of Gance Creek, Nevada. Pages 15-19 *in* California-Nevada Wildl. Trans.

———, O. CASEY, and V. CRISPIN. 1983. Riparian-stream habitat conditions on Tabor Creek, Nevada, under grazed and ungrazed conditions. Pages 10-14 *in* Proc. Ann. Conf. Western Assoc. Fish and Wildl. Agencies. 63:10-14.

REID, E.H. and G.D. PICKFORD. 1946. Judging mountain meadow range condition in eastern Oregon and eastern Washington. U.S. Dep. Agric., Circular 748.

RICE, J., B.W. ANDERSON, and R.D. OHMART. 1984. Comparison of the importance of different habitat attributes of avian community organization. J. Wildl. Manage. 48:895-911.

ROATH, L.R. and W.C. KRUEGER. 1982. Cattle grazing influence on a mountain riparian zone. J. Range Manage. 35:100-104.

RUBY, K.B., D.C. ERMAN, and J.D. NEWBOLD. 1977. Biological assessment of timber management activity impacts and bufferstrip effectiveness on National Forest streams of northern California. Earth Resources Monogr. 1, U.S. Dep. Agric., For. Serv., Reg. 5, San Francisco, CA. 170pp.

SALWASSER, H. and K. SHIMAMOTO. 1984. Pronghorn, cattle and feral horse use of wetland and upland habitats. Pages 210-213 *in* Warner, R.E. and K.M. Hendrix, eds. California Riparian Systems: Ecology, Conservation, and Productive Management. Univ. California, Berkeley. 1035pp.

SCOTT, L.B. 1984. Economic values of three furbearers inhabiting California riparian systems. Pages 731-738 *in* Warner, R.E. and K.M. Hendrix, eds. California Riparian Systems: Ecology, Conservation, and Productive Management. Univ. California, Berkeley. 1035pp.

SCOTT, V.E. 1979. Bird responses to snag removal in ponderosa pine. J. Forestry. 77:26-28.

———, K.E. EVANS, D.R. PATTON, and C.P. STONE. 1977. Cavity-nesting birds of North American forests. U.S. Dep. Agric., For. Serv. Agric. Handbook 511, Washington, DC. 112pp.

SEVERSON, K.E. and C.E. BOLDT. 1978. Cattle, wildlife, and riparian habitats in the western Dakotas. Pages 94-103 *in* Management and Use of Northern Plain Rangeland. Reg. Rangeland Symp., Bismarck, ND.

SIEKERT, R.E., Q.D. SKINNER, M.A. SMITH, J.L. DODD, and J.D. RODGERS. 1985. Channel response of an ephemeral stream in Wyoming to selected grazing treatments. Pages 276-278 *in* Johnson, R.R., C.D. Ziebell, D.R. Patton, P.F. Ffolliott, and R. H. Hamre, tech. coords. Riparian Ecosystems and Their Management: Reconciling Conflicting Uses. Proc. First North Am. Riparian Conf. U.S. Dep. Agric., For. Serv. Gen. Tech. Rep. RM-120. 523pp.

SKOVLIN, J.M. 1967. Fluctuations in forage quality on summer range in the Blue Mountains. U.S. Dep. Agric., For. Serv. PNW-Res. Paper 44.

———. 1984. Impacts of grazing on wetlands and riparian habitat: A review of our knowledge. Pages 1001-1104 *in* Committee on Developing Strategies for Rangeland Management. Natl. Resour. Council/Natl. Acad. Sci., Westview Press, Boulder, CO.

———, R.W. HARRIS, G.S. STRICKLER, and G.A. GARRISON. 1976. Effects of cattle grazing methods on ponderosa pine-bunchgrass range in the Pacific Northwest. U.S. Dep. Agric., Tech. Bull. 1531. Washington, DC. 40pp.

———, W.R. MEEHAN, J.C. BUCKHOUSE, and M. VAVRA. 1977. A method of study for determining the influence of grazing on riparian and aquatic habitats in the Blue Mountains of Oregon. Pages 164-169 *in* Livestock Interactions with Wildlife, Fisheries, and Their Environments. Proceedings of the Symposium. U.S. Dep. Agric., For. Serv. Pacific Southwest For. Range Exp. Sta., Berkeley, CA.

SMITH, F. 1977. A short review of the status of riparian forests in California. Pages 1-2 *in* Sands, A., ed. Riparian Forests in California: Their Ecology and Conservation. Inst. Ecol., Publ. 15, Univ. California, Davis. 122pp.

STAMP, N. and R.D. OHMART. 1979. Rodents of desert shrub and riparian woodland habitats in the Sonoran Desert. Southwestern Nat. 24:279-289.

SULLIVAN, B.K. 1981. Distribution and relative abundance of snakes along a transect in California. J. Herpert.

15:247-248.

SWANSON, F.J., S.V. GREGORY, J.R. SEDELL, and A.G. CAMPBELL. 1982. Land-water interactions: The riparian zone. Pages 267-291 *in* Analysis of Coniferous Forest Ecosystems in the Western United States. US/IBP Synthesis Series 14, Hutchinson Ross Publ. Co., Stroudsburg, PA.

SZARO, R.C., S.C. BELFIT, J.K. AITKIN, and J.N. RINNE. 1985. Impact of grazing on a riparian garter snake. Pages 359-363 *in* Johnson, R.R., C.D. Ziebell, D.R. Patton, P.F. Ffolliott, and R. H. Hamre, tech. coords. Riparian Ecosystems and Their Management: Reconciling Conflicting Uses. Proc. First North Am. Riparian Conf. U.S. Dep. Agric., For. Serv. Gen. Tech. Rep. RM-120. 523pp.

THOMAS, J.W., C. MASER, and J.E. RODIEK. 1979. Wildlife habitat in managed rangelands—the Great Basin of southeastern Oregon-riparian zone. U.S. Dep. Agric., For. Serv. Gen. Tech. Rep. RNW-80. 18pp.

———, R.J. MILLER, H. BLACK, J.E. RODIEK, and C. MASER. 1976. Guidelines for maintaining and enhancing wildlife habitat in forest management in the Blue Mountains of Oregon and Washington. Trans. North Am. Wildl. Nat. Resour. Conf. 41:452-476.

U.S. COUNCIL ON ENVIRONMENTAL QUALITY. 1978. Environmental quality. The ninth report of the Council on Environmental Quality. U.S. Govt. Printing Office, Washington, DC. (Stock No. 041-011-00040-8). 599pp.

U.S. DEPARTMENT OF AGRICULTURE, FOREST SERVICE. 1972. Western regional working conference—results of work group sessions—delegate meetings. National Program of Research for Forest and Associated Rangelands. U.S. Dep. Agric., For. Serv. Intermountain For. Range Exper. Sta., Ogden, UT. 39pp.

U.S. DEPARTMENT OF THE INTERIOR, BUREAU OF LAND MANAGEMENT. 1978. Recreational carrying capacity in the California Desert. U.S. Dep. Inter., Bur. Land Manage., Sacramento, CA. 115pp.

———. 1980. The California desert conservation area plan. U.S. Govt. Printing Office, San Francisco, CA.

U.S. DEPARTMENT OF THE INTERIOR, BUREAU OF RECLAMATION. 1979. Pecos River Basin water salvage project: Final environmental statement. U.S. Dep. Inter., Bur. Rec., Southwest Reg. Off., Amarillo, TX.

VAN VELSON, R. 1979. Effects of livestock grazing upon rainbow trout in Otter Creek, Nebraska. Pages 53-55 *in* Cope, O.B., ed. Proc. of the Forum—Grazing and Riparian/Stream Ecosystems. Trout Unlimited, Inc., Vienna, VA. 94pp.

WARNER, R.E., recorder. 1979a. Fish and wildlife resource needs in riparian ecosystems: Proc. of a workshop. Nat. Water Resour. Analysis Group, Eastern Energy and Land Use Team, U.S. Dep. Inter., Fish Wildl. Serv., Kearneysville, WV. 53pp.

———. 1979b. California riparian study program: Background information and proposed study design. Planning Branch, California Dep. Fish and Game, Sacramento. 177pp.

——— and K.M. HENDRIX, eds. 1984. California riparian systems: Ecology, conservation, and productive management. Univ. California Press, Berkeley. 1035pp.

WAUER, R.H. 1977. Significance of Rio Grande riparian systems upon the avifauna. Pages 165-174 *in* Johnson, R.R. and D.A. Jones, tech. coords. Importance, Preservation and Management of Riparian Habitat: A Symposium. U.S. Dep. Agric., For. Serv. Gen. Tech. Rep. RM-43. 217pp.

WEBSTER'S NEW COLLEGIATE DICTIONARY. 1979. G.&C. Merriam Co., Springfield, MA. 1532pp.

WILLIAMS, D.F. 1985. Mammalian species of special concern in California. California Dep. Fish and Game, Nongame Wildl. Invest., Final Rep., Project E-W-4, IV-14.l. Sacramento. 184pp.

——— and K.S. KILBURN. 1984. Sensitive, threatened, and endangered mammals of riparian and other wetland communities in California. Pages 950-957 *in* Warner, R.E. and K.M. Hendrix, eds. California Riparian Systems: Ecology, Conservation, and Productive Management. Univ. California Press, Berkeley. 1035pp.

WINEGAR, H.H. 1977. Camp Creek channel fencing—plant, wildlife, soil, and water response. Rangeman's J. 4:10-12.

WINTERNITZ, B.L. 1973. Ecological patterns in a montane breeding bird community. Ph.D. dissertation, Univ. Colorado, Boulder.

——— 1976. Temporal change and habitat preference of some montane breeding birds. Condor 78:383-393.

——— and H. CAHN. 1983. Nestholes in live and dead aspen. Pages 102-106 *in* Davis, J.W., G.A. Goodwin, and R.A. Ockenfels, tech. coords. Snag Habitat Management: Proceedings of the Symposium. U.S. Dep. Agric., For. Serv. Gen. Tech. Rep. RM-99. 226pp.

YOUNG, R.A., T. HUNTRODS, and W. ANDERSON. 1980. Effectiveness of vegetated bufferstrips in controlling pollution from feedlot runoff. J. Environ. Qual. 9:483-487.

10

MARSHES

Milton W. Weller

Department of Wildlife & Fisheries Sciences
Texas A&M University
College Station, TX   77843

"Greater familiarity with marshes on the part of
more people could give man a truer and a more
wholesome view of himself in relation to Nature.
. . . Marshes comprise their own form of wilderness.
They have their own life-rich genuineness and reflect
forces that are much older, much more permanent,
and much mightier than man."

———Paul L. Errington, from *Of Men and
Marshes*

*Editor's Note: Wetlands compose a small percentage
of lands in the western U.S., but their importance
for wildlife far outweighs their acreage. In this publication, marshes are considered to be wetlands associated with standing water. Among the most
complex habitats, marshes are therefore most difficult to inventory or monitor. As the author emphasizes, evaluation, impact assessment, and management decisions require first-hand, mud-on-your-
boots experience in the marsh.*

INTRODUCTION

Marshes, the dynamic meeting places of land
and water, are among the most productive and exciting of all wildlife habitats. Not only do they attract a
great diversity of wildlife, but numbers of some species can be overwhelming. As a result, the value of
marshes for recreation such as hunting or bird
watching can outweigh those activities on far larger
tracts of other habitats. Moreover, their values in
damping flood surges, in water purification, and in
water recharge make marshes highly important. Inventory and monitoring are essential to identify critical habitats and resource values. With this knowledge biologists can develop management alternatives
or mitigation plans on these numerically restricted
but highly valued habitats.

Wetlands are characterized by hydric soils and
water-loving plants (Cowardin et al. 1979). Of the
many diverse types of wetlands, marshes are the
most widely distributed and the best-known form.
They are dominated by emergent plants such as cattail (*Typha* sp.), bulrushes (*Scirpus* sp.), sedges
(*Carex* sp.), and water-tolerant grasses. The general
height and structure of such plant communities distinguish marshes from swamps (wooded and shrub-
dominated wetlands) or from bogs (moss and heath-
covered wet organic soils). Whereas swamps and
bogs are restricted in distribution by climatic regime, marshes may be found anywhere. They are the
characteristic wetland of intermountain lowlands of
the western U.S. where they form a true oasis for
wildlife, both aquatic and terrestrial.

Marshes often are complete entities, found in
shallow basins. The term may also be used for any
emergent hydrophyte community. The emphasis
here is on shallow basins that are marshes in the
geomorphic as well as biological sense.

Water is the driving force in determining wetland type and habitat quality. Water permanency and
associated vegetation are key factors in classifying
wetlands. Because water cycles are variable, marshes
are rarely constant. These fluctuations induce "boom
and bust" in wildlife numbers, but are essential to
nutrient recycling. In shallow marshes such as

ephemeral prairie potholes, dense vegetation produced during natural drawdowns is the major food for detritus-feeding macroinvertebrates (those larger aquatic invertebrates visible to the unaided eye) which are in turn important food resources for waterbirds and fish (McKnight and Low 1969; Krapu 1974). In deeper marshes or shallow lakes, drying allows decomposition of bottom organic deposits that provide nutrients for a new surge of vegetation that germinates under the low water conditions.

The character of marshes—water, sediment, organic matter, and dense vegetation—makes walking or boating difficult. The tendency is to circle around the area rather than go through it. But evaluation, impact assessment, and management decisions require first-hand experience in the marsh. It is hoped that this chapter will provide the inducement to gain this experience.

Bureau of Biological Survey employees, 1935.

Because of the dynamics of water and season, observations of conditions or populations in a single year have relatively little meaning except when viewed in relation to the following: (1) past records of the same marsh, or (2) a predicted potential based on knowledge of similar wetlands for which data are available. Long-term monitoring is vital to understanding the quality, importance, and condition of a marsh.

Losses of wetlands occur in many ways. Drainage for agriculture is the major cause of loss of marshes (Frayer et al. 1983). Filling of small marshes for agriculture and other uses occurs occasionally, but even large marshes have been filled for urban and industrial development. Because marshes that have constant water levels become lake-like, permanent flooding may have serious detrimental impacts on marsh wildlife (Weller 1981b). The impact of total loss is obvious. Less measurable negative influences include modified water flow, increased eutrophication or turbidity, and introduction of exotic animals or plants. These impacts are both long-term and widespread, but they are difficult to assess without ecological and biological baseline data for making comparisons.

A number of wildlife species inhabiting western marshes are classified as endangered, mostly because of disappearing habitats. Three subspecies of Clapper Rail—Yuma (*Rallus longirostris yumaensis*), California (*R. l. obsoletus*), and Light-footed (*R. l. levipes*)—are endangered due to loss of river or coastal marsh. The salt marsh harvest mouse (*Reithrodontomys raviventris*) now occurs in only a few scattered marshes in San Francisco Bay. Wetlands are important not only for local wildlife populations but also for migratory birds, a national and international resource. Protection, restoration, and management of marshes are essential to restore these species.

Yuma clapper rail.

CLASSIFICATION SYSTEMS AND DESCRIPTORS FOR MARSHES

Interest in wetlands has been dominated by biologists studying semiaquatic animal and plant life. Acquisition of marshes was promoted by waterfowl hunters, fur trappers, and fishery managers. Different species of wildlife were associated with different types of marshes, and efforts to preserve species through acquisition or management required a method of choosing different wetlands and assessing how many of each existed. Hence, biologists developed classification systems to broadly define and inventory wetlands (e.g., Martin et al. 1953).

A classic document by Shaw and Fredine (1956) outlined 20 types of wetlands across the U.S., described their use by wildlife, and estimated the extent of losses since the earliest surveys. A significant advancement was made in classification precision by a detailed regional study in the North Dakota prairie pothole region (Stewart and Kantrud 1971). This system is strongly influenced by data on water permanence and vegetation patterns. The system devised by Millar (1979) for western Canada also used data on basin, area, watershed, and other limnological variables to develop a precise classification system that could be used when wetlands were dry or devoid of vegetation. Data on wildlife generally have not been used as a means of defining or clarifying types of wetlands except by Bergman et al. (1977) for Alaskan tundra wetlands.

With the advent of widespread interest in wetland values for food chain support systems, flood and erosion control, and energy and sewage treatment, a broader classification system was needed. An interagency task force, headed by the U.S. Fish and Wildlife Service, devised a system ranging from the general to more and more specific. Known as the "Classification of Wetlands and Deepwater Habitats of the United States" (Cowardin et al. 1979), it is being used for the National Wetland Inventory. It is hierarchical, like a taxonomic key. All wetlands are first placed into one of five "systems" by means of ecological terms of broad usage:

Palustrine	vegetated wetlands such as marshes
Estuarine	brackish water which may include marshes or swamps
Lacustrine	lake-like
Riverine	stream-related but not including marshes or oxbow lakes
Marine	deepwater habitats

These systems are then divided into subsystems except for Palustrine wetlands. The Palustrine System is divided into units called Classes which are based on dominant vegetative type. A marsh is termed an Emergent Wetland as opposed to a Moss-lichen Wetland (bog) or a Forested Wetland (swamp). Further subdivisions allow more and more precise descriptors, so that Emergent Wetlands can be divided into subclasses by the presence of persistent (lasting over winter or more) plants such as cattail or bulrushes, to the nonpersistent (rapidly decomposing) plants such as arrowhead (*Sagittaria* sp.) or dock (*Rumex* sp.). The precise plant species or community is referred to as **dominance type,** which allows a rather precise taxonomic description of the community. However, the habitat significance of these descriptors is not evident from the classification.

Sagittaria breviorstra

On a local basis, some of the earlier classification systems are still in use and may be extremely helpful in wildlife evaluations. They should be used as an addition to rather than replacement for the interagency system.

For the western U.S., especially the glaciated pothole region, the Stewart and Kantrud (1971) system is useful because of the use of common terms related to hydroperiods. Classes I through V reflect pattern of flooding or mean water depth and are self explanatory: **Ephemeral, Temporary, Seasonal, Semipermanent,** and **Permanent.** Special wetland classes include VI-**Alkali ponds** and shallow lakes rich in submergents and VII-**Fens** (or alkaline bogs). Subclasses were used to denote five ranges from fresh to subsaline.

Because wetlands are so dynamic in water level, a wetland of the same class can range from bare mud flat to emergent vegetation through the action of water levels and herbivores (Weller and Spatcher 1965; Weller and Fredrickson 1974). Special terminology reflecting those short-term successional stages was used by Stewart and Kantrud (1971) to assist in detailed descriptions: emergent phase, open-water phase, drawdown phase, and bare-soil phase—the last two inducing germination conditions that ultimately result in reestablishment of emergent vegetation.

Another set of descriptive terms denotes the typical combination of plants found under mean prevailing water conditions as well as topography. Millar's (1979) system uses traditional terms for vegetation zones of large wetlands, or for classifying a marsh by the vegetation of the central part of the marsh:

1. wet meadow
2. shallow marsh
3. emergent deep marsh
4. open water marsh
5. shallow open water
6. open alkali wetland
7. disturbed areas (due to drought or agricultural activities).

A wet-meadow community is made up mostly of nonpersistent annuals and is commonly flooded only in spring. A deep marsh is dominated by those persistent perennials in the center that do well with regular flooding, but the edge will have species characteristic of wet meadow or shallow marsh.

Most classification and inventory systems deal with one basin or a part of one basin. Yet values for wildlife and fish are enhanced by the proximity of several different wetlands. The importance of contiguity has not been documented, but birds and mammals move from area to area. Adult fish that move from lakes to wetlands to spawn, or fry that mature in nursery marshes, must have connecting links (Forney 1968). Such relations sometimes can be detected from aerial photographs or detailed maps, but the extra value to be placed on such spatial relationships is uncertain. Data need to be gathered and analyzed from this perspective because acquisition, protection, and management of marshes would be strongly influenced by this information.

One of the most difficult descriptive decisions of wetlands is the demarcation of the wetland boundary. Marsh edges often grade imperceptibly into the uplands, and plants at the marsh edge may be tolerant of both wet and dry conditions. Moreover, the hydrologic influence of a wetland may affect upland vegetation since increased water availability near the wetland may encourage or maintain terrestrial vegetation that might otherwise not exist.

Coastal wetlands may have the additional complicating variables of lunar tidal regime, wind and storm surges, and salinity. These too are dynamic processes with tides varying seasonally, and freshwater inflow varying with rainfall. At times, estuarine marshes may be totally fresh due to high rates of inflow, whereas marine storm tides may modify and even reverse the situation periodically. As a result, a much reduced flora dominated by grasses such as salt marsh cordgrasses (*Spartina* sp.) and saltgrass (*Distichlis spicata*) characterizes vast areas of coastal marsh. Mean tide ranges have produced zones of high (less commonly flooded) and low (wet) marsh based on the relative degree of flooding and the influence of salt water (Nixon 1982; Zedler 1982).

MAJOR SPECIES GROUPS

The availability of water, diverse plants, and rich invertebrate life make marshes ideal for many species of wildlife and fish. Some species evolved with more permanent water and are equipped with gills for total water emersion throughout life (fish and some salamanders) or for part of their life cycle (most salamanders, frogs, and toads). Others are semiaquatic, being air breathers throughout life as a secondary adaptation to fluctuating water regimes found in marshes. Some species have highly modified feet (beaver, *Castor canadensis,* and river otters, *Lutra canadensis*) or flattened tails for swimming (muskrats, *Ondatra zibethicus*). Some avian species have long legs for wading (herons and storks), or adaptions for swimming and diving (ducks and grebes). Still other species retain greater range of habitat by means of less inhibiting adaptations to water, but are common around marshes (mink, *Mustela vision,* and raccoons, *Procyon lotor*). All degrees of variation are found between these extremes. Some species frequent marsh areas and exploit their resources without being intimately associated. Swallows and bats, for example, catch insects there but do not use marshes for nesting or cover. Some terrestrial species may invade during drawdown stages to seek out stranded invertebrates or fish. Red foxes (*Vulpes vulpes*) take advantage of muskrats unprotected by water or lodges.

A review of some common taxonomic groups will facilitate a view of the more complex communities of vertebrates common to marshes of the western U.S. For further detail, see Weller (1979a).

Fish

Considering both freshwater (about 95) and estuarine (about 109) species, wetlands serve over 200 species on a national basis (Adamus 1983). Interior palustrine wetlands may have several species or none at all. The most abundant are small minnow-like fishes that feed on tiny invertebrates, such as mosquito fish (*Gambusia* sp.). Other species include herbivores or omnivores like crappie (*Pomoxis* sp.) and bluegill (*Lepomis macrochirus*); herbivore-detritivores like carp (*Cyprinus carpio*); and carnivores like walleye (*Stizostedium vitreum*), pike (*Esox lucius*), and largemouth bass (*Macropterus sal-*

moides). The exact complement varies with size and permanence of the water. Association with source streams may contribute to pioneering. Oxygen shortage is perhaps the most important limiting influence because marshes may be oxygen depleted during the summer.

Amphibians

Dominant amphibians range from the most aquatic sirens (*Siren* sp.) that have gills throughout life, to frogs that breathe air as adults. Some frogs stay in or near water always (bullfrogs, *Rana catesbeiana*). Others stay near water but feed in wet meadows and grassy areas (northern leopard frogs, *Rana pipiens*). A few are highly terrestrial species that associate with moist forest most of the year (tree frogs, *Hyla* sp.). The most terrestrial amphibians are toads (*Bufo* sp.) that range in habitat from moist uplands to near-desert. Amphibians are important as food for various fish, reptile, avian, and mammalian predators.

Reptiles

Although the species vary locally, turtles are the most widespread and often abundant reptilian predator or omnivore in marshes. Some like the musk turtles (*Sternotherus* sp.), mud turtles (*Kinosternon* sp.), cooters and sliders (*Pseudemys* sp.) loaf on logs or vegetation in the sun and are conspicuous. A few are true marsh turtles, found nowhere else: Blanding's turtle (*Emydoidea blandingii*) and chicken turtles (*Deirochelys reticularia*). Others like the common (*Chelydra* sp.) and alligator snapping turtles (*Macroclemys temminckii*) may be inconspicuous until they move into uplands during egg-laying or are exposed during droughts. Snakes, especially water snakes of the genus *Nerodius,* are widespread. The massasauga (*Sistrurus catenatus*) occurs in either swamps or wet prairies. Some species like rat snakes (*Elapha* sp.) and garter snakes (*Thamnophis* sp.) go into any habitat, including marshes, for birds and their eggs.

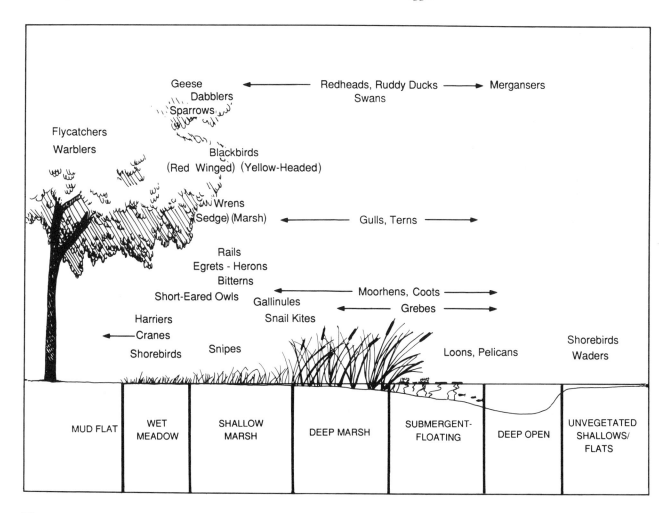

Figure 1. Waterbirds of wetlands—with emphasis on habitat selection for breeding and feeding.

Birds

Over 140 species of birds are associated with wetlands intimately or casually (Adamus 1983). Like fish, but with still greater flexibility, birds may use marshes only part of the year to fulfill certain life functions. These include summer breeding and feeding sites (see Figure 1), molting sites (ducks), feeding sites away from the nest (pelicans and waders), migration stops (shore birds, ducks, and geese), food exploration zones (most waders moving north after breeding), and wintering (all migratory species). Although breeding sites tend to be valued more highly, each area plays a vital role in the life cycle of mobile species. All are essential.

Mammals

Compared with other classes of vertebrates, few mammals are semiaquatic and very few are adapted to marshes. Lack of species numbers is compensated for by numbers of individuals. Several small rodents characteristic of damp areas swim easily and do not avoid water or flooded areas: marsh rice rat (*Oryzomys palustris*) in Gulf Coast marshes (Esher et al. 1978), and California vole (*Microtus californicus*) in tidal marshes (Fisler 1961). Both are omnivorous. Beavers may create their own marsh by damming of streams, but also use large marshes and build lodges of willows and cattail.

Communities of Vertebrates

Species associations and numbers are influenced by (1) plant structure, (2) size and diversity of the unit, and (3) water depth and permanence. Hence, a wet meadow dominated by nonpersistent, temporary plants and water cover is likely to be used for breeding by smaller species requiring only low cover (sparrows, mice, rats, shore birds, rails) or by transients using the area for food (muskrats, shorebirds,

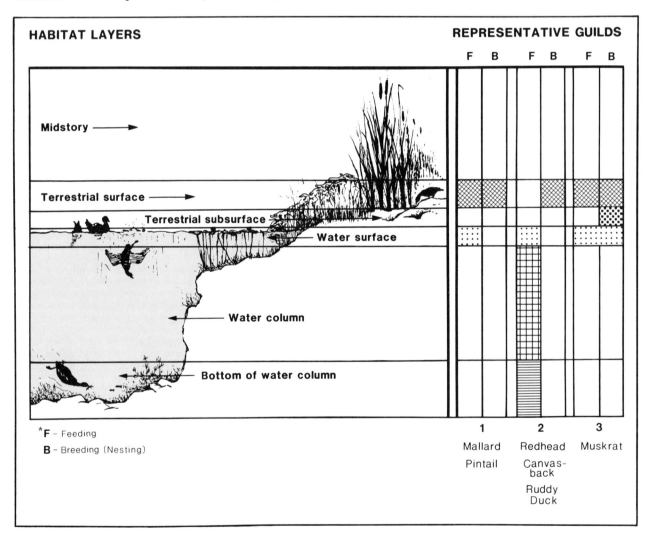

Relationship between habitat layers and guilds.

waders, dabbling ducks). Shallow marshes may harbor nesting king rails (*Rallus elegans*), purple gallinules (*Porphyrula martinica*) or common moorhens (*Gallinula chloropus*), and species of blackbirds that vary by geographic area. More persistent and taller vegetation of deep marshes support larger species that need cover, support for nests, and the foods induced by more permanent water (diving ducks, swans, cranes, some geese, American coots [*Fulica atra*], bitterns, and wader colonies).

Because many vertebrates may use the general structural layer of vegetation, ecologists often use the term **guild** to reflect taxonomically unrelated species that use the same habitat in the same way (Short and Burnham 1982). In marshes, bird nests may be built at three layers: (1) in tall and robust emergents, (2) in short and nonpersistent emergents, and (3) at the water's surface. For feeding, birds may forage in all three of the nesting layers, and divers may seek foods in the water column or on the bottom.

Surface feeding birds that specialize on foliage include gadwall (*Anas strepera*) and American widgeon (*Anas americana*). Northern shovelers (*Anas clypeata*) can feed in the open because they can strain plankton or in shallow water where they may eat snails or seeds. Phalaropes prey on plankton forms by swimming and picking. Blue-winged teal (*Anas discors*), however, are typical of many dabblers that have generalized bill structure and food habits. These species can take invertebrates in summer when hens need protein for eggs and young need it for body growth (Swanson, et al. 1979), or seeds and foliage in nonbreeding periods. Predators include mergansers, grebes and loons, and others that feed on fish in open marshes. Mink may occur around or in any of these wetland types, but dens are most common by semipermanent water, presumably because of the food supply.

CRITICAL HABITAT FEATURES

To appreciate the features of a marsh that make it valuable to wildlife, it is essential to relate these components to wildlife needs. Regardless of the climatic conditions or the season, wildlife often seek shelter from sun, wind, rain, and hail. Cover also is essential for protection from predators. No wonder predatory mink and weasels are long-bodied, and aerial predators like the northern harrier (*Circus cyaneus*) hover to follow and catch their prey.

The concentrated nutrients of the marsh produce high primary productivity in plants. The secondary production of invertebrates produces an array of potential food exceeded in few if any habitats.

The major herbivores in marshes are mammals like muskrats which not only eat leaves and tubers of various emergent plants but build lodges for winter use, thereby cutting vast quantities of emergents. Geese, especially Snow Geese (*Anser coerulescens*), also may utilize tubers and rootstocks in wintering areas. Swans, widgeons, gadwalls, and coots devour huge quantities of submergent vegetation. Additionally, many bottom (benthic) invertebrates utilize decomposing plant matter, or feed on tiny organisms like bacteria and fungi that live on old stems. Invertebrate abundance must be directly related to plant productivity at an earlier stage, but there has been little effort at quantitating such energy flow in freshwater marshes.

Marsh vegetation is vital for many species of birds that nest—often colonially—in marshes: ibis, egrets, herons, grebes, ducks, gulls, etc. Diverse vegetation, whether it be for food, cover, or nest substrate, clearly influences the potential richness of species found in the system by its various heights, coverage, foods potential, and food-chain support for other lower organisms.

Water Chemistry and Plant Communities

Water that enters a marsh is a product of precipitation and hydrologic processes. Much of the water may enter the system from surface runoff and slow moving underground flows at various depths. The timing of water availability (hydroperiod) and depth determine the character and type of marsh through influence on chemical characteristics of the water and subsequently on vegetation and invertebrates used by wildlife.

Typically, rainwater carries with it few dissolved chemicals except where it collects wind-driven soil particles or salt spray. Water that flows over soil or rock strata or through porous substrates may dissolve and carry a wide range of dissolved solids which may serve as plant nutrients or, in extreme instances, be so concentrated as to be toxic to life. Thus, general characters of the water in marshes and lakes reflect the character of the watershed as shown by Moyle (1945) in Minnesota and Metcalf (1931) in North Dakota. Moyle's work spanned more diverse water chemistry and plant types, which he classified as (1) soft waters (low dissolved salts) of northeastern Minnesota Laurentian Shield country, (2) hard water morainic lakes of central and southern areas, and (3) alkali lakes of western Minnesota. He pointed out the plant community that reflects each of these types is distinctive (Table 1), but it is a product of individual tolerance to chemical characteristics, as shown by Bourn (1935) and others on salt tolerance. Significant measured features were total alkalinity, sulfate ions, and hydrogen ions (pH).

Soft water flora are limited due to poor nutrients and are characterized by underwater leaves

Table 1. Some examples of lake waters' influence on aquatic plants of Minnesota (selected from Moyle 1945).

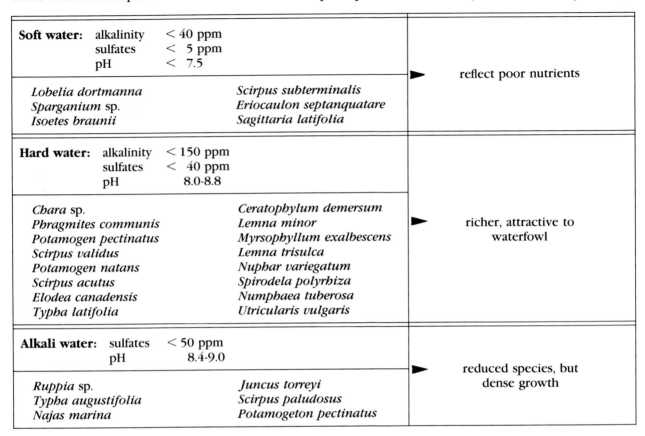

Soft water:	alkalinity	< 40 ppm	
	sulfates	< 5 ppm	reflect poor nutrients
	pH	< 7.5	
Lobelia dortmanna	*Scirpus subterminalis*		
Sparganium sp.	*Eriocaulon septanquatare*		
Isoetes braunii	*Sagittaria latifolia*		

Hard water:	alkalinity	< 150 ppm	
	sulfates	< 40 ppm	
	pH	8.0-8.8	
Chara sp.	*Ceratophylum demersum*		
Phragmites communis	*Lemna minor*		richer, attractive to waterfowl
Potamogen pectinatus	*Myrsophyllum exalbescens*		
Scirpus validus	*Lemna trisulca*		
Potamogen natans	*Nuphar variegatum*		
Scirpus acutus	*Spirodela polyrhiza*		
Elodea canadensis	*Numphaea tuberosa*		
Typha latifolia	*Utricularia vulgaris*		

Alkali water:	sulfates	< 50 ppm	
	pH	8.4-9.0	reduced species, but dense growth
Ruppia sp.	*Juncus torreyi*		
Typha augustifolia	*Scirpus paludosus*		
Najas marina	*Potamogeton pectinatus*		

and rosettes. Floating plants are rare. Hard water floras are richer, more abundant, and are attractive to waterfowl. Alkali floras have reduced species but often have dense growth of a few well-adapted species.

Stewart and Kantrud (1972) found that specific conductivity measured dissolved solids simply and reliably to indicate alkalinity or salinity of prairie marshes. Means ranged from fresh (about 300 micromhos per cm at 25° C) to brackish (6,300) to saline (37,500) in their North Dakota ponds. Plant species composition in relation to conductivity readings are reproduced in modified form in Figures 2 through 5 for wet meadow, shallow marsh, and deep marsh communities. Despite broad ranges of tolerance, common emergent hydrophytes tended to be associated with the following mean dissolved solids measured by Stewart and Kantrud (1972): Slender bulrush (*Scirpus heterochaetus*) 350 mh/cm, cattail 1000 mh/cm, and alkali bulrush (*Scirpus paludosus*) 3,500-32,000 mh/cm (Figure 6).

Salinity is clearly one of the more important chemical factors of coastal and certain western marshes. For example, the effects of salinity in establishment and growth of widgeongrass (*Ruppia mar-*

tina) are well known (Bourn 1935; Joanen and Glasgow 1966). Inland saline waters support many salt-tolerant species (halophytes), and their salt concentrations strongly influence plant species composition and growth as shown by Rawson and Moore (1944). Experimental studies of vegetation in the Great Salt Lake basin and efforts to freshen such areas to induce more suitable plants for waterfowl have provided excellent insights into plant species and water quality influences in these extreme conditions (Nelson 1954; Christiansen 1970). Additionally, observations of marshes and marsh hydrophytes associated with warm, salt springs in Utah provide excellent data on species composition and the role of water tables in salt deposition so important to wetland plants (Bolen 1964).

Key to Figures 2 thru 5:
Width of bars indicates relative abundance.
• Thick bars = frequently common or abundant.
• Thinner bars = common, occasionally abundant to occasionally fairly common.

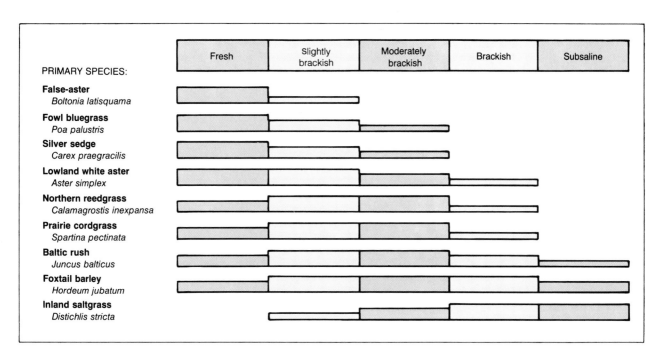

Figure 2. Characteristic plant species of wet meadows arranged from fresh to salt water tolerance.

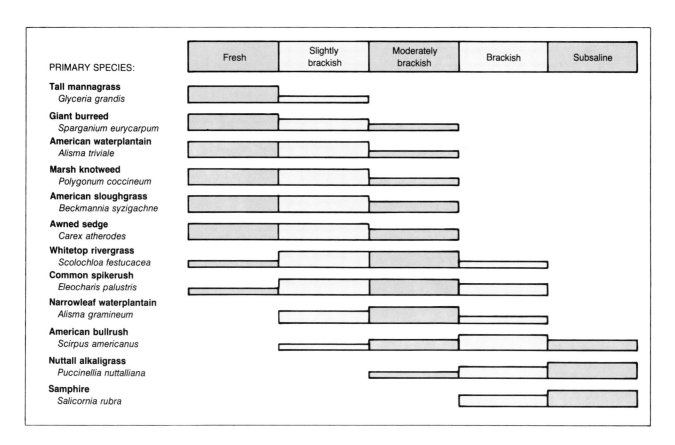

Figure 3. Characteristic plant species of shallow marsh emergent vegetation.

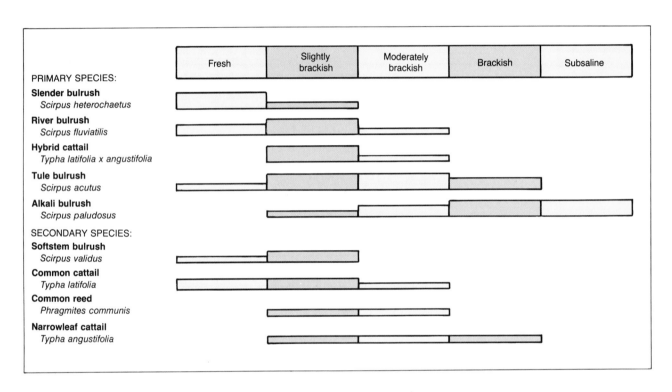

Figure 4. Characteristic plant species of deep-marsh emergent vegetation.

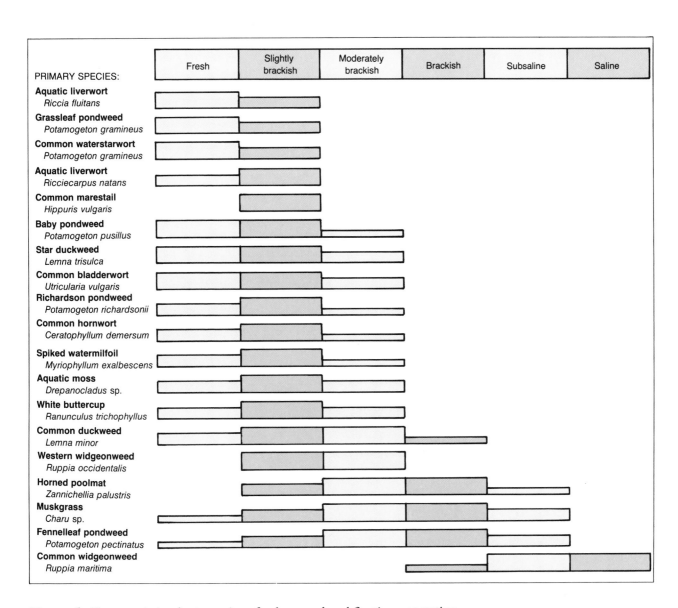

Figure 5. Characteristic plant species of submerged and floating vegetation.

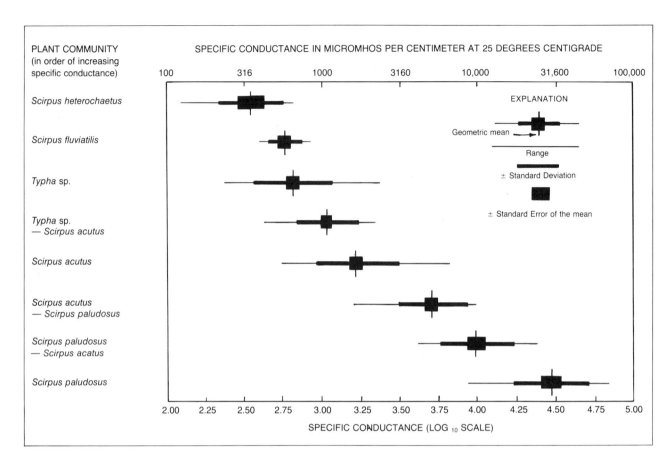

PLANT COMMUNITY
(in order of increasing
specific conductance)

SPECIFIC CONDUCTANCE IN MICROMHOS PER CENTIMETER AT 25 DEGREES CENTIGRADE

SPECIFIC CONDUCTANCE (LOG₁₀ SCALE)

Figure 6. Relationship of dominant deep-marsh vegetation to specific conductance.

Many water characteristics are influenced by processes within a basin. These include the years of alternate flooding and drying which may concentrate deposits, the rate of water flow through the system that carries away dissolved materials (including nutrients), and the processes of storage and decomposition of dissolved chemicals. Marshes also vary seasonally in concentrations of dissolved solids.

Community Structure

Life Form and Zonation. Wildlife of marshes respond visually to plant structure and by trial and error to the associated cover and food. Diversity of structure is produced by various species of plants adapted to marshes and also by zonation resulting from basin configuration.

Plants of marshes have life forms, growth, and reproductive strategies that result from adaptation to water depth and hydroperiod. Their mechanisms of germination, growth, and spread also influence how they are used as food and cover by wildlife. The dominant life form, rooted emergents, represents the easiest adaptation of hydrophytes to the semiaquatic environment. Seeds typically germinate on mud flats or in very shallow water, deriving their nutrients

(1) emergents

from soil or organic substrate. **Emergents** are diverse and complex. The continuum can be subdivided several ways. Nonpersistent, soft and often short grasses, sedges, and forbs decompose usually in less than one growth season. Larger, more robust, and persistent emergents like cattail, some bulrushes, and reeds may stand for several years. This category normally does not include woody plants like willow (*Salix* sp.) which are classified as shrubs or trees.

Still more truly aquatic plants are the **submergents,** most of which are rooted. They have much dissected or linear leaves efficient at tapping reduced sunlight at considerable depths. Such plants, like the pondweeds (*Potamogen* sp.), may have flowers and seedheads that reach the water's surface. Others like stonewort (*Chara* sp.) are bottom plants with totally submerged fruiting bodies.

Plants adapted to deeper water may have floating leaves rising from long stems resting on the water's surface ("pad" plants). They reproduce by means of large seeds or well-established tubers (example: water lily). Such **floating-leaf plants** can tolerate considerable water fluctuation in spite of their general preference for deeper water.

The most aquatic plants are **floating plants** that may have roots dangling in the water for nutrients, such as duckweed (*Lemna* sp.) or the introduced water-hyacinth (*Eichornia crassipes*). Another species of *Lemna,* star duckweed (*L. trisulca*), drifts in the water column like the many species of microscopic plankton.

Marshes are characterized by concentric zones of vegetation, often intergrading or changing in a continuum. Sometimes they change abruptly, which adds diversity of structure horizontally as well as plant species richness. Thus, a deep-marsh which results from semipermanent water has a shallow-marsh zone around the perimeter. It may grade into a wet-meadow or damp situation where water occurs in spring but dries out in early summer (Figure 7). The shallow-marsh or wet-meadow plants are those one finds in smaller basins which hold shallow water only temporarily in spring, but these lack the vegetative diversity in structure and layering found in a deep marsh with gradual shorelines (Figure 7). Nonetheless, some concentric zonation is expected in any marsh, providing a horizontal change in structure which also induces vertical or layering diversity. Few marsh basins have perfect symmetry, and other diversity of pattern is created by flow-through chan-

---

Life forms of marshes: (1) emergents, (2) submergents, (3) floating-leaf plants, (4) floating plants.

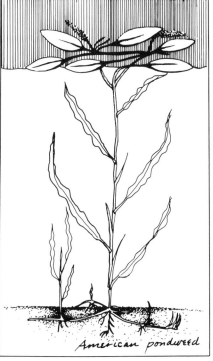

(2) submergents

(3) floating-leaf plants

(4) floating plants

A. Three examples of small marshes with water regimes varying from ephemeral to shallow to deep, resulting in: wet-meadow, shallow-marsh, and deep-marsh vegetation.

B. Typical deep marsh displaying zonation with deep-marsh vegetation in center, shallow-marsh peripherally, and wet-meadow at the edge.

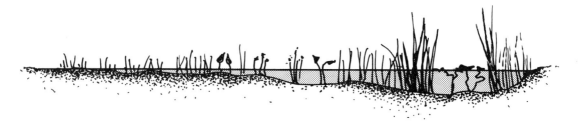

C. Open-water marsh resulting from loss of vegetation (due to continued high water or muskrats).

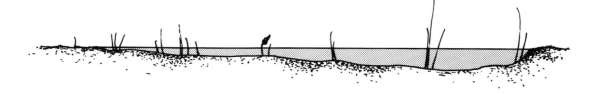

D. Germination phase at low water with a mix of annuals and perennials, persistent, and nonpersistent plants.

Figure 7. Common vegetational patterns of marshes.

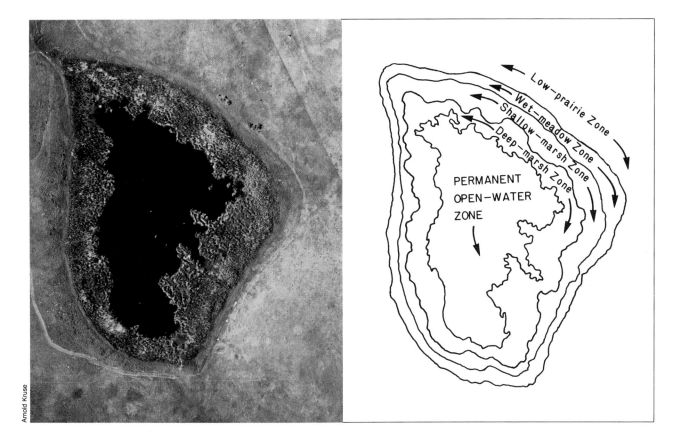

Concentric zones of marsh vegetation.

nels, islands of soil, clumps of trees, or other unique vegetation established at a lower water level.

Patterns of Vegetation and Water. The above comments might suggest that the more abundant and diverse the vegetation, the better; but this is not always true for breeding birds. Many bird species that are attracted to vegetation also need open water for landing and swimming. Openings in emergents create edge, providing access to vegetation. Openings also allow sunlight penetration essential to submergents and some animals. Thus, interspersion of cover and water is best. Various species respond to different cover-water ratios. Weller and Fredrickson (1974) showed an increase in species richness of marsh birds and numbers of individuals with increasing numbers of openings or pools in nearly pure cattail up to the point where too little vegetation reduced nest sites and food resources. Various cover-water ratios supported the idea that ducks were more attracted to 50-50 cover-water patterns (Kaminski and Prince 1981; Murkin et al. 1982), although the reasons are more complex than earlier thought.

Marsh Size and Wetland Complexes

Wetland size is an important influence of the presence or absence of wildlife species and richness only because larger areas tend to have more habitat types (i.e., diversity). Certain birds (red-winged blackbirds *Agelaius phoniceus*, blue-winged teal, and some rails) are well adapted to small units or are ubiquitous, and use these as well as perimeters of large marshes. Other species (ruddy ducks, *Osyura jamaicensis*, yellow-headed blackbirds, *X. xanthocephalus*) occur mainly in larger, deeper areas with persistent emergents and submergents. Thus, clusters of diverse wetlands may function like larger and more complex wetlands in having more bird species in the community (Smith 1971; Weller 1981a).

Marsh Succession and Vegetation Dynamics

Because marshes are shallow, dynamic, water bodies, they undergo changes in depth, chemical characteristics of the water, vegetation (species, density, and coverage), and associated wildlife. Water regimes over long periods dictate most or all of these changes; and the presence, richness, success, and duration of the plant community is in response to this regime. Hence, it is vital to have records of water depth and extent of water coverage of the marsh bottom, and to document seasonal or year-to-year variation in hydroperiods to interpret responses by vegetation and wildlife. Moreover, the seed bank of long-lived seeds is a product of this water history (Van der Valk and Davis 1978). The lack of vegetative response in a management setting may mean that seeds are lacking (Pederson 1981). Logically, shallow or temporary marshes have seeds of pioneering, annual, or short-lived plants. They are adapted to quick response and maturation that enhance the seed bank. Ducks and other seed eaters respond to this stage as well, but sufficient seeds survive that the species is not eliminated locally. When conditions such as mud flats are again available, these seeds will germinate. In deep, open waters dominated by submergents, there may be fewer seeds of emergents, although this situation varies by site. More importantly, terrestrial sites flooded artificially may lack the seed bank entirely, and establishment of vegetation may take several years.

The usual pattern in natural shallow marshes is that diverse seeds of annuals and perennials are present. With natural drought at various times of the year, different seeds respond (Van der Valk 1981). Harris and Marshall (1963) showed that early drawdown with fairly moist soil induces germinations of persistent, perennial emergents (e.g., cattail). Later and drier drawdown conditions may result in quick-maturing and short-lived annuals like smartweed. They still produce seeds that survive over winter—and often for many years—until conditions are suitable (see Weller 1981a).

If water levels in subsequent years remain low, vegetation tends to be annual plants or a few perennials characteristic of shallow marshes: sedges, rushes, and softstem bulrush. If the water level increases, it is the perennials that prosper. Cattail, tule bulrush, common reed, and other plants tolerant of deep water survive. In addition to the development of masses of seeds, some floating-leaf and submergent plants reproduce by tubers or bulbs. They store energy in one year that allows vegetative growth in the next season—before the availability of suitable seed germination substrate such as mudflats. These perennials may go for years without germination of seeds, as an influence on the local population of the plant. However, seeds spread by wind or birds may influence the establishment of these species in other areas.

Several studies have been cited demonstrating the impacts of successional changes on wildlife of single marshes. Because of long-term water cycles or random changes, wetland habitats in large regions are sometimes adversely affected for wildlife. Yeager and Swope (1956), Smith (1971), and Pospahala et al. (1974) all observed major population responses to droughts. Several workers have shown how waterfowl populations in wetter or more stable areas increase when drought strikes the interior grassland marshes (Derksen and Eldridge 1980).

Macroinvertebrates

Diverse and often abundant invertebrates provide needed protein for reproduction and growth of many fish, amphibians, birds, and some mammals. Invertebrates occupy every habitat in marshes and exploit every food resource. They have evolved life history strategies attuned to dynamic water regimes, seasonal temperature cycles, and differing salinities and acidities. Life cycles are intimately tied to water regimes. Marshes characterized by deeper and more constant water levels will have populations of dragonflies and other long-lived insects that may require several years to mature. Shallow and more temporary bodies have annual crops of invertebrates (fairy shrimps, mosquitoes, some midges) that hatch from drought-tolerant eggs and mature rapidly, to leave eggs for another time (Wiggins et al. 1980).

Population fluctuations among invertebrates are dramatic. The emergences of annual crops of insects like midges and caddisflies, or the "blooms" of planktonic crustaceans such as Daphnia or Cyclops represent discrete seasonal energy flow patterns as well as reproductive cycles. The abundance and species richness of invertebrates vary with marsh type or successional stage (Voigts 1973), and are influenced by nutrient availability and shifts in food abundance. Vertebrate consumers respond promptly. An emergence of midges in mid to late summer feeds fish, amphibians and ducks in the water, ducks and terns at the water's surface, plus gulls and swallows in the air column up several hundred feet. Plankton blooms are exploited by shovelers with a straining bill, phalaropes that pick out individual targets, and fish and amphibians in the water column. The predators and scavengers too must be adaptive, because emergences or blooms may last a few days to a few weeks, and other foods may appear that require different feeding methods.

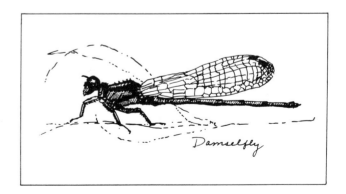

Damselfly

Wetland biologists now recognize the vital role that macroinvertebrates play in dictating the presence or absence of wildlife that need these for food. Some managers are even manipulating water levels to induce high invertebrate populations to attract waterfowl and shorebirds. Most biologists who have worked with invertebrates use them as indicators of marsh condition, but few techniques have been developed to monitor populations or interpret such data for rapid assessments in the field.

INVENTORY AND MONITORING SYSTEMS FOR MARSH HABITATS AND THEIR WILDLIFE

As discrete, often small and self-contained ecosystems, marshes usually are more easily inventoried than more extensive terrestrial habitats. But evaluating them or monitoring changes can present difficult problems. First, biologists are often not as familiar with the plants and invertebrates or their use by wildlife as in terrestrial ecosystems. Second, biologists lack technology, manpower, and precise evaluation systems. To examine these problems and possible solutions, I will first define the systems. I will then outline the ways in which one might want to use these systems or devise procedures to meet particular goals.

Inventory

Inventory is the determination of number, size, and distribution of marshes. Mapping involves the

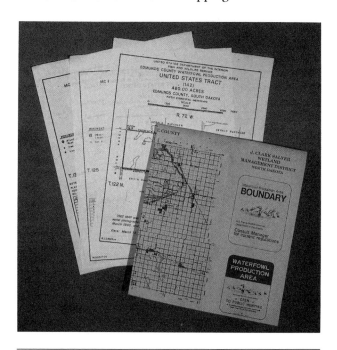

Wetland maps, such as these, are available from the U.S. Fish and Wildlife Service.

geographic aspect of location and distribution patterns. The most extensive national wetland inventory ever attempted is in progress. It is a multiagency Federal effort to record the number, size, and distribution of all wetlands of the contiguous United States. Much of the survey is already complete. Some maps have been published and are available from the U.S. Fish and Wildlife Service. Other areas are still being mapped or have not been mapped in detailed scale. Vegetation zones may be gross or lacking on these maps. A general summary of wetland changes over time has resulted from these inventories (Frayer et al. 1983). They suggest a loss in vegetated palustrine wetlands (marshes) of 94,770 ha (234,000 a.) per year from the 1950s to the 1970s. The data on wetland number, area, and modifications thereof are stored in computer data bases, and more detailed analysis can be expected in the future.

On a regional or local scale, the inventory process may produce greater detail, not only in identifying smaller areas but in perceiving changes due to dynamic water regimes. Additionally, on-the-ground vegetation and water depth measurements can be taken.

On a very gross scale, the number of wetlands has been related to waterfowl populations over vast areas of the northern U.S. and Canada. In addition to the standard annual aerial waterfowl censuses, observers have recorded the number of prairie wetlands to reflect year-to-year climatic conditions. Correlations of mallard population size and distributions with pond numbers reflect the impact of habitat quality on breeding conditions for mallards (Pospahala et al. 1974). On a smaller scale, a simple positive correlation between pond numbers and canvasback pairs was noted by Sugden (1978) over a series of years of observations.

Cover Mapping

Cover mapping produces a detailed analysis of the vegetation patterns found within a marsh or other wetland. Coupled with these is classification, which describes vegetation, basin, and water regimes to place marshes or other wetlands into identifiable types or classes. Vegetation mapping is a vital first step in understanding potential for wildlife use. It establishes baseline information necessary for monitoring. Mappers gain a familiarity with the area that assists in devising census methods or observation sites. On a national scale, the National Wetlands Inventory is using aerial photographs almost exclusively with ground truthing in various wetland types (Montanari and Townsend 1977). Periodic black-and-white photo series by the Soil Conservation Service usually are available for baseline maps. Current color photos have excellent potential for indicating significant characteristics in wildlife habitat evaluation (Cowardin et al. 1981). Local overflights can provide views of marshes that add great appreciation and understanding as well as an opportunity for photographs. Out-of-the-window obliques are useful for records of vegetation and water patterns, but are very misleading for mapping due to the dramatic distortion that even a small angle produces. A plane with a "belly" port is ideal for low-level (915-1,830m; 3,000-6,000 ft) 35mm pictures. Where this equipment is not available, out-of-the-window verticals can be taken with an externally-mounted camera (Meyer and Grumstrup 1978).

A series of aerial photographs and the resulting maps can be used to demonstrate seasonal or yearly changes in vegetation and coverage, cover-water ratios, and numbers of muskrat lodges in a given wetland. Vegetation surveys are necessary in the marsh to provide detailed data on species richness or diversity, stem density, water depth, submergent plant distribution, etc. Moreover, work in the marsh is vital to understanding wildlife-plant-water relationships. There is no substitute for a good pair of hip boots or chest waders!

Monitoring Habitat and Wildlife

Monitoring implies biological assessment with a series of timed observations for a stated purpose. Objectives can include assessment of habitat and wildlife values to prevent habitat deterioration, measurement of fluctuation in populations or vegetation as natural entities of the system, or establishment of a baseline for evaluating the consequences of human activities on wetland quality. All of these activities are essential for making sound resource decisions. Ordinarily, the process requires measurement of habitat and wildlife populations. Many of these techniques are covered elsewhere. Here it is important only to consider the combination of individual techniques to form a "system" that will satisfy your particular needs or goals. The following are possible features of the habitat, and use by wildlife and fish that might be measured.

Water Depth and Fluctuation. Water level changes are important to understanding vegetation germination, growth, and loss. Water levels also affect nests of birds or litters of muskrats, potential predation by terrestrial predators, and the survival of duck broods. Where practical, gauges should read in tenths and hundredths of a foot in relation to known mean sea level. This relation is an engineering standard that has practical mathematical and communication advantages when working with managed or artificial impoundments.

Water depth and extent of coverage in a marsh determines wildlife use and seasonally influences plant germination, growth, and seed production. Mud flats may be viewed negatively at times of nesting, but may be beneficial in the long run because the resulting germination creates emergent vegetation suitable for nesting in subsequent years.

Vegetation. The species composition, density, height, distribution, and cover-water interspersion patterns by water depth are among the features of the plant community that might be assessed. However, time and financial constraints prevent measurement of all these details unless the goals of the monitoring demand them. Moreover, there is significant vertical layering in marsh vegetation as a result of the four dominant life forms of aquatic plants: rooted emergents, floating-leaf, rooted submergents, and free-floating (surface or water column). There also are some epiphytic filamentous algaes that can be abundant, suitable food for fish and ducks, and substrates for macroinvertebrates. Sampling systems must be suitable for this variety.

Point-counts are especially useful because they are rapid and can be used to assess all life forms of plants above, at, and below water level as well as water depth (Weller and Voigts 1983). However, they provide only a crude index to density of less common plants. Additional sampling systems such as quadrats or relevés (Mueller-Dumbois and Ellenberg 1978) may be necessary. Several studies have demonstrated dramatic year-to-year changes in vegetation that strongly influenced wildlife populations (Weller and Fredrickson 1974).

Wildlife Census. Investigators censusing wildlife in marshes use strategies similar to those for terrestrial wildlife, but are complicated by access and visibility. This is why aerial census of waterfowl and large wading birds of open water developed early, and is used in place of an index to population change (Henny et al. 1972). Boats, canoes, air boats, and marsh buggies also have been used when aerial survey is either financially impossible or the size of the area is too small. Air boats and marsh buggies are expensive to buy and maintain, and can only be justified in large marsh units. Boats often will not go through emergents or submergents and thus do not perfect survey techniques. Canoes have the advantage of being quiet, but are slow and sometimes awkward, and like walking, visibility may be impaired. Hence, biologists often use subsamples, indexes, and indirect estimates. Certainly no simple technique can be advised for all areas.

Censusing wildlife in marshes requires preliminary experimentation because each area differs. Constancy in technique will then provide an index even when abundance or density figures cannot be obtained. No one technique will work for all birds or mammals. Fish, amphibians, and reptiles are still more difficult because of poor visibility, and require subsampling techniques that will produce different levels of success.

Fish. Seines are not useful in marshes because of the vegetation and organic debris. Kushlan (1974) used lift-traps, drop-traps, and bottom nets to get estimates of species richness and species composition. Rotenone and electrofishing also can be useful, but no technique is equally suitable for all species and all vegetation types. Submergents are a particular hindrance. Some minnows and smaller species in prairie marshes have been studied by trapping (Payer and Scalet 1978). Much needs to be learned about census techniques that assess communities of fish in marshes.

Amphibians. I know of no accurate method of censusing various kinds of frogs in various habitats. Bullfrogs are conspicuous at night with a flashlight, but leopard frogs and small peepers are difficult to count. Incidence observed per unit time by habitat category is possibly the best available index.

Birds. I have been well satisfied with counts of territorial male songbirds on quadrats from observation towers or raised shorelines. Red-winged and yel-

low-headed blackbirds are especially conspicuous. Even less visible but vocal species like marsh wrens can be pinpointed by triangulation and repeated surveys. At least three early morning surveys at the peak of breeding activity are required for statistical reasons as well as to compensate for variation in activity of birds. In small marshes and ponds where access is enhanced by walking on knolls, biologists were able to survey blue-winged teal and other pairs of ducks and get fairly consistent results on each of three annual pair counts (Weller 1979c).

Rails represent one of the most difficult of all birds to census in any habitat. Except for vocalizations, and an occasional nest accidentally discovered, rails can be present in large numbers and remain undetected. Some workers have been successful in stimulating calling by playing back recorded vocalizations (Zimmerman 1977). Nest density of larger species has been recorded as a product of very intensive effort (Tanner and Hendrickson 1956). Least Bitterns belong in the same difficult-to-census class.

The above examples demonstrate the difficulty of finding one technique that works for species using several different strata of vegetation and several different reproductive strategies. The line transect method of sighting and vocalization is now in fairly widespread use and holds promise for providing indexes to various species (Mikol 1980). Whether the method is equally functional in a marsh in early-season low vegetation and after a full season's growth is still uncertain.

Nest counts are favored for conspicuous colony birds such as ibises, egrets, and herons. They have also been used for ducks where chain drags and other devices are used to arouse hens from their incubation (Higgins et al. 1969). In some instances, post-breeding season surveys have been used to correct for partial counts or counts in dense vegetation.

Mammals. Censuses in marshes have focused around sign or dens as opposed to visual count, since many species are nocturnal or hidden in dense vegetation. Muskrats are censused by numbers of "lodges" with a fall per-house number of five commonly used to estimate totals (Dozier 1948). Numbers and home range size of swamp rabbits in southeast Missouri were derived by driving with men and dogs and by grid trapping (Toll et al. 1960).

Evaluation

Goals of Evaluation. Evaluation of marshes is complex. It involves some method of correlating characteristics of the marsh with a value in which there is special interest, such as wildlife populations or variety. Qualities that will attract an endangered species are also evaluated. There are no well-defined procedures. Biologists are usually dependent on simple correlations or associations rather than cause-and-effect relationships described in quantitative terms. Dependent upon objectives, such evaluations may be simplified by comparing two wetlands on qualitative rather than quantitative terms. Thus, assessing the quality of a marsh for wildlife is a skill that is still evolving. Unfortunately, we have a small data base, and our parameters usually are qualitative rather than quantitative. Hence, it is imperative that we clarify the objectives and the parameters of an evaluation.

Often we limit our interest and evaluation to a single species (e.g., whooping cranes, as an endangered species) or a group of recreational importance (waterfowl) or a nuisance group (blackbirds). Using individuals per hectare (or square mile on vast areas), or duck-use days, we identify marshes that are highly productive or much used versus those with low numbers. If we use a wetland classification system, we associate number of species and individuals with types of wetlands as did Stewart and Kantrud (1973) in North Dakota. Or we may map the cover of zones or areas of a single marsh to denote where nesting occurs, where feeding occurs, etc. We can then determine how much of any one habitat is needed to attract and maintain a single species.

There are dangers in species or group-oriented assessments in that we ignore the community of vertebrates as a whole and bias our effort toward species of our choosing. Other species may be of importance to other persons for other reasons. Another danger rests with a comparative approach of choosing between two marshes because two wetlands in the same area may have different water regimes and be in different phases of the drawdown-reflooding cycle. Their potential to produce may be just as great but each is on a different time schedule. Without long-term observations, or experience in a certain climatic-geomorphic area, a highly erroneous conclusion might be reached. Generally, such relations between maximum wildlife populations and some habitat feature are based on one or few studies, so confidence levels may be low. Clearly, additional work is needed.

Tools for Evaluation. For marsh wildlife, we look positively on certain features as being important enhancements in marshes and use them as parameters of a quality habitat.

Complexity or diversity of vegetative structures is measured by cover-water ratio, vertical layering, and possibly plant species richness. Cover-cover edges or cover-water edges were identified as attractive to nesting birds by Beecher (1942), and maximum species richness of birds was noted with a ratio of 30% cover to 70% open water (Weller and Frederickson 1974). Using experimental approaches,

workers found the 50-50 cover-water ratio most attractive to feeding dabbling ducks as well (Kaminski and Prince 1981; Murkin et al. 1982). Vertical layering (strata) has been suggested as important for nesting marsh birds by Weller and Spatcher (1965) and Short (1982). These measures of structural diversity suggest that increased variety and numbers of birds would be expected with increased water, cover ratio, or number of strata, but that low numbers and different species may be expected in the extremes of either a dense monoculture or sparse vegetation (open marsh).

A wetland has characteristic water regimes due to local climate, surface drainage patterns, and subsurface hydrology. Determining what is a favorable regime is a moot issue, and dependent on the values and functions attributed to the wetland. For wildlife, water level stability during breeding seasons is ideal to prevent flooding of duck nests (Low 1945) or drowning of young muskrats (Errington 1937). Periodic drawdowns are essential to establishment of diverse wetland plants in reestablishment of vegetation after a flood-out or an eat-out by herbivores. Muskrats or nutria are more vulnerable to predators in dry or shallow marshes (Errington 1961). Permanent changes producing higher water level may be nearly as detrimental to wildlife as is drainage of a wetland. Such "flooding" reduces submergent growth (Robel 1962), availability of benthic organisms to some species (Boyer and Psejek 1977), and covers established beds of emergents (Weller 1981b).

Shoreline gradient and vegetative cover can be very important to suitability of an area for wildlife. Steep shores reduce emergent growth and induce more terrestrial plants. Such shorelines may be ideal loafing sites for ducks or muskrats, but are less suitable for invertebrates that favor shallow water and aquatic plants.

Turbidity reduces growth of important submergents like sago pondweed, *P. pectinatus* (Robel 1961). Current or wave action tends to reduce perimeter emergents and takes out nutrients from the system. Nutrient levels in water and soil can be measured by various chemical means. Usually, some simple measurements of alkalinity are used to reflect nutrient-rich waters (eutrophic conditions) as opposed to less enriched (oligotrophic) water. Conductivity, an electrical measure of dissolved solids, is a common, quick technique to assess whether water is extremely pure, highly alkaline, or saline due to concentrations of minerals. Extreme levels of salt content may inhibit plant growth.

Nutrient cycling also is involved as nutrients tend to be tied up quickly (seasonally) by plants, and returned to water and substrate reservoirs by decomposition of plants. Where decomposition is extensive in late stages of succession or following eat-outs, extensive surface floating plants or algal blooms may be common. Again, this is not easily measured but one must be conscious that fluctuation in floating duckweed or other seasonal events is not necessarily negative. Floating duckweed can be valuable as food itself, and for the snails and amphipods it harbors. But continuous spring to fall crops suggest excess nutrients and duckweed will screen out growth of submergents that produce seeds and tubers valuable to waterfowl later in the year. Filamentous algae can have the same effects but is less valuable as a food.

Food resources are a product of water regimes plus plant and invertebrate communities. Generally, there are positive correlations between vegetative complexity and bird populations (Weller and Fredrickson 1974) and between invertebrate abundance and duck populations (Whitman 1976; Eriksson 1978; Joyner 1980). The presence of seed-producing plants like smartweed and sago, or of foliage-producing plants like sago and widgeongrass, is of high value for wildlife (Fredrickson and Taylor 1982). But data are not available for all foods or all wildlife species. What causes the increase in populations of amphibians like frogs and salamanders is complicated by complex food chains of algae, phytoplankton, zooplankton, and small invertebrates, and cannot be quickly or easily assessed. The presence of fish is a strong influence on quality of habitat for mergansers and grebes, but large predatory fish may prey heavily on ducklings (Lagler 1956).

The presence of macroinvertebrates is positive. Cover-water ratios do not always enhance invertebrate numbers (Murkin et al. 1982), but variation in type and numbers of invertebrates varies with successional stage of the marsh (Voigts 1973). Because invertebrates are not easily assessed by any simple and easily obtained measurement, taxon richness is being explored as the most simple way to assess relative importance. However, one must be cautious when associating abundance with availability as deep water can prevent some ducks from obtaining food (Boyer and Psujek 1977).

Nest sites and materials are a product of vegetation types and patterns. Plant density could influence suitability of cover for nests—although data are not available to clearly support this assumption. Sparse vegetation may serve coots and grebes that carry dead vegetation for nests and need only the sparse material to hold the nest in a wind. But ducks do not carry vegetation to build nests. Dead and live materials on the site must be sufficient to create a nest bowl and sometimes a canopy. Songbirds seem to need vertical stalks of vegetation that are sufficiently robust that the weight of the nest, eggs, female, and young do not cause collapse. The stalks must be sufficiently close that weaving of nest materials be-

tween the uprights provides support and cover (Weller and Spatcher 1965).

Muskrats carry lodge material, but build large lodges where material is abundant, and small platforms in suboptimal habitats. Breeding sites for fish, frogs, and most reptiles really have not been evaluated in marshes; it is believed that they too are at peak levels when the entire ecosystem is responding to nutrient availability, successional stages, invertebrate variety, and water depths that allow completion of life cycles.

Evaluation Systems. Evaluation of wetlands for wildlife is not new, and several systems are currently in use. The **Habitat Evaluation Procedures** (HEP) developed by the U.S. Fish and Wildlife Service (USFWS 1980) utilizes individual species models called **Habitat Suitability Index** (HSI) models. These models are used to build a composite of key species within the habitat (Edwards and Twomey 1982; Schroeder 1982). HSI models are not available for all species but are being prepared by USFWS. Such a system is used in mitigation but also has wide applicability to biological survey work in marshes. The system has been criticized for being species rather than community oriented. This and other systems are described in the chapter on habitat evaluation systems.

The U.S. Army Corps of Engineers has a more ecosystem-oriented method (**Habitat Evaluation System**), but it has not reached the same level of development and now deals mainly with terrestrial systems (U.S. Army Corps of Engineers 1980).

The need for evaluation is so great for so many diverse fields that less rigorous approaches are being developed. A system in progress by the Federal Highway Administration evaluates wetlands in their entirety for all values and functions, with qualitative ratings of high, moderate, and low for some 75 predictors (Adamus 1983; Adamus and Stockwell 1983). Waterfowl and other water birds are used as the major indicator groups so that much of the wildlife community is not represented, but there are several important predictors related to values for wildlife. These include contiguity between wetlands, size, vegetation form and density, salinity-conductivity, pH, flooding, water depths, edge, waterfowl food values of plants, invertebrate density, alkalinity, and eutrophication. Collectively, these include many of the important factors that have been identified as contributing to quality habitat for marsh wildlife. But no one has derived a mechanism for rating these and developing a cumulative rating without going to the detail used in the HEP.

Several states (Michigan, New York, and Wisconsin) also have wetland evaluation or rating systems that emphasize wildlife and fish values, but they tend to have only regional applicability. Numerous individuals and groups are experimenting with group-specific evaluation systems incorporating current ecological community factors such as species richness and species diversity in addition to population data (Williams 1980). Thus, at the present stage of development, the options are – –

- make qualitative judgments based on items of special interest to the evaluator (done consistently and comparatively),

- use HEP if the HSI models are available and seem to fit the needs, or

- make a series of gross to detailed surveys and measurements that provide indices to those items of special interest or importance at the site or sites in question.

DISCUSSION

Compared with other habitats, marshes are so dynamic they create difficult situations for assessment as wildlife habitats. Marshes require – –

- long-term observations or use of past aerial photos to aid in interpretation,

- careful selection of parameters that fit the local situation,

- testing of measurements for reliability as indicators of wildlife habitats,

- standardization of times and techniques when reassessing habitats,

- experimental efforts to improve technologies, and

- data gathering on localized areas to reflect local water regimes and wildlife populations.

Marshes are exciting because of their diversity and dynamics, but they can be disappointing and deceiving as well. A rich habitat once lost causes outcries from an uninformed public for correction of a problem that may not exist. Public information on the "boom and bust" dynamics of wetlands is essential to prevent wasted and needless action on areas best left alone. Concurrently, gradual changes can be hidden among the extremes, and only long-term monitoring will indicate trends that induce concern and investigation.

The accuracy of predictors, qualitative judgments, or even detailed measurements is poorly known. It is difficult to encourage extensive effort when the variability of the system may mask important events. Yet, there is no option. The alternative of no evaluation, census, or monitoring is too likely to result in irreparable damage to the system. The level of accuracy can only be set by the needs, and even detailed evaluation can ignore obvious truths. If goals are established first, and the level of detail set by need, many of the otherwise difficult decisions become obvious.

Above all, do not assume someone else knows all the answers. Instead, learn the system by repeated visits and careful observation, search for the obvious truths, use common sense in devising an evaluation system, then stick with it as much as possible to provide comparable data between observations.

LITERATURE CITED

ADAMUS, P.R. 1983. A method for wetland functional assessment, Vol. II. FHWA assessment method. U.S. Dep. of Transportation. Federal Highway Admin. Rep. FHWA-IP-82-24. 138pp.
——— P.R. and L.T. STOCKWELL. 1983. A method for wetland functional assessment: Vol. I. Critical review and evaluation concepts. U.S. Dep. of Transportation. Federal Highway Admin. Rep. FHWA-IP-82-23. 181pp.
BEECHER, W.J. 1940. Nesting birds and the vegetative substrate. Chicago: Chicago Ornith. Soc. 69pp.
BERGMAN, R.D., R.L. HOWARD, K.F. ABRAHAM, and M.W. WELLER. 1977. Waterbirds and their wetland resources in relation to oil development at Storkersen Point, Alaska. U.S. Dep. Inter., Fish and Wildl. Serv. Resour. Publ. 129. 38pp.
BOLEN, E.G. 1964. Plant ecology of spring-fed salt marshes in western Utah. Ecol. Monogr. 34:143-166.
BOURN, W.S. 1935. Sea-water tolerance of *Ruppia maritima.* Contrib. Boyce Thompson Inst. 7:249-255.
BOYER, R.L. and M.J. PSUJEK. 1977. A comparison of wetland bird aggregations and macrobenthos. Trans., Ill. State Acad. Sci. 70:332-340
CHABRECK, R.H. 1972. Vegetation, water and soil characteristics of the Louisiana coastal region. Louisiana St. Univ. Bull. 664. 72pp.
CHRISTIANSEN, J.E. 1970. Water requirements of waterfowl marshlands in northern Utah. Utah Div. of Fish and Game. Publ. 69-12. 108pp.
COWARDIN, L.M. and D.H. JOHNSON. 1973. A preliminary classification of wetland plant communities in north-central Minnesota. U.S. Dep. Inter., Fish and Wildl. Serv. Special Sci. Rep.—Wildl. 168. 33pp.
———, D.S. GILMER, and L.M. MECHLIN. 1981. Characteristics of central North Dakota wetlands determined from sample aerial photographs and ground study. Wildl. Soc. Bull. 9:280-288.
———, V. CARTER, F.C. GOLET, and E.T. LAROE. 1979. Classification of wetlands and deepwater habitats of the United States. U.S. Dep. Inter., Fish and Wildl. Serv. FWS/OBS-79/31. 103pp.
DERKSEN, D.V. and W.D. ELDRIDGE. 1980. Drought-displacement of pintails to the arctic coastal plain, Alaska. J. Wildl. Manage. 44:224-229.

DOZIER, H.L. 1948. Estimating muskrat populations by house counts. Trans. North Am. Wildl. Conf. 13:372-392.

EDWARDS, E.A. and K. TWOMEY. 1982. Habitat suitability index models: common carp. U.S. Dep. Inter., Fish and Wildl. Serv. FWS/OBS-82/10.12. 28pp.

ERIKSSON, O.G. 1978. Lake selection by goldeneye ducklings in relation to the abundance of food. Wildfowl 29:81-85.

———. 1979. Competition between freshwater fish and goldeneyes (*Bucephala clangula*) for prey. Oceologia 41:99-107.

ERRINGTON, P.L. 1937. Drowning as a cause of mortality in muskrats. J. Wildl. Manage. 18:497-500.

———. 1961. Muskrats and marsh management. The Stackpole Co., Harrisburg, PA and The Wildl. Manage. Inst., Washington, DC. 183pp.

——— and T.G. SCOTT. 1945. Reduction in productivity of muskrat pelts on an Iowa marsh through depredations of red fox. J. Agric. Res. 71:137-148.

ESHER, R.J., R.L. WOLFE, and J.H. LAYNE. 1978. Swimming behavior of rice rats (*Oryzomya palustris*) and cotton rats (*Sigmodon hispidis*). J. Mammal. 59:551-558.

FISLER, G.F. 1961. Behavior of salt marsh *Microtus* during winter high tides. J. Mammal. 42:37-43.

FORNEY, J.L. 1968. Production of young northern pike in a regulated marsh. N.Y. Fish and Game J. 15:143-154.

FRAYER, W.E., D.C. BOWDEN, F.A. GRAYGILL, and T.J. MONAHAN. 1983. Status and trends of wetlands and deepwater habitats. U.S. Dep. Inter., Fish and Wildl. Serv. 31pp.

FREDRICKSON, L.H. and T.S. TAYLOR. 1982. Management of seasonally flooded impoundments for wildlife. U.S. Dep. Inter., Fish and Wildl. Serv. Resour. Publ. 148. 29pp.

GOLET, F.C. and J.S. LARSON. 1974. Classification of freshwater wetlands in the glaciated Northeast. U.S. Dep. Inter., Fish and Wildl. Serv. Resour. Publ. 116. 56pp.

HARRIS, S.W. and W.H. MARSHALL. 1963. Ecology of water-level manipulations on a northern marsh. Ecol. 44:331-343.

HENNY, C.J., D.R. ANDERSON, and R.S. POSPAHALA. 1972. Aerial surveys of waterfowl production in North America, 1955-71. U.S. Dep. Inter., Fish and Wildl. Serv. Special Sci. Rep.–Wildl. 160. 48pp.

HIGGINS, K.F., L.M. KIRSCH, and I.J. BALL. 1969. A cable-chain device for locating duck nests. J. Wildl. Manage. 33:1009-1011.

JOANEN, J.T. and L.L. GLASGOW. 1966. Factors influencing the establishment of widgeongrass stands in Louisiana. Proc. Ann. Conf. SE Assoc. Game and Fish Comm. 19:78-92.

JOYNER, D.E. 1980. Influence of invertebrates on pond selection by ducks in Ontario. J. Wildl. Manage. 44:700-705.

KAMINISKI, R.M. and H.H. PRINCE. 1981. Dabbling duck and aquatic macroinvertebrate responses to manipulated wetland habitat. J. Wildl. Manage. 45:1-15.

KRAPU, G. 1974. Feeding ecology of pintail hens during reproduction. Auk 91:278-290.

KUSHLAN, J.A. 1974. Quantitative sampling of fish populations in shallow, freshwater environments. Trans. Am. Fish. Soc. 103:348-352.

LAGLER, K.F. 1956. The pike, *Esox lucius* Linnaeus, in relation to waterfowl on the Seney National Wildlife Refuge, Michigan. J. Wildl. Manage. 20:114-124.

LOW, J.B. 1945. Ecology and management of the redhead, *Nyroca americana*, in Iowa. Ecol. Monogr. 15:35-69.

MARTIN, A.C., N. HOTCHKISS, F.S. UHLER, and W.S. BOURN. 1953. Classification of wetlands of the United States. U.S. Dep. Inter., Fish and Wildl. Serv. Special Sci. Rep.–Wildl. 20. 14pp.

McILHENNY, E.A. 1976. The alligator's life history. Soc. for the Study of Amphibians and Reptiles. 117pp.

McKNIGHT, D. and J.B. LOW. 1969. Factors affecting waterfowl production on a spring-fed salt marsh in Utah. Trans. North Am. Wildl. Nat. Resour. Conf. 34:307-314.

METCALF, F.P. 1931. Wild duck foods of North Dakota lakes. U.S. Dep. Agric. Tech. Bull. 221. 72pp.

MEYER, M.P. and P.D. GRUMSTRUP. 1978. Remote sensing applications in agriculture and forestry. Univ. of Minnesota, St. Paul. IAFHE RSL Res. Rep. 78-1. 60pp.

MIKOL, S.A. 1980. Field guidelines for using transects to sample nongame bird populations. U.S. Dep. Inter., Fish and Wildl. Serv. FWS/OBS-80/58.

MONTANARI, J.H. and J.E. TOWNSEND. 1977. Status of the national wetlands inventory. Trans. North Am. Wildl. Nat. Resour. Conf. 42:66-72

MOYLE, J.B. 1945. Some chemical factors influencing the distribution of aquatic plants in Minnesota. Am. Midl. Naturalist. 34:402-420.

MUELLER-DUMBOIS, D. and H. ELLENBERG. 1974. Aims and methods of vegetation ecology. John Wiley & Sons, Inc. 545pp.

MURKIN, H.R., R.M. KAMINSKI, and R.D. TITMAN. 1982. Responses by dabbling ducks and aquatic invertebrates to an experimentally manipulated cattail marsh. Can. J. of Zool. 60:2324-2332.

NELSON, N.F. 1954. Factors in the development and restoration of waterfowl habitat at Ogden Bay Refuge, Weber County, Utah. Utah Dep. of Fish and Game. Publ. 6. 87pp.

NIXON, S.W. 1982. The ecology of New England high salt marshes: a community profile. U.S. Dep. Inter., Fish and Wildl. Serv. FWS/OBS-81-55. 70pp.

PAYER, R.D. and C.G. SCALET. 1978. Population and production estimates of fathead minnows in a South Dakota prairie marsh. Prog. Fish-Cult. 40:63-66.

PEDERSON, R.L. 1981. Seed bank characteristics of the Delta Marsh, Manitoba: applications for wetland management. Pages 61-82 *in* Richardson, B., Selected Proceedings of the Midwest Conference on Wetland Values and Management. 660pp.

PENFOUND, W.T. and E.S. HATHAWAY. 1938. Plant communities in the marshland of southeastern Louisiana. Ecol. Monogr. 8:1-56.

POSPAHALA, R.S., D.R. ANDERSON, and C.J. HENNY. 1974. Population ecology of the mallard: II Breeding habitat conditions, size of breeding populations, and production indices. U.S. Dep. Inter., Fish and Wildl. Serv. Resour. Publ. 115. 73pp.

RAWSON, D.S. and G.T. MOORE. 1944. Saline lakes of Saskatchewan. Can. J. of Res. 22:141-201.

ROBEL, R.J. 1961. The effects of carp populations on the production of waterfowl food plants on a western waterfowl marsh. Trans. North Am. Wildl. Nat. Resour. Conf. 26:147-159.

ROBEL, R.J. 1962. Changes in submersed vegetation following a change in water level. J. Wildl. Manage. 26:221-224.

SCHROEDER, R.L. 1982. Habitat suitability index models: yellow-headed blackbird. U.S. Dep. Inter., Fish and Wildl. Serv. FWS/OBS-82/10.26. 12pp.

SHAW, S.P. and C.G. FREDINE. 1956. Wetlands of the United States: their extent and their value to waterfowl and other wildlife. U.S. Dep. Inter., Fish and Wildl. Serv. Circular 39. 67pp.

SHORT, H.L. 1982. Use of northern prairie and wetland habitat by breeding birds. U.S. Dep. Inter., Fish and Wildl. Serv. 27 pp.

——— and K.P. BURNHAM. 1982. Technique for structuring wildlife guilds to evaluate impacts on wildlife communities. U.S. Dep. Inter., Fish and Wildl. Serv. Spec. Sci. Rep.–Wildl. 244. 34pp.

SMITH, A.G. 1971. Ecological factors affecting waterfowl production in the Alberta parklands. U.S. Dep. Inter., Fish and Wildl. Serv. Resour. Publ. 98. 49pp.

STEWART, R.E. and H.A. KANTRUD. 1971. Classification of natural ponds and lakes in the glaciated prairie region. U.S. Dep. Inter., Fish and Wildl. Serv. Resour. Publ. 92. 57pp.

———. 1972. Vegetation of prairie potholes, North Dakota, in relation to quality of water and other environmental factors. U.S. Dep. Inter., Fish and Wildl. Serv. and Geological Survey. Geological Survey Professional Paper 585-D. 36pp.

———. 1973. Ecological distribution of breeding waterfowl populations in North Dakota. J. Wildl. Manage. 37:39-50.

SUGDEN, L.G. 1978. Canvasback habitat use and production in Saskatchewan parklands. Can. Wildl. Serv. Occ. Pap. 34. 32pp.

SWANSON, G.A., G.L. KRAPU, and J.R. SERIE. 1979. Foods of laying female dabbling ducks on the breeding grounds. Pages 47-57 in Bookhout, T.A., ed. Proc. 1977 Symp. Waterfowl and Wetlands. The Wildlife Society. Madison, WI.

TANNER, W.D. and G.O. HENDRICKSON. 1956. Ecology of the king rail in Clay County, Iowa. Iowa Bird Life. 26:54-56.

TOLL, J.E., T.S. BASKETT, and C.H. CONAWAY. 1960. Home range, reproduction, and foods of the swamp rabbit in Missouri. Am. Midl. Naturalist. 63:398-412.

U.S. ARMY CORPS OF ENGINEERS. 1980. A habitat evaluation system for water resources planning. U.S. Army Corps of Engineers, Lower Mississippi Valley Division. 158pp.

U.S. FISH AND WILDLIFE SERVICE. 1980. Habitat evaluation procedures (HEP). U.S. Dep. Inter., Fish and Wildl. Serv. ESM 102. 27pp.

VAN DER VALK, A.G. 1981. Succession in wetlands: a gleasonian approach. Ecol. 62:688-696.

——— and C.B. DAVIS. 1978. The role of seed banks in the vegetation dynamics of prairie glacial marshes. Ecol. 59:322-335.

VOIGTS, D.K. 1973. Food niche overlap of two Iowa marsh icterids. Condor. 75:392-399.

WELLER, M.W. 1979a. Wetland habitats. Pages 210-234 in Greeson, P.E., J.R. Clark and J.E. Clark, eds. Wetland Functions and Values: the State of Our Understanding. Am. Water Resour. Assoc. 674pp.

———. 1979b. Birds of some Iowa wetlands in relation to concepts of faunal preservation. Proc. Ia. Acad. Sci. 86:81-88.

———. 1979c. Density and habitat relationships of blue-winged teal nesting in Northwestern Iowa. J. Wildl. Manage. 43:367-374.

———. 1981a. Freshwater marshes: ecology and wildlife management. Univ. Minn. Press. 146pp.

———. 1981b. Estimating wildlife and other wetland losses due to drainage and other perturbations. Pages 337-346 in Richardson, B., ed. Selected Proceedings of the Midwest Conference on Wetland Values and Management. Minn. Water Planning Board, St. Paul, MN. 660pp.

——— and L.H. FREDRICKSON. 1974. Avian ecology of a managed glacial marsh. Living Bird. 12:269-291.

——— and C.E. SPATCHER. 1965. Role of habitat in the distribution and abundance of marsh birds. Iowa State Univ. Agric. and Home Econ. Exp. Sta. Spec. Rep. 43. 31pp.

——— and D.K. VOIGTS. 1983. Changes in the vegetation and wildlife use of a small prairie wetland following a drought. Proc. Iowa Acad. Sci. 90:50-54.

WHITMAN, W.R. 1976. Impoundments for waterfowl. Can. Wildl. Serv. Occ. Pap. 22. 22pp.

WIGGINS, G.B., R.J. MACKAY, and I.M. SMITH. 1980. Evolutionary and ecological strategies of animals in annual temporary pools. Arch. Hydrobiol. Suppl. Bd. 58. 206pp.

WILLIAMS, G. 1980. An index for the ranking of wildfowl habitats, as applied to eleven sites in West Surrey, England. Biol. Conserv. 18:93-99.

YEAGER, L.E. and H.M. SWOPE. 1956. Waterfowl production during wet and dry years in north-central Colorado. J. Wildl. Manage. 20:442-446.

ZEDLER, J.B. 1982. The ecology of southern California coastal salt marshes: a community profile. U.S. Dep. Inter., Fish and Wildl. Serv. FWS/OBS-81/54. 110pp.

ZIMMERMAN, J.L. 1977. Management of migratory shore and upland game birds. Pages 45-46 in Sanderson, G.C., ed. Virginia Rail (*Rallus limicola*). International Assoc. Fish and Wildlife Agencies, Washington, DC. 358pp.

11

STREAMS

Paul Cuplin

U.S. Bureau of Land Management
Service Center
Denver, CO 80225

"I love any discourse of rivers, and fish, and fishing."

—Izaak Walton, *Compleat Angler*

Editor's Note: This chapter is the first of two on aquatic habitats, and covers moving water habitat (rivers and streams). The emphasis is on the smaller streams typical of the western United States, as opposed to large systems such as the Mississippi River. As with all other natural systems, the streams cannot be understood or measured without looking at the associated wetlands and uplands. Therefore, stream inventory and monitoring involves measuring or estimating factors such as stream bank stability and dominant riparian vegetation. Nevertheless, the focus of a study is often the stream and its potential for supporting fish and other aquatic vertebrates. This chapter covers the basic measurements and measurement systems for describing stream habitat.

INTRODUCTION

Eighty-five thousand miles of fishing streams occur on public lands managed by the U.S. Bureau of Land Management (BLM) in the 11 western States and Alaska (Table 1). Streams provide recreational opportunities ranging from white-water boating to family picnicking. Important wildlife habitat associated with streams include riparian vegetation which provides food and cover for many wildlife species. Fresh-water fishing in terms of sportsfishing dollars is estimated to be $11 per fisherman per day. About 36.4 million Americans made 620.5 million fishing trips in 1980. Total dollars expended annually for fresh-water fishing in the U.S. is estimated to be $7.8 billion (U.S. Department of the Interior, Fish and Wildlife Service and U.S. Department of Commerce 1982). Salmon and steelhead originating from public land streams that are taken in commercial fisheries of Alaska and Oregon totaled 58,358,000 pounds in 1983 (U.S. Department of the Interior, Bureau of Land Management 1983). Commercial fisheries catch statistics can be related to dollar values by fish species.

Stream habitat management requires an awareness of land uses that can improve, stabilize, or destroy stream habitat. A starting point is a baseline description of existing habitat conditions. Changes in habitat conditions are detected by monitoring specific attributes of the stream over time. Stream habitat features, i.e., stream bank stability, streambed siltation, stream channel stability, shade, water quality, stream width and depth, and other features are monitored to detect changes in stream habitat conditions.

STREAM CLASSIFICATION

Although classification of streams has received some attention in the U.S., there is no universally accepted method of classification. The U.S. Fish and

Wildlife Service has developed a wetland and deep-water classification for a national wetland inventory (Cowardin et al. 1979) to comply with the Clean Water Act of 1977. This classification is very useful for broad-base wetland inventory and mapping, but it does not provide information on condition that is needed by the public land resource specialist or manager.

A stream classification would be useful for comparing streams that are similar in size, water quality, elevation, and geomorphology. Common classification terminology would allow for predicting aquatic habitat potential relative to aquatic habitat improvement.

Stream order, which provides a concept of stream size and characteristics for the biologist and manager, was first defined by Horton (1945). He designated unbranched tributaries as first-order streams; streams that receive first-order tributaries, as second-order streams; those that receive second- or first- and second-order streams as third-order streams, and so on until the mouth of the stream is reached. Strahler (1952) modified Horton's stream order and called all unbranched tributaries first-order streams; two first-order streams join to make a second-order stream, and so on downstream to the stream mouth (Figure 1).

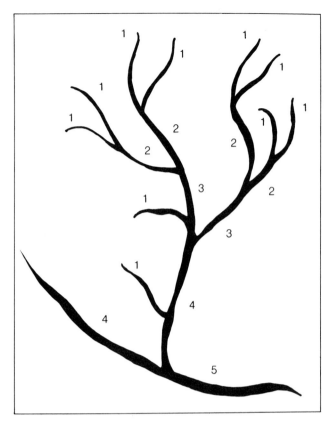

Figure 1. Stream order by A.N. Strahler (1952).

Table 1. Estimated miles of existing fishing streams, and acres of lakes and reservoirs on public lands administered by U.S. Bureau of Land Management (1983).

State	Lakes[1]	Reservoirs[1]	Streams[2]
Alaska	3,874	0	65,000
Arizona	1	26	439
California	19	2	818
Colorado	1	19	1,822
Idaho	10	39	3,577
Montana	16	22	996
Nevada	23	5	1,134
New Mexico	2	3	176
Oregon, Washington	29	18	7,136
Utah	1	8	2,300
Wyoming	7	32	2,537
Total	**3,983**	**174**	**85,935**

[1]In thousands of acres.
[2]Includes only miles of fishable streams.

Third-order and larger streams generally have gradients less than 0.5%, and streambed is usually rubble, gravel, sand, silt, and organic detritus. These streams are meandering with abundant riparian shrubs and trees; stream stability is generally fair. Sediment discharge is higher than the smaller first- and second-order streams. Fishery habitat is good.

Map scale influences determination of stream order. For example, a 1:500,000-scale map would not show most first- and second-order streams. Although 1:24,000-scale maps will show first-order and larger streams, Boehne and House (1983) suggested 1:12,000 as a minimum scale for mapping stream orders of Oregon streams.

Stream order descriptions vary within physiographic regions. Streams in mountainous regions are used as an example for a general description of stream orders.

In my experience, first- and second-order streams generally have steep gradients (3% or more) and large coarse streambed and streambank material. Stream meander is moderate; riparian shrubs and trees are present; and debris jams are common. Fishery habitat is suitable in some reaches for spawning and rearing.

STREAM HABITAT FEATURES

Stream habitat feature is a convenient term used to identify the variables that make up stream habitat. Stream habitat features are streamflow patterns, streambank stability, stream channel stability, riparian vegetation, riffles, pools, streambed, stream depth, stream width, stream gradient, stream diversity, stream water chemistry, and macroinvertebrates.

Streamflow Pattern

Streamflow pattern significantly affects the biotic life of the stream. The most desirable streamflow pattern for aquatic production is one of perennial flow with moderate spring runoff. Perennial streams can provide year-round spawning, rearing, and feeding requirements for fish. However, extreme drought may cause drying of perennial streams. The type of spring runoff will govern habitat stability.

Intermittent streams flow only part of each year. Generally streamflow occurs during the rainy season or during snow melt; otherwise the streambed is dry. Intermittent streams are indicated by a dashed line on U.S. Geological Survey (USGS) 7.5-minute quad maps. Intermittent streams often provide spawning and rearing habitat for fish before the streambed dries up during the summer months.

Ephemeral streams are those that flow only in response to a rain shower. The ephemeral stream provides marginal habitat for aquatic life but it may be very important to amphibians.

Instream Flow Needs

The amount of water needed to maintain stream habitat on a year-round basis is termed "instream flow needs." It can be determined by several methods as summarized by Cuplin et al. (1979). Where detailed, precise, legally defensible information is required, the multiple transect-incremental flow method is recommended. This method is described in detail in Bovee and Milhous (1978).

For rapid assessment, a single transect method is available (Cuplin et al. 1979). This technique requires less time for field work and data analysis but it produces less precise results than the incremental flow method.

Computer programs have been developed for analyzing stream channel cross-section survey data collected in conjunction with instream flow assessments (Parsons and Hudson 1985). A single transect method can be used for rapid assessment. A computer analysis program is available for BLM offices through the Denver Service Center, Division of Resource Systems (Parsons and Hudson 1985).

The flow of a stream is measured in cubic feet per second (cfs) to provide information on stream water volume. Water flow is estimated to the nearest cfs during stream inventory. The U.S. Geological Survey maintains permanent streamflow measuring weirs and annually publishes surface water reports for each State. These reports include data on streamflow and water chemistry of selected streams.

Streambank Stability

Stable streambanks and abundant riparian vegetation provide good habitat for aquatic and terrestrial wildlife. Aquatic systems depend on the condition of the adjacent land. Removal of riparian vegetation through timber harvest, road construction, overgrazing, or excessive recreational use can cause unstable streambank conditions. Eroding streambanks allow sediment to enter the stream and degrade the streambed. Silt and sediment fill the spaces between streambed gravel and rubble and prevent the flow of water and oxygen necessary for the survival of fish eggs, larval fish, and macroinvertebrates.

Stream Channel Stability

Stream channel stability is related to the water flow of the stream and the sediment load carried by the stream. Material that enters the stream from the watershed or streambanks is either washed downstream or becomes part of the bed material (Bovee 1982). Schumm and Meyer (1979) related the shape of the stream channel to the amount and kind of load it carries. Channels can be classified as suspended load (silt and clay), mixed load, or bed load channels (sand and gravel). Five channel patterns have been identified which correspond to each of the types of load and transitions between load types (Figure 2; Shen et al. 1981).

Riparian Vegetation

Woody riparian vegetation, shrubs and trees, are most important to smaller streams. Streamside woody vegetation provides shade that prevents excessive warming of water during summer months. Overhanging trees provide cover for fish and the leaves and twigs provide stream energy through nutrient cycling. Riparian vegetation provides a buffer from upland activities as well as a filter for overland soil erosion.

A method of predicting riparian vegetation potential has been developed by Crouse and Kindschy (1981). This method provides guidelines for predicting the riparian vegetation that can exist under various conditions of soil and water flow if protection through fencing or grazing management system is applied to a stream/riparian area.

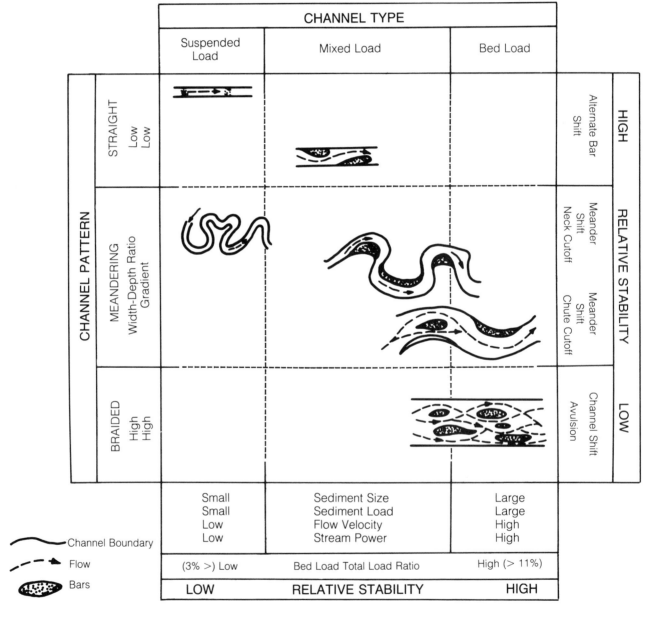

Figure 2. Channel classification showing relative stability and types of hazards encountered with each pattern (from Shen et al. 1981).

Typical riparian vegetation along a foothills' stream.

Low gradient stream.

Riffles

Riffles are the steeper gradient, high-water velocity stream sections. Macroinvertebrates reproduce in the riffle, and fish feed on them at the base of riffles in either pools or runs. Steep gradient streams that are largely composed of riffles provide food and some spawning area but not the necessary resting and shelter mix to provide good habitat for salmonids. Other fishes, e.g., certain suckers and minnows, are almost exclusively found over riffles.

Pools

Pools are the deeper, slow-moving-water portions of streams. Pools can be classified by width and depth (Duff and Cooper 1978; Hamilton and Bergersen 1984) and they provide resting areas for fish.

Runs

Runs are shallow troughs that generally have sand or gravel bottoms. Runs are smooth, laminar flows of slow to moderate velocity, intermediate between a pool and a riffle.

Streambed

The streambed consists of various amounts and sizes of material. These are classified by particle size (Table 2). The amount of different-sized particles that compose/make up the streambed determines the uses of the stream bottom by fish, macroinvertebrates, and other aquatic life. For example, coarse gravel (2.5-7.5 cm [1-3 in. diameter]) is most commonly used by salmonids for spawning, whereas small rubble (7.5-15.0 cm [3-6 in. diameter]) free of silt and sand, provides good habitat for macroinvertebrates. Silt and sand inhibit the flow of water and oxygen through rocks in the streambed and reduce the success of fish egg incubation and aquatic organism survival.

Table 2. Classification of streambed material (Duff and Cooper 1976).

Material	Particle Size
Bedrock	Exposed solid rock
Boulder	12″ (305 mm)
Large rubble	6-12″ (152-305 mm)
Small rubble	3-6″ (76-152 mm)
Coarse gravel	1-3″ (25-76 mm)
Fine gravel	0.1-1.0″ (2.5-25 mm)
Sand	(0.074-2.5 mm)
Clay	(0.074 mm)
Sapropel	Reduced organic matter
Detritus	Particulate organic matter

Stream Width and Depth

The average width of a stream is the average distance between the water's edges, perpendicular to the stream flow (Hays et al. 1981). Stream depth is the average vertical distance from the surface to the bottom (Hays et al. 1981).

Wide shallow streams provide reduced habitat for aquatic life. They usually lack resting cover for fish and allow water temperature to rise beyond the tolerance limits of some fishes. Narrow deep streams, in comparison, maintain lower water temperatures because of less surface area exposure to solar warming, and the deep water provides good resting cover for fish.

Stream Gradient

A steep, torrential mountain stream provides very little habitat for fish. A moderate gradient will provide some of the requirements for food production, spawning, and rearing of fish. A very low gradient, deepwater stream provides the greatest stability and warmer water. Large, low gradient streams, free of pollution, provide the greatest habitat diversity and the largest number of aquatic species.

Stream Water Chemistry

Suspended Solids and Turbidity. Suspended solids in the form of silt, clays, and other fine materials can cause temporary to permanent turbidity or murkiness.

Prolonged turbidity caused by runoff or disturbance in normally clear streams can cover the streambed with silt which can smother macroinvertebrates, cover spawning areas, and reduce photosynthetic rates. Turbidity can cause feeding problems for sight-feeding trout and gill irritation to most fishes with the exception of those that are adapted to year-round turbidity.

Turbidity caused by suspended solids can be judged in terms of visibility of objects in water, such as muddy water (0.5-1 foot of visibility), murky water (1-5 feet of visibility), and clear water (5 feet of visibility). Turbidity can be measured and reported in Nephelometric Turbidity Units (NTUs), which are measures of light transmittance in a water sample. Turbidity in excess of 25 NTUs is judged to be too high for sight-feeding fish.

Water Temperature. Water temperature range is an important criterion of the resident fish and aquatic species in a stream. Species that are acclimated to various maximum water temperatures in their life cycle are listed in Table 3 (U.S. Environmental Protection Agency 1971). An increase in temperature of a few degrees can upset the natural balance in a stream. Fish and other organisms exposed to maximum temperatures for long periods may suffer from unusual stresses, disease, and reduced appetite.

Table 3. Maximum temperature probably compatible with the well-being of various species of fish and their associated biota in °C and °F (U.S. Environmental Protection Agency 1971).

Temperature	Taxa
34°C (93.2°F)	Growth of catfish (*Ictaluridae*), gar (*Lepisosteus* sp.), white bass (*Morone chrysops*), yellow bass (*M. mississippiensis*), spotted bass (*Micropterus punctulatus*), buffalo (*Ictiobus* sp.), carpsucker (*Carpiodes* sp.), threadfin shad (*Dorosoma petenense*), and gizzard shad (*D. cepedianum*)
32°C (89.6°F)	Growth of large-mouth bass (*M. salmoides*), drum (*Aplodinotus grunniens*), bluegill (*Lepomis macrochirus*), and crappie (*Pomoxis* sp.)
29°C (84.2°F)	Growth of pike (*Esox lucius*), perch (*Percina* sp.), walleye (*Stizostedion vitreum*), small-mouth bass (*M. dolomieui*), sauger (*S. canadense*), California killifish (*Fundulus parvipinnis*), and topsmelt (*Atherinops affinis*)
27°C (80.6°F)	Spawning and egg development of catfish, buffalo, threadfin shad, gizzard shad, California grunion (*Leuresthes tenuis*), opaleye (*Girella nigricans*), and northern swellfish (*Sphoeroides maculatus*)
24°C (75.2°F)	Spawning and egg development of largemouth bass, white and yellow bass, spotted bass, sea lamprey (*Petromyzon marinus*), alewife (*Alosa pseudoharengus*), and striped bass (*Morone saxitilis*)
19°C (66.2°F)	Growth of migration routes of salmonids and for egg development of perch, smallmouth bass, winter flounder (*Pseudopleuronectes americanus*), and herring (*Clupea* sp.)
12°C (53.6°F)	Spawning and egg development of all salmonidae (other than lake trout [*Salvelinus namayacush*])
9°C (48°F)	Spawning and egg development of lake trout, walleye, northern pike, sauger, and Atlantic salmon (*Salmo salar*)

Chemical Variables. The three most important chemical measurements in stream water are dissolved oxygen, pH (hydrogen ion concentration), and specific conductance which can be converted to represent total dissolved solids in milligrams per liter (mg/L).

Dissolved Oxygen. The dissolved oxygen content of water is an indicator of the biochemical condition of water. It also indicates the balance between oxygen-consuming and oxygen-producing processes. Fish and other desirable clean-water biota require relatively high dissolved oxygen levels at all times. Dissolved oxygen levels below 6 mg/L are dangerous to sensitive or higher elevation fish. Desert fishes can survive and withstand low oxygen tensions to 1 mg/L.

Streams with large loads of organic material may have oxygen-consuming and inorganic reactions that deplete oxygen to levels unfavorable for the clean-water species.

pH. The pH is the abbreviation for the negative base 10 log of the hydrogen ion concentration. Stream water not influenced by pollution has a pH between 6.5 and 9.0, which is the acceptable range of pH for fish.

Specific Conductance. Specific conductance is the measure of the ability of water to conduct an electrical current and is expressed in micromhos per centimeter at 25°C (7°F). It can be used for approximating the dissolved solids in water by using the formula—

Specific conductance × (0.65 ± 0.05) = mg/L dissolved solids or total dissolved solids (see below).

The formula should be verified by comparing specific conductance with total dissloved solids determined by a chemist.

Total Dissolved Solids Total dissolved solids (TDS) are all of the dissolved materials present in natural waters and consist of carbonates, bicarbonates, chlorides, sulfates, phosphates, and other substances. Most productive fresh water has a TDS above 350 mg/L. The maximum safe level is about 1,500 mg/L TDS in fresh water. Chemical laboratory assistance will be needed for the analysis of heavy metals, TDS, pesticides, and pollutants.

Macroinvertebrates

Macroinvertebrates are aquatic organisms that can be seen with the naked eye, such as mayfly, stonefly, and caddis fly larvae; *Gammarus* sp., aquatic worms, beetles, clams, and snails. These animals provide an important food supply for fish.

Macroinvertebrate production in streams is related to water temperature, water chemistry, and habitat diversity. A stream that is low in TDS and has low average temperatures will produce few macroinvertebrates per square foot of stream bottom.

Rock and rubble 7.5-15 cm (3-6 in.) in diameter provide good habitat for macroinvertebrates. Smaller rocks from 2.5-7.5 cm (1-3 in.) provide less desirable habitat, hence fewer numbers of macroinvertebrates. Sand and silt provide little habitat except for tubificid worms if nutrient levels are high.

Plant-eating macroinvertebrates consume algae, detritus, diatoms, wood, and leaves. Some macroinvertebrates are carnivorous and prey on other stream dwellers.

Stream Diversity

The pools, riffles, runs, boulders, streambed gravel and rubble, shade, downed trees, and gradient all provide habitat diversity in a stream. Streams with good habitat diversity provide the essential requirements of food, cover, spawning, and rearing for fish.

Stream habitat improvement enhances diversity and provides the missing habitat features such as pools, streambed spawning gravel, cover, and streambank stabilization.

An example of diversity destruction, which was once a common practice, is the removal of all downed trees and logs from a stream. It is now recognized that the natural tree fall into a stream adds to the diversity and to the flow of energy to support the food chain.

STREAM INVENTORY AND MONITORING SYSTEMS

Stream Habitat Inventory

Streams are inventoried to determine existing and potential aquatic and terrestrial wildlife habitat related to existing or planned land uses. A general system that can be used for photointerpretation and on-the-ground assessment is the stream habitat inventory developed by the Oregon State Office, BLM (Cuplin 1981). This method uses five criteria (shade, riparian zone condition, streambank stability, stream channel stability, and sedimentation of streambed) to classify a stream as poor, fair, good, or excellent. Each of these attributes is rated in one of three or four categories and the ratings are then summed to give an overall stream condition rating (Figure 3). This classification has limited applicability on southern desert erosional streams.

(This form to be used for field inventory or photo interpretation)

Stream _____ Date _____ State _____ Dist. _____

Planning Unit _____ Site No. _____ Surveyor(s) _____

Field Survey _____ Length of Stream Surveyed _____

Aerial Photograph _____

	4	3	2	1
% Shade	80% +	60 - 80%	40 - 60%	40% or less
Riparian Zone Condition (% Bare Soil)	5% or less	6 - 15%	16 - 25%	25% or more
Stream Bank Stability (% Bank Damage)	0 - 10%	20% or less	40% or less	41% or more
Stream Channel Stability (% Channel Movement)	5% or less	6 - 10%	11 - 15%	16% or more
Sedimentation of Streambed (% Silt)		10% or less	11 - 25%	26% or more
Column Totals				

Stream Condition Rating for Length of Stream Evaluated - (Enter total score in appropriate space)

Excellent 17 _____
Good 14-16 _____
Fair 10-13 _____
Poor 5-9 _____

Percent Shade is important for 1st, 2nd, 3rd order streams but less important to large, wide streams where riparian vegetation cannot affect water temperature by shading.

Figure 3. Stream habitat inventory.

Habitat Quality Index (HQI)

Binns (1979) developed a Habitat Quality Index (HQI) which relates habitat quality to trout biomass in streams. He field-tested 13 physical habitat attributes, 5 water chemistry attributes, and 4 biological attributes and chose 9 attributes for the HQI (Table 4). The attributes chosen for the HQI are late summer streamflow, annual streamflow variation, maximum summer stream temperature, water velocity, cover, stream width, eroding banks, substrate, and nitrate nitrogen.

The HQI is given by the expression:

$$\log_{10}(\hat{Y} + 1) = [(-0.903) + (0.807)\log_{10}(X_1 + 1) + \\ (0.877)\log_{10}(X_2 + 1) + (1.233) \\ \log_{10}(X_3 + 1) + (0.631)\log_{10}(F + \\ 1) + (0.182)\log_{10}(S + 1)] \\ [1.12085]$$

Where:

$\hat{Y}$ = Predicted trout standing crop (biomass)
X_1 = Late summer stream flow
X_2 = Annual stream flow variation
X_3 = Maximum summer stream temperature
F = Food index = $X_3 (X_4) (X_9) (X_{10})$
S = Shelter index = $X_7 (X_8) (X_{11})$
X_4 = Nitrate nitrogen
X_7 = Cover

X_8 = Eroding stream banks
X_9 = Substrate
X_{10} = Water velocity
X_{11} = Stream width

Binns (1979) found a close correlation between predicted and measured standing crop of trout in 36 Wyoming streams.

Riparian Aquatic Information Data System (RAIDS)

A computer-based system for summarizing riparian and aquatic data has been developed by the U.S. Bureau of Land Management, Service Center. This system, called the Riparian Aquatic Information Data System (RAIDS), can accommodate most stream inventory methods. It is available to BLM offices; more detailed information can be obtained from the BLM Service Center, Division of Resource Systems.

DISCUSSION

A recurring problem in BLM is the failure of biologists to record their stream inventory data in the data base. Monitoring changes in a stream ecosystem requires that baseline data are available in an analyzed and recorded format. Inventory data must be on a specific area and have repeatable variables, otherwise monitoring will be of little value. Variables that can be measured with good to excellent repeatability over time are stream width, stream depth,

Table 4. Stream habitat attributes selected for field testing during development of a stream Habitat Quality Index (HQI) for trout (Binns 1979).

Attribute Class		
Physical	*Chemical*	*Biological*
Late summer stream flow[1]	Nitrate nitrogen	Streambank vegetation
Annual stream flow variation	Total alkalinity	Fish food abundance
Maximum summer stream temperature	Total phosphorous	Fish food diversity
Water velocity	Total dissolved solids	Fish food type
Turbidity	Hydrogen ion	
Cover		
Stream width		
Stream depth		
Stream morphology		
Eroding banks		
Substrate		
Bed material		
Silt deposition		

[1]Attributes underlined were ones selected for use in the HQI.

steambank undercut, and streambank angle. Variables that have poor repeatability are percentage pools, pool quality, percentage riffle, bank-to-bank width, high stream water width, and stream rock content (Table 5).

LAND-USE IMPACTS ON STREAM HABITAT

Land uses such as livestock grazing, timber harvest, road construction, mining, and recreation can adversely affect stream habitat if good management practices are ignored.

Timber harvest impacts are reduced by leaving buffer strips of uncut trees in a 75-ft. or wider zone on each side of the stream. Stream habitat can be destroyed by snagging, log dragging, crossing with heavy equipment, and slash and sawdust dumping.

Livestock grazing in the riparian zone can cause streambank sloughing, reduced shrub and tree reproduction, compacted soils, and increased bacterial count in the water.

Hydraulic mining affects all stream habitat features as well as the riparian zone, especially if streamside settling ponds are required. Mining exploration should be conducted a safe distance away from a stream to prevent erosion and degradation of the streambed.

Recreation activities such as picnics and overnight camping facilities should be carefully designed to prevent water pollution and deterioration of the riparian zone.

Road construction should be confined to areas other than riparian zones. Culvert design must conform to accepted practices for fish passage.

Stream channelization destroys stream diversity and causes long-term damage to stream productivity. The impact of each of these activities on stream habitat features is summarized in Table 6.

Streams are extremely important on arid lands. The variety of uses received in stream/riparian areas are compounded by the attractiveness of these areas to all users. Livestock and wildlife congregate in stream/riparian areas because of the availability of food, cover, and water. Recreationists enjoy boating and aesthetic values, and fishermen enjoy the pursuit of their sport. Road construction is the least costly in the riparian zone. Hydraulic mining must of necessity be carried on in the streambed.

These competing uses require biologists to have a data base on stream habitat conditions as well as a knowledge of the impacts from all land uses on such conditions.

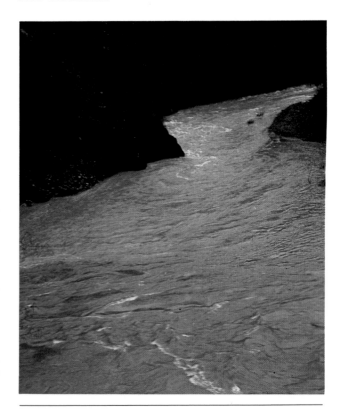

Unregulated logging can destroy stream habitat.

Hydraulic mining residues can pollute main stem streams in addition to side streams.

Table 5. Average expected repeatability, precision, and confidence intervals of water column and streambank measurement means from six selected streams in Idaho and Nevada. Confidence intervals are at the 95% level and expressed as percentage of the mean (from Platts 1981).

Item	Confidence Interval	Precision	Repeatability over Time
Water Column			
Stream width	5.4	◒	◒
Stream depth	8.2	◒	◒ – ●
Streamside water depth	16.6	⊖	⊖ – ⊖
Pool (percent)	10.3	◒	○
Pool (quality)	8.0	◒	○ – ⊖
Riffle (percent)	12.5	⊖	○
Sun arc angle	1.1	●	◒
Bank-to-bank width	Very wide	○	○
High water stream width	Very wide	○	○
Streambank			
Soil alteration	12.3	⊖	⊖ – ◒
Vegetative stability	3.1	●	⊖ – ◒
Undercut	18.5	⊖	◒
Angle	4.4	●	◒
Rock content	Very wide	○	○

● = Excellent   ◒ = Good   ⊖ = Fair   ○ = Poor

Table 6. Land uses in stream/riparian zones and their impacts on stream habitat features (from American Fisheries Society, Western Division 1982).

Stream Habitat Feature	Livestock Grazing	Mining	Road Construction	Stream Channeli-zation	Timber Harvest	Recreation (Fishing, Picnicking)
Stream flow pattern, increased runoff	●	●	●		●	
Vegetation removal, shade and cover reduced	●	●	●		●	
Stream temperature increased	●	●	●		●	
Streambank stability reduced	●	●	●	●	●	
Channel stability reduced	●	●	●		●	
Streambed siltation increased	●	●	●	●	●	
Stream width increased	●				●	
Stream depth decreased	●				●	
Bacterial count increased	●					●
Suspended solids increased	●	●	●	●	●	
Stream diversity reduced	●	●	●	●	●	

LITERATURE CITED

AMERICAN FISHERIES SOCIETY, WESTERN DIVISION. 1982. The best management practices for the management protection of western riparian stream ecosystems. Riparian Habitat Committee, Western Division, Am. Fisheries Soc. 45pp.

BINNS, N.A. 1979. A habitat quality index for Wyoming trout streams. Fishery Research Report Monograph Series, 2. Wyoming Game and Fish Dep., Cheyenne. 75pp.

BOEHNE, P.L. and R.A. HOUSE. 1983. Stream ordering: a tool for land managers to classify western Oregon streams. U.S. Dep. Inter., Bur. Land Manage. TN OR 3, Oregon State Office, Portland. 6pp.

BOVEE, K.D. 1982. A guide to stream habitat analysis using the instream flow incremental methodology. Instream Flow Information Paper 12. Cooperative Instream Flow Service Group, U.S. Dep. Inter., Fish and Wildl. Serv., Ft. Collins, CO. FWS/OBS-82/26. 248pp.

———— and R. MILHOUS. 1978. Hydraulic simulation in instream flow studies: theory and techniques. IFIP 5, Cooperative Instream Flow Service Group, U.S. Fish and Wildl. Serv., Ft. Collins, CO. 130pp.

COWARDIN, L.M., V. CARTER, F.C. GOLET, and E.T. LAROE. 1979. Classification of wetlands and deepwater habitats of the United States. U.S. Dep. Inter., Fish and Wildl. Serv., Washington, DC. 103pp.

CROUSE, M.R. and R.R. KINDSCHY. 1981. A method for predicting riparian vegetation potential of semiarid rangelands. Pages 110-116 *in* Acquisition and Utilization of Aquatic Habitat Information. Western Div. of Amer. Fisheries Soc. Portland, OR.

CUPLIN, P. 1981. The use of large scale, color-infrared photography for stream habitat and riparian vegetation inventory. U.S. Dep. Inter., Bur. Land Manage., Denver, CO. 57pp.

————, B. VAN HAVEREN, R. BOROUICKA, J. ERDMANN, L. LEE, R. MCQUISTEN, and M. WHITTINGTON. 1979. Instream flow guidelines. U.S. Dep. Inter., Bur. Land Manage., Denver, CO. 57pp.

DUFF, D.A. and J.L. COOPER. 1978. Techniques for conducting stream habitat surveys on national resource land. U.S. Dep. Inter., Bur. Land Manage. Denver, CO. Tech. Note 283. 72pp.

HAMILTON, K. and E.P. BERGERSEN. 1984. Methods to estimate aquatic habitat variables. U.S. Dep. Inter., Bur. Reclamation. Eng. Res. Center. Denver, CO. 1984.

HAYS, R.L., C. SUMMERS, and W. SEITZ. 1981. Estimating wildlife habitat variables. U.S. Dep. Inter., Fish and Wildl. Serv. FWS/OBS-81/47. 111pp.

HORTON, R.E. 1945. Erosional development of streams and their drainage basins—hydrophysical approach to quantitative morphology. Bull. Geol. Soc. Amer. 56:275–370.

PARSONS, S.C. and S. HUDSON. 1985. Stream channel cross-section surveys and data analysis. Pam. 228. U.S. Dep. Inter., Bur. Land Manage. Denver, CO. 48pp.

PLATTS, W.S. 1981. A plea for fishery habitat classification. Fisheries 5(1):2–6.

SCHUMM, S.A. and D.F. MEYER. 1979. Morphology of alluvial rivers of the Great Plains. Pages 9–14 *in* Agric. Council Publ. 91. U.S. Dep. Agric., For. Serv. Fort Collins, CO.

SHEN, H.W., S.A. SCHUMM, J.D. NELSON, D.O. DOEHRING, M.M. SKINNER, and G.L. SMITH. 1981. Assessment of stream-related hazards to highways and bridges. Federal Highway Admin., Washington, DC. 241pp.

STRAHLER, A.N. 1952. Dynamic basis of geomorphology. Bull. Geol. Soc. Am. 63:923–938.

U.S. DEPARTMENT OF THE INTERIOR, BUREAU OF LAND MANAGEMENT. 1983. Public land statistics, Vol. 168. U.S. Govt. Print. Off. Washington, DC.

U.S. DEPARTMENT OF THE INTERIOR, FISH AND WILDLIFE SERVICE and U.S. DEPARTMENT OF COMMERCE. 1982. 1980 National survey of fishing, hunting, and wildlife-associated recreation. U.S. Govt. Print. Off. Washington, DC.

U.S. ENVIRONMENTAL PROTECTION AGENCY. 1971. Freshwater biology and pollution ecology training manual. Training Manual, Water Quality Office, Washington, DC.

12

LAKES

James F. LaBounty

U.S. Bureau of Reclamation
Denver, CO 80225

"A lake . . . forms a little world within itself—a microcosm within which all elemental forces are at work and the play of life goes on in full, but on so small a scale as to bring it easily within the mental grasp."

—Stephen A. Forbes

Editor's Note: This second chapter on aquatic habitats covers bodies of standing water, including lakes, ponds, and reservoirs. These habitats are as important to the many aquatic and terrestrial species that depend on them as flowing water is in the arid western States. However, the techniques for inventorying and monitoring these habitats and their fauna are often different from those used for flowing bodies of water. Entire books and complete courses have been devoted to the study and measurement of aquatic life in lakes. This chapter summarizes this complex subject and provides guidance for inventorying and monitoring of lakes.

INTRODUCTION

In a very simple sense, lakes are bodies of standing fresh water. In reality, they are complicated systems of living and nonliving features that influence each other immensely. Lakes may be shallow or deep, large or small, but the features that give them their most distinctive characteristics are all related to their standing water. A lake basin can be thought of as a trap or catchment area, both for water and materials from within the watershed. Typically, lakes have inlets and outlets so that some of the water and materials that enter a lake are discharged from the lake at some future time.

Even though one can go back to a particular lake year after year and it appears to remain the same, it is constantly changing. Lakes are only temporary features on the landscape. Most lakes in the U.S. were formed between 10,000 and 12,000 years ago after the last retreat of the glaciers (Figure 1; Odum 1971). Others were formed as a result of volcanic activity or a change in the earth's crust (e.g., earthquakes). Lakes will eventually fill with the materials that accumulate and become a portion of the terrestrial landscape. The life span of lakes varies considerably, but the outcome is always the same. The stage of development of a lake is very important in preparing management strategies. Generally, there is an increase in the complexity and diversity of life within a lake as it ages.

Most consider reservoirs (Figure 2) to be just another kind of lake, but there are two major differences between reservoirs and natural lakes that should be considered. First, reservoirs are man-made and their water levels are controlled. Many lakes have control structures placed on their outlets. However, the degree of control between reservoirs and lakes is very different. The deepest point in a reservoir is generally at its outlet—the dam. Therefore it could be drained. On the other hand, the deepest point of a lake is somewhere near its center. The lake's natural outlet is logically the shallowest point

Figure 1. A mountain lake at 9,200 feet in elevation in Colorado.

Figure 2. Seminoe Reservoir located in the high plains of southern Wyoming.

in the body of water. Thus, without some major excavation or catastrophic event such as an earthquake, a lake could not be emptied. These two differences are very important considerations in putting together management strategies for a body of water.

Ponds (Figure 3) can, in a small way, exhibit all of the characteristics of a lake or a reservoir. They play important roles in watershed management in the western U.S.

Figure 3. A pond located along Lake Creek in central Colorado.

CLASSIFICATION SYSTEMS

Lakes (Figure 1) possess a great variety of combinations of properties (Odum 1971). This makes it difficult to select any one basis to classify lakes. Therefore, one can find all sorts of terminology applied to lake types. To illustrate this, Hutchinson (1957) listed at least 75 lake types based on geomorphology and origin. In this chapter, Odum's

1971 use of three-lake categorization schemes will introduce the most commonly encountered terminology as applied to lake types:

(1) the oligotrophic-eutrophic series of ordinary, clear-water lakes based on productivity;

(2) special lake types; and

(3) impoundments.

Oligotrophic—Eutrophic Series

These terms, implying productivity or fertility, are probably the most commonly used to describe lakes. The classic **oligotrophic** lake is one that has low primary productivity and is relatively deep. In contrast, **eutrophic** ("good foods") lakes are shallower and have a greater primary productivity. The term **mesotrophic** implies moderate productivity, meaning the lake falls in a category somewhere between oligotrophic and eutrophic.

Other categories—ultraoligotrophic, oligomesotrophic, and hypereutrophic—modify the above-mentioned terms. However, emphasis should remain on using the oligotrophic, mesotrophic, and eutrophic terms because they will suffice when referring to a lake's productivity. Many times the term eutrophic is improperly used as a synonym for polluted. Pollution does not always correlate with the process of eutrophication when referring to increasing the nutrient (nitrogen and phosphorus) content of a lake from sewage effluent. A lake can, in fact, be "polluted" by a heavy metal or other toxic substance and become more oligotrophic. Care and thought should then be made before using the term eutrophic in describing a lake, even though increased eutrophication of a lake frequently results from untreated or little-treated effluent, such as runoff from a cattle feed lot or nearby town.

In relatively natural situations, lakes become more eutrophic as they age. Another general rule is that there is a trend of increasing productivity (or eutrophication) with decreasing depth of a lake. Therefore, a rule of thumb is that eutrophic lakes are shallow and have greater primary productivity, and oligotrophic lakes are deep and have lower productivity.

Special Lake Types

Odum (1971) listed seven special lake types:

(1) Dystrophic lakes generally have high concentrations of humic acid. The water appears brown and the lakes eventually develop into peat bogs.

(2) Deep, ancient lakes contain animals that are found nowhere else on earth.

(3) Desert salt lakes occur in sedimentary drainages in arid climates where evaporation exceeds precipitation. They are sumps for drainages where salts build up that have no outlets such as the Great Salt Lake. Communities of few species are the rule for these lakes.

(4) Desert alkali lakes occur in igneous drainages in arid climates. Being alkaline, their pH values and concentrations of carbonates are high. Pyramid Lake, Nevada is an example.

(5) Volcanic lakes occur in areas with active volcanoes and may be acid or alkaline.

(6) Chemically stratified meromictic or partly-mixed lakes become permanently stratified due to such things as intrusion of saline water or salts liberated from sediments. This sets up a permanent density difference between surface and bottom waters. The boundary between the upper, circulating waters and the lower, non-circulating layer is termed a chemocline. The bottom layers are free of any organisms. Big Soda Lake, Nevada is an example of a meromictic lake. In addition, Flaming Gorge Reservoir on the Green River of Utah and Wyoming had a chemocline from the time it was filled in 1967 until 1982. The chemocline resulted from salts being liberated from the sediments.

(7) Polar or alpine lakes have surface temperatures that remain below 4°C (39°F) except for brief periods during the ice-free summer. Plankton populations grow rapidly and store fat for the long winter. These lakes are not productive enough to obtain optimum growth of fish.

Impoundments

Impoundments (Figure 2) are artificial lakes created by placing a dam on a river or stream. Beaver ponds are the smallest example in this category. A tall concrete dam such as the Hoover and Glen Canyon dams on the Colorado River are examples of the other extreme. The limnological characteristics of an impoundment vary according to the nature of the drainage, the climate, and probably most of all, the operation of the reservoir. Wright (1967) and Odum (1971) listed a number of effects of dams. Some of the more notable include the fact that water is released from the surface of natural lakes

and from the bottom of most reservoirs. Therefore, the releases from the deep layers of a reservoir will have higher salinities, be colder during the ice-free period, have a lower concentration of dissolved oxygen, be higher in some of the reducing compounds (such as hydrogen sulfide), and have higher nutrient concentrations than would normally be stored in a natural lake. The advent of using multilevel outlets on dams has resulted in the moderation of some of the above effects. Nevertheless, water levels of reservoirs can fluctuate greatly whereas lake levels remain relatively stable. This operational difference, along with all the ramifications, puts impoundments in a category of lakes that require different management techniques than natural lakes.

CRITICAL HABITAT FEATURES

The physical feature that exerts the most direct control on a lake's characteristics is its thermal stratification. The maximum density of pure water is just under 4°C (39°F). All fresh water at any other temperature is lighter and found on the surface. Thus, ice floats and in summer, the upper layer of a lake is warmest. The thermal regime of a lake definitely reflects its ambient temperatures as they fluctuate over a day and over a season.

The following is a scenario of a temperate lake. The example will also be used to define some terms. Consider a deep lake whose temperature in late spring is fairly uniform from top to bottom at about 4°C (39°F). As the day lengthens, solar radiation is absorbed by the water, mostly by the upper layers of the lake. Light intensity decreases with increasing depth until the point is reached where complete darkness occurs. Wind mixes the surface water rather thoroughly but does not reach down to the deeper water. As heating and mixing of the surface layers continue to midsummer, a typical pattern of temperature distribution develops (Figure 4). The warm top layer, which is heated by the sun and mixed by the wind and other currents, is called the **epilimnion.** The bottom layer (neither heated by the sun nor mixed by the wind) is called the **hypolimnion.** The transition between the two is the metalimnion or **thermocline.** The thermocline is generally recognized where the water temperature drops at a rate of 1°C per m of water depth, although this is a textbook definition and may in reality be better described as a biological barrier.

Once a thermocline has formed, the two layers are virtually separated and no water is exchanged between them; even the current patterns within them are different. These layers are maintained strictly because warmer water is lighter than colder water. As fall progresses, heat is lost from the epilimnion to the atmosphere faster than it is absorbed and the temperature drops. At the same time, the

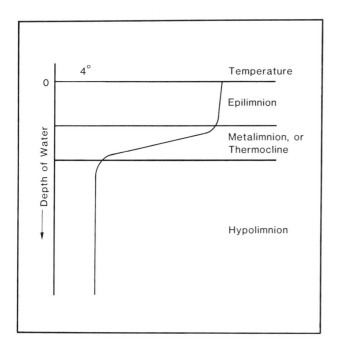

Figure 4. Typical pattern of temperature distribution in a deep lake in the summer zone during the summer.

thermocline continues to sink. The difference between water temperatures at the surface and at the bottom steadily decreases until the thermocline no longer exists and the lake "turns over" as the wind mixes it.

As winter intensifies, stratification, in reverse of summer, is setup. Ice forms on the surface of the water at about 0°C (32°F) and temperatures at the bottom are about 4°C (39°F). In typical temperate-zone lakes, the winter stratification is not as strongly developed as the summer stratification; and in some areas ice never forms and the lakes, more or less, continually turn over the entire winter due to wind driving their circulation.

In spring, the lake again absorbs heat from the sun and its temperature rises until it is uniform at about 4°C (39°F) from top to bottom. The cycle begins again. Lakes that undergo two turnovers per year are called **dimictic.** Those that turn over only once and never manage to form ice are called **monomictic.** There is a range of lakes found in each of the two categories.

The determining factors for the complexity of life in a lake are a combination of the physical and chemical factors in and around a lake. Factors other than temperature include the basin configuration, depth of lake, water clarity, dissolved oxygen and dissolved solids, inflow-outflow volume versus lake volume (flushing rate), nutrient (e.g., nitrogen, phosphorus, and silica), and a myriad of other chemical and physical factors including many caused by man.

Lakes are ephemeral features, considering the geologic time scale. The length of their life is extremely variable, but they all progress toward the eutrophic state. This rate of change is influenced tremendously by man's activities. Water is a precious commodity in the western U.S. and numerous factors compete for the limited supply. Therefore, man has varying degrees of influence on all the lakes, ponds, and reservoirs in the western U.S. The watershed that supplies water to lakes may have cattle grazing, which causes added nutrient input and erosion of streambeds from vegetation loss. Added nutrient input tends to increase eutrophication of a lake whereas erosion of streambeds adds turbidity. Mining activities in a watershed may add heavy metals to a lake. Acid mine pollution can essentially kill a lake. In some areas, acid mine effluent from old mine shafts or tailing piles has been continually polluting area streams and lakes for over 100 years. The ultimate influence of this acid mine effluent is to actually suppress a lake's development, keeping its living component at a minimum.

Proper management of the watershed will avoid disasters and reduce problems that may later be too expensive or impractical to fix. The paramount consideration is that a lake is only part of the entire watershed; therefore, proper management of the lake alone will not be enough.

Different lakes and even different parts of a lake have different communities of animal and plant life. These differences are functions of many things, including lake size and depth, substrate, light, thermal stratification, and geographic location. All of these factors should be considered in the management scheme of a lake.

MAIN LIFE ZONES OF A LAKE

Figure 5 diagrams the main life zones within a lake. All open water, where the bottom is too deep to be inhabited by living plants, is termed the **pelagic zone.** Within the pelagic zone there are two subzones: the **limnetic,** where there is enough light for photosynthesis to occur, and the **profundal,** the dark bottom layers. The layer of most biological importance in the pelagic zone is above the compensation point where light is just sufficient to produce exactly what is used up (e.g., photosynthesis = decomposition). Above this level, autotrophs (such as algae) can produce food through photosynthesis. These autotrophs form the base of the food web as they are the main source of primary production for the lake. Diversity of life in the limnetic zone is greatest. Below the compensation level is the profundal zone. Here autotrophs cannot produce food (lack of enough light) and the main source of energy is detritus that "rains" out of the limnetic zone. All organisms in the profundal zone are called **heterotrophs** and are either detritus feeders or carnivores.

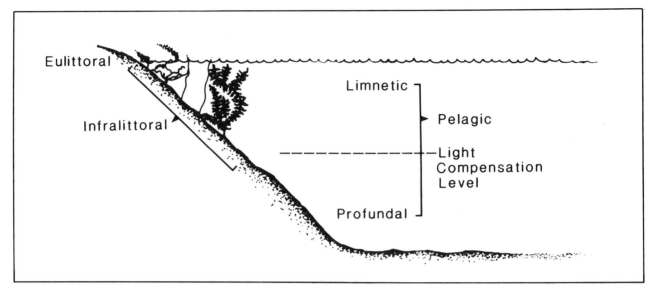

Figure 5. The main life zones of a lake.

One final way a lake is partitioned is by the bottom. The lake bottom may be of original rock in younger lakes; in older lakes the bottom is covered with sediments to form a uniform substrate of mud or sand. The area of bottom below the compensation level is the **profundal benthic zone.** The area from the lower limit of rooted vegetation to the shore is known as the **littoral zone.** The littoral zone has the lake's greatest diversity both in habitat and community. The littoral zone is further broken down into the **infralittoral zone,** which is always under water and contains rooted vegetation; and the **eulittoral zone,** which is nearest the shore and may be covered by water only part of the time. Much erosion can occur in this zone as agitation is greatest.

MAJOR SPECIES GROUPS

Lakes are used for many forms of recreation. These include swimming, boating, water skiing, sailing and, of course, fishing. As the population of the western U.S. increases, so does the fishing pressure on its limited number of lakes, ponds, and reservoirs. The fishery must then be closely managed by stocking and other techniques. Above all other forms of life, fish are generally the primary concern. To put this into a proper perspective, along with the fish themselves, other aspects about a particular lake govern the fishery and must be considered and known.

The variety of animal and plant assemblages found in lakes is as great as the variety of different kinds of lakes. In addition, different parts of a lake have different characteristics and therefore have different animal and plant communities. Probably the most influential factor in determining the kind of plant and animal communities that occur in a lake is

temperature. One commonly encounters the terms *cold-water fishery, cool-water fishery,* and *warm-water fishery.* The term two-story fishery is also commonly used by fishery biologists. The following are rules of thumb: A cold-water fishery in the western U.S. usually means a trout fishery. Therefore, it could include any kind of native or introduced salmonid such as rainbow (*Salmo gairdneri*), brown (*S. trutta*), or brook trout (*Salvelinus fontinalis*), or a variety of salmon. A cool-water fishery includes walleye (*Stinostedion rutreum*), sauger (*S. canadense*), yellow perch (*Perca flavescens*), northern pike (*Esox lucius*), and muskellunge (*Esox masquinongy*) (Trandahl 1978). A warm-water fishery in the western U.S. usually includes spiny-rayed fishes, such as sunfish (*Centrarchidae*) and bass (*Micropterus sp.*), and also catfish, bullheads (*Ictaluridae*), and carp (*Cyprinus carpio*). A two-story fishery is one that includes both cold-water and warm-water fishes.

The situation for a two-story fishery is special in that thermal stratification during the summer is strong enough that the epilimnion is generally above 20° to 25°C (68° to 77°F) in midsummer while the hypolimnion (lower layer) is around 10° to 15°C (50° to 59°F). For a successful two-story fishery, thermal conditions during winter cannot be so severe as to violate the ecological requirements of warm-water species. In addition, the proper kinds and amounts of food must be available for the cold-water and warm-water fish. Thus, considerable information on a particular lake must be available to determine if it will sustain a two-story fishery. All of the fisheries mentioned are found throughout the western U.S.

Both recreationally and commercially, fish are the most important living component in a lake. However, other living components within the lake dictate what the fishery is and how successful it is (or could be if managed correctly). The differences in communities between lakes and within any particular lake are functions of many other physical and chemical factors besides temperature. These include substrate, light, cation-anion concentrations, and geographic position of communities within the lake. The communities within the different life zones (e.g., limnetic, profundal, pelagic, and littoral) of a lake are not completely separate, as some species overlap two or more zones.

The upper portion (limnetic zone) of the open water (pelagic) area is of the most obvious biological importance, as it is where autotrophs can produce food through photosynthesis. The simplest form of life in the food chain of a lake would most likely be found in its upper zone. The autotroph is algae that converts the sun's energy and inorganic material to living material. There are many kinds of algae, ranging from diatoms dominating in lakes of low production to blue-greens that dominate more productive lakes during midsummer. The algae are grazed on by microscopic animals collectively called zooplankton. These range from relatively small rotifers (10 microns) to fresh-water shrimp (20-30 mm [1 in.] long) that feed on the smaller zooplankton.

Zooplankton provide the food base for fish. Some species of fish only eat zooplankton for a short time in their life cycle, while they are very small. Other fish (commonly called filter feeders because they filter the water) feed on zooplankton their entire life. The next predator in this simple food chain is a fish that feeds on other fish. An example is a largemouth bass feeding on minnows. Man, other fish-eating mammals, or some fish-eating birds would be the final link in this food chain. The following illustration is a sample food chain.

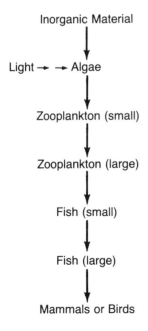

In reality, the community of a lake is a food web. That is, there are many kinds and species of plants and animals, and a variety of conditions and factors that result in a web pattern versus the simple chain described above. The following illustration is a sample food web.

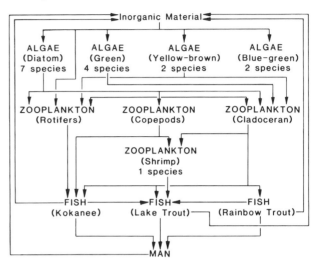

The benthic and littoral components of the community also play significant roles in the food web. The benthic community may consist of insect larvae, true worms, and clams. These animals break down the organic material (e.g., dead fish) that falls to the bottom into the inorganic material that reenters the food web when the lake circulates at spring and fall turnover. The littoral zone contains an even greater diversity of insect larvae, worms, clams, and rooted and floating aquatic plants. The littoral zone often provides the most diverse aquatic habitat within a lake; it also may have the most complex food web of a lake.

INVENTORY AND MONITORING METHODS FOR LAKES

A number of useful manuals and books can be consulted for methodology of studying lakes. They range from sections of limnology and fishery text books to entire manuals devoted to methods. Some of the more common manuals or textbooks that include methods are listed in Appendix 1.

The U.S. Geological Survey publication entitled **National Handbook of Recommended Methods for Water Data Acquisition** (1977) is considered to be the "bible" by users and collectors of data relating to hydrology, chemical quality, groundwater, sediment, biological quality soil water, evapotranspiration, and hydrometeorology. It should be referred to by anyone surveying or monitoring lakes, ponds, reservoirs, or streams. Compiled by agencies that acquire information on or related to water in the U.S., it contains standardized methodology to assure greater comparability, compatibility, and usability of water data. It is easily obtainable from the Office of Water Data Coordination, U.S. Geological Survey, Department of the Interior, Reston, VA 22092.

Levels of Inventory or Monitoring

There are, of course, several ways (and levels of effort) to conduct limnological or fishery surveys of lakes. The goals and needs should first be identified, which will dictate both the type of survey and the level of effort. If, for example, several hundred lakes need to be characterized as eutrophic versus oligotrophic, a remote sensing survey with a minimum of ground-truthing during midsummer could provide the information necessary. It should be cautioned, however, that in almost every situation there would not be enough information provided from a survey of this type to make judgments as to the fishery. Also, a lake one year could be classified as eutrophic, whereas another year it could not.

The most difficult level of effort would include a long-term (5-year), twice-monthly to monthly, survey of the physical, chemical, and biological limnology and frequent netting or creel census data collection of each lake or lakes. The long-term survey could involve expenditures of more than $200,000 per year, whereas the remote sensing survey may cost only a few hundred dollars. Although a prudent manager is likely to opt for the remote sensing survey, the needs and long-term usefulness of the data should be considered. The following are descriptions of several levels of effort that can be chosen or blended to fit a needed situation. Level I is the least amount of effort; Level IV the most.

The first thing that needs to be determined is why a survey is needed. When that question is answered, the tests to be run and samples to be collected can be planned. Upon completion of the reconnaissance survey, when the data are in hand, it is important for the manager to realize the limitation of the data. That is, a one-shot collection of data during midsummer reveals little of the lake's ecology during winter or even for the month before and after the collection of data. Nevertheless, remember that by doing the reconnaissance survey, managers can know things about the lake not previously known. As long as the data are kept in proper perspective, such a survey is useful.

Level I—Minimum Effort Inventory. This level, which is a simple inventory, can also be described as a reconnaissance survey. Reconnaissance surveys are usually used to determine the general ecological trend of a system and should be conducted in midsummer. They may also be used to identify areas in which more detailed or synoptic surveys should be done.

A Level I survey can be approached in various ways, depending upon the need. If there is need to simply characterize a lake as to cold water versus warm water, measuring depth and surface and bottom temperatures during midsummer may be sufficient. If there is need to characterize the trophic status of a lake or several lakes, remote sensing may be used, or carefully collected and properly handled water samples may be analyzed for phosphorus and nitrogen concentrations.

If there is a need to know the quality of a lake's fish food base (i.e., plankton), a top to bottom plankton sample needs to be collected with a proper plankton net and analyzed. If some information on a lake's fishery needs to be known, creel-censusing (interviewing fishermen) or spot-netting with appropriate gill nets is necessary.

All of the above are examples of information that would be obtained at a "one-shot" reconnaissance level for a specific need. It may be that several things need to be known about a lake; therefore, a reconnaissance survey would include many of the above tests. It must be remembered that there are several approaches to obtaining information for any one particular need. I recommend that the **National Handbook of Recommended Methods for Water-Data Acquisition** (U.S. Geological Survey 1977) be consulted for each test.

Level II—Maximum Level Inventory. This level would also be classified as a reconnaissance survey, with several tests done to obtain more knowledge of the subject lake. For example, suppose a manager wanted to know the general characteristics of four or five lakes so that future studies could be planned to develop an intensively managed fishery. An approach I recommend would involve not more than four workdays per lake, preferably on the same day. Each lake's survey would be in two parts—fishery and limnology. The limnology would involve choosing the deepest part (or parts if it is relatively large) of the lake and collecting some critical profile data and samples there. A profile of temperatures each 1-2 m (3.3-6.6 ft) from surface to bottom is essential; dissolved oxygen concentration, at least at the bottom, is desirable.

Also, some information on other water quality variables is desirable. A determination must be made as to what kind of water quality data are needed and what is to be done with them. This will determine how many samples are collected and how these samples are handled. At a minimum, a sample or samples of water should be collected from at least three depths—surface, mid-depth (thermocline), and near-bottom.

Nitrogen and phosphorous concentrations are always important data to collect as they indicate trophic status of a body of water. The samples for these nutrient analyses must be collected in clean, approved plastic bottles, with no contamination from handling. Usually 0.5 L (0.5 qt) is a sufficient sample for these analyses. After collection of the samples, they need to be analyzed by a qualified laboratory or preserved by freezing until they are sent to a laboratory.

Next, a sample of the lake's plankton should be collected with a sock-like plankton net which is pulled from bottom to top or within layers of the lake (e.g., 5 m [16 ft] to surface; 10 m [33 ft] to surface), depending on the equipment available and the need for a detailed study. These samples provide information on the food base for fish. The samples need to be placed in acceptable bottles (0.5 L [0.5 qt]) and preserved with several drops of formalin or other preservative. The samples are then analyzed qualitatively and quantitatively, if desired, in the laboratory. A binocular, low-power microscope, standard counting cell, and simple pipette are needed to do these analyses.

Next, benthic samples of the lake could be collected. This involves using one of several types of dredges, a standard No. 30 sieve bucket, and some forceps. The bottom mud is collected, washed in the sieve bucket, and the sample plus residue preserved in a bottle with a few milliliters of formalin. These samples will reveal many things about the lake, such as the benthos food base, past stratification strength, hypolimnion chemistry, and general status of the lake. These samples would also be analyzed in a laboratory.

Finally, in this brief reconnaissance limnological survey, some indication of light penetration is desirable. The simplest way to do this is with a Secchi disc. This is a circular metal plate, 20 cm (8 in.) in diameter, the upper surface of which is divided into quarter sections painted black and white. It is attached to a line by a center eyebolt. The point at which the eyebolt can no longer be seen upon lowering is the Secchi depth. This simple piece of information is extremely valuable since light is one of the important qualities of the lake's limnology. The lake in question can be easily compared to others by this method.

The second portion of this reconnaissance is to examine the fishery. If no data exist, a gill-net survey is a good place to start. This involves first having the proper collecting permit, which should be obtained well ahead of time from the state game and fish agencies. Assistance from the agencies is desirable and often essential. They can assist in using proper equipment, such as gill nets, shocking boats, and beach seines. Without their involvement, a survey of the fishery will most likely lack some important knowledge.

Often, a one-night set of experimental gill nets in some strategic locations will yield information that will help managers make some preliminary decisions as to what kind of a fishery exists and what needs to be done. Sometimes beach seining during late summer or early fall can give fishery biologists and ichthyologists a good indication of the type of fishery existing in a lake where little is known. The Level II survey involves much preparation and follow-up to be done properly.

Level III—Minimum Effort Monitoring. This level of effort involves part or all of the tasks described under Level II except they are performed on a seasonal basis, that is, four times a year at midseason. Again, details of the study depend on the questions being asked. The Level III studies are the first stage of synoptic or detailed studies. Instead of an inventory, a monitoring study is being performed. These synoptic or detailed studies are done to determine ecological baselines from which change can be determined in the future. In general, the premise on which synoptic surveys are based is that an evaluation of kinds, numbers, and relative abundance of species enables one to establish the biological health of a lake, pond, or reservoir (or any other ecological system). As with the other levels of effort, this monitoring should be attempted only after careful planning and preparation. If several lakes are involved, some coordination is beneficial so that inter-lake comparisons can be made.

If the needs dictate a Level III effort, costs can add up to tens of thousands of dollars per lake per year. However, if there is only a need to monitor lake temperatures, all that is needed is a boat and motor, a thermometer probe with enough cable to reach the bottom, and a readout. If plankton species need to be documented, all that is needed is a boat and motor, a plankton net, a collection bottle, and some preservative. Seasonal samples of plankton would then reveal not only if certain kinds required for certain species of fish are present, they would reveal many things about the lake's health.

Level IV—Maximum Effort Monitoring. Level IV should be chosen only when a highly synoptic set of data is needed. Monitoring studies at this level become more involved and more frequent. The main thing is that they are more synoptic, and routine field sampling dates need to be selected. An example would be every other month, or monthly during turnover, and every third month at other times. A resource specialist or manager needs to ask why the data are needed, when the most significant information can be collected, and how much and what kind of data are needed to solve the problem. It cannot be overemphasized that the studies must constantly be adjusted and fine-tuned to keep them in a proper perspective. It is common for a resource specialist to convince a manager of the need to perform a certain study, yet the manager may not understand the utility of collecting a lot of data. Both resource specialists and managers should agree how the data are to be used by their agency.

For example, the need may exist to monitor a lake that is involved in a water resources development scheme. Suppose that its ecosystem is likely to be modified considerably. For this example, consider that the lake is a natural subalpine lake with a surface area of about 700 ha (1,750 a.). Furthermore, consider that the lake is to be raised behind a newly constructed dam. In addition, a pumped storage power plant will be constructed that will pump lake water 150 m (495 ft) up to a newly constructed reservoir. During the generation phase, water will pass from the upper reservoir through the power plant back to the natural lake. Current environmental laws require that the environmental effects be recognized and some values protected. Therefore, the ecosystem must be understood. Limnology and fishery investigations would be necessary before, during, and after changes were made. The lake's food chain should be studied in enough detail to be able to first predict, then detail and quantify changes to the lake that are accountable to the development project.

The actual level of detail of each study will vary from location to location and will be dictated by needs identified by resource specialists. The manuals and textbooks listed in Literature Cited should be referred to as a guide in determining how the outlined needs will be met. One of the more difficult tasks for a manager is knowing how much and what kind of information are necessary for a particular situation. Many times, not enough information is collected to provide managers or resource specialists with the evidence they need to make a critical decision. This not only can do an injustice to the resource, it can be embarrassing for the decisionmaker. On the other hand, some studies become "gold-plated" and the information may not apply to the need. An example may be that an adequate amount of chemistry data is available on a particular lake for the manager to determine if the inflow actually is contributing to the lake pollution. However, these data need summarization by a resource specialist so that managers can use them in their decisions. Suppose the investigators selected to do the summarization are involved deeply in computer modeling and their product is a detailed and highly technical model of the lake. There have been instances when the manager has not been able to use this product because it is too technical.

The more practical way to handle this situation would be to have the summarization done by a resource specialist who will also know the practical

need. The manager may be less technically qualified than a professional statistician or modeler, but the manager's grasp of the situation will allow the data to be useful and allow a decision to be made. This does not mean that models are not useful. The point is that there will always be difficulty in knowing exactly how much information is needed. A consensus of resource personnel and management should be sought as to how much information is necessary to make a wise decision regarding a lake, pond, or reservoir.

Field Techniques

This section includes a summarization of some of the accepted field methods and the types of gear needed for the various studies that are done for the levels described in the previous section. Three aspects of a survey are used to facilitate this presentation: physical-chemical limnology, biological limnology, and fishery.

For all the studies listed below, a boat, outboard motor, field book, and pen or pencil are required. At all times, approved life jackets or vests are required equipment for a survey. The following summarizes the requirements for specific tests.

Physical-chemical surveys. Collecting profile information on a lake requires some instrument(s) that measures the desired features. The most primitive way is to lower a water bottle (described below) to each desired depth; collect a sample; bring it to the surface; and measure the temperature, conductance, and dissolved oxygen (DO) of water in the bottles with a simple hand-held thermometer and other portable gear. This method is acceptable if errors of up to several degrees temperature can be tolerated. Also, the methodology for DO measurement requires clear glass bottles that hold about 300 ml (9 oz) and have glass stoppers (called BOD bottles), and several chemicals. In many situations, this sampling method is adequate, but in others, more sophisticated gear is needed. This gear may be very complex electronic equipment that measures five or six variables at once (temperature, pH, DO, conductance, oxidation-reduction potential, and depth) and stores the data on internal memory chips.

Practically speaking, a multiparameter probe (see Figure 6) is a fairly basic piece of equipment where routine lake surveys are being done. These instruments cost from $4,000 to $8,000, but are accurate and save much time in the field and laboratory.

Water chemistry data generally require that water samples be collected, placed into acceptable

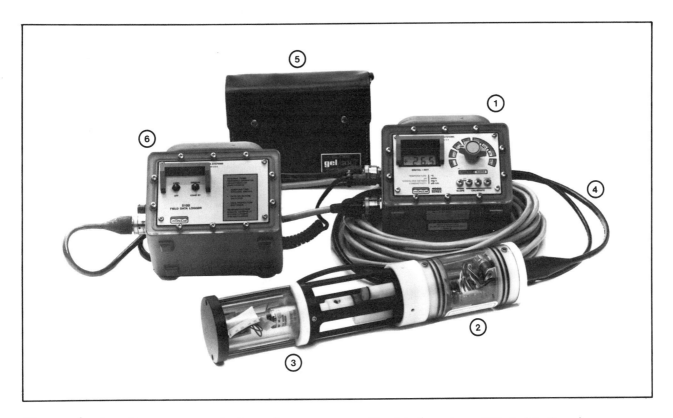

Figure 6. A multiparameter probe is used to measure profile data (courtesy of Hydrolab Corp.). (1) Digital Display Unit, (2) Sohole Unit, (3) Circulatory Assembly, (4) Cables, (5) Battery Pack, and (6) Digital Field Datalogger.

containers, preserved, and taken to a qualified laboratory for analyses. Portable water chemistry kits are available and the data obtained from their use are acceptable for some measurements when the analyst is qualified. However, for synoptic studies or where data are required for critical decisions, the samples should be carefully collected and analyzed by a qualified laboratory.

Ideally, the sample bottles should be provided by the laboratory that does the analyses. The laboratory should be consulted as to the amount of water they need for the requested analysis. A water bottle of the Van Dorn or Kemmerer types (see Figure 7) is necessary if more than surface samples are to be collected. The water bottle must be attached to a reel of cable of sufficient length. Along with the water bottle, a messenger or something to trigger or close the bottle at the desired sampling depth is needed. Samples for chemical analyses should include both inflow and outflow water to determine quantitatively the chemical elements that flow in and out of a lake or reservoir and those that are retained. Finally, the proper preservative is needed. For normal cation and anion analysis, only refrigeration is needed; for nitrogen and phosphorus nutrients, freezing is best; and for most heavy metal analyses, lowering the pH with nitric acid below a value of 2 is recommended.

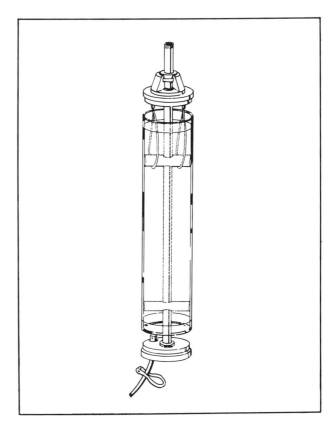

Figure 7. A Kemmerer water sample bottle in the open position.

The amount of light that enters a lake is an important quality. It can be measured easily with a Secchi disc. If more quantitative information on light is desired, instrumentation called limnophotometers may be used. These cost between $3,000 and $5,000 and actually measure light in units as the photocell is lowered into the water.

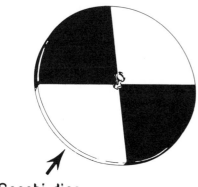

Secchi disc

The following list of equipment will be sufficient to perform a physical-chemical survey:

- map of the lake (optional);

- reel with enough cable or rope to reach desired depth;

- thermometer, multiparameter probe, or whatever is appropriate to measure temperature, dissolved oxygen, conductance, pH, redox potential, and depth;

- water sample bottle (Kemmerer or Van Dorn type);

- appropriate containers to hold samples for water analysis;

- appropriate preservative; and

- messenger (heavy metal weight made especially to trigger sampling gear).

Biological Limnology. The selection of equipment here is as broad as the kinds of data that need to be collected. The following is by no means exhaustive. A limnological text should be consulted before proceeding. Some examples are nevertheless given.

Primary production is commonly measured by two methods—chlorophyll or light versus dark bottle studies. An analysis of chlorophyll pigments in a known volume of lake water will provide an indication of the algae biomass. This then gives direct evidence of the amount of primary products in the lake. The entire process involves access to a laboratory with a filtration system, spectrophotometer, test tubes, and acetone. Water is collected and stored for a short period until the samples are filtered (usu-

ally with a pressure filter) through recommended fiberglass filters. These are kept frozen until they are put into a test tube of acetone and crushed. The test tubes are centrifuged and the decanted sample is put into a spectrophotometer. Light penetration at wavelengths 630, 645, and 667 is recorded and the results put into equations found in Wood (1975) or Maitland (1978).

An actual measurement of photosynthetic rate may be done in several ways. Most involve comparing activity in light versus dark BOD bottles left in the lake at desired depths for specified times. One common method is to measure the DO before and after a predetermined time period in both dark and light bottles. The difference in dissolved oxygen between the light and dark bottle then represents an indication of the amount of primary production. Specific methodology for this is available in Wood (1975). Another commonly used method is even more direct and involves spiking the light and dark bottles with a known concentration of radioisotope tagged source of carbon ($NaH^{14}CO_3$). The theory is that algae during photosyntheses use carbon-12 and by putting tagged carbon-14 in, filtering the algae later, and measuring the amount of radioactivity, the amount of carbon uptake by algae will be known. The amount of carbon assimilation then indicates the primary productivity rate at the time of the survey. The carbon-14 methodology requires expensive laboratory equipment, a radioactive source, and individuals licensed by the Nuclear Regulatory Commission. Nevertheless, when done properly, it is the best indication of a lake's primary production rate.

The next step is to collect the plankton (both phytoplankton and zooplankton) and measure densities (i.e., number per volume). Again, there are numerous ways to accomplish this task. Probably the most common method is to use a closing net (Figure 8). This is a sock-like net that is lowered into the water column to various depths. It strains the water as it is raised through the water column. A cup at the lower end is emptied into a collection jar and preserved with a few drops of formalin, alcohol, or other preservative.

A subsample (e.g., 1 ml) of the plankton is put into a counting cell for counting and identification under a microscope. The densities of each kind of plankton are then calculated. Other commonly used methods include towing a metered Clark-Bumpus plankton net horizontally a short distance across the lake or collecting a known volume of water with the water bottle and pouring it through a net. All of these involve counting and identifying the samples in the laboratory by qualified personnel. A note of caution: some of the zooplankton may not be there when and where sampling is done. For example, the freshwater shrimp (*Mysis relicta*) that live in cold-

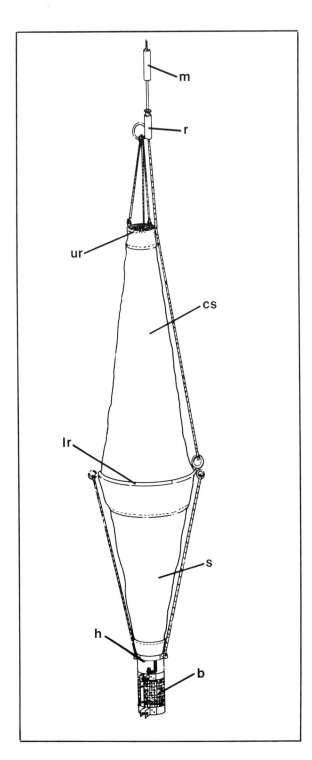

Figure 8. The closing style plankton net—

- (b)   detatchable bucket
- (cs) canvas sleeve
- (h)   headpiece
- (lr) lower ring
- (m) messenger
- (r)   release
- (s)   sleeve of silk bolting cloth or other suitable material
- (ur) upper ring

water lakes are nocturnal and will not be collected during daylight hours. Therefore, adequate sampling techniques would include spatial and temporal considerations.

The benthos of a lake are collected by gathering a known area of bottom mud and straining it through a sieve. Sampling gear includes Ponar, Peterson, and Ekman dredges (Figures 9 and 10). They all have their most appropriate uses—an Ekman for shallow or soft mud, Peterson for hard lake bottom, and Ponar for deep lakes of either type.

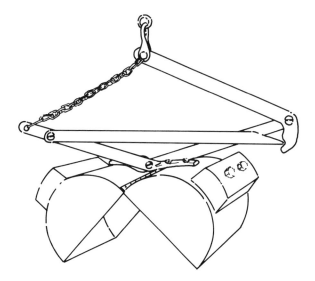

Figure 9. Ponar dredge in the open position.

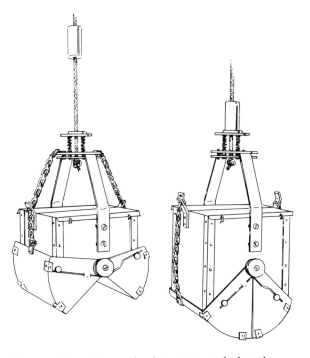

Figure 10. Ekman dredge, open and closed positions.

Samples are preserved in formalin and analyzed in the laboratory (identification and enumeration). Qualified personnel are required for the laboratory procedure.

One aspect of a lake's limnology that is frequently ignored is the emergent and submergent plants (macrophytes). This is because it is difficult to collect information on these, especially underwater. Usually found in the shallow waters of littoral zones of lakes, these plants may be free-floating or attached. They serve as habitat for a variety of other aquatic organisms. The contribution of macrophytes to the primary production of lakes, ponds, and even reservoirs has been grossly underestimated or ignored in many synoptic studies. However, rooted aquatic plants are becoming increasingly significant in the study of aquatic communities, supplementing data obtained on algae (Patrick and Martin 1974). Collection of these plants is normally done by harvesting. Species identification, biomass, and regrowth measurements are done in the laboratory. A surface plot is harvested and the regrowth rate is determined as a function of nutrients and productivity. A qualified aquatic botanist with access to laboratory and greenhouse facilities should be employed to accurately determine the macrophytes of a lake.

Bacterial counts may be important in some surveys. They give an indication of the amount and type of pollution in the water. These surveys are particularly important where water is used for contact sports, drinking water, or water in which fish live. There are a number of techniques available for determining bacteria counts (see Am. Public Health Assoc. 1971). A qualified bacteriologist should be employed to perform the study and analyze the data.

Figure 11 lists the equipment or alternatives that will be sufficient to perform biological limnology studies. Appendix II lists sources of equipment.

Fishery Studies. Fish are considered by many to be the most important component of a lake's food chain. This may or may not be true, but under any circumstance, the entire food chain needs to be considered. Emphasis is usually on the fish because of fishermen's demands. There are many ways to approach a fishery survey and, therefore, the equipment needed also varies. As previously mentioned, the state game and fish agency should be aware and involved in many of these studies. In all states, a collection permit is required before any work begins. A creel census can take many hours because fishermen need to be frequently interviewed. On the other hand, a netting survey can require very expensive, sophisticated gear.

There are basically two categories of methods for actually collecting fish—those that trap and hold the fish and those that physically incapacitate them. Those two can further be broken down by the various habitats in which each individual method is applicable. No one method is the best for all sizes

Studies	Reel with Cable or Rope	Water Sample Bottle and Messenger	Sample Bottles	Preservative	Laboratory Facility Includes	Other Equipment
Primary Productivity	●	●	●	●	— NRC licensed personnel for C^{14} techniques	— BOD light and dark bottles with clips — Anchor with float
Plankton	●	●	●	●	— Binocular microscope — Counting cell	— Suitable plankton net
Chlorophyll	●	●	●		— Filtration system — Fiberglass filters	— Cooler — Spectrophoto-meter
Benthos	●		●	●	— Binocular microscope — Wash pans — Forceps	— No. 30 sieve wash bucket — Ponar, or similar dredge
Macrophyte					— Greenhouse facilities — Aquaria/bell jars	— Tape measure and plot frame — Plastic bags — Digging device

Figure 11. Equipment recommended for biological limnology studies.

and species of fish in all locations. Trawls (Figure 12) are useful where water depth and bottom composition are favorable; trawls are most successfully used at night. The boat must tow the trammel net efficiently, so sufficient water depth is needed. The only fish not sampled with a trawl are the very fast swimmers and very small ones.

A variety of nets or seines are available for taking fish. Nets are usually referred to as fixed or passive sampling devices. Seines are usually indicative of an action device, one that is moved through the water and traps fish. Gill nets (Figure 13) are stationary and fish swim into them and become captured; hoop or trap nets are those that fish swim into and are held in the enclosed device until removed. Horizontal gill nets are most commonly used, but vertical gill nets are also used to determine depth of water occupied by fish. The best nets for reconnaissance surveys are termed "experimental gill nets" since they include a variety of mesh sizes sewn together. Gill nets are most commonly fished overnight. After reconnaissance is done and the desired size of fish to be studied is determined, the size mesh to be used is selected.

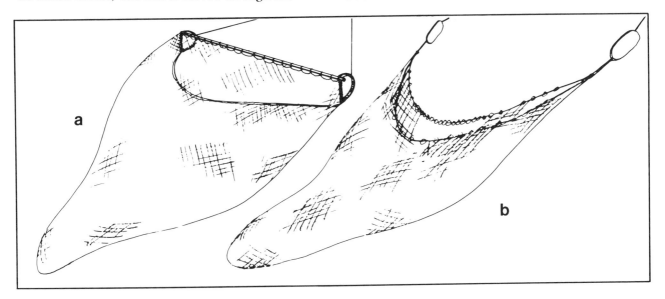

Figure 12. The Beam Fish Trawl (a) and the Otter Fish Trawl (b).

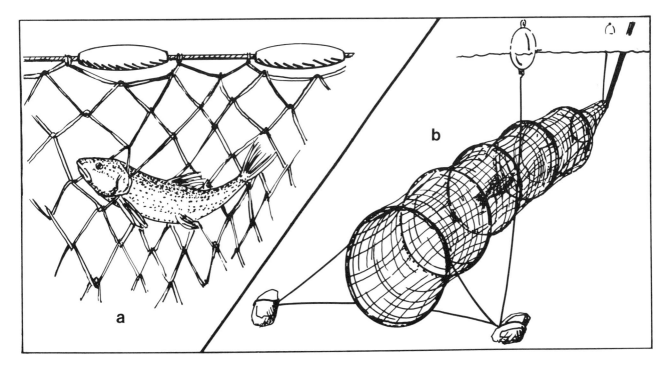

Figure 13. Gill net (a) and hoop net (b).

Seines commonly used are the straight or minnow seine. Two individuals wading (or one wading and one in a boat) pull it near the shore. These are good for littoral zone sampling. The minnow (or haul) seine has a trailing bag. There are several methods of incapacitating fish. One is the use of piscicide chemicals. The most commonly used of these is rotenone. Creol and cyanide are also used. All of these require, in some states at least, personnel that are licensed piscicide applicators. Use of these piscicides can cause serious damage to fish and other biota. Care in their application should be taken.

Another way of incapacitating fish is the use of electrofishing techniques. This method works well in very shallow lakes or portions of lakes. Where aquatic vegetation precludes efficient seining, electrofishing gear is very applicable. The gear can be either portable or mounted on a boat. Night is the best time to electrofish in lakes, ponds, and reservoirs.

The last method is the use of hook and line. This method, however, is highly selective to preferred game species. After fish are collected, species identification, number of fish captured per unit effort, length, weight, sex, and age should all be recorded. These data can usually be collected without harm to the fish. Some individuals are collected and preserved for both verification purposes and also for further analysis (e.g., food habit studies).

DISCUSSION

Each lake is a world within itself. One lake may be similar to another lake, but each is still unique. That is, two lakes may both have rainbow trout, freeze every winter, be too cold for people to ever swim in comfortably, contain sparkling clear water, have a stream flowing in and a stream flowing out, and even have pine trees up to their shoreline. A closer look reveals, however, that one lake is twice as deep as the other and has stronger thermal stratification; twice the abundance of plant nutrients; three times the densities of plankton; a relatively large, shallow littoral area in its upper end; and almost four times more fish caught in any year.

From the above facts, a biologist can see that one lake probably needs a little closer attention and

perhaps a good management plan, whereas the other lake with richer flora and fauna should be left alone. They then are different internally. As knowledge is gained from their similarities, knowledge also is gained from their differences.

As alternative management decisions regarding a resource are being considered, it is advisable that as many concerned resource specialists and managers as possible be consulted for their opinions. This is, of course, a difficult task. I know from experience that as the number of interests (agencies and people) in natural resources increases, the complexity of any decision increases and the reality of achieving a wise decision seems more remote. However, biologists and resource managers should not shy away from seeking all opinions possible, no matter how diverse they may become, so that decisionmakers can make decisions based on the best information.

The questions are always how much data is needed and how many times do things need to be measured? These questions should be asked and answers sought from resource personnel from all interested resource agencies. The decision that is finally made may strongly influence the future of a particular resource. For example, some decisions may result in irreversible changes to a system (e.g., introduction of a new species of game fish), whereas others may be reversed (e.g., change in the annual flow regime from a reservoir). Having the most and best information possible adds to the credibility of these important decisions.

The final important step that is neglected most of the time is to follow up on the actual influence and success of the decision. A good rule for the resource's sake is to see that follow-up monitoring investigations are performed. For example, suppose it had been decided, based on scientific evidence, that a forage species of fish was desirable in a certain lake because walleye did not have enough to eat after they became 15 cm (6 in.) long. It would be desirable to monitor whether the introduction of forage fish was successful or not, also to know if forage fish are reproducing naturally in sufficient numbers to provide an adequate food base for walleye in the future. Certainly monitoring this situation would make the next similar decision easier to make. Post-decision monitoring then makes each future decision easier to make.

LITERATURE CITED

AMERICAN PUBLIC HEALTH ASSOCIATION and AMER-
ICAN WATER WORKS ASSOCIATION. 1971. Standard methods for the examination of water and
wastewater. Water Control Bull. 1971. 13th ed. Am.
Pub. Health Assoc. Washington, DC. 874pp.

HUTCHINSON, G.E. 1957. A treatise on limnology, Volume I, geography, physics and chemistry. John Wiley
& Sons, Inc. New York, NY. 1015pp.

MAITLAND, P.S. 1978. Biology of freshwaters. John Wiley
& Sons, New York, NY. 244pp.

ODUM, E.P. 1971. Fundamentals of ecology. W.B. Saunders
Co. Philadelphia, PA. 574pp.

PATRICK, R. and D.M. MARTIN. 1974. Biological surveys
and biological monitoring in freshwaters. Number 5.
Contributions from Dep. Limnology, Acad. Nat. Sci.
Philadelphia, PA. 63pp.

TRANDAHL, A. 1978. Preface, Page x in Kendall, R.L. ed.,
Cool-water Fishes of North America. Special Publication 11, Am. Fish. Soc. Washington, DC. 437pp.

U.S. GEOLOGICAL SURVEY, Office of Water-Data Coordination. 1977. National handbook of recommended
methods for water-data acquisition. Two Volumes.
U.S. Dep. Inter. Reston, VA.

WOOD, R.D. 1975. Hydrobotanical methods. Univ. Park
Press. Baltimore, MD. 173pp.

WRIGHT, J.C. 1967. Effects of impoundments on productivity, water chemistry, and heat budgets of rivers.
Pages 188-199 in Reservoir Fishery Resources Symposium. Am. Fish. Soc. Washington, DC.

APPENDIX I.

Manuals and Textbooks with Inventory and Monitoring Methods for Lakes.

CAIRNS, J., Jr. and K.L. DICKSON. 1973. Biological methods for the assessment of water quality. ASTM Special Publication 528. Am. Soc. for Test & Mat. Philadelphia, PA. 256pp.

EDDY, S. and J. UNDERHILL. 1978. The freshwater fishes. Wm. C. Brown Co. Dubuque, IA. 215pp.

EVERHARDT, W.H., A.W. EIPPER, and W.D. YOUNG. 1975. Principles of fishery science. Cornell Univ. Press. Ithaca, NY. 288pp.

HUTCHINSON, G.E. 1967. A treatise on limnology, Volume II. Introduction to lake biology and the limnoplankton. John Wiley & Sons, Inc. New York, NY. 1115pp.

LAGER, K.F. 1956. Freshwater fishery biology. Wm. C. Brown Co. Dubuque, IA. 421pp.

LIETH, H. and R.H. WHITTAKER, eds. 1975. Primary productivity of the biosphere. Ecological Studies 14, Springer-Verlag, New York, NY. 339pp.

LIND, O.T. 1979. Handbook of common methods in limnology, Second Edition. The C.V. Mosby Co. St. Louis, MO. 154pp.

WELCH, P.S. 1948. Limnological methods. McGraw Hill, Inc. New York, NY. 381pp.

APPENDIX II.

Sources of Limnological and Fishery Equipment.

This list implies no endorsement of product or service. A more complete listing is "Sources of Limnological and Oceanographic Apparatus and Supplies" (special publication No. 1, third revision) available from the American Society of Limnology and Oceanography, 1530 12th Avenue, Grafton, Wisconsin 53024.

Test kits
  Hach Chemical Co.
  P.O. Box 389
  Loveland, CO 80539

General Sampling & Field Equipment
  Wildlife Supply Company
    (Wildco)
  2200 S. Hamilton St.
  Saginaw, MI 48602

  Kalh Scientific
    Instrument Co.
  P.O. Box 1166
  El Cajon, CA 92022

Fish Nets and Fish Sampling Gear
  Nylon Net Company
  7 Vance Avenue
  P.O. Box 592
  Memphis, TN 38101

  Cofelt Electronic Co.,
    Inc.
  3910 So. Windermere St.
  Englewood, CO 80110

Radio Isotopes
  Amersham-Searle Corp.
  2636 Clearbrook Dr.
  Arlington Heights, IL
    60005

  New England Nuclear
  575 Albany St.
  Boston, MA 02118

Multiparameter Instruments Submarine Photometers
  Hydrolab
  P.O. Box 50116
  Austin, TX 78763

  Kalh Scientific
    Instrument Co.
  P.O. Box 1166
  El Cajon CA 92022

III SPECIES GROUPS

13

FISH

Paul Cuplin

U.S. Bureau of Land Management
Service Center
Denver, CO 80225

Editor's Note: This chapter is the first of a series in which the focus is on species groups. In this book, species are lumped into groups based upon similarity of the techniques used to inventory and monitor their habitat or populations. Fish are of course a diverse and widespread group, and fisheries management is often considered as a separate discipline from wildlife management. However, inventory and monitoring of an area of land would be incomplete without taking into consideration the aquatic resources, of which fish are extremely important. One chapter cannot cover, except in the briefest manner, the massive field of fisheries biology. However, it can serve as a starting point for the biologist with little experience in this area. The references cited provide further guidance.

INTRODUCTION

The purpose of this chapter is to assist biologists in identifying information needed to inventory and monitor fish-producing waters including streams, lakes, ponds, and reservoirs. Fishery biology is a well-developed profession with academic curricula and degrees, professional societies, and scientific publications. A single chapter on fish cannot cover the entire subject of fish habitat and population techniques in any depth. This chapter emphasizes the techniques appropriate for inland fisheries investigations in the western U.S., particularly for salmonids and for smaller streams and ponds in arid lands. For more detailed information, consult Nielsen and Johnson (1983) or the papers cited in this chapter. Carlson and Gifford (1983) provide guidance on locating and accessing fisheries literature.

State fish and game agencies have historically managed fish populations; federal land agencies manage habitat on public land. There must of necessity be some overlapping of responsibility since federal agencies cannot evaluate the habitats properly without knowing something about existing fish populations. Likewise, State agencies need to know habitat variables in order to manage fish populations. Nor can critical habitat for threatened or endangered fish species be preserved without knowledge of habitat variables needed to sustain listed fish species.

AQUATIC HABITAT FEATURES

Important habitat features for fish are described in this section. Methods for measuring many of the following attributes or components are described by Hamilton and Bergersen (1984).

Soils

The ability of the resource specialist to determine potential of riparian zones through the analysis of soil and water flows will direct rehabilitation efforts to riparian areas with the highest potential. Streams in improved riparian habitat will support larger fish populations.

Crouse and Kindschy (1981) described soil conditions required by various riparian plant species along streams in southeastern Oregon. In the western U.S., highly alkaline soils along perennial streams will predictably produce alkali bullrush (*Scirpus paludosus*), greasewood (*Sarcobatus* sp.), buffaloberry (*Shepherdia* sp.), and salt cedar (*Tamarix* sp.); less alkaline soils will produce sedges (*Carex* sp.), forbs, grasses, cattails (*Typha* sp.), and few woody species. Soil that is extremely rocky will support willow (*Salix* sp.), mock orange (*Philadelphus* sp.), chokecherry (*Prunus* sp.), and sparse stands of grasses and forbs. Fine textured soil will support tree willow, cottonwood (*Populus* sp.), alder (*Alnus* sp.), aspen, dogwood (*Cornus* sp.), mock orange and other shrubs, dense stands of grasses, sedges, and forbs.

Physical Features

Physical features of streams and lakes such as stream gradient, may be correlated with the capability of the water to support or produce fish. These are described in more detail in the Lakes and Streams chapters. Methods for measuring such attributes are described in the Aquatic Physical Features chapter.

Vegetation

Along streams, the capability of the stream to produce or support fish populations is often a function of or correlated with the condition of the riparian vegetation. Shrubs, trees, and other woody riparian vegetation are needed to shade smaller streams and control high summer water temperatures for cold-water fishes such as the Salmonidae, which include trout, salmon, and grayling. Streambanks are strengthened and stabilized by the root structure of trees and shrubs. Streams with only grass and forb cover are subject to streambank erosion during high water flows.

Food of salmonids sometimes consists of as much as 35% terrestrial insects during the summer months. If woody riparian vegetation is absent, this source of food is also absent.

Shrubs and trees also provide much of the energy source for the stream from leaf fall and twigs. Tree fall across the stream provides resting shelter and stream habitat diversity. Healthy riparian vegetation acts as a filter to prevent soil from reaching the stream during heavy rainstorms or snowmelt (Odum 1978).

Water Quality

The chemical and physical properties of water are extremely important habitat characteristics for fish. Three of the most important attributes are pH, dissolved materials, and dissolved oxygen. Other properties are described in the chapters on Streams and Lakes. Methods for measuring water quality are described in the chapter on that subject.

pH. Most fresh-water fishes can accommodate pH ranging from 6.0 to 9.5, although some species can adapt below 6.0 or above 9.5 pH.

Dissolved Materials. Total dissolved materials in excess of 1,500 mg/L NaCl cannot be tolerated by most fresh-water fish species. Most waters in the West fall in a range of less than 400 mg/L except for the lower Colorado River, saline seeps, and springs.

Dissolved Oxygen. For warm-water fish the dissolved oxygen (DO) concentration should be 5 mg/L or greater. Cold-water fishes prefer the DO concentration to be at saturation which varies with water temperature and elevation. Under extreme conditions the DO may range to 5 mg/L or lower during the winter. The critical periods for DO are during late summer and during long periods of ice and snow cover during winter months.

Macroinvertebrates

Macroinvertebrates can be used to characterize stream water quality by the diversity of species, number of species, and by the presence or absence of certain species (see the Macroinvertebrates chapter).

The simplified stream-aquatic organism relationship is presented in Figure 1. Macroinvertebrates play a major role in consuming aquatic plants and detritus and providing fish with most of their food supply. A wide diversity of macroinvertebrates is produced in the stream substrate under optimum conditions.

Food Supply

The flow of nutrients into the stream system governs the number and species of macroinvertebrates that are available to fish for food.

Fish feeding habits vary widely by family, species, young of the year, juvenile, and adult. Examples of planktivores, plankton feeding species; benthic or bottom feeders; and piscivores or carnivorous fish are shown in Table 1. Not listed are sockeye or kokanee (non-migratory) salmon that are planktivores throughout all life stages.

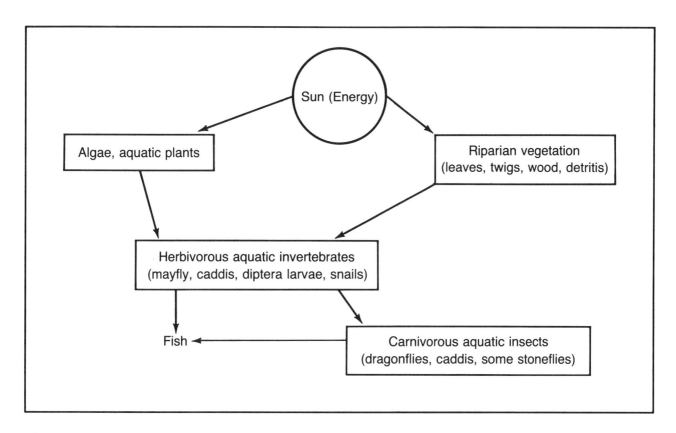

Figure 1. Simplified stream-aquatic organism relationships.

Table 1. Examples of families and species of planktivores, benthic feeding fish, and piscivores (from Fritz et al. 1980).

Group	Family	Species
Planktivores	Clupeids	Alewife (*Alosa pseudoharengus*) Gizzard shad (*Dorosoma cepedianum*)
	Corregonids	Lake whitefish (*Coregonus clupeaformis*) Ciscoe (*Coregonus* sp.) Round whitefish (*Prosopium cylindraceum*)
Benthic feeding fish	Catostomids	White sucker (*Catostomus commersomi*) Longnose sucker (*C. catostomus*) Carp (*Cyprinus carpio*)
	Cyprinids	Spottail shiner (*Notropis hudsonius*)
	Percopsids	Troutperch (*Percopsis omiscomaycus*)
	Cottids	Sculpins (*Cottidae*)
	Ictalurids	Catfish (*Ictalurus* sp.) Bullhead (*Ictalurus* sp.)
	Percids	Walleye (*Stizostedion vitreum*) Yellow perch (*Perca flavescens*)
Piscivores	Salmonids	Lake trout (*Salvelinus namaycush*) Brown trout (*Salmo trutta*) Rainbow trout (*Salmo gairdneri*) Chinook salmon (*Oncorhynchus tshawytscha*) Coho salmon (*O. kisutch*)
	Osmerids	Rainbow smelt (*Osmerus mordax*)
	Esocids	Northern pike (*Esox lucius*)

The food supply may be an important habitat component limiting fish populations or productivity. This may be important primarily during one season of the year or during one life stage. Bowen (1983) describes methods for determining fish diets.

HABITAT OF IMPORTANT FISH FAMILIES

Families of fishes have developed under various ecological conditions. The habitat requirements of each family of fish are well known, and habitat studies continue to add to our knowledge.

The families of fishes inhabiting public land waters in the western States and Alaska can be grouped into cold-water, cool-water, and warm-water fishes.

Cold-Water Families

Salmonidae. Family Salmonidae, for example, is represented by trout, salmon, whitefish, and grayling. This family represents important game and commercial species. Their life requirements are similar in that they inhabit cold water, and most spawn in or on stream substrate in the fall or spring. Anadromous members (migrating from the ocean up a fresh water stream to spawn), such as the Pacific salmon (*Oncorhynchus* sp.), migrate to the ocean in the first or second year of life and return to fresh water to spawn and die after spending 1 to 3 years in saltwater. Unlike the Pacific salmon, the sea-run rainbow trout (steelhead), sea-run cutthroat trout (*S. clarki*), and Dolly Varden trout (*Salvelinus malma*) return from the ocean to spawn in fresh water but do not die after spawning. They can repeat the ocean—fresh water spawning migration cycle. Whitefish and grayling (*Thymallus arcticus*) spend their entire life as residents of a lake or stream.

Cottidae. The family Cottidae, sculpins or cottids, lives on the stream bottom of cold-water streams. Sculpins or cottids inhabit much of the same stream habitat occupied by trout and provide food for them.

Cool-Water Families

Catostomidae. The family Catostomidae, suckers, uses some of the same habitat as trout. Suckers migrate upstream to spawn during the spring months and compete with trout for spawning space. They are common in degraded trout streams which have silted streambeds and higher than normal summer water temperatures.

Escoidae. The family Escoidae, pike and pickerels, inhabits streams, lakes, and reservoirs and is a native east of the Rocky Mountains to Alaska. Introductions have been made in western waters. The best known representative is the northern pike (*Esox lucius*). Preferred habitats are weedy areas of lakes and reservoirs. Spawning takes place in the spring. The eggs adhere to the stream substrate.

Percidae. Family Percidae, yellow perch (*Perca flavescens*) and walleye (*Stizostedion vitreum*), originally occurred in lakes and reservoirs east of the Continental Divide. They have been widely introduced into the western States. They prefer the cool water in lakes and reservoirs.

Warm-Water Families

Centrarchidae. The family Centrarchidae, sunfishes, is best known for bluegill (*Lepomis macrochirus*), largemouth bass (*Micropterus salmoides*), and crappie (*Pomoxis* sp.). Most of these species prefer warm-water lakes and reservoirs. Smallmouth bass (*M. dolomieui*), however, inhabit the larger, warmer streams. Only one member of this family, the

Grayling.

Northern pike (top) and sauger (bottom).

Sacramento perch (*Archoplites interruptus*), is native west of the Continental Divide, primarily found in the Sacramento and San Joaquin River Basins in California (Simpson and Wallace 1978).

Cyprinidae. The family Cyprinidae, minnows and carps, is best represented by the common carp (*Cyprinus carpio*), squawfish (*Ptychocheilus* sp.), and the goldfish (*Carassius auratus*). Carp, introduced from Asia, thrive in warm, shallow streams and lakes with abundant aquatic vegetation. The rooting habits of carp contribute to the high turbidity of water.

Squawfish are found in a variety of habitats from reservoirs to the largest western rivers. Squawfish once achieved a very large size—as much as 27 kg (60 pounds) in the Colorado River. The numbers of Colorado squawfish have been severely reduced due to dam construction which altered their required stream habitat and water temperatures for spawning.

Cyprinodontidae. The family Cyprinodontidae, killifishes, inhabits ponds, springs, and streams of the southwestern deserts. The most well known of this group is the Devil's Hole Pupfish (*Cyprinodon diabolis*) which exists in the most restricted fish habitat on earth, a spring-fed pond in Nevada with a surface area not much larger than a bathtub; the total population is 300 to 350 individuals. The habitat for this and other similar fishes of the desert is in jeopardy due to the use of water for crop irrigation.

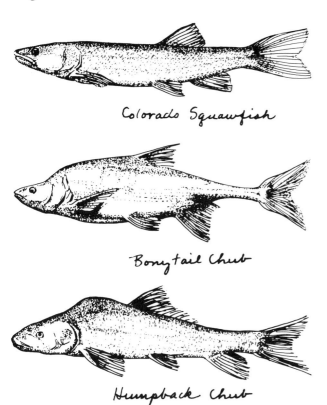

Colorado Squawfish

Bonytail Chub

Humpback Chub

Ictaluridae. The family Ictaluridae, catfishes, originally found east of the Continental Divide, can now be found in lakes, reservoirs, and streams throughout the West. The family is represented by black bullhead (*Ictalurus melas*), brown bullhead (*I. nebulosus*), channel catfish (*I. punctatus*), flathead catfish (*Pylodictis alivaris*), and blue catfish (*I. furcatus*). The channel, flathead, and blue catfish are most commonly found in the large warmer ponds and reservoirs and large warm-water streams.

Endangered Fish Species

Twenty-seven of the 44 U.S. fish species listed under the Endangered Species Act of 1973 are endemic to the southwestern U.S. (Johnson and Rinne 1982), an indication of the rapidly disappearing aquatic habitat of the southwestern deserts.

Dewatering of desert springs through groundwater pumping and continued drying of desert aquatic habitats has seriously reduced habitats for desert fishes. Water impoundments on the Colorado River have reduced water temperatures and therefore the reproduction capabilities of the four native "large river" species, Colorado Squawfish, razorback sucker (*Xyrauchen texanus*), humpback chub (*Gila cypha*), and bonytail chub (*Gila elegans*).

POPULATION MEASUREMENT TECHNIQUES

Fish population studies are conducted to relate fish biomass to habitat conditions, observe change in relative fish numbers, determine habitat preference by species, and determine use periods of the year at various life stages. A method of sampling should be selected to provide the required information at a minimum cost.

Johnson and Nielsen (1983) compared relative costs to obtain different types of information on fish populations and communities (Table 2). The lowest level (easiest to get but least valuable) of information about fish communities is the number of species present and susceptible to sampling gear. At the other end of the scale are radio tracking and food habit information; both activities are very expensive, but the resultant information may be extensive. Between these extremes are a series of activities that will provide more information at increasing cost. Table 2 lists these activities and an estimate of their relative cost. Each activity is compared to the first activity, and each activity is affected by sampling bias. Since the relative cost in dollars and personnel of different types of studies vary considerably, the biologist should be careful not to collect more information than is required for the problem being addressed.

Table 2. A cost-benefit hierarchy for information about fish populations and communities (from Johnson and Nielsen 1983).

Level	Activity	Information	Relative Cost	Comments
1	Species enumeration	Number of species present.	1	Useful in sampling.
2	Numbers of fish caught of each species	Relative abundance of the species present.	x2	Usually the minimal level of information needed.
3	Length of fish	Length distributions can give relative year-class strength, growth, and mortality, especially for young fish.	x4	A great deal of helpful information added, particularly for fast growing, temperate latitude.
4	Weight of fish	Length-weight curves, condition factors, relative weight.	x12	Most field scales are not accurate enough. Must construct special shelter or move indoors. Condition factors need both accurate lengths and weights.
5	Age determination	More accurate than length distributions for calculating year-class strength, age distribution, growth history, and mortality.	x120	Must have accurate length measurements; requires extra handling of fish and laboratory time for analysis.
6	Radio or sonar tagging	Exact information about fish location and measurements. May be combined with information about water depth, temperature.	x1,200	Much information gained about movements of relatively few fish. Equipment cost and maintenance can be quite high.

Paul Cuplin

Inventorying a small stream by electrofishing.

General Considerations

Life Stages of Fishes. The terms applied to the developmental life stages of fish assist in describing and understanding fishery reports and studies.

Developmental stage terms most commonly used are as follows:

Egg—Fertilized ovum with developing embryo.

Eyed Egg—Embryo developed to the state where the eyes can be readily observed.

Larva—Prolarva still bear yolk sacs, sometimes called sac fry. With postlarva, yolk sacs have been completely absorbed.

Alevin—The newly hatched salmon, with yolk sac still attached.

Fry—The same as postlarva; yolk sac has been completely absorbed.

Fingerling—A fish in the first or second year of life, 5 to 10 cm (2 to 4 in.) long.

Young of the Year—Young fish added to the fish population during the current year.

Smolt—One- or 2-year-old anadromous fish physiologically prepared for migration into saltwater.

Grilse—Early maturing salmon, mostly male fish.

Adult—Mature fish capable of spawning.

Kelt—Spent salmon or sea-run trout after spawning, in a weak, emaciated condition.

In the past, most fish population work has concentrated on mature stages of fish (from fry through kelt). Awareness is growing of the need to collect, identify, and gather data on larval fish. In many cases, habitat for larval fish is quite different from that of mature stages; it may be geographically separated also. If larval habitat is deteriorating, then it should be identified and monitored.

Laboratories are available for assisting in larval fish sampling and identification. Since 1977 a larval fish conference has been held annually in the U.S. or Canada. Information on larval fish procedures are described by Snyder (1983); more information on the conferences and on procedures can be obtained from the Larval Fish Laboratory, Colorado State University, Fort Collins, CO 80523.

Fish Collection. Fish specimens sometimes need to be collected and stored for later identification or tagged or marked for population surveys. Biologists must comply with State and federal laws including collection permit requirements when sampling or collecting fish. Procedures for tagging and marking fish are described by Wydoski and Emery (1983).

Fish Preservation. Specimens should be preserved in 4% formaldehyde solution (10% formalin) containing about 3 g of borax per liter (Greeson et al. 1977). Fish more than 3 inches long should be slit on the right side to allow preservatives to penetrate the body cavity.

Identify samples with date, species, location where collection was made, and name of collector. If individual fish from separate locations are to be stored in the same container, they can be wrapped in cheesecloth with an identification tag attached.

Capture Methods. Fisheries surveys beyond Level 1 (presence; Table 2) normally require fish capture. Fish capture can also be used to determine presence. Many methods for capturing fish are available. Seining, electrofishing, fish toxicants, and hook-and-line sampling are commonly used on small inland waters.

Seining Small seines are useful in small ponds but are less effective in small streams. Details about seining techniques are described by Hayes (1983:139–143).

Electrofishing. Electrofishing can be used to determine fish presence, species composition, and to make fish population estimates. Electrofishing is the most effective method of fish population sampling for a stream. The most effective time for electrofishing is from midsummer to the fall months when the streamflow is at a low point.

A 600-m (1/10-mi.) sampling area is blocked with block nets at the upper and lower ends of the sampling area. Population estimates for important game, sensitive, and endangered or threatened fishes are made by the Seber-LeCren (1967) method. A fish population estimate, relative abundance estimate, fish length distribution, and pounds of fish can be calculated for each fish population sample. Reynolds (1983) describes in detail procedures for electrofishing.

Other. Many other techniques for capturing fish are available including use of toxicants and hook-and-line. Hubert (1983) and Hayes (1983) describe procedures for passive and active capture techniques, and Davies (1983) describes use of toxicants.

Specific Techniques

Appropriate techniques that correspond with each of the 6 levels of survey (Table 2) are described below.

Presence (Level 1).

Counting Weirs and Spawning Ground Surveys, Aerial Redd Counts. Observations of salmon and other anadromous fish species in spawning runs have often been made at counting wiers and by the enumeration of dead fish on the spawning grounds. The latter method is used to determine numbers and species on specific streams. Redd counts can be made during the spawning season with helicopter or fixed-wing aircraft (Neilson and Green 1981).

Visual Observation of Stream Fish. Stream surveyors can recognize species by observing, determining presence, and estimating relative numbers per measured distance of a stream.

Relative Abundance—Population Estimation (Level 2).
Relative abundance can be expressed as the numbers of fish, by species, per unit of capture effort, e.g., number of brook trout (*S. fontinalis*) per miles of stream shocked.

For important species, population estimates can be made using one of the techniques described below. Express population estimates in numbers per linear mile for streams or numbers per surface acre for lakes, ponds, and reservoirs. For details of statistical analyses or information on alternative methods, see Lagler (1956), Ricker (1958), Armour and Platts (1983), Otis et al. (1978), or White et al. (1982).

Two-Catch Depletion (Seber-LeCren) Estimator. Depletion methods require that the fish from samples not be re-placed (put back into the water). In the two-catch depletion method, a first sample is taken (without re-placement) followed by a second sample. Equipment and effort must be standardized so that the expected proportion of the population caught is the same for each sample.

The total population can then be estimated with the formula (Seber and LeCren 1967):

$$N = \frac{(C_1)^2}{C_1 - C_2}$$

Where N = estimated number of fish in population

$\quad C_1$ = number of fish caught in first sample

$\quad C_2$ = number of fish caught in second sample

Otis et al. (1978) provide a formula for calculating sampling variance. However, White et al. (1982) recommended using three or more captures to test the assumption of equal capture probability and to increase precision. They describe assumptions and statistical analyses for three or more samples.

Mark and Release. Mark and release techniques have most often been used in lakes, ponds, and reservoirs to study fish population numbers. Fish populations can be estimated by capturing and releasing a number of marked fish and then recapturing marked and unmarked fish.

The population can then be estimated by the formula (Davis and Winstead 1980).

$$N = \frac{M \, n}{m}$$

Where N = estimated number of fish in population

$\quad M$ = number of fish marked

$\quad n$ = total number of fish captured in second sample

$\quad m$ = number of marked fish in second sample

Assumptions applied to this type of population study are (1) fish do not lose their marks, (2) marked fish are randomly distributed in the population, (3) marked and unmarked fish are equally capturable, and (4) numbers of unmarked fish are not added to the population through recruitment or immigration (Lagler 1956). Many variations on the mark-recapture technique have been developed. For details of these see Lagler (1956), Ricker (1958), Otis et al. (1978), or White et al. (1982).

Length of Fish (Level 3).
Rate of change in length of individuals and length-frequency distributions are key attributes of fish populations (Anderson and Gutreuter 1983). Fish length distributions can be developed from samples. For details of measurement and analysis techniques, see Anderson and Gutreuter (1983).

Weight of Fish (Level 4).
Weight of individual fish and fish populations are also key attributes of fish populations (Anderson and Gutreuter 1983). The relationship between weight and length can also be used to develop condition indexes. For details of these techniques see Anderson and Gutreuter (1983).

Age Determination (Level 5).
Age determination requires a substantial increase in time and money (Table 2) and should only be done where the problem(s) being addressed require such information. See Jearld (1983) for details on techniques and analysis.

Radio or Sonar Tagging (Level 6). Radio or sonar tagging is extremely costly (Table 2) and the biologist should be sure that such an investment is justified before beginning a study. Thorne (1983) describes the use of sonar or hydroacoustics. Winter et al. (1978) and Winter (1983) describe underwater biotelemetry including sonar and radiotelemetry.

HABITAT INVENTORY AND MONITORING SYSTEMS

Inventory and monitoring fish habitat allow the land manager to identify trends in habitat conditions needed for fish production and to adjust land use to stabilize or improve habitat conditions. No fish inventory will provide all of the data needed to describe habitat conditions for specific fish species.

A number of systems have been developed to inventory fish habitat conditions and to relate habitat conditions to actual or potential fish populations. Three of these are described below.

Habitat Quality Index (HQI)

Binns (1979) has developed a habitat quality index (HQI) for predicting biomass of trout in streams based on nine measurable habitat attributes. The index is described in more detail in the Streams chapter.

Habitat Evaluation Procedures (HEP) and Habitat Suitability Index (HSI) Models

The U.S. Fish and Wildlife Service has developed Habitat Evaluation Procedures (HEP) which provide numerical ratings of habitat quality for pre- and post-project conditions (U.S. Department of Interior, Fish and Wildlife Service 1976). HEP uses one or more Habitat Suitability Index (HSI) models for such analyses. These models use one or more habitat variables to generate an index of habitat quality between 0 and 1 for individual fish species. Aquatic applications of HEP and HSI models are described in detail by Terrell et al. (1982). HSI models have been developed and published for many fish species. The biologist may find these useful in developing an inventory and monitoring system or program other than HEP. Models and their use in HEP are described in more detail in the chapter on Habitat Evaluation Systems. More information on HEP and HSI models and on availability of HSI models for fish can be obtained from "the National Ecology Center," U.S. Fish and Wildlife Service, Drake Creekside Building One, 2627 Redwing Road, Fort Collins, CO 80526-2899.

Riparian/Aquatic Information Data Summary (RAIDS)

Riparian/Aquatic Information Data Summary (RAIDS) is a computer-based system for storing data on aquatic habitat and the associated fish populations. It does not specify how such data must be collected. Details on the system can be obtained from the BLM's Denver Service Center, Division of Resources.

SUMMARY

Inventory of fish and fish habitat is needed to provide baseline information for the land manager. After baseline conditions have been assessed, monitoring helps evaluate land management actions and provides justification for leads toward adjusting land use where necessary. This chapter provides guidance for planning and organizing inventories and monitoring studies of fish-producing waters. For detailed descriptions of techniques, equipment, and analyses, the biologist will need to consult the Literature Cited section in this chapter.

LITERATURE CITED

ANDERSON, R.O. and S.J. GUTREUTER 1983. Length, weight, and associated structural indices. Pages 283–300 *in* Nielsen, L.A. and D.L. Johnson, eds., Fisheries Techniques. Am. Fish. Soc. Bethesda, MD. 468pp.

ARMOUR, C.L. and W.S. PLATTS 1983. Field methods and statistical analyses for monitoring small salmonid streams. U.S. Dep. Inter., Fish and Wildl. Serv., FWS/OBS-83/33. 200pp.

BINNS, N.A. 1979. A habitat quality index for Wyoming trout streams. Fishery Research Report Monograph Series 2. Wyoming Game and Fish Dep., Cheyenne, 82002. 75pp.

BOWEN, S.H. 1983. Quantitative description of the diet. Pages 325–336 *in* Nielsen, L.A. and D.L. Johnson, eds., Fisheries Techniques. Am. Fish. Soc. Bethesda, MD. 468pp.

CARLSON, C.A. and C.L. GIFFORD 1983. Finding literature and reports. Pages 23–42 *in* Nielsen, L.A. and D.L. Johnson, eds., Fisheries Techniques. Am. Fish. Soc. Bethesda, MD. 468pp.

CROUSE, M.R. and R.R. KINDSCHY. 1981. A method for predicting riparian vegetation potential of semiarid rangelands. Pages 110-114 *in* Proc. of Symp., Acquisition and Utilization of Aquatic Habitat Inventory Information, Western Div. Am. Fish. Soc. Portland, OR. Oct. 1981.

DAVIES, W.D. 1983. Sampling with toxicants. Pages 199–214 *in* Nielsen, L.A. and D.L. Johnson, eds., Fisheries Techniques. Am. Fish. Soc. Bethesda, MD. 468pp.

DAVIS, D.E. and R.L. WINSTEAD. 1980. Estimating the numbers of wildlife populations. Pages 221–246 *in* Schemnitz, S.D., ed., Wildlife Management Techniques Manual. 4th ed. revised, The Wildl. Soc., Washington, DC. 686pp.

EISERMAN, F.M. 1979. Quantification of fluvial trout habitat in Wyoming. Trans. Am. Fish. Soc. 108:215–228.

FRITZ, E.S., P.J. RAGO, and I.P. MURARKA. 1980. Strategy for assessing impacts of power plants on fish and shellfish populations. U.S. Dep. Inter., Fish and Wildl. Serv., Biological Services Program, National Power Plant Team, FWS/OBS-08/34. 68pp.

GREESON, P.E., T.A. EHLKE, G.A. IRWIN, B.W. LIUM, and K.V. SLACK. 1977. Techniques of water resources investigations of the U.S. Geological Survey, Chapter A4. 332pp.

HAMILTON, K. and E.P. BERGERSEN. 1984. Methods to estimate aquatic habitat variables. Colorado Coop. Fishery Res. Unit, Colorado State University, Ft. Collins.

HAYES, M.L. 1983. Active fish capture methods. Pages 123-146 *in* Nielsen, L.A. and D.L. Johnson, eds., Fisheries Techniques. Am. Fish. Soc. Bethesda, MD. 468pp.

HUBERT, W.A. 1983. Passive capture techniques. Pages 95–122 *in* Nielsen, L.A. and D.L. Johnson, eds., Fisheries Techniques. Am. Fish. Soc. Bethesda, MD. 468pp.

JEARLD, A. Jr. 1983. Age determination. Pages 301-324 *in* Nielsen, L.A. and D.L. Johnson, eds., Fisheries Techniques. Am. Fish. Soc. Bethesda, MD.

JOHNSON, D.L. and L.A. NIELSEN. 1983. Sampling considerations. Pages 1–21 *in* Nielsen, L.A. and D.L. Johnson, eds., Fisheries Techniques. Am. Fish. Soc. Bethesda, MD. 468pp.

JOHNSON, J.E. and J.N. RINNE. 1982. The Endangered Species Act and Southwest fishes. Pages 2–7 *in* Fisheries Bulletin, 7(4), Am. Fish. Soc.

LAGLER, K.R. 1956. Freshwater fishery biology, 2nd ed. Wm. C. Brown Co., Dubuque, IA. 421pp.

NEILSON, J.D. and G.H. GREEN. 1981. Enumeration of spawning salmon from spawner residence time and aerial counts. Trans. Am. Fish. Soc. 110(4):554-556.

NIELSEN, L.A. and D.L. JOHNSON, eds. 1983. Fisheries techniques. Am. Fish. Soc. Bethesda, MD. 468pp.

ODUM, E.P. 1978. Ecological importance of the riparian zone, strategies for protection and management of floodplain wetlands and other riparian ecosystems, in Proc. of Symp., U.S. Dep. Agric., For. Serv., Washington, DC.

ORTH, D.J. 1983. Aquatic Habitat Measurements. Pages 61–84 *in* Nielsen, L.A. and D.L. Johnson, eds., Fisheries Techniques. Am. Fish. Soc. Bethesda, MD. 468pp.

OTIS, D.L., K.P. BURNHAM, G.C. WHITE, and D.R. ANDERSON. 1978. Statistical inference from capture data on closed animal populations. Wildl. Monogr. 62. 135pp.

REYNOLDS, J.B. 1983. Electrofishing. Pages 147–164 *in* Nielsen, L.A. and D.L. Johnson, eds., Fisheries Techniques. Am. Fish. Soc. Bethesda, MD. 468pp.

RICKER, W.E. 1958. Handbook of computations for biological statistics of fish populations. Fish. Res. Board, Can. Bull. 119. 300pp.

SEBER, G.A.F. and E.D. LECREN. 1967. Estimating population parameters from large catches relative to a population. J. Animal Ecol. 36(3):631–643.

SIMPSON, J.C. and R.L. WALLACE. 1978. Fishes of Idaho. The University Press of Idaho. Idaho Research Foundation, Inc. Moscow. 237pp.

SNYDER, D.E. 1983. Fish eggs and larvae. Pages 165–198 *in* Nielsen, L.A. and D.L. Johnson, eds., Fisheries Techniques. Am. Fish. Soc. Bethesda, MD. 468pp.

TERRELL, J.W., T.E. MCMAHON, P.D. INSKIP, R.F. RALEIGH, and K.L. WILLIAMSON. 1982. Habitat suitability index models: Appendix A. Guidelines for riverine and lacustrine applications of fish HSI models with the habitat evaluation procedures. U.S. Dep. Inter., Fish and Wildl. Serv., FWS/OBS-82/10.A. 54pp.

THORNE, R.E. 1983. Hydroacoustics. Pages 239–259 *in* Nielsen, L.A. and D.L. Johnson, eds., Fisheries Techniques. Am. Fish. Soc., Bethesda, MD. 468pp.

U.S. DEPARTMENT OF INTERIOR, FISH AND WILDLIFE SERVICE. 1976. Habitat evaluation procedures. Division of Ecological Services. Washington, DC. 30pp.

WHITE, G.C., D.R. ANDERSON, K.P. BURNHAM, and D.L. OTIS. 1982. Capture-recapture and removal methods for sampling closed populations. Los Alamos National Laboratory, Los Alamos, NM. LA-8787-NERP. 235pp.

WINTER, J.D. 1983. Underwater biotelemetry. Pages 371–396 *in* Nielsen, L.A. and D.L. Johnson, eds., Fisheries Techniques. Am. Fish. Soc. Bethesda, MD. 468pp.

———, V.B. BUECHLE, D.B. SINIFF, and J.R. TESTER. 1978. Equipment and methods for radio tracking freshwater fish. Univ. Minnesota, Agric. Experiment Sta. Misc. Rep. 152-1978. 18pp.

WYDOSKI, R. and L. EMERY. 1983. Tagging and marking. Pages 215–238 *in* Nielsen, L.A. and D.L. Johnson, eds., Fisheries Techniques. Am. Fish. Soc., Bethesda, MD. 468pp.

14

AMPHIBIANS AND REPTILES

K. Bruce Jones[1]

U.S. Bureau of Land Management
Phoenix Training Center
Phoenix, AZ 85015

Editor's Note: Among the vertebrates, amphibians and reptiles have often been ignored. "Traditional" biologists trained in game management may not be familiar with studies or techniques for these species. Very little has been published, and what's available tends to be located in hard-to-get publications—not the journals or manuals familiar to most biologists.

Nonetheless, amphibians and reptiles are important components of many ecosystems. This chapter brings together the diffuse techniques for studying these species and their habitats.

INTRODUCTION

Until recently, amphibians and reptiles have been largely overlooked in land management considerations. Federal and State agencies have spent most of their time and money on commercially important species, and the public is generally unaware of how important these animals are in natural ecosystems. Only within the past 10 years have we become concerned about conditions of these animals and their habitats.

Public awareness of the importance of the entire wildlife community has led to legislation (e.g., the Federal Land Policy and Management Act of 1976) requiring study and management of nongame wildlife such as amphibians and reptiles. Studies have demonstrated the importance of these animals in natural ecosystems. Terrestrial amphibians, lizards, and burrowing snakes are excellent indicators of the relative amounts of microhabitats in ecosystems. For example, the Sacramento Mountain salamander *(Aneides hardii)* is entirely dependent on moist, downed logs and litter on north- and northeast-facing slopes (Wiegman et al. 1980). In addition, information on amphibian and reptile abundance and diversity helps determine the relative health of ecosystems. For example, lizard abundance and diversity fluctuate directly with changes in the composition and amount of microhabitats. These microhabitat changes often result from land management practices (Jones 1981a; Ortega et al. 1982; Tinkle 1982; Luckenbach and Bury 1983).

Aquatic amphibians and snakes are good indicators of the health of aquatic systems. These animals are especially sensitive to pollution and loss of aquatic habitat (Hall 1980).

Amphibians and reptiles are also important in food chains, and they make up large proportions of vertebrates in certain ecosystems (Bury and Raphael

[1]Current address: Office of Endangered Species, U.S. Fish and Wildlife Service, Washington,DC 20240.

1983). Many carnivorous mammals and raptorial birds rely on these animals for food. For example, up to 50% of the spring diet of common black hawks *(Buteogallus anthracinus)* consists of aquatic herpetofauna (Millsap and Harrison 1981). Recent studies have also demonstrated the economic importance, both consumptive and nonconsumptive, of these animals (see Bury et al. 1980).

Because of recent concern for nongame wildlife, biologists and land managers find themselves faced with studies and management needs for a group of animals they know little about. Only a few biologists and virtually no land managers have had any formal education in herpetology.

There is a wealth of information on the ecology of individual amphibians and reptiles in literature. Unfortunately, few papers deal with amphibian and reptile communities, and even fewer summarize information needs, data collection, and management on public lands.

This chapter is designed to help biologists who have little or no education or experience with amphibians and reptiles organize and run inventories or monitoring studies on selected species or major groups (e.g., lizards).

HABITAT FEATURES

The most important factor affecting amphibian and reptile distribution and habitat use is horizontal and vertical habitat availability. In studying population condition, trend, and cause and effect factors, biologists must collect data on habitat.

Sixteen habitat components and attributes are important determinants of amphibian and reptile abundance (Table 1).

Microhabitat components are site-specific, physical entities that provide environmental conditions necessary for a wide variety of ecological functions such as reproduction, foraging, predator avoidance or escape, thermoregulation, and resting. Amphibians and reptiles are ectothermic (cold-blooded); body temperatures are not derived from metabolic processes but rather from the surrounding environment. Therefore, behavioral adaptations and use of different microhabitats by amphibians and reptiles are diverse. These animals often demonstrate a high dependence on certain microhabitats to thermoregulate. Removal or reduction of microhabitats necessary for thermoregulation can detrimentally affect all other ecological functions because internal temperature regulation determines the intensity of activity (see Brattstrom 1965 for examples). For example, certain basking turtles can be extirpated from a pond if floating logs are eliminated.

Amphibians are even further restricted to moist or wet habitats with varying degrees of free-standing water. Many larval toads, frogs, and salamanders require water for development into adult stages (Stebbins 1966). Additionally, some adult frogs and salamanders require water to avoid desiccation and to respirate cutaneously. For example, many *Plethodon* (lungless) salamanders require moist, rotting logs and litter for egg development and adult cutaneous respiration (Stebbins 1966). Without rotting logs and associated litter, there is insufficient moisture for egg development and adult survival.

Although most biologists and some land managers understand the significance of vegetation structure and composition to wildlife, few realize how important litter (fallen logs, leaves), soil, plant root structure, and horizontal vegetation structure are to most forms of wildlife, especially amphibians and reptiles. Litter provides moisture regimes necessary for development of terrestrial salamanders, but it also provides cool surface and below-the-surface temperature regimes. Often this is the only microhabitat with moderate environmental temperatures in otherwise hot, dry regions. Because of low preferred body temperature ranges, many species such as the Arizona alligator lizard *(Elgaria kingii)* and Gilbert skink *(Eumeces gilberti)* are entirely restricted to deciduous riparian habitats within desert regions (Stebbins 1966). In addition, litter provides feeding substrate for several common lizards, especially members of the genus *Sceloporus* (fence or spiny lizards). Loss of fallen logs and trees can drastically reduce populations of these lizards (see discussions of Jones 1981a & b and Vitt et al. 1974, for dependence on woody vegetation).

Soil depth, texture, and diversity are extremely important in determining amphibian and reptile distribution in an area. For example, soil depth and

Fallen logs provide important microhabitats for terrestrial salamanders.

Table 1. Important components and attributes of amphibian and reptile habitat.

Habitat Component	Types	Variables/ Factors	Amphibian and Reptile Associations	Relations of Species' Ecology to Components							
				Defense	Escape cover	Feeding substrate	Food or prey	Nest substrate	Physiological	Reproduction	Thermoregulation
Microhabitat Component Water (Lotic)	Rivers and streams	Riffle/run/pool ratios, water temperature, turbidity, DO, organic content, siltation, pollutants	AQAL, SAAL		•	•		•	•	•	•
Water (Permanent Lentic)	Ponds, marshes, lakes, reservoirs, natural catchments, agricultural run-off	Water temperature, DO, organic content, siltation, pollutants, emergent vegetation, logs and other litter, substrate	AQAL, SAAL		•	•		•	•	•	•
Water (Temporary Lentic)	Temporary rain pools, irrigation ditches	DO, water temperatures, siltation, pollutants, duration, frequency, emergent vegetation, substrate	SATD, SASA SATU, SASN		•	•		•	•	•	•
Rock	Talus slopes, cliffs, boulders, substrate	Rock size, heterogeneity, interfaces, origin, vertical and horizontal structure	AQAL, SAAL (Where interfaced with aquatic habitats), TAL	•	•	•		•		•	•
Vegetation— Litter/Debris	Leaves, logs, limbs	Litter size, depth, heterogeneity, horizontal structure, type, moisture retention, temperature	AQAL, SAAL (Where interfaced with aquatic habitats), TAL		•	•		•		•	•
Vegetation— Live	All vegetation including roots	Horizontal and vertical structure, interfaces with abiotic components, heterogeneity	AQAL, SAAL (Where interfaced with aquatic habitats) TAL	•	•	•	•	•		•	•
Vegetation— Dead	Standing vegetation, roots	Size, interface with other habitats, heterogeneity, vertical and horizontal structure, soils (roots only)	AQAL, SAAL (Where interfaced with aquatic habitats) TAL	•	•	•		•		•	•
Vegetation— Plant Species	Individual plant species	Individual plant species abundance and occurrence	TL, TSN				•	•			•

Habitat Component	Types	Variables/ Factors	Amphibian and Reptile Associations	Relations of Species' Ecology to Components							
				Defense	Escape cover	Feeding substrate	Food or prey	Nest substrate	Physiological	Reproduction	Thermoregulation
Microhabitat Component (cont.) Soil	Surface and subsurface soil types	Types, death, heterogeneity, horizontal and vertical structure, interfaces with other habitat components	AQAL, SAAL (Where interfaced with aquatic habitats), TAL	•	•	•		•		•	•
Macrohabitat Components/Factors Slope	% angle of area from horizontal	% slope, moisture availability, thermal regimes, vegetation structure	SAAL, TAL		•	•		•		•	•
Aspect	South, north, east, and west facing	Direction, moisture availability, temperature regimes, vegetation structure	SAAL, TAL		•		•	•		•	•
Elevation	Vertical, above or below sea level	Vertical distance, moisture availability, thermal regimes, vegetation structure	AQAL, SAAL, TAL		•	•	•	•		•	•
Precipitation	All forms	Quantity, type, duration, frequency, moisture availability, thermal regimes, vegetation structure	AQAL, SAAL TAL		•	•	•	•	•	•	•
Ecotones/Habitat Juxtaposition	Habitat interfaces and locations	Heterogenity, interface size and cumulative numbers, position of habitats	AQAL, SAAL TAL	•	•	•	•	•		•	•
Topography	General	Slope, aspect, and physical feature mixture and position	SAAL, TAL	•	•	•	•	•		•	•
Geographic Location	Major geographic boundaries and barriers	Size, location and frequency, habitat size and disjunction	AQAL, SAAL, TAL							•	

Codes for Amphibian and Reptile Associations:

AQ—aquatic	TD—toads
SA—semiaquatic	SA—salamanders
T—terrestrial	LI—lizards
TU—turtles	SN—snakes
FR—frogs	AL—all amphibians and reptiles

texture determine the rate of percolation and soil layer moisture.

In some areas with heavy clay soils, water accumulates on the surface, especially during rainy seasons. Because surface water may be available for up to 3 weeks, many semiaquatic amphibians occur in these regions. For example, six species of semiaquatic toads were verified within a small, hot region of the Sonoran Desert that had deep clay soils (Jones et al. 1983).

Although moist, clay soils enhance the distribution of toads in some regions, hard, shallow, or rocky soils may prevent species colonization of an area. For example, spadefoot toads (*Scaphiopus* sp.) are well adapted to survive in dry, desert regions, but without soils loose enough for burrowing, generally will not occur in an area (unless rodent burrows are present).

The diversity of soils interfaced with rocks and other structures often determines amphibian and reptile species richness. Diversity provides more niches for amphibian and reptile colonization and existence.

Plant root structure also contributes greatly to amphibian and reptile species richness by providing avenues into subsurface space. These plant-created avenues often account for greater species richness than expected in what are thought to be structureless plant communities. For example, deserts dominated by creosotebush (*Larrea* sp.) appear very homogeneous with little horizontal or vertical structure. However, the root systems of creosote are extensive, and they provide a wide variety of subsurface opportunities to many of the desert's nocturnal amphibians and reptiles. The result is a diverse amphibian and reptile community.

Generally, horizontal vegetation structure determines amphibian and reptile composition more often than vertical structure, especially in lizards. This results primarily from foraging and thermoregulation which are generally conducted on the surface (there are exceptions—some amphibians and reptiles forage in trees and below the surface). For example, zebra-tailed lizards *(Callisaurus draconoides)* prefer brushy, open habitats where they ambush prey while sitting in the open and then move into shade to thermoregulate (Pianka 1966; Jones 1981a & b). Some species such as desert iguanas *(Dipsosaurus dorsalis)* are common in very open, sparsely vegetated creosotebush habitats; this habitat allows them to reach high preferred body temperatures and obtain specific food items (creosotebush buds). Other species that forage in or on litter and have moderate internal temperature ranges prefer densely vegetated habitats with large amounts of surface litter (e.g., alligator lizard).

Macrohabitat components are physical phenomena that affect environmental conditions of microhabitats and in some instances entire regions. Different types of microhabitat and macrohabitat components are listed with corresponding variables or factors that affect the ecological requirements of species (Table 1). Amphibians and reptiles are listed by major taxonomic group (e.g., frogs, lizards). Table 1 serves primarily as a checklist of habitat components and variables that biologists should consider when conducting habitat and amphibian and reptile surveys or studies. Biologists should collect data on soils, litter, water availability, and horizontal vegetation on each amphibian and reptile sample site. This information will allow the biologist to accurately assess the relation between microhabitat availability and presence or absence of certain species. By being aware of macrohabitat conditions, biologists will better understand causes of microhabitat variables, and how and where to set up samples (e.g., biologists can reduce sample variability due to slope by sampling only north-facing slopes, or they may elect to sample all different aspects to determine their effect on species composition).

K. Bruce Jones

Zebra-tailed lizard.

POPULATION MEASUREMENT TECHNIQUES

Sources of Information

Although amphibian and reptile data collection generally does not require the degree of expertise required for surveys of animals such as birds, a biologist with little or no previous experience will need to review certain literature and, when possible, contact local or regional experts. Field guides and keys that provide characteristics for identifying various herpetofauna (Table 2) are available for most regions of the U.S. The biologist should thoroughly review species characteristics before starting field surveys.

Review of field guides, books, and amphibian and reptile journals will also provide ecological background on various species that will help biologists select the most appropriate sampling methods.

Museum and individual collection records and publications can be used to verify amphibian and reptile species occurrence within a geographic area. Searches of these sources should be made before starting censuses to avoid duplication.

Several large museums in the U.S. hold vast records of amphibians and reptiles. Edwards (1975) lists U.S. collections of amphibians and reptiles, their locations, and major sources of records (e.g., Desert Southwest). This publication serves as an excellent starting point for record searches.

Expert herpetologists often possess personal locality records that can add to species lists in specific geographic regions. Herpetologists with regional expertise should be consulted before field work is initiated.

Many journals contain valuable amphibian and reptile occurrence and ecological data (Table 2).

Problems Affecting Sampling

Biologists should be aware of several factors that may affect their results when sampling amphibians and reptiles. Perhaps the largest problem in assessing amphibian and reptile populations is that these animals' activities and reproduction vary with natural environmental fluctuations, such as precipitation and temperature (Whitford and Creusere 1977; Gibbons and Semlitsch 1981; Vogt and Hine 1982). Therefore, biologists should be cautious in interpreting cause and effect data because observed differences may result from natural fluctuations in weather

Table 2. Examples of major references providing preliminary and supplemental data for amphibian and reptile surveys and studies.

Journal or Publication	Behavioral	Distributional	Ecological	Habitat/species relationships	Identification	Management	Physiological	Bibliographies	Systematic	Taxonomic	Geographic Applicability
Herpetologica	•	•	•	•			•		•		WH
Copeia			•	•			•		•		WH
Journal of Herpetology	•	•	•	•			•		•		WW
Ecology	•	•	•	•		○	•				WW
Ecological Monographs	•	•	•	•			•				WW
Herpetological Review	•	•	•	•		•	•	•	•		Primarily US
American Midland Naturalist	•	•	•	•		○			•		Primarily CUS
Great Basin Naturalist	•	•	•	•		○			•		Primarily WUS
Southwestern Naturalist	•	•	•	•		•	○		•		Primarily SW and ME
Academy of Sciences publications (Arizona, Utah, Kansas, Texas, etc.)	•	•	•	•		•	•	•	•		Limited generally to regions around applicable states
Bulletin of the Maryland Herpetological Society	•	•	•	•		•	•	•	•		Primarily US and ME
American Museum Novitiates	•	•	•						•		WW
University of Kansas Publications in Zoology	•	•	•	•	•		•		•		Primarily CUS and WUS
University of California Publications in Zoology	•	•	•	•			•		•		Primarily WUS
Smithsonian Herpetological Information Service	•	•	•	•			•	•	•		WW

○ Limited

Table 2. Examples of major references providing preliminary and supplemental data for amphibian and reptile surveys and studies (concluded).

Journal or Publication	Behavioral	Distributional	Ecological	Habitat/species relationships	Identification	Management	Physiological	Bibliographies	Systematic	Taxonomic	Geographic Applicability
					Types of Information						
Examples of books with broad geographic coverage											
Turtles of the United States by C. H. Ernst and R. W. Barbour (1973)	•	•	•	•	•		•			•	US
Handbook of Lizards by H. M. Smith (1946)	•	•	•	•	•		•			•	US
A Field Guide to Western Reptiles and Amphibians by R. C. Stebbins (1966)	•	•	•	•	•					•	CUS, WUS
Handbook of Frogs and Toads of the United States and Canada by A.H. Wright and A.A. Wright	•	•	•	•	•					•	US and CA
Handbook of Snakes of the United States and Canada by A.H. Wright and A.A. Wright (1957)	•	•	•	•	•					•	US and CA
Handbook of Salamanders by S.C. Bishop (1947)	•	•	•	•	•		•		•	•	US and CA
A Field Guide to Reptiles and Amphibians of Eastern and Central North America by R. Conant (1975)	•	•	•	•	•		•		•	•	CUS and EUS
Example of books with regional geographic coverage[a]											
Amphibians and Reptiles of the Pacific Northwest by R. Nussbaum et al. (1983)											

[a]Be sure to check thoroughly for these. There are many regional- and area-specific books.

Codes for Geographic Applicability:

CA —Canada
CUS—Central United States
EUS —Eastern United States
ME —Mexico

SW —Southwestern United States
US —United States
WH —Western hemisphere
WUS—Western United States
WW —Worldwide

rather than man-caused changes. Gibbons and Semlitsch (1981) recommend long-duration studies (> 5 years) in assessing amphibian and reptile populations. Shorter-duration studies in an area can yield species occurrences, and they are also used to compare composition of herpetological communities provided sample areas are roughly adjacent to each other and climatic factors are considered (Jones 1981a).

Other major factors affecting amphibian and reptile sampling are differences in species morphology, physiology, and behavior such as activity patterns and movement. For example, certain lizards and snakes are too large (e.g., desert iguana) to capture in pitfall traps. Other methods should be used in conjunction with pitfall trapping to adequately census large lizards and snakes. Populations of relatively sedentary, microhabitat-specific animals are also underestimated by pitfall and other trapping methods because the probability of these animals falling into traps is far less than those species that move over larger areas. An active searching method such as turning logs, rocks, and debris (Bury and Raphael 1983) would yield more accurate estimates of sedentary species occurrence and abundance than traps.

The frequency and type of amphibian and reptile movement will also affect sampling. For example, there are many burrowing, nocturnal snakes in the Sonoran Desert. Transects run during daylight hours rarely verify nocturnal, burrowing species even when rocks and debris are searched. Addition of pitfall traps and drift fences to a diurnal transect greatly increases the accuracy of the sample.

Yearly fluctuations in amphibian and reptile activity also affect verification of species occurrence in an area. Toads within the Desert Southwest are active primarily during thunderstorms in July and August. Samples taken other than in July and August yield poor results.

Certain microhabitat-specific species tend to move in nonrandom patterns between preferred habitats (see Pianka 1966 for lizard examples), and this affects accuracy of census methods (Gibbons and Semlitsch 1981). Placement of traps and fences is extremely important when considering different movement patterns in lizards. For example, zebra-tailed lizards move between large bushes along drainages (Pianka 1966). Pitfall traps and drift fences placed in open areas with few bushes will catch few zebra-tailed lizards, whereas fences and traps placed between bushes will catch more lizards.

Daily and weekly weather patterns also affect amphibian and reptile activity. Species with narrow preferred temperature ranges are more likely to be active during a smaller range of environmental temperatures. Therefore, samples can be variable during weeks with large temperature differences. There may also be considerable daily and seasonal differences in movement between different age and size classes and sexes.

Abilities of the biologist will also affect the accuracy of samples, especially transect and tape-recording techniques where animals are not closely viewed. For example, a high degree of expertise is needed to identify lizards on a walk-through transect. Similarly, a biologist must be familiar with toad and frog calls if auditory data are to be used for species identification. Conversely, pitfall and other trapping methods do not require specific expertise because amphibians and reptiles can be closely viewed.

Other life history limitations may also affect the interpretation of sampling data. Whereas one lizard may produce multiple clutches within a year, another may reproduce only every other year. This type of result could be easily misinterpreted if the biologist does not consider differences in reproductive strategies. Similarly, size and age class ratios can be misinterpreted if the surveyor is not familiar with differences in species' life history. For example, juveniles tend to move less and, therefore, would be underestimated by techniques such as pitfall trapping.

Relatively accurate samples can be obtained for individual species and entire amphibian and reptile communities provided that species' life histories and sampling method limitations are clearly understood.

Sampling Methods

There are many methods used to sample amphibians and reptiles. The method chosen by a biologist will depend on the objectives. For example, if biologists need to develop a species list by habitat type for a planning document, then they should select some combination of verification techniques. However, if biologists need to show differences in species abundance between habitat types, then they must select a method that yields relative abundance. Generally, data on species presence are adequate for assessing species richness of habitat types. Abundance and density techniques provide additional data for comparing habitat types and also provide information about individual species fitness. For example, density estimates provide biologists with data on the relative fitness of special status reptiles such as the desert tortoise (Gopherus agassizii).

Depending on the biologist's objectives, there are generally two ways to collect species information: direct and indirect. Direct sampling of amphibians and reptiles involves observation of animals occurring on a sample site. Indirect sampling involves obtaining species information on a sample site without observing the animal. Before initiating any sampling, the biologist should contact the State game and fish agency to obtain the necessary regulations and collecting permits.

Direct Search Methods

One of the simplest ways of verifying species occurrence in an area is to walk or drive through the area, recording all amphibians and reptiles seen. Because species are separated in time as well as space (see Creusere and Whitford 1982 for an example in a lizard community), searches run at different times of the day will yield different species in varying numbers (searches run during the daylight hours verify some diurnal species and those run at night some nocturnal species).

Searches of areas are either random and opportunistic or systematic within a defined time and area. Many records of amphibians and reptiles result from casual, opportunistic observations made during field work. Cumulatively, these observations have contributed more to known occurrence of amphibians and reptiles than any other method. Although this method often yields valuable locality records, it generally involves a great deal of search time. It also verifies only those species that spend a great deal of time on the surface or under rocks and debris such as logs. Generally, only a small percentage of species that occupy an area are verified during searches. Only through months and often years are all species in an area verified by search methods.

Road riding (road cruising) is one of the most popular search methods used to verify and collect amphibians and reptiles, especially nocturnal species (see discussion by Campbell and Christman 1982). Generally road riding consists of cruising secondary roads at speeds of 35-55 km/h (22-34 mph), using low headlight beams. Many small nocturnal snakes, lizards, and frogs not normally found during daytime field searches are obtained by this method when conducted between dusk and 2 to 3 hours after dusk. Use a spotlight or strong flashlight while road riding to spot animals moving off of roads. Flashlights are useful for locating amphibians and reptiles on sides of roads (see Vitt and Ohmart 1978 for an example of road-riding results). Road riding is most productive when run without moonlight. Road-riding routes can be systematically established, and relative abundance of amphibians and reptiles can be obtained by standardizing sampling efforts by units of time in each habitat. For example, biologists can measure the distance of each habitat along a road, and measure the amount of time spent in each segment of the habitat. They can then express individual species abundance data as the number of animals seen per mile of habitat per hour. This allows for comparison of habitats using road-riding procedures. Bury and Raphael (1983) refer to searches conducted per unit effort of time as time-constraint procedures.

Although providing occurrence and abundance data on some nocturnal and secretive herpetofauna, road riding:

(1) is time-consuming;

(2) yields relatively few records;

(3) verifies only nocturnal species that migrate across roads;

(4) biases samples because it is limited to areas with roads; and

(5) is sometimes dangerous to observers, especially on well-traveled routes.

Tortoises (especially desert tortoises) and other turtles are often verified by systematic searches. Burge (1979) used a series of 1.6-km and 4.8-km (1-mi. and 3-mi.) search transects in the Arizona Sonoran Desert to verify occurrence of desert tortoises. The 4.8-km (3-mi.) transect consisted of a triangle (1.6 km [1 mi.] each side) set on a random compass line. Along each line, observers look for live tortoises, scat, burrows, and tracks. Data are then recorded on standard forms.

Systematic searches of defined areas yield species occurrence data and allow for further assessment of populations of amphibians and reptiles. This method is especially valuable when the biologist needs population estimates of special status amphibians and reptiles. Bury (1982) used 2-ha (4.9-a.) quadrats to verify and study diurnal reptile populations in the Mojave Desert. He used a removal method to determine densities of reptiles on his quadrats (discussed in more detail later in this chapter). Bury and Luckenbach (1977) successfully censused tortoise populations with a quadrat and grid location system. They established 25- to 100-ha (62- to 247-a.) quadrats, subdividing each into 1-ha (2.47-a.) sections. Systematic searches of each section accurately located tortoises and served as permanent sites for monitoring tortoise populations. Schneider (1981) used 2.59-km^2 (1-mi.^{2}) plots to collect population data on desert tortoises in Arizona. Both Bury (1982) and Schneider (1981) used systematic searches of these grids to determine occurrence and population structure.

Systematic search procedures in defined areas are very time-consuming and should only be used if the biologist needs an accurate estimate of population density. Generally this involves only special status species such as federally threatened and endangered amphibians and reptiles where density data are needed to assess populations.

Another systematic search method commonly used involves scouring known habitats of certain amphibians and reptiles. For example, canyon tree frogs (*Hyla* sp.) are most easily observed in rocky, boulder-strewn canyons with permanent water, primarily pools (Jones 1981b). Secretive diurnal and nocturnal species can be verified along systematic search routes by lifting rocks, vegetative debris, and uprooting animal shelters such as pack rat dens. Zweifel and Lowe (1966) obtained desert night lizard specimens (*Xantusia vigilis*) by lifting downed Joshua tree (*Yucca brevifolia*) limbs. Without search of their preferred habitat (surface debris), these lizards cannot be verified. Amphibians and reptiles also use a variety of other animal cover sites; therefore, a large number of amphibians and reptiles can be verified by searching mammal dens and burrows (Lee 1968).

These microhabitat specific searches are generally used to verify and collect data on the abundance of a few species. If used for verification only, this method can be quick and easy. When relative abundance or density is needed, this method is considerably more time-consuming.

There are several small tools that increase effectiveness of searches. Mirrors, in particular, locate and identify animals in burrows, especially turtles and snakes. Similarly, flashlights increase light in and around burrows and are extremely helpful in verifying species such as tortoises.

Several types of poles have been used to locate inactive, partially, or completely concealed reptiles, especially turtles. Noodling is an effective way to locate aquatic turtles concealed in muddy creek bottoms (Lagler 1943). The technique involves cruising shallow lakes and ponds using a blunt steel rod to protrude through mud and emergent vegetation. A hollow sound is given off when a turtle is hit. Noodling can also be used to protrude through terrestrial litter and soil to verify hidden turtles (Carpenter 1955).

Another extremely effective method of determining species occurrence in an area is to search nests of predators for amphibian and reptile remains. Large proportions of certain raptor diets consist of reptiles (Millsap 1981). A total of 13 species of reptiles were verified in and below red-tailed hawks *(Buteo jamaicensis)* nests by Millsap (1981). Red-tailed hawks forage over relatively large areas and, therefore, reptile occurrence in nests cannot be correlated with specific areas or habitats. However, some raptors forage over extremely limited areas or in specific habitats (e.g., riparian and aquatic habitats). For example, black hawks are highly dependent on aquatic prey within western Arizona (over 90% of their diets are aquatic organisms). Millsap and Harrison (1981) identified six species of reptiles at black hawk nests, including a mud turtle (*Kinosternon* sp.). Generally raptor nests cannot be used to identify amphibian species because entire animals are usually consumed. However, prey items can be identified as they come into raptor nests.

Owl pellet dissections also verify amphibian and reptile occurrence in an area (B.A. Millsap, pers. commun.). Positive identifications are obtained by comparing samples with skeletal references.

Although examination of predator nests and feces provides species occurrence for a region, it does not consistently indicate relative abundance of amphibians and reptiles because predators eat what they prefer and not necessarily what is most abundant.

Black hawk feeding nestling.

Trapping and Collecting Methods

Trapping methods have been designed around specific life histories of certain amphibians and reptiles. For example, a trout fly was extended over a pitfall trap to lure zebra-tailed and fringe-toed lizards (*Uma* sp.) into traps (Lannon 1962). Both of these lizards are sit-and-wait species that forage out in open spaces (see Pianka 1966). They remain relatively stationary until visual contact is made with an invertebrate and then attempt to capture and swallow the prey. Although Lannon's method may attract lizards that forage in similar ways on similar prey, it will not attract other amphibians and reptiles that forage in different ways.

Two basic procedures exist for collecting or capturing amphibians and reptiles: direct and indirect capture. Direct capture consists of actively seeking animals and using various equipment to increase capture success. Indirect capture involves use of equipment capable of securing animals without active searching by the biologist.

Several types of equipment are used to capture animals during active pursuit. I will highlight some of the most commonly used equipment.

Large samples of frogs, toads, salamanders, tadpoles, and turtles can be obtained because their habitats (water and water/land ecotones) are limited to relatively small areas (as compared with terrestrial habitats).

Dip nets increase effectiveness of capturing turtles, frogs, toads, and salamanders during active pursuit or while turning stones and logs in streams. Svihla (1959) greatly increased capture of tailed frog tadpoles *(Ascaphus truei)* by simultaneously placing a dip net directly downstream while turning rocks. Without the net, many tadpoles escaped unnoticed.

Lagler (1943) also described dip nets of various sizes used to collect small tadpoles, salamander larvae, and small turtles.

Seines, placed across a stream or creek, greatly increase capture success of salamander and salamander larvae, and frog and toad tadpoles (Balgooyen 1977). With a seine placed downstream, biologists move toward the net, turning rocks, debris, and vegetation. Disturbed animals are then swept downstream into the net by the stream's current.

Stationary, polyethylene plastic dams can be used to corral stream-dwelling organisms including shovel-nosed salamander larvae (*Leurognathus* sp.) (Martof 1963). The damming effect causes larval salamanders to congregate at the bottom of the plastic sheet.

Electroshocking is an effective means of collecting and censusing aquatic habitats. Although more traditionally used for collecting fish, direct current electroshockers have been used to census aquatic amphibians and reptiles (Gunning and Lewis 1959; Williams et al. 1981). Electroshocking stuns adult and larval salamanders, adult and larval frogs, and to a lesser degree, small turtles, making capture easier. Several combinations of aquatic collecting techniques were tested on hellbenders (*Cryptobranchus alleganiensis*). Combinations of electroshocking and dip nets were most effective although results varied in different aquatic habitats. Electroshocking and dip nets were most successful in pools and slow-moving stream sections because dip nets capture hellbenders before they sink. Conversely, seines captured hellbenders more effectively in fast-moving, riffle-dominated stream sections because animals are more easily swept into a seine than into a dip net. Williams et al. (1981) found conventional dip-netting and seining to be inferior to netting with electroshocking. Both Williams et al. (1981) and

Gunning and Lewis (1959) reported low mortality rates when using shockers that generated direct current fields.

Abundance and density of aquatic amphibians can be determined for a reach of stream by using the previously described equipment. First, an area of the stream is selected and measured in square meters. Second, a seine is stretched across the stream at the station's farthest point downstream. Finally, the biologist systematically walks downstream, swooping the electrical field across the stream. Shocked amphibians are then placed in the net and counted. A second swoop is conducted to shock the remaining amphibians. The biologist then obtains a number of each species for the area shocked.

Seining by itself provides verification of species, but is too slow to provide an absolute count (unless sampling a small isolated pool). Electroshocking, although more effective, is generally not effective on large species with small surface to volume ratios. As a quantitative method, electroshocking is limited to relatively narrow, shallow, non-turbid reaches.

Anderson and Smith (1950) designed and tested an electrical apparatus that effectively stunned both aquatic and terrestrial amphibians and reptiles (Figure 1). Mortality rates of shocked animals varied, usually with size. Large snakes such as water moccasins (*Agkistrodon* sp.) must be shocked on the upper third of their body to obtain paralysis, whereas single shocks to small amphibians (e.g., tree frogs) are often fatal.

In water with thick vegetation and organic debris, dredges can increase collecting success. Goin (1942) used a double-trough dredge held together by hinges (Figure 2). The upper trough is constructed of larger mesh hardware cloth than the

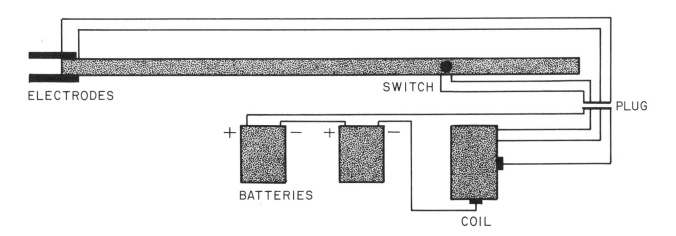

Figure 1. Electrical stunning apparatus.

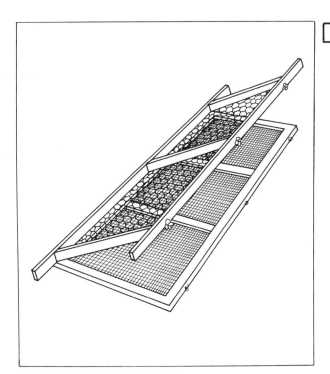

Figure 2. Double-trough dredge.

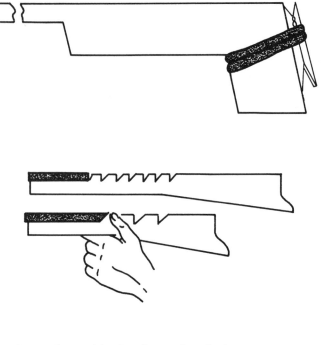

Figure 3. Rubberband-stunning devices.

lower trough. Vegetation-dwelling larvae and adult salamanders, tadpoles, frogs, and turtles are captured when the dredge is lifted up through vegetation and debris. Different sized animals can be collected by varying the size of the screen mesh.

Other methods, such as gaffing and setting lines of baited fish hooks, have been used to verify aquatic turtles (Lagler 1943). A gaff consists of a sharp hook placed on the end of a pole. Turtles are caught by spearing the hook through the shell. This method, although not used as a quantitative procedure, produces records of large turtles.

A snare has been designed and successfully tested to capture water snakes (Franklin 1947). The snare consists of a three-prong sterilizing forcep attached by a scissor grip to the end of a 3.7-m (12-ft) lightweight cane pole. The snare is particularly effective in capturing large, swimming water snakes (e.g. water moccasin) and provides a means of verifying certain species.

An alternative to collecting amphibians and reptiles with a gun is to use a rubberband mechanism. This type of collecting method is considerably safer than a firearm and, with practice, yields live specimens. Neill (1956) and Dundee (1950) designed effective rubberband-launching devices that they reported using successfully to immobilize frogs and lizards (see Figure 3).

Hand snares are used to secure reptiles, especially lizards. Eakin (1957) designed a copper wire

slip noose (Am. Stand. Wire, gauge 34, [0.15 mm]) attached to a light pole. Lizards are captured by slowly placing the noose over their heads and jerking the wire tight. Stickel (1944) designed and successfully tested a snare that has a trigger mechanism and a thread (Figure 4). He stated that his mechanism is superior to hand-pulled snares because of the speed of the snare mechanism. Fishing line (0.91-1.36 kg [2-3 lb.] test) can also be used to form the noose (R. Bowker, pers. commun.).

All of the previously described equipment such as snares, nooses, and dredges help biologists verify occurrence of species on a site or in a habitat. Rarely is this equipment used to determine relative abundances or densities unless they are part of a systematic search or procedure.

Perhaps the most widely and successfully used amphibian and reptile collecting and censusing techniques are those that involve indirect capture, specifically traps and funnels. Traps and funnels have the advantage of capturing animals while the biologist is not present. Generally they provide a greater number of species per sampling effort than active, direct capture methods. Funnels and traps are used widely for both terrestrial and aquatic sampling. Most trap and funnel procedures are designed to maximize capture of certain types of herpetofauna. Their placement in certain microhabitats and the use of different baits also bias sampling toward certain species.

Several investigators successfully designed and tested hoop funnel traps for capturing turtles (Lagler 1943, 1960; Pirnie 1935; Iverson 1979; Feuer 1980).

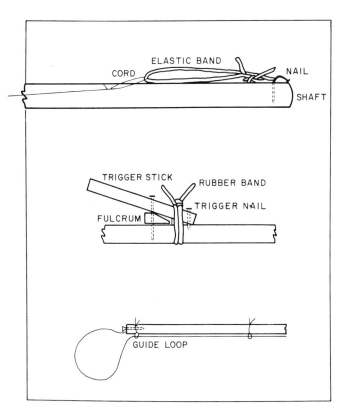

Figure 4. Trigger snare.

Generally, traps consist of mesh netting connected to four aluminum hoops or guide lines (Figure 5). A purse-string regulated opening provides turtles with access through the throat to a piece of suspended bait. Funnels can have single or double throats. Iverson's (1979) funnel trap is constructed of chicken wire rather than netting. These funnel traps are most effective in shallow water and should be checked frequently to avoid drowning the specimen.

Funnel traps have also been designed to capture larvae and adult salamanders and frogs (Carpenter 1953; Moulton 1954). Carpenter's trap consists of a

6.35-mm (0.25-in.) mesh hardware cloth formed into a funnel that is lowered into deep pools by a 1.8- to 3.0-m (6- to 10-ft) rope. This method collects larval and adult salamanders in pools too deep for seines. Funnel openings should face toward shores of ponds to take advantage of animal movements.

Moulton's trap is slightly different than Carpenter's, consisting of a rectangular wire screen box placed on a wooden frame with an access funnel placed 63.5 cm (25 in.) above the box floor. The trap is placed in a shallow depression along the shore of a pond or lake with the funnel facing toward land. Salamander and anuran prey accumulate in the trap and lure animals toward the trap during movements between land and water.

Funnel traps have been used extensively in capturing terrestrial and semiaquatic frogs, salamanders, lizards, and snakes. Generally these traps function similarly to aquatic funnel traps; they encourage entrance into traps and restrict access out. These traps are usually constructed of hardware cloth, shaped into cylindrical form, and accessed at one or both ends by funnels (Vogt 1941; Lagler 1943). Many minor variations of this general construction have been used. Fitch (1951) used a transparent, cellulose pivotal door at the entrance to the trap, preventing lizards and snakes from crawling out (Figure 6). Clark (1966) and Hall (1967) further modified the trap by using mason jars and 0.45-kg (1-lb) coffee cans, respectively, as the collecting area. Both used hardware cloth to funnel animals into the trap (Figure 7). Many of these investigators used bait to attract animals.

Many investigators have also combined funnel trapping with other techniques, especially use of drift fence. Dargan and Stickel (1949) used a 0.10-m (4-in.) high, 7.6-m (25-ft) long hardware cloth drift fence to guide snakes into hardware cloth funnel

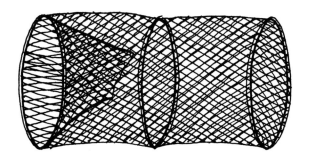

Figure 5. Standard funnel trap for capturing turtles.

Drift fence reptile trap.

traps. Clark (1966) found that rolled aluminum (0.019 gauge) and board drift fences (2.4 to 3.0 m [8 to 10 ft]) used with funnel traps increased trapping success of small snakes. Migrating salamanders and frogs can be surveyed by completely enclosing ponds with 6.35 mm (1/4 in.), 0.25-m (10-in.) high hardware cloth, placing hardware cloth and bronze screen funnel traps inside and outside the enclosure along the fence (Storm and Pimentel 1954).

Pitfall trapping is one of the most widely used methods for collecting data on amphibians and reptiles. Generally this method involves placing a square or round container below water or ground with the container top flush with the surface. Container sizes and shapes vary greatly, depending on which species is trapped.

Floating pitfall traps can be used in water for capturing turtles. Lagler (1943), Breen (1949), and Petokas and Alexander (1979) successfully used these traps for turtles in ponds and lakes. Lagler (1943) and Petokas and Alexander (1979) used a floating wood frame with a submerged trap to capture basking turtles (Figure 8). Breen (1949) used a submerged wooden barrel with the top above the water surface. Wooden planks were extended from the barrel top to the water with bait placed at the top of each plank. Turtles fell into the barrel while attempting to swallow bait. Pitfall traps capture mostly basking turtles that spend time on or above the water's surface.

Pitfall traps have been used extensively in terrestrial amphibian and reptile surveys and studies. Generally pitfall traps are various sized containers placed in the ground with tops flush to the surface. There are a number of variations in pitfall traps ranging from wooden box traps to 18.9-L (5-gal.) plastic containers.

Rogers (1939) used a trapdoor box-trap buried with the top flush to the surface to capture lizards. Banta (1957) used 4.7-L (5-qt) tin cans and covered tops (cardboard) leaving a few inches between tops and pitfall openings (Figure 9). Lizards fell into traps while attempting to seek shade. Whitaker (1967) increased pitfall trapping success of some lizards by using fruit and honey bait. Besides providing occurrence data, pitfall traps obtain specimens for population, reproductive, and taxonomic studies. Porzer (1982) used double-depth 18.9-L (5-gal.) plastic containers to capture Gila monsters (*Heloderma suspectum*) for radio telemetry studies.

When arranged systematically and standardized per unit effort (e.g., animals caught in a 24-hour trapping period), pitfall and other trapping data can be quantified and compared. For example, biologists can compare relative abundance of certain species between two or more habitat types if they set out traps in a standardized way (similar arrangement and size) during the same season. Bury and Raphael (1983) described a systematic pitfall trapping system

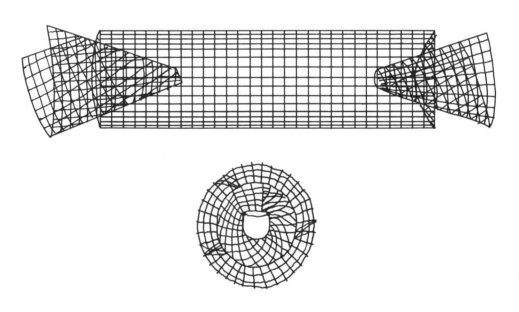

Figure 6. Funnel trap for capturing terrestrial amphibians and reptiles.

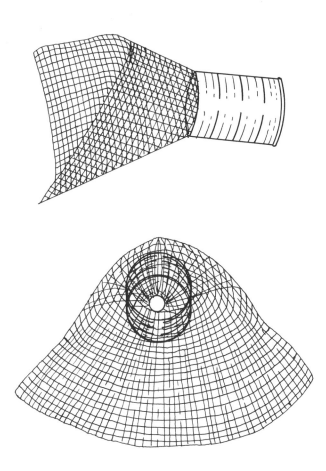

Figure 7. Jar funnel trap.

consisting of 7.6-L (2 gal.) sized pitfall traps, arranged in a 5- x 13-cm (2- x 5-in.) grid, 20 m (66 ft) apart. This procedure captured seven times the number of lizards than a technique of searching a predefined area, lifting logs and rocks (previously described as time-constraint collecting), but produced only one-half the number of salamanders. K.B. Jones (unpubl. data) and Price (pers. commun.) used a large (26- x 30-cm [10- x 12-in.] trap grid) 2-ha (5-a.) pitfall grid to determine relative abundance of lizards in riparian and Chihuahuan Desert habitats, respectively (Figure 10). Both used double-deep, 1.35-kg (3-lb) coffee cans spaced 15 m (49.5 ft) apart with wooden tops placed 15.2-20.3 cm (6-8 in.) over the traps for shade. Jones and Price (unpubl. data) accumulated large samples of most lizards in a period of less than a month during the spring.

By marking amphibians and reptiles for individual identification while using a pitfall grid, biologists can determine species home ranges and population sizes (mark and recapture).

Drift fences have been widely used in combination with pitfall traps, especially in recent years.

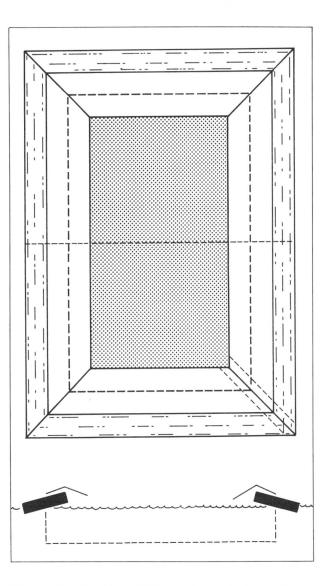

Figure 8. Floating pitfall trap for capturing turtles.

Gibbons and Semlitsch (1981) used several configurations of pitfall traps and drift fences for capturing amphibians, reptiles, and small mammals. They found these methods yielded a large number of species and accurately estimated the abundances of readily trapped species. They also provide time and cost estimates for trapping. Campbell and Christman (1982) described an array-trapping method consisting of eight 18.9-L (5-gal.) plastic containers, 7.6-m (25-ft) drift fences, and hardware cloth funnel traps (Figure 11). The array technique yielded a large number of amphibian and reptile species, especially secretive species not normally verified by other techniques. Jones (1981a & b) modified Campbell's and Christman's (1982) array system by using only three drift fences and four 18.9-L (5-gal.) plastic containers (Figure 12). As in Campbell and Christman's (1982) studies, Jones verified a large number of lizards and snakes, especially secretive forms, but with about one-half the equipment at each site.

Figure 9. Simple pitfall trap for terrestrial amphibians and reptiles.

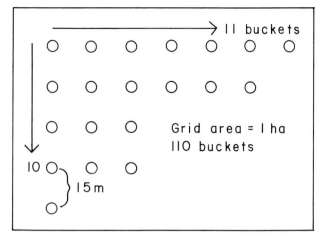

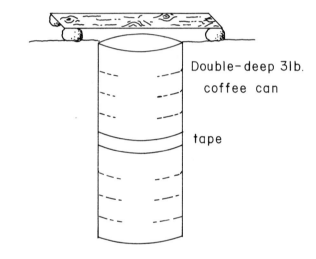

Figure 10. Grid pitfall trapping system.

Vogt and Hine (1982) also used a wide variety of pitfall/drift fence configurations (Figure 13) to sample amphibians and reptiles. These configurations were designed to maximize trapping success in each habitat. Although Vogt and Hine (1982) reported drift fence lengths of less than 15 m (49.5 ft) as generally ineffective, Jones (1981a & b) demonstrated that a 7.6-m (25-ft) fence length was very effective. These differences may reflect different types of habitat and animals sampled by the two investigators (wet woodland versus desert).

The sampling duration and seasons when array or pitfall/drift fence trapping is most successful depends on general climatic features of an area, and the species and habitats to be sampled. For example, Vogt and Hine (1982) suggested that several short sampling periods, staggered over an activity season (especially after rains), yield the most accurate estimate of species composition and species abundance. They believed this procedure takes advantage of increased herpetofauna activity resulting from rain. Unlike Wisconsin, the Desert Southwest receives infrequent precipitation and has a far greater number of habitats where temperature and moisture availability vary. In Arizona, desert habitats are most effectively trapped in April and May, and forest and woodland habitats between May and July. I have also found that broken, short-duration sampling suggested by Vogt and Hine (1982) does not verify all species,

especially many secretive desert snakes, present in a habitat. I attribute this finding to infrequent, erratic rainfall and suggest sample periods of not less than 30 days.

To obtain differences in species composition and abundance, biologists should place arrays in different habitats, provided that a standard configuration is used. Fences located so that amphibian and reptile migration routes are dissected will increase capture success. Jones (1981a & b) used arrays for assessing lizard and small snake relative abundances in a variety of habitats in western Arizona. Array abundance data can be expressed as the number of animals caught in 24 hours (Jones 1981a & b).

Pitfall/drift fence or array trapping most accurately assesses lizard and small snake composition and abundance, but is less effective in estimating salamander, frog, and toad abundances, although it does provide some excellent records for these herpetofauna. This method is not recommended for assessment of most terrestrial turtles and large snakes. There is some amphibian and reptile mortality, especially salamanders, frogs, and toads, associated with most trapping methods previously listed. To reduce mortality, biologists should check traps as often as possible, generally every other day. Mortality due to exposure can be reduced by placing traps in shaded areas, by covering trap openings with shades, or by placing about 2 to 4 cm (1 to 2 in.) of soil or litter at the bottom of the trap. These precautions will also reduce predation on trapped animals.

Water accumulation in pitfall traps, especially in wet regions, can cause significant mortality. Whereas punching holes in the bottom of traps provides little drainage, floatable objects such as styrofoam reduce mortality due to drowning.

Baited snap traps, such as those commonly used to census small mammals, can be used to collect large diurnal lizards. Heatwole et al. (1964) trapped several large, diurnal lizards by baiting museum snap traps with live insects, meat, fruit, and peanut butter.

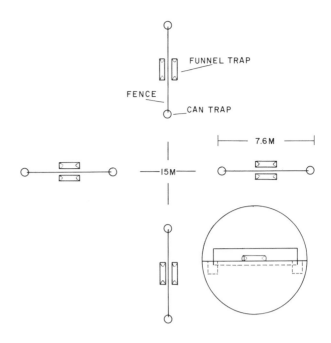

Figure 11. Array pitfall trapping technique, with funnels.

Table 3. Comparison of mean relative abundance and species diversity for lizards of five heavily grazed vegetative communities. Tests are based on Student's t-test values at the 95% confidence interval. Each heavily and lightly grazed site is based on seven sample sites.

H = Heavily grazed   L = Lightly grazed

Vegetative Community				Mean Relative Abundance ± SD	Species Diversity (H')
	Grazed	Array-Nights	Lizards Trapped		
Chaparral	H	672	782	1.18 ± 32	1.02
	L	623	1050	1.69 ± .41[a]	1.09
Desert grassland	H	294	179	0.56 ± .08	0.88
	L	224	176	0.77 ± .13	1.01
Mixed riparian scrub	H	392	295	0.73 ± 0.5	0.69
	L	252	310	1.20 ± .06[a]	0.90
Cottonwood-willow riparian	H	658	419	0.64 ± .23	0.59
	L	175	201	1.13 ± .15[a]	0.86
Sonoran desert scrub	H	714	757	1.06 ± .10	0.93
	L	238	244	1.03 ± .12	0.93

[a]The comparison of heavily grazed with lightly grazed is significantly different at the 95% confidence interval in three vegetative communities.

Large, man-made developments such as canals act as large traps and can provide valuable distributional records of amphibians and reptiles. Hawken (1951) captured large numbers of amphibians and reptiles by a flume located downstream from a lake.

A total of 582 specimens (15 species) of amphibians and reptiles were trapped by this man-made system.

Because some records obtained during trapping represent significant range extensions, biologists should collect voucher specimens of amphibians and reptiles taken out of their published geographic range. Pisani (1973) discussed field notes and preservation techniques for amphibians and reptiles. After preserving range extension specimens, biologists should contact regional experts to verify records. These animals should then be deposited in a university, regional, or national museum. For example, range extension specimens collected by the BLM's Phoenix District were placed in the National Museum of Natural History at the Smithsonian Institute in Washington, DC.

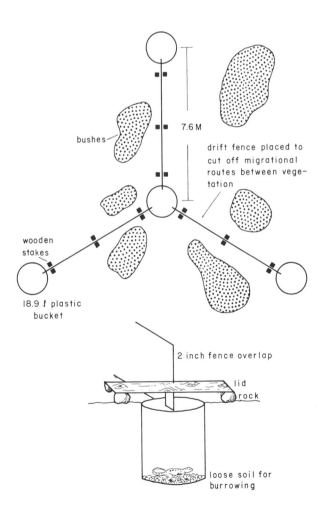

Figure 12. Modified array pitfall trapping technique.

Certain field procedures have been developed to identify amphibians and reptiles where direct observations are not possible. Many frogs and toads produce specific calls that can be recorded and used to identify individual species (see Michaud 1964; Brown and Littlejohn 1972; Fouquette 1980 for examples).

Certain species of reptiles, especially lizards and snakes, leave characteristic tracks and when compared to standards developed for each species, can be used to identify species occurrence in an area. Lillywhite (1982) used tracks left in fine-textured soils and on roads to identify common snakes such as sidewinders *(Crotalus cerastes)* and whipsnakes *(Masticophis* sp.). Although this procedure provides some indication of species and habitat use, track identification does not provide accurate estimates of abundance, and it may not be practical to use because of precipitation and wind. A biologist may want to use this method when movement and habitat use data are needed for priority species that leave easily-recognized tracks.

Species and Population Measurements

Depending on the specific objectives of a survey or study, a number of morphological, behavioral, and ecological measurements can be taken. Only a few measurements such as general age class and size are taken from opportunistic and systematic observations when animals are not captured.

Capture methods allow biologists to obtain a number of measurements such as total length (e.g., snakes), snout-vent length (lizards), weight, sex (from coloration or sex probes), reproductive condition (swollen testes or coloration that indicates breeding), and limb and other morphological traits (used to tie species to habitats) such as jaw width/length ratios. All of these measurements provide biologists with indicators of species' conditions, especially when animals are released and recaptured.

Stomach analysis of captured animals can also be obtained, especially on lizards and snakes. Pietruszka (1981) found that stomach-flushing devices provided data on lizard prey. Kephart and Arnold (1982) determined garter snake *(Thamnophis* sp.) diets by running their hands tightly up snakes, forcing regurgitation.

Diet information of lizards and snakes can be used to determine these animals' food needs, and it also provides information on the quantity and trends of certain prey species (see Kephart and Arnold 1982).

Fecal analyses of certain herbivorous reptiles can be conducted to determine dietary preferences.

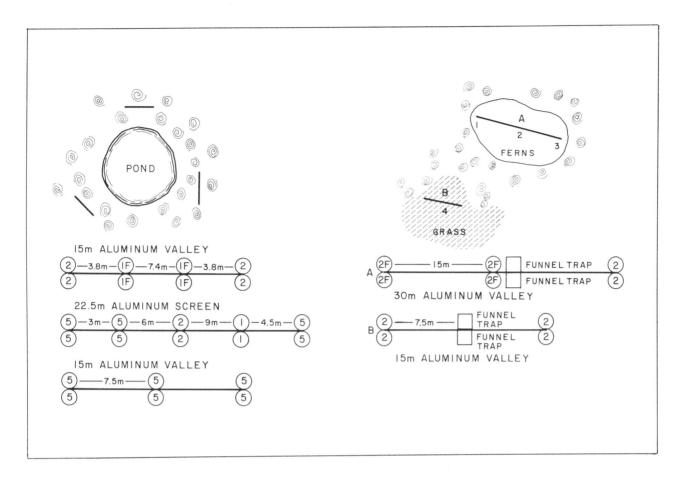

Figure 13. Pitfall/drift fence trapping schemes in different habitats.

Hansen et al. (1976) used a microhistological analysis of fecal droppings to determine dietary preferences of the desert tortoise.

When individual amphibians and reptiles are marked, released, and recaptured at a later date, a number of statistical treatments can be used to determine species' density, movement, and activity patterns. Capture of amphibians and reptiles allows biologists to mark individual animals for future identification. A wide variety of marking techniques, ranging from tagging (including radioactive) to sequential toe-clipping, have been used. Pough (1970) attached plastic plug tags to identale clipped just anterior to the cloaca (Figure 14). Shell notching is perhaps the most common method of marking turtles, although tagging, branding, and painting are also used for individual identification (Ferner 1979; Figure 14).

Heckel and Roughgarden (1979) used a paint spray gun to mark lizards. Although the marking technique did not provide individual lizard recognition necessary to determine movements, it provided quick and accurate data necessary to determine home range and population size.

Although more commonly used for fish, removal methods yield data that can be submitted to certain statistical treatments to estimate amphibian and reptile population size. Bury (1982) used a removal method to estimate population size of diurnal lizards. He verified all resident diurnal lizards after 2 days of sampling and used the total number of lizards removed over the 2-day period as the population size.

Trailing devices and radiotelemetry provide data on individual reptile movement and activity. Scott and Dobie (1980) used an aluminum-canister, thread-trailing device to determine movements of turtles (Figure 15).

All of the previously described procedures and measurements can be used by biologists to determine the relative health of amphibians and reptile species and communities. Most methods involved with marking, tracking, and recapture are time-consuming and, in some instances, expensive (e.g., telemetry). These methods should be used when detailed information on the condition of a species (e.g., threatened or endangered) or a group of species in a specific habitat (e.g., riparian) is needed.

K. Bruce Jones

Gila monster leaving tracks in the sand.

Community Surveys

Broader, more extensive surveys of entire amphibian and reptile faunas in a variety of habitat types do not allow for intensive study of individual species. In a community survey, biologists attempt to determine species composition of each major habitat type; some rough estimate of abundance; and, if possible, species' uses of microhabitats.

Because individual amphibian and reptile morphology, behavior, and ecology vary, biologists should use several censusing methods for determining herpetofauna community composition. Campbell and Christman (1982) and Gibbons and Semlitsch (1981) emphasized the need to use combinations of opportunistic observations, transects, pitfall and funnel traps, drift fence, and road riding for deriving complete species lists (occurrences) within specific areas or habitats. Jones (1981b) used several methods to determine amphibian and reptile composition and abundance in 14 major habitat types. Conducted during spring, summer, and fall of a year, the survey generated 27 significant range extensions for the region. Information gained from the survey also contributed heavily to management decisions made for the area. Bury and Raphael (1983) recommend a combination of time-constraint and pitfall array techniques for generating data useful in making most types of management decisions.

Herpetofauna richness and abundance data can help determine the effects of land use on these animals. Busack and Bury (1974) and Jones (1981a) provided examples of studies describing land-use impacts, including grazing effects on lizards. Data such as in Table 3 can be used to assess impacts of land use.

There are other statistical analyses that assess amphibian and reptile community structure. These analyses, which include Horn's Overlap Index (Horn 1966) and several similarity coefficients, are treated in a later chapter.

DISCUSSION

The primary difference between inventory and monitoring of amphibians and reptiles and their habitat is the objective established by the biologist. An inventory and monitoring study may involve similar data collection methods. However, inventories usually verify what is there and how habitat resources are being used, whereas monitoring determines how individual species or communities change as a result of specific types of land use. An inventory can successfully verify most amphibians and reptiles in representative habitat types within a year, provided that—

(1) there are multiple samples in each habitat;

(2) samples are taken during all peak activity periods; and

(3) a variety of methods are used.

If funds prohibit complete community samples, the biologist must then decide which species or habitats will produce the most useful information for the money.

Monitoring generally requires sampling over several years so that species and community health can be accurately estimated. This is especially needed in sampling amphibians and reptiles because populations fluctuate greatly from year to year with environmental changes, particularly precipitation. Multiyear data collection allows the biologist to determine which population trends are due to naturally fluctuating environmental conditions and which ones are due to land-use practices.

Most agency budgets will not permit long-term, intensive, multiyear samples of individual species or entire communities. To offset budget limitations, biologists should concentrate on long-term changes in species richness and important microhabitats, especially when losses are involved. To determine these changes, the biologist does not need to use expensive, time-consuming species trend techniques,

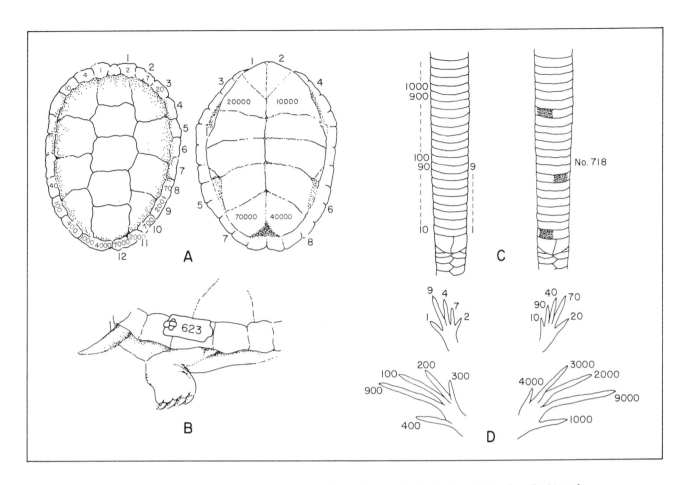

Figure 14. Marking techniques for amphibians and reptiles. A & B. Turtles C. Snakes D. Lizards

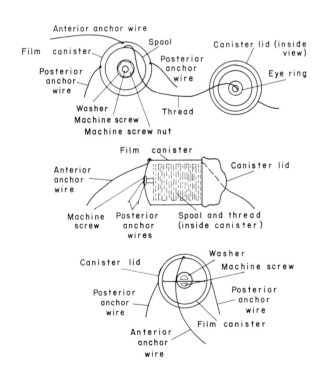

Figure 15. Trailing device to determine turtle movement.

Short-term method of marking desert tortoises.

but rather species verification and habitat measurement techniques. Data can also be obtained intermittently over 3- to 5-year intervals to reduce costs. Generally these types of data will provide biologists with adequate information for management decisions, although some management situations may require intensive, multiyear monitoring.

Another way of reducing costs, while obtaining community data on amphibians and reptiles, is to sample indicator species. There are two general types of indicator species:

- amphibians and reptiles that represent species assemblages that use habitats in similar ways (species guilds), or
- species that use specific habitat components.

For example, population trend data can be collected on one of several species that require downed litter. The trend of the species sampled should reflect trends of the entire species assemblage because they require the same habitat component. However, some tests have revealed that species within delineated guilds respond differently to land-use practices. Mannan et al. (1984) found that 67% of birds within guilds responded differently to timber harvest. The problem with guilds is that all species occupy separate niches, some more specific than others. Therefore, many amphibians and reptiles within the same guild as the indicator may respond differently to habitat changes. Mannan et al. (1984) pointed out that guilding works either when the investigator defines very specific guilds or the land-use impact is so severe that several habitat components are lost.

The other use of indicator species is to determine conditions of a habitat component based on condition and trend of an amphibian or reptile. Although certain microhabitat specific species could be used in this manner, greater accuracy and less sample cost may be obtained by sampling the habitat components directly.

In selecting indicator amphibians and reptiles, a biologist must again be fully aware of sampling method and species life history limitations. Amphibians and reptiles whose populations respond to climatic conditions should not be used as indicator species, especially in short-duration studies. However, it may be possible to use these species in long-term studies where climatic effects can be separated.

Presence and absence can be used to assess gross species assemblage and habitat component trends provided sampling techniques are adequate. For example, absence of a salamander reflects the lack of required habitat components on one site, and presence of the species on a similar site reflects the presence of required habitat components. The key phrase in the previous sentence is "on a similar site." To be compared, these sites must have similar topography, rainfall, temperature, and vegetation. If these variables are not similar on each site, the biologist cannot determine whether lack of habitat components on one site limits the salamander's occurrence. Biologists should select species that rely heavily on a specific microhabitat. This will increase the accuracy of predictions made about microhabitat conditions.

LITERATURE CITED

ANDERSON, K. and C.L. SMITH. 1950. An electrical apparatus for herpetological collecting. Copeia 1950:322.

BALGOOYEN, T.G. 1977. Collecting methods for amphibians and reptiles. U.S. Dep. Inter., Bur. Land Manage. Tech. Note 299. Denver, CO.

BANTA, B.H. 1957. A simple trap for collecting desert reptiles. Herpetologica 13:174-176.

BRATTSTROM, B.H. 1965. Body temperatures of reptiles. Am. Midl. Nat. 73:376-422.

BREEN, J.F. 1949. Reptiles: their habits and care. All-Pets Mag.

BROWN, L.E. and M.J. LITTLEJOHN. 1972. Male release call in the *Bufo americanus* group. Pages 310-323 *in* W.F. Blair, ed. Evolution in the Genus *Bufo*. Univ. Texas Press, Austin.

BURGE, B.L. 1979. Survey of the present distribution of the desert tortoise, *Gopherus agassizii*, in Arizona. U.S. Dep. Inter., Bur. Land Manage. Contract YA-512-CT8-108. Denver, CO.

BURY, R.B. 1982. Structure and composition of Mojave Desert reptile communities determined with a removal method. Herpetological Communities, U.S. Dep. Inter., Fish and Wildl. Serv. Wildl. Res. Rep. 13.

———, H.W. CAMPBELL, and N.J. SCOTT, Jr. 1980. Role and importance of nongame wildlife. Pages 197-207 *in* Trans. 45th North Am. Wildl. Nat. Res. Conf. Washington, DC.

——— and R.A. LUCKENBACH. 1977. Censusing desert tortoise populations using a quadrat and grid location system. Desert Tortoise Council Symp. Proc. 1977:169-178.

——— and M.G. RAPHAEL. 1983. Inventory methods for amphibians and reptiles. Proc. Int. Conf. Renewable Resour. Inventories for Monitoring Changes and Trends. Oregon State Univ., Corvallis.

BUSACK, S.D. and R.B. BURY. 1974. Some effects of off-road vehicles and sheep grazing on lizard populations in the Mojave Desert. Biol. Consev. 6:179-183.

CAMPBELL, H.W. and S.P. CHRISTMAN. 1982. Field techniques for herpetofaunal community analysis. Herpetological Communities, U.S. Dep. Inter., Fish and Wildl. Serv. Wildl. Res. Rep. 13.

CARPENTER, C.C. 1953. Trapping technique for aquatic salamanders. Herpetologica 8(4):183.

———. 1955. Sounding turtles: a field location technique. Herpetologica 11:120.

CLARK, D.R., Jr. 1966. A funnel trap for small snakes. Trans. Kansas Acad. Sci. 69(1):91-95.

CREUSERE, F.M. and W.G. WHITFORD 1982. Use of time and space by lizards. Herpetological Communities, U.S. Dep. Inter., Fish and Wildl. Serv. Wildl. Res. Rep. 13.

DARGAN, L.M. and W.H. STICKEL. 1949. An experiment with snake trapping. Copeia 1949:264-268.

DUNDEE, H.A. 1950. An improved method for collecting living lizards and frogs. Herpetologica 6(3):78-79.

EAKIN, R.M. 1957. Use of copper wire in noosing lizards. Copeia 1957:148.

EDWARDS, S.R. 1975. Collections of preserved amphibians and reptiles in the United States. SSAR Misc. Publ. Herpetological Circular 3.

FERNER, J.W. 1979. A review of marking techniques for amphibians and reptiles. SSAR. Herpetological Circular 9.

FEUER, R.C. 1980. Underwater traps for aquatic turtles. Herp. Review 11(4):107-108

FITCH, H.S. 1951. A simplified type of funnel trap for reptiles. Herpetologica 7:77-80.

FOUQUETTE, M.J., Jr. 1980. Effect of environmental temperatures on body temperature of aquatic-calling anurans. J. Herpetol. 14(4):347-352.

FRANKLIN, M.A. 1947. An inexpensive snare for water snakes. Copeia 1947:143.

GIBBONS, J.W. and R.D. SEMLITSCH. 1981. Terrestrial drift fences with pitfall traps: an effective technique for quantitative sampling of animal populations. Brimleyana 7:1-16.

GOIN, C.J. 1942. A method of collecting the vertebrates associated with water hyacinths. Copeia (3):183-184.

GUNNING, G.E. and W.M. LEWIS. 1957. An electrical shocker for the collection of amphibians and reptiles in the aquatic environment. Copeia 1957:52.

HALL, R.J. 1967. A simplified live-trap for reptiles. Trans. Kansas Acad. Sci. 70(3):402-404.

———. 1980. Effects of environmental contaminants on reptiles: a review. U.S. Dep. Inter., Fish and Wildl. Serv. Spec. Sci. Rep. 228. Washington, DC.

HANSEN, R.M., M.K. JOHNSON, and T.R. VAN DEVENDER. 1976. Foods of the desert tortoise, *Gopherus agassizii*, in Arizona and Utah. Herpetologica 32(3):247-251.

HAWKEN, J.L. 1951. Water system acts as reptile and amphibian trap. Herpetologica 7:81-83.

HEATWOLE, H., A. MALDONADO, and J. OJASTI. 1964. A trapping method for capturing lizards. Herpetologica 20(3):212-213.

HECKEL, D.G. and J. ROUGHGARDEN. 1979. A technique for estimating the size of lizard populations. Ecology 60(5):966-975.

HORN, H.S. 1966. Measurement of overlap in comparative ecological studies. Am. Nat. 100:419-424.

IVERSON, J.B. 1979. Another inexpensive turtle trap. Harp. Review 10(2):55.

JONES, K.B. 1981a. Effects of grazing on lizard abundance and diversity in western Arizona. Southwest Nat. 26(2):107-115.

———. 1981b. Distribution, ecology, and habitat management of the reptiles and amphibians of the Hualapai-Aquarius planning area, Mohave and Yavapai Counties, Arizona. U.S. Dep. Inter., Bur. Land Manage. Tech. Note 353. Denver, CO.

———, L.P. KEPNER, and W.G. KEPNER. 1983. Anurans of Vekol Valley, Central Arizona. Southwest Nat. 28(4):469-470.

KEPHART, D.G. and S.J. ARNOLD. 1982. Garter snake diets in a fluctuating environment: a seven-year study. Ecology 63(5):1232-1236.

LAGLER, K.F. 1943. Methods of collecting freshwater turtles. Copeia 1943:21-25.

LANNON, J.R., Jr. 1962. A different method of catching the desert lizards, *Callisaurus* and *Uma.* Copeia 1962:437-438.

LEE, D.S. 1968. Herpetofauna associated with central Florida mammals. Herpetologica 24(1):83-84.

LEGLER, J.M. 1960. A simple and inexpensive device for trapping aquatic turtles. Utah Acad. Sci. Proc. 37:63-66.

LILLYWHITE, H.B. 1982. Tracking as an aid in ecological studies of snakes. Herpetological Communities, U.S. Dep. Inter., Fish and Wildl. Serv. Wildl. Res. Rep. 13.

LUCKENBACH, R.A. and R.B. BURY. 1983. Effects of off-road vehicles on the biota of the Algodones Dunes, Imperial County, California. J. Appl. Ecol. 20:265-286.

MANNAN, R.W., M.L. MORRISON, and E.C. MESLOW. 1984. Comment: The use of guilds in forest bird management. The Wildl. Soc. Bull. 12(4):426-430.

MARTOF, B.S. 1963. An effective technique for capturing stream-dwelling organisms. Copeia 1963:439-440.

MICHAUD, T.C. 1964. Vocal variation in two species of chorus frogs, *Pseudacris nigrita* and *Pseudacris clarki*, in Texas. Evolution 18:498-506.

MILLSAP, B.A. 1981. Distributional status of Falconiformes in west-central Arizona: with notes on ecology, reproductive success, and management. U.S. Dep. Inter., Bur. Land Manage. Tech. Note 355. Denver, CO.

MILLSAP, B.A. and W. HARRISON. 1981. Food and foraging habitats of common black hawks *(Buteogallus anthracinus)* in western Arizona. U.S. Dep. Inter., Bur. Land Manage. Phoenix District, AZ. Unpubl.

MOULTON, J.M. 1954. Notes on the natural history, collection, and maintenance of the salamander *Ambystoma maculatum* Copeia 1954:64-65.

NEILL, W.T. 1956. Another device for collecting lizards. Copeia 1956:124-125.

ORTEGA, A., M.E. MAURY, and R. BARBAULT. 1982. Spatial organization and habitat partitioning in a mountain lizard community of Mexico. Ecol. Gen. 3(3):323-330.

PETOKAS, P.J. and M.M. ALEXANDER. 1979. A new trap for basking turtles. Herp. Review 10(3):90.

PIANKA, E.R. 1966. Convexity, desert lizards, and spatial heterogeneity. Ecology 47(6):1055-1059.

PIETRUSZKA, R.D. 1981. An evaluation of stomach flushing for desert lizard diet analysis. Southwest. Nat. 26(2):101-105.

PIRNIE, M.D. 1935. Michigan waterfowl management. Michigan Dep. Conserv., Lansing, MI.

PISANI, G.R. 1973. A guide to preservation techniques for amphibians and reptiles. SSAR Misc. Publ. Herpetological Circular 1.

PORZER, L.M. 1982. Movements, behavior, and body temperatures of the Gila monster (*Heloderma suspectum* Cope) in the vicinity of Queen Creek, Arizona. M.S. Thesis, Arizona State Univ., Tempe.

POUGH, F.H. 1970. A quick method for permanently marking snakes and turtles. Herpetologica 26:428-430.

ROGERS, T.L. 1939. A lizard live-trap. Copeia 1939:51.

SCHNEIDER, P.B. 1981. A population analysis of the desert tortoise, *Gopherus agassizii*, in Arizona. U.S. Dep.

Inter., Bur. Land Manage. Phoenix District Office. Contract AZ-950-CT9-0014.

SCOTT, A.F. and J.L. DOBIE. 1980. An improved design for a thread-trailing device used to study terrestrial movements of turtles. Herp. Review 11(4):106-107.

STEBBINS, R.C. 1966. A field guide to western reptiles and amphibians. Houghton Mifflin Co. Boston, MA. 27pp.

STICKEL, W.H. 1944. A simple and effective lizard snare. Copeia 1944:251-252.

STORM, R.M. and R.A. PIMENTEL. 1954. A method of studying amphibian breeding populations. Herpetologica 10:161-166.

SVIHLA, A. 1959. A simple method of collecting *Ascaphus truei* tadpoles. Copeia 1959:72.

TINKLE, D.W. 1982. Results of experimental density manipulation in an Arizona lizard community. Ecology 63(1):57-65.

VITT, L.J., A.C. HULSE, and R.D. OHMART. 1974. Reproduction and ecology of a Colorado River population of *Sceloporus magister*. Herpetologica 30:410-417.

VITT, L.J. and R.D. OHMART. 1978. Herpetofauna of the lower Colorado River: Davis Dam to the Mexican border. Proc. West. Found. Vert. Zool. 2(2):35-72.

VOGT, R.C. and R.L. HINE. 1982. Evaluation of techniques for assessment of amphibian and reptile populations in Wisconsin. Pages 201-217 *in* Scott, N.J., Jr. ed. Herpetological Communities. U.S. Dep. Inter., Fish and Wildl. Serv. Wildl. Res. Rep. 13.

VOGT, W. 1941. A practical lizard trap. Copeia 1941:115.

WHITAKER, A.H. 1967. Baiting pitfall traps for small lizards. Herpetologica 23(4):309-310.

WHITFORD, W.G. and F.M. CREUSERE. 1977. Seasonal and yearly fluctuations in Chihuahuan Desert lizard communities. Herpetologica 33:54-65.

WIEGMAN, D.L., M. HAKKILA, K. WHITMORE, and R.A. COLE. 1980. Survey of the Sacramento Mountain salamander *(Aneides hardyi)* habitat on the Cloudcroft and Mayhill Districts in the Lincoln National Forest. U.S. Dep. Agric., For. Serv. Contract OM-40-7512-O-632.

WILLIAMS, R.D., J.E. GATES, and C.H. HOCUTT. 1981. An evaluation of known and potential sampling techniques for hellbender, *Cryptobranchus alleganiensis*. J. Herpetol. 15(1):23-27.

ZWEIFEL, R.G. and C.H. LOWE. 1966. The ecology of a population of *Xantusia vigilis*, the desert night lizard. Am. Mus. Novit. 2247:1-57.

15

SONGBIRDS

Ronald A. Ryder

Department of Fishery & Wildlife Biology
Colorado State University
Fort Collins, CO 80523

Editor's Note: This chapter on Songbirds is the first of six chapters on birds. The chapter covers the true songbirds (Order Passeriformes) and also other orders that require similar techniques for habitat and population surveys. Techniques for surveying songbirds are relatively well-described and formalized, and this chapter provides an overview of these along with references to the appropriate publication for step-by-step procedures.

In addition, the chapter covers general sources of information on birds. In North America, birds are actively observed, counted, and recorded by millions of avid, amateur birdwatchers as well as more limited numbers of professional ornithologists. The observations of these people, as summarized in publications such as local bird lists and periodicals such as American Birds, are valuable sources of background information on distribution and habitat use, for not only songbirds but for all bird species. To avoid repetition, these sources of information are covered in this chapter and not in the others.

INTRODUCTION

Songbirds will be considered to include not only birds of the order perching birds (Passeriformes), but also cuckoos (Cuculiformes), nighthawks (Caprimulgiformes), swifts and hummingbirds (Apodiformes), trogons (Trogoniformes), kingfishers (Coraciiformes), and woodpeckers (Piciformes), constituting over 350 species in North America, north of Mexico. With few exceptions, most are extremely mobile, and many are migratory, moving latitudinally or altitudinally between breeding grounds and wintering areas each year. Most have relatively high breeding potentials, and their numbers and densities may fluctuate greatly from season to season due to recruitment and climatic changes. Some even shift their centers of abundance based on vegetation and prey densities—especially in the West—depending on seasonal and regional variations in precipitation.

Although it is possible to obtain comparatively accurate estimates of absolute densities for a few endangered forms (such as Kirtland's warbler [*Dendroica kirtlandii*] and dusky seaside sparrow [*Ammodramus maritimus nigrescens*]), for most species it is neither physically possible nor economically reasonable to obtain absolute densities. For most management purposes, estimates of relative density are adequate.

The literature concerning inventorying and monitoring songbirds is vast, if not overwhelming. Ralph and Scott (1981) edited symposium proceedings which are probably the best available references on methods for estimating numbers of terrestrial birds. Franzeb (1977) and Call (1981) discussed songbirds in their U.S. Bureau of Land Management (BLM) Technical Notes on terrestrial wildlife inventories. Davis (1982) and Davis and Winstead (1980) also provided useful references; they gave specific inventory methods for many species of songbirds. The U.S. Forest Service has published proceedings of several symposiums and workshops relating songbird numbers to habitats and their management (Smith 1975; DeGraff 1978a, b; DeGraff and Evans 1979; DeGraff and Tilghman 1980). Verner (1985) critically evaluated many counting techniques suitable for songbirds. *American Birds* (and earlier *Audubon Field Notes* and *Bird Lore*) regularly summarizes Christmas Bird Counts (CBCs) in its July-August issue, and winter bird-population studies and breeding bird censuses in its January-February issue. Not only do the main ornithological journals such as *Auk, Condor, Wilson Bulletin,* and the *Journal for Field Ornithology* regularly contain songbird-habitat papers, but a multitude of state and regional bird periodicals are also useful sources of such information. Many of these periodicals are indexed in *Wildlife Review* and *Wildlife Abstracts.*

This chapter describes habitat characteristics, such as cliffs and other physical features, as well as vegetative structure and composition as they relate to the over 20 families of songbirds found in the West. Throughout, key references to major avian groups are given, which can be consulted for specific habitat requirements (See Table 1).

The major methods or techniques used to monitor or inventory songbirds are described, with critical evaluations made of their applicability, especially in the western U.S. (See Table 2).

Ornithologists and land-use managers believed that numbers of bird species and individuals might serve as a "litmus test of the environment." It was thought that a decline in species richness and diversity, as determined by routine monitoring, would serve as an early warning of environmental degradation. More specifically, overgrazing, overcutting, or too heavy recreational use of forest and range ecosystems would be revealed by changes in bird populations.

Efforts to use songbird trends as indicators of habitat quality and habitat changes, however, have not been as successful as many had hoped. Songbirds are highly mobile and many individuals may, at most, spend only 3 to 4 months per year on a given area. Migratory species are probably more affected by habitat destruction and pesticide use on their wintering grounds in the Neotropics, where they spend more of their annual life cycle, than they are by changes on their breeding grounds in the western U.S., where they may spend one third or less of the year.

Lark bunting.

The skill, time, and dedication required to thoroughly inventory and monitor bird populations is probably more than the average land-use manager can provide. Identification of the many species, by sight and sound, and determination of sex and age classes of songbirds to be found in a BLM District require more knowledge and skill than most typical "wildlifers" possess or can acquire without considerable training and practice.

Also, most songbirds are not primary consumers but insectivores, at least during the breeding season. Thus, cause-and-effect relationships with vegetative changes are not as direct as with resident primary consumers, such as most rodents.

With these reservations in mind, some monitoring approaches that might be used to ascertain trends in bird numbers follow.

HABITAT FEATURES CORRELATED WITH SPECIES GROUPS

Physical Features

Most songbirds are associated with vegetation of a variety of types, but a few species, especially for nesting, are largely dependent on cliffs (cliff swallows [*Hirundo pyrrhonota*] and white-throated swifts [*Aeronautes saxatalis*], for example). Others use earthen banks (bank swallows [*Riparia riparia*] and belted kingfishers [*Ceryle alcyon*]). These special features are described in Chapters 27 and 31 and listed in Table 1.

An increasing number of songbirds are adapting to nesting and roosting in or on structures, such as buildings and bridges, as well as utilizing artificial nest boxes and platforms.

Table 1. Selected taxa of birds of western North America, structural features used, and some key references to avian ecology.

| Taxa | Common Names | Structural Features Used (mainly for nesting) | | | | | | | | | Key References |
		man-made	bare ground	cliffs and ravines	grass	grass/forb	low shrub	shrub/tree	tree	tall shrub	
PASSERI-FORMES	Perching birds	●	●	●	●	●	●	●	●	●	Anderson (1979), Balda (1975), Call (1981), Ralph & Scott (1981), Trimble (1975)
Tyrannidae	Tyrant flycatchers	●		●			●	●	●	●	Bent (1942), Forest Service (1982), Graber et al. (1974), Maser et al. (1984)
Alaudidae	Larks		●		●	●	●				Beason & Franks (1973, 1974), Boyd (1976), Pickwell (1931)
Hirundinidae	Swallows	●	●	●	●	●	●	●	●	●	Bent (1942), Graber et al. (1972), Harrison (1975)
Corvidae	Jays, magpies, & crows			●				●	●	●	Balda & Bateman (1972), Bent (1946), Goodwin (1976)
Paridae	Chickadees & titmice							●	●	●	Bailey & Niedrach (1965), Bent (1946), Dixon (1961)
Sittidae	Nuthatches								●		Bent (1948), Bock & Lepthien (1972), Norris (1958)
Certhiidae	Creepers								●		Bent (1948), McClelland & Frissell (1975)
Troglodytidae	Wrens	●		●			●	●	●	●	Anderson & Anderson (1973), Armstrong (1955), Bent (1948)
Cinclidae	Dippers			●							Bakus (1959a, 1959b), Price & Bock (1983)
Sylviinae	Kinglets & gnatcatchers							●	●	●	Bent (1949), Root (1967), Trimble (1975)
Turdinae	Solitaires, thrushes, & allies	●	●	●	●	●	●	●	●	●	Bent (1949), Graber et al. (1971), Jackman & Scott (1975), Young (1955), Zeleny (1976)
Mimidae	Mockingbirds & thrushes	●	●	●	●	●	●	●	●	●	Bent (1948), Brazier (1964), Graber et al. (1970)
Motacillidae	Wagtails & pipits		●		●						Bent (1950), Verbeek (1970)
Bombycillidae	Waxwings							●	●	●	Bent (1950), Lea (1942), Putnam (1949)
Ptilogonatidae	Silky flycatchers							●	●	●	Bent (1950), Verner & Boss (1980)
Laniidae	Shrikes						●	●	●	●	Bystrak (1983), Graber et al. (1973), Miller (1931), Porter et al. (1975)
Sturnidae	Starlings	●	●	●	●	●	●	●	●	●	DeHaven & DeHaven (1973), Feare (1984), Kessel (1957)

Table 1. Selected taxa of birds of western North America, structural features used, and some key references to avian ecology (concluded).

Taxa	Common Names	man-made	bare ground	cliffs and ravines	grass	grass/forb	low shrub	shrub/tree	tree	tall shrub	Key References
		Structural Features Used (mainly for nesting)									
Vireonidae	Vireos							●	●	●	Barlow (1962), Bent (1950), Verner & Boss (1980), Winternitz (1976)
Parulinae	Wood-warblers							●	●	●	Bent (1953), Graber et al. (1983), Griscom & Sprunt (1957), Harrison (1984)
Thraupinae	Tanagers							●	●		Bent (1958), Verner & Boss (1980)
Cardinalinae	Cardinals, grosbeaks, & allies				●	●	●	●	●	●	Austin (1968), Verner & Boss (1980)
Emberizinae	Emberizine finches				●	●	●	●	●	●	Austin (1968), Forest Service (1982)
Icterinae	Blackbirds & allies	●	●	●	●	●	●	●	●	●	Bent (1958), Nero (1984), Orians (1980)
Fringillinae	Fringilline finches				●	●	●	●	●	●	Austin (1968), Maser et al. (1984), Trimble (1975)
Carduelinae	Cardueline finches				●	●	●	●	●	●	Austin (1968), Trimble (1975), Verner & Boss (1980)
Passeridae	Old world sparrows	●							●		Packard (1966), Summers-Smith (1963, 1967)
CUCULIFORMES											
Cuculidae	Cuckoos, roadrunners, & anis						●	●	●	●	Bent (1940), Ohmart (1973), Preble (1957)
CAPRIMULGI-FORMES											
Caprimulgidae	Goatsuckers		●								Bent (1940), Caccamise (1974), Verner & Boss (1980)
APODIFORMES											
Apodidae	Swifts	●		●							Bent (1940), Knorr (1961)
Trochilidae	Hummingbirds	●					●	●	●	●	Calder (1973), Johnsgard (1983)
TROGONI-FORMES											
Trogonidae	Trogons							●	●	●	Bent (1940), Forest Service (1975), Phillips et al. (1964)
CORACII-FORMES											
Alacedinidae	Kingfishers			●							Bent (1940), Cornwell (1963), Eipper (1956)
PICIFORMES											
Picidae	Woodpeckers and allies							●	●	●	Bent (1939), Bock (1970), Jackson & Scott (1975)

Table 2. Some methods for monitoring songbirds—advantages and disadvantages. (See text for more details.)

Method	Season of Use	Advantages	Disadvantages
Checklist	All	Quick, relatively cheap to compile. Use literature and volunteers. Can visually portray arrival and departure dates and relative abundance.	Mainly qualitative, only relative abundance and gross habitat preferences.
Atlas	Mainly stress-breeding season (can show other seasons also)	Gives "big picture." Fairly understandable to the public.	Usually rather large scale (1° blocks of latitude and longitude). Requires considerable organization and cooperation of many observers.
Christmas Bird Count (CBC)	Winter	Many areas covered in past. Large sample size nationally.	Only one coverage/area/year. Area of special interest may not have been covered. Urban areas stressed. Only indexes, no absolute densities.
Winter bird-population studies	Winter	More coverages/season than CBC. Replications, hence greater possibility of statistical analysis.	Smaller area and number of areas covered than CBCs. More time and effort required.
Spot-mapping	Mainly breeding season (some winter territorial mapping possible)	Usually considered to give good estimates of breeding densities.	Requires repeated coverages by skilled observer. Need good vegetative map and vegetative measurements to be most useful.
Transects (mainly walked)	Any season	Quicker, cheaper to conduct than spot-mapping. More random samplings possible.	Accuracy highly variable species to species, habitat to habitat. Less accurate in nonbreeding season.
North American Breeding Bird Survey (BBS)	Breeding season (has been used for other seasons)	Large sample size nationally. Relatively cheap and quick to conduct.	Only single coverage of a given route each year. Habitat data not regularly gathered. Only indexes of abundance. Area must be accessible by road.
Point count (IPA)	Breeding season	Good statistical reliance reported for Europe (not well tested in U.S.).	Only two coverages/plot/season, normally. Considerable time (20 min) per stop. Only frequency data.
Density-frequency relationship (EFP)	Breeding	As above. Said to give density correlations.	More time-consuming than point count.
Maryland winter bird survey	Winter	Can be used where roads are lacking. Comparatively quick and cheap.	Walked (unlike roadside count), requires more time and effort than BBS. Not well tested in western U.S.
Variable-circular plots	All seasons (but mainly used in breeding season)	Can cover large geographical areas, compare different habitats, and work in rugged and remote terrain.	Requires considerable training in estimating or time in measuring distances (aural as well as visual distances).

Table 2. Some methods for monitoring songbirds—advantages and disadvantages. (See text for more details.) (concluded).

Method	Season of Use	Advantages	Disadvantages
Playback of tape recordings	Mainly breeding season	Quick way to get male responses. Speeds up spot-mapping.	Only certain species respond. Can alter behavior (interfere with nesting success?).
Mark and recapture	Any season	Can use similar population estimates as used with game species.	Not highly efficient. Considerable time and effort required. Special permits required. Many biases involved (trap-happy vs. trap-shy individuals).
Nest monitoring	Breeding season	Relates to actual nesting efforts.	Very time-consuming. Highly variable with species and habitats involved. Can increase predation and desertion.

Vegetation

Structure. Vegetative structure and habitat configuration (physiognomy) are generally considered more important in distribution and abundance of birds than plant species composition (floristics—Anderson and Shugart 1974; Hilden 1965; James 1971; Wiens 1969). However, some believe floristics may be more important within gross habitat types (Rotenberry, pers. commun.). Rotenberry's analysis of International Biological Program data from grasslands disclosed that 55% of the variation in bird community composition was associated with floristic variation and only 35% was associated with physiognomy.

Others have shown patterns of avian distribution strongly correlated with vegetational structure (MacArthur and MacArthur 1961; Willson 1974 et al.). Structural features commonly measured include density, mean distance to nearest plant neighbors, height, diameter at breast height (DBH) for trees, relative dominance, and canopy cover. Readers of *American Birds* are urged to follow "A Quantitative Method of Habitat Description" by James and Shugart (1970). Numerous review papers on bird-habitat structure studies are included in Abbott (1976), Anderson (1979), Anderson and Shugart (1974), Balda (1975), Cody (1981), Hilden (1965), Holmes et al. (1979), Holmes and Robinson (1981), James (1971), Karr (1980), Meents et al. (1983), Rice et al. (1983), Rotenberry and Wiens (1980a, b), Roth (1981), Taylor and Littlefield (1984), Wiens (1973, 1983), and Willson (1974). Capen (1981) discusses the use of multivariate statistics in describing avian habitats. Principal component analysis and discriminate function analysis are frequently used to examine avian habitat selection (Sedgwick 1981).

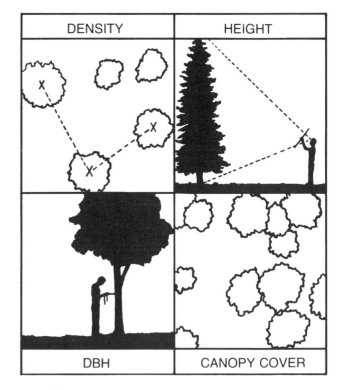

Species Composition. Although some researchers have recently shown floristics, or species of plants making up songbird habitat, to be important (Rotenberry, pers. commun.), most past studies have placed more importance on vegetative structure. Notable exceptions are the close dependence of Kirtland's warbler on young-growth jack pine (*Pinus banksiana*) and the red-cockaded woodpecker (*Picoides borealis*) on southern pines (*P. palustris, P. elliottii, P. taeda,* and *P. echinata*) that are infected with red heart (*Formes pini*).

STRUCTURE	FLORISTICS
Canopy Cover by Type	Species Composition
38% Trees	5% Ponderosa pine
32% Shrubs	10% True mountain mahogany
20% Grass	30% Arizona fescue
5% Forbs	30% Bluebunch wheatgrass
5% Bare ground	25% Other

Clay Bridges

Western tanager.

POPULATION MEASUREMENT TECHNIQUES

Presence

Sometimes mere lists of species or maps showing species distribution are adequate for making management decisions (for example, the location of red-cockaded woodpecker colonies and decisions to log or not log). Most state ornithological societies have official state lists of birds and often have "official records" committees and procedures for deciding the validity of records. Many local chapters of the National Audubon Society have checklists of birds for local areas, as do various land use agencies (e.g., BLM, U.S. Forest Service, U.S. National Park Service, U.S. Fish and Wildlife Service, and state conservation agencies).

Breeding Bird Atlases

Breeding bird "atlasing" has become a popular pastime among bird observers in Europe during the past decade. Atlases showing breeding distribution maps for each species have recently been published for the British Isles, France, and Denmark. Similar atlases are in progress in 16 other European nations (Sharrock 1975), Australia (Serventy 1980), and New Zealand (Gibb 1980).

The original purpose of preparing a breeding bird atlas was to correlate bird distribution with that of plants as shown in the *Atlas of British Flora* (Perring and Walters 1962). In a government-sponsored program carried out through the British Trust for

Ornithology and the Irish Wildbird Conservancy, observers visited every one of the 3,862 10-km squares (100 km² [38.6 mi.²] each) of land throughout the British Isles during a 5-year period and reported the presence or absence of each bird species (Sharrock 1976). Twelve transparent overlays, ordered separately, facilitate correlation of bird distribution with selected environmental factors. Sampling blocks have been different sizes in other countries, depending on the size of the area to be sampled and the standard maps available. In France, the sampling unit was 20 by 27 km (12.4 by 16.8 mi.; Yeatman 1976) and in Denmark it was 5-km (3.1-mi.) square (Dybbro 1976). Several countries modified the method to include some indication of abundance rather than merely presence or absence.

No large-scale atlas has been attempted in the U.S. because the U.S. Fish and Wildlife Service's Breeding Bird Survey (BBS) provides an annual sample of changing abundance of each species and also gives a density of coverage roughly comparable with that of the projected European atlas of the 1980s. Nevertheless, atlas studies have been initiated in several states (Laughlin 1982; Laughlin et al. 1982). These state atlases will provide information on presence or absence of the various species in many forested areas. In the Rocky Mountains, they are often termed "Latilong" studies, a word originally coined by Skaar (1969) to denote 1° of latitude and longitude blocks (Figure 1).

Although western state atlases use grids larger than the British 10-km (6.1-mi.) model, in most eastern states a 5-km (3.1-mi.) grid (six blocks on a 7 ½-minute topographic map) is used. The Maryland Ornithological Society, however, uses 2 ½-km (1 ½-mi.) "quarter blocks" (about 600 ha [1,500 a.]). The quarter blocks make it possible to pinpoint the location of rare species and others of special interest and are much better for outlining areas where a particular species is not present (Klimkiewicz and Robbins 1974). This accuracy is particularly important where commercial or residential communities are expanding or where habitats are being lost to other types of development. In areas where large forests are being destroyed by changes in land use, quarter-block atlas data have been of immense value in showing the degree various breeding species disappear when forested areas are fragmented into smaller tracts. Raynor (1983) proposed a method for evaluating atlas coverages.

Christmas Bird Count (CBC)

The CBC is the best known and probably most used source of information on geographical distribution of nongame birds in winter (Table 3). Started in 1900, the counts now involve over 1,300 circles, each 24 km (15 mi.) in diameter, which are covered by varying numbers of birders in an 8-hour period, sometime between December 20 and January 2 each year. Dawn-to-dusk (or longer) counts are preferred.

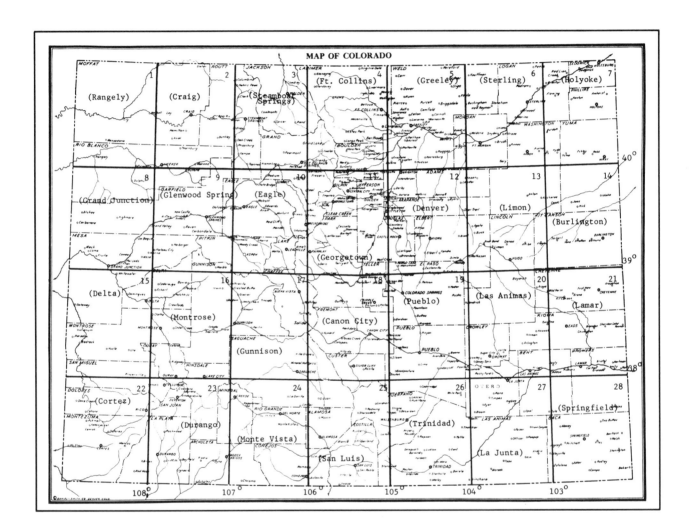

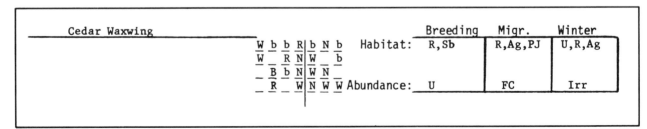

Cedar Waxwing							Breeding	Migr.	Winter
	W	b	b R	b N	b	Habitat:	R,Sb	R,Ag,PJ	U,R,Ag
	W		R N	W	b				
		B	b N	W	N				
		R	W N	W	W	Abundance:	U	FC	Irr

Figure 1. Example of bird distribution by Latilong blocks in Colorado.

Counts less than 8 hours long, except in arctic areas or at sea, are not acceptable. Results are summarized on standardized forms which include entries for weather, habitat description, and quality of the food supply. Summaries are published annually in *American Birds* (Arbib 1978) (Figure 2). In 1980, 1,320 counts were included, covering a vast area from Newfoundland to Alaska, south to Panama and Hawaii. In 1982, 36 countries and 6 continents were involved (Arbib 1982). Popular evaluations of the CBC have been written by Robbins (1966), Bock (1979), and Wing and Jenks (1939).

Individual birds reported on CBCs in 1979 ranged from 92 at Churchill, Manitoba, to 22,352,044 at Pine Prairie, Louisiana. Sixty-five counts had 150 or more species. The most meaningful data are expressed in number of birds observed per party-hour. Other bases, such as birds per mile and birds per observer, have proven unreliable (Bock 1979).

Winter Bird Population Study

In 1948, the National Audubon Society inaugurated an annual Winter Bird Population Study which, like the CBC, is published in *American Birds*. The purpose of this type of count is to estimate the average number of birds using a particular habitat. Many observers use the same plot in which they have conducted a breeding bird census by spot-mapping. Most plots range from 6 to 20 ha (14.8 to 49.4 a.). Plots are visited 6 to 10 times in midwinter, and the totals for each species are averaged (Kolb 1965). Results are expressed in terms of birds per kilometer squared [1 km^2] and birds per 40.5 ha (100 a.). In 1979-80, 92 counts were reported in *American Birds* (Cink and Boyd 1981), only a fraction of the 1,300 Christmas counts reported that winter. Several visits per winter are necessary because populations, and even the species present in a given plot, vary from day to day and from morning to afternoon. Finches (*Carpodacus* sp.), robins (*Turdus* sp.), and waxwings (*Bombycilla* sp.), for example, often range over many square kilometers in the course of 2 or 3 days. Other species, in mixed flocks, may range in and out of a study plot. Such flocks tend, especially on cold days, to favor sunny exposures, concentrate in better feeding sites, and avoid windy areas (Robbins 1978).

Difficulties notwithstanding, the Winter Bird Population Study does enable one to compare populations of different habitats and, to a lesser degree, to follow population trends over a period of years. Webster (1966) analyzed the results of 248 winter studies in forest habitats and 25 studies in grasslands. By plotting species richness against population density, he found that southern pine forests mixed with oaks or gums tended to have a higher species richness than other eastern forests. Webster, however,

Table 3. Key references to uses of Christmas Bird Counts in North America.

Topic Considered	References
Evaluation of method	Arbib (1967), Bock & Lepthien (1975b), Burtt & Burtt (1982), Bystrak (1974), Preston (1958), Tramer (1974)
General application	Bock (1979, 1984)
Nuthatches	Bock & Lepthien (1972, 1974, 1976d)
Woodpeckers	Bock & Lepthien (1975a)
Finches	Bock & Lepthien (1976a, 1976b)
Various species	Bock & Lepthien (1972, 1976b, 1976c), Bock et al. (1977), Bock & Root (1981), Bock & Smith (1971)

1176. Aspen, Colo. 39°15'N 106°54'W, center n.e. corner Sec. 29, R85W, T9S, as described 1982; elevation 7000 to 8200 ft; habitat coverage: residential 35%, oak/serviceberry/chokecherry 21%, willow/cottonwood riverbottom 15%, spruce fir 12%, aspen grove 9%, sage/rabbitbrush 3%, open meadow 3%, pinyon juniper 2%.—Dec. 19; 8 a.m. to 5 p.m. Clear. Temp. 9° to 46°F. Wind SE-W, 0-5 m.p.h. Snow cover 0 to 24 in. Water mostly frozen. Wild food crop excellent. Nineteen observers, 11-14 in 8 parties, 5-8 at feeders. Total party-hours, 37 (18 on foot, 5 by car, 14 on skis) plus 19 hours at feeders; total party-miles, 119.5 (13.5 on foot, 93 by car, 13 on skis).

● Canada Goose 51; Mallard 304; Am. Wigeon 1; Wood Duck 1; Goshawk 1; Cooper's Hawk 2; Great Horned Owl 1; Com. (Redsh.) Flicker 10; Hairy Woodpecker 5; Downy Woodpecker 4; Gray Jay 4; Steller's Jay 47; Scrub Jay 12; Black-billed Magpie 121; Com. Raven 5; Black-capped Chickadee 116; Mountain Chickadee 27; White-breasted Nuthatch 7; Brown Creeper 1; Dipper 7; Am. Robin 121; Townsend's Solitaire 3; Cedar Waxwing 67; Starling 95; House Sparrow 356; Red-winged Blackbird 54; Evening Grosbeak 46; Cassin's Finch 37; Pine Grosbeak 6; (Gray-crowned) Rosy Finch 24; (Brown-capped) Rosy Finch 4; Pine Siskin 1; Rufous-sided Towhee 1; Dark-eyed (Slate-col.) Junco 23; Dark-eyed (Oregon) Junco 36; Dark-eyed (Gray-headed) Junco 13.

Total, 33 species (3 additional races); 1615 individuals. (In count area count week but not seen count day: Bald Eagle ad., Com. Snipe,

Blue Jay 9; Crow 1; Blatain Chicka in 19; Wat 1761; Hous 128; Red-w Blackbird 2 **Cowbird 1** 170; Pine S eyed (Slate-gon) Junco Junco 1; T Sparrow 25

Total, 54 individuals. Barry Knap W. 9th Pl. Ward, Judy

1178. E 104°38'W, described 1 habitat cov 19; 7:30 a.n to 60°F. Wi to 6 in. Wat fair. Fifteen party-hours, party-miles,

● Cooper Rough-legge Marsh Hawk 2; Com. Snij Owl 1; Cor Woodpecker Horned Larl 3; Black-bill Com. Crow

Figure 2. Example of winter bird population study taken from *American Birds*, January/February 1984.

did not list actual species involved but merely cited 17 years of data published originally in *Audubon Field Notes*.

This method can be used to obtain indexes of winter use. However, because winter bird populations vary enormously from year to year in any location, a minimum of 2 years is required for a meaningful study. In a critique of this method, Robbins (1972) showed that in forest habitats six traps were sufficient to obtain a stable minimum estimate of the total wintering bird population, but that at least 8 to 10 trips were required to obtain such estimates for individual species. Brewer (1972) and Engstrom and James (1981) also evaluated the technique.

Spot-Mapping Census

The spot-mapping technique, also called the plot census or simply mapping census, was first used in North America by Williams (1936) and in Sweden by Enemar (1959). Basically, this count involves 8 to 10 census trips through an area of specified size and preferably uniform habitat, which has been surveyed and mapped with a grid system (Figure 3). On each visit, the position of each bird seen or heard is recorded on the plot map. Kendeigh (1944), Lack (1937), and Udvardy (1957) gave good historical accounts, described the method in detail, and included comprehensive bibliographies. An important feature of spot-mapping is to designate, with appropriate symbols, those individual birds that are heard singing at the same time (simultaneous registrations). These, in conjunction with clusters of single registrations, make it possible to outline the approximate territorial limits of each male bird and make reasonable estimates of the total number of territorial males of each species present in the area.

Spot-mapping has been widely adopted in Europe and North America. Procedures have been standardized by the International Bird Census Committee (1969) so that results obtained in different countries can be compared. Spot-mapping has been widely used in England since 1962 to monitor bird population changes (Batten and Marchant 1977). The British Trust for Ornithology refers to such counts as the Common Bird Census (their CBS, not to be confused with CBC, Christmas Bird Count). A quantitative description of habitat (James and Shugart 1970) is now a standard feature of many of the breeding bird censuses in forest habitats published in *American Birds*.

Results from over 200 spot-mapping censuses were published in *American Birds* in 1981 (Van Velzen 1981). Many private consultants and government biologists regularly use the spot-mapping technique, although their results are not published in *American Birds*. Dickson (1978) compared the technique with winter bird-population count techniques (also referred to as "mean detections per count") and Palmgren's (1930) "summation method" and concluded that spot-mapping gave the highest population estimates.

Robbins (1978) considered spot-mapping to be the most accurate of the various bird census methods because it—

(1) gives the greatest opportunity to record all species breeding in the area,

(2) most closely approximates the absolute number of breeding pairs,

(3) is more accurate in estimating whether the birds recorded are inside or outside plot boundaries, and

(4) involves less observer bias.

The chief disadvantage of the technique is the amount of time required to set up the plot and conduct a minimum of eight census trips.

The results of 228 breeding bird censuses conducted in Canada were summarized in three catalogs by Erskine (1971, 1972, 1976). Censuses published in *American Birds* since 1937 are on magnetic tape at the Migratory Bird and Habitat Research Laboratory, U.S. Fish and Wildlife Service. They provide a valuable resource for comparing habitat, bird species, or other variables included in the computer record. The files contain information on 1,000 plots (Robbins 1978).

Ladder-backed woodpecker.

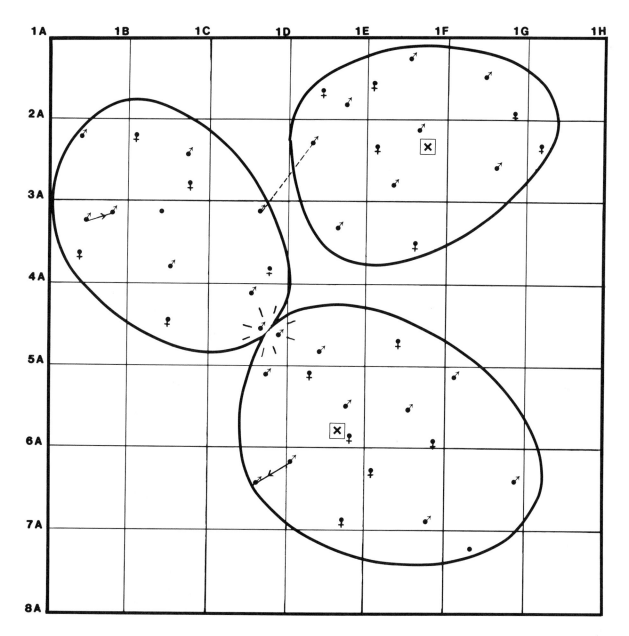

Figure 3. Spot-map for the yellow-rumped warbler (*Dendroica coronata*) in a mixed-coniferous forest. (Blocks are 50 m by 50 m producing a grid plot of 12.25 ha. Total breeding bird density is 3 territories x 2 = 6 breeding yellow-rumped warblers per 12.25 ha or a density of 19.6/40 ha [19.6/100a.]).

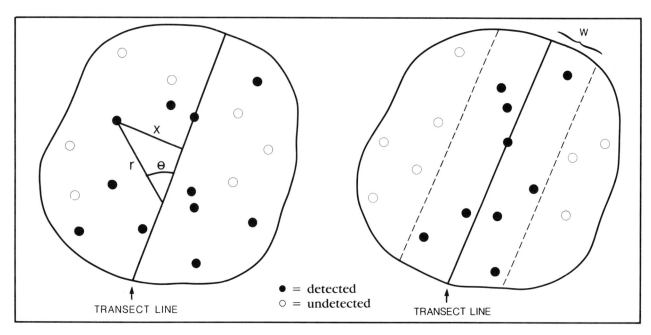

● = detected
○ = undetected

TRANSECT LINE

TRANSECT LINE

Figure 4. In line transect sampling, the observer records either the right angle distance (x), or both the flushing distance (r) and the sighting angle (O) for each bird detected. Bird density is estimated mathematically using the distribution of distances (x or r).

Figure 5. In belt transect sampling, all birds are assumed to be detected within a specified, fixed distance (w) from the transect line of length L. Birds outside the belt are not recorded. Bird density = n/2Lw, where n is the number of birds recorded.

Transects

Transect methods (Figures 4 and 5) involve counting birds on one or both sides of a line through one or more habitats. Usually either the width of the transect is defined or the distance to each bird encountered is estimated. The transect method was first used extensively in the U.S. in 1906-09 by S.A. Forbes and A.O. Gross (Graber and Graber 1963) and in Finland in 1941-56 by Merikallio (1958). In both studies, the transect results were used to estimate total populations by habitat for an entire state or nation. The Forbes and Gross study was later repeated by Graber and Graber (1963) to show bird population changes over a 50-year period in Illinois.

One advantage of the transect method is that a relatively large area can be sampled in a short time. Flack (1976), for example, used 45-m (150-ft)-wide and 1,097-m (1,200-yd)-long transects to compare breeding bird populations in 41 aspen forests in 9 western states and provinces in 1966-69.

The transect method may be used throughout the year, but the results are less accurate outside the breeding season. However, the chief disadvantage of the transect method is that a single coverage of a transect does not permit a good estimate of the number of birds missed. Anderson and Pospahala (1970), using data from 2,574 km (1,600 mi.) of transects, generated a curvilinear (quadratic) equa-

tion to show the fraction of waterfowl nests missed at various distances from the center line of the transect. However, they pointed out, that to adequately correct for the number of fixed objects missed, one needs a large sample and must also assume that all the objects closest to the center of the transect are detected.

Emlen (1971) also considered how the error in the transect count may be reduced by first estimating the lateral distance to each bird encountered and then deriving a coefficient of detectability. He assumed that no bird close to the observer goes undetected. In actual practice, a large number of birds within a few meters of the transect line may be undetected (Jarvinen and Vaisanen 1976), especially in a mature forest habitat. Even during the height of the breeding season, there are enormous differences in the singing behavior and conspicuousness of birds. A noisy, active species such as the tufted titmouse (*Parus bicolor*) may be recorded on 68% of the visits if within 50 m (54.7 yd) of the observer. Species such as the ruby-throated hummingbird (*Archilochus colubris*), worm-eating warbler (*Helmitheros vermivorus*), and even the American redstart (*Setophaga ruticilla*) may be recorded only 36% to 39% of the time (Stewart et al. 1952). Emlen (1977) estimated the number of unrecorded males of common species by running each transect five times, plotting all singing birds on maps, outlining the territory of each, and determining what European workers call the "effectivity" of a single trip for each species. He then

302 **Songbirds**

used the computed effectivity for correcting his breeding season transect results.

The transect method is effective for comparing the abundance of a given species in two or more plots of similar habitat. Also, unless visibility is strongly influenced by the structure of the habitat, the transect method may be used to compare abundance of a given species from one habitat to another (Robbins 1978). It is not, however, a desirable method for comparing abundance of two species that may not be equally conspicuous, unless appropriate corrections are made, species by species. These corrections can be made by taking a series of transect counts through plots where the population has been estimated by other methods (Ferry and Frochot 1970; Enemar and Sjostrand 1970).

Although most transect workers record birds per unit of distance or area—kilometer (or mile) or square kilometer (or 100 acres)—a few have preferred to use units of time, such as birds per 10 hours (Colquhoun 1940). Conner and Dickson (1980) discussed sampling design and statistical treatment of data gathered by transect censusing.

North American Breeding Bird Survey (BBS)

The North American Breeding Bird Survey (BBS) (Figure 6) was developed by the U.S. Fish and

Figure 6. Breeding Bird Survey summaries are published in *American Birds*.

Wildlife Service to monitor bird population changes in North America over a period of years (Bystrak and Robbins 1978; Erskine 1978; Robbins and Van Velzen 1967, 1969, 1974). Each survey route is a series of 50, 3-minute point counts at 800-m (½-mi.) intervals along a 39.4-km (24 ½-mi.) roadside transect selected randomly. Coverage extends from half an hour before sunrise to about 4 hours after sunrise, embracing the period of greatest bird activity. At each of the 50 points (counts), all birds heard and all birds seen within 400 m (¼ mi.) of the counting position are tallied. The BBS, which now embraces the populated areas of Canada and all of the U.S. except Hawaii, provides an annual sample from 1,700 or more roadside transects (Robbins 1978).

The BBS results are used primarily for statistical analysis of population changes over the years and for mapping relative breeding densities throughout the North American range of a species. A 15-year summary of the BBS results is presented by Robbins et al. (1986).

For intensive local studies, BBS routes can be laid out in a non-random way so that all or most secondary roads within the area of interest are included in a sample. The route is termed "mini-route" because 25 instead of 50 stops are made. By using a shorter route, observers are able to cover the route before working hours in the morning. Covering each route twice (once in each direction) and combining the results of the two counts eliminated most of the difference in activity resulting from time of day. D. Bystrak and others (Klimkiewicz and Solem 1974) used mini-routes to map relative abundance of breeding birds throughout two Maryland counties as part of a *Breeding Bird Atlas* program for these counties. Although the mini-route technique was designed for roadside use, with slight modifications, it could be used to cover forested areas by horseback or off-road vehicles. Such application would make it possible to map distribution of breeding birds over a wide area in a relatively short time. Differences in bird populations could then be correlated with differences in vegetation obtained from aerial surveys or by ground survey methods.

The Indexes Ponctuels d'Abondance (IPA) or Point Count Method

The point count or IPA method was developed in France by Ferry and Frochot (1970) as a means of obtaining indexes of abundance for comparing bird populations of different habitats (or of the same habitat in different locations) during the breeding season (Robbins 1978).

The IPA counts by the French ornithologists consist of establishing a network of points regularly distributed through the habitat to be studied. An observer then stands at each designated spot for 20 minutes in the early morning in good weather and notes all birds seen or heard. Each spot is censused twice during the breeding season. The higher of the two counts of pair numbers is used as an index of abundance for each species. Each singing male, occupied nest, or family of birds out of the nest counts as one pair, whereas a bird merely seen or heard calling counts as half a pair. The efficiency of a 20-minute stop seemed satisfactory to the French investigators because during the last 5 of the 20 minutes only 3% more species and 9% more individuals were recorded in forest habitat.

In Denmark, Jorgensen (1974) conducted 81 IPA censuses on eight mornings from mid-May to mid-June. The 13 ½ hours of effective field work was about 50% less than would have been needed for covering one census plot by the spot-mapping method. Jorgensen compared the density of each species in different habitats, using the Mann-Whitney U-test. He concluded that the IPA method was well-suited to a study of forest succession in which statistical comparisons are necessary or desirable. He summarized habitat use (based on 15 to 18 counts in each habitat) in terms of a list of dominant species, each making up 5% or more of the registrations, and subdominants (2% to 5%). Then, using only the dominant species, he computed similarity indexes for the various habitats using the formula:

$$S = \frac{2c}{(a+b)}$$

Where:

S = the index.

a and b = the numbers of species in each sample.

c = the number of species common to the two samples.

Density-Frequency Relationship. Blondel (1975) introduced a further modification of the IPA method, Echantillonnage Frequentiel Progressif (EFP). The EFP method uses the presence or absence of a species on each of the 20-minute IPA counts to determine frequency of that species in each plot. Comparison of the IPA with EFP figures allows one to determine for each species the relationship between its density and frequency. The frequency of a species is closely correlated with the logarithm of its density; the lower the frequency, the better the correlation. Rotenberry and Wiens (1976) found a similar correlation between density and frequency, using BBS roadside transect data.

Blondel claimed that the EFP method, which is highly standardized, is very useful for a rigorous statistical interpretation of data. He used the EFP method to calculate ecological profiles and niche breadth for each species and analyzed the structure of bird communities according to the structure of the vegetation. For each community, he determined the species richness, the species diversity index (H'), the equitability (J'), and the level of fit to Galton's log-normal model. He also discussed the influence of reforestation on bird communities. Blondel concluded that the EFP method is "very well adapted to solve problems of theoretical and applied ecology at the community level, and can be used fruitfully for environmental monitoring" (Robbins 1978). Unfortunately, the method has not been tested in the West but seems worthy of consideration.

Comparison with Spot-Mapping. In comparing point counts (IPA) with mapping census in the Bialowieza Forest in Poland, Tomialojc et al. (1978) found that point counts overestimated the population when the density was low and underestimated it when the density was high. IPA counts also require better trained observers and involve more problems in the separation of migrants or other non-breeding birds from breeding individuals than mapping censuses.

Transect and Point Count Combination. Bond (1957) used a method that was essentially a combination of the transect and point count methods to compare bird populations in 64 upland hardwood stands in Wisconsin. After entering a woodland, he walked about 50 m (55 yds) along a transect line. At this point, he stopped for 5 minutes and counted all birds seen or heard ahead of him. He then walked ahead slowly for 5 minutes, averaging 150 to 175 m (164 to 191 yds). He repeated this procedure until he had made five 10-minute counts from each forest interior. Two early morning visits were made to each woodlot, and the highest count for each species was used. In these counts, he detected 76%, 78%, and 70% as many pairs as he found by spot-mapping censuses in three of the same woodlands. Palmgren (1930) and Kendeigh (1944) found that 81% and 63% of their birds in spot-mapping censuses were detected on the first two visits.

Winter Transects

The Maryland Ornithological Society (MOS) devised a winter bird survey in central Maryland, using walked transects (Robbins 1970). Preliminary tests showed that the winter bird survey method was not practical because of heavy traffic on many roads during the first few hours after sunrise. Also, because the birds were not singing, those that could not be seen from the roadside could not be detected. The walked transects, away from roads, would reduce the problem caused by traffic noises.

The winter bird survey method involves transects of 8 km (5 mi.) that are covered on foot during the first 4 hours after sunrise. One route was established at the center of each 7 ½-minute U.S. Geological Survey map of central Maryland, representing an 11- by 14-km (6.8- by 8.7-mi.) grid. An effort was made to lay out each route in the form of a square, 2 km (1.2 mi.) to a side. Many routes could not be formed into a square because of streams, ponds, buildings, high fences, or other obstacles; despite changes in shape, the total length of 8 km (5 mi.) was maintained. By timing their walking speed for the first quarter of the route, observers were able to return to the starting point within a few minutes of the prescribed 4-hour period. Separate counts were kept for each hour, and birds identified at a distance greater than 402 m (¼ mi.) were recorded in a separate column on the form (Robbins 1978). The winter survey should be applicable for key wintering areas in the Southwest.

Variable-Circular Plots

Reynolds et al. (1980) described a count, using a combination of a transect and circular plots (Figure 7). This count method has been widely used

in studies of endangered species in dense Hawaiian forests (Ramsey and Scott 1979; Scott and Ramsey 1981; Scott et al. 1981), oak-pine woodlands (Verner and Ritter 1985), ponderosa pine forest (Szaro and Balda 1982), and desert habitats (Szaro and Jakle 1982). De Sante (1981) found that the variable circular plot underestimated the densities of breeding birds in California coastal scrub by 2% to 70% (depending on the species of bird) when compared with estimates derived from a combination of color banding, spot-mapping, and nest monitoring. De Sante (1985) found similar discrepancies in lodgepole (*Pinus contorta*) populations of birds in the Sierras.

For many species, tape recordings can be played back to induce songs from silent territorial males (Down 1970). The technique may increase census accuracy (especially for species with low song activity) with little expenditure of time and can be used to determine territorial boundaries. Repeated use of tape recordings during the breeding season, however, can bias results because birds may alter their habits or their territorial boundaries if they believe a competing member of the same species has a territory nearby (Robbins 1978; McNicholl 1981). Recordings have proven useful in censusing various songbirds (Falls 1981; Johnson et al. 1981; Marion et al. 1981). Although recordings are probably most useful for non-songbirds such as rails and owls, they have been used successfully to monitor Kirtland and golden-cheeked warblers as well as trogons.

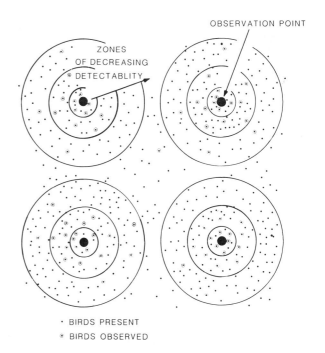

Figure 7. Variable circular-plot method is based on principles of the variable-strip transect method.

Mark and Recapture Methods

Several investigators in the U.S., Sweden, and France have marked and recaptured birds as a means of studying the effectiveness of other census methods (De Sante 1981, 1985; Robbins 1978). Capture, mark, and recapture methods are often called Lincoln or Peterson indexes (Davis and Winstead 1980).

Trapping and banding in itself is neither an efficient nor a highly accurate way of measuring entire breeding bird populations. It is, however, a very effective way in determining how many pairs of certain species are present and in distinguishing migrants from summer residents and, to some degree, non-breeding from breeding individuals. Color-banding or radiotelemetry can be used to define the ranges of individual birds and also can point out errors in judgment that occasionally occur when the observer relies entirely on the mapping method (Robbins 1978).

In France, Frochot et al. (1978) compared spot-mapping, IPA, and capture-recapture methods in a 100-ha (247-a.) oak forest plot. Comparing the results for 12 common species, he estimated 49.9 breeding pairs per 10 ha (24.7 a.) by the mapping method and 47.0 by the IPA method (with appropriate corrections for conspicuousness). Banding data

sufficient for computation of population estimates were available for only 4 of the 12 species, but for 3 of these 4, the estimate from capture-recapture was higher than obtained by either of the other two methods. Frochot et al. (1978) reported that while the IPA census required less than 10 hours of prime time in the early morning, the mapping census required 43 hours and the banding study, 400. They emphasized three major advantages of the capture-recapture method:

(1) It permits a census of females and young as well as of singing males;

(2) It can be used for testing mapping and IPA methods; and

(3) It gives additional information about daily range and habitat use of the individual birds.

In Colorado, Porter (1973) also used capture-recapture methods to check other census methods in grasslands.

Hewitt (1967) devised a roadside count to estimate breeding populations of red-winged blackbirds (*Agelaius phoeniceus*), which basically is a Lincoln Index without having to capture and mark. It should work well for other blackbirds found in western marshes.

Western bluebird.

Colorado Chapter, The Wildlife Society

Red-breasted nuthatch.

Nest Monitoring

Perhaps nest monitoring would seem an obvious way to accurately determine breeding bird populations. In actual practice, however, it is seldom possible to find enough active nests of a species to use this method for measuring the breeding population, especially in forest habitats.

A good example of a nesting study of a single species is an investigation of wood thrushes (*Hylocichla mustelina*) made by Longcore and Jones (1969) in a 14.4 ha (35.6 a.) Delaware woodlot. Systematic nest searches were conducted during a 3-month period in 1965 and 1966. Grid lines located at 45.7-m (150-ft) intervals were traversed at least once every 3 days, except for a 2-week period in July 1965. A total of 142 wood thrush nesting attempts were documented, of which 54 (38%) were successful. Nest finding was supplemented by intensive banding efforts every 2 to 3 weeks during the 1966 breeding season, which resulted in the banding of 46 wood thrushes. The aim of this study was to determine reproductive success rather than to measure the population, but it gives an idea of how much effort would be required to gather enough information about a single species to get an accurate measurement of the breeding population. Similar approaches should work for western thrushes.

De Sante (1981) used nest monitoring in conjunction with color-banding and spot-mapping to estimate breeding densities of eight species of California coastal scrub at Point Reyes National Seashore. De Sante (1985) used a similar approach to count individuals of 19 species of breeding birds in a subalpine lodgepole pine forest in the Sierras.

Conclusion

Many techniques are available to inventory and monitor songbird numbers and the habitats they utilize. For breeding birds, the best overall method involves spot-mapping territorial males, but considerable time and effort are required. Eight to 10 early morning counts of 10- to 20-ha (24.7- to 49.4-a.) plots are recommended. Additional time is required to analyze the habitat. Walked-line transects or variable-circular plots along transects can also be used to estimate avian populations. These usually require fewer coverages than spot-mapping, but greater skill and training are needed to estimate distances to birds detected. Playback of recorded calls can be used to elicit responses from more elusive species but must be used consistently or not at all. Roadside counts, such as the North American Breeding Bird Survey (BBS), can sample larger areas but only give indexes to bird numbers. BBS results can be correlated to habitat if such data are recorded for each stop. A variety of point-counts and capture, mark, and recapture methods are available but, especially if

trapping is involved, require considerable effort. The results of Christmas Bird Counts and winter bird population studies sponsored by the National Audubon Society are published regularly in *American Birds* and are valuable sources of information on winter distribution and trends in bird numbers. Table 2 summarizes the comparative advantages and disadvantages of several monitoring methods.

Rather than attempting to monitor all species of birds in many different habitats, one might want to concentrate on just a few species in selected habitats. Often threatened or endangered species in "critical" habitats are stressed. Szaro and Balda (1982) recommended selecting bird species for use as "indicator" species by considering:

(1) residency status (i.e., summer, winter, or permanent residence),

(2) foraging and/or nesting substrate,

(3) adequate data base,

(4) ease of monitoring,

(5) sensitivity to habitat perturbations,

(6) sensitivity to environmental fluctuations,

(7) the condition or range of conditions a given species will indicate, and

(8) biogeographic considerations based on fragmentation of the habitat.

Graul et al. (1976) and Graul and Miller (1984) recommended an ecological-indicator approach for management, where the species in an area having the most exacting ecological requirements are monitored. This "steno" (as opposed to "eury") species approach is based on the idea that by managing to create habitat conditions for the species with the narrowest requirements, a manager will provide for all species. Other related approaches have stressed a featured-species concept where a single species, not necessarily stenotypic, is selected, and a unit of habitat managed primarily to benefit or feature that species. Graul and Miller (1984) reviewed still other ecosystem management approaches in which songbirds might be emphasized. An example of a stenotypic songbird that might be monitored as an early warning of excessive human disruption of its environment would be the loggerhead shrike (*Lanius ludovicianus*; Bystrak 1983). The species has demonstrated a considerable population decline, which suggests a narrow range of tolerance, thus qualifying it as an indicator species. The BBS provides good population trends for loggerhead shrike (Robbins et al., in press).

LITERATURE CITED

ABBOTT, I. 1976. Comparisons of habitat structure and plant, arthropod, and bird diversity between mainland and island sites near Perth, Western Australia. Australian J. Ecol. 1:275-280.

ANDERSON, A.H. and A. ANDERSON. 1973. The cactus wren. Univ. Arizona Press, Tucson. 226pp.

ANDERSON, D.R. and R.S. POSPAHALA. 1970. Correction of bias in belt transect studies of immobile objects. J. Wildl. Manage. 34:141-146.

ANDERSON, S.H. 1979. Habitat structure, succession and bird communities. Pages 9-21 in Proceedings of Workshop: Management of North Central and Northeastern Forests for Nongame Birds, U.S. Dep. Agric., For. Serv. Gen. Tech. Rep. NC-51. Minneapolis, MN.

——— and H.H. SHUGART, Jr. 1974. Habitat selection of breeding birds in an east Tennessee deciduous forest. Ecology 55:828-837.

ARBIB, R.S., Jr. 1967. Considering the Christmas count. Audubon Field Notes 21(1):39-42.

———. 1978. The National Audubon Society and amateur ornithologists. Pages 26-29 in McCrimmon, Jr., D.A. and A. Sprunt, IV, eds. Proceedings of a Conference on the Amateur and North American Ornithology. Natl. Audubon Soc. Res. Dep. Ithaca, NY. 80pp.

———. 1982. The Christmas bird count and the world. Am. Birds 36:365-368.

ARMSTRONG, E.A. 1955. The wren. Macmillan Co. New York, NY. 312pp.

AUSTIN, O.L., Jr., ed. 1968. Life histories of North American cardinals, grosbeaks, buntings, towhees, finches, sparrows, and allies. U.S. Natl. Mus. Bull. 237, 3 vols. 1889pp.

BAILEY, A.M. and R.J. NIEDRACH. 1965. Birds of Colorado. Denver Mus. Nat. Hist., 2 vols. 895pp.

BAKUS, G.J. 1959a. Observations on the life history of the dipper in Montana. Auk 76:190-207.

———. 1959b. Territoriality, movements, and population density of the dipper in Montana. Condor 61:410-425.

BALDA, R.P. 1975. Vegetation structure and breeding bird diversity. Pages 59-80 in Smith, D.R., ed. Proceedings of the Symposium on Management of Forest and Range Habitats for Nongame Birds. U.S. Dep. Agric., For. Serv., Gen. Tech. Rep. WO-1, Washington, DC.

——— and G.C. BATEMAN. 1972. The breeding biology of the pinon jay. Living Bird 11:5-42.

BARLOW, J.C. 1962. Natural history of the Bell vireo (Vireo bellii) Audubon. Univ. Kansas Publ., Mus. Nat. Hist. 12:241-296.

BATTEN, L.A. and J.H. MARCHANT. 1977. Bird population changes for the years 1975-76. Bird Study 24:159-164.

BEASON, R.C. 1974. Breeding behavior of the horned lark. Auk 91:65-74.

——— and E.C. FRANKS. 1973. Development of young horned larks. Auk 90:359-363.

BENT, A.C. 1939. Life histories of North American woodpeckers. U.S. Natl. Mus. Bull. 174:1-334.

———. 1940. Life histories of North American cuckoos, goatsuckers, hummingbirds, and their allies. U.S. Natl. Mus. Bull. 176:1-506.

———. 1942. Life histories of North American flycatchers, larks, swallows, and their allies. U.S. Natl. Mus. Bull. 179:1-555.

———. 1946. Life histories of North American jays, crows, and titmice. U.S. Natl. Mus. Bull. 191:1-495.

———. 1948. Life histories of North American nuthatches, wrens, thrashers, and their allies. U.S. Natl. Mus. Bull. 195:1-475.

———. 1949. Life histories of North American thrushes, kinglets, and their allies. U.S. Natl. Mus. Bull. 196:1-454.

———. 1950. Life histories of North American wagtails, shrikes, vireos, and their allies. U.S. Natl. Mus. Bull. 197:25-38.

———. 1953. Life histories of North American wood warblers. U.S. Natl. Mus. Bull. 203:1-734.

———. 1958. Life histories of North American blackbirds, orioles, tanagers, and allies. U.S. Natl. Mus. Bull. 211:1-549.

BLONDEL, J. 1975. L'analyses des peuplements d'oiseaux, elements d'un diagnostic ecologique. La Terre et la Vie. 29:533-589.

BOCK, C.E. 1970. The ecology and behavior of the Lewis woodpecker (Asyndesmus lewis). Univ. California Publ. in Zoology 92:1-100.

———. 1979. Christmas bird count. Nat. Hist. 88(10):7-11.

———. 1984. Geographical correlates of abundance versus rarity in some North American winter landbirds. Auk 101:266-273.

———, J.H. BOCK, and L.W. LEPTHIEN. 1977. Abundance patterns of some bird species wintering on the Great Plains of the U.S.A. J. Biogeography 4:101-110.

——— and L.W. LEPTHIEN. 1972. Winter eruptions of red-breasted nuthatches in North America, 1950-1970. Am. Birds 26:558-561.

——— and ———. 1975a. A Christmas count analysis of woodpecker abundance in the United States. Wilson Bull. 87:355-366.

——— and ———. 1975b. Patterns of bird species diversity revealed by Christmas counts versus breeding bird surveys. Western Birds 6:95-100.

——— and ———. 1976a. Growth in the eastern house finch population, 1962-1971. Am. Birds 30:791-792.

——— and ———. 1976b. Synchronous eruptions of boreal seed-eating birds. Am. Nat. 110:559-571.

——— and ———. 1976c. Geographical ecology of the common species of Buteo and Parabuteo wintering in North America. Condor 78:554-557.

——— and T.L. ROOT. 1981. Winter abundance patterns of landbirds in the U.S. and southern Canada. Am. Birds 35:891-897.

——— and R.B. SMITH. 1971. An analysis of Colorado Christmas counts. Am. Birds 25:945-947.

BOND, R.R. 1957. Ecological distribution of breeding birds in the upland forests of southern Wisconsin. Ecol. Monogr. 27:351-384.

BOYD, R.L. 1976. Behavioral biology and energy expenditure in a horned lark population. Ph.D. dissertation, Colorado State Univ., Fort Collins. 194pp.

BRAZIER, F.H. 1964. Status of the mockingbird in the northern Great Plains. Blue Jay 22:63-75.

BREWER, R. 1972. An evaluation of winter bird population studies. Wilson Bull. 84:261-277.

BURTT, H.E. and B.P. BURTT. 1982. Reliability of the Christmas bird count. Redstart 49:90-93.

BYSTRAK, D., ed. 1974. Wintering areas of bird species potentially hazardous to aircraft. Natl. Audubon Soc., NY.

————. 1983. Loggerhead shrike (*Lanius ludovicianus*). Pages 301-310 *in* Armbruster, J.S., ed. Impacts of Coal Surface Mining on 25 Migratory Bird Species of High Federal Interest. U.S. Dep. Inter., Fish and Wildl. Serv. FWS/OBS-83/35. 348pp.

———— and C.S. ROBBINS. 1978. Bird population trends detected by the North American breeding bird survey. Polish Ecol. Studies 3(4):131-143.

CACCAMISE, D.F. 1974. Competitive relationships of the common and lesser nighthawks. Condor 76:1-20.

CALDER, W.A. 1973. Microhabitat selection during nesting of hummingbirds in the Rocky Mountains. Ecol. 54:127-134.

CALL, M.W. 1981. Terrestrial wildlife inventories: Some methods and concepts. U.S. Dep. Inter., Bur. Land Manage. Tech. Note 349:1-171.

CAPEN, D.E., ed. 1981. The use of multivariate statistics in studies of wildlife habitat. U.S. Dep. Agric., For. Serv. Gen. Tech. Rep. RM087. 249pp.

CINK, C.L. and R.L. BOYD. 1981. Thirty-third winter bird-population study. Am. Birds 35:21-45.

CODY, M.L. 1981. Habitat selection in birds: The roles of vegetation structure, competitors, and productivity. BioScience 31:107-113.

COLQUHOUN, M.K. 1940. Visual and auditory conspicuousness in a woodland bird community: A quantitative analysis. Proceedings, Zoological Soc. London 110:129-148.

CONNER, R.N. and J.G. DICKSON. 1980. Strip transect sampling and analysis for avian habitat studies. Wildl. Soc. Bull. 8:4-10.

CORNWELL, G.W. 1963. Observations on the breeding biology and behavior of a nesting population of belted kingfishers. Condor 65:426-431.

DAVIS, D.E., ed. 1982. CRC handbook of census methods for terrestrial vertebrates. CRC Press, Inc. Boca Raton, FL. 397pp.

———— and R.L. WINSTEAD. 1980. Estimating the numbers of wildlife populations. Pages 221-245 *in* Schemnitz, S.D., ed. Wildlife Management Techniques Manual. The Wildlife Soc. Washington, DC. 686pp.

DEGRAFF, R.M., tech. coord. 1978a. Proceedings of the workshop on management of southern forests for nongame birds. U.S. Dep. Agric., For. Serv. Gen. Tech. Rep. SE-14.

————. 1978b. Proceedings of workshop on nongame bird management in the coniferous forests of the western U.S. U.S. Dep. Agric., For. Serv. Gen. Tech. Rep. PNW-64.

———— and K.E. EVANS, compilers. 1979. Management of north-central and northeastern forests for nongame birds. U.S. Dep. Agric., For. Serv. Gen. Tech. Rep. NC-51.

———— and N.G. TILGHMAN, eds. 1980. Workshop proceedings, management of western forests and grasslands for nongame birds. U.S. Dep. Agric., For. Serv. Gen. Tech. Rep. INT-86.

DEHAVEN, R.W. and P.J. DEHAVEN. 1973. A contribution toward a bibliography on the starling. U.S. Dep. Inter., Fish and Wildl. Service. Denver, CO. 92pp.

DESANTE, D.F. 1981. A field test of the variable circular-plot censusing technique in a California coastal scrub breeding bird community. Pages 177-185 *in* Ralph, C.J. and V.M. Scott, eds. Estimating the numbers of terrestrial birds. Studies Avian Biol. 6.

————. 1985. A field test of the variable circular-plot censusing technique in a Sierran subalpine forest breed-
ing bird community. Abstract of paper presented at fourth joint meeting of Wilson and Cooper Ornithological Societies, Univ. Colorado, Boulder, June 4-9. 11pp.

DICKSON, J.G. 1978. Comparison of breeding bird census techniques. Am. Birds 32:10-13.

DIXON, K.L. 1961. Habitat distribution and niche relationships in North American species of *Parus*. Pages 179-216 *in* Blair, W.F., ed. Vertebrate Speciation. Univ. Texas Press, Austin.

DOWN, D.D. 1970. Indexing population densities of the cardinal with tape-recorded calls. Wilson Bull. 86:83-91.

DYBBRO, T. 1976. De danoke gorglefulgles udbredelse. Dansk Ornith Forening, Copenhagen. 293pp.

EIPPER, A.W. 1956. Differences in vulnerability of the prey of nesting kingfishers. J. Wildl. Manage. 20:177-183.

EMLEN, J.T. 1971. Population densities of birds derived from transect counts. Auk 88:323-342.

————. 1977. Estimating breeding season bird densities from transect counts. Auk 94:455-468.

ENEMAR, A. 1959. On the determination of the size and composition of a passerine bird population during the breeding season. Var Fagelvard, Supplement 2:1-114.

———— and B. SJOSTRAND. 1970. Bird species densities derived from study area investigations and line transects. Swedish Nat. Sci. Res. Council, Ecol. Res. Comm. Bull. 9:33-37.

ENGSTROM, R.T. and F.C. JAMES. 1981. Plot size as a factor in winter bird-population studies. Condor 83:34-41.

ERSKINE, A.J. 1971. A preliminary catalogue of bird census plot studies in Canada. Canadian Wildl. Serv. Progress Notes 20:1-78.

————. 1972. A preliminary catalogue of bird census plot studies in Canada. Part 2, Canadian Wildl. Serv. Progress Notes 30:1-42.

————. 1976. A preliminary catalogue of bird census plot studies in Canada. Part 3, Canadian Wildl. Serv. Progress Notes 59:1-24.

————. 1978. The first 10 years of the cooperative breeding bird survey in Canada. Canadian Wildl. Serv. Rep., Serial 42:1-59.

FALLS, J.B. 1981. Mapping territories with playback: An accurate census method for songbirds. Pages 86-91 *in* Ralph, C.J. and J.M. Scott, eds. Estimating the numbers of terrestrial birds. Studies Avian Biol. 6.

FEARE, C. 1984. The starling. Oxford Univ. Press. New York, NY. 315pp.

FERRY, C. and B. FROCHOT. 1970. L'airfaune nidofreatrice d'une foret de chenes pedoncules en bourgogne etude de deux successions ecologiques. La Terre et la Vie 24:153-250.

FLACK, J.A.D. 1976. Bird populations of aspen forests in western North America. Ornith. Monogr. 19. 97pp.

FRANZEB, K.E. 1977. Inventory techniques for sampling avian populations. U.S. Dep. Inter., Bur. Land Manage. Tech. Note 307. 17pp.

FROCHOT, B., D. REUDET, and Y. LERUTH. 1978. A comparison of three different methods of census applied to the same population of forest birds. Polish Ecol. Studies 3(4):71-76.

GIBB, J.A. 1980. New Zealand ornithology during the past 50 years. Bull. British Ornith. Club 100:93-96.

GOODWIN, D. 1976. Crows of the world. Cornell Univ. Press. Ithaca, NY. 354pp.

GRABER, R.R. 1971. Illinois birds: Turdidae. Illinois Nat. Hist. Surv. Biol. Notes 75:1-44.

————. 1972. Illinois birds: Hirundenidae. Illinois Nat. Hist. Surv. Biol. Notes 80:1-36.

————. 1973. Illinois birds: Laniidae. Illinois Nat. Hist. Surv. Biol. Notes 83:1-18.

————. 1974. Illinois birds: Tyrannidae. Illinois Nat. Hist. Surv. Biol. Notes 86:1-56.

———— and J.W. GRABER. 1963. A comparative study of bird populations in Illinois, 1906-1909 and 1956-1958. Illinois Nat. Hist. Surv. Bull. 28:377-528.

————, ————, and E.L. KIRK. 1970. Illinois birds: Mimidel. Illinois Nat. Hist. Surv. Biol. Notes 68:1-38.

GRABER, V.W., R.R. GRABER, and E.L. KIRK. 1983. Illinois birds: Wood warblers. Illinois Nat. Hist. Surv. Biol. Notes 118. 144pp.

GRAUL, W.D. and G.C. MILLER. 1984. Strengthening ecosystem management approaches. Wildl. Soc. Bull. 12:282-289.

————, J. TORRES, and R. DENNEY. 1976. A species-ecosystem approach for nongame programs. Wildl. Soc. Bull. 4:79-80.

GRISCOM, L. and A. SPRUNT, Jr. 1957. The warblers of America. Devin-Adair Co. New York, NY. 356pp.

HARRISON, H.H. 1975. A field guide to birds' nests. Houghton Mifflin Co., Boston, MA. 257pp.

————. 1984. Wood warbler's world. Simon & Schuster, New York, NY. 335pp.

HEWITT, D.H. 1967. A road-count index to breeding populations of red-winged blackbirds. J. Wildl. Manage. 31:39-47.

HILDEN, O. 1965. Habitat selection in birds. Ann. Zoology Fennici 2:53-75.

HOLMES, R.T., R.E. BONNEY, and S.W. PACALA. 1979. Guild structure of the Hubbard Brook bird community: A multivariate approach. Ecol. 60:512-520.

———— and S.K. ROBINSON. 1981. Tree species preference of foraging insectivorous birds in a northern hardwoods forest. Oecologia 48:31-35.

INTERNATIONAL BIRD CENSUS COMMITTEE. 1969. Recommendations for an international standard for a mapping method in bird census work. Bird Study 16:249-255 (also 1970, Audubon Field Notes 24:723-726.)

JACKMAN, S.M. and J.M. SCOTT. 1975. Literature review of 23 selected forest birds of the Pacific Northwest. U.S. Dep. Agric., For. Serv. Portland, OR. 382pp.

JAMES, F.C. 1971. Ordinations of habitat relationships among breeding birds. Wilson Bull. 83:215-236.

———— and H.H. SHUGART, Jr. 1970. A quantitative method of habitat description.

JARVINEN, O. and R.A. VAISANEN. 1976. Finnish line transect censuses. Ornis Fenn 53:115-118.

JOHNSGARD, P.A. 1983. The hummingbirds of North America. Smithsonian Inst. Press, Washington, DC. 303pp.

JOHNSON, R.R., B.T. BROCON, L.T. HAIGHT, and J.M. SIMPSON. 1981. Playback recordings as a special avian censusing technique. Pages 68-75 in Ralph, C.J. and J.M. Scott, eds. Estimating the numbers of terrestrial birds. Studies Avian Biol. 6.

JORGENSEN, O.H. 1974. Results of IPA-censuses on Danish farmland. Acta Ornithologica 14:310-321.

KARR, J.R. 1980. History of the habitat concept in birds and the measurement of avian habitats. Pages 991-997 in Nohring, R., ed. Acta XVII Int. Congress Ornithologica, Berlin.

KENDEIGH, S.C. 1944. Measurement of bird populations. Ecol. Monogr. 14:67-106.

KESSEL, B. 1957. A study of the breeding biology of the European starling (Sturnus vulgaris L.) in North America. Am. Midl. Nat. 58:257-331.

KLIMKIEWICZ, M.K. and C.S. ROBBINS. 1974. The breeding bird atlas of Montgomery County, Maryland, USA. Acta Ornithologica 14:446-458.

———— and J.K. SOLEM. 1974. First year of breeding bird atlas, Howard County, Maryland. Maryland Birdlife 30:27-35.

KNORR, O.A. 1961. The geographical and ecological distribution of the black swift in Colorado. Wilson Bull. 73:155-170.

KOLB, H. 1965. The Audubon winter bird-population study. Audubon Field Notes 19:432-434.

LACK, D. 1937. A review of bird census work and bird population problems. Ibis 79:369-395.

LAUGHLIN, S.D., ed. 1982. Proceedings of the northeastern breeding bird atlas conference. Vermont Inst. of Nat. Sci., Woodstock, VT.

————, D.F. KIBBE, and P.F.J. EAGLES. 1982. Atlasing the distribution of the breeding birds of North America. Am. Birds 35:6-19.

LEA, R.B. 1942. A study of the nesting habits of the cedar waxwing. Wilson Bull. 54:225-237.

LONGCORE, J.R. and R.E. JONES. 1969. Reproductive success of the wood thrush in a Delaware woodlot. Wilson Bull. 81:396-406.

MACARTHUR, R.W. and J.W. MACARTHUR. 1961. On bird species diversity. Ecol. 42:594-598.

MARION, W.R., T.E. OMEARA, and D.S. MAEHR. 1981. Use of playback recordings in sampling elusive or secretive birds. Pages 81-85 in Ralph, C.J. and J.M. Scott, eds. Estimating the Numbers of Terrestrial Birds. Studies Avian Biol. 6.

MASER, C., J.W. THOMAS, and R.G. ANDERSON. 1984. The relationship of terrestrial vertebrates to plant communities and structural conditions. U.S. Dep. Agric., For. Serv. Gen. Tech. Rep. PNW-172, 2 parts. 237pp.

MCCLELLAND, B.R. and S.S. FRISSELL. 1975. Identifying forest snags for hole-nesting birds. J. Forestry 73:414-417.

MCNICHOLL, M.K. 1981. Caution needed in use of playbacks to census bird populations. Am. Birds 35:235-236.

MEENTS, J.K., J.R. RICE, B.W. ANDERSON, and R.D. OHMART. 1983. Nonlinear relationships between birds and vegetation. Ecol. 64:1022-1027.

MERIKALLIO, E. 1958. Finnish birds, their distribution and numbers. Fauna Fennica 5:1-181.

MILLER, A.H. 1931. Systematic revision and natural history of the American shrikes. Univ. California Publ. in Zoology 38:11-242.

NERO, R.W. 1984. Redwings. Smithsonian Institute Press, Washington, DC. 160pp.

NORRIS, R.A. 1958. Comparative biosystematics and life history of the nuthatches (Sitta pygmaoa and Sitta pusilla). Univ. California Publ. Zoology 56:119-300.

OHMART, R.D. 1973. Observations on the breeding adaptations of the roadrunner. Condor 75:140-149.

ORIANS, G.H. 1980. Some adaptations of marsh-nesting blackbirds. Princeton Univ. Press, Princeton, NJ. 295pp.

PACKARD, G.C. 1966. Evolution of North American house sparrows in relation to altitude and aridity. Ph.D.

thesis, Univ. Kansas, Lawrence. 86pp.

PALMGREN, P. 1930. Quantitative Untersuchesogen uber die Vogelfauna in den Waldern Sudfinnlands mit besonderer Beruckshigring Alands. Acta Zod. Fenn. 7:1-218.

PERRING, F.H. and S.M. WALTERS. 1962. Atlas of the British flora. Botanical Soc. British Isles. Nelson Press, New York, NY. 32pp.

PHILLIPS, A.R., J. MARSHALL, and G. MONSON. 1964. The birds of Arizona. Univ. Arizona Press, Tucson. 220pp.

PICKWELL, G.A. 1931. The prairie horned lark. Trans. Acad. Sci., St. Louis, MO. 27:1-153.

PORTER, D.K. 1973. Accuracy in censusing breeding passerines on the short-grass prairie. M.S. thesis, Coloado State Univ., Fort Collins. 107pp.

————, M.A. STRONG, J.B. GIEZENTANNER, and R.A. RYDER. 1975. Nest ecology, productivity, and growth of the loggerhead shrike on the short-grass prairie. Southwestern Nat. 19:429-436.

PREBLE, N.A. 1957. Nesting habits of the yellow-billed cuckoo. Am. Midl. Nat. 57:474-482.

PRESTON, F.W. 1958. Analysis of the Audubon Christmas counts in terms of the lognormal curve. Ecol. 39:620-624.

PRICE, F.E. and C.E. BOCK. 1983. Population ecology of the dipper (*Cinclus mexicanus*) in the Front Range of Colorado. Cooper Ornith. Soc., Studies Avian Biol. 7. 84pp.

PUTNAM, L.S. 1949. Life history of the waxwing. Wilson Bull. 61:141-181.

RALPH, C.J. and J.M. SCOTT, eds. 1981. Estimating number of terrestrial birds. Studies Avian Biol. 6. 630pp.

RAMSEY, F.L. and J.M. SCOTT. 1979. Estimating population densities from variable circular plot surveys. Pages 155-181 *in* Cormack, R.M., G.P. Patel, and D.S. Rolson, eds. Sampling Biological Populations. Int. Co-op Publ. House, Fairfield, MD.

RAYNOR, G.S. 1983. A method for evaluating quality of coverage in breeding bird atlas projects. Am. Birds 37:9-13.

REYNOLDS, R.T., J.M. SCOTT, and R.A. NUSSBAUM. 1980. A variable circular-plot method for estimating bird numbers. Condor 82:309-313.

RICE, J.C., R.D. OHMART, and B.W. ANDERSON. 1983. Habitat selection attributes of an avian community: A discriminant analysis investigation. Ecol. Monogr. 53:263-290.

ROBBINS, C.S. 1966. The Christmas count. Pages 154-163 *in* Stefferud, A., ed. Birds in Our Lives. U.S. Dep. Inter., Fish and Wildl. Serv. Washington, DC. 561pp.

————. 1969. The breeding bird survey of 1967 and 1968. U.S. Dep. Inter., Fish and Wildl. Serv. Spec. Sci. Rep.—Wildl. 124:1-107.

————. 1970. Winter bird survey technique tested in Maryland. Maryland Birdlife. 26:11-20.

————. 1972. An appraisal of the winter bird-population study technique. Am. Birds 26:688-692.

————. 1974. Progress report on the North American breeding bird survey. Acta Ornithologica 14:170-191.

————. 1978. Census techniques for forest birds. Pages 142-163 *in* Proceedings of Workshop: Management of southern forests for nongame birds. U.S. Dep. Agric., For. Serv. Gen. Tech. Rep. SE-14.

————, D. BYSTRAK, and P.H. GEISSLER. 1986. The breeding bird survey: its first 15 years, 1965-1979. U.S. Dep. Inter., Fish and Wildl. Serv., Resour. Publ. 157:1-154.

———— and W.T. VAN VELZEN. 1967. The breeding bird survey, 1966. U.S. Dep. Inter., Fish & Wildl. Serv. Spec. Sci. Rep.—Wildl. 102:1-43.

ROOT, R.B. 1967. The niche exploitation pattern of the blue-gray gnatcatcher. Ecol. Monogr. 37:317-350.

ROTENBERRY, J.T. 1980a. Temporal variation in habitat structure and shrub-steppe bird dynamics. Oecologia 47:1-9.

————. 1980b. Habitat structure, patchiness, and avian communities in North American steppe vegetation: A multivariate analysis. Ecol. 61:1228-1250.

———— and J.A. WIENS. 1976. A method for estimating species dispersion from transect data. Am. Midl. Nat. 95:64-78.

ROTH, R.R. 1981. Vegetation as a determinant in avian ecology. Pages 162-174 *in* Proceedings First Welder Wildl. Foundation Symp.

SCOTT, J.M. and F.L. RAMSEY. 1981. Effects of abundant species on the ability of observers to make accurate counts of birds. Auk 98:610-612.

————, ————, and C.B. KEPLER. 1981. Distance estimation as a variable in estimating bird numbers. Pages 366-371 *in* Ralph, C.J. and Scott, J.M., eds. Estimating the Numbers of Terrestrial Birds. Studies Avian Biol. 6.

SEDGWICK, J.A. 1981. Breeding bird and small mammal habitat relationships in northwestern Colorado. Ph.D dissertation, Colorado State Univ., Fort Collins. 139pp.

SERVENTY, D.L. 1980. Developments in Australian ornithology. Bull. British Ornith. Club. 100:89-93.

SHARROCK, J.T.R. 1975. Dot distribution mapping of breeding birds in Europe. Ardeola 21:797-810.

————. 1976. The atlas of breeding birds in Britain and Ireland. British Trust for Ornith., Tring. Herts. 477pp.

SKAAR, P.D. 1969. Birds of Bozeman Latilong. Published by author, 501 S. Third, Bozeman, MT. 131pp.

SMITH, D.R. 1975. Proceedings of the symposium on management of forest and range habitats for nongame birds. U.S. Dep. Agric., For. Serv. Gen. Tech. Rep. WO-1.

STEWART, R.E., J.B. COPE, C.S. ROBBINS, and J.W. BRAINERD. 1952. Seasonal distribution of bird populations at the Patuxent Research Refuge. Am. Midl. Nat. 47:257-363.

SUMMERS-SMITH, J.D. 1963. The house sparrow. Collins. London. 269pp.

————. 1967. Bibliography of the genus *Passer*. Intl. Studies of Sparrows. Warsaw, Poland. 82pp.

SZARO, R.C. and R.P. BALDA. 1982. Selection and monitoring of avian indicator species: An example from a ponderosa pine forest in the Southwest. U.S. Dep. Agric., For. Serv. Gen. Tech. Rep. RM-89. 8pp.

———— and M.D. JAKLE. 1982. Comparison of variable circular-plot and spot-mag methods in desert riparian and scrub habitats. Wilson Bull. 94:546-550.

TAYLOR, D.M. and C.D. LITTLEFIELD. 1984. Willow flycatcher and yellow warbler responses to reduced cattle use of willow habitat. Abstract of paper presented at 54th Ann. Meeting, Cooper Ornith. Soc. Humboldt State Univ., Arcata, CA. June 19-23. 26pp.

TOMIALOJC, L., W. WALANKIEWICZ, and T. WESOLOWSKI. 1978. Methods and preliminary results of the collective bird census work in the primeval forest of the Bialowieza National Park. Polish Ecol. Studies 3(4):215-224.

TRAMER, E.J. 1974. An analysis of the species density of U.S. landbirds during the winter using the 1971

Christmas bird count. Am. Birds 28:563-567.

TRIMBLE, S. 1975. Non-game birds of the West: An annotated bibliography. U.S. Dep. Inter., Bur. Land Manage. Tech. Note 269. 320pp.

UDVARDY, M.D.F. 1957. An evaluation of quantitative studies in birds. Cold Spring Harbor Symp. Quantitative Biol. 22:301-311.

U.S. DEPARTMENT OF AGRICULTURE, FOREST SERVICE, Rocky Mountain Region. 1982. Wildlife and fish habitat relationships. 2 vols. Denver, CO.

————, Southwestern Region. 1975. Endangered and unique fish and wildlife of the Southwestern National Forests. Albuquerque, NM. 203pp.

VAN VELZEN, W.T., ed. 1981. Forty-fourth breeding bird census. Am. Birds 35:46-112.

VERBEEK, N.A.M. 1970. Breeding-ecology of the water pipit. Auk 87:425-451.

VERNER, J. 1985. Assessment of counting techniques. Chapter 8 *in* Current Ornithology 2:247-302.

———— and A.S. BOSS. 1980. California wildlife and their habitats: western Sierra Nevada. U.S. Dep. Agric., For. Serv. Gen. Tech. Rep. PSW-37. 439pp.

———— and J.V. RITTER. 1985. A comparison of transects and point counts in oak-pine woodlands of California. Condor 87:46-68.

WEBSTER, J.D. 1966. An analysis of winter bird-population studies. Wilson Bull. 78:456-461.

WIENS, J.A. 1969. An approach to the study of ecological relationships among grassland birds. Ornith. Monogr. 8:1-93.

————. 1973. Pattern and process in grassland bird communities. Ecol. Monogr. 43:237-270.

————. 1983. Avian community ecology: An iconoclastic view. Pages 355-403 *in* Brush, A.H. and G.A. Clark, Jr., eds. Perspectives in Ornithology. Cambridge Univ. Press. New York, NY. 560pp.

WILLIAMS, A.B. 1936. The composition and dynamics of a beech-maple climax community. Ecol. Monogr. 6:317-408.

WILLSON, M.F. 1974. Avian community organization and habitat structure. Ecol. 55:1017-1029.

WING, L. and M. JENKS. 1939. Christmas censuses: The amateur's contribution to science. Bird Lore 41:343-350.

WINTERNITZ, B.L. 1976. Temporal change and habitat preference of the montane breeding birds. Condor 78:382-393.

YEATMAN, L. 1976. Atlas des oiseaux nicheur de France de 1970 a 1975. Soc. Ornithology de France, 55 Rue de Buffon, Paris. 283pp.

YOUNG, H. 1955. Territorial behavior and nesting of the eastern robin. Am. Midl. Nat. 53:329-352.

ZELENY, L. 1976. The bluebird: How you can help its fight for survival. Indiana Univ. Press, Bloomington. 170pp.

16

RAPTORS

Michael N. Kochert

U.S. Bureau of Land Management
Snake River Birds of Prey Research Project
Boise, ID 83705

Editor's Note: The importance of raptors is widely recognized. Interest in these species has resulted in many studies and much literature. At times, biologists can have trouble wading through this material to find what they need. This chapter summarizes the available information on raptors and refers the biologist to major studies and reports.

INTRODUCTION

Raptors are difficult to accurately count because they often nest in inaccessible areas at relatively low densities. They can be secretive and difficult to find, and are wide-ranging and rapid-moving. Because of these difficulties, a census (complete count) is rarely possible. In most raptor surveys, population and productivity estimates are based on samples. Because data are sometimes hard to obtain, it may be impractical to obtain adequate sample sizes and results may differ depending on how the data were collected. These problems can be compounded by poor sampling design and methods of interpretation (Steenhof and Kochert 1982), and may result in a waste of time and money.

Surveys should provide adequate information to determine population changes. The type and intensity of an inventory or monitoring effort may be dictated by personnel, funding, or logistics. Because of these restrictions, biologists may be required to use low resolution surveys. However, statistically sound sampling procedures must be used regardless of the resolution.

When designing an inventory or monitoring effort, biologists should obtain general information about the raptor species or group they intend to survey and the habitats in which it occurs (Fuller and Mosher 1981). They also must consider the biases that influence survey results. Observer competence, experience in identifying raptors and conducting surveys, and knowledge of raptor behavior are important factors influencing survey results and can be sources of variability. This variability is compounded when several species in many different habitats are surveyed simultaneously.

This chapter provides information necessary to design a raptor inventory and monitoring effort. The first section presents the principal habitat features related to the major species and the use of these features. The second section briefly describes the major techniques for measuring raptor populations and evaluates their limitations, biases, and utility in an inventory or monitoring program.

HABITAT FEATURES CORRELATED WITH SPECIES GROUPS

Raptors, like other animals, are associated with specific habitat features. Often the occurrence of a raptor species can be predicted by the presence of certain habitat characteristics. Knowledge of the relationships between raptors and habitat features can assist biologists in designing and conducting an inventory or monitoring effort. This section summarizes the main habitat features for the major raptor species in the western United States (Table 1) and discusses how biologists should apply these features in an inventory or monitoring effort. Although western habitats are emphasized, eastern habitats are described if the species also occurs in the eastern United States.

Vegetation and physical (topographic and physiographic) features are the two most important habitat features that influence the abundance and distribution of raptors (Newton 1979). These features influence availability of nest sites and foraging habitat. Some raptors are adapted to forests (e.g., accipiters) whereas others are adapted to open grasslands and shrublands (e.g., prairie falcons and ferruginous hawks; Table 1). Some species occur in a wide variety of topographic and physiographic situations and others require a relatively narrow set of physical features. Great-horned owls, for example, nest in numerous types of topographic and physiographic situations, but nest dispersion of cliff-nesting species, such as prairie falcons, is directly influenced by the distribution of rock outcroppings and escarpments. Other raptor species are closely associated with water or riparian areas (Table 1).

Nesting habitats are emphasized in Table 1 because more is known about nesting requirements than requirements during other portions of raptors' life cycles, and successful nesting is critical in maintaining population stability (Newton 1979). Nesting habitat features in Table 1 are presented in the form of a hierarchy. The vegetation category includes the major vegetation types (Kuchler 1964; Brown et al. 1980) in which a species occurs throughout its range. Physical features represent specific physiographic and topographic situations within the vegetation types which are associated with a particular species. Habitat characteristics reflect special features of the vegetation where the species nests, and can be related to age class (e.g., old-growth) or vegetative structure (e.g., closed, dense canopy, or open low shrubs). For example, northern goshawks and Cooper's hawks both nest in conifer forests in the west; however, goshawks occur in dense mature stands with a multi-layered canopy and Cooper's hawks occur in even-aged second growth stands with a dense canopy (Table 1). Associations with farmland and urban development are included in this category of habitat characteristics. Farmland habitat includes cultivated lands or pasture lands, whereas urban habitat consists of small towns, large cities, and suburban areas.

Cliffs furnish nest sites and overlook hunting areas.

Within these areas of specific habitat characteristics, different raptors use different substrates for nesting. Some species have a very narrow range of requirements whereas others nest on many different substrates. Knowledge of these requirements aids in locating nests and predicting the occurrence of nesting birds. Also, certain populations can be restricted by the availability of nesting sites (Newton 1979), especially for tree nesting raptors in the Great Plains and those that use snags.

Availability of food is the second factor that regulates raptor abundance and distribution (Newton 1979). Knowledge of foraging habitat requirements can help biologists predict raptor occurrence. This knowledge is important in managing and maintaining foraging habitat that can be critical to raptor survival and nesting success. The ranges in foraging habitat presented in Table 1 are based on a few studies in the literature and should be considered guidelines instead of absolute rules.

Wintering habitat may be as important as nesting habitat because habitat quality may influence juvenile survival and the condition of breeding females the following spring (Newton 1979). Wintering habitat is less predictable than nesting habitat because raptors usually use more varied habitats in the winter. Biologists should be aware that species such as bald eagles, northern harriers, and long-eared owls communally roost during the winter, and protection and management of these roosts are important in maintaining wintering habitat for these species.

Little is known about migration routes and habitat use during migration. Certain raptor species, however, use migration corridors dictated by geographic features or barriers (e.g., mountain ranges or water bodies) which cause migrating birds to congregate (Newton 1979). In the western United States, migrating raptors tend to follow north-south mountain ranges where birds use deflective air currents caused by escarpments. Surveys of migrating raptors are of little value for local inventory or monitoring efforts because the origin of the birds is mostly unknown and migration counts are subject to many biases (Fuller and Mosher 1981). These counts, however, can have value on a regional basis in determining general population trends.

Biologists should use the information presented in Table 1 as guidelines for predicting possible presence of species and for developing inventory and monitoring designs, especially those using stratified sampling procedures. However, biologists should not use these features as a sole means of assessing relative raptor abundance or habitat quality because many environmental factors can influence actual population numbers.

POPULATION MEASUREMENT TECHNIQUES

This section describes the major techniques for surveying raptor populations that can be applied in a BLM inventory and monitoring program. However, before designing a survey, biologists should consult Steenhof (1986) and Fuller and Mosher (1986) for further discussion of biases, limitations, and application of these techniques. Discussions in this section focus on the utility of each technique in assessing relative population changes, including evaluations of accuracy and precision. Accuracy is the closeness of the value computed or measured by the technique to the true or known value and is expressed as a percentage of the true or known value. Precision is the closeness of repeated measurements of the same variable and is the amount of variation expressed as a percentage of the mean. Therefore, measurements with greater precision have less variation in relation to the mean and thus smaller precision values. I used coefficients of variation (Sokal and Rohlf 1981) to measure precision. When that was not possible, and if 95% confidence intervals were reported, I followed Postovit (1979) and used the following formula which gave a measure roughly double the coefficient of variation.

$$\text{Percent precision} = \frac{\pm 95\% \text{ Confidence Interval}}{\text{Mean}} \times 100$$

Presence

A survey to determine presence is often the first step in evaluating potential impacts of land use and is also used to describe geographical range of a species and changes in distribution (Fuller and Mosher 1981). Specific techniques for assessing presence are not discussed in this section because they are essentially the same as those used to assess relative abundance, which I describe in a later section. Use of information about presence of a species does not require careful enumeration of birds, and data collection and analysis requirements are more rigorous for surveys to determine relative abundance.

The method used to determine presence will depend on funding and logistics as well as the raptor species to be surveyed. Although data collection requirements are the least rigorous, methods are subjected to biases with detectability being the main bias (Fuller and Mosher 1981). The literature, habitat models, and knowledgeable people are initial information sources in assessing presence. Aerial surveys are an expeditious way to determine presence of conspicuous raptors over large areas. Surveys from boats and land vehicles can be more efficient than those from aircraft because of less cost and more opportunity to see inconspicuous raptors. Vocalizations provide a quick means to detect the presence

Table 1. Habitat features correlated with selected Falconiform species in the United States.

SPECIES	Vegetation	Physical Features	NESTING HABITAT Habitat Characteristics
Black vulture (*Coragyps atratus*)	Shrubland; grassland; eastern and southern deciduous, coniferous, and mixed forest types.	Varied. Flatlands to rolling hills and foothills, canyons, and ravines.	In or near open to semi-open habitat including farmland.
Turkey vulture (*Cathartes aura*)	Numerous shrubland, grassland, coniferous, and deciduous forest types.	Varied. Flatlands to mountainous to 3750 m (12000 ft). Canyons, ravines, and hillsides.	In or near open to semi-open habitat including farmland.
California condor (*Gymnogyps californianus*)	Primarily chaparral vegetation type. One nest located in a redwood (*Sequoia* sp.) type.	Rugged mountainous terrain between 610-1370 m (2000-4500 ft).	Open to semi-open habitats.
Mississippi kite (*Ictinia mississippiensis*)	Eastern deciduous forest, grassland, and shrubland types.	Level to rolling uplands; also floodplain.	Tree groves, shelter belts; gallery and riparian forests near open habitat including farmland and urban areas.
Black-shouldered kite (*Elanus caeruleus*)	Grassland and oak (*Quercus* sp.) savannas.	Coastal valleys and grassy foothills.	Open to semi-open habitats including farmland.
Northern goshawk (*Accipiter gentilis*)	Coniferous, deciduous, and mixed forest types.	Gentle slopes or flat areas near a steep incline or canyon often near water. Northerly exposure in western U.S. Southerly exposure in Alaska.	Dense mature stands with a multilayered canopy and dense to open understory.
Cooper's hawk (*Accipiter cooperii*)	Coniferous, deciduous, and mixed forest types. Also shrubland and grassland types.	Flat terrain or gentle slopes (30°), sometimes near water. Low elevations. Sea level to 2700 m (8700 ft) in western U.S. on northerly exposures.	Wooded areas exceeding 6-8 ha (15-20 a.); occasionally smaller areas or isolated trees. Mature deciduous, coniferous, or mixed forest with dense understory in the East. In western mountainous, old or even-aged second growth stands (30-80 years) with a dense canopy and sparse ground cover. Also oakwoodland habitat. Riparian forests in grassland and shrubland types.
Common barn-owl (*Tyto alba*)	Nearly every shrubland, grassland, and forest type except in montane areas and north of 50°.	Variable. Absent in mountainous terrain.	Open to semi-open habitat. Common in farmland and urban habitats.
Western screech-owl (*Otus kennicottii*)	Most forest associations, shrubland, and grassland types.	Variable below 2470 m (8000 ft). Also riparian areas.	Woodland habitat near open areas. Also farmland and urban habitats.
Whiskered screech-owl (*Otus trichopsis*)	Oak and oak-pine forests in the Southwest.	Usually canyons.	Usually riparian habitat and dense stands.

Nesting Substrate	FORAGING HABITAT	WINTERING HABITAT	SOURCES
Ground, hollow logs, and stumps; occasionally caves and old buildings.	Open to semi-open areas where carrion is available.	Similar to nesting; also urban habitat.	Scott et al. (1977); Am. Ornithol. Union (1983).
Cliff cavities and caves, ground, hollow logs, and trees near ground level.	See black vulture.	Similar to nesting.	Scott et al. (1977); Call (1978).
Cavities, caves and crevices of cliffs, and rarely hollow trees.	Grassland and oak savanna foothills up to 60-70 km (35-45 mi.) from nests where large mammal carrion is available.	Same as nesting.	Wilbur (1978); Studer (1983).
Trees.	Open areas near colonies or above the forest canopy for insects.	N/A*	Parker (1975, pers. commun.); Parker and Ogden (1979).
Trees.	Open pasturelands, grasslands, and forest canopy for insects.	Same as nesting.	Waian and Stendall (1970); Bammann (1975).
Tall trees, greater than 8 m (25 ft) high.	Same as nesting. Also ecotone between forest and openings. Areas containing rodents and large birds up to 2.8 km (1.8 mi.) from nests.	Varied forested and open habitats. More open than nesting habitat.	McGowan (1975); Reynolds et al. (1982); Reynolds (1983).
Medium high trees, greater than 6 m (20 ft) high.	Same as nesting. Use areas containing medium to large passerines within 2.4 km (1.5 mi.) of nests.	Diverse habitats. Woodland, grassland, shrubland, farmland, and urban. More open than nesting.	Jones (1979); Millsap (1981); Titus and Mosher (1981); Reynolds et al. (1982); Reynolds (1983); Fuller and Partelow (1983).
Cavities in trees, cliffs, and banks. Wide variety of man-made structures.	Open habitats containing small rodents within 5.6 km (3.5 mi.) of nests.	Similar to nesting.	Scott et al. (1977); Call (1978); C. Marti (pers. commun.); Hegdal and Blaskiewicz (1984).
Cavities, woodpecker or flicker holes in trees, saguaro cactus, and occasionally snags. Man-made structure.	Open habitats containing rodents and insects usually within 0.5 km (0.3 mi.) of nest.	Similar to nesting.	Scott et al. (1977); Call (1978); Johnson et al. (1979); Marti (1979).
Cavities and flicker holes in trees.	Areas near nest containing insects.	N/A*	Marshall (1967); Scott et al. (1977).

Table 1. Habitat features correlated with selected Falconiform species in the United States (continued).

| SPECIES | NESTING HABITAT | | |
	Vegetation	Physical Features	Habitat Characteristics
Flammulated owl (*Otus flammeolus*)	Coniferous forest and mixed coniferous-deciduous forest types.	Mountainous areas between 1000-3100 m (3250-10000 ft). Usually on dry hillsides or on ridge tops.	Usually mature forest with dense canopies and a brush understory or intermixture of oaks. Occasionally in second growth forest. Rarely in logged-over areas.
Northern hawk-owl (*Surnia ulula*)	Northern boreal forests.	Open woods, parklands, and barrens with low shrubs and scattered trees.	Forest edge areas or open canopy (20-60% canopy cover) stands.
Northern pygmy-owl (*Glaucidium gnoma*)	Most coniferous associations throughout the West.	Mountainous up to 3750 m (12000 ft).	Open to semi-open forests.
Elf owl (*Micrathene whitneyi*)	Palo verde-saguaro associations and occasionally coniferous-deciduous forests at higher elevations.	Steep canyons, riparian areas, hillsides, and flats.	Variable.
Sharp-shinned hawk (*Accipiter striatus*)	Coniferous, deciduous, or mixed forest types.	Canyons, valleys, and riparian areas. In canyons, nest 50-100 m (162-325 ft) upslope from a stream.	Dense stands with well-developed canopy (60%) and dense understory. Dense, young (25-50 year), even-aged, second growth stands with single-layered canopy in western coniferous forests. Also in conifers within dense mixed stands.
Osprey (*Pandion haliaetus*)	Numerous shrubland, grassland, coniferous forest, and deciduous forest types.	Proximity to water (can be up to 11 km or 7 mi. away).	Varied habitats including farmland and urban. Old growth stands better than even-age second growth stands.
Bald eagle (*Haliaetus leucocephalus*)	Numerous shrubland, deciduous forest, and mixed forest types.	Proximity to water (usually within 3.2 km or 2 mi.).	Uneven-aged, multi-layered forests with an availability of large trees with sturdy branches.
Golden eagle (*Aquila chrysaetos*)	Shrubland and grassland types. Also tundra, coniferous forests, and woodland-brushland.	Canyons, buttes, and mountainous escarpments between 600-3100 m (1950-10000 ft) in elevation.	Open to semi-open habitats. Sometimes riparian and farmland habitats.

Nesting Substrate	FORAGING HABITAT	WINTERING HABITAT	SOURCES
Woodpecker or flicker holes in trees or snags. Also nest boxes.	17-27 ha (43-63 a.) areas around nests containing insects.	N/A*	Bull and Anderson (1978); Franzreb and Omart (1978); Winter (1979); Reynolds and Linkhart (1984).
Cavities in trees, sometimes snags. Occasionally corvid nests in trees or on cliffs.	Open areas containing microtines, small rodents, and birds.	Same as nesting. Sometimes open habitat in temperate areas.	Grossman and Hamlet (1964); Scott et al. (1977); Meehan and Ritchie (1982).
Woodpecker holes in trees or snags.	Areas near nests containing insects and small rodents.	Open to semi-open habitats.	Scott et al. (1977); Call (1978); Hayward (1983).
Woodpecker holes in saguaro cactus or snags. Also cavities in dead branches of living trees.	Small area around nest containing insects, particularly beetles, moths, and crickets.	N/A*	Scott et al. (1977); Call (1978); Johnson et al. (1979); Millsap (pers. commun.).
Small trees (less than 6 m [20 ft] high).	Same as nesting areas containing small passerine birds within approximately 1.5 km (0.9 mi.) of nests.	Diverse habitats including riparian, woodland, farmland, and urban habitats. More open than nesting. Perches have substantial arboreal cover.	Platt (1973); Jones (1979); Millsap (1981); Clarke (1982); Reynolds et al. (1982); Reynolds (1983).
Tops of trees, rock and dirt pinnacles, cactus, and numerous man-made structures (snags or trees with dead tops preferred).	Slow-moving water usually within a few km of the nest. Can be up to 11 km (7 mi.) away.	N/A*	Johnson and Melquist (1973); Zarn (1974c); Melquist (1975).
Primarily trees, occasionally cliffs. Nest below crown in super canopy trees. Occasionally man-made structures.	Primarily slow-moving water within a few km of the nest. During winter, bodies of water; occasionally upland habitats. Winter foraging areas can be up to 27 km (17 mi.) from roost.	Same as nesting, but also in farmland and urban habitats. Open water most important; however, shrubland also used. Diurnal perches primarily in trees close to a food source. Night roosts more protected than day roosts. Stands generally have large, old, open-structured trees with horizontal branches.	Call (1978); Fraser (1978); Steenhof (1978); Steenhof et al. (1980); Anthony et al. (1982); Keister and Anthony (1983); U.S. Fish and Wildlife Service (1983).
Primarily cliffs, sometimes trees, and occasionally ground and man-made structures.	Open habitats where rabbits and small rodents are available, usually within 7 km (4.4 mi.) of nests.	Same as nesting. In the West below 1400 m (4500 ft) in elevation. In the East coastal plains and wetlands.	Snow (1973); Wrakestraw (1973); U.S. Bureau of Land Management (1979); Kochert (1980); Millsap and Vana (1984).

Table 1. Habitat features correlated with selected Falconiform species in the United States (continued).

SPECIES	Vegetation	Physical Features	NESTING HABITAT Habitat Characteristics
Northern harrier (*Circus cyaneus*)	Grassland and shrubland associations; also large open expanses in deciduous forests.	Relatively flat and open terrain from sea level to 3200 m (10,400 ft) in elevation.	Open habitat with short vegetation. Mainly wetland and riparian habitats, but also shrub and grass upland and farmland habitats.
Red-tailed hawk (*Buteo jamaicensis*)	Nearly every open to semi-open vegetation type. Absent in tundra and uncommon in dense forests.	Canyons, hillsides, and level terrain. In East occupy forested uplands, ridges, and steep slopes. Riparian floodplain in Alaska.	In or near open to semi-open habitats. Nests situated for unobstructed access in riparian and dense forested areas.
Swainson's hawk (*Buteo swainsoni*)	Shrubland and grassland types.	Low to moderate elevations, valleys, foothills, and level uplands. In areas moist enough to support trees.	Small tree groves in open habitats, including farmland.
Ferruginous hawk (*Bueto regalis*)	Grassland, shrubland, and juniper-pinyon (*Juniperus-Pinus*) woodland types.	More xeric sites than other sympatric buteos. Avoid mountainous areas, steep canyons, and high cliffs.	Open habitat. Avoid heavily farmed areas.
Red-shouldered hawk (*Buteo lineatus*)	Deciduous forest associations in East. Riparian and sycamore (*Platanus*) woodland in West.	Mosaic lowlands, riparian areas, floodplains, and valleys.	Mature forests with fairly closed canopy and large amount of floodplain edge in the East. In the West, riparian habitat with taller-than-average trees.
Broad-winged hawk (*Buteo platypterus*)	Deciduous and mixed deciduous forest types.	Wet, poorly drained areas. More upland than red-shouldered hawk areas.	Much like red-shouldered hawk. Nest close to small streams, lakes or swampy areas.
Rough-legged hawk (*Buteo lagopus*)	Tundra and taiga.	Foothills and mountain valleys with bluffs and rock formations.	Open habitat.
Zone-tailed hawk (*Buteo albonotatus*)	Various shrubland types in the Southwest; also the Arizona Pine Forest type.	Rugged terrain. Deep, broad canyons and tablelands up to 2750 m (9000 ft) in elevation.	Large trees required. Usually in perennial and intermittent streams; occasionally in tablelands away from water.
Gray hawk (*Buteo nitidus*)	Riparian forests in mesquite and shrubland types.	Floodplain areas.	Presently mature gallery trees. Historically mesquite trees.

Nesting Substrate	FORAGING HABITAT	WINTERING HABITAT	SOURCES
Ground. In rank vegetation.	Open habitats up to 18 km (11.2 mi.) from the nest.	Same as nesting, but at lower elevations. Use uplands more often. Will communally roost in depressions.	Call (1978); Apfelbaum and Seelbach (1983); Thompson-Hanson (1984).
Trees preferred, also cliffs and man-made structures. Higher and in taller trees than other sympatric *Buteo* species.	Open habitats containing lagomorphs, small rodents, and snakes, usually within 3 km (1.9 mi.) of nest.	Same as nesting. Absent from high elevations.	Brown and Amadon (1968); U.S. Bureau of Land Management (1979); Schmutz et al. (1980); Cottrell (1981); Millsap (1981); Titus and Mosher (1981); Bednarz and Dinsmore (1982).
Primarily trees and small shrubs, occasionally man-made structures. Closer to the ground than other sympatric *Buteo* species.	Open habitats with short vegetation containing small rodents and insects within 3 km (1.9 mi.) of the nest and a home range of approximately 9 km^2 (3.5 mi.^{2}).	N/A*	Fitzner (1980); Schmutz et al. (1980); Cottrell (1981); Bechard (1982); Gilmer and Stewart (1984).
Low rocky outcrops (preferred), trees in small groves, on cut banks, and a variety of man-made structures.	Open habitats with short vegetation containing ground squirrels, pocket gophers, and rabbits usually within 2-3 km (1.2-1.9 mi.) of nest.	Same as nesting habitat, also pastureland.	Wakely (1978); Schmutz et al. (1980); Cottrell (1981); Millsap (1981); Evans (1983).
Trees, larger than those used by broad-winged hawks. Farther below canopy than red-tailed hawks.	Closed to semi-closed woodland in and near wet areas containing small rodents, reptiles, amphibians, and crayfish in an area 0.6-0.9 km^2 (0.2-3.5 mi.^{2}) around nest. Up to 1.0-2.3 km (0.6-1.4 mi.) from nest.	Similar to nesting; also forest edge and openings.	Brown and Amadon (1968); Wiley (1975); Titus and Mosher (1981); McCrary (1981); Bednarz and Dinsmore (1982).
Trees (see red-shouldered hawk).	Closed to semi-open habitat in an approximately 13 km^2 (5.1 mi.^{2}) range containing small mammals, reptiles, amphibians, and large insects.	N/A*	Brown and Amadon (1968); Matray (1974); Fuller (1979); Titus and Mosher (1981).
Primarily river bluffs, lesser degree upland outcroppings and escarpments. Occasionally the ground, sometimes trees.	Wet meadows, bogs, marshes, open riparian areas, pastures. Also shrub and grass uplands containing small rodents.	Open shrub and grass habitats in temperate areas (see foraging habitat).	Zarn (1975); Bildstein (1978); BLM (unpubl. data).
Primarily trees, rarely cliffs.	Upland habitats, open shrubland containing an abundance of lizards up to 27 km (16.0 mi.) from nests.	N/A* Rare winter sightings in southwest U.S.	Call (1978); Millsap (1981, pers. commun.); Fuller (1983).
Trees.	Thorn shrub-mesquite bosque with an abundance of lizards.	N/A* Rare winter sightings in southwest U.S.	Millsap (pers. commun.).

Table 1. Habitat features correlated with selected Falconiform species in the United States (continued).

| SPECIES | NESTING HABITAT | | |
	Vegetation	Physical Features	Habitat Characteristics
Common black-hawk (*Buteogallus anthracinus*)	Shrubland types of the Southwest.	Riparian and floodplain between 430-1850 m (1400-6000 ft) in elevation. Perennial streams essential.	Mature riparian habitat. Tree groves preferred over single trees.
Harris' hawk (*Parabuteo unicinctus*)	Mesquite (*Prosopis* sp.) and Palo verde (*Cercidium* sp.) vegetation types.	Flatlands with washes and ravines that give way to low hills.	Structurally complex and diverse vegetation. Multilayered and semi-closed shrub.
Gyrfalcon (*Falco rusticolus*)	Tundra, occasionally in taiga.	Foothills and mountain valleys with rock formations, bluffs, and rock outcroppings.	Varied. Vast expanses of open habitat.
Peregrine falcon (*Falco peregrinus*)	Nearly all shrubland, grassland, and forest types. Rare in alpine areas.	Flat terrain to rugged canyons. Usually on high cliffs (62 m or 200 ft), in areas of open expanses and high topographic relief, and near (within 4.8 km or 3.0 mi.) permanent or semi-permanent sources of water.	Open habitats, including farmland and urban habitats.
Prairie falcon (*Falco mexicanus*)	Arid and semi-arid shrubland and grassland types. Sometimes the open parklands of coniferous forest types.	Canyons, buttes, mountainous escarpments, outcroppings to elevations of 3100 m (10,000 ft).	Open habitat with short vegetation.
Merlin (*Falco columbarius*)	Shrubland, grassland, boreal forest, and coastal coniferous forest types.	Varied. Uncommon in rugged-mountainous terrain.	Near open habitat. Forests broken by expanses of open country. Openings in dense forests. Tree groves, riparian forests.
American kestrel (*Falco sparverius*)	Nearly all shrubland, grassland, and forest types.	Variable terrain associated with open areas up to 3750 m (12,000 ft).	Wide variety of open to semi-open habitats, including farmland and urban habitats.
Spotted owl (*Strix occidentalis*) Northern spotted owl	Douglas-fir (*Pseudotsuga menziesii*), cedar (*Thuja* sp.), and hemlock (*Tsuga* sp.) forests.	Usually below 1700 m (5500 ft) elevation on 75% slopes half way down hillside.	Multilayered old growth (100-200 + years) forests with deep ravines and 50-90% canopy closure.
California spotted owl	Fir-pine/Douglas-fir forests and oak woodlands.	Steep slopes.	Heavily timbered old growth.
Mexican spotted owl	Spruce, Douglas-fir, and pinyon-juniper forests. Aspen and maple stands.	Deep narrow timbered canyons below 2770 m (9000 ft) in elevation	Timbered riparian habitat.

Nesting Substrate	FORAGING HABITAT	WINTERING HABITAT	SOURCES
Trees.	Riparian habitat (mostly in the water) containing fish, amphibians, reptiles, and small mammals within 0.5 km (3.1 mi.) of nests.	N/A*	Schnell (1979); Millsap (pers. commun.).
Palo verde, mesquite, other trees, and saguaro cactus (Cereus giganteus).	Semi-closed areas (more closed than those used by red-tailed hawks) containing rabbits, medium to small rodents and birds (quail) in a 5 km^2 (2.0 mi.^{2}) area around the nest.	Same as nesting, also occur in farmland.	Call (1978); Mader (1976, 1978); Millsap (1981).
Primarily cliffs (6-90 m) occasionally trees in taiga.	Open habitats with an abundance of hare and ptarmigan.	Same as nesting. Sometimes in the northern conterminous U.S.	Cade (1982); Mindell (1983).
Cliffs (60 m), rarely in trees.	Open habitats. Usually riparian and shoreline areas. Also upland habitats containing shorebirds and passerines. Usually within 5 km (3.1 mi.) of nests, but up to 24 km (15 mi.).	N/A*	Porter and White (1973); Cade (1982); Ellis (1982).
Cliffs and rock outcroppings, rarely abandoned raptor nests in trees.	Open areas of low vegetation containing ground squirrels and passerine birds up to 24 km (15 mi.) from nests.	Similar to nesting, also farmland habitats.	U.S. Bureau of Land Management (1979); Cade (1982); Becker and Ball (1983a).
Abandoned corvid nests in trees, occasionally in tree cavities or on the ground.	Open shrub and grass habitats containing passerine birds up to 9 km^2 (5.6 mi.^{2}) from nests. Also forage for insects above forest canopy.	Coastal, marsh, grassland, farmland, and urban habitats where passerine and shore birds concentrate.	Trimble (1975); Scott et al. (1977); Cade (1982); Becker and Ball (1983b); Becker (1984); Millsap (pers. commun.).
Old flicker holes or cavities in banks and cliffs, buildings, abandoned magpie nests, and nest boxes.	Open habitats mostly in marshland, grassland, savanna, shrubland, open forest, farmland, and urban habitats.	Similar to nesting. Absent in high elevations.	Scott et al. (1977); Cade (1982).
Tree cavities or other raptor nests.	Old growth stands, primarily second growth stands secondarily containing flying squirrels (Glaucomys sp.) and woodrats (Neotoma sp.) in a 0.5-3.4 km^2 (0.2-1.3 mi.^{2}) area around nest.	Similar to nesting.	Forsman (1983a); Forsman et al. (1984).
Tree cavities, other raptor nests, cavities in cliffs; occasionally on the ground.	Same as nesting.	Lower elevations. Tend to be more open.	Zarn (1974a); Layman (pers. commun.).
Tree cavities, cliff ledges and cavities, empty raptor nests.	Same as nesting.	Similar to nesting.	Zarn (1974a); C. Marti (pers. commun.).

Table 1. Habitat features correlated with selected Falconiform species in the United States (concluded).

SPECIES	NESTING HABITAT		
	Vegetation	*Physical Features*	*Habitat Characteristics*
Barred owl (*Strix varia*)	Eastern deciduous and mixed coniferous forests; boreal and montane coniferous forests.	In lowlands in East. In West, features similar to spotted owl habitats.	In the West, resembles northern spotted owl habitat; however, less affiliation with old-growth forests. In East, dense stands in swamps and river bottoms.
Boreal owl (*Aegolius funereus*)	Boreal and montane coniferous forests.	Variable from flat boreal uplands to mountainous terrain.	Dense, closed canopy stands.
Northern saw-whet owl (*Aegolius acadicus*)	Most forest types up to 3400 m (10,000 ft) in elevation.	Variable.	Dense, closed canopy stands with smaller trees, fewer openings; greater canopy than those used by boreal owls.
Great horned owl (*Bubo virginianus*)	Nearly every grassland, shrubland, and forest type. Absent in tundra.	Variable.	Wide variety of open to semi-open habitats including farmland and urban habitats.
Great gray owl (*Strix nebulosa*)	Northern boreal forests and montane coniferous forests.	Flat lowlands to mountainous terrain between 1850-2500 m (6000-8100 ft) in elevation.	Old growth conifer or mixed deciduous stands in montane forests. Mature poplar, and to lesser degree, conifer stands in boreal forests. Nests usually near a wet meadow or marsh.
Long-eared owl (*Asio otus*)	Most shrubland, grassland, and forest types.	Variable, level, to mountainous terrain.	Semi-open to dense wooded areas, tree groves, and dense shrubs near open areas including farmlands. Nests usually within a few meters of the woodland edge.
Burrowing owl (*Athene cunicularia*)	Arid and semi-arid shrubland and grassland types.	Level to rolling hills.	Open habitats including farmland and urban areas with short vegetation and an availability of burrows.
Short-eared owl (*Asio flammeus*)	Most shrubland and grassland types north of 37° north latitude. Also in tundra.	Open terrain. Absent from mountainous areas.	Open habitat including grassland, shrubland, meadow, marsh, and farmland habitat.
Snowy owl (*Nyctea scandiaca*)	Tundra.	Open flats or slopes. Nests usually on highest point; occasionally on a rocky ledge.	Open habitat. Nests sometimes near marshes or small lakes.

Nesting Substrate	FORAGING HABITAT	WINTERING HABITAT	SOURCES
Large hollow trees; occasionally corvid and raptor nests. Sometimes snags. Also nest boxes.	Wooded areas with an open understory in a home range between 0.8-3.6 km^2 (0.3-1.4 mi.^{2}).	Similar to nesting.	Nicholls and Warner (1972); Scott et al. (1977); Apfelbaum and Seelbach (1983); Taylor and Forsman (1976); Boxall and Stepney (1982).
Woodpecker holes in snags.	Semi-open areas containing microtines.	Similar to nesting.	Scott et al. (1977); Meehan and Ritchie (1982); Hayward (1983).
Woodpecker holes in snags and trees. Also nest boxes.	Areas containing small rodents and insects in a range up to 0.5 km^2 (0.2 mi.^{2}).	Similar to nesting.	Forbes and Warner (1974); Scott et al. (1977); Hayward (1983).
Abandoned large bird nests in trees and on cliffs. Also cliff ledges and cavities.	Open to semi-open areas containing medium to small mammals in a 1.3-3.7 km^2 (0.5-1.4 mi.^{2}) area.	Similar to nesting.	Call (1978); Fuller (1979); Am. Ornithol. Union (1983).
Abandoned raptor or corvid nests in trees.	Marsh and wet meadows containing microtines.	Similar to nesting. Occasionally farmland and urban habitat.	Winter (1979); Nero (1980).
Abandoned corvid nests in small scrubby trees or large bushes.	Open habitats containing microtines and other small rodents in 1.8-3.7 km^2 (0.7-1.4 mi.^{2}) range.	Similar to nesting.	Call (1978); Marti (1979); Wijnandts (1984); Marks (1984).
Abandoned mammal burrows. Occasional cavities in small basalt outcroppings.	Open habitat with short vegetation containing small rodents, insects, lizards, and passerine birds.	Similar to nesting.	Zarn (1974b); Marks and Ball (1983).
Ground	Open habitat (see characteristics) containing microtines in a 0.2-1.2 km^2 (0.07-0.5 mi.^{2}) range.	Similar to nesting.	Clark (1975); Call (1978).
Ground	Open uplands and meadows with a supply of small rodents.	Same as nesting. Also coastal, grassland, farmland, and urban habitats.	Grossman and Hamlet (1964); Lein and Weber (1979).

*Migrates outside the United States.

of secretive raptors over large areas, and walking surveys are useful for locating raptors that are difficult to detect.

Relative Abundance—Non-Nesting Surveys

Road Counts.

Description. Road surveys can be conducted by either the continuous count or point count methods (Fuller and Mosher 1986). Routes either wander through different habitats (Craighead and Craighead 1956), circle or cut through an area (Craig 1978), or consist of transects arranged to completely cover an area (Marion and Ryder 1975).

When conducting continuous counts, observers repeatedly drive specified routes in a vehicle at speeds between 16-40 km/h (10-25 mph) and count all birds seen on either side of the road. They record the perpendicular distance from the transect for each bird seen. Because birds are counted on either side of the road two observers are necessary.

For the point count method, observers stop at systematically placed stations (usually 0.8 km or 0.5 mi. apart) along the road (Fuller and Mosher 1986). During a prescribed time period (usually 3 min), they count all raptors seen or heard within a predetermined radius of the station. The radius at stations can be fixed (usually 0.4 km [0.25 mi.]), variable, or unlimited. In either situation, biologists must record the distance from the station of each bird seen or heard. An advantage of this method is that each station (or circular plot) can be treated as an independent sample with its own habitat characteristics, thus increasing sample size and enhancing statistical analysis.

Before conducting road surveys, biologists should list raptor species and habitat types they need to survey. They should delineate habitat types on maps and compute the linear distance of each type along the road. Transects should be run at least once to delineate the habitat types, to assess effective detection distances, and to identify any biases that may affect the count. Routes should be selected so that all major communities are represented in the sample area (Craighead and Craighead 1956; Millsap 1981).

Road counts should be made under similar weather conditions because weather conditions can affect raptor activity (Craighead and Craighead 1956). The time, weather (at least precipitation, wind, cloud cover, and temperature), and vehicle odometer reading (read to 0.16 km [0.1 mi.] and estimated to nearest 0.08 km [0.05 mi.]) should be recorded at the beginning and end of the survey. For each sighting, observers should record the species, age class, sex (if possible), and activity (perched or flying) of the raptor as well as the time, habitat type, vehicle odometer reading (read to 0.16 km [0.1 mi.] and estimated to nearest 0.08 km [0.05 mi.]), and perpendicular distance from the bird to the road (Millsap 1981).

All road count methods have inherent biases for which biologists must compensate (Fuller and Mosher 1986). The season, time of day, weather, and activity of the birds can bias counts (Fuller and Mosher 1981). To compensate for this, researchers have alternated the direction of each survey run, restricted runs to specific times of the day, or run transects at several times of the day (Craig 1978; Thiollay 1978; Millsap 1981). Repeated runs of the transect in a sampling period increase accuracy, and at least three repeated runs are desirable. The estimated number of birds per transect for each survey period is the maximum number of birds seen on a single run. Man-made structures such as fences, powerlines, and towers provide perches that draw birds along census routes and cause inflated population estimates. If possible, routes adjacent to these structures should be avoided, especially when contrasting abundance among areas. This bias may not be critical when assessing population changes in the same area over time. Temporary influxes of birds, concentrations of birds, and interspecific interactions may also bias counts and should be considered in data analysis (Fuller and Mosher 1981).

Because the detectable distance of a raptor varies with species and habitat type, substantial biases occur when comparisons are made among areas or habitats. To compensate for this problem, surveyors can reduce strip width and only count birds within a narrow width which reflects detection (Millsap 1981). A better alternative is to record all birds seen and their perpendicular distances from the transect center line regardless of their distance, and to analyze these data with the line transect computer program TRANSECT (Burnham et al. 1980). This program compensates for variable detection distances and is available to all BLM employees on the computer at the BLM Service Center. The main problem with program TRANSECT is that the ideal sample size is $\geq$ 40 individuals (Burnham et al. 1980; Mikol 1980). Transects can be analyzed with less than 40 individuals, but resolution is greatly reduced. The problem can be compensated for by (1) increasing transect length, (2) increasing the number of repetitions, or (3) pooling species and habitats (Millsap pers. commun.).

A criticism of road surveys is that transects usually are not random and data are not collected for statistical analysis. However, appropriate methods can reduce this problem. If many roads exist in a large area of homogeneous habitat, investigators can randomly select transects from the array of available roads. Often these conditions do not exist, and dividing the transects into segments provides a viable alternative. Transects should be established in habitat and land use types that need to be surveyed. Transect segments can be delineated by the actual distance of specific habitat types along the transect, resulting in segments of unequal length. These segments of specific habitats are conceptually linked together and treated as one long transect. Data are analyzed with line transect programs, and comparisons among years and habitat types can be made (Mikol 1980).

Another method divides transects into equal 1.6 km (1.0 mi.) segments (Koplin pers. commun.). Each segment is treated as an independent sample plot with specific habitat, land use, and visibility characteristics. The entire transect is surveyed, and the exact location of each bird is recorded during repeated runs. The mean number (and variance) of birds per sample plot is calculated; comparisons are made among years within and among habitats, as well as among habitats within years. To test for clumping, one can compare the number of plots with various numbers of birds with a Poisson Model. More simply, biologists can compute the coefficient of dispersion (Sokal and Rohlf 1981) of the plots.

$$CD = \frac{s^2}{Y}$$

This value will be near 1 if the distribution is essentially Poisson (random), >1 in clumped samples, and < 1 in uniformly distributed samples. Habitat-specific sample plots can also be linked to form a long conceptual transect and analyzed with the line transect program (Mikol 1980). The advantage of this method is that each segment can be considered a replication, thus increasing sample size. In addition, sample plots can be randomly selected on a stratified basis.

Accuracy and Precision. Road counts appear to have variable accuracy which may be affected by transect width. Craighead and Craighead (1956) made repeated vehicle surveys during the winter in a partially forested area in Michigan. They believed that 92% of the buteos, 43% of the northern harriers, 33% of the Cooper's hawks, and 33% of the American kestrels were located by using a belt of 0.4 km (0.25 mi.) on both sides of the road. In Virginia, B. Millsap and M. LeFranc (pers. commun.) found much lower accuracy from preliminary results of one summer-fall field season. Models of perched raptors representing various size classes were randomly distributed within a 0.4-km (0.25-mi.) strip on either side of the road. By using this belt, the proportion of models detected ranged (depending on size) from 11 to 64% in grassland habitat, 2 to 32%

in woodland habitat, and 5 to 26% in heavily forested habitat. However, when effective transect width was adjusted to habitat specific detection distances within each vegetation type, accuracy averaged 90% (Millsap pers. commun.).

Craighead and Craighead (1956:49) and Fuller and Mosher (1981) discussed factors that affect accuracy of road surveys. Results are more reliable for determining relative densities of conspicuous species (buteos, vultures, and eagles) with similar detectability in open country of homogeneous habitat types. Accuracy greatly decreases when many raptor species are sampled in habitats that differ greatly in vegetation and terrain. This gives relatively inflated density estimates in open areas compared with estimates in the more vegetated areas.

Although road surveys can be inaccurate, they are precise. Coefficients of variation calculated from seven surveys, which counted medium-large raptors in a 0.4 km (0.25 mi.) strip in open to semi-open habitats, ranged from 6 to 14% (Craighead and Craighead 1956; Schnell 1967; Kochert et al. 1975, 1976; Craig 1978). Millsap and LeFranc (pers. commun.) found that their road transect data were more precise when they adjusted effective transect width.

Equipment. No special equipment is required except binoculars, spotting scope (minimum 20x), thermometer, wind meter, watch, field forms, and a vehicle. Biologists should use a range finder to assist in estimating perpendicular distances from the transect.

Cost. Road transects are inexpensive, and large areas can be surveyed by two people in a short time. Two people in the Snake River Birds of Prey Area covered 112 km (70 mi.) of transect in 4 hours (1 person-day). This is a reasonable estimate for a survey day considering travel time to and from the survey site.

Training. At least one observer must be trained in raptor identification and should be able to identify color phases and age classes of those species in the survey area. Short courses in raptor identification are recommended.

Discussion. Road counts are a fast, inexpensive means of surveying raptors over large areas. The method, however, is ineffective for nest surveys and monitoring owls and forest raptors. It is a reliable means for assessing occurrence, species composition, and age structure of populations of suitable species. The technique is useful for assessing long-term population trends through relative measures; however, it is plagued with many biases (Fuller and Mosher 1981, 1986). For meaningful surveys, biologists must work within the limitation of those biases, primarily detectability and observer biases, and use only experienced observers on surveys.

Aerial Surveys.

Essentially two types of aerial surveys can be used to census large raptors. Random transects are used to survey raptors that are scattered throughout a survey area. Searches of specific habitats (e.g., lakes and riparian areas) are used to survey species that congregate in specific habitats. These surveys are used primarily to census wintering birds.

Description. Random aerial transects have been used primarily for golden eagles and occasionally for other large raptors (Fuller and Mosher 1981). Starting from a randomly selected section line, investigators randomly select sample transects from all possible transects that can be placed at fixed 0.8-km (0.5-mi.) intervals in the survey area (Wrakestraw 1972; BLM unpubl. data). Transects should be of equal length (usually 80 km [50 mi.]) and separated enough to avoid duplicate sightings (at least 6.4 km [4.0 mi.]). However, because of irregular survey area boundaries, some investigators have used transects of unequal lengths (Boeker and Bolen 1972; Craig 1974). They considered all transect lines collectively as a large transect which was divided into 80-km (50-mi.) segments. This approach is valid only if the transects and the beginning point for the first segment are randomly selected; however, biologists should avoid this approach because segments may not be totally independent.

Transects should be flown at about 15 m (50 ft) to 92 m (300 ft) above ground level (AGL) at speeds between 160-190 km/h (100-120 mph) (Boeker and Bolen 1972; Boeker 1974). All birds seen on each side of the plane, regardless of distance, should be counted and their perpendicular distance from the transect should be recorded. This increases analytical flexibility, and data can be analyzed within a fixed belt (Boeker and Bolen 1972), or by using line transect analysis (Mikol 1980).

Because birds are counted on both sides of the aircraft, two observers and a pilot are necessary. The right side observer sits in the right front seat and searches from the center line out to the right side of the aircraft, scanning both the sky and the ground. The left side observer sits in the left rear seat of the aircraft and searches the left side of the aircraft. To reduce biases, surveys must be flown in as few consecutive days as possible, but days should not be excessively long. After 3-4 hours of flying, fatigue and eyestrain affect a person's ability to see birds (Roseneau 1972); a survey day should be 6-7 hours maximum of flying, interrupted with a necessary 1-hour rest period. A 1600-km (1000-mi.) survey is most efficiently flown in 3 consecutive days.

Kochert et al. (1983) analyzed 3 years of golden eagle transect data by using both the belt transect method and line transect analysis (program TRANSECT, Burnham et al. 1980). The belt method gave consistently lower estimates of wintering population levels than TRANSECT—they believed the results from line transect analysis yielded a more realistic view of the actual population size. Belt transects typically underestimate population densities when the size of the belt is too wide to detect all animals within the belt (Franzbeb 1981); however, effective transect width varies from survey to survey with program transect, depending on probabilities of detection (Burnham et al. 1980). Although TRANSECT can be compromised by small sample sizes (see Road Count section), it appears to be a reliable analytical method.

Aerial surveys of specific habitats are used primarily for bald eagles, and biologists can either completely search habitat patches or randomly sample them. In designing the initial inventory, they should identify habitat areas from aerial photographs where

Aerial surveys can easily identify bald eagle nests in forest habitats.

birds are known to concentrate and should then chart survey routes on maps. U.S. Fish and Wildlife Service (1983) presents detailed guidelines for wintering bald eagle surveys and stresses the need for subsequent surveys throughout the winter. Areas can be surveyed by either helicopters or fixed-wing aircraft at a recommended height of 31-93 m (100-300 ft) AGL and speed between 96-120 km/h (60-70 mph). The best time to survey feeding activity is 1-3 hours after daylight. Entire habitat areas should be flown to count all birds present; large areas can be covered by systematic parallel transects or concentric contours of the habitat border (Hancock 1964). Where potential bald eagle foraging area is vast, surveys along systematic transect lines should be spaced 2.4 km (1.5 mi.) apart and extend no more than 27 km (15 mi.) from roosts (U.S. Fish and Wildlife Service 1983).

Often areas are too large to survey all habitats. In this situation, biologists should consider surveying a random sample of quadrats of the area (King et al. 1972; Grier 1977; Grier et al. 1981). This method provides population estimates with confidence limits and allows statistical comparison of subsequent surveys (Hodges et al. 1979). If the objective is to survey a large amount of linear habitat (i.e., a river), surveyors should segment the linear habitat and randomly sample the segments, preferably on a stratified basis.

Gilmer et al. (1981) and Grier et al. (1981) described aircraft certification, preflight preparations, safety precautions, and special considerations for aerial surveys. Surveys should be flown on clear days with no precipitation. Though not mandatory, winds should be less than 32 km/h (20 mph). Safety is a prime concern, and only experienced pilots and aircraft with sufficient power should be used. Helicopters should not be used in canyons and areas with many powerlines. Pilot attitude and experience can also influence error (Hoskinson 1976).

Accuracy and Precision. Caughley (1974) discussed biases of aerial transect surveys. He believed that the method had moderate to low accuracy because many animals were not seen; accuracy deteriorated progressively with increasing transect width, cruising speed, and altitude. Although inaccurate, transect surveys from fixed-wing aircraft are precise. Precision (based on 95% confidence intervals) of fixed-wing transect surveys in Wyoming and Idaho for golden eagles ranged between 14.0 and 16.5% (Wrakestraw 1972, 1973; BLM unpubl. data).

Fixed-wing aircraft surveys of bald eagles in specific habitats on flat terrain appear to be fairly accurate. Steenhof (1976) surveyed an area for bald eagles from both the ground and a fixed-wing aircraft

on the same day and obtained nearly the same results. Also, helicopter surveys may be more accurate than fixed-wing surveys (U.S. Fish and Wildlife Service 1983).

Slight biases may occur in assessing age structure of bald eagles from airplanes. Hancock (1964) believed that perched adult bald eagles were more conspicuous than immatures and assumed that he underestimated immatures by 20-35%, compared with only 10-15% for adults. These biases may not be significant for golden eagle surveys because plumage difference between adults and sub-adults are not striking, and all perched birds must be flushed and inspected at close range before they are aged.

Perched adult bald eagles are twice as easy to see as immature ones.

Equipment. No special equipment is required except for the aircraft. Certain aircraft may have advantages over others. Readers should see the Equipment section of Aerial Nesting Surveys discussed in this chapter. Some observers prefer to use a small cassette tape recorder to record data. Others carry binoculars; however, I have found them of limited value for aerial surveys. Also, hearing protectors can reduce fatigue.

Training. Observers must be able to identify eagles and other raptors to species and age class. See Training in the Road Transect section.

Cost. Cost can vary considerably depending on type of survey and aircraft. In the Birds of Prey Area it has taken 20 hours (including ferry time) for two observers to survey 20 transects 80 km (50 mi.) long (BLM unpubl. data). The same survey in a helicopter would take about 30 hours for two people. Costs of surveying specific habitats can vary greatly depending on the amount of ferry time and aircraft used.

Discussion. Both random aerial transects and aerial surveys of specific habitats provide a reliable and expeditious means of assessing raptor presence, including smaller conspicuous species over large areas. Random aerial transects are an effective means to count large raptors over broad areas as demonstrated by the statewide survey of golden eagles in Wyoming (Wrakestraw 1972, 1973). This method is also reliable for assessing age structure of golden eagles for population dynamics studies. Although the method has inherent biases, they affect accuracy more than precision (Caughley 1974), making it a reliable means of assessing relative densities and monitoring long-term population trends. Aerial surveys of wintering habitat can be an accurate and reliable means of surveying bald eagle concentrations, and randomly sampled quadrats could be a reliable way to monitor numbers of wintering raptors in large areas.

Weather, raptor activity, time of day, foliage condition, and snow cover can affect raptor detectability and bias surveys. Biases can be reduced by standardizing survey times, season, and weather conditions. Because observer competence is a major source of variability in survey results, the same experienced observer(s) should conduct all surveys in a particular area with the same pilot (U.S. Fish and Wildlife Service 1983).

Counts at Roosts and Colonies.

All kite species in North America nest either colonially or semi-colonially, and many falconiforms and strigiforms use communal roosts (Newton 1979; Allen and Young 1982). This section focuses on techniques used to locate colonies or communal roosts and to estimate bird numbers. Often the same techniques are used to survey roosts and colonies.

Description. Before searching for roosts or colonies, biologists should identify potential nesting or roosting habitat from aerial photographs and vegetation maps. A common method of locating roosts or colonies employs non-random ground or aerial searches of these potential areas for concentrations of raptors (Bildstein 1979; Fuller and Mosher 1986; Glinski and Ohmart 1983). A few investigators, however, have searched for roosts or colonies by running systematically spaced transects (Sykes 1979). Roost searches are most effective during the last 90 minutes of daylight (Keister 1981). Eagle roosts may be identified by low level aerial photography. Roosts or colonies can also be located by following birds back from feeding areas to the roost or colony by direct observation or with the aid of radio telemetry (Keister 1981). The location of suspected roosts or colonies can be obtained by observing birds from a vantage point, and the exact location and relative size of roosts can be determined from the distribution of feces and castings (Keister 1981).

The most common method of enumerating individuals in a roost or colony is by directly counting the number of birds (Parker 1975; Steenhof 1976; Keister 1981). Night roost counts for diurnal raptors should be made between 60 minutes before sunset to 30 minutes after sunset (Keister 1981). Evening counts are usually more accurate than morning counts (Hein 1961; U.S. Fish and Wildlife Service 1983). Most Mississippi kite nesting colonies are small enough that investigators can enter the colony and count the number of nesting attempts (Parker pers. commun.); however, caution should be taken to minimize disturbance.

Bald eagles are easily counted at winter roost concentrations.

Sometimes roosts are inaccessible, or birds cannot be seen (e.g., northern harriers), and biologists must estimate numbers of individuals by counting birds as they fly to and from roosts (Hein 1961; Bildstein 1979; U.S. Fish and Wildlife Service 1983). This technique has an advantage in that it minimizes disturbance. Hein (1961) gave detailed procedures for conducting roost flight counts. Roosting flight counts should be made from 90 minutes before sunset to 30 minutes after sunset, with a subsequent count the next morning from 30 minutes before sunrise to 90 minutes after sunrise. The maximum number of the two counts should be used. Sometimes several counters stationed around the roost are required when birds depart in different directions (Weller et al. 1955).

Biologists sometimes use flight counts to census nesting colonies (Fuller and Mosher 1981). Glinski and Ohmart (1983) estimated Mississippi kite numbers in colonies by counting birds during courtship, foraging, and predator-mobbing flights. They used these numbers and counts of nesting attempts to estimate the nonbreeding component. Accurate counts, however, can only be made by many periodic visits to the colony or roost starting early in the season (Bildstein 1979; Parker and Ogden 1979). Although long-eared owls can be counted at roosts,

Long-eared owl.

Millsap (pers. commun.) found that morning counts of birds flying to the roost were very similar to direct counts of birds in the roost. This method may also work for short-eared owls. Some investigators have counted these owls by walking through roosts and flushing individuals (Clark 1975), but this is not desirable because of disturbance.

Keister (1981) discussed other methods of enumerating roosting eagles such as thermal infrared remote sensing, radar, and infrared photography. These methods have limited utility for a BLM monitoring or inventory program. However, in the Birds of Prey Area, biologists have experimented with standard photography using 1000 ASA print film to count communally roosting ravens on transmission towers and have had encouraging results (BLM unpubl. data).

Discussion. This method is effective in assessing presence of birds in specific areas. It is also useful in population dynamics studies, and combined with other surveys over a large area, it may also be a means of assessing long-term trends. The number,

distribution, and relative size of colonies and roosts are more important for most monitoring and inventory programs than absolute counts or changes in absolute numbers of individuals. Changes in numbers of individuals may not reflect changes in the population. Many colonial raptors tend to be nomadic (Newton 1979), and changes in bird numbers in a colony or roost may only reflect a local or regional shift. To account for any inter-roost shifts, investigators should periodically make simultaneous counts at all roosts in an area.

Because many factors influence counts at roosts (e.g., weather and shifts in prey abundance), counts should be considered indexes (Bildstein 1979; Fuller and Mosher 1981; Keister 1981; U.S. Fish and Wildlife Service 1983). Although direct counts are indexes, and indirect counts (e.g., flight counts) may underestimate the number of birds (U.S. Fish and Wildlife Service 1983), both methods provide a reliable means of assessing relative abundance. Counts at night roosts provide a more accurate index of wintering bald eagle abundance than day counts on feeding areas (U.S. Fish and Wildlife Service 1983). Compared with other census techniques, roost and colony counts are very reliable. As with any census technique, there are problems with detectability, and when communally roosting birds bunch up they are difficult to count. However, accuracy of counting methods can be increased by taking the average of numerous repeated counts made during a sampling period.

Relative Abundance—Nesting Surveys

General Considerations.

Survey Design. When designing an inventory, investigators should gather all available relevant historical information on the area to be surveyed (Fuller and Mosher 1981). This information can be obtained through the literature, records (e.g., Federal and State agencies, museums, or the Laboratory of Ornithology at Cornell University), and inquiries of local residents, falconers, wildlife managers and biologists, and amateur ornithologists. Because many species have relatively restricted nest site requirements and use structures that last many years (e.g., ledges), historic data can lead one to specific nest sites. Historic information can provide data on species occurrence and distribution.

Inventory or monitoring objectives will determine the sampling approach. In certain unique habitats or areas of special concern, like the Birds of Prey Area, biologists may be required to design systematic searches of the entire area staggered over the nesting period (U.S. Bureau of Land Management 1979). However, in most situations, investigators will not be able to survey the entire area, and the most efficient approach in terms of time and people is to sample the area in a simple random or stratified random manner.

Biologists should consider quadrat sampling to estimate populations over large areas (King et al. 1972; Grier 1977; Postovit 1979; Grier et al. 1981; Gilmer and Stewart 1984). Quadrats are randomly selected from grids on maps or aerial photos. Selections can be simple random or stratified to habitat characteristics or quality. Investigators can survey either the entire quadrat or just the primary nesting habitat (e.g., shorelines or cliffs) within the quadrat. Quadrat sampling provides population estimates with confidence limits (Grier 1977), and quadrats can be easily monitored with statistical comparisons among surveys (Hodges et al. 1979). Surveys that include more than primary habitat may be more precise (Leighton et al. 1979).

To survey long stretches of linear habitat (e.g., cliff, shoreline, or riparian areas), biologists can divide the habitat into equal segments and select segments to survey on a stratified random basis. Each segment can be treated as a sample plot for statistical comparisons. Random sampling of segments gives an inference of the entire habitat stretch sampled, but non-randomly-sampled segments give information only on the segment sampled.

Locating Nests and Nesting Areas. Successful location of raptor nests or nesting areas requires knowledge of the distribution, habitat relationships, nesting chronology, spacing, and nesting behavior of the species or group of species to be surveyed. This knowledge and understanding can be derived from several sources (Craighead and Craighead 1956; Call 1978; Newton 1979; and various technical notes available from the BLM Service Center).

Typical ferruginous hawk nest on rock outcrop.

For a territory to be classified "occupied," it must satisfy the criteria for occupancy (see Productivity section). There are a variety of visible signs that advertise raptor occupancy and nesting attempts (Craighead and Craighead 1956; Call 1978; Jones 1979; Fuller and Mosher 1981, 1986; Reynolds 1982; Forsman 1983b). These signs differ with species and nesting habitat. In cliff areas, rocks stained with feces (whitewash) are the primary feature. Decorated or repaired nests, perches, plucking perches, and regurgitated pellets are also important. In forested areas, stick nests, perches, molted feathers, plucking perches, and prey remains below a nest are common signs of occupancy.

Behavioral observations are also important for locating nests. These include courtship displays, food carries, food transfers, copulation, nest building, active defense and calling by adults, and food begging by young (Craighead and Craighead 1956; Call 1978; Jones 1979; Fuller and Mosher 1981; Reynolds 1982; Mindell 1983). A single observation of an unrepaired nest does not mean the site is vacant (Fuller and Mosher 1981). Nesting areas should be visited more than once to confirm vacancy.

Biases. Many factors influence detection of nests and nesting areas (Fuller and Mosher 1981, 1986). Visibility biases are influenced by light conditions, time of day, weather, type of nesting habitat, seasonal changes in the habitat, seasonal changes in the behavior of raptors, and observer competence and experience (Craighead and Craighead 1956; Henny et al. 1974, 1977; Postovit 1979; Grier et al. 1981). Raptor behavior can bias observations; secretive raptors that stay away from nests are easily missed, whereas extremely aggressive birds are easily found (Craighead and Craighead 1956; Call 1978; Postovit 1979). Also, pairs arriving late and those that have multiple broods (e.g., barn owls) or renest can influence accuracy because they are often missed.

Aerial Surveys.

Description. Boeker (1970), Hickman (1972), Roseneau (1972), Grier (1977), Fraser (1978), Leighton et al. (1979), and Grier et al. (1981) described techniques for surveying cliff and tree nesting raptors with fixed-wing aircraft. They discussed types of aircraft, safety precautions, and costs, and stressed the need to retain only experienced pilots. Observers fly predetermined routes and search for nests, presence of adults, or other signs of occupancy. Surveys for conspicuous bald eagle and osprey nests are flown relatively fast at speeds between 112 and 160 km/h (70-100 mph) at about 100 m (325 ft) AGL (Grier et al. 1981). Cliff nesting surveys tend to be flown slower (between 72 and 112 km/h [45 and 70 mph]) at distances of 15-62 m (50-200 ft) from the cliff (Boeker 1970; Hickman 1972; Roseneau 1972). Observers fly slightly below the rim, scan the cliff, and search for evidence of occupancy. Often a second pass is required to determine the nest contents, and these approaches should be made going "down hill" after checking air movement (Boeker 1970). Additional passes in a tiered fashion descending down the cliff are necessary to completely cover large cliff faces.

White and Sherrod (1973) and Carrier and Melquist (1976) described survey techniques and safety precautions for surveying from a helicopter. Techniques for locating nests are similar to those for fixed-wing aircraft. A desired speed to survey cliffs is 48-70 km/h (30-40 mph), and open nests on powerline structures can be adequately surveyed at 80-96 km/h (50-60 mph). Once a suspected nest is located, observers can hover or slow to speeds less than 32 km/h (20 mph) to provide a better view of the nest. I have found that glare on the helicopter bubble reduces one's ability to see nests; this can be remedied by removing the door. White and Sherrod (1973) advised approaching nests from upwind to avoid hitting flushed birds; however, Carrier and Melquist (1976) did not believe this was a problem. Many times downwind approaches are necessary in canyon surveys for hovering or maneuvering at slow speeds. Biologists and pilots should always be alert because occasionally birds will attack the aircraft or fly in its path (Nelson pers. commun.).

Surveys can be systematic grids of an area, random quadrat samples of an area, or random or nonrandom surveys of nesting habitat (see General Considerations). Systematically spaced transects are used primarily to survey entire areas for tree-nesting species (Petersen 1979). Both fixed-wing and helicopter nest surveys should be made with at least two observers on calm (winds less than 24 km/h [15 mph]) days (Carrier and Melquist 1976; Grier et al. 1981). Helicopters, however, are more stable and effective in winds greater than 24 km/h (15 mph) (Call 1978). Surveys can be conducted at any time of day, but mornings are usually the best time for canyon surveys because of the reduced wind conditions. Although Grier et al. (1981) found no difference in visibility due to season, if possible, observers should survey tree-nesting raptors before foliation in deciduous forests. Also, possible errors can be avoided by observers recording observations independently.

Accuracy and Precision. Two types of error characterize aerial nesting surveys: failure to locate occupied sites and failure to properly classify them. Estimates are conservative at best because some birds and nests are not seen, and visibility biases are common and often unavoidable (Caughley 1974; Grier 1977).

Accuracy varies with species surveyed, observers, and number of flights in each survey. Henny et al. (1974, 1977) calculated that only about 64% of the occupied osprey sites on various substrates were located in a single, fixed-wing flight. Accuracy for similar single-flight surveys of cliff-nesting golden eagles was estimated at 81% (Phillips et al. 1984). Accuracy of single flight fixed-wing surveys for occupied breeding areas of tree nesting bald eagles in three areas ranged between 84 and 85% (Leighton et al. 1979; Grier et al. 1981; Fraser et al. 1983). Accuracy increased to 98% by adding a second flight (Grier et al. 1981). Although differences were not significant, the proportion of bald eagle tree nests found by experienced observers ranged from 67 to 87% (Grier et al. 1981). Specific data are lacking for the smaller, less conspicuous raptors (gyrfalcons, rough-legged hawks, and red-tailed hawks). Accuracy of surveys for these species may be lower than those for eagles, considering accuracy in locating osprey pairs (Henny 1974, 1977) and raven tree nests (12%; Grier et al. 1981).

Little has been published on accuracy of nest surveys from helicopters. In a single-flight survey, Wier (1982) located seven of the eight (88%) golden eagle, rough-legged hawk, and gyrfalcon nesting attempts on a cliff in Alaska. Birds of Prey Area personnel located 96% of a sample of 48 golden-eagle nesting attempts during a single flight (BLM unpubl. data). Accuracy of occupancy classifications may be related to the proportion of pairs laying eggs. In a single-flight occupancy survey for cliff-nesting golden eagles during incubation, Birds of Prey Area personnel correctly classified 88% of 77 sites when only 67% of the pairs laid eggs; however, all sites were correctly classified during a year when all pairs bred (BLM unpubl. data). Most of the misclassified nesting areas contained nonbreeding pairs.

Timing and classification criteria can also influence accuracy of aerial surveys. Surveys for occupancy are most accurate after completion of all clutches, but before the first brood hatches (Fraser et al. 1983; Steenhof 1986). Fraser (1978) increased accuracy in classifying bald eagle breeding areas for occupancy from 85% to 89% when criteria required that only one adult instead of two be seen in the breeding area. However, sites where one bird is observed must satisfy the criteria for occupancy (see Productivity section), and biologists must note whether one or two birds were seen on their surveys so data can be compared with other studies. If they find no evidence of egg laying, no freshly decorated nests, and only a single adult, the site should be revisited, preferably on the ground, to verify occupancy (Steenhof 1986).

Fixed-wing aerial surveys are fairly precise for locating occupied bald eagle territories (Grier 1977; Leighton et al. 1979). However, the precision of extrapolating population estimates from random aerial survey blocks appears low. Leighton et al. (1979) calculated that their aerial surveys of random blocks could not detect population changes of less than 27%. Surveyors can refine precision by stratified random sampling (Grier 1977). However, Grier and Hamilton (1978) observed no reduction in variance when they subsampled clusters of random samples on a stratified basis using optimum allocation of samples. Fraser (1978) found that when he included a single adult bald eagle at the nest, or single adults or pairs away from the nest in his criteria for site occupancy, it increased accuracy but reduced precision.

Equipment. Often local availability will determine the type of aircraft to be used. Smaller fixed-wing aircraft (e.g., Piper Super Cub) may be better for raptor nest surveys than larger ones (Cessna 180 or 182) because smaller craft are slower, more maneuverable, and offer better observer visibility (Hickman 1972; Roseneau 1972; Grier et al. 1981). For helicopter surveys, the smaller jet-turbine aircraft (e.g., Hiller/Soloy) may be more effective because of lower hourly cost and the ability to hover in unstable air conditions. However, if surveys involve a large amount of ferry distance, the faster medium-sized helicopters (e.g., Bell Jet Ranger) are more efficient.

Cost. Depending on the aircraft, fixed wing surveys cost 1/3 (Cessna 180) to 1/10 (Piper Super Cub) of an equivalent ground survey. A Super Cub took 25% less survey time per linear mile (1.6 km) of cliff to locate golden eagle nests than did the Cessna 180 and 98% less time than ground surveys (Boeker 1970; Hickman 1972). Quadrat surveys for tree nesting bald eagles covered 150 km² (58 mi.²)/h using a Cessna 180 and 71 km² (28 mi.²)/h with a Piper Super Cub (King et al. 1972; Grier 1977; Hodges et al. 1979). By cluster sampling, Grier and Hamilton (1978) reduced their flight time by 15%. Considering salaries, travel, and per diem, helicopter surveys cost about 5% less than that of equivalent ground surveys, and they were completed 10 times faster (Carrier and Melquist 1976; BLM unpubl. data).

Discussion. Aerial surveys are most successful with large conspicuous raptors that have high visibility, limited nesting habitat, and synchronized nesting cycle (Henny et al. 1977; Call 1978; Leighton et al. 1979). Although aerial nesting surveys have been successful for ospreys, gyrfalcons, rough-legged hawks, and goshawks (McGowan 1975; Call 1978; Fuller and Mosher 1981), they are most accurate for bald and golden eagles. Accuracy appears to decrease for smaller, less conspicuous raptors. Although peregrine falcons, snowy owls, great horned owls, and red-tailed hawks have also been surveyed by aircraft, these surveys have usually supplemented ground searches (Fuller and Mosher 1981). The technique has limited value on cavity-nesting raptors (e.g., prairie falcons, owls; Call 1978).

Aerial surveys can be more effective than ground surveys because they cost less, they are an expeditious means of surveying large areas, and they provide ready access to remote country. Investigators, however, must consider many factors when choosing an aircraft. Although more costly in comparison, helicopters provide more visibility (they can hover to allow a better view of nests), better maneuverability and stability, and in many instances, greater accuracy than fixed-wing aircraft. Furthermore, helicopters can land in the field for ground inspection of nests.

Aerial surveys have many biases and limitations (Fuller and Mosher 1981, 1986). Detectability and classification biases are most important, and can be reduced by supplementing flights with follow-up ground searches or flying additional surveys. Also, problems with precision can be reduced with larger sample sizes. The technique is fairly repeatable, and if biologists work within the limitations of these biases, it can be a reliable means of surveying large areas.

Calling Surveys.

Detection of calls has been used primarily to survey owls, but recently the technique has been applied to some falconiforms (Fuller and Mosher 1981). Every North American owl species, except the common barn-owl, snowy owl, short-eared owl, and northern hawk-owl, has responded to human broadcasted owl vocalizations (Foster 1965; Martin 1973; Call 1978; Fuller and Mosher 1981; Hayward 1983). Falconiforms presently known to respond to these calls are the red-shouldered hawk, red-tailed hawk, broad-winged hawk, goshawk, Cooper's hawk, sharp-shinned hawk, common black-hawk, gray hawk, and zone-tailed hawk (Fuller and Mosher 1981; Rosenfield et al. 1985; Mosher et al. unpubl. ms.; Millsap pers. commun.).

Description. Two basic methods are used to locate raptors by their calls. The first is to listen for calls and note their location. This method, used mainly to supplement other survey techniques, entails walking or driving through an area and periodically listening for calls. The other method is to elicit responses either by imitating calls or broadcasting recordings of calls; responses can be either return calling or the silent approach of a bird. This method involves periodic broadcasting of calls followed by periods of silence during which surveyors look and listen for responses (Forsman et al. 1977; Fuller and Mosher 1981; Forsman 1983b).

Raptors can be surveyed by the continuous transect method (Forsman et al. 1977; Forsman 1983b) or the calling station method (Fuller and Mosher 1981). In the continuous transect method, investigators walk along a road and play recorded calls at fixed intervals (often every 15-20 sec). After a bird responds, surveyors move a fixed distance (often 0.8 km or 0.5 mi.) down the road (presumably out of the responding owl's territory) before calling again. A relative density estimate of the number of pairs per linear distance is calculated from this method.

The calling station method involves broadcasting calls from established stations. Stations can be non-randomly placed in specific habitat types or placed at fixed distances to ensure full coverage of an area (Siminski 1976; Smith 1978; Springer 1978). Stations can be systematically placed along a road or transect (sometimes called point count transects; Simpson 1972; Ellison 1980; Mosher et al. unpubl. ms.), along parallel transects to form a grid (Cink 1975), or in quadrats randomly selected from a grid (Nowicki 1974). Calls are usually broadcast for 15 seconds followed by a 15-60 second listening period, after which the sequence is repeated. Investigators usually call at each stop for 4 to 15 minutes. Mosher et al. (unpubl. ms.) recommended that observers look and listen for an additional 5 minutes before proceeding to the next stop. Also at each stop they broadcast to one side of the road, turned the speaker 180 degrees and broadcast again, and repeated this process until three recordings had been broadcast to each side of the road. In contrast, Balding and Dibble (1984) played calls through four speakers each pointed in a different direction. Relative densities derived by this method can be reported as the number of birds per calling station, number of birds per linear distance, or number of birds in an area.

Call surveys should be conducted under relatively calm conditions with no precipitation or fog (Simpson 1972; Forsman et al. 1977; Smith 1978; Springer 1978; Forsman 1983b). Minimum data to be recorded at each calling stop are weather (at least temperature, precipitation, wind speed, and cloud cover), moon phase, terrain, vegetation, and raptor response. If a response is elicited, investigators should record species, approximate location, time of response, type of response (vocal or visual), habitat type, and sex (if distinguishable). However, inexperienced observers may not be able to distinguish between sexes.

Most researchers call owls at night, usually between 30 minutes after sunset to 1 hour before sunrise (Bell 1964; Simpson 1972; Nowicki 1974; Forsman et al. 1977; Hayward 1983); however, Siminski (1976) and Springer (1978) successfully called great horned owls during daylight. Little information exists on when owl calling is most successful. Some workers believe time of night has no effect (Cink 1975); however, nesting barred owls appeared most responsive near the middle of the night (Smith 1978), and wintering eastern screech-owls responded more towards dawn (Beatty 1977).

Calling for nesting diurnal raptors is usually conducted between 30 minutes after sunrise to mid-morning, and birds may be more responsive toward mid-morning (Balding and Dibble 1984; Mosher et al. unpubl. ms.; Millsap pers. commun.). Responses to calls appear to be immediate, mostly within 5 minutes of broadcasting (Rosenfield et al. 1985; Mosher et al. unpubl. ms.). Although hawks respond to calls during all stages of the nesting cycle (Mosher et al. unpubl. ms.), Cooper's hawks appeared to be less responsive during incubation (Rosenfield et al. 1985).

If the objective is to estimate the number of birds present in an area, it is important to know the range over which the sample is being taken. However, biologists should avoid using the absolute measure, number of birds per unit area, because not all birds respond to calls. However, some researchers have calculated number of birds responding per unit area by dividing the area contained in an arbitrarily delineated study area by the number of birds responding to calls (Siminski 1976; Springer 1978; Smith 1978). This measure is meaningless if the entire area is not covered by vocalizations. Conversely, it may overestimate the density if it draws birds in from outside the study area. To estimate the number of birds in a large area, Nowicki (1974) randomly selected quadrats from the area and calculated a density based on the number of owls responding, divided by the area contained in all sample quadrats. Total number of owls were estimated by multiplying this figure by the size of the total study area. This method is valid if quadrats are randomly selected, the entire area of the quadrat is covered by the calls, and no owls from adjacent quadrats are drawn in and respond to the calls.

Some researchers estimated the distance their broadcast calls carried and used this "effective listening distance" to determine the size of their sampling area (Cink 1975). This approach has many biases. Vegetation and topography influence the distance that calls carry, and effective listening distances based on human detection may be inaccurate because of differences between raptor and human hearing (Nowicki 1974; Fuller and Mosher 1981). However, one should know the audio range and effectiveness of equipment. Mosher et al. (unpubl. ms.) measured sound levels from their equipment and suggested that vocalizations would be audible to about 800 m (2640 ft), at which distance sound levels were similar to background noise (30-40 dB); however, they believed calls could carry up to 1.6 km (1.0 mi.).

Sometimes owls are difficult to locate, and when many birds simultaneously respond to the calls, individuals or pairs are difficult to differentiate. Also many owls, particularly flammulated owls, have ventriloquial abilities which make it extremely difficult to pinpoint the source of the call without considerable effort (Millsap pers. commun.). To more precisely locate calling barred owls, Bell (1964) triangulated from two stations. When western screech-owl and elf owl nests were concentrated (50 m [165 ft] apart) in limited riparian zones, Johnson et al. (1979) placed at least three people 50-100 m (165-330 ft) apart to differentiate among simultaneously responding pairs. At best, locations of responding owls are estimates, and often a reasonable estimate is extremely difficult. This problem is compounded because birds responding to calls may approach the caller beyond the limits of their normal home range or territory (Reynolds pers. commun.). This can impose great limitations when assigning habitat types based on call responses.

Accuracy and Precision. Although certain raptors respond to calls year-round (Foster 1965), vocalization surveys are most reliable during the breeding season (Fuller and Mosher 1981). Not all individuals will respond to calls (Nowicki 1974; Beatty 1977; Johnson et al. 1979; Balding and Dibble 1984). Siminski (1976), Forsman et al. (1977), and Springer (1978) found that from 75 to 85% of the nesting spotted owls and great horned owls in their study areas responded to broadcasted calls. Male owls appear to be more responsive to broadcasted calls than females (Siminski 1976; Springer 1978). Results on accuracy of this method on diurnal raptors are preliminary (Mosher pers. commun.). However, Mosher et al. (unpubl. ms.) found a significant positive correlation between the number of nesting

diurnal pairs and the number of responses to recorded calls of conspecifics. To increase accuracy, they recommended calling on ten different occasions during the nesting season and establishing more and longer transects when surveying large areas.

Equipment. Necessary equipment consists of a cassette tape player, amplifier, speaker, and cassette tape recordings of calls. Surveyors have used many kinds of tape recorders, amplifiers, and speakers that have ranged from simple units to sophisticated component systems. Examples are the Model 600 BM Game Tape Caller (Springer 1978), Sony Model TC 100 Tape Recorder (Smith 1978), and Marantz C-205 Tape Recorder with 10-in. (25-cm), 8-ohm trumpet speakers (Mosher et al. unpubl ms.). Regardless of equipment, its audible range should be no less than 0.4 km (1/4 mi.). Mosher et al. (unpubl. ms.) recommended a tape player with a frequency of about 40 Hz to 12 kHz and a power output of about 1.2 watts at 1 kHz. Some owls have local dialects which could make them less responsive to calls of the same species from a different geographic region (Siminski 1976; Fuller and Mosher 1981). Surveyors should try to use calls recorded in the geographic region where the survey is being conducted.

Taped vocalizations are available from the following sources:

Laboratory of Ornithology
Cornell University
Sapsucker Woods
Ithaca, NY 14850

National Audubon Society
Western Education Center
376 Greenwood Beach Road
Tiburon, CA 94920

National Geographic L.P. Records
National Geographic Society
17th & M Streets NW
Washington, DC 20036

Oregon State Office
Bureau of Land Management
P.O. Box 2965
Portland, OR 97208 (for spotted owl tapes)

Training. Investigators must be thoroughly familiar with the repertoire of calls (including any differences between sexes) of the species they are surveying. Training for both new and experienced surveyors is essential. Listening to recorded calls from the many field guide series is the simplest repertoire of the species (Johnson et al. 1979). It may be necessary to obtain taped calls from an expert on a particular species.

Cost. Vocalization surveys are relatively inexpensive to conduct, and fairly large areas can be surveyed in a short period of time. Forsman et al. (1977) surveyed an average of 12.8 km (8.0 mi.) of road per night using the continuous transect method. Ellison (1980) averaged 12 calling stations per night. Using the procedure recommended by Mosher et al. (unpubl. ms.), it is possible for one person to complete 16 calling stations or cover 12.8 km (8.0 mi.) of transect in 4 hours if all stations are easily accessible.

Discussion. Vocalization surveys result in significantly more bird contacts than simply looking and listening for inconspicuous raptors. They greatly reduce the time required to find birds and may be the only reliable means to locate owls and forest-inhabiting hawks. Although responsiveness varies with species, the method is reliable for assessing species occurrence (Mosher pers. commun.). Results suggest that calling from point counts can be useful in developing indexes to local populations and perhaps for estimates of density (Mosher et al. unpubl. ms.). Accuracy, however, is reduced when the method is used to count individuals in a given area. Estimates of birds in an area should only be used if it is certain that the broadcast calls covered the sample area. Otherwise, a more realistic measure of relative density would be number of birds per linear distance (Forsman et al. 1977) or contacts per station (Ellison 1980).

Although the method is used to assess relative abundance of nesting raptors, it is valuable in supplementing road counts and other types of nest searches (Fuller and Mosher 1981). Biologists use nocturnal calling to obtain the general location of spotted owl territories and diurnal calling to specifically locate roosts and nests (Forsman 1983b). To locate diurnal raptor nests, biologists concentrate their searches in areas where most contacts occur (Mosher et al. unpubl. ms.) or search in the direction of departing birds after a contact has been made (Rosenfield et al. 1985). Whenever possible, surveyors should supplement call surveys with ground searches for birds or nests. These searches are essential to confirm breeding attempts, and they also serve to assess survey accuracy.

Investigators should be cautious when using broadcast calls alone to assess relative densities because several factors contribute to the difficulty in estimating numbers, and many variables can influence the reliability of a vocal census. Fuller and Mosher (1981) discussed the main variables, including time of year, time of day, behavioral differences, and differences in vocalizations and in responses between sexes. Both sexes of the great horned owl, spotted owl, screech-owl, and flammulated owl respond to calls, and there may be sexual differences in call responses (Marshall 1939; Siminski 1976; Forsman et al. 1977; Springer 1978; Smith 1978; Johnson et al. 1979). They demonstrate sexual differences in the pitch of their calls; the male call is softer and lower. Also, one cannot assume if a male responds to a call that a pair is occupying a territory, because many responding males may not be paired, and unpaired male spotted owls and flammulated owls appear more responsive during the nesting season (Reynolds pers. commun.).

Spotted owl.

Great horned owl.

Equipment and environmental variables can also affect response rates (Fuller and Mosher 1981). Background noise produced by the equipment or the environment (e.g., traffic noise) may interfere with efficient transmission and should be avoided if possible. Effects of wind on sound transmission and the observer's ability to hear the calls vary with the habitat type but have less of an influence in open habitats. Steep terrain, thick vegetation, and running water can greatly restrict the audible distance of the call or the observer's ability to hear a response. Response rates may be affected by the lunar cycle, and owls may be more responsive during a bright, waxing moon (Johnson et al. 1979). Ellison (1980) adjusted his systematic calling sequence monthly to avoid synchronizing calling station visits with the moon phase.

Surveyors need to understand ranges and dispersion of target species pairs. If call stops are too far apart, some birds may be missed, and if too close, the same pair may be counted twice. Mosher et al. (unpubl. ms.) recommended stations spaced at 0.8 km (0.48 mi.) for larger raptors; however, points can be only 0.25 km (790 ft) for smaller raptors such as screech-owls. It is worthwhile to test the audio range of equipment on raptors in a known location in the vegetational and topographic areas to be sampled.

Certain factors should be considered when broadcasting calls. Johnson et al. (1981) believed that if western screech-owls were censused too often they could become habituated to broadcasts and be less responsive; however, Mosher et al. (unpubl. ms.) saw no indication of this with diurnal raptors. When calling different species from the same station, Call (1978) recommended that calls of the smallest species be played first because response behavior of the smaller species may be inhibited by the vocalization of a larger owl. However, some researchers do not recommend calling different species from the same station because of the possible biases (Mosher pers. commun.).

Ground Surveys.

I include searches by foot, horseback, boat, and land vehicle (e.g., automobile, motorcycle, bicycle) in this category. The methods involve similar techniques, allow time for close inspection, and are often used to complement each other.

Description. Biologists should be concerned with collecting two types of data during ground surveys: the general location of a pair (i.e., nesting territory) and the exact nest location. The latter requires more time and effort, and slightly different

techniques. In most monitoring programs it is not necessary to determine the exact nest location. Therefore, biologists should only be concerned with obtaining general locations of pairs unless specific management needs require the exact locations of nests. Biologists should use multiple techniques; one negative observation does not necessarily mean that a site is vacant. Subsequent visits and checks for signs of occupancy should be made before concluding vacancy.

Surveyors must be aware of the potential hazards from disturbance caused by nest searches. Precautions are discussed by Fyfe and Olendorff (1976), Call (1978), and Steenhof and Kochert (1982). Although investigators need to locate nests before hatching, they must observe them from a safe distance and avoid entering nests and disturbing parent birds until the young can thermoregulate (Steenhof and Kochert 1982).

Craighead and Craighead (1956), Call (1978), Jones (1979), Reynolds (1982), and Forsman (1983b) described survey techniques for forest-nesting raptors. To determine general nest locations in deciduous forests, biologists often canvass wooded areas before foliation in the spring and look for stick nests. These searches are often supplemented by aerial surveys (Petersen 1979). Observations of aerial courtship displays of raptors above the canopy yield the general nest location for signs of occupancy (see General Considerations) and defending adults are required to locate the nest. Workers sometimes locate pairs and follow them to nests (Village 1984). Searches for forest-nesting raptors, especially cavity nesting owls, are facilitated by calling surveys (Forsman 1983b; Fuller and Mosher 1986). Occupancy of suspected cavities by smaller raptors may be confirmed by rapping the tree and observing the bird at the cavity entrance (Call 1978); however, this does not necessarily mean there is a nest in it. Also, this method may not be reliable because certain species, such as flammulated owls, are seldom brought to the cavity entrance by rapping (Reynolds pers. commun.). Exact nest locations of spotted owls have been determined by baiting the birds with a tethered mouse and following the owl with prey back to its nest (Forsman 1983b).

Call (1978) and Mindell (1983) discussed survey techniques for cliff-nesting raptors; decorated stick nests, whitewash on the cliff, and behavior of adult birds are the most commonly used clues. Cliffs should be surveyed early in the nesting season to obtain general locations of breeding pairs and to locate stick nests. These searches are often later augmented by aerial surveys. If the nest or scrape is not located during the early survey, a thorough search of the general location for field signs (see General Considerations) or defending adults is required to determine the exact nest location. To locate scrapes, some workers have flushed falcons by clapping hands or throwing rocks. These techniques should be used with caution because they disturb birds, and they may not be totally reliable because some birds do not flush when disturbed (BLM unpubl. data). Sometimes the only way to locate nests involves many hours of observing the cliff and watching for adults or young.

Searches for ground nesters sometimes require unique techniques. General nesting locations of harriers and other ground-nesting raptors are obtained by observing consistent nesting behavior (i.e., courtship flights, territorial defense, copulation, prey exchanges, and nest building) in an area; however, behavior must be interpreted with caution because unmated harriers sometimes exhibit courtship behavior (Call 1978; Thompson-Hanson 1984). Exact nest locations can be determined by observing the female flying consistently to the same spot with prey during the brood-rearing period or by systematically searching a general nesting location, sometimes with a trained dog (Call 1978; Thompson-Hanson 1984). Burrowing owl nests are located by observing perched owls, prey remains, and perches in areas with burrows (Call 1978).

Accuracy and Precision. Little published information exists on accuracy and precision of ground surveys for nesting raptors; however, accuracy varies with species, habitat, and methods. In most instances, foot surveys are most accurate because observers are able to see inconspicuous nests (Fuller and Mosher 1981), and accuracy increases with each subsequent survey (Craighead and Craighead 1956; Postovit 1979). As with the other methods, surveys are most accurate after completion of all clutches, but before the first brood hatches. Village (1984) showed a 20-30% decrease in accuracy when European kestrel (Falco tinnunculus) nests were visited on foot late in the season because he missed nonbreeding pairs and those which failed early. Craighead and Craighead (1956) used both foot and vehicle surveys of a deciduous forest area; they believed that 85% of all raptor nests were easily found and the remaining 15% required numerous repeated searches. Olendorff (1975) believed that by using repeated vehicle and foot surveys he located over 95% of the raptor pairs nesting on trees and cliffs in a grassland area. Large conspicuous nests are easily found; Hodges and Robards (1982) believed that a trained observer could locate 90% of the bald eagle nests within 200 m (660 ft) of the shoreline in a single pass in a boat and accurately assess nesting status of 90% of the nests as well. Accuracy for boat surveys of cliff-nesting falcons would probably be much less.

Village (1984) presented two sources of error in assessing nesting density: (1) study areas are not chosen at random, and (2) nests may be more easily missed in large study areas than small ones. This problem is compounded because clusters of sightings, normally recorded as one pair, may be two pairs. Biases can be so large that they may have masked any variation in breeding density.

Precision of ground surveys can vary greatly depending on size of the sampling unit, sampling intensity, and number of species surveyed. Postovit (1979) refined precision of raptor surveys of a 223 km^2 (93 mi.^{2}) area 2.6 times (from 63 to 24% based on 95% confidence intervals) by reducing sample quadrat size from 2.56 km^2 to 0.65 km^2 (1.02 mi.^{2} to 0.26 mi.^{2}) and increasing sampling intensity from 10 to 33% of the study area. However, surveys still lacked sensitivity, and population changes less than 39% could not be detected. Because precision may be increased by sampling a large proportion of an area in a short period using a correction factor for visibility bias (Postovit 1979), other more intensive surveys may be more precise. Stratified random sampling apparently does not increase precision when surveying a collection of raptor species (Postovit 1979), but it increases precision when sampling for a single species that occurs in restricted habitats (Leighton et al. 1979; Grier et al. 1981).

Equipment. Binoculars (at least 7x35) and a spotting scope (minimum 20x) with a sun shade are essential.

Training. Observer competence is one of the many factors that influence accuracy of nesting surveys. Survey manuals (e.g., Call 1978) and short courses are helpful; however, novice biologists should survey with an experienced biologist until they have developed a satisfactory "search image."

Cost. Cost will vary depending on species and accessibility, and ruggedness and remoteness of the terrain. Village (1984) believed that one full-time worker could properly survey about 100 km^2 (39 mi.^{2}) of reasonably accessible habitat for European kestrels during a nesting season. When travel costs and salaries are considered, ground surveys cost nearly the same as equivalent helicopter surveys and more than fixed-wing surveys.

Discussion. Ground surveys are most effective for inconspicuous secretive raptors. This method, especially on foot, is useful for intensive searches of small areas of specialized habitat; however, these searches are the most time-consuming of all. Surveys on foot or horseback may be more accurate than those by boat or automobile because the former allow for closer inspection. These techniques, however, should complement each other. Large areas can be surveyed quickly by automobile, and boats provide ready access to remote areas. However, these surveys have some error, and questionable nesting areas should be reinspected on foot.

Although ground surveys may be the most accurate survey method for nesting raptors, they have certain limitations and biases (Postovit 1979; Steenhof and Kochert 1982; Steenhof 1986; Fuller and Mosher 1986). Observer and visibility biases are most significant, and because of possible poor precision, especially with sampling of large areas, there may be problems using single surveys to monitor nesting populations. Biases can be reduced and precision increased by repeated surveys of sample areas, increased sample size, and by using only experienced surveyors. However, ground surveys are time-consuming, and time is one of the main limitations of the technique. This problem can be reduced by augmenting ground surveys with more expedient methods (e.g., aerial surveys).

Productivity Surveys

Data Collection and Analysis.

General Considerations. Data on raptor reproductive rates are useful to managers for assessing the status and reproductive health of a raptor population. Information required, biases, and timing of productivity surveys are briefly discussed in this section. Postupalsky (1974), Steenhof and Kochert (1982), Fraser et al. (1983), and Steenhof (1986) discussed them in more detail.

Productivity Data. Clutch size and number of young hatched usually are not necessary for productivity surveys; however, the following basic information is used for estimates of reproductive success and production (Steenhof 1986):

(1) *Number of pairs in the area.* This refers to the number of occupied "breeding areas" or "nesting territories" (Postupalsky 1974; Steenhof 1986). Occupancy classification requires at least one of the following observations during the nesting season:

   (a) Evidence that an egg was laid (i.e., observation of an incubating bird, eggs, eggshell fragments, young, or a decorated nest with fresh prey and feces).

   (b) Observation of two breeding-age birds that appear to be paired within a nesting territory.

(c) Observations of one or more birds attending a nest, engaging in reproductive behavior, or defending an area.

Some researchers disagree with the last criterion, but observation of one adult attending a nest or defending an area usually constitutes enough evidence that a pair is present (Steenhof 1986). Also the presence of a freshly decorated nest usually is evidence of occupancy for species such as golden eagles and red-tailed hawks. Caution must be used, however, because of the difficulty in distinguishing new nesting material from old, and because wintering birds in some areas decorate nests and then move elsewhere (Steenhof 1986). Areas where only decorated nests are observed should be revisited on the ground to confirm occupancy.

(2) *Number of breeding pairs.* This is the number of pairs that lay eggs (see 1 above); however, this information is not mandatory. Useful information can be obtained without knowing the number of breeding pairs (Steenhof and Kochert 1982). Biologists should remember that observations of raptors near a nest are not always evidence of a breeding attempt (Fuller and Mosher 1981); nonbreeding pairs sometimes decorate or repair nests. Some birds may also assume incubation posture without having laid an egg; but because of the difficulty of distinguishing these situations, birds observed in incubation position should be considered "breeding" for analysis (Steenhof 1986).

(3) *Number of successful pairs.* These are pairs that raise at least one young to "acceptable" fledging age which is defined as 80% of the average age that most young leave the nest (Steenhof and Kochert 1982; Steenhof 1986). Full counts of broods at fledging are not necessary.

(4) *Number of young to reach acceptable fledging age.* The number of young fledged per pair is the most important measure of productivity (Steenhof 1986). This value can be calculated directly from all known pairs or a random sample of preselected pairs in an area. It can also be estimated indirectly by combining independent estimates of percentage breeding, percentage success, and number fledged per successful nest (Steenhof and Kochert 1982; Steenhof 1986).

Red-tailed hawk on nest.

Biases. As with other surveys, two broad types of error can bias productivity surveys: measurement error and sampling error (Steenhof 1986). Measurement error occurs when data are incorrectly collected or interpreted because of the technique, visibility problems, or observer incompetence. Proper timing of surveys can reduce measurement error (Fraser et al. 1983). Also, by calculating a measurement error rate and an estimated standard error, true differences in productivity can be tested where all breeding pairs are known and are repeatedly sampled in a given year (Fraser et al. 1984).

Sampling error occurs when the pairs sampled do not represent the population. Biases can be reduced by randomly selecting pairs (either preselecting known pairs or sampling areas), using only pairs found during or before incubation, or using the Mayfield Model (Mayfield 1961) to calculate success (Steenhof and Kochert 1982). An unbiased estimate of percentage of pairs breeding can be obtained only from samples of traditional pairs selected before the nesting season (Steenhof and Kochert 1982). Only these nests and those found during incubation should be used for calculating reproductive success and productivity; inclusion of pairs found late yields inflated estimates. The Mayfield Model allows workers to maximize use of data sets with small sample sizes by including nests found late in the season (Steenhof 1986). A computer program is available to handle the tedious calculations required by the Mayfield approach (contact the Birds of Prey Research Staff, Boise District, BLM for details).

Timing of Surveys. For single species surveys, a minimum of two surveys are required (Fraser et al. 1983), and more may be necessary (Steenhof 1986). The first survey, to count occupied territories and pairs with eggs, should be done during incubation, ideally after completion of all clutches but before hatching of the first brood. A middle survey may be necessary if there is a wide latitude in nesting chronology. It should be conducted after the oldest broods reach acceptable fledging age but have not left the nest. The function of this survey is to assess fledging of the oldest broods and to age the remaining young to establish the optimal time of the third survey. The last or "productivity" survey should be conducted after the youngest brood reaches acceptable fledging age but before the oldest chicks, who were less than acceptable fledging age on the middle survey, leave the nest. For multiple-species surveys in the Birds of Prey Area, investigators found it necessary to conduct a minimum of four surveys. Because of the wide range in chronology, a second occupancy survey is necessary to compensate for the wide latitude in starting dates (BLM unpubl. data).

Survey Methods

Aerial Surveys.

Description. Techniques for assessing productivity from aircraft are the same as those used during aerial nesting surveys; however, the former requires a closer inspection of the nest contents.

Accuracy and Precision. Aerial productivity surveys are fairly accurate for large conspicuous raptors. An average 82% of the breeding pairs were correctly classified and 86% of the young were seen during fixed-wing surveys of nesting bald eagles (Fraser et al. 1983).

In the Birds of Prey Area, accuracy of helicopter surveys for cliff nesting golden eagles was 86% for assessing breeding status and 95% for counting young (BLM unpubl. data). Accuracy can be enhanced by adjusting survey timing. By properly timing surveys, Fraser et al. (1983) increased accuracy for both estimates by about 12%. Accuracy in the Birds of Prey Area was also increased with properly timed helicopter surveys.

Poole (1981) found fixed-wing surveys of osprey breeding pairs and fledged young were as accurate as ground counts. However, accuracy may be lower for smaller, less conspicuous raptors. During helicopter surveys in the Birds of Prey Area, investigators have been unable to obtain accurate brood counts at some red-tailed and ferruginous hawk nests because the parents covered their young (BLM unpubl. data).

Discussion. Aircraft provide a fast and expeditious way to collect productivity data for large conspicuous raptors, especially if surveys are optimally timed. Multiple productivity surveys are often required and additional flights further increase accuracy (Grier et al. 1981). Aerial surveys can be reliable for monitoring eagle productivity, especially if all breeding sites are known and surveyed at the proper time (Fraser et al. 1984). Lastly, helicopters cost more than fixed-wing aircraft, but they are usually more accurate because they can hover to allow more opportunity to correctly count broods.

Ground Surveys.

Description. Techniques for assessing productivity from ground surveys are the same as those used for nesting surveys except exact location of the nest and inspection of its contents are required. Inspections can be accomplished by distant observations with the aid of telescopes or binoculars; close observations from a nearby vantage point, or with the aid of a mirror attached to a pole (Parker 1972); or by entering nests (Call 1978; Steenhof 1986).

Discussion. The usefulness of methods for inspecting nests depends on survey purpose and environmental conditions (Steenhof 1986). Distant observations are necessary and adequate to confirm an incubating bird, but less useful for brood counts, especially if the entire nest cannot be seen. Climbing into the nest is undoubtedly the most accurate method to obtain productivity data. However, it is extremely time-consuming and causes disturbance to the birds. Close inspections and distant observations require less time but are subject to error. Foliage and topographic features often do not allow full view of the nest or complete brood counts; Millsap (pers. commun.) minimized this error and used a 15 m (49.5 ft) range pole and mirror to count eggs and young in 150 tree nests. He spent an average of 3 minutes at each nest with very little disturbance and high accuracy.

SYSTEMS FOR CORRELATING HABITAT VARIABLES WITH POPULATION MEASUREMENTS

Habitat models provide useful information for management biologists. They can be used to predict potential species occurrence and to evaluate potential habitat quality. The models are also useful in designing an inventory. Biologists are cautioned from using these models alone as a population measure or as a management tool. They still need to inventory the area of concern by using the techniques described in this chapter to gather the information necessary for management decisions.

Climbing into raptor nests is the most accurate method of obtaining productivity information.

Few habitat models have been published. I will discuss those that are available or being developed. The U.S. Fish and Wildlife Service (FWS), Office of Biological Services' Habitat Evaluation Procedures (HEP) Group in Fort Collins, Colorado, has developed Habitat Suitability Index Models for the ferruginous hawk, prairie falcon, sharp-shinned hawk, golden eagle, northern spotted owl, short-eared owl, burrowing owl, and northern harrier. The only published model (Jasikoff 1982) is on ferruginous hawks; others are in draft form. Model narratives describe habitat relationships for the raptor. The FWS's Division of Ecological Services in Anchorage, Alaska, has also developed a draft habitat model for bald eagles. Ellis (1982) developed a system for evaluating the potential for peregrine falcon habitat in Arizona. It provides a good means for predicting possible occurrence, and it may be applied to other habitats in the arid West. Mosher et al. (1985) developed a management model to predict nesting habitat for eastern woodland hawks. Lastly, Stalmaster (1983) developed a detailed energetics model for bald eagles wintering in the Pacific Northwest that determines eagle carrying capacity in salmon spawning drainages and estimates use of salmon by eagles. This model also provides broad scale management recommendations.

DISCUSSION

Raptor inventory and monitoring programs are frequently limited because raptors are often difficult to detect and count. Raptors often occur at relatively low densities in a diversity of habitats, and it is extremely laborious to obtain complete counts of nesting pairs. Estimates usually must be obtained through sampling, and adequate sampling is often costly and arduous.

Design and implementation of a successful raptor inventory or monitoring program is affected by sampling, measurement, and interpretation problems. Many sampling problems affect estimates of numbers and population changes. Although reliable for assessing abundance, the usefulness of many indirect techniques (e.g., calling surveys) is limited if studies do not relate the sample to the actual population size

(Fuller and Mosher 1981). Often relative indexes are of limited value because surveys are not conducted in a standardized manner or samples are not adequately collected for statistical analysis. However, these problems can be eliminated by proper sampling procedures. Real problems occur when logistics prevent implementation of a proper sampling design, when sampling intensity is inadequate to allow the necessary comparisons to be made, or when samples are biased and do not represent the population.

Accurate measurement of raptor populations is also compromised by many biases. The greatest bias is detectability; not all birds can be found or seen. Next is observer competence. Every technique discussed here is affected by these two biases. Their effects can be reduced by adequate sampling intensity and by using only experienced observers. Environmental factors (e.g., weather) and biological variability (e.g., changes in food or bird behavior) also cause error, and each technique has its own inherent measurement biases.

Interpretation problems usually stem from incomplete knowledge of how raptors interact with their environment. For example, lack of knowledge of the effects of climate and food supply hampers one's ability to distinguish true population changes from regional shifts in distribution. Interpretation errors also result from a poor selection of estimators. Some variables may remain the same when the population actually changes. For example, production of successful pairs often will show no change when productivity of the population actually has changed (BLM unpubl. data). To conduct a meaningful inventory and monitoring program, biologists must use those features that best reflect the population (Fuller and Mosher 1986; Steenhof 1986).

These problems can be reduced by using efficient, standardized techniques suitable for use with a diversity of raptor species and habitats. Standardization of estimated variables, including measures of variability (e.g., confidence limits, standard error), is as important as standardization of survey techniques (Fraser 1978). This allows valid comparisons to be made among areas.

Through an understanding of the inherent biases of the methods used to measure raptor populations, surveys can be designed and implemented to give results of optimal accuracy and precision. By recognizing the limitations of the resultant data and the necessity for careful interpretation, it is possible to reach conclusions that are useful and effective inputs to management decisions.

LITERATURE CITED

ALLEN, H.L. and L.S. YOUNG. 1982. An annotated bibliography of avian communal roosting. Washington Dep. Game, Olympia. 177pp.

AMERICAN ORNITHOLOGISTS UNION. 1983. Check-list of North American birds, 6th ed. Allen Press. Lawrence, KS. 877pp.

ANTHONY, R.G., R.L. KNIGHT, G.T. ALLEN, B.R. MCCLELLAND, and J.I. HODGES. 1982. Habitat use by nesting and roosting bald eagles in the Pacific Northwest. Trans. North Am. Wildl. Nat. Resour. Conf. 47:332-342.

APFELBAUM, S.I. and P. SEELBACH. 1983. Nest tree, habitat selection and productivity of seven North American raptors based on the Cornell University nest record card program. Raptor Res. 17:97-113.

BALDING, T. and E. DIBBLE. 1984. Responses of red-tailed, red-shouldered, and broad-winged hawks to high volume playback recordings. Passenger Pigeon 46:71-75.

BAMMANN, A.R. 1975. Ecology of predation and social interactions of wintering white-tailed kites. M.S. Thesis, Humboldt State Univ. Arcata, CA. 81pp.

BEATTY, W.H. 1977. Attracting screech owls. Redstart 44:102-104.

BECHARD, M.J. 1982. Effect of vegetative cover on foraging site selection by Swainson's hawk. Condor 84:153-159.

BECKER, D.M. 1984. Reproductive ecology and habitat utilization of Richardson's merlins in southeastern Montana. M.S. Thesis, Univ. Montana, Missoula. 62pp.

——— and I.J. BALL. 1983a. Prairie falcon (*Falco mexicanus*). Pages 138-153 in Armbruster, J.S. ed. Impacts of Coal Surface Mining on 25 Migratory Bird Species of High Federal Interest. FWS/OBS-83/85. U.S. Dep. Inter., Fish and Wildl. Serv. Fort Collins, CO.

——— and I.J. BALL. 1983b. Merlin (*Falco columbarius*). Pages 124-137 in Armbruster, J.S. ed. Impacts of Coal Surface Mining on 25 Migratory Bird Species of High Federal Interest. FWS/OBS-83/85. U.S. Dep. Inter., Fish and Wildl. Serv., Fort Collins, CO.

BEDNARZ, J.C. and J.J. DINSMORE. 1982. Nest-sites and habitat of red-shouldered hawks and red-tailed hawks in Iowa. Wilson Bull. 94:31-45.

BELL, R.E. 1964. A sound triangulation method for counting barred owls. Wilson Bull. 76:292-294.

BILDSTEIN, K.L. 1978. Behavioral ecology of red-tailed hawks (*Buteo jamaicensis*), rough-legged hawks (*B. lagopus*), northern harriers (*Circus cyaneus*), American kestrels (*Falco sparverius*) and other raptorial birds wintering in south central Ohio. Ph.D. dissertation. Ohio State Univ., Columbus. 364pp.

——— 1979. Fluctuations in the number of northern harriers (*Circus cyaneus hudsonius*) at communal roosts in south central Ohio. Raptor Res. 13:40-46.

BOEKER, E.L. 1970. Use of aircraft to determine golden eagle (*Aquila chrysaetos*) nesting activity. Southwest. Nat. 15:136-137.

——— 1974. Status of golden eagle surveys in the western states. Wildl. Soc. Bull. 2:46-49.

——— and E.B. BOLEN. 1972. Winter golden eagle populations in the Southwest. J. Wildl. Manage. 36:477-484.

BOXALL, P.C. and P.H.R. STEPNEY. 1982. The distribution and status of the barred owl in Alberta, Can. Field-Nat. 96:46-50.

BROWN, D., C. LOWE, and C. PASE. 1980. Digitized systematic classification for ecosystems with an illustrated summary of the natural vegetation of North America. Gen. Tech. Rep. RM-73. U.S. Dep. Agric., For. Serv., Fort Collins, CO. 93pp.

BROWN, L.H. and D. AMADON. 1968. Eagles, hawks and falcons of the world. McGraw-Hill. New York, NY. 945pp.

BULL, E.L. and R.G. ANDERSON. 1978. Notes on flammulated owls in northeastern Oregon. Murrelet 59:26-27.

BURNHAM, K.P., D.R. ANDERSON, and J.L. LAAKE. 1980. Estimation of density from line transect sampling of biological populations. Wildl. Monogr.72. 202pp.

CADE, T.J. 1982. The falcons of the world. Cornell Univ. Press. Ithaca, NY. 188pp.

CALL, M.W. 1978. Nesting habitats and surveying techniques for common western raptors. Tech. Note 316. U.S. Dep. Inter., Bur. Land Manage. Serv. Cen. Denver, CO. 115pp.

CARRIER, W.D. and W.E. MELQUIST. 1976. The use of a rotor-winged aircraft in conducting nesting surveys of ospreys in northern Idaho. Raptor Res. 10:77-83.

CAUGHLEY, G. 1974. Bias in aerial survey. J. Wildl. Manage. 38:921-933.

CINK, C.L. 1975. Population densities of screech owls in northeastern Kansas. Kansas Ornithol. Soc. Bull. 26:13-16.

CLARK, R.J. 1975. A field study of the short-eared owl (*Asio flammeus pontoppidan*) in North America. Wildl. Monogr. No. 47. 67pp.

CLARKE, R.G. 1982. Nest site selection by sharp-shinned hawks in interior Alaska. Pages 155-162 in Ladd, W.N. and P.F. Schempf, eds. Raptor Management Biology in Alaska and Western Canada. FWS/AK/PROC-82. U.S. Dep. Inter., Fish and Wildl. Serv. Anchorage, AK.

COTTRELL, M.J. 1981. Resource partitioning and reproductive success of three species of hawks (*Buteo sp.*) in an Oregon prairie. M.S. Thesis, Oregon State Univ., Corvallis. 72pp.

CRAIG, G.R. 1974. Raptor populations and characteristics studies. Job Prog. Rep. No. W-124-R-1. Colorado Div. Wildl., Denver. 36pp.

CRAIG, T.H. 1978. A car survey of raptors in southeastern Idaho 1974-1976. Raptor Res. 12:40-45.

CRAIGHEAD, J.J. and F.C. CRAIGHEAD. 1956. Hawks, owls, and wildlife. Wildl. Manage. Inst. Washington, DC. 443pp.

ELLIS, D.H. 1982. The peregrine falcon in Arizona: habitat utilization and management recommendations. Rep. 1. Inst. Raptor Stud. Oracle, AZ. 24pp.

ELLISON, P.T. 1980. Habitat use by resident screech owls (*Otus asio*). M.S. Thesis, Univ. Massachusetts, Amherst. 86pp.

EVANS, D.L. 1983. Ferruginous hawk (*Buteo regalis*). Pages 109-123 in Armbruster, ed. Impacts of Coal Surface Mining on 25 Migratory Bird Species of High Federal Interest. FWS/OBS-83/85. U.S. Dep. Inter., Fish and Wildl. Serv. Fort Collins, CO.

FITZNER, R.E. 1980. Behavioral ecology of the Swainson's hawk (*Buteo swainsoni*) in Washington. PNL-2754 UC-11. Battelle Pac. Northwest Lab. Richland, WA. 15pp.

FORBES, J.E. and D.W. WARNER. 1974. Behavior of a radio-tagged saw whet owl. Auk 91:783-795.

FORSMAN, E.D. 1983a. Spotted owl (*Strix occidentalis*). Pages 243-255 *in* Armbruster, J.S. ed. Impacts of Coal Surface Mining on 25 Migratory Bird Species of High Federal Interest. FWS/OBS-83/85. U.S. Dep. Inter., Fish and Wildl. Serv. Fort Collins, CO.

———. 1983b. Methods and materials for locating and studying spotted owls. U.S. Dep. Agric., For. Serv. Gen. Tech. Rep. PNW-162. 8pp.

———, E.C. MESLOW, and M.J. STRUB. 1977. Spotted owl abundance in young versus old-growth forests, Oregon. Wildl. Soc. Bull. 5:43-47.

——— and H.M. WIGHT. 1984. Distribution and biology of the spotted owl in Oregon. Wildl. Monogr. 87. 64pp.

FOSTER, F. 1965. An early reference of the technique of owl calling. Auk 82:651-653.

FRANZREB, K.E. 1981. The determination of avian densities using the variable-strip and fixed-width transect survey methods. Stud. Avian Biol. 6:139-145.

——— and R.D. OHMART. 1978. The effects of timber harvesting on breeding birds in a mixed coniferous forest type. Condor 80:431-441.

FRASER, J.D. 1978. Bald eagle reproductive surveys: accuracy, precision, and timing. M.S. Thesis. Univ. Minnesota, Minneapolis. 82pp.

———, L.D. FRENZEL, J.E. MATHISEN, F. MARTIN, and M.E. SHOUGH. 1983. Scheduling bald eagle reproduction surveys. Wildl. Soc. Bull. 11:13-16.

———, F. MARTIN, L.D. FRENZEL, and J.E. MATHISEN. 1984. Accounting for measurement errors in bald eagle reproduction surveys. J. Wildl. Manage. 48:595-598.

FULLER, M.R. 1979. Spatiotemporal ecology of four sympatric raptor species. Ph.D. dissertation. Univ. Minnesota, Minneapolis. 220pp.

———. 1983. Zone-tailed hawk (*Buteo albonotatus*). Pages 98-108 *in* Armbruster, J.S. ed. Impacts of Coal Surface Mining on 25 Migratory Bird Species of High Federal Interest. FWS/OBS-83/85. U.S. Dep. Inter., Fish and Wildl. Serv. Fort Collins, CO.

——— and J.A. MOSHER. 1981. Methods of detecting and counting raptors: a review. Stud. Avian Biol. 6:235-246.

——— and ———. 1986. Raptor survey techniques *in* Millsap, B.A. and K.W. Kline, eds. Raptor Management Techniques Manual. Vol. 1. Natl. Wildl. Fed. Washington, DC.

——— and J.R. PARTELOW. 1983. Cooper's hawk. (*Accipiter cooperii*). Pages 74-97 *in* Armbruster, J.S. ed. Impacts of Coal Surface Mining on 25 Migratory Bird Species of High Federal Interest. FWS/OBS-83/85. U.S. Dep. Inter., Fish and Wildl. Serv., Fort Collins, CO.

FYFE, R.W. and R.R. OLENDORFF. 1976. Minimizing the dangers of nesting studies to raptors and other sensitive species. Can. Wildl. Serv. Occas. Pap. 23. Can. Wildl. Serv. Ottawa, Ont. 17pp.

GILMER, D.S., L.M. COWARDIN, R.L. DUVAL, L.M. MECHLIN, C.W. SHAIFFER, and V.B. KUECHLE. 1981. Procedures for the use of aircraft in wildlife bio-telemetry studies. Resour. Publ. 140. U.S. Dep. Inter., Fish and Wildl. Serv., Washington, DC. 19pp.

——— and R.E. STEWART. 1984. Swainson's hawk nesting ecology in North Dakota. Condor 82:12-18.

GLINSKI, R.L. and R.D. OHMART. 1983. Breeding ecology of the Mississippi kite in Arizona. Auk 85:200-207.

GRIER, J.W. 1977. Quadrat sampling of a nesting population of bald eagles. J. Wildl. Manage. 41:438-443.

———, J.M. GERRARD, G.D. HAMILTON, and P.A. GRAY. 1981. Aerial visibility bias and survey techniques for nesting bald eagles in northwestern Ontario. J. Wildl. Manage. 45:83-92.

——— and G.D. HAMILTON. 1978. Aerial census of bald eagles in the West Patricia Planning Area. West Patricia Land Use Plan. Wildl. Tech. Rep. 7. Ontario Min. Nat. Resour., Ottawa. 25pp.

GROSSMAN, M.L. and J. HAMLET. 1964. Birds of prey of the world. Bonanza Books, New York, NY. 496pp.

HANCOCK, D. 1964. Bald eagles wintering in the southern Gulf Islands, British Columbia. Wilson Bull. 76:111-120.

HAYWARD, G.D. 1983. Resource partitioning among six forest owls in the River of No Return Wilderness, Idaho. M.S. Thesis. Univ. Idaho, Moscow. 127pp.

HEGDAL, P.L. and R.W. BLASSKIEWICZ. 1984. Evaluation of the potential hazard to barn owls of TALON (brodifacoum bait) used to control rats and house mice. Environ. Toxicol. Chem. 3:167-179.

HEIN, E. 1961. Wood duck roosting flights at Paint Creek, Iowa. Proc. Iowa Acad. Sci. 68:264-270.

HENNY, C.J., M.M. SMITH, and V.D. STOTTS. 1974. The 1973 distribution and abundance of breeding ospreys in the Chesapeake Bay. Chesapeake Sci. 15:125-133.

———, M.A. BYRD, J.A. JACOBS, P.D. McLAIN, M.R. TODD, and B.F. HALLA. 1977. Mid-Atlantic Coast osprey population: present numbers, productivity, pollutant contamination, and status. J. Wildl. Manage. 41:254-265.

HICKMAN, G.L. 1972. Aerial determination of golden eagle nesting status. J. Wildl. Manage. 36:1289-1292.

HODGES, J.I., J.G. KING, and F.C. ROBARDS. 1979. Resurvey of the bald eagle breeding populations in southeast Alaska. J. Wildl. Manage. 43:219-221.

——— and F.C. ROBARDS. 1982. Observations of 3850 bald eagle nests in southeast Alaska. Pages 37-46 *in* Ladd, W.N. and P.F. Schempf, eds. Raptor Management and Biology in Alaska and Western Canada. U.S. Dep. Inter., Fish and Wildl. Serv. FWS/AK/Proc. 82. Anchorage, AK.

HOSKINSON, R.L. 1976. The effect of different pilots on aerial telemetry error. J. Wildl. Manage. 40:137-139.

JASIKOFF, T.M. 1982. Habitat suitability index models: ferruginous hawk. U.S. Dep. Inter., Fish and Wildl. Serv. FWS/BS-82/10.10. Washington, DC. 18pp.

JOHNSON, D.R. and W.E. MELQUIST. 1973. Unique, rare, and endangered raptorial birds of northern Idaho: nesting success and management recommendations. Publ. No. R1-73-021. Univ. Idaho and U.S. Dep. Agric., For. Serv. Moscow, ID. 42pp.

JOHNSON, R.R., B.T. BROWN, L.T. HAIGHT, and J.M. SIMPSON. 1981. Playback recording as a special avian censusing technique. Stud. Avian Biol. 6:68-75.

———, L.T. HAIGHT, and J.M. SIMPSON. 1979. Owl populations and species status in the southwestern United States. Pages 40-59 *in* Schaeffer, P.P. and S.M. Ehlers, eds. Owls of the West: Their Ecology and Conservation. Natl. Audubon Soc. Tiburon, CA.

JONES, S. 1979. Habitat management series for unique or endangered species. Report No. 17 - The accipiters goshawk, Cooper's hawk, sharp-shinned hawk. Tech.

Note 335. U.S. Dep. Inter., Bur. Land Manage. Denver, CO. 51pp.

KEISTER, G.P., Jr. 1981. An assessment of bald eagle communal roosting in northwestern Washington. Wash. Dep. Game, Olympia. 39pp.

——— and R.G. ANTHONY. 1983. Characteristics of bald eagle communal roosts in the Klamath Basin, Oregon and California. J. Wildl. Manage. 47:1072-1079.

KING, J., F.C. ROBARDS, and C.J. LENSINK. 1972. Census of the bald eagle breeding population in southeastern Alaska. J. Wildl. Manage. 36:1292-1295.

KOCHERT, M.N. 1980. Golden eagle reproduction and population changes in relation to jackrabbit cycles: implications to eagle electrocutions. Pages 71-86 in Howard, R.P. and J.F. Gores, eds. A Workshop on Raptors and Energy Development. Idaho Chapter Wildl. Soc., Boise.

———, A.R. BAMMANN, R.P. HOWARD, J.H. DOREMUS, M. DELATE, and D. DONAHUE. 1975. Reproductive performance, food habits and population dynamics of raptors in the Snake River Birds of Prey Natural Area. Pages 1-50 in Snake River Birds of Prey Res. Proj. Ann. Rep. U.S. Dep. Inter., Bur. Land Manage. Boise, ID.

———, A.R. BAMMANN, J.H. DOREMUS, M. DELATE, and J. WYATT. 1976. Reproductive performance, food habits and population dynamics of raptors in the Snake River Birds of Prey Natural Area. Pages 1-57 in Snake River Birds of Prey Res. Proj. Ann. Rep. U.S. Dep. Inter., Bur. Land Manage., Boise, ID.

———, J.H. DOREMUS, K. STEENHOF, D.R. DUNCAN, M.Q. MORITSCH, A.C. DOLDE, D.M. RAMIREZ, S.A. ADAMS, and D. DELSORDO. 1983. Density and reproductive performance of raptors in the Snake River Birds of Prey Area. Pages 6-15 in Snake River Birds of Prey Res. Proj. Ann. Rep, U.S. Dep. Inter., Bur. Land Manage. Boise, ID.

KUCHLER, A.W. 1964. Potential natural vegetation of the conterminous United States. Am. Geogr. Soc. Spec. Publ. 36. Am. Geogr. Soc. New York, NY. 116pp.

LEIGHTON, F.A., J.M. GERRARD, P. GERRARD, D.W.A. WHITFIELD, and W.J. MAHER. 1979. An aerial census of bald eagles in Saskatchewan. J. Wildl. Manage. 43:61-69.

LEIN, M.R. and G.A. WEBER. 1979. Habitat selection by wintering snowy owls (Nyctea scandiaca). Can. Field-Nat. 93:176-178.

MADER, W.J. 1976. Biology of Harris' hawks in southern Arizona. Living Bird 14:59-85.

———. 1978. A comparative study of red-tailed hawks and Harris' hawks in southern Arizona. Auk 95:327-337.

MARION, W.R. and R.A. RYDER. 1975. Perch-site preferences of four diurnal raptors in northeastern Colorado. Condor 77:350-352.

MARKS, J.S. 1984. Nest site characteristics, reproductive success and food habits of long-eared owls in southwestern Idaho. M.S. Thesis, Univ. Montana, Missoula. 91pp.

——— and I.J. BALL. 1983. Burrowing owl (Athene cunicularia). Pages 227-242 in Armbruster, J.S., ed. Impacts of Coal Surface Mining on 25 Migratory Bird Species of High Federal Interst. U.S. Dep. Inter., Fish and Wildl. Serv. FWS/OBS-83/85. Fort Collins, CO.

MARSHALL, J.R., Jr. 1939. Territorial behavior of the flammulated screech owl. Condor 41:71-78.

MARSHALL, J.T. 1967. Parallel variation of North and Middle American screech owls. Monogr. 1. West Found. Vert. Zool. Los Angeles, CA. 72pp.

MARTI, C.D. 1979. Status of barn owls in Utah. Pages 29-35 in Schaeffer, P. and S.M. Ehlers, eds. Owls of the West: Their Ecology and Conservation. Natl. Audubon Soc. Tiburon, CA.

MARTIN, D.J. 1973. Selected aspects of burrowing owl ecology and behavior. Condor 75:446-456.

MATRAY, P.F. 1974. Broad-winged hawk nesting and ecology. Auk 91:307-324.

MAYFIELD, E.G. 1961. Nest success calculated from exposure. Wilson Bull. 73:255-261.

MEEHAN, R.H. and R.J. RITCHIE. 1982. Habitat requirements of boreal and hawk owls in interior Alaska. Pages 188-196 in Ladd, W.N. and P.F. Schempf, eds. Raptor Management and Biology in Alaska and Western Canada. FWS/AK/Proc. 82. U.S. Dep. Inter., Fish and Wildl. Serv., Anchorage, AK.

MELQUIST, W.E. 1975. Eagles and osprey: abstracts and discussion. Page 142 in Murphy, J.R., C.M. White, and B.E. Harrell, eds. Population status of raptors. Proc. Conf. Raptor Conserv. Tech. Raptor Res. Rep. 3. Raptor Res. Found. Vermillion, SD.

MIKOL, S.A. 1980. Field guidelines for using transects to sample nongame bird populations. FWS/OBS-80/58. U.S. Dep. Inter., Fish and Wildl. Serv. Fort Collins, CO. 26pp.

MILLSAP, B.A. 1981. Distributional status of falconiforms in west central Arizona: with notes on ecology, reproductive success and management. Tech. Note 355. U.S. Dep. Inter., Bur. Land Manage. Serv. Cen. Denver, CO. 102pp.

——— and S.L. VANA. 1984. Distribution of wintering golden eagles in the eastern United States. Wilson Bull. 96:692-701.

MINDELL, D.P. 1983. Nesting raptors in southwestern Alaska: status, distribution, and aspects of biology. Tech. Rep. 8. U.S. Dep. Inter., Bur. Land Manage. Anchorage, AK. 59pp.

MOSHER, J.A., K. TITUS, and M.R. FULLER. 1985. Developing a practical model to predict nesting habitat of woodland hawks in Verner, J., M.L. Morrison, and C.J. Ralph, eds. Modeling Habitat Relationships of Terrestrial Vertebrates. Univ. Wisconsin Press, Madison.

———, M.R. FULLER, and M. KOPENY. (Unpubl. ms.). Surveying woodland raptors: I. Responsiveness to broadcast of conspecific vocalizations. (To be submitted to J. Wildl. Manage.).

———, ———, and M. KOPENY. (Unpubl. ms.). Surveying woodland raptors: II. Density and distribution of nesting hawks. (To be submitted to J. Wildl. Manage.).

McCRARY, M.D. 1981. Space and habitat utilization by red-shouldered hawks (Buteo lineatus elegans) in southern California. M.S. Thesis, California State Univ., Long Beach. 85pp.

McGOWAN, J.D. 1975. Distribution, density and productivity of goshawks in interior Alaska. Fed. Aid Wildl. Restoration Proj. Rep. W 17-3, 4, 5, 6. Alaska Dep. Fish & Game, Juneau. 55pp.

NERO, R.W. 1980. The great gray owl. Smithsonian Inst. Press, Washington, DC. 167pp.

NEWTON, I. 1979. Population ecology of raptors. Buteo Books. Vermillion, SD. 399pp.

NICHOLLS, T.H. and D.W. WARNER. 1972. Barred owl habitat use as determined by radiotelemetry. J. Wildl. Manage. 36:213-224.

NOWICKI, T. 1974. A census of screech owls using tape-recorded calls. Jack-Pine Warbler 52:98-101.

OLENDORFF, R.R. 1975. Population status of large raptors in northeastern Colorado 1970-1972. Pages 185-295 *in* Murphy, J.R., C.M. White, and B.E. Harrell, eds. Proc. Conf. Raptor Conserv. Tech. Raptor Res. Rep. 3. Raptor Res. Found. Vermillion, SD.

PARKER, J.W. 1972. A mirror and pole device for examining high nests. Bird-Banding 43:216-218.

———. 1975. Populations of the Mississippi kite in the great plains. Pages 159-172 *in* Murphy, J.R., C.M. White, and B.E. Harrell, eds. Proc. Conf. Raptor Conserv. Tech. Raptor Res. Rep. 3. Raptor Res. Found. Vermillion, SD.

——— and J.C. OGDEN. 1979. The recent history and status of the Mississippi kite. Am. Birds 33:119-130.

PETERSEN, L. 1979. Ecology of great horned owls and red-tailed hawks in southeastern Wisconsin. Tech. Bull. 111. Wisconsin Dep. Nat. Resour. Madison. 63pp.

PHILLIPS, R.L., T.P. McENEANEY, and A.E. BESKE. 1984. Population densities of breeding golden eagles in Wyoming. Wildl. Soc. Bull. 12:269-273.

PLATT, J.B. 1973. Habitat and time utilization of a pair of nesting sharp-shinned hawks (*Accipiter striatus velox*)—a telemetry study. M.S. Thesis, Brigham Young Univ. Provo UT. 42pp.

POOLE, A. 1981. The effects of human disturbance on osprey reproductive success. Colonial Waterbirds 4:20-27.

PORTER, R.D. and C.M. WHITE. 1973. The peregrine falcon in Utah, emphasizing ecology and competition with the prairie falcon. Brigham Young Univ. Sci. Bull. Biol. Ser. 18:1-74.

POSTOVIT, H.R. 1979. Population estimates of breeding raptors in North Dakota Badlands. M.S. Thesis, North Dakota State Univ., Fargo. 55pp.

POSTUPALSKY, S. 1974. Raptor reproductive success: some problems with methods, criteria, and terminology. Pages 21-31 *in* Hamerstrom, F.N. Jr., B.E. Harrell, and R.R. Olendorff, eds. Management of Raptors. Raptor Res. Found. Vermillion, SD.

REYNOLDS, R.T. 1982. North American accipiter hawks. Pages 288-289 *in* Davis, D.E., ed. Handbook of Census Methods for Terrestrial Vertebrates. CRC Press. Boca Raton, FL.

———. 1983. Management of western coniferous forest habitat for nesting accipiter hawks. U.S. Dep. Agric., For. Serv. Gen. Tech. Rep. RM-102. 7pp.

——— and B.D. LINKHART. 1984. Methods and materials for capturing and monitoring flammulated owls. Great Basin Nat. 44:49-51.

———, E.C. MESLOW, and H.M. WIGHT. 1982. Nesting habitat of coexisting accipiters in Oregon. J. Wildl. Manage. 46:124-138.

ROSENEAU, D.G. 1972. Summer distribution, numbers, and food habits of the gyrfalcon (*Falco rusticolus* L.) on the Seward Peninsula, Alaska. M.S. Thesis, Univ. Alaska, Fairbanks. 124pp.

ROSENFIELD, R.M., J. BIELEFELDT, R.K. ANDERSON, and W.A. SMITH. 1985. Taped calls as an aid in locating Cooper's Hawk nests. Wildl. Soc. Bull. 13:62-63.

SCHMUTZ, J.K., S.M. SCHMUTZ, and D.A. BOAG. 1980. Coexistence of three species of hawks (*Buteo* sp.) in the prairie parkland ecotone. Can. J. Zool. 58:1075-1089.

SCHNELL, G.D. 1967. Population fluctuations, spatial distribution, and food habits of rough-legged hawks in Illinois. Kansas Ornithol. Soc. Bull. 18:21-28.

SCHNELL, J. 1979. Black hawk (*Buteogallus anthracinus*). Tech. Note TN-329. U.S. Dep. Inter., Bur. Land Manage. Serv. Cen. Denver, CO. 25pp.

SCOTT, V.E., K.E. EVANS, D.R. PATTON, and C.P. STONE. 1977. Cavity nesting birds of North American forests. Agric. Handb. 511. U.S. Dep. Agric., For. Serv. Washington, DC. 122pp.

SIMINSKI, D.P. 1976. A study of great horned owl (*Bubo virginianus*) population density with recorded calls in northwestern Ohio. M.S. Thesis, Bowling Green State Univ., Bowling Green, OH. 35pp.

SIMPSON, M.B. Jr. 1972. Saw-whet owl population of North Carolina's southern Great Balsam Mountains. Chat. 36:47.

SMITH, C.F. 1978. Distributional ecology of barred and great horned owls in relation to human disturbance. M.S. Thesis, Univ. Connecticut, Storrs. 104pp.

SNOW, C. 1973. Golden eagle. Tech. Note 239. U.S. Dep. Inter., Bur. Land Manage. Serv. Cen. Denver, CO. 52pp.

SOKAL, R.R. and F.J. ROHLF. 1981. Biometry. The principles and practice of statistics in biological research, 2nd ed. W.H. Freeman, San Francisco, CA. 859pp.

SPRINGER, M.A. 1978. Foot surveys versus owl calling surveys: a comparative study of two great horned owl censusing techniques. Inland Bird-Banding News 50:83-92.

STALMASTER, M.V. 1983. An energetics simulation model for managing wintering bald eagles. J. Wildl. Manage. 47:349-359.

STEENHOF, K. 1976. The ecology of wintering bald eagles in southeastern South Dakota. M.S. Thesis, Univ. Missouri, Columbia. 147pp.

———. 1978. Management of wintering bald eagles. FWS/OBS/78-79. U.S. Dep. Inter., Fish and Wildl. Serv. Washington, DC. 59pp.

———. 1986. Assessing raptor reproductive success and productivity *in* Millsap, B.A. and K.W. Kline, eds. Raptor Management Techniques Manual. Vol. 1. Natl. Wildl. Fed. Washington, DC.

———, S.S. BERLINGER, and L.H. FREDRICKSON. 1980. Habitat use by wintering bald eagles in South Dakota. J. Wildl. Manage. 44:798-805.

——— and M.N. KOCHERT. 1982. An evaluation of methods used to estimate raptor nesting success. J. Wildl. Manage. 46:885-893.

STUDER, C.D. 1983. Where is condor habitat? Outdoor California 44:17-18.

SYKES, P.W. Jr. 1979. Status of the Everglade kite in Florida 1968-1978. Wilson Bull. 91:495-511.

TAYLOR, A.L. Jr. and E.D. FORSMAN. 1976. Recent range extension of the barred owl in western North America, including the first records for Oregon. Condor 78:560-561.

THIOLLAY, J.M. 1978. Population structure and seasonal fluctuations of the falconiforms in Uganda national parks. East Afr. Wildl. J. 16:145-151.

THOMPSON-HANSON, P.A. 1984. Nesting ecology of northern harriers on the Hanford site, south-central Washington. M.S. Thesis, Washington State Univ., Pullman. 99pp.

TITUS, K. and J.A. MOSHER. 1981. Nest site habitat selected by woodland hawks in the central Appalachians. Auk 98:270-281.

TRIMBLE, S.A. 1975. Habitat management series for unique or endangered species, merlin (*Falco columbarius*). Tech. Note TN-271. U.S. Dep. Inter., Bur. Land Manage. Serv. Cen. Denver, CO. 41pp.

U.S BUREAU OF LAND MANAGEMENT. 1979. Special research report to the Secretary of the Interior. Bur. Land Manage., Boise, ID. 141pp.

U.S. FISH AND WILDLIFE SERVICE. 1983. Northern States bald eagle recovery plan. U.S. Dep. Inter., Fish and Wildl. Serv. Denver, CO. 117pp.

VILLAGE, A. 1984. Problems in estimating kestrel breeding density. Bird Study 31:121-125.

WAIAN, L.B. and R.C. STENDALL. 1970. The white-tailed kite in California with observations of the Santa Barbara population. Calif. Fish Game. 56:188-189.

WAKELEY, J.S. 1978. Factors affecting the use of hunting sites by ferruginous hawks. Condor 80:316-326.

WELLER, M.W., I.C. ADAMS, Jr., and B.J. ROSE. 1955. Winter roosts of marsh hawks and short-eared owls in central Missouri. Wilson Bull. 67:189-193.

WHITE, C.M. and S. SHERROD. 1973. Advantages and disadvantages of the use of rotor-winged aircraft in raptor surveys. Raptor Res. 7:97-104.

WIER, D.N. 1982. Cliff nesting raptors of the Kisaralik River, western Alaska. Pages 138-152 in Ladd, W.N. and P.F. Schempf, eds. Raptor Management and Biology in Alaska and Western Canada. WS/AK Proc. 82. U.S. Dep. Inter., Fish and Wildl. Serv. Anchorage, AK.

WIJNANDTS, H. 1984. Ecological energetics of the long-eared owl (*Asio otus*). Ardea 72:1-92.

WILBUR, S.R. 1978. The California Condor, 1966-76: a look at its past and future. North Am. Fauna 72. U.S. Dep. Inter., Fish and Wildl. Serv. Washington, DC. 136pp.

WILEY, J.W. 1975. The nesting and reproductive success of red-tailed hawks and red-shouldered hawks in Orange County, California, 1973. Condor 77:133-139.

WINTER, J. 1979. Status and distribution of the great gray owl and the flammulated owl in California. Pages 60-85, *in* Schaffer, P.P. and S.M. Ehlers, eds. Owls of the West: Their Ecology and Conservation. Nat. Audubon Soc. Tiburon, CA.

WRAKESTRAW, G.F. 1972. 1972 Wyoming bald and golden eagle survey. Job Completion Rep. W-50-4-21. Wyoming Game Fish Comm., Cheyenne. 7pp.

———. 1973. The 1973 Wyoming bald and golden eagle survey. Am. Birds 27:716-718.

ZARN, M. 1974a. Spotted owl (*Strix occidentalis*). Tech. Note TN-242. U.S. Dep. Inter., Bur. Land Manage. Serv. Cen. Denver, CO. 22pp.

———. 1974b. Burrowing owl (*Speotyto cunicularia hypugaea*). Tech. Note TN-250. U.S. Dep. Inter., Bur. Land Manage. Serv. Cen. Denver, CO. 25pp.

———. 1974c. Osprey (*Pandion haliaetus carolinensis*). Tech. Note TN-254. U.S. Dep. Inter., Bur. Land Manage. Serv. Cen. Denver, CO. 41pp.

———. 1975. Rough-legged hawk (*Buteo lagopus sanctijohannis*). Tech. Note TN-270. U.S. Dep. Inter., Bur. Land Manage. Serv. Cen. Denver, CO. 23pp.

17

MARSH AND SHOREBIRDS

Peter G. Connors

Bodega Research Associates
P.O. Box 247
Bodega Bay, CA 94923

Editor's Note: Marsh and shorebirds, because of the habitat they occupy and the unique adaptations for feeding and breeding, require inventory and monitoring techniques quite different from those used for songbirds, for example. Although marsh and shorebirds are not a homogeneous group in terms of habitat, size, taxonomic affinity, or life history, they nevertheless require methodology that differs significantly from any other species group, including waterfowl with which they often coexist. This chapter describes these specialized techniques and their application.

INTRODUCTION

Few general statements concerning habitat relationships will apply accurately to all the groups of birds addressed in this chapter. Marsh and shorebirds include two families in the order Gruiformes and five families in the order Charadriiformes (Table 1). Typical nesting habitats range from arctic tundra to Colorado River marshes and from western rangelands to the rocky California coastline. As if that habitat diversity were not enough, species range from permanent residents to some of the longest distance migrants in the world. Shorebirds are more consistently and emphatically migratory than any other taxonomic group of North American birds, and the habitats occupied in different seasons and different areas often contrast sharply. Finally, species range in size from least sandpipers *(Calidris minutilla)* to sandhill cranes *(Grus canadensis)* and in behavior and accessibility, from visually prominent, frequently flocking species seen in open landscapes to some of the world's most secretive denizens of densely vegetated marshes, the rails.

Table 1. Families of birds addressed in this chapter occurring regularly in Alaska and western States.

Order Family	Number of Species

Gruiformes—marsh birds
  Rallidae—rails and coots
  Gruidae—cranes
	
	7
	2

Charadriiformes—shorebirds
  Charadriidae—plovers
  Haematopodidae—
    oystercatchers
  Recurvirostridae—stilts and
    avocets
  Scolopacidae—sandpipers,
    phalaropes, and close
    relatives
	
	7
	1
	
	2
	
	35

This great diversity of habitats, life cycles, and behaviors requires a divided approach to this discussion of habitat relationships and population estimation techniques. In the interest of brevity, however, not all species can be individually addressed. Instead I consider four major categories of habitat, attempting to discuss the most general features of species group habitat use within each category. This approach will unavoidably omit some species that do not share characteristics with other species discussed below; some of these will be mentioned only briefly, with appropriate references if available. Others can best be investigated by methods discussed for other species groups with similar habitat use, behavior, and size. For example, American coots *(Fulica americana)* in breeding marshes can be studied with grebes *(Podiceps* sp.) and, in winter, with small waterfowl; sandhill cranes can be partly addressed with large arctic breeding waterfowl.

The four habitat categories addressed in this chapter are tundra, rangeland, shorelines (coastal and inland), and marshes. Table 2 outlines the species groups treated under each habitat heading and emphasizes the generalizations applied to efficiently treat the diversity of this chapter's subject. These combinations of habitats and species groups define the sections and limit the scope of the discussion in this chapter.

Table 2. Major habitats and associated species groups.

Habitat	Species Group
Tundra— Arctic and subarctic	Breeding shorebirds and cranes
Rangeland— Upland and wetlands	Breeding shorebirds and cranes
Shorelines— Coastal and inland	Non-breeding shorebirds
Marshes— Coastal and inland	Breeding and non-breeding rails and coots

TUNDRA—BREEDING SHOREBIRDS

At most arctic and many subarctic sites, shorebirds are a major, conspicuous element of the avifauna. On the arctic coastal plain of Alaska near Prudhoe Bay, Troy et al. (1983) found 13 of 24 nesting species to be shorebirds, including 8 of the 10 species with nesting densities above 1 nest/km^2 (0.4 mi.^{2}).

Comparable results have been recorded at Barrow (Myers and Pitelka 1980) and Point Storkersen (Bergman et al. 1977) as well as at other Alaska sites. Total shorebird densities are usually higher on tundra with numerous small wetlands than on well-drained sites and, therefore, higher on most coastal plain tundra than in inland elevated areas, although densities of some species reverse this trend because of habitat preferences. All tundra-breeding shorebirds are migratory, arriving at nesting sites in May or early June in Alaska and departing soon after nesting duties are finished, from late June to September. Timing of breeding seasons matches the hatching of insects on which adults and newly hatched chicks depend (Holmes and Pitelka 1968). In many areas, shorebirds move from breeding tundra areas to nearby coastal areas in late summer before beginning southward migration (Connors et al. 1979).

Habitat Features

Many studies have related tundra habitat features to shorebird populations in Alaska, but few have dealt quantitatively with fine-scale variation in habitat types or with basic features of habitat structure. The most detailed studies dealing principally with shorebirds were conducted by Myers and Pitelka (1980) at Barrow and Atkasook and by Troy et al. (1983) at Prudhoe Bay. Many other studies describe habitat characteristics somewhat more generally, often relating shorebird densities to different classes of habitat. These include Spindler (1978), Martin and Moiteret (1981), Bergman et al. (1977), Connors et al. (1979), Williamson et al. (1966), and Holmes and Black (1973). Several other government reports and a few graduate theses also address this topic, and many papers deal with habitat preferences of particular species. The most quantitatively derived and most generally applicable conclusions from these sources will be discussed here.

Physical Features

Myers and Pitelka (1980) measured several physical features of shorebird habitat use at Barrow and Atkasook, Alaska. They measured average and maximum microtopographic relief on transect units, average slope of unit diagonals, average water depth, and proportion of sampling points with different degrees of saturation or surface water present. Combining these variables with vegetation measurements, they used multivariate factor analysis to identify major gradients underlying the habitat variation at these sites and found corresponding differences in shorebird densities across these gradients, as well as species differences in habitat use. Other researchers have used classification schemes based principally on differences in topography, wetness, and vegetation to identify differences among species and among habitats (Bergman et al. 1977; Spindler 1978; Martin and Moiteret 1981; Troy et al. 1983). Because both these approaches relate bird use to integrated descriptions of habitat, it is difficult to identify individual features of prime importance, but topographic relief and the occurrence of surface water certainly influence shorebird populations.

Individual species differ in habitat preferences, but total shorebird densities are usually highest during the breeding season on tundra of variable topography (such as the polygons of ridges and troughs produced by frost action), with numerous shallow wet troughs or small ponds. This combination provides habitat for nesting and foraging for several of the most common tundra shorebirds. Well-drained sites without ponds, including highly polygonized areas, support lower densities, although some species such as golden plovers *(Pluvialis dominica)* and buff-breasted sandpipers *(Tryngites subruficollis)* may select these habitats. Areas of continuous marsh, lacking elevated dry sites, are also less used during the breeding season because of the scarcity of nest sites, but species such as pectoral sandpiper *(Calidris melanotos)* use these areas after chicks hatch.

These generations do not apply strictly to all sites and to all seasons. However, on the Canning River Delta, Martin and Moiteret (1981) measured higher breeding densities on a mosaic of wet and dry polygonized tundra than on sites of more homogeneous wet or dry habitat. Spindler (1978) found similar results at the Okpilak Delta, although densities in low wetlands were also high. At Barrow, a region of little topographic relief but extensive wetlands, Myers and Pitelka (1980) measured highest densities of breeding season shorebirds in areas of low to intermediate polygonization, with many small ponds, and in areas of high polygonization, with fewer ponds. Inland on the coastal plain at Atkasook, where well-drained tundra is more widespread, they found most shorebirds nesting in low, non-polygonized areas having a wide range in density of ponds. These patterns changed seasonally, however, as shorebird use in all three studies became heavier in low wetland sites after shorebirds finished nesting duties.

Thus assessment of habitat value for shorebirds is not a simple matter of measuring features such as density of ponds or height of polygons, for example. Furthermore, regional differences in species present or in gross geomorphology between sites may override the influences of particular habitat feature studies at one site. For example, the highest shorebird nesting densities on the Yukon Delta occur in areas of heath tundra interspersed with marsh, delta channels, and ponds (Holmes and Black 1973)

that provide a variety of nesting and foraging habitats. However, this habitat mix is not well-represented at the arctic sites where detailed shorebird-habitat relationships have been studied. Directly censusing shorebird populations is, therefore, often preferable to habitat measurements, except when habitat measurements are obtained primarily by aerial photography and are compared with bird-habitat studies done in similar terrain within the same region.

Vegetation

On most arctic tundra, vegetation structure is relatively monotonous compared with temperate ecosystems. Tundra ranges from almost unvegetated soils to dense stands of grasses, sedges, and forbs, with areas of low woody shrubs such as birches and willows, often lower than the surrounding grasses. Plant species composition and, therefore, vegetation structure are to a great extent determined by the physical features of the tundra within a region. Most habitat classification schemes have defined tundra types by combining these factors. For some species, vegetation height or density may strongly influence bird use, and gross differences in plant species composition (as between shrubby heath tundra and graminoid tundra, for example) may separate some species. In general, however, vegetation is not a simple predictor of total shorebird populations except as it corresponds with the differences in physical features discussed above.

Population Measurement Techniques

Direct measurement of tundra shorebird densities may often be preferred over indirect population evaluation based on habitat measurements, primarily because tundra shorebirds are easier to census than most other non-colonial nesting birds. In areas of tundra, such as the North Slope and arctic coastal areas of Alaska, low vegetation reduces visibility problems that plague most censuses of birds in habitats with complex vegetation structure, such as woodlands. Censusing shorebirds does not require singing birds or estimates of distances to unseen singing birds.

On arctic coastal plain tundra in Alaska, most shorebird individuals, except some incubating sandpipers and secretive species such as long-billed dowitcher *(Limnodromus scolopaceus)* and common snipe *(Gallinago gallinago),* can be located by an experienced observer on a walking transect. The relative tameness of most shorebirds allows a closer approach by the census taker than is possible for more elusive species such as waterfowl and cranes. Reliable estimates of absolute density are often possible with an acceptable amount of effort. Measurement of simple presence or absence of shorebirds is therefore seldom justified, because relative density estimates, at least, can usually be obtained with little extra effort.

Sandhill cranes, breeding in some of the same tundra habitats, require a very different approach because of their lower densities and greater flushing distances. Their large size, however, permits aerial censusing for relative or absolute density measurements (Riley 1982). This species is not addressed in the discussions below of techniques designed to assess densities of groups of shorebirds species.

Relative Density—Encounter Rate Method.

For a simple estimate of relative density of shorebirds, by species, an observer walks through a site recording all birds seen per distance or time traveled. The census path can be straight or meandering, provided that it does not incorporate any strong bias toward habitat of a particular type that is not equally abundant at all sites compared. A continuous, roughly circular route from a point of departure such as an airplane landing site may be most efficient when comparing several remote sites. Distances are best estimated from topographic maps; alternatively, time elapsed at a reasonably constant hiking rate can be used.

This method has relatively low accuracy and precision, but it quickly and cheaply obtains a list of most or all common species at a site and a rough estimate of their relative abundances. Reliability of this estimate depends on distance traveled (I suggest 4 to 12 km [2 to 7 mi.]); consistency; and experience of the observer, weather conditions, hiking conditions, and season. For example, windy weather reduces the number of birds heard and then observed; hiking rates through tussocky or very marshy tundra will be slower than in easier terrain; and birds differ in visibility seasonally, depending on their behaviors, such as displaying, incubating, or mobbing. Furthermore, because species differ in detectability within a season, relative densities of certain species detected by this method incorporate a somewhat predictable bias.

For best results, the census should be along straight-line paths chosen from topographic maps, during the same period of the breeding season, at all sites or in all years. Early breeding season is best for estimating relative breeding densities, about mid-June at arctic locations.

This method requires only binoculars, notebook, and hip boots, plus an experienced observer familiar with displays, vocalizations, behavior, and identification of the species that may be encountered. Cost is low except for transportation to the sites. The method should only be used when time and funds are very limited; when many sites will be visited

briefly, usually only one time each; or when bird observations must be supplemental to other observer duties. In these circumstances, it becomes a very efficient method of obtaining relative density data of limited accuracy. When more time is available or greater accuracy is needed, the following methods should be used.

Absolute Density.

Method 1—Territory Spot Mapping. On a marked study area, an observer records the location of all birds, noting especially locations of territorial displays and nests. Study plots and data sheets should be correspondingly marked with grid lines indicating 50 m (165 ft) intervals. Censuses should take place on several dates during the early and middle breeding season. I suggest three to eight censuses per study plot. Combining censuses for each species using overlay maps, the observer plots territories or nest sites. Densities can be calculated only from fractional portions of territories that cross plot boundaries within the study area.

This method is reasonably accurate and precise. Successive censuses add to the information base, increasing accuracy each time. Data from all censuses are combined to estimate the actual resident population. This process requires judgment in the analysis and should be done by the field observer, revising the map as required after each census. The observer must know displays, nesting behavior, and identification of all the local species, and must be familiar with nest location techniques for shorebirds. Study plots should be large enough to include several territories of common species (typically 20 to 100 ha [50 to 250 a.]).

Little equipment is needed, as in the preceding method. One observer can map 30 to 60 ha (75 to 150 a.) of study plot per day. Many of the interfering factors discussed above apply also to this method. However, the marked boundaries, measured area, and repeated censuses greatly increase the accuracy of the density estimate. In addition, densities correspond to known or strongly suspected breeding birds only, providing what is often the most useful population measure. Multiple censuses, however, require much greater personnel time and, therefore, increase costs.

Method 2—Rope-Drag Nest Mapping. The rope-dragging technique can be used independently or as a supplement to the previous method. Two observers drag a rope (about 50 m [165 ft] long) across the tundra, while a third observer follows behind, noting locations of any birds that flush from nests as the rope passes over or near them. This simple method locates incubating birds that "sit

Rope-drag technique using vehicles.

close," not flushing, unless the observer almost steps on them. These are the most difficult of shorebird nests to locate by usual mapping techniques and are frequent among some species such as the long-billed dowitcher.

Method 3—Marked Plot Strip Transect. To measure changes in total bird populations (not just nesting pairs) within a season, between seasons, or between sites, many researchers have used permanently marked transects treated as study plots (Connors et al. 1979; Myers and Pitelka 1980; Troy et al. 1983). Numbered wooden stakes or similar markers are placed in a straight line at 50 m (165 ft) intervals, indicating the center line of two adjacent rows of 50 x 50 m (165 x 165 ft) plots. A single observer walks a rectangular zigzag path across all transect plots, walking within 25 or 18 m (82 or 59 ft) of all points on the plots. Alternatively, two observers walk the center lines of the parallel rows of plots.

The plot markers help observers estimate lateral distances, and additional stakes can be placed on outer transect edges to aid the estimation. Time required averages about 1 observer-hour/kilometer (1/2 mile) of transect on arctic plain tundra. In areas of taller shrubby vegetation, visual obstructions may require increasing the amount of zigzagging and the time required per transect. All birds are recorded, and the observer must note locations and movements to avoid counting individuals more than once. Censuses can be repeated at regular intervals

and averaged to obtain mean densities and changes in bird use with time. Transects can be placed within single habitats or randomly crossing all habitats, depending on sampling design.

These plot transects work well because of the relatively high visibility of tundra shorebirds, but they are subject to errors caused by differential visibility of species. Experienced observers are confident that almost all shorebirds are recorded by this method (J.P. Myers, F.A. Pitelka, D. Troy, pers. commun.). The most difficult application of the technique occurs after chicks hatch and some shorebird parents engage in mobbing activities, flying across several transect plots to display, near the observer, a potential predator. The observer must note the origins of these birds to avoid overcounting during this period.

Precision and, to some extent, accuracy of this technique can be assessed by replicate censusing of control plots or of all plots. This might be done by comparing different observers or a single observer over time intervals of one hour, several hours, or single days. This assessment greatly aids the interpretation of data collected from single counts at comparable sites. A similar approach of replicate censuses is useful for all the techniques mentioned in this chapter.

Method 4—Unmarked Strip Transect. When several sites must be evaluated, usually with single visits, an unmarked strip transect of fixed width (I recommend 50 m [165 ft] total width) can be used. This is an upgraded version of the Encounter Rate Method for relative density. By controlling the width of the census path, absolute densities can be calculated. Density accuracy depends on factors mentioned earlier, plus any error in estimating the 25 m (82 ft) width on either side of the observer's path. Accuracy also suffers compared with Marked Plot Transects by the absence of replicate estimates, but Method 4 has an obvious advantage by saving time and money.

Method 5—Variable Width Line Transect. Several variations of this method have been developed, principally for passerine censusing in wooded habitats. Corrections have been applied to account for differential detectability of species (Emlen 1971, 1977; Jarvinen and Vaisanen 1975; Ralph and Scott 1981). Briefly, all birds are recorded on either side of a central transect line, along with the perpendicular distance from each bird to the transect line. Tundra shorebirds do not pose the same visibility problems as woodland songbirds, so the additional complication of estimating horizontal distances to all birds is probably not warranted.

Discussion

Tundra shorebird habitat relationships have been investigated at several arctic sites. The closest scrutiny focused on individual species preferences and seasonal changes in habitat use. Nevertheless, no clear definition of habitat features that can predict shorebird abundances has yet emerged. The most widely applicable generalization from these studies suggests that total shorebird densities will usually be highest in areas of numerous small wetlands with moderate microtopographic relief, providing a fine-grained mosaic of nest sites and foraging sites.

The low tundra vegetation, moderate conspicuousness, and non-elusive character of most shorebird species at most tundra sites make shorebird censusing on breeding grounds relatively easy. For this reason, measures of simple presence or absence are not recommended, because they are easily replaced with estimates of relative or absolute density. All these techniques require at least the ability to easily identify all local species in a variety of plumages, and all are more reliable when observers know the behavioral peculiarities and vocalizations of shorebird species. Methods should be chosen on the basis of available time and personnel, number of sites to be monitored, duration of monitoring planned, and the information needs of the monitoring program.

RANGELAND—BREEDING SHOREBIRDS

In contrast to their prominence on arctic tundra, shorebirds are much less common and conspicuous on western rangelands, but several species nest

there, and additional species are found throughout the West during migration. A brief summary of habitat affinities and census techniques follows.

Habitat Features

Western rangeland encompasses a greater variety of contrasting habitat types than can readily be treated in this short section, from prairies and plains to mountain slopes and valleys; from deserts to rich grasslands, including marshes, streams, fresh and saline lakes, over a wide range of elevations and winter climates. Most nesting shorebird species can be assigned to groups associated with prairie grasslands, marshes, or stream and lake shores, although these categories overlap for some species.

Grassland-nesting shorebird species include mountain plover (*Charadrius montanus*), a long-billed curlew (*Numenius americanus*), upland sandpiper (*Bartramia longicauda*), and sometimes killdeer (*Charadrius vociferus*). Physical characteristics of different grasslands can be described by measuring such factors as mean vegetation height; percentage vegetation cover types (grass, forb, shrub, cactus); slope and topographic diversity; and distance to water.

Intensive studies of long-billed curlews in Idaho (Jenni et al. 1982; Redmond et al. 1981; Redmond 1984) have demonstrated that curlew densities in that area are highest in areas of low topographic slope, low vegetation height, and low vertical vegetative cover. Mountain plovers in Colorado also selected low slope, shortgrass habitats (Graul 1975). Upland plovers occur in tallgrass or mixed grass prairie habitats (Wiens 1973). Since these species are conspicuous enough in these habitats, direct censusing of birds during the breeding season is more effective than attempts to assess habitat suitability.

Marsh and pond nesting shorebirds occurring within western rangelands are American avocet (*Recurvirostra americana*), black-necked stilt (*Himantopus mexicanus*), willet (*Catoptrophorus semipalmatus*), marbled godwit (*Limosa fedoa*), common snipe, and Wilson's phalarope (*Phalaropus tricolor*). Distributions and habitats of these species vary widely and have not all been the subjects of intensive habitat studies. Furthermore, habitat use by a single species may change regionally as wetland types change over large distances of western North America. Wetlands in many of these areas are seasonal or semipermanent and have been classified according to permanence by Stewart and Kantrud (1971) for the northern prairie region.

Black-necked stilts and American avocets nest in similar habitats, usually along shorelines and grassy or unvegetated flats near fresh water, brackish or

U.S. Fish and Wildlife Service

Black-necked stilt turning eggs.

Shoreline nesting species include killdeer, snowy plover *(Charadrius alexandrinus),* spotted sandpiper *(Actitis macularia),* and in some northern prairie regions, piping plover *(Charadrius melodus).* These are usually associated with lakes, ponds, or streams (except that killdeer may nest well away from water) and nest in open areas or areas of sparse or short vegetation (Bent 1929; Renaud 1979; Page et al. 1983; Oring et al. 1983; Weseloh and Weseloh 1983).

Sandhill cranes also nest in western rangeland areas, in or near marshes or ponds (Bent 1926; Littlefield and Ryder 1968; Drewien 1973).

As with shorebirds breeding on tundra, many rangeland species are relatively conspicuous in the sparsely vegetated or shortgrass habitats they occupy in western rangelands. This circumstance facilitates direct measurement of shorebird or crane densities. For species associated with wetlands, however, locating and mapping areas of wetlands by wetland type may provide a large-scale estimate of relative abundance of these species. This approach requires calibration from bird studies done within the same region. Information relating presence, absence, or relative or absolute densities of species to wetland type or wetland size class can then be applied to areawide inventories of wetlands. Weber et al. (1982) provided an example of the kind of calibration information required on northern prairies.

Population Measurement Techniques

Census methods must be chosen to match the species or habitat characteristics within this diverse group of species. Many of the methods listed for tundra shorebirds are also applicable to rangeland species and are listed here briefly with the habitats or species of concern. A few additional approaches are described more fully.

Relative Density—Encounter Rate Method.
The encounter rate method is generally less useful in rangeland shorebird habitats than in tundra, where the nesting habitats of large numbers of species occur in a fine-grained mosaic. Nevertheless, walking around wetlands or along shorelines during the breeding season, or traversing grasslands on foot or horseback, can provide easy but limited information on relative density of nesting birds. Large areas can be covered by aircraft searching for cranes, but the effort involved argues for attempting absolute density estimates.

Absolute Density.

Method 1—Nest Spot Mapping. Most studies of shorebird populations breeding in the western U.S. have been concentrated on locating all nests

alkaline marshes, and ponds. Foraging habitats, usually shallow water areas or wet mud flats, may be continuous with or separated from nest territories (Gibson 1971; Hamilton 1975). In prime areas, nest densities may be very high, clustered in semi-colonial situations. This distribution of nests and the usually low vegetation facilitate direct spot-mapping techniques for nesting birds.

Willets and marbled godwits nest near prairie marshes and ponds surrounded by grasslands. Both species prefer permanent or semipermanent pond types, either fresh or brackish, and nest in adjacent grassy areas (Ryan 1985). Godwits use surrounding uplands in addition to marshes for foraging and prefer short to medium grass heights for nesting. Willets use taller grass areas (Ryan, unpubl. ms). Wilson's phalaropes nest in ponds and marshy wetlands of prairie and basin areas, both fresh and saline, and common snipes nest in marshes of the northern States.

within a study area. Techniques depend, to some extent, on the species involved and habitat features, but in all instances, actual ground searching is required. This is usually initiated by observing locations of birds flushing from or returning to brooding activities, from a vantage point inside or outside the studied habitat. For large birds (sandhill crane, long-billed curlew, marbled godwit, avocet), initial observations may be made from a road, dike, or even an airplane. For smaller birds, initial observations may require field work within the habitat. For many species, thorough hiking may be required to flush brooding birds or to elicit antipredator responses. For species nesting in high densities within limited habitats, such as the loosely colonial breeders, American avocet and black-necked stilt, spot-mapping techniques to locate all nests or territories can be fairly efficient. In other situations, this would be time-consuming.

Method 2—Rope-Drag Nest Mapping. This method is usually used only as a supplement to Method 1 and is most useful for species that nest in dense vegetation and those that may not flush without a close approach, such as the marbled godwit (Ryan 1985). The technique is described in the tundra section.

Method 3—Strip Transect. This method, which requires locating birds within a linear transect of a fixed width, can be applied as a walking transect through grasslands, around wetlands, or near shorelines in a manner similar to the tundra transect described in the preceding section. Alternatively, to deal with the low densities of some rangeland species and the patchy distribution of their habitats, the method can be (1) a driving transect along a road, counting all individuals of large species within a standard perpendicular distance; (2) driving along a road and stopping at predetermined stations for censusing; or (3) a road transect linking wetland censusing stations. An aircraft flying transect lines with observers censusing a specified width along the transect line is a useful variant for cranes.

Method 4—Variable Width Line Transect. Variations of this approach, described for tundra, can also be applied to solve the particular problems of rangeland species and habitats. Unlike most tundra and shoreline shorebirds, long-billed curlews present special difficulties, in both size and breeding habitat, which affect census techniques. Redmond et al. (1981) compared three methods of censusing curlew breeding populations in Idaho and recommended a modified Finnish Line Transect method. Observers drive a route along existing roads, recording all curlews sighted within 500 m (1,650 ft) of the road, and estimate perpendicular distances to all birds sighted. The census is repeated five times on different days, and pooled data are corrected for

U.S. Fish and Wildlife Service

Avocet turning eggs.

distance effects of detectability (Emlen 1971; Jarvinen and Vaisanen 1975) before calculating densities. Censuses should be done soon after curlews arrive on breeding grounds (late March or early April). Results of this and the strip transect method were fairly accurate when compared with results of territory mapping studies done on the same area (Redmond et al. 1981). As with tundra shorebird censusing, the change in behavior during the brood-rearing period, with adults flying long distances to mob potential predators, introduces errors. Censusing early in the breeding season avoids this problem.

Discussion

Western rangeland, including such diverse habitats as grasslands, shrub deserts, mountain slopes, marshes, and alkali lakes, to name a few, poses greater problems for generalizing conclusions than other major habitat areas addressed in this chapter. Most rangeland nesting shorebirds, however, fall into three habitat categories, as described above, and census techniques applicable to these categories and species are similar to those for comparable situations elsewhere. The major modifications necessary arise from the large size and low density of grassland shorebirds or cranes, compared with most tundra shorebirds, and the patchy distribution of western ponds, marshes, and lakeshores. On a large-scale area, the patchiness of gross habitat types, such as marshy wetlands, permits successful assessment of probable shorebird locations, but assessments of fine habitat distinctions will usually be less useful than direct censuses of birds.

SHORELINES—MIGRANT SHOREBIRDS

During much of the year, from late summer to late spring, shorebirds are most common in or near shoreline habitats, predominantly coastal but including inland shores of lakes and marshes. This description encompasses a great variety of habitats ranging from muddy freshwater ponds and flooded fields, to sandy coastal beaches; from tidal mudflats and saltmarshes, to exposed rocky coastlines; and from arctic Alaska, to southern California and beyond. Naturally, shorebird use, habitat features, and census methods vary over this range, but some habitat characteristics are common and these guide the choice of census techniques.

First, most shoreline habitats of importance to shorebirds are open and free of much vegetation structure or topographic relief. Shorebirds in these circumstances are even more readily located than on tundra or rangelands. Second, most of these habitats occur where land meets water, in areas where accessible invertebrate prey in high densities cause foraging shorebirds to concentrate locally. This factor also facilitates shorebird censusing. However, the tidal nature of most coastal shoreline habitats and the flocking habits of most migrant and wintering shorebirds inject elements of instability into shorebird density measurements.

Migrant marsh and shorebirds move frequently to exploit food sources, escape predators, or continue migrations. This instability can usually be accommodated in at least one of several ways. For example, biologists might census when shorebirds are most predictably concentrated and stable, as at high tide roosts in coastal areas. They might always census under the same set of conditions that relate to movements, such as tide height, time of day, and calendar date. They might census regularly and repeatedly throughout a period of migration or simultaneously census an entire local population, using multiple observers. The following discussion addresses the most generally important habitat features and most widely applicable census methods for inland and coastal shoreline habitats throughout Alaska and the western States.

Habitat Features

Most migrating and wintering shorebirds do not require vegetative cover for nests or chicks or for their own protection. This frees them to use habitats where their food, mainly small invertebrates of many orders, are most abundant. In coastal locations, these habitats are usually bare or sparsely vegetated, the exceptions being mainly algae-covered rocks and mudflats, and saltmarshes with low or sparse vegetation.

Hans Stuart

Greater sandhill cranes, a western rangeland nester.

The primary features of habitat that relate to shorebird densities must usually be those features that result in the highest densities of available shorebird prey in an area, because shorebirds in winter are generally distributed in relation to availability of prey (Goss-Custard 1970; Bryant 1979; Myers et al. 1979; Rands and Barkham 1981). In arctic Alaska, these conditions prevail in two separate situations in late summer after shorebird breeding has been completed on the tundra. Densities of some species (red phalaropes [*Phalaropus fulicaria*], red-necked phalaropes [*P. lobatus*], and sanderlings [*Calidris alba*]) are highest along beaches or spits, bars, and barrier islands. Numbers of several other species (especially dunlin [*Calidris alpina*], semipalmated [*C. pusilla*], western [*C. mauri*] and pectoral sandpipers, and long-billed dowitchers) are highest on mudflats, at edges of sloughs, and around shallow pools in short vegetation saltmarshes (Connors et al. 1979; Connors 1984). These habitats usually support higher shorebird use than other arctic shorelines, but densities are highly variable from one site to another and cannot be predicted with accuracy.

On the Bering Sea coast, similar habitats, especially river deltas, lagoon mudflats, and saltmarsh margins, attract highest shorebird densities during post-breeding movements, from July through October (Shields and Peyton 1979; Gill et al 1981; Gill and Handel 1981). From a large-scale view, these coastal habitats in arctic and subarctic Alaska are localized and discrete, and their occurrences correlate well with post-breeding shorebird densities throughout the region. Field recognition of these habitats is straightforward and is frequently possible from maps and aerial photography. Quantitative characterization of these gross habitat features is easily accomplished by referencing properties of water depth, slope, distance, or extent from the water's edge; substrate sediment size; substrate penetrability; vegetation density and height; plant species composition; salinity or saltwater influence; and surrounding landform type.

On a finer scale, little quantitative work has been done to isolate those features within mudflats or saltmarsh, for example, that correlate with bird density distributions within the habitat. As in other coastal mudflat environments, density of available invertebrate prey is probably the best predictive feature to relate to shorebird densities. This is not always easily measured, and habitat correlates of prey densities are unstudied in these areas. For most management purposes, the simple presence of more than trace amounts of wet mudflats, shallow muddy pools, and sparsely vegetated saltmarsh with wet mud and shallow pools is sufficient to predict elevated levels of seasonal shorebird use.

A few physical and vegetative features can be used to identify and separate arctic saltmarshes from freshwater tundra. First, because lunar tidal fluctuations are so slight (about 15 cm [6 in.] at Barrow, Alaska, for example), saltmarsh areas are maintained by occasional flooding during storms in late summer and fall. Therefore, saltmarsh is always located in areas with access routes for storm-flood saltwater from oceans or lagoons. The importance of storm flooding leaves another clue in the form of driftwood lines on coastal land, inland from any saltmarshes. Depending on the frequency of storm flooding represented by different driftwood lines, vegetation shoreward of the driftwood may be very salt-tolerant, mildly salt-tolerant, or fresh tundra pioneers invading after the previous salt-killing of tundra vegetation.

In the permanent arctic saltmarsh zone of most interest, two salt-tolerant plants are characteristic indicators: *Puccinellia phryganodes,* a prostrate grass, and *Carex subspathacea,* a very short sedge. Both have a pronounced reddish color in some life stages and, together with the reddish iron oxides in saltmarsh mud, create a final color attribute that is helpful in identifying and delineating arctic saltmarshes. Within these vegetated areas, however, the shallow pools, wet mudflats, and muddy margins show the heaviest shorebird use.

For phalaropes, sanderlings, and lesser numbers of several other species feeding primarily on zooplankton along arctic shorelines, the habitat feature of most importance seems to be the landform on which arctic beaches occur. Spits and islands generally have higher densities of these species than mainland beaches (Johnson and Richardson 1981; Connors 1984). Vegetation and substrate characteristics are less important than landform in predicting these bird densities.

Farther south in Alaska, coastal shorebird densities are usually highest in areas of extensive mudflats and, for some species, on rocky intertidal beaches. The Copper River Delta is an important habitat area with such large numbers of migrating shorebirds, especially during spring, that total population numbers can only be estimated rather than directly counted (Isleib 1979; Mickelson et al. 1980; Senner 1979). The ample prey base, principally of small molluscs on the extensive mudflats and sandflats of that area, is responsible for the massive shorebird concentrations (Senner 1979). In Washington, Oregon, and California, the largest numbers of shorebirds occur on mudflats and sandflats of lagoons, estuaries, and fresh- and saltwater marshes; on coastal beaches; and on rocky intertidal shorelines, with different groups of species in different habitats.

Several studies have addressed species habitat preferences among coastal wetland habitat types (for example, Recher 1966; Gerstenberg 1979; Page et al. 1979). These do not, however, permit assessment of wildlife values of different examples of a single wetland type, except on the basis of the extent of habitat. Indeed, the population densities of some wetland habitat areas seem to depend on the locations of nearby wetlands of other types, rather than on strictly intrinsic properties (Page et al. 1979; Connors et al. 1981). Thus, one cannot yet profitably judge shorebird wetland habitats by measuring particular habitat variables, except in a few specialized instances. Sanderling densities on beaches in central California, for example, are sometimes correlated with beach slope and sediment size, because these are correlated with prey densities (Myers et al. 1979; Connors et al. 1981). On a larger scale, however, one can assess areas by the presence and extent of wetland habitats that provide foraging areas of the types selected by particular species.

The situation for inland areas is similar. Wetlands providing appropriate species foraging areas will attract shorebirds, but measurements of physical or vegetational features within those habitats do not permit assessment of relative value. This is not generally a handicap, however, because direct measurement of the shorebird populations in different areas gives the best assessment of their relative values, and this measurement is usually not prohibitively difficult to obtain.

On a large scale, total area of different wetland types sets limits on migrant marsh or shorebird populations of most species at inland sites. For example, most migrant sandpipers will occur only on mudflats and flooded fields or the beaches and shorelines of ponds and lakes; Wilson's phalaropes concentrate in large saline lakes during fall migration. Sandhill cranes roost on river bars and forage in croplands. The most efficient way of assessing the value of habitat to shorebirds of different habitats, however, remains the direct censusing of bird populations found there. For example, recent efforts to relate numbers of roosting sandhill cranes on Nebraska river bars to habitat features such as water depth and water velocity have established significant relationships. These do not permit model predictions of crane numbers at other river locations away from the studied sites (Latka and Yahnke, unpubl. ms), however.

Except for the influence of the tidal period on bird movements and habitat availability, most aspects of the census techniques discussed below apply equally well to coastal and inland habitats. In the western U.S., however, most inland and coastal wetlands differ in annual seasonality of bird use, because inland wetlands away from the coast or away from low elevations in the Southwest are usually frozen during winter. These areas are used by shorebirds only during spring and fall migration, mainly April through May and July through September. During these periods, however, densities of migrant shorebirds may be very high, even in temporary, seasonal wetlands. Flooded fields in springtime, in particular,

may attract large numbers of northbound migrant shorebirds, perhaps because of elevated densities of invertebrate prey (Krapu 1974). The temporary nature of this shorebird habitat, of course, requires that any habitat evaluation program, like shorebird census studies, focus on conditions during the brief migration period.

Population Measurement Techniques

Presence—Aerial Survey Method. Flying in a helicopter or fixed-wing aircraft, one or two observers record, on tape or on maps, the presence of flocks of shorebirds in different wetland locations over large surveyed areas. Flight elevation should be 25 to 60 m (80 to 200 ft) to promote flushing of roosting or foraging birds. Observers can record flock size or identify species or species groups whenever possible.

This method is useful only in areas where almost nothing is known of shorebird distributions for the time period surveyed. Except in unusual circumstances, aerial surveys cannot provide accurate estimates of population size because of the low reliability with which birds are sighted or counted from the air. Compounding this problem, only well-marked species that fly under the aircraft (dowitchers, willets, black-bellied plovers [*Pluvialis squatarola*]; or phalaropes sitting on calm water, etc.) can be identified consistently. Nevertheless, if large inaccessible areas or large numbers of inaccessible, small wetlands must be surveyed for presence of migrant shorebird flocks, the high cost of aircraft may be justified.

Relative Density. Most techniques of ground censusing for migrant shorebirds can be targeted to either relative or absolute density estimates, depending on the physical arrangement of local habitat areas and the schedule and range of shorebird movements among different areas. In general, relative density estimates are obtained when shorebirds are patchily distributed over the available habitat of interest, when counts are too limited to sample enough of the patchiness, or when parts of local populations are counted in special circumstances, such as at roosting sites. Actual censusing methods are discussed only under Absolute Density below, but the applicability of census results must be judged by biologists on the basis of factors just mentioned. Although actual numbers of birds in an area are counted in either situation, local population distributions and movements and local habitat distributions may require interpreting census numbers as relative rather than absolute densities.

Absolute Density. For most of the methods described here, important choices must be made beforehand, to set some conditions for the census. In coastal areas, the most important decision concerns tidal conditions. Birds can be counted at high or low tides, at specified time intervals before or after high or low tides, or at particular tide levels on either rising or falling tides. Setting these conditions is central to intertidal shorebird censusing because shorebirds move between habitat areas on a tidal schedule, and the area of available habitat changes on a tidal schedule (Connors et al. 1981).

The choice of conditions should be coordinated with the census method chosen. For foraging birds on mudflats, a falling tide is generally best, because birds usually forage most intensively on falling tides, having been prohibited from access to feeding areas during the previous high tide. Selecting a particular interval of tide levels permits the observer to locate census plots conveniently. If very low tide levels expose extensive mudflats, birds may forage too far from convenient observation points along shorelines; a mid-tide level may be more practical (Page et al. 1979). For censusing birds on beaches or at roosting sites, a very high tide level may be best, because this forces birds out of foraging areas on nearby mudflats (Connors et al. 1981). In nontidal areas, time of day assumes greater importance, and foraging birds should usually be censused in early morning or late afternoon when most are active.

Frequency and duration of censusing also must be determined, because migrant shorebird populations may change quickly. To determine peak migration densities or timing of migration, multiple counts are needed, spaced every 1 to 5 days. Single counts or longer intervals between counts will be useful, but could miss peak movements of short duration.

Method 1—Sample Plot Count. In the sample plot technique, an observer counts all birds within a specified area. The observer can select areas with natural topographic boundaries, mark plots with stakes, or count a circular plot with a specified radius around the observing station. This last scheme, also called a fixed-distance point count, is most useful when an area will be censused only once, because it permits sampling many points without mapping or staking. However, it requires the observer to walk through the open shorebird habitat, potentially disturbing the birds, and its accuracy depends on the observer's ability to estimate the specified radial distance.

Choosing sample plots with permanently marked boundaries avoids this last problem and, in many instances, the observer can count the entire plot from one observing station, frequently positioned on a plot boundary (which may be the shoreline). Because of the open character and lack of vegetation or topographic diversity in many migrant shorebird habitats, an observer with binoculars or a telescope can count and identify birds at great distances (to 200 m [660 ft]) under good viewing conditions. This permits large sample plot areas to be covered from a single station or from a series of stations along a shoreline. This method is well-suited to regular repetitive censusing. Densities are determined by field measurement or map estimation of sample plot areas.

Accuracy of the sample plot method is generally high, limited mainly by difficulties in counting birds that may move appreciably during the brief count period. Poor visibility, estimates of large flocks, difficulties with identifications at long distances, and parallax problems of estimating plot boundary locations may also affect accuracy. As with all methods listed here, equipment is minimal, training is easy if observers have mastered shorebird identification, and cost depends mainly on the number and frequency of sample plot counts.

Method 2—Marked Plot Strip Transect. This technique is essentially identical to Method 3 for tundra-breeding shorebirds. It is especially well-suited to marshy areas or wetlands with open pools and mudflats, interspersed with marsh, because the observer moves through the transect close enough to all points to discover birds partially obscured by vegetation. The division of the transect into small plots permits association of birds with habitat information for each plot, an advantage in some studies. In open mudflat habitats, the excellent visibility allows the observer to walk directly along the center line of a 100 m (330 ft) wide transect, accelerating the census. As with the preceding method, accuracy is high except when birds move on or off the transect during the count. The time required to mark the transect is a good investment only when a series of censuses are planned at the same site, such as censuses throughout a migration or winter period.

Method 3—Unmarked Strip Transect. In this variant of Method 2, with no permanent transect markers, the observer must estimate a census width to either side of the transect line, a factor that reduces the accuracy and precision of the census. However, the technique requires no setup time, and is useful for surveying areas when only single censuses are possible.

Method 4—Linear Density Transects. Several variations of this technique all obtain a linear density estimate along shorelines, rather than the conventional density measured over two-dimensional areas. The observer moves parallel to the shoreline, walking or riding a vehicle (three-wheeled motorcycles are effective on arctic beaches), counting birds continually. The counting width may be constant, centered on the water's edge or landward from the water's edge, or it may be variable, including for example, all of a beach from water to dunes or all of a specific habitat, such as the wave-washed zone of a sandy beach or the rocky intertidal zone below a cliff. Densities are typically expressed as birds per kilometer (0.6 mile). Linear density transects share the same properties of accuracy, precision, and required training as comparable area transect methods.

Method 5—Roosting Flock Counts. If consistent roosting areas are known from prior observations, specific areas can be treated as sample plots, or general areas can be searched for the daily location of total roosting flocks. This method clearly depends on properly choosing sampling times, usually dusk or midday for inland areas and high tide for coastal areas. It may provide an absolute density for a roosting area, but the real values of such a count are usually (1) as an index to the population using nearby areas for foraging or (2) in some circumstances, as an estimate of the total local population size. In counting roosting flocks, accuracy and precision are sometimes reduced by the inability to visually separate and count all individuals in very large flocks of small birds. A vantage point providing some elevation above the roosting flock is helpful in these situations.

Method 6—Total Population Counts. Because migrating shorebirds are so concentrated in specific, limited habitats, total population size estimates for a local area may be obtainable. This is unusual compared with most avian censusing situations and is often the most useful of population variables. This technique also requires prior knowledge of the local distributions of shorebird habitats or the behavior of shorebird species, and usually more than one observer censusing different areas simultaneously. It has been used to estimate total populations of a single estuary (Page et al. 1979; Connors et al. 1981) or of hundreds of kilometers of a coastline (J.P. Myers, pers. commun.). This technique is costly in personnel and its accuracy depends on the physical layout of the area censused and on movements of birds during the census period. However, the numbers obtained are frequently the most useful in management studies.

Method 7—Aerial Counts. As discussed above, transect counts from aircraft are not usually accurate for shorebirds because of shorebirds' small size and their frequent occurrence in large flocks of several species. For cranes, however, the large size of the birds makes this approach feasible and efficient when large areas must be sampled.

Method 8—Photographic Counts. For very large numbers of roosting birds, especially shorebirds or sandhill cranes in migration, photographs taken from aircraft or from an elevated fixed point near a roost may provide the best means of obtaining an accurate count. A photograph can be taken quickly, before birds flush or while they are flying but still concentrated. It can then be analyzed methodically and carefully at a later time.

Discussion

Shorebirds in migration occupy such a wide range of habitats that profitable generalizations are difficult. However, in most migrant shorebird situations, the open nature of the habitat and the conspicuousness and high densities of the birds make shorebird censusing relatively simple. In these situations, monitoring shorebird densities directly is usually preferable to measuring habitat features as a means of evaluating probable shorebird use. For the same reasons, counting actual shorebird totals in monitored areas can often give absolute density estimates at little extra cost over simple presence/absence or relative density estimates. However, interpreting census results, in light of information on local habitat distributions and bird movements, is more centrally important than for most other bird-habitat groups, as is the proper choice of census conditions, especially with tidal fluctuations. Because of the disjunct distribution of most migrant and wintering shorebird habitats, estimates of total size of temporarily discrete local populations are frequently possible and may be more meaningful than estimates of bird densities in particular habitats under particular conditions.

Finally, dealing with populations in migration at a site carries certain complications that differ from breeding population studies. Most notable is the inherent instability of the population, which requires frequent regular censuses to estimate peak or mean densities during a migration period. Furthermore, unless rates of individual turnover at a site are known, single census results or even continuous census results do not provide estimates of total population numbers using the site—a relationship that is markedly different from that which applies to breeding bird studies.

MARSHES—RAILS AND COOTS

Five of the six North American rail species breed and winter in the western U.S. where they constitute a characteristic segment of the avifauna of fresh, brackish, and saltmarshes. They are secretive and inconspicuous, spending most of their time in wetlands surrounded by dense vegetative cover, a situation that has led to the development of specialized census techniques. Coots and gallinules nest in some of the same marshes, and coots in winter are widespread in open water situations, both fresh- and saltwater, where waterfowl are common.

Habitat Features

Rails are among the strictest of all bird groups in their consistency of habitat use. They seldom venture out of marshes or the muddy borders of marshes. This basic requirement of vegetated wetlands provides the best, albeit rough, guide to assessing rail habitat. Within this general description, however, suitable marshlands vary from freshwater to brackish to saltwater; from edges of ponds, lakes, or rivers to large estuaries; and from moderately low vegetation, such as pickleweed (*Salicornia* sp.), to tall cattails (*Typha* sp.), sedges (*Scirpus* sp.), and rushes (*Juncus* sp.). Species habitat preferences and seasonal habitat use patterns differ (Repking and Ohmart 1977; Gill 1979; Glahn 1974; Griese et al. 1980; Sayre and Rundle 1984). Even within a single species and a single region, questions remain concerning the differences in rail population densities between superficially similar marshes, as with populations of clapper rail *(Rallus longirostris)* in San Francisco Bay (Gill 1979; T. Harvey, pers. commun.).

Coots are abundant and fairly conspicuous at wetland nesting sites in western North America, where they use a wide variety of marsh and pond types. Habitat requirements, in terms of pond size, permanency, and characteristics of emergent vegetation at nest sites, have been studied by Sugden (1979) and Nudds (1982).

Population Measurement Techniques

Presence. Because of the difficulty of observing secretive rails in dense cover, presence and absence is sometimes the only information one can obtain. There are no special techniques for determining presence, however, other than direct observation of individuals, usually during foraging periods, or calls and observations recorded by the methods listed under Relative or Absolute Density.

Relative Density.

Method 1—Breeding Vocalization. The breeding vocalization technique relies on naturally occurring vocalizations of territorial breeding rails during the early breeding season (April, May, and June in most areas). An observer familiar with rail calls listens at selected points within or on the periphery of a marsh. Listening periods should be of

Coots in an open-water habitat.

the same duration and similar in time of day, date, and weather conditions at all sites to be compared. Relative density can be expressed as calling birds per time of observation or per listening station. Recordings or rail vocalizations are available for training purposes. Precision and accuracy of this technique are unknown, but may be low. Costs are also low.

Method 2—Tape Playback Response. The tape playback technique is more widely used, requires little extra effort, and increases the chance of hearing a rail that is present during the station count. Glahn (1974) located 71% more territories of rails in Colorado using playback techniques, compared with territory mapping without playback. Accuracy is therefore increased but may still be low, depending mainly on the consistency with which rails respond.

Although taped response techniques are most effective during the breeding season, they also have been used with appropriate taped calls to assess winter populations (Tomlinson and Todd 1973; Marion et al. 1981). Use of a variety of calls, preferably

recorded within the local region of the species' range, is recommended (Johnson et al. 1981). A consistent schedule of tape playback duration and listening duration must be maintained, on the order of 1 min. of playback followed by 5 min. of listening, possibly repeated, at each station. Training and data treatment are similar to Method 1.

Method 3—Flood Tide Counts. In tidal areas, some rails can be located visually during extremely high tides, when almost all marsh vegetation is inundated. In San Francisco Bay, clapper rails are forced onto small patches of high ground or floating debris during the highest tides of the year, which occur during daylight only in winter. They can be located from vantage points surrounding the marsh or in extensive marsh areas from a canoe or an airboat traveling through the marsh. Detection of birds can be increased if the observer works with a competent hunting dog (T. Harvey, pers. commun.).

With sufficiently high tides and scarce, accessible refuges, this method can be accurate in terms of total birds sighted, but the distance over which birds have traveled to a refuge is generally unknown. For

U.S. Fish and Wildlife Service

Gallinule in a typical marsh habitat.

this reason it is listed first as a relative density technique, but this technique and the two previous techniques can all be adapted to absolute density estimation.

Method 4—Open Water Counts (Coots). American coots are the only species in this group to regularly forage in open water away from emergent vegetation. Direct visual counts, made from shore or in boats, can provide an index of numbers of coots nesting in wetlands. The fraction of the population missed will remain unknown and may vary in different types of wetlands. All counts of comparative purposes should be made at the same time of day and over as short a calendar interval as practical.

Absolute Density.

Method 1—Breeding Vocalization. Combining the breeding vocalization technique with a territory mapping effort, a variable width line transect method, or a variable circular plot method permits estimation of absolute densities. Accuracy is probably low in most situations, however, because an unknown percentage of rails present will not call during the census period. All three approaches require the observer to estimate distances to unseen vocalizing rails, a difficult task.

Method 2—Tape Playback Response. Similarly, the tape playback method is the combination of the technique discussed under Relative Density and the area estimating techniques of mapping, variable width line transect, or variable circular plot method. It suffers the same limitations of accuracy and precision as Method 1 in this section, but the tape playback elicits vocalizations at a higher frequency than the natural calling rates, so fewer birds are missed.

Method 3—Flood Tide Counts. Methods for this technique are described under Relative Density. However, when discrete patches of saltmarsh or extensive areas of continuous saltmarsh can be searched thoroughly, absolute density measurements result. Local movements of birds to refuges within their population area do not distort the density estimate if the entire population area is censused. (Transect sampling, under these circumstances, may produce large errors.) If all potential refuges can be carefully searched, accuracy and precision of these estimates should be high. Costs may also be high, however, because of logistics, especially with the use of airboats at high tides. This method is only useful in winter, when high tides occur during daylight hours.

Method 4—Rope-Drag Nest Mapping. As described for Tundra—Breeding Shorebirds, two observers walk through potential nesting habitat dragging a rope (about 50 m [165 ft] of 1/4-in. rope) between them; a third observer walks behind, recording locations of nests and adults when birds flush. The technique greatly increases the numbers of nests located and is especially valuable when used in conjunction with Methods 1 and 2, because it provides an independent estimate of breeding density. Furthermore, information from one method can sometimes be added to information from the other when clear discrepancies occur. The combined census may be more accurate than either census alone.

Method 5—Nest Searches (Coots). Direct nest searches in marshes can provide reliable estimates of coot nest densities (Sugden 1979). This can be combined with observations of bird-nesting behavior and territoriality to narrow the search areas, but will usually require a time-consuming field effort.

Discussion

Rails in marshes share one characteristic with shorebirds in migration. Their habitats are often clearly distinguished from surrounding areas (marsh or mudflat versus uplands, for example) and are easily recognized and mapped. Habitat evaluation at this very general level is straightforward. At the finer scale, which requires distinguishing better from poorer marshlands, knowledge is limited.

The two bird groups contrast markedly in ease and accuracy of censusing populations for absolute density estimates. For all the reasons that shorebirds are extremely tractable, rails are difficult to treat. Their secretiveness and the densely vegetated, relatively inaccessible habitats they favor impose stumbling blocks in any rail population studies. The methods just described have limited accuracy and precision, but provide useful estimates of population sizes in most situations.

CONCLUSIONS

The 54 species of marsh and shorebirds that occur in Alaska and the western States cover such a wide range of sizes, habitats, and natural histories that the difficulty of any neat generalizations of bird-habitat relationships or of preferred census techniques is not surprising. Most of these species are relatively easy to assign to large-scale habitat types (marsh versus forest, for example) and some can be partially defined by minor habitat differences in habitat features, such as vegetation height or water depth. In almost no situations beyond a local study area, however, can one predict densities of bird use based on habitat measurements with a sufficient degree of accuracy to justify such an approach. For most shorebirds and cranes, this is not a serious lack, because these species are usually so visible in their breeding and non-breeding habitats that a direct censusing method can be efficient and acceptably accurate. Rails, by their secretive habits and the dense vegetative cover in their habitats, present a much more difficult censusing challenge.

For these reasons, presence and absence techniques are usually warranted only for rails and gallinules. Relative density census techniques have much wider application for many shorebirds, rails, coots,

and cranes. With an increase in effort and minor modifications, many of these techniques provide absolute density measurements. The range of absolute density census techniques is especially large for shorebirds nesting on tundra or migrating along shorelines, because in these situations a large mixture of species often occurs at high densities under conditions of good detectability. Even these generalizations, however, gloss over individual species differences that may be of major importance in selecting research and management techniques. The Literature Cited section in this chapter should be consulted directly for additional details concerning particular species, areas, or habitats before field work is initiated.

LITERATURE CITED

BENT, A.C. 1926. Life histories of North American marsh birds. U.S. Natl. Mus. Bull. 135.

———. 1929. Life histories of North American shorebirds. U.S. Natl. Mus. Bull. 146.

BERGMAN, R.D., R. HOWARD, K. ABRAHAM, and M. WELLER. 1977. Water birds and their wetland resources in relation to oil development at Storkersen Point, Alaska. U.S. Dep. Inter., Fish and Wildl. Serv. Resour. Publ. 129. 39pp.

BRYANT, D.M. 1979. Effects of prey density and site character on estuary usage by overwintering waders (Charadrii). Estuarine and Coastal Marine Science 9: 369-384.

CONNORS, P.G. 1984. Ecology of shorebirds in the Alaskan Beaufort littoral zone. Pages 403-416 in Barnes, P., E. Reimnitz, and D. Schell, eds. The Alaskan Beaufort Sea: Ecosystems and Environments. Academic Press.

———, J.P. MYERS, C.S.W. CONNORS, and F.A. PITELKA. 1981. Interhabitat movements by sanderlings in relation to foraging profitability and the tidal cycle. Auk 98:49-64.

———, ———, and F.A. PITELKA. 1979. Seasonal habitat use by arctic Alaskan shorebirds. Studies Avian Biol. 2:101-111.

DREWIEN, R.C. 1973. Ecology of Rocky Mountain greater sandhill cranes. Ph.D. dissertation, Univ. Idaho, Moscow. 152pp.

EMLEN, J.T. 1971. Population densities of birds derived from transect counts. Auk 88:323-342.

———. 1977. Estimating breeding season bird densities from transect counts. Auk 94:455-468.

GERSTENBERG, R.H. 1979. Habitat utilization by wintering and migrating shorebirds on Humboldt Bay, California. Studies Avian Biol. 2:33-40.

GIBSON, F. 1971. The breeding biology of the American avocet (Recurvirostra americana) in central Oregon. Condor 73:444-454.

GILL, R.E., Jr. 1979. Status and distribution of the California clapper rail (Rallus longirostris obsoletus). California Fish and Game 65:36-49.

——— and C.M. HANDEL. 1981. Shorebirds of the eastern Bering Sea, Pages 719-738 in Hood, D.W. and J.A. Calder, eds. Eastern Bering Sea Shelf: Oceanography and Resources, Vol. 2. Univ. Washington Press, Seattle.

———, M.R. PETERSEN, and P.D. JORGENSEN. 1981. Birds of the north Alaska Peninsula, 1976-1980. Arctic 34:286-306.

GLAHN, J.F. 1974. Study of breeding rails with recorded calls in north-central Colorado. Wilson Bull. 86:206-214.

GOSS-CUSTARD, J.D. 1970. The response of redshank (Tringa totanus L.) to spatial variations in the density of their prey. J. Animal Ecol. 39:91-113.

GRAUL, W.D. 1975. Breeding biology of the mountain plover. Wilson Bull. 87:6-31.

GRIESE, H.J., R.A. RYDER, and C.E. BRAUN. 1980. Spatial and temporal distribution of rails in Colorado. Wilson Bull. 92:96-102.

HAMILTON, R.C. 1975. Comparative behavior of the American avocet and the black-necked stilt (Recurvirostridae). A.O.U. Monographs, 17.

HOLMES, R.T. and C.P. BLACK. 1973. Ecological distribution of birds in the Kolomak River-Askinuk Mountain Region, Yukon-Kuskokwim Delta, Alaska. Condor 75:150-163.

——— and F.A. PITELKA. 1968. Food overlap among coexisting sandpipers on northern Alaska tundra. Systematic Zoology 17:305-318.

ISLEIB, M.E.P. 1979. Migratory shorebird populations on the Copper River Delta and eastern Prince William Sound, Alaska. Studies Avian Biol. 2:125-130.

JARVINEN, O. and R.A. VAISANEN. 1975. Estimating relative densities of breeding birds by the line transect method. Oikos 26:316-322.

JENNI, D.A., R.L. REDMOND, and T.K. BICAK. 1982. Behavioral ecology and habitat relationships of long-billed curlews in western Idaho. Unpubl. Rep. to U.S. Dep. Inter., Bur. Land Manage., Boise, ID. 234pp.

JOHNSON, R.R., B.T. BROWN, L.T. HAIGHT, and J.M. SIMPSON. 1981. Playback recordings as a special avian censusing technique. Studies Avian Biol. 6:68-75.

JOHNSON, S.R. and W.J. RICHARDSON. 1981. Beaufort Sea—Barrier Island— lagoon ecological processes studies: Final report, Simpson Lagoon: birds. Pages 109-383 in Environmental Assessment Alaskan Continental Shelf. Vol. 7.

KRAPU, G.L. 1974. Feeding ecology of pintail hens during reproduction. Auk 91:278-290.

LATKA, D.C. and J.W. YAHNKE. 1984. Simulating roosting habitat of sandhill cranes and validation of suitability-of-use indices. Unpubl. abstract of poster presented at Wildlife 2000 Conference, Fallen Leaf Lake, CA.

LITTLEFIELD, C.D. and R.A. RYDER. 1968. Breeding biology of the greater sandhill crane on Malheur National Wildlife Refuge, Oregon. Trans. North Am. Wildl. Nat. Resour. Conf. 33:444-454.

MARION, W.R., T.E. O'MEARA, and D.S. MAEHR. 1981. Use of playback recordings in sampling elusive or secretive birds. Studies Avian Biol. 6:81-85.

MARTIN, P.D. and C.S. MOITERET. 1981. Bird populations and habitat use, Canning River Delta, Alaska. Unpubl. Rep. to U.S. Dep. Inter., Fish and Wildl. Serv., Fairbanks, AK. 196pp.

MICKELSON, P.S., J.S. HAWKINS, D.R. HERTER, and S.M. MURPHY. 1980. Habitat use by birds and other wildlife on the Eastern Copper River Delta, AK. Unpublished Report. Alaska Coop. Wildl. Res. Unit, Univ. Alaska, Fairbanks. 189pp.

MYERS, J.P., P.G. CONNORS, and F.A. PITELKA. 1979. Territory size in wintering sanderlings: The effects of prey abundance and intruder density. Auk 96:551-561.

——— and F.A. PITELKA. 1980. Effect of habitat conditions on spatial parameters of shorebird populations. Rep. to the U.S. Dep. Energy. 82pp.

NUDDS, T.D. 1982. Ecological separation of grebes and coots: Interference competition or microhabitat selection? Wilson Bull. 94:505-514.

ORING, L.W., D.B. LANK, and S.J. MAXSON. 1983. Population studies of the polyandrous spotted sandpiper. Auk 100:272-285.

PAGE, G.W., L.E. STENZEL, D.W. WINKLER, and C.W. SWARTH. 1983. Spacing out at Mono Lake: Breeding success, nest density, and predation in the snowy plover. Auk 100:13-24.

———, ———, and C.M. WOLFE. 1979. Aspects of the occurrence of shorebirds on a central California estuary. Studies Avian Biol. 2:15-32.

RALPH, C.J. and J.M. SCOTT, eds. 1981. Estimating numbers of terrestrial birds. Studies Avian Biol. 630pp.

RANDS, M.R.W. and J.P. BARKHAM. 1981. Factors controlling within-flock feeding densities in three species of wading bird. Ornis Scandinavica 12:28-36.

RECHER, H.F. 1966. Some aspects of the ecology of migrant shorebirds. Ecology 47:393-407.

REDMOND, R.L. 1984. The behavioral ecology of long-billed curlews *(Numenius americanus)* breeding in western Idaho. Ph.D. dissertation, Univ. Montana, Missoula.

———, T. K. BICAK, and D.A. JENNI. 1981. An evaluation of breeding season census techniques for long-billed curlews *(Numenius americanus).* Studies Avian Biol. 6:197-201.

RENAUD, W.E. 1979. The piping plover in Saskatchewan. Blue Jay 37:90-103.

REPKING, C.F. and R.D. OHMART. 1977. Distribution and density of black rail populations along the lower Colorado River. Condor 79:486-489.

RILEY, J.L. 1982. Habitats of sandhill cranes in the southern Hudson Bay lowland, Ontario. Canada Field-Nat. 96:51-55.

RYAN, M.R. 1985. Marbled godwit habitat selection in the northern prairie region. J. Wildl. Manage., in press.

SAYRE, M.W. and W.D. RUNDLE. 1984. Comparison of habitat use by migrant soras and Virginia rails. J. Wildl. Manage. 48:599-605.

SENNER, S.E. 1979. An evaluation of the Copper River Delta as a critical habitat for migrating shorebirds. Studies Avian Biol. 2:131-146.

SHIELDS, G.F. and L.J. PEYTON. 1979. Avian community ecology of the Akulik-Inglutalik River Delta, Norton Bay-Alaska. Environmental Assessment, Alaskan Continental Shelf, Ann. Reps. 5:608-710. NOAA, Boulder, CO.

SPINDLER, M.A. 1978. Bird populations and habitat use in the Okpilak River Delta area, Arctic National Wildlife Range, Alaska, 1978. Unpubl. Rep. to U.S. Dep. Inter., Fish and Wildl. Serv., Fairbanks, AK. 86pp.

STEWART, R.E. and H.A. KANTRUD. 1971. Classification of natural ponds and lakes in the glaciated prairie region. U.S. Dep. Inter., Fish and Wildl. Serv. Resour. Publ. 92. 57pp.

SUGDEN, L.G. 1979. Habitat use by nesting American coots in Saskatchewan parklands. Wilson Bull. 91:599-607.

TOMLINSON, R.E. and R.L. TODD. 1973. Distribution of two western clapper rail races as determined by responses to taped calls. Condor 75:177-183.

TROY, D.M., D. HERTER, and R. BURGESS. 1983. Prudhoe Bay Waterflood Project tundra bird monitoring program. Unpubl. Rep. to Dep. Army, Corps of Engineers, Anchorage, AK. 98pp.

WEBER, M.J., P.A. VOHS, Jr., and L.D. FLAKE. 1982. Use of prairie wetlands by selected bird species in South Dakota. Wilson Bull. 94: 550-554.

WESELOH, D.V. and L.M. WESELOH. 1983. Numbers and nest site characteristics of the piping plover in central Alberta, 1974-1977. Blue Jay 41:155-161.

WIENS, J.A. 1973. Pattern and process in grassland bird communities. Ecol. Monogr. 43:237-270.

WILLIAMSON, F.S.L., M.C. THOMPSON, and J.Q. HINES. 1966. Avifaunal investigations, Pages 437-480 *in* Wilimovsky, N. J., ed. Environment of the Cape Thompson Region, Alaska. U.S. Atomic Energy Commission, Oak Ridge, TN.

18

WATERFOWL

Robert L. Eng

Montana State University
Bozeman, MT 59717-0001

Editor's Note: Waterfowl, because of their economic and recreational value have received much attention for many years. And because of their obligate association with wetlands, habitat has long been a concern with these species. Thus, inventory, monitoring, and management of waterfowl habitat has a long history compared to species groups whose management has focused on population management. However, waterfowl biology has become a specialized discipline and has tended to focus on major wetland areas. Yet large numbers of waterfowl depend on smaller wetlands scattered throughout the West. These areas, if managed at all, are probably managed by biologists with no specialized expertise in waterfowl. This chapter provides such biologists an introduction to inventory and monitoring of waterfowl and waterfowl habitat.

INTRODUCTION

The term waterfowl includes ducks, geese, and swans. In the most recently published classification, a single family, the Anatidae, is separated into two subfamilies, the Anserinae (whistling-ducks, swans, and geese) and the Anatinae (ducks; Check-List of North American Birds, American Ornithologists Union, 1983). Both subfamilies are further divided into species, groups, or tribes—the Anserinae, into three and the Anatinae, into five.

Most species of waterfowl are migratory to some extent, with many participating in lengthy seasonal movements. Thus habitat features for different species or species groups will vary considerably throughout the year, both as a result of geographic availability and by demands placed upon the species as a result of seasonal behavior.

As with upland game birds, most early waterfowl investigations emphasized the reproductive season (Chabreck 1979). This is somewhat understandable because it covers the period when offspring are produced. The nesting season also embraces the time of the year when waterfowl habitat is most important, because self-imposed isolation of pairs results in a density far below that which may be found during other seasons. Also, nesting habitat seemingly was the most threatened by land uses by man and consequently was thrust into the limelight.

In recent years, attention has increased on wintering and migration habitat. Even though the gregarious nature of waterfowl during these periods permits rather large numbers in relatively small areas, winter habitats in parts of the Atlantic Flyway have deteriorated to the extent that they are no longer suitable for ducks (Addy 1964). As was pointed out by Chabreck (1979), dabbling ducks may spend two-thirds of the year on the winter habitat, and the quality of that habitat may greatly influence their reproductive performance in the spring.

The habitat features for the various tribes of waterfowl appear more distinguishable for the breeding season than for other times of the year. This may in part be a result of the greater investigative effort during the breeding season. It may also be a result of less diverse activities by all species during winter (largely feeding and loafing), permitting a more intense use of a resource by many members of the same or different species. Thus, in this chapter, the habitat features for the nesting season are discussed by species groups for the more widely distributed or numerically important tribes with references to individual species when deemed pertinent. Winter habitat is discussed in a more general fashion for the entire family.

HABITAT FEATURES CORRELATED WITH WATERFOWL

Swans (Cygnini)

Two species of swans are native to North America. The tundra swan *(Cygnus columbianus),* until recently called the whistling swan, is the most abundant; about 150,000 were reported in 1971 (Bellrose 1978). The trumpeter swan *(C. buccinator),* once believed to number less than 100 birds in the U.S. and Canada, now constitutes a population of about 1,500 plus about 9,000 in Alaska.

Physical Features. As the name implies, tundra swans nest in the arctic from north of Hudson Bay to the coast of Alaska (Bellrose 1978). Lensink (in Bellrose 1978) reported nest site locations as follows: 50% on the shore of a lake or pond within 18 m (20 yd) of water, 30% on small islands or points, and the remainder in a variety of situations. In most instances the nest was elevated aboveground.

Trumpeter swans in Alaska showed a nest preference for small beaver impoundments over other larger bodies of water; one-half of the 40 nests were located in beaver ponds of less than 5.6 ha (14 a.). This preference appeared to be related to a stable water level and little wave action, which promoted the development and maintenance of extensive stands of emerging and floating vegetation in which and from which the nests were constructed (Hansen et al. 1971). Trumpeter swans in the Targhee Forest in Idaho and Wyoming use older, more eutrophic lakes, which are relatively shallow (average 1.2 m [4 ft]), have a large part of the surface covered with vegetation (80%), and have at least 25% of their total area less than 1 m deep. Aquatic vegetation is used for the nest site and nest material (Maj 1983).

Trumpeter swans, adults, and cygnet.

Vegetation.

Structure. Whereas the trumpeter swan nests almost exclusively over water in emergent aquatic vegetation, the tundra swan seems to prefer more upland sites not associated with emergent vegetation (Hansen et al. 1971), but close enough to water that water was often exposed when vegetation was removed from a circle around the nest (Lensink in Bellrose 1978). Both species also feed largely on aquatic plants, both submergents and emergents, although the tundra swan will feed on upland sources when marshes freeze (Nagel 1965). Upland feeding in cornfields by tundra swans has become relatively common along Chesapeake Bay and can be readily observed during spring migration through Montana.

Species Composition. Tundra swans, as inhabitants of the open tundra and somewhat more terrestrial than trumpeter swans, construct nests from material which may include mosses, grasses, and sedges (*Carex* sp.). In Alaska, nests of trumpeter swans were usually constructed with the stems and rhizomes of *Carex* sp., *Equisetum fluviatile,* or *Potentilla* sp. (Hanson et al. 1971). In Idaho and Wyoming, nests were frequently in and constructed of *Typha* sp., *Scirpus* sp., or *Carex* sp. Occasional nests were found on islands or beaver (*Castor canadensis*) lodges, near the water's edge, and constructed largely of aquatic vegetation (Maj 1983).

Both species feed largely on aquatic plants, including the seeds, stems, and tubers of several species. Sago pondweed (*Potamogeton pectinatus*) is a prominent plant in the diet of tundra (Sherwood 1960; Nagel 1965) and trumpeter swans (Bellrose 1978). Other plants frequently mentioned as food are widgeon grass (*Ruppia* sp.), duck potato (*Sagittaria* sp.), other pondweeds (*Potamogeton* sp.), and water milfoil (*Myriophyllum* sp.).

Geese (Anserini)

Of the several species of geese that winter in the U.S., only one, the Canada goose *(Branta canadensis)*, nests within the U.S. south of Canada. This species has great morphological and ecological breadth, with sizes ranging from a large duck to a small swan, and nesting distribution from farm ponds to forested lakes to arctic tundra. This diversity has led to considerable discussion as to the number of identifiable races. Bellrose (1978) illustrated the ranges of 12 populations of this species, established largely on the basis of the close alliances shown during the winter. Two races nest south of Canada, the giant Canada goose *(B. c. maxima)* and the western Canada goose *(B. c. moffitti)*, whereas at least nine other races nest across the breadth of the arctic or northern Canada (Bellrose 1978).

Physical Features. Nesting habitat for Canada geese is extremely diverse, particularly for the two races nesting south of Canada. This is probably because of the diverse habitats into which the two races have been introduced through management (transplant) programs. Canada geese have been observed to nest in the vicinity of lakes, ponds, marsh, and river habitat; on the ground; on muskrat houses; in trees in unused raptor, heron, and magpie *(Pica pica)* nests; and on cliffs. However, in spite of the great variety of reported nest sites, the preference for islands as nest sites appears to dominate (Hammond and Mann 1956; Ewaschuk and Boag 1972; Giroux 1981; Giroux et al. 1983). This preference is also shown by some of the smaller arctic nesting Canada geese (MacInnes 1962), but less so by the colonial nesting snow geese *(Chen caerulescens;* Lemieux 1959) and Ross' goose *(C. rossii;* Ryder 1967).

Colorado Division of Wildlife

Terrestrial nesting Canada geese.

Geese are very terrestrial compared with most ducks and swans. Consequently, secure brood-rearing areas are an integral part of breeding habitat. The habitat usually consists of a meadow or flat area providing a grazing area with good visibility and access to water. Such areas are frequently near the nest sites but some birds nesting on western rivers may move several miles to congregate on desirable brood-rearing areas.

Another habitat requirement of geese used during the breeding season, but usually distinct from breeding areas, is the molting area. Nonproductive geese, primarily yearlings (65%), 2-year-olds (20%), and older birds (15%), leave the breeding areas in late spring for traditional molting areas (Krohn and Bizeau 1979). The migration is usually in a northerly direction. Although several molting areas are present in the western U.S., many of the Canada geese from this area migrate to the Northwest Territories to molt (Krohn and Bizeau 1979). Key physical characteristics of a molting area are a large body of water for security, a good food supply, and little human disturbance. One such area in southwestern Montana, under the jurisdiction of the U.S. Bureau of Land Management, annually harbors 8,000 to 10,000 geese. This site has received special consideration to maintain its integrity as an important molting area (Hildebrand 1979).

Vegetation.

Structure. Protective cover near goose nests seems optimal when it at least breaks the outline of the incubating bird, but is not so high as to prevent visibility from the nest. Thus, in areas where vegetation was relatively short and nesting densities high, geese selected islands that had greater coverage of forbs and grass (Giroux 1981). Conversely, where vegetation was relatively high and nesting densities low, geese selected islands with less dense vegetation (Kaminski and Prince 1977). In areas where high densities of geese are nesting, visual barriers between nest sites (vegetation or topography) permit pairs to nest closer to one another with less aggressive encounters (Giroux 1981).

Structure of vegetation in brood-rearing areas should be short enough to permit visibility, at least by the adults. Grazing geese generally avoid dense or high vegetation because both adults and goslings are often flightless.

Species Composition. Where nesting cover is concerned, vegetation structure is more critical than species composition. Migrating and wintering geese make extensive use of agricultural crops, including cereal grains and green forage. However, on brood-rearing areas where flightless birds must graze adjacent to the water, a wide variety of green forage is utilized. At Canyon Ferry Wildlife Management Area near Townsend, Montana, where about 1,000 goslings are produced annually, I have observed Canada geese grazing heavily on wheatgrass (*Agropyron* sp.), spikerushes (*Eleocharis* sp.), new shoots of bulrush (*Scirpus* sp.), alfalfa *(Medicago sativa),* and reed canarygrass *(Phalaris arundinacea),* while virtually ignoring abundant plants of sweet clover *(Melilotus officinalis).*

Dabbling Ducks (Anatini) and Wood Ducks (Cairinini)

Under the subfamily Anatinae (ducks), more than one tribe may be treated as a single species group because they will frequently share some common habitat feature. Although many ducks have breeding ranges extending far into Canada, unlike most geese, many also nest south into the U.S. Some have very extensive breeding ranges, being abundant on both the prairies and the tundra (e.g., pintail *[Anas acuta]* whereas the black duck *(A. rubripes)* and the mottled duck *(A. fulvigula)* are considerably more restricted geographically. Many dabbling ducks and some diving ducks reach their highest density of breeding birds in the north-central U.S. and south-central Canada in an area called the Prairie Pothole region. Among the dabblers in this group are the mallard *(A. platyrhynchos),* pintail, gadwall *(A. strepera),* blue-winged teal *(A. discors),* and shoveler *(A. clypeata).*

Physical Features. Most species of this group are birds that breed primarily in the prairies, parklands, or tundra, all of which provide relatively open shallow marshes. Notable exceptions include the black duck, which is found in fresh and marine marshes, swamps, and lakes (and prefers wooded marshes for breeding), and the wood duck *(Aix sponsa),* which prefers small, quiet inland streams and ponds near woodland.

Because all of these ducks are territorial to some degree, breeding habitat is enhanced with an abundance of water areas of varying sizes, depths, and configurations that provide a diversity of aquatic vegetation structure. Patterson (1976) found a seasonal shift in habitat requirements by prairie-dwelling ducks, where the breeding pairs disperse to all bodies of water, irrespective of the productivity of the waters. As the breeding chronology progressed, the broods and fledged ducks (which had greater demands for nutrition but less demands for isolation) moved selectively to the more productive waters, thus allowing full utilization of a spatially heterogeneous aquatic habitat.

Stock ponds often provide valuable habitats (Bue et al. 1964). Although in comparatively low densities (seldom exceeding 1/km² [1/247 a.²] on arid grazing lands in the West), these ponds are often more stable (Brewster et al. 1976) and more productive over the years than many natural wetlands. The merits of different types of stock ponds as waterfowl habitat were discussed by Eng et al. (1979).

Stock pond in Great Basin Desert used by waterfowl.

As with geese, several species of ducks are attracted to island habitats for nesting. From this species group, mallards and gadwalls are very likely to nest on islands. In the absence of mammalian predation, a high nest success combines with a high degree of homing in ensuing years by surviving young, resulting in some rather high nest densities (Duebbert 1982; Duebbert et al. 1983).

Vegetation.

Structure. Most dabbling ducks nest on the ground. Black ducks nest in tree cavities and stumps (Cowardin et al. 1967), whereas wood ducks are obligate cavity nesters (Bellrose et al. 1964). The mallard, although typically a ground-nesting bird, will nest in a variety of elevated sites, natural and artificial (Cowardin et al. 1967; Bishop and Barratt 1970).

Of the ground-nesting ducks in this group, the pintail appears more prone to nest in the least cover situation than any of the others. In a study of duck nesting in intensively farmed areas, pintail nests were in near-equal densities in summer fallow, mulched stubble, standing stubble, and untilled uplands, whereas 72% or more of other duck nests were in the untilled uplands (Higgins 1977).

Duck-nesting density in idle grasslands was studied in North Dakota for 3 years; the 3-year average nesting density was 76.6 nests/km² (30 nests/mi.²;

Duebbert and Lokemoen 1976). Nesting density on the idle acres for one of the years was four times higher than that found on nearby agricultural lands (farmed and grazed) during the same year. Vegetation measurements on the idle lands in May showed an average of 90 dead stems/m^2 (108/yd^2) and heights of 71, 47, and 28 cm (28, 19, and 11 in.) on dead stems, dead leaves, and live leaves, respectively. The preference that nesting hens had for this vegetation density and structure was shown by flights up to 1.6 km (1 mi.) from wetlands to nest in the idle lands.

Species Composition. As with geese, when vegetation is used as cover, species composition appears to take a secondary role to structure. Several species used heavily for nesting cover by dabbling ducks in Alberta (*Calamovilfa longifolia, Hordeum jubatum, Spartina gracilis*) had one common denominator—they were unpalatable to cattle and consequently provided the structure for cover (Keith 1961). The same could probably be said for dense thickets of snowberry (*Symphoricarpos* sp.) and rose (*Rosa* sp.), which are frequently found on the prairie and have had high usage by nesting ducks (Hines and Mitchell 1983; Lokemoen et al. 1984).

Successful brood-rearing involves a proper combination of cover and food. Aquatic cover can be provided by a variety of emergent plants, some of which provide cover only (Cattails [*Typha* sp.]) whereas others (bulrush, spikerush, arrowhead [*Sagittaria* sp.], smartweeds [*Polygonum* sp.]) provide food from tubers, foliage, or fruiting bodies, as well as cover. Cattail, although often used as cover for nesting ducks, can detract from the attractiveness of a pond, at least to certain species. Keith (1961) reported an increase in waterfowl usage of ponds when shoreline cattail was reduced.

Submerged aquatics, such as water milfoil and pondweeds combined with seeds of spikerush, were used heavily by adult dabblers in the spring (Keith 1961). Ducklings showed a heavy use of spikerush seeds suggesting a feeding pattern along the shore where this plant was prevalent. Flying juveniles fed more heavily on submergents, indicating more intense feeding in the open water.

Major foods found in stock pond habitat in Montana include pondweeds, water milfoil, common hornwort (*Ceratophyllum demersum*), Canadian waterweed (*Elodea canadensis*), watercrowfoot buttercup (*Ranunculus aquatilis*), and longspike spikerush (*Eleocharis macrostachya*). At least 5 years must pass for newly constructed stock ponds to develop aquatic vegetation to provide adequate food and cover (Hudson 1983).

Bay Ducks (Aythyini) and Ruddy Ducks (Oxyurini)

Five species of the tribe Aythyini, all of a single genus, are common to North America. These five are the canvasback (*Aythya valisineria*), redhead (*A. americana*), ring-necked duck (*A. collaris*), greater scaup (*A. marila*), and lesser scaup (*A. affinis*). The ruddy duck (*Oxyura jamaicensis*), although a member of a different tribe (stiff-tailed ducks), is included here because it has some similar habitat requirements during the breeding season. These two tribes and a third, Mergini, are often included under the descriptive term diving ducks as opposed to the dabbling ducks discussed earlier.

Although many diving and dabbling ducks may be observed on the same bodies of water, particularly during the breeding season, the morphological differences between the two groups are reflected in many of their activities and often in the segments of a pond that each uses. Divers have lobed hind toes and generally much larger feet than the dabbling ducks, which aid in their underwater swimming capabilities. The legs on divers are located farther back on the body which enhances their diving ability, but reduces their walking capabilities—resulting in little or no utilization of terrestrial habitats.

Body contour, method for taking flight, and feeding methods also separate divers from dabblers. On the water, divers provide a much lower profile than dabbling ducks; their shorter tail feathers provide an appearance of the back sloping down to the water's surface. In taking flight, divers patter along the water before lift-off, whereas the dabblers leap immediately into the air. Divers commonly go well below the surface to feed, whereas the dabbling ducks simply tip to reach below the surface for aquatic foods. Primarily because of the divers' inability to maneuver on land, ducks observed feeding in grain fields will be dabblers.

Physical Features. All except two of the species within this group normally inhabit the open prairie marshes. One of these exceptions, the ring-necked duck, seems to show preference for marshes bordered by woodland. The other, the greater scaup, is primarily an inhabitant of marshy tundra. The lesser scaup, although commonly found associated with prairie marshes, also extends its breeding range into boreal lakes and tundra habitat.

When nesting, canvasbacks, redheads, and ruddy ducks all inhabit a variety of prairie marshes, sloughs, and potholes with stands of emergent vegetation. Of the three species, canvasbacks seem most prone to nest in the small ponds; ruddy ducks and especially redheads seem to favor the larger, deeper bodies of water. This preference, in conjunction with its

Ring-necked duck.

gregarious nesting habits, makes the redhead an important nesting species in many marshes of the Intermountain West—20-25 times more abundant than canvasbacks. Although not evenly distributed throughout the Intermountain West—nor the marsh habitat—redheads in particular, but also ruddy ducks, lesser scaup, and canvasbacks reach rather high breeding densities in western marsh habitats. Some Nevada, Utah, and Montana marshes attain very high breeding densities (919 redheads/km^2 [355/mi.^{2}] of wetlands on Salt Lake marshes; Bellrose 1978).

All of the species in this group are inclined to nest closer to the water than most dabbling ducks, a reflection of their close tie to the aquatic environment. Canvasbacks and ruddy ducks invariably nest over water. Redheads nest over water, but also on land (Keith 1961) and often on islands (Vermeer 1970; Carlsen 1984). Ring-necked ducks usually nest within marshes; over 85% nest on small clumps of floating vegetation or within clumps of marsh vegetation (Mendall 1958). Although both the greater and the lesser scaup will nest on islands, the latter seems to show a greater preference for such sites (Vermeer et al. 1972; Vermeer 1970).

Vegetation.

Structure. The canvasback, redhead, and ruddy duck, all of which commonly nest over the water, are highly selective to nesting ponds that provide emergent vegetation and often band around the shoreline of small ponds. Redheads tend to avoid large stands of emergents without breaks of open water (Low 1945). Ring-necked ducks and scaup all prefer to nest close to water and consequently use a variety of structural cover over water (ring-necks) or near the water (scaup).

Canvasback broods mostly used permanent type wetlands, larger and deeper wetlands (0.4 ha [1 a.]),

and wetlands with less than one-third of the water area covered by emergent vegetation (Stoudt 1982). Broods of redheads, ruddy ducks (Evans and Black 1956), and lesser scaup (Sugden 1973) showed a propensity for feeding in the deeper, more open water segments of the pond. Although amphipods, a favored food of young scaup, appeared to be more numerous in larger and deeper ponds, Sugden (1973) believed that the movement to larger ponds by older scaup was related to security and not food.

Species Composition. A variety of species of emergent vegetation have been noted as nesting cover for canvasbacks, redheads, and ruddy ducks. Cattails, bulrush, whitetop *(Fluminia festucacea)*, willows *(Salix* sp), sedges, and reeds *(Phragmites communis)* were listed by Stoudt (1982) in Manitoba. Bellrose (1978) reported that for nesting cover, redheads appeared to have a preference for bulrushes, cattails, and sedges, in that order. He also stated that ruddy ducks seemed to select the vegetation characteristic of the nesting pond, availability playing a key role. I have observed this on stock dams in eastern Montana, when in good moisture years, ruddy ducks will readily nest in a relatively short emergent, longspike spikerush, the only emergent cover present.

Most food habits studies of divers point out the heavy intake of animal matter by young ducklings and an increase in plant food as the birds get older (Bartonek and Hickey 1969; Sugden 1973). Although specific foods will vary considerably with location and availability within this species group, ruddy ducks appear to feed most heavily on plant materials. Both species of scaup are most inclined to an animal diet.

Plants frequently used are pondweeds, muskgrass *(Chara* sp.), bulrush, wild celery *(Valisneria americana),* duckweeds *(Lemna* sp.), water milfoil, and widgeon grass. Depending on the species of plant and season of year, leafy parts, seeds, and tubers of the various plants may be fed upon.

Eiders, Scoters, Mergansers, and Allies (Mergini)

This relatively diverse tribe is represented in North America by seven genera, all different in appearance as adults, but grouped together at least partially as a result of similarity in voice and display (Delacour and Mayr 1945). Members of this entire group are referred to as "sea ducks," primarily because most of them winter along the sea coasts. However, several members breed inland on fresh water, and a few winter in the interior.

Included in the genus *Somateria* are three eiders, the common eider *(S. mollissima),* king eider *(S. spectabilis),* and spectacled eider *(S. fischeri),* all of which breed along the arctic coasts. The common and king eiders winter along the northern coasts; the spectacled eider's wintering areas remain somewhat obscure. Steller's eider *(Polysticta stelleri),* the sole member of this genus, nests along the northern coasts of Alaska and Siberia and winters along the Alaska peninsula and the Aleutians (Bellrose 1978).

The harlequin duck *(Histrionicus histrionicus)* has a distinct eastern and western range. It breeds from the northern coasts of Canada and Alaska southward into the Cascades and Sierra Nevadas and the Rocky Mountains (Bellrose 1978), and winters along both coasts as far south as California and Long Island.

Harlequin duck.

Oldsquaws *(Clangula hyemalis)* are found throughout arctic Canada and Alaska during the breeding season; they winter along both coasts, commonly south to northern California and northern North Carolina and interior on the Great Lakes.

Three scoters are included under the genus *Melanitta:* the black scoter *(M. nigra americana),* surf scoter *(M. perspicillata),* and white-winged scoter *(M. fusca deglandi).* The black scoter breeds in Alaska and probably in Canada (Bellrose 1978). Breeding surf and white-winged scoters are both well distributed across Canada in the open and closed boreal forest. All three species winter along most of the east and west coasts of the U.S.

The genus *Bucephala* includes the bufflehead *(B. albeola)* and two goldeneyes, the Barrow's *(B. islandica)* and common *(B. clangula americana).* The bufflehead has a rather extensive breeding range throughout Canada; the largest numbers are in northwestern North America (Bellrose 1978). A few isolated breeding populations are found in mountainous areas of the U.S. and in some timbered areas of the northern prairies. The primary breeding populations of Barrow's goldeneyes are in northwestern North America extending from the mountains of Wyoming

and northern California, north into Alaska. The common goldeneye is more widespread, breeding in forest areas across the breadth of Canada and into Alaska. All three species of this genus concentrate along both the Atlantic and Pacific coasts during the winter, but can also be found in small concentrations along rivers and lakes in the interior.

Bufflehead.

Male and female common goldeneye.

Three species of mergansers *(Mergus)* are common to North America: the hooded *(M. cucullatus),* red-breasted *(M. serrator),* and common *(M. merganser americanus).* The hooded merganser nests throughout most of the eastern half of the U.S., extending into adjoining provinces in Canada. It also nests in the northwest U.S. from northern California to southeast Alaska (Bellrose 1978).

The red-breasted merganser breeds throughout eastern Canada, across the southern tundra and northern boreal forest into Alaska. The common merganser has a somewhat similar distribution more to the south although with a broad overlap zone where both may be found. The common merganser breeds in the northeast and lake States, and extends southward along mountain ranges in the West.

The hooded merganser winters along the east, west, and gulf coasts and several southeastern States; the red-breasted winters largely on the Great Lakes and along both coasts. The common merganser, by contrast, winters largely (58%) in the interior (Bellrose 1978).

Physical Features. Of the three *Somateria* eiders, the common is the most marine, occurring primarily along rocky shores and islands and only rarely on open fresh water. The king and spectacled eiders, although they both winter along seacoasts, breed near fresh-water ponds, lakes, deltas, and tidal inlets. The Stellar's eider nests along the coast or inland near grassy ponds or lakes but winters along coasts in shallow marine habitat.

The harlequin duck usually nests along fast-flowing coastal or mountain streams and winters along rocky sea coasts.

Oldsquaws, unlike the eiders, nest along the coast and inland on lakes and ponds throughout the tundra. Like most of the other sea ducks, it winters along coastal areas but also on large inland lakes (e.g., Great Lakes).

All three scoters nest in fresh-water situations, the black and the surf showing a preference for more brushy, taller cover near the water, whereas the white-winged scoter is more prone to nest in open prairie or tundra and frequently at considerable distances from the water. Dense ground cover for nesting is a prominent characteristic (Bellrose 1978).

Goldeneyes and buffleheads are cavity nesters, so breeding habitat usually consists of trees surrounding fresh-water lakes, ponds, and streams. All three species winter along the coasts in bays or estuaries as well as lakes and rivers inland.

Hooded and common mergansers are also cavity nesters. The hooded merganser seems more restricted to tree cavities or wood duck houses than the common merganser, which frequently uses cavities in rock cliffs along major western rivers. The red-breasted merganser nests on the ground, often under shrubs (Weller et al. 1969).

Wintering habitat for the three mergansers varies: the common winters largely on open lakes and rivers and only rarely in coastal habitat; the hooded winters mostly in fresh water, but it is also commonly found in estuaries and bays; the red-breasted

Hooded merganser.

merganser winters primarily in coastal areas and rarely in fresh-water.

Vegetation. Less can be concluded regarding the vegetational aspect of sea duck habitat than with most other tribes of waterfowl. Several reasons may be put forth as a partial explanation.

Nesting by many of the species is carried out in the tundra or in open or closed boreal forest. Residual vegetation from previous years' growth is critical because the short season requires that nesting be initiated before the appearance of much of the current season's growth.

The importance of structural cover for nests rather than species composition is reflected in the selection of shrubs, rocks, burrows, and overhanging banks by many species. Several species (eiders, oldsquaw, some scoters) nest on islands in rather large numbers (colonial) and as such rely less on cover and more on the mammal-free island habitat.

Also, several species (goldeneyes, bufflehead, common and hooded mergansers) are cavity nesters, and as such the dominating feature is the proper-sized cavity and not the plant species providing the cavity. However, certain trees appear more prone to natural cavities and species composition may thus influence selection of a particular habitat. Erskine (1972) in British Columbia noted that of 11 trees that provided cavities for nesting buffleheads, 52% were aspen *(Populus tremuloides).*

The relative minor importance of vegetation structure and composition to sea ducks is also indicated by the little se made of plants in their food habits. Results from several studies showed that animal matter in the diet ranged from about 70 to 95% for eiders, harlequins, oldsquaws, scoters, buffleheads, and goldeneyes, and 100% (largely fishes) for mergansers (Bellrose 1978). Many of the insect larvae taken as food by young ducks of several tribes or adult dabbling ducks are in close association with aquatic vegetation. However, many of the animal foods eaten by sea ducks are crustaceans and mollusks taken during bottom feeding and have relatively less relationship to aquatic macrophytes.

CHARACTERISTICS OF WINTER HABITAT

Winter habitat for waterfowl has only recently received the attention it deserves. For 6 to 8 months of the year, this habitat must provide security and a food source capable of sustaining the bird. For many species it must also provide an energy base for pairing and initiation of migration. With the wide range of species requirements present within the waterfowl for breeding habitat, differences would also be expected in winter habitat requirements.

Probably the least variability in winter habitat is found among the tribes that are most aquatic. Groups within the tribe Mergini, which feed largely on aquatic invertebrates, are confined to coastal waters, or if wintering inland, are usually found on larger lakes or rivers. Heitmeyer and Vohs (1984), in looking at wintering waterfowl habitat in Oklahoma, found common mergansers and common goldeneyes more abundant on the large reservoirs.

The diving ducks (Aythyini), another highly aquatic group, tend to concentrate along certain coastal areas. In contrast with many of the Mergini which winter in marine habitat, the diving ducks seek out estuarine habitat. In 1955, slightly less than one-half of the canvasbacks recorded in North America were found in Chesapeake Bay (Perry et al. 1981), whereas about 78% of the redheads in existence normally winter on Laguna Madre along the Texas coast (Weller 1964).

Both species of scaup make heavy use of coastal areas, the greater, more abundant in the Atlantic Flyway and the lesser, more prominent in coastal marshes of the Mississippi Flyway. Both scaup also winter inland as far north as the Great Lakes (Bellrose 1978).

Dabbling ducks show considerable variability in selecting winter habitat, both between and within species. Mallards and pintails show different feeding preferences depending on which portion of their respective ranges they may be occupying (Chabreck 1979). Fredrickson and Drobney (1979) pointed out the importance of a food resource on wintering areas and referred to specific feeding habits that permit several species of ducks to fully and at times simultaneously exploit an aquatic food resource.

Thus, with high densities of ducks so often found in wintering areas, a highly productive aquatic food source is a key component of winter habitat. Gadwalls and widgeon in Oklahoma wintered primarily on wetlands where submergent and emergent vegetation were abundant (Heitmeyer and Vohs 1984). All species of dabbling ducks preferred natural wetlands over farm ponds, probably a reflection of the absence of biologically productive littoral zones on the steep-sided farm ponds. In determining values for 13 physical, limnological, and vegetative features on a series of flood-prevention lakes in Texas, Hobaugh and Teer (1981) concluded that the most important characteristics influencing winter waterfowl use were amounts of aquatic vegetation and lake surface area.

Some species of waterfowl have been able to capitalize on land-use changes by modifying their food habits to include certain upland agricultural crops. Historically, upland feeding in cultivated fields in Manitoba was first recorded for geese, which could be expected in light of the terrestrial habits of this group. Use of cultivated fields by ducks seemingly developed later and initially appeared with mallards and pintails (Bossenmaier and Marshall 1958). Field feeding, although initially considered a fall activity, has to be a major contributor in the northward extension of wintering ducks (primarily mallards) into Montana and the two Dakotas. Many of these birds winter on large bodies of water that are totally devoid of available aquatic vegetation, thus forcing a total subsistence on cultivated grains. On wintering areas farther south, American widgeons *(Anas americana),* and blue-winged and green-winged teal *(A. crecca)* join the mallard and northern pintail as regular field feeders (Baldassarre and Bolen 1984).

POPULATION MEASUREMENT TECHNIQUES

Virtually all techniques employed for population measurements of waterfowl are based on direct observations of the birds. This contrasts with techniques, such as auditory counts, employed in monitoring upland bird populations. The obvious reason for this difference is that waterfowl are closely associated with water for much of the time and although they are no more equally visible between different bodies of water and between seasons, they are easier to observe and count than many other species of birds. Because the methods are based on direct observation, they all detect presence with varying degrees of precision and accuracy.

On a continental scale, breeding and winter populations are surveyed annually by the U.S. Fish and Wildlife Service, Canadian Wildlife Service, and State and Provincial conservation agencies. Most of such surveys are conducted from the air and are used for determining long-term trends (Bellrose 1978:17-19).

Breeding Population

Description. Annual trend data on North American populations of breeding waterfowl are gathered in May and June along aerial east-west transects (Bellrose 1978:18). The transects, which are censused cooperatively by State, Federal, and Canadian biologists, are distributed throughout prime breeding areas from the prairies to the boreal forest and into the tundra. Because visibility varies between species and years, segments of transects are covered intensively by a ground crew within 24 hours of the air count and a visibility index applied to the aerial count. This annual survey, which also provides data on habitat (water) conditions, is conducted over about 80,500 km (50,000 linear mi.) representing about 2% of the breeding habitat (Bellrose 1978).

This basic technique, involving ground counts only, has been modified and refined making it more useable on a smaller scale. The count, called a breeding pair count, may be conducted on specific bodies of water, along roadside transects, or on all water areas within a predescribed area. The counts are based on the knowledge that breeding pairs of dabblers, once established on a breeding home range, will localize their activities to one or two ponds. Thus, from the time of pair bond formation (often on arrival because many species form pair bonds on the wintering ground or enroute north) until the female is well into incubation, the locations of pairs or lone drakes are plotted during four or five censuses. Pairs or lone drakes of any dabbler species occurring on a given unit of habitat three or four times are recorded as part of the assigned breeding population (Dzubin 1969). The counts should be made when the highest percentage of pairs are in the pre-nesting, laying, or incubation stage. This may include a period of 20 to 30 days to include early-nesting pintails and mallards, as well as late-nesting, blue-winged teal and gadwalls. Although this technique is often described to include all ducks, Dzubin (1969) believed the large home ranges of canvasbacks and redheads and the tendency for pairs of these two species and lesser scaup to congregate on deep ponds termed "primary waiting areas," precluded enumerating divers in smaller census units.

For additional precision, Dzubin (1969) proposed an "Indicated Breeding Population" where, until a certain date, grouped males and males in aerial flights temporarily on censused ponds were also considered pairs. After that date, grouped males of five or more were not counted as pairs (six or more were considered post-breeding males). Different cutoff dates were established for early nesters (pintails and mallards), intermediates (widgeon and shovelers), and late nesters (blue-winged teal and gadwalls); dates may vary between areas and years but are based on nesting chronology of the respective groups.

Lastly, a sex-ratio corrected population figure was suggested. This consisted of taking the mean-indicated breeding population from four or five census efforts and applying a sex-ratio correction factor based upon sex-ratio data obtained from each species before egg laying.

The following are some of the recommendations by Dzubin (1969) for breeding-pair census on a grassland type. This type, which has little visual obstruction from emergent vegetation, is appropriate for much of the waterfowl habitat on public lands in the West.

(1) Census during that portion of the breeding season when site attachment by pairs and drakes is greatest (pre-nesting, laying, and early incubation).

(2) Census between 0800 and 1200 hours; this is the period of least mobility, and most pairs and lone drakes will be on waiting stations.

(3) Census only on bright days with temperatures above 4° C (40° F) and winds less than 24 km/h (15 mph). Avoid inclement weather (rain, heavy overcast, and low temperatures) which affects mobility and visibility of ducks (Diem and Lu 1960).

(4) Conduct at least two censuses when sampling a multiple species population; four to six counts would be preferable, permitting a calculated average number of pairs for each species.

(5) Take counts from a vehicle, positioned at a vantage point at an adequate distance to prevent flushing birds.

(6) Tally all lone pairs and lone drakes greater than 5 m (15 ft) apart as pairs; this type enumeration, if conducted four to six times on the census area with proper timing, will provide relative abundance data between areas or between years on a given area. Greater precision can be obtained, if the objectives warrant, by a more refined timetable as recommended by Dzubin (1969:220).

Breeding populations of Canada geese are commonly censused along rivers either from the ground (boat) or air at which time pairs and lone geese (ganders) are recorded as pairs and groups as nonbreeders (Hanson and Eberhardt 1971; Allen et al. 1978). Unlike most ducks, geese remain paired throughout the nesting season so lone ganders will be available for tally (as pairs) throughout the incubation period.

Prime breeding areas on the prairies are censused in May and June along aerial transects.

Accuracy and Precision. Sauder et al. (1971), in evaluating the roadside census for breeding waterfowl in South Dakota, found that to be within 20% of the mean at the 90% confidence level on an 86.4 km (54 mi.) route, at least four counts of lone drakes and pairs were needed for blue-winged teal and three for gadwalls and mallards. They also stated that additional counts were necessary to maintain the same degree of accuracy when routes were shorter or when water areas were less numerous. Although Dzubin (1969) did not recommend lone drake and pair counts for divers, Sugden and Butler (1980), after an evaluation, concluded that lone male and pair counts for canvasbacks and total female counts for redheads provided the best index to breeding populations of these species.

In spite of the obvious shortcomings with the breeding pair counts, indications are good that it will provide useable data for certain management problems. Pair and lone drake counts were conducted on 33 stock ponds during a 5-year study to measure waterfowl responses to a changing land use (Gjersing 1975; Mundinger 1976). Although the changes in waterfowl numbers were fairly pronounced over the period, production data obtained from intensive brood counts for the same period followed a similar trend. For many evaluations of waterfowl habitat on western ranges, carefully timed and conducted breeding pair counts (lone pairs and drakes) should fulfill the objectives.

Discussion. Without knowing what percentage of the actual breeding population is being counted, counts of breeding pairs at best provide yearly trends. Timing of the count is critical. The chronology of the nesting effort of a single species may extend over a 70-day period (Humburg et al. 1978) and longer when several species are considered. Thus for intensive work, several counts are necessary, well-dispersed over the entire breeding season.

Nest Counts

Nest counts are often incorporated in (or substituted for) breeding pair counts. Dzubin (1969:2217) suggested this as a better method on block-type studies for divers and ruddy ducks, although he pointed out potential problems in uneven nest distribution, failure to locate all nests, and difficulty in separating first and second nest attempts.

Sugden and Butler (1980) considered nest searching as an impractical technique for recording canvasback and redhead breeding densities, primarily because the variability in nest distribution made it necessary to have a large sample. Nest counts are effective for enumerating breeding populations of Canada geese, particularly when nesting is largely accomplished on islands in rivers (Hansen and Eberhardt 1971) or ponds (Childress and Eng 1979).

A measure of various upland habitats may be made by comparing nest densities or nest success. Nests are located by systematically covering the area in question at specified time intervals to locate early and late nesting birds. This effort is frequently facilitated by the cable-chain drag method (Higgins et al. 1969).

With early, intermediate, and late nesting species plus renesting by most species, a continued initiation of nests will be occurring throughout the nesting season. It is not practical (nor advisable) to search an area daily; thus many nests may be initiated and destroyed between search periods and consequently not found. Also, nests located early (during laying or early incubation) suffer a greater chance of destruction before hatching than a nest first located shortly before hatching. If all nests are considered equal regardless of their stage when first found, the nest density would be biased downward (e.g., nests destroyed early are not found) and the hatch rate (nest success) biased upward. The recommended method for standardizing waterfowl nest density and success data is the Mayfield method (Mayfield 1975; Miller and Johnson 1978) in which a hatch rate is determined and applied to each nest depending on its stage of development toward hatching.

Brood Counts

Production surveys are conducted by U.S. Fish and Wildlife Service biologists to assess annual waterfowl breeding success. Brood counts are conducted from the air along many of the same transects as the breeding bird counts and are subject to many of the same problems. However, Pospahala et al. (1974) supported the general contention that the number of Class II and III broods observed along aerial transects in July, when adjusted for visibility,

Nesting coot.

is related to the density of breeding birds observed in the May survey.

Although broods are less mobile than flying adults, they are usually more secretive. By the time most broods are on the water, the emergent vegetation is more lush—reducing visibility. A serious need for aerial-ground indexes as adjustments for the vagaries of aerial counts alone was stressed by Diem and Lu (1960).

Brood counts conducted more intensively from the ground appear more acceptable. Gollop and Marshall (1954) presented a method for brood counts that basically calls for several counts to be made and broods recorded by species and age, which tends to eliminate duplication of counts. This method has been employed extensively on studies where more precise production data are important (Berg 1956; Mundinger 1976; Kirby 1980).

Stock ponds in Montana generally have far less emergent vegetation than prairie potholes. Mundinger (1976), in making brood counts, would usually approach the pond unobtrusively in an attempt to count undisturbed broods. Even so, brood movement ("transient broods") made it necessary to record broods by age class to prevent duplication.

Kirby (1980) analyzed intensive observations of breeding pairs and broods of ducks in forested habitats of northern Minnesota. Aerial censuses in such areas appeared inadequate because of the difficulty in observing birds at low densities. Kirby (1980) found that indexes to breeding birds and brood numbers were highly correlated, and that censusing was a distinct possibility as a source for population trend data in this type habitat.

Winter Surveys (Counts)

The annual January inventory was initiated in the U.S. in 1935 and has increased in scope until it now encompasses most wintering areas in Alaska, Canada, the conterminous U.S., and Mexico. The survey is coordinated by the U.S. Fish and Wildlife Service, and although the purpose is to determine the size and distribution of the midwinter waterfowl population, the potential for error (at least in determining total population) is obvious and great. Black ducks and wood ducks winter in small groups more easily counted, but winter in habitat where they would be more easily overlooked. Canvasbacks and redheads often concentrate in open areas where they can be easily seen, but in such large flocks that estimates of numbers are often subject to error. Population status of wintering canvasbacks on Chesapeake Bay and coastal North Carolina were efficiently and accurately obtained with low-level aerial photography (Haramis et al. 1985).

A detailed description of the winter survey was presented by Stewart et al. (1958:366-367). Bellrose (1978:20) acknowledged that winter counts, for several reasons, were undoubtedly underestimated. However, he defended their use because they provided the distribution of ducks at that time of the year and provided the major annual population data for geese. Most geese nest in such widely distributed parts of the arctic and subarctic that annual counts are impractical.

DISCUSSION

Tiner (1984) provided an excellent summary of the current status and recent trends of wetlands in the U.S. Although some recent modest gains were recorded as a result of man-made lakes and reservoirs, a net loss of 3.6 million ha (9 million a.) occurred in a 20-year period starting in the mid-1950s. Frayer et al. (1983) attributed 87% of these losses to agricultural activities, 8% to urban development, and 5% to other development. The geographical distribution is no more evenly distributed, but clearly related as to the causes. In the fertile farmlands of Iowa, 99% of the natural marshes have been drained compared with 32% of Wisconsin's wetlands (Tiner 1984, p.34).

The major waterfowl habitats within the U.S. are important primarily as breeding habitat, wintering habitat, or both (Figure 1). The prairie pothole region, for example, encompasses the most valuable waterfowl production marshes in North America. Representing no more than 10% of the continent's waterfowl breeding area, in a wet year it produces over 50% of the ducks. Included are many of the popular species including the mallard, pintail, teal, widgeon, canvasback, and redhead. Of more recent

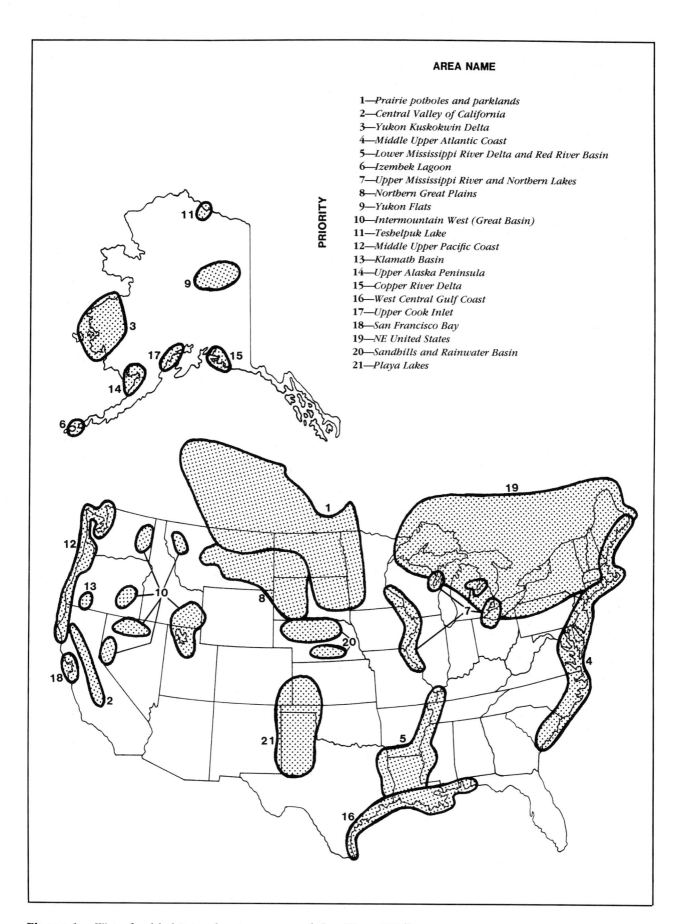

AREA NAME

1—*Prairie potholes and parklands*
2—*Central Valley of California*
3—*Yukon Kuskokwin Delta*
4—*Middle Upper Atlantic Coast*
5—*Lower Mississippi River Delta and Red River Basin*
6—*Izembek Lagoon*
7—*Upper Mississippi River and Northern Lakes*
8—*Northern Great Plains*
9—*Yukon Flats*
10—*Intermountain West (Great Basin)*
11—*Teshelpuk Lake*
12—*Middle Upper Pacific Coast*
13—*Klamath Basin*
14—*Upper Alaska Peninsula*
15—*Copper River Delta*
16—*West Central Gulf Coast*
17—*Upper Cook Inlet*
18—*San Francisco Bay*
19—*NE United States*
20—*Sandhills and Rainwater Basin*
21—*Playa Lakes*

PRIORITY

Figure 1. Waterfowl habitats of major concern (after Tiner 1984).

and justified concern has been the importance of wintering habitat (Fredrickson and Drobney 1979) and its rate of loss reported along coastal marshes (Tiner 1984:35). Although wetland losses are not confined to the areas illustrated in Figure 1, they represent areas of high use, and consequently any effort toward their preservation or enhancement would pay great dividends toward waterfowl welfare.

One of the annual measures of potential waterfowl productivity has been an index to the number of water areas along the aerial transects used for breeding birds. It has been assumed that good water conditions in a given year would speak well for the productivity of waterfowl in the area. However, with ever-intensifying agricultural efforts in the surrounding uplands, at least the dabbling ducks, which rely on secure upland nesting cover, may not be able to respond favorably with good water conditions only. Higgins (1977), in measuring waterfowl production in an area of intense farming, believed that upland nesting ducks could not reproduce themselves during most years in areas that were 85% or more tilled. He recorded a 21% nest success on his study area, with 76% of the failures attributed to predators and 16% to farming operations.

In the northern Great Plains, grazing is a more prevalent land use, and where grazing is not excessive, waterfowl nest success is often high (77%, Smith 1953; 67%, Rundquist 1973). Of the two major ingredients to successful dabbling duck production, quality water areas and secure upland nesting habitat, the former is currently at a premium in the northern Great Plains—the latter in the prairie pothole area. Thus the two areas, although adjacent to one another, offer different options in terms of type of investment and return for effort expended toward enhancing habitat.

Intensive agriculture, although detrimental on the breeding habitat, may be providing at least an acceptable substitute for some food sources on wintering areas. Fredrickson and Drobney (1979) suggested that abundant food supplies (domestic grains) may be holding some populations farther north than previously, thereby reducing competition on traditional (but negatively altered) winter habitat. This is particularly true for the mallard, which in the Columbia Basin in Washington, increased from a wintering population of 86,000 in the entire State in 1947 to 730,000 in 1960, largely as a result of additional food sources from irrigated grain farms (Bellrose 1978). Baldassarre and Bolen (1984) suggested a possible increasing importance of field-feeding by wintering waterfowl, because of wetland distribution, and presented management recommendations toward enhancement of this activity.

LITERATURE CITED

ADDY, C.E. 1964. Atlantic Flyway. Pages 167-184 *in* Linduska, J.P. ed. Waterfowl Tomorrow. U.S. Govt. Print. Off., Washington, DC.

ALLEN, G.T., S.E. FAST, B.J. LANGSTAFF, D.W. TOMRDLE, and B.L. TROUTMAN.1978. Census of Canada geese on the Palouse River, Washington, during the spring of 1977. The Murrelet 59:96-100.

AMERICAN ORNITHOLOGISTS UNION. 1983. Checklist of North American birds, Sixth Edition. Allen Press, Inc., Lawrence, KS.

BALDASSARRE, G.A. and E.G. BOLEN. 1984. Field-feeding ecology of waterfowl wintering on the southern high plains of Texas. J. Wildl. Manage. 48:63-71.

BARTONEK, J.C. and J.J. HICKEY. 1969. Food habits of canvasbacks, redheads and lesser scaup in Manitoba. Condor 71:280-290.

BELLROSE, F.C. 1978. Ducks, geese and swans of North America. The Stackpole Co., Harrisburg, PA, and Wildl. Manage. Inst., Washington, DC. 540pp.

———, K.L. JOHNSON, and T.U. MEYERS. 1964. Relative value of natural cavities and nesting houses for wood ducks. J. Wildl. Manage. 28:661-676.

BERG, P.F. 1956. A study of waterfowl broods in eastern Montana with special reference to movements and the relationship of reservoir fencing to production. J. Wildl. Manage. 20:253-262.

BISHOP, R.A. and R. BARRATT. 1970. Use of artificial nest baskets by mallards. J. Wildl. Manage. 34:734-738.

BOSSENMAIER, E.F. and W.H. MARSHALL. 1958. Field-feeding by waterfowl in southeast Manitoba. Wildl. Monogr. 1. 32pp.

BREWSTER, W.G., J.M. GATES, and L.D. FLAKE. 1976. Breeding waterfowl populations and their distribution in South Dakota. J. Wildl. Manage. 40:50-59.

BUE, I.G., H.G. UHLIG, and D.J. SMITH 1964. Stock ponds and dugouts. Pages 391-398 *in* Linduska, J.P. ed., Waterfowl Tomorrow, U.S. Govt. Print. Off., Washington, DC. 770pp.

CARLSEN, T.L. 1984. Waterfowl nesting in two ponds of the Canyon Ferry Wildlife Management Area, Montana. M.S. Thesis. Montana State Univ., Bozeman. 91pp.

CHABRECK, R.H. 1979. Winter habitat of dabbling ducks—physical, chemical, and biological aspects. Pages 133-142 *in* Bookhout, T.A. ed., Waterfowl and Wetlands—An Integrated Review. North-central Sect., The Wildl. Soc., Madison, WI

CHILDRESS, D.A. and R.L. ENG. 1979. Dust abatement project with wildlife enhancement on Canyon Ferry Reservoir, Montana. Pages 282-288 *in* The Mitigation Symposium: a National Workshop On Mitigating Losses of Fish and Wildlife Habitats. Colorado State Univ., Ft. Collins.

COWARDIN, L.M., G.E. CUMMINGS, and P.B. REED, Jr. 1967. Stump and tree nesting by mallards and black ducks. J. Wildl. Manage. 31:229-235.

DELACOUR, J. and E. MAYR. 1945. The family Anatidae. Wilson Bull. 57:3-55.

DIEM, K.L. and K.H. LU. 1960. Factors influencing waterfowl censuses in the parklands, Alberta, Canada. J. Wildl. Manage. 24:113-133.

DUEBBERT, H.F. 1982. Nesting waterfowl on islands in Lake Audubon, North Dakota. Wildl. Soc. Bull. 10:232-237.

——— and J.T. LOKEMOEN. 1976. Duck nesting in fields of undisturbed grass-legume cover. J. Wildl. Manage. 40:39-49.

———, J.T. LOKEMOEN, and D.E. SHARP. 1983. Concentrated nesting of mallards and gadwalls on Miller Lake Island, North Dakota. J. Wildl. Manage. 47:729-740.

DZUBIN, A. 1969. Assessing breeding populations of ducks by ground counts. Pages 178-230 *in* Saskatoon Wetlands Seminar. Can. Wildl. Serv. Rep. Series 6.

ENG, R.L., J.D. JONES, and F.M. GJERSING. 1979. Construction and management of stock ponds for waterfowl. U.S. Dep. Inter., Bur. Land Manage. Tech. Note 327. Denver, CO. 39pp.

ERSKINE, A.J. 1972. Buffleheads. Can. Wildl. Serv. Monogr. Series 4. 240pp.

EVANS, C.D. and K.E. BLACK. 1956. Duck production studies on the prairie potholes of South Dakota. U.S. Dep. Inter., Fish and Wildl. Serv. Spec. Sci. Rep. Wildl. 32. 59pp.

EWASCHUK, E. and D.A. BOAG. 1972. Factors affecting hatching success of densely nesting Canada geese. J. Wildl. Manage. 36:1097-1106.

FRAYER, W.E., T.J. MONAHAN, D.C. BOWDEN, and F.A. GRAYBILL. 1983. Status and trends of wetlands and deep water habitats in the conterminous United States, 1950s to 1970s. Dep. of Forest and Wood Sciences. Colorado State Univ., Ft. Collins. 32pp.

FREDRICKSON, L.H. and R.D. DROBNEY. 1979. Habitat utilization by post-breeding waterfowl. Pages 119-131 *in* Bookhout, T.A. ed., Waterfowl and Wetlands—An Integrated Review. North-central Sect., The Wildl. Soc., Madison, WI.

GIROUX, J.F. 1981. Use of artificial islands by nesting waterfowl in southeastern Alberta. J. Wildl. Manage. 45:669-679.

———, D.E. JELINSKI, and R.W. BOYCHUK. 1983. Use of rock lands and round, straw bales by nesting Canada geese. Wildl. Soc. Bull. 11:172-177.

GJERSING, F.M. 1975. Waterfowl production in relation to rest-rotation grazing. J. Range Manage. 28:37-42.

GOLLOP, J.G. and W.H. MARSHALL. 1954. A guide for aging duck broods in the field. Mississippi Flyway Council Tech. Sect. 14pp. (mimeo.).

HAMMOND, M.C. and G.E. MANN. 1956. Waterfowl nesting islands. J. Wildl. Manage. 20:345-352.

HANSEN, H.A., P.E.K. SHEPHERD, J.G. KING, and W.A. TROYER. 1971. The trumpeter swan in Alaska. Wildl. Monogr. 26. 83pp.

HANSON, W.C. and L.L. EBERHARDT. 1971. A Columbia River Canada goose population, 1950-1970. Wildl. Monogr. 28. 61pp.

HARAMIS, G.M., J.R. GOLDSBERRY, D.G. MCAULEY, and E.L. DERLETH. 1985. An aerial photographic census of Chesapeake Bay and North Carolina canvasbacks. J. Wildl. Manage. 491:449-454.

HEITMEYER, M.E. and P.A. VOHS, Jr. 1984. Distribution and habitat use of waterfowl wintering in Oklahoma. J. Wildl. Manage. 48:51-62.

HIGGINS, K.F., L.M. KIRSCH, and I.J. BALL. 1969. A cable-chain device for locating duck nests. J. Wildl. Manage. 33(4):1009-1011.

———. 1977. Duck nesting in intensively farmed areas of North Dakota. J. Wildl. Manage. 41:232-242.

HILDEBRAND, B.D. 1979. Habitat requirements of molting Canada geese at Lima Reservoir, Montana. M.S. Thesis. Montana State Univ., Bozeman. 79pp.

HINES, J.E. and G.J. MITCHELL. 1983. Gadwall nest-site selection and nesting success. J. Wildl. Manage. 47:1063-1071.

HOBAUGH, W.C. and J.G. TEER. 1981. Waterfowl use characteristics of flood-prevention lakes in north-central Texas. J. Wildl. Manage. 45:16-26.

HUDSON, M.S. 1983. Waterfowl production in three age classes of stock ponds in Montana. J. Wildl. Manage. 47:112-117.

HUMBURG, D.D., N.H. PRINCE, and R.A. BISHOP. 1978. The social organization of a mallard population in northern Iowa. J. Wildl. Manage. 42:72-80.

KAMINSKI, R.M. and H.H. PRINCE. 1977. Nesting habitat of Canada geese in southeastern Michigan. Wilson Bull. 89:523-531.

KEITH, L.B. 1961. A study of waterfowl ecology on small impoundments in southeastern Alberta. Wildl. Monogr. 6. 88pp.

KIRBY, R.E. 1980. Waterfowl production estimates on forested wetlands from pair and brood counts. Wildl. Soc. Bull. 8:273-278.

KROHN, W.B. and E.G. BIZEAU. 1979. Molt migration of the Rocky Mountain population of the western Canada goose. Pages 130-140 in Management and Biology of Pacific Flyway Geese Symp. N.W. Sect. Wildl. Soc. Portland, OR.

LEMIEUX, L. 1959. The breeding biology of the greater snow goose on Bylot Island, Northwest Territories. Can. Field-Nat. 73:117-128.

LOKEMOEN, J.T., H.F. DUEBBERT, and D.E. SHARP. 1984. Nest spacing, habitat selection, and behavior of waterfowl on Miller Lake Island, North Dakota. J. Wildl. Manage. 48:309-321.

LOW, J.B. 1945. Ecology and management of the redhead (Nyroca americana) in Iowa. Ecol. Monogr. 15:35-69.

MACINNES, C.D. 1962. Nesting of small Canada geese near Eskimo Point, Northwest Territories. J. Wildl. Manage. 26:247-256.

MAJ, M.E. 1983. Analysis of trumpeter swan habitat on the Targhee National Forest of Idaho and Wyoming. M.S. Thesis. Montana State Univ., Bozeman. 102pp.

MAYFIELD, H. 1975. Suggestions for calculating nest success. Wilson Bull. 87:456-466.

MENDALL, H.L. 1958. The ring-necked duck in the Northeast. Univ. of Maine Bull. 60(16). 317pp.

MILLER, H.W. and D.H. JOHNSON. 1978. Interpreting the results of nesting studies. J. Wildl. Manage. 42:471-476.

MUNDINGER, J.G. 1976. Waterfowl response to rest-rotation grazing. J. Wildl. Manage. 40:60-68.

NAGEL, J. 1965. Field-feeding of whistling swans in northern Utah. Condor 67:446-447.

PATTERSON, J.N. 1976. The role of environmental heterogeneity in the regulation of duck populations. J. Wildl. Manage. 40:22-32.

PERRY, M.C., R.E. MUNRO, and G.M. HARAMIS. 1981. Twenty-five-year trends in Chesapeake Bay diving duck populations. Trans. North Am. Wildl. Nat. Resour. Conf. 46:299-310.

POSPAHALA, R.S., D.R. ANDERSON, and C.J. HENNY. 1974. Population ecology of the mallard. II. Breeding habitat conditions, size of the breeding populations and production indices. U.S. Dep. Inter., Fish and Wildl. Serv. Resour. Publ. 115. 73pp.

RUNDQUIST, V.M. 1973. Avian ecology on stock ponds in two vegetational types in north-central Montana. PH.D. Thesis, Montana State Univ., Bozeman. 116pp.

RYDER, J.P. 1967. The breeding biology of Ross' goose in the Perry River region, Northwest Territories. Can. Wildl. Serv. Rep. Series 3. 56pp.

SAUDER, D.W., T.L. LINDER, R.B. DAHLGREN, and W.L. TUCKER. 1971. An evaluation of the roadside technique for censusing breeding waterfowl. J. Wildl. Manage. 35:538-543.

SHERWOOD, G.A. 1960. The whistling swan in the West, with particular reference to Great Salt Lake Valley, Utah. Condor 62:370-377.

SMITH, R.H. 1953. A study of waterfowl production in artificial reservoirs in eastern Montana. J. Wildl. Manage. 17:276-291.

STEWART, R.E., A.E. GEIS, and C.D. EVANS. 1958. Distribution of populations and hunting kill of the canvasback. J. Wildl. Manage. 22:333-370.

STOUDT, J.H. 1982. Habitat use and productivity of canvasbacks in southwestern Manitoba, 1961-72. U.S. Dep. Inter., Fish and Wildl. Serv. Spec. Sci. Rep. Wildl. 248. 31pp.

SUGDEN, L.G. 1973. Feeding ecology of pintail, gadwall, American widgeon, and lesser scaup ducklings. Can. Wildl. Serv. Rep. Series 24. 45pp.

——— and G. BUTLER. 1980. Estimating densities of breeding canvasbacks and redheads. J. Wildl. Manage. 44:814-821.

TINER, R.W., Jr. 1984. Wetlands of the United States: Current status and recent trends. U.S. Dep. Inter., Fish and Wildl. Serv. Habitat Resources. Newton Corner, MA. 59pp.

VERMEER, K. 1970. Some aspects of the nesting of ducks on islands in Lake Newell, Alberta. J. Wildl. Manage. 34:126-129.

———, D.R.M. HATCH, and J.A. WINDSOR. 1972. Greater scaup as common breeder on northern Lake Winnipeg. Can. Field-Nat. 86:168.

WELLER, M.W. 1964. Distribution and migration of the redhead. J. Wildl. Manage. 28:64-103.

———, D.L. TRAUGER, and G.L. KRAPU. 1969. Breeding birds of the West Mirage Islands, Great Slave Lake, Northwest Territories, Can. Field Nat. 83:344-360.

19

COLONIAL WATERBIRDS

Steven M. Speich

Cascadia Research Collective
Waterstreet Building, Suite 201
218 1/2 W. 4th Avenue
Olympia, WA 98501

Editor's Note: Like marsh and shorebirds, colonial waterbirds are a taxonomically diverse group, yet they require similar management and survey techniques. Because of their colonial nesting behavior, they can be very sensitive to impacts and disturbances to nesting areas, including those caused by biologists conducting inventories and monitoring studies. This chapter provides guidelines on survey techniques and methods to minimize impacts to the birds from such efforts.

INTRODUCTION

Any bird that predominantly feeds in aquatic systems, marine, fresh water, or both, and tends to nest in groups of closely associated nests, is considered a colonial waterbird (Table 1). Some species nest both in groups and singly, and all colonial nesting birds nest as solitary pairs at times. Discussions of the biology of colonial waterbirds are found in Emlen and DeMong (1975), Evans (1982), Krebs (1974, 1978), Kushlan (1978), and Pratt (1980). Waterfowl (Anseriformes) are generally not thought of as colonial nesting waterbirds and therefore, are not discussed in this chapter.

Species of colonial waterbirds range from small storm petrels to large pelicans. Some species, such as storm petrels, lead a truly pelagic existence, except when they come to offshore rocks and islands to nest, often in dense colonies. Other colonial nesting species (alcids and cormorants, brown pelican [*Pelecanus occidentalis*], and some gulls and terns) are less pelagic, with coastal and nearshore affinities throughout the year, or at least portions of the year. A few species bridge the gap between marine and fresh-water environments, with at least segments of the species' population feeding in marine or fresh water systems. Indeed, some individuals (some gulls and terns, great blue heron [*Ardea herodias*], and double-crested cormorant [*Phalacrocorax auritus*]) feed in both systems while nesting. And still other species are truly specific to fresh water while nesting, i.e., grebes; white pelican (*P. erythrorhynchos*); and some egrets, gulls, and terns.

There are several reasons why it is important to survey and census colonial nesting waterbirds. Most species are near or at the top of food chains and are thus sensitive to the health of fresh-water and marine ecosystems. Changes or reductions in food chain biomass and species composition often cause stress in colonial waterbirds, expressed as failure to breed, abandonment of eggs and young, late nesting, depressed growth rates, or reduced fledging success. Over long periods, populations may decline; this can be monitored through a censusing program.

Table 1. Habitat and nesting characteristics of colonial waterbirds found in western North America.

Family and Species	Habitat	Nest Type and Substrate	Nest Location
Grebes (Podicipedidae)			
Red-necked (*Podiceps grisegena*)	coastal waters, lakes	floating, reeds	surface
Eared (*P. nigricollis*)	lakes, bays, ocean	floating, reeds	surface
Western (*Aechmophorus occidentalis*)	lakes, sloughs, bays	floating, reeds	surface
Fulmars (Procellariidae)			
Northern (*Fulmarus glacialis*)	ocean	herbage, dried grass	seal cliffs
Storm Petrels (Hydrobatidae)			
Fork-tailed (*Oceanodroma furcata*)	ocean	burrow	sea islands
Leach's (*O. leucorhoa*)	ocean	burrow	sea islands
Ashy (*O. homochroa*)	ocean	under rocks	sea islands
Black (*O. melania*)	ocean	burrow	sea islands
Pelicans (Pelecanidae)			
American White (*Pelecanus erythrorhynchos*)	lakes, marshes, salt bays, beaches	on ground or in bulrushes	surfaces, bare ground
Brown (*P. occidentalis*)	ocean, salt bays	on ground	islands
Cormorants (Phalacrocoracidae)			
Double-crested (*Phalacrocorax auritus*)	coast, bays, lakes, rivers	sticks, brush, seaweed	trees, marshes, islands, or cliffs
Brandt's (*P. penicillatus*)	ocean, coast, littoral	seaweed, sticks	rocky island, cliffs
Pelagic (*P. pelagicus*)	coast, bays, sounds	seaweed, grass	ledges, cliffs
Red-faced (*P. urile*)	ocean, coast	seaweed, grass	rocky islands
Herons and Egrets (Ardeidae)			
Great Blue Heron (*Ardea herodias*)	marshes, swamps, streams, shores, tideflats, ditches	sticks	trees, rocky islands
Great Egret (*Casmerodius albus*)	marshes, ponds, shores	sticks, brush	trees, brush over water
Snowy Egret (*Egretta thula*)	marshes, ponds, tideflats	sticks, tules, bushes in marsh	willow thickets in marshes
Cattle Egret (*Bubuleus ibis*)	cow pastures, fields and marshes	sticks	in bush or trees
Black-crowned Night Heron (*Nycticorax nycticorax*)	marshes, lake margins, shores	sticks, stalks	trees, willow thickets in marshes
Ibises (Threskiornithidae)			
Glossy Ibis (*Plegadis falcinellus*)	marshes, lake margins	sticks, stalks	bushes in marshy areas
Gulls and Terns (Laridae)			
Laughing Gull (*Larus atricilla*)	salt water marshes, bays	grass platforms	marsh islands
Franklin's Gull (*L. pipixcan*)	prairies, marshes, lakes	among reeds	prairie marshes
Bonaparte's Gull (*L. Philadelphia*)	ocean, bays, rivers, lakes	in conifers	wooded muskeg
Mew Gull (*L. canus*)	coasts, rivers, lakes	rocks or trees	marsh or beach
Ring-billed Gull (*L. delawarensis*)	coast, estuaries, rivers, lakes, fields, refuse dumps	dried grass, weeds, sticks	islands in lakes
California Gull (*L. californicus*)	coast, beach, lake, river, farmland, cities	on ground	islands in lakes
Herring Gull (*L. argentatus*)	ocean coast, bays, beaches, lakes, farmlands, dumps	grass or seaweeds	ground or cliff, islands

Table 1. Habitat and nesting characteristics of colonial waterbirds found in western North America (concluded).

Family and Species	Habitat	Nest Type and Substrate	Nest Location
Gulls and Terns (Laridae) (continued)			
Thayer's Gull *(L. thayeri)*	ocean coast, bays, beaches	vegetation on rocks	on ground
Western Gull *(L. Occidentalis)*	coastal waters, estuaries, beaches	grass	offshore islets, seacliffs
Glaucous-winged Gull *(L. glaucescens)*	ocean, coast, bays, beaches, piers, dumps, waterfronts	seaweed or grass	coastal islands, headlands
Black-legged Kittiwake *(Rissa tridactyla)*	ocean	seaweed	ledges of seacliffs
Red-legged Kittiwake *(R. brevirostris)*	ocean	seaweed or grass	ledges of seacliffs
Sabine's Gull *(Xema sabini)*	ocean, tundra (summer)	grass	depressions in low tundra
Gull-billed Tern *(Sterna nilotica)*	lakes, marshes, fields	surface depression lined with shells and straw	sandy islands
Caspian Tern *(S. caspia)*	lakes, bays, coast	large, deep hollows lined with sticks and shells	sandy islands or dikes of lakes
Elegant Tern *(S. elegans)*	coast	scrape on sand	islands
Common Tern *(S. hirundo)*	ocean, bays, beaches, lakes (summer)	surface depression	lake islands
Arctic Tern *(S. paradisaea)*	ocean, coast, tundra lakes (summer)	surface depression	island, beach, tundra
Aleutian Tern *(S. aleutica)*	ocean, coast	depression in moss	islands
Forster's Tern *(S. forsteri)*	ocean, lakes, bays, marshes, beaches	marsh vegetation	marshes or on muskrat houses
Least Tern *(S. antillarum)*	ocean, bays, beaches, estuaries	scrape	sandy beaches or gravel bars
Black Tern *(Chlidonias niger)*	coasts, lakes, freshwater marshes	marsh vegetation	floating or on muskrat houses
Murres, Guillemots, Auks, etc. (Alcidae)			
Common Murre *(Uria aalge)*	ocean, large bays	bare rock or loose soil	bare ledges, cliffs, or rocky islands
Thick-billed Murre *(U. lomvia)*	ocean	bare ledges	bare rock, sea cliffs
Black Guillemot *(Cepphus grylle)*	ocean, rocky coast	crevices, burrows	sea cliffs
Pigeon Guillemot *(C. columba)*	ocean, rocky coast	crevices, burrows	sea cliffs
Xantu's Murrelet *(Synthliboramphus hypolecus)*	ocean	rock crevices	sea islands
Ancient Murrelet *(S. antiquus)*	ocean, sounds	burrows or bare rock	sea islands
Cassin's Auklet *(Ptychoramphus aleuticus)*	ocean	crevices or burrows	sea islands
Parakeet Auklet *(Cyclorrhynchus psittacula)*	ocean	crevices	sea cliffs
Least Auklet *(Aethia pusilla)*	ocean	under rocks	sea islands
Wiskered Auklet *(A. pygmaea)*	ocean	crevices	sea cliffs
Crested Auklet *(A. cristatella)*	ocean, tide-rip	crevices	sea cliffs
Rhinoceros Auklet *(Cerorhinca monocerata)*	ocean, tide-rip	burrows	sea islands
Tufted Puffin *(Fratercula cirrhata)*	ocean	burrows	sea islands or headlands
Horned Puffin *(F. corniculata)*	ocean	burrows or crevices	sea cliffs

Colonial nesting waterbirds have served, coincidently, as indicators of man-made contaminants in the environment. The effects have included reproductive failure, which can be detected through careful censusing and surveying programs. Knowledge of the numbers and locations of colonies provides an immediate source of biological materials for the geographical monitoring of the levels and types of pollutants in the environment and their subtle effects on body and egg tissues.

Information that can be obtained from censusing and surveying programs, includes quantification of the numbers and geographic locations of colonies, numbers and species present in each colony, and habitats occupied by species and colonies. Collecting quantified information about colonies for long periods, decades and preferably longer, allows a meaningful monitoring of populations. There is often a large variation in reproductive success from year to year. Long-term population trends cannot be reliably derived from short-term studies (those lasting 5 years or less).

Determining the numbers of waterbirds is more efficient when they are concentrated at breeding sites. During the nonbreeding portion of the year, the individuals of most species are dispersed over large geographic areas, such as all or part of North America, Central and South Americas, the continental margins, or the Pacific Ocean. Even when numbers are determined away from breeding colonies in remote areas, the origin of observed birds is almost always unknown. The efficiency and accuracy obtainable from censusing breeding colonies is usually superior to those from censusing wintering colonies.

The material presented here is intended to aid investigators in the design and execution of censusing, surveying, and monitoring programs. Primarily, the biology of colonial nesting waterbirds relevant to such programs, measurement techniques, examples and comparisons of techniques actually applied, and limitations on observers of colonial nesting waterbirds relevant to disturbance and its effects are discussed. These materials are meant to guide potential users in formulating specific programs, according to species, nesting sites, and program goals.

COLONIAL WATERBIRD BIOLOGY

Several aspects of the biology of colonial nesting waterbirds are both unique and important. Since most of these aspects vary greatly, it is helpful to be aware of them. Knowledge of these aspects of biology will improve the design and conduct of any inventory or monitoring study. The following aspects of the biology of colonial nesting waterbirds are relevant to study design and execution.

Colony Size

In most cases, it is not possible to make a definitive statement of the exact size of a given colony. The failure of nesting birds, and the occurrence of renesters and late nesters, makes any determination imprecise. Thus, any statement of colony size must be accompanied by qualifying statements, such as survey date, stage of nesting, and timing of the survey in relation to the colony nesting cycle. If precise information on any of these nesting aspects is known, it should accompany the colony census data.

For each species, there is a range in the number of active nests found in its colonies. Solitary nesting pairs occur in most species. The upper colony size limit varies with each species. If a histogram of colony size were constructed for each species, all would be different. The frequency distribution of colony size is, more or less, species specific (Blacklock et al. 1978; Buckley and Buckley 1972; Des-Granges and Laporte 1979, 1981; DesGranges et al. 1979; Sowls et al. 1978, 1980; Speich and Wahl 1985; Thompson 1982; Werschkul et al. 1976, 1977).

Colony size varies geographically in some species. In marine species, a good example is the common murre (*Uria aalge*). In the Pacific Ocean basin, it breeds along the continental margin from central California to Alaska. Colonies in California, Oregon, and Washington usually number hundreds, thousands, or low tens-of-thousands. Colonies of just a few pairs or tens-of-pairs are present. However, in Alaska, colonies are known to contain up to hundreds-of-thousands of birds. A similar pattern is present in Leach's storm petrel (*Oceanodroma leucorhoa*), and to a lesser extent, tufted puffin (*Fratercula cirrhata*). However, other species do not show geographic variation in colony size along the same coast line: double-crested cormorant, pelagic cormorant (*Phalacrocorax pelagicus*), glaucous-winged gull (*Larus glaucescens*), and pigeon guillemot (*Cepphus columba*) (Sowls et al. 1978, 1980; Speich and Wahl 1985).

Inland fresh-water species also show a range in colony size, but the upper limit is dramatically lower than the large colonies of marine birds (English 1978).

Colony Size Stability

The number of nesting individuals of a species at a site varies over time. To document this, it is necessary to determine the number of nests or nesting adults at a site with the same methods at the same time in the nesting cycle over several years, preferably at least a decade (Erwin et al. 1981). In general, survey data are lacking for most species and most sites over long periods of time, seldom allowing analysis of colony site trends. Data are usually fragmentary and imprecise. There are examples of species colonizing new sites, ceasing to nest at sites, and switching sites (Ainley and Lewis 1974; Buckley and Buckley 1980; Conover and Conover 1981; DesGranges 1980; Drent and Guiguet 1961; Drent et al. 1964; Nettleship 1975; Ogden 1978; Penland 1982; Pratt 1972, 1974; Speich and Wahl 1985; Stowe 1982; Thompson et al. 1979; Tuck 1961).

Nesting

Of critical importance to the censusing and monitoring of colonial nesting species is the knowledge of the time of nesting and the breeding synchrony of the subject species, as a whole, and its colonies. The time of breeding and synchrony are distorted by renesting and late nesting pairs. Although the time of nesting at any site tends to take place at the same time each year, there is, nonetheless, variation in the time of nesting (Bayer and McMahon 1981; Drent 1965; Ogden 1978; Pratt 1970, 1972, 1974; Thompson and Tabor 1981; Tuck 1961). At times this can vary as much as a month (Drent et al. 1964; Speich and Wahl 1985). A few studies have documented geographical variation in the time of nesting. Even colonies close together can be out of phase (Bailey and Terman 1983; Bayer and McMahon 1981; Speich and Wahl 1985; Thompson and Tabor 1981; Tuck 1961; Werschkul et al. 1977; pers. obs.).

Renesting. Generally egg laying is clumped and can be described statistically by calculating mean, variance, range, etc. However, some nesters fail through loss of nest, eggs, young, or even mates. The number of failed nests can range from a small percentage to, at times, the entire colony.

Often the individuals that failed in their initial attempt will renest later in the same season. After nest failure, there is a recycle time before they attempt to renest. The re-entering of these individuals into the colony prolongs the active nesting phase of the colony and negates the usual pronounced breeding synchrony observed at the onset of nesting in the colony.

Non-nesters. In most populations there is a segment that does not breed. It may be quite small, or sizable and measurable, depending on the species. These non-nesting individuals may not be present in the nesting colony at all, or may be present for only a short time. Generally, non-nesters are thought to be young inexperienced birds, without previous nesting experience (Rodgers 1978). However, occasionally yearling birds do attempt to nest (Lowe 1954; Pratt 1973; Rodgers 1978; Speich and Manuwal 1974).

Late Nesters. Although nesting colonies often initially appear to be synchronous in nesting, this frequently is dispelled by the arrival of late nesting individuals. The numbers can be just a few pairs or so numerous that they double the colony size, or more (Rodgers 1978). The appearance of late nesting birds is often gradual, or in mass (Massey and Atwood 1981).

Mixed Species Colonies. In mixed species colonies, nesting species are often out of phase with one another. This is usually preceded by different arrival times for each species (Burger 1978; Drent et al. 1964; McCrimmon 1978a; Thompson 1981; Thompson and Tabor 1981; pers. obs.).

A colony of adult nesting pelicans.

Colorado Division of Wildlife

A mixed-species colony consisting of great blue herons, double-crested cormorants, and black-crowned night herons.

Attendance Patterns

When censusing colonial nesting species and counting adults, it is critical to determine daily colony attendance patterns of the nesting adults because the proportion of nesting adults in the colony varies with the time of day, the stage of nesting, and other environmental patterns (Birkhead 1978; Brun 1972; Burger 1976; Conover and Miller 1980; Custer and Osborn 1978; Drent 1965, 1967; Galusha and Amlaner 1978; Gibson 1950; Lloyd 1972; Manuwal 1974b; Patterson 1965; Slater 1980; Tuck 1961).

Distribution and Habitat

When working with colonial nesting waterbirds, two aspects of distribution should be considered: (1) the distribution of colony sites over often broad geographic regions and (2) the distribution of the nests in a colony.

The geographic distribution of a species' colonies may cover a considerable area, such as large portions of western North America (Godfrey 1966; Palmer 1962; Ryder 1978; Sowls et al. 1978, 1980; Speich and Wahl 1985; general bird guides). The distribution of colony sites within overall ranges may evidence one or more distribution patterns. Colonies may be distributed non-randomly, with clusters near lakes, streams, or coastlines (Drent and Guiguet 1961; English 1978; Sowls et al. 1978, 1980; Speich and Wahl 1985). Within an area, such as a corridor along a river or around a lake, the nests there may be evenly or randomly spaced. Knowledge of the study species' distribution pattern is important to any plan to locate colony sites for all programs.

The geographic distribution of a species is partially determined by the interactions of its ability to reach new areas, the extent it is a specialist or generalist in feeding and nesting requirements, and the extent of its preferred habitat(s) (Udvardy 1969).

Colony Site Selection

The factors involved in colony site selection are only partially understood and undoubtedly vary with each species. They may include (1) suitable nest site substrate or support for nest placement, (2) shelter from adverse environmental conditions, (3) apparent freedom from predators, and (4) proximity to food sources (English 1978; Buckley and Buckley 1972). Individuals of colonial nesting species usually nest in colonies with conspecifics and often with other species as well, while suitable nearby sites are often left unused with all individuals in the area nesting at one or a few sites (Weise 1978). Behavioral factors may be as important as those of selecting nest sites (Buckley and Buckley 1980).

Nest Site Selection

Nest density varies with each species. Inter-nest (how far apart nests are constructed) distance is the result of nest site selection and appears to be affected by nest site structure as it relates to habitat suitability and social interactions (Buckley and Buckley 1977; Burger 1978; McCrimmon 1978a).

Habitat Suitability. The placement of a nest ultimately depends on whether the substrate is appropriate for a particular species' nests. The nests of some species are found in several habitat types; the habitat structure for nest placement is apparently important (Burger 1978). Great blue heron nests are found on the ground, cliff ledges, in bushes and shrubs, deciduous trees, coniferous trees, dead trees, and man-made structures (DesGranges 1979; Henny and Kurtz 1978; Werschkul et al. 1976). In this

Typical white pelican colony.

Great blue heron nests in cottonwood grove.

species, if the substrate will support the nest, it can be used for nesting. Finding suitable places that support a nest in a colony limit in part nest placement, nest density, and colony size. For most species that nest in vegetation, the species of plants used are not necessarily important, as long as the structures of the plants meet the support and shelter requirements of the species' nest (Bailey and Terman 1983; Bayer and McMahon 1981; Werschkul et al. 1976).

Burrow nesting species require a substrate that allows the digging of a burrow, yet will not collapse once the burrow is complete. In rocky soil, density may be limited by a scarcity of "clean" soil that allows burrowing. Talus slopes contain only a limited number of openings that lead deep enough into the slope to afford nesting sites for alcids and storm-petrels (pers. obs.).

Social Interactions.
The presence of a species nesting in a colony may affect the choice of nest sites of another species (Burger 1978). If all suitable nest sites are taken, other individuals (conspecifics or otherwise) have four choices: (1) displace the occupants of a nest site, (2) wait until a site is open, (3) nest in a less favorable site, or (4) go elsewhere (Thompson 1981).

Inter-nest distance is determined in part by social interaction (territory defense) with conspecifics (Buckley and Buckley 1977; Meyerriecks 1960) or other species (Burger 1978). The space between nests is open if a new nest, territory, can "fit" between existing nests.

The density of burrowing birds, such as Cassin's auklet, is limited by aggressive interactions on the colony surface (Manuwal 1974a, b; Thoresen 1964). Burrow occupants vigorously defend the burrow opening and small area around the burrow entrance. Glaucous-winged gulls and western gulls (*L. occidentalis*) nest in higher densities where the substrate surface is irregular with many large objects on the ground. These are visual barriers and allow closer packing of the nests. Herons and egrets nest in lower densities, allowing for large body size and the reach of long necks of birds at their nests (Burger 1978). Pelecaniformes defend nest sites and a small area around nests (Van Tets 1965), probably resulting from the observed nest densities in colonies.

Nest Types, Placement, and Habitat

Colonial nesting waterbirds in western North America construct a variety of nests and place them in characteristic locations and habitats depending on the needs of the particular species.

Floating Platform. Floating nests are generally constructed in marshes or areas of slow moving water. The nests are attached to the edge of patches of anchored, emergent vegetation; areas of variable plant density; and often in thick stands of emergent vegetation. The visibility of nests varies, with edge nests easily observable, while nests in areas of dense vegetation are often visible only when the observer is next to the nest. Nests in dense stands are often obscured from sight from the air; the nests are built with vegetation forming a natural overhead shelter. (For species nest descriptions see Bent 1922; Godfrey 1966; Palmer 1962.)

Subsurface Chamber. Subsurface nests are used or constructed by a variety of marine birds. (For species' nest descriptions see Bent 1919; Palmer 1962; Sowls et al. 1978.) In some cases, nesting chambers are naturally occurring. The sites range from talus slopes, rubble piles, boulder piles, sea caves, driftwood, various holes and cracks in cliffs, and burrows dug by other species (Manuwal 1974b). Existing holes are often extended and enlarged, but at least usually cleaned out. Birds nesting in natural cavities are often particularly difficult to census and the numbers present in a colony cannot always be determined from surface features (Byrd et al. 1983; Sowls et al. 1978).

In other cases, nesting chambers are constructed. For instance, many species of marine birds excavate burrows for nesting. Chambers are often excavated new each season or used for several nesting seasons. Burrow sites vary with each species and show considerable range in some species. Sites must allow burrowing and be stable enough to permit the structure to survive the nesting season. Burrows vary in length, shape, and depth, depending on the species and the nesting substrate. Surface cover is not critical providing the vegetation can be penetrated.

Ronald A. Ryder

Glaucous gull.

Surface Nests. Nests placed on the surface of the ground range from simple, virtually no nest at all, to large complex structures. (For species' nest descriptions see Bent 1919, 1921, 1922, 1927; Godfrey 1966; Palmer 1962; others.)

The simplest nests are in reality no nest at all, with the egg placed directly on the substrate. This is seen in the ledge nesting common murre and thick-billed murre (*U. lomvia*). The murres bring a few small stones and other objects to the nest site (Tuck 1961). Birds nesting on ledges are usually highly visible at the proper angle of observation.

The simplest "nest" of ground nesting birds is the scrape, a small hollow made in the soil, often sand. This is common in terns, such as the Caspian tern (*Sterna caspia*; Penland 1981). These nests are precarious, and are often filled with drifting sand. Nests of this type are difficult to see from a distance, especially from aircraft. The birds themselves are counted, unless the colony is entered.

The next order of nest complexity is seen in the small rings of material that are constructed of gathered vegetation and other debris. These nests have a bottom and a rim that hold the eggs in place and off the substrate. These are commonly seen in gulls and cormorants. Nests of sticks, such as those built by cormorants, often survive the winter and are used again, with new material added. Other rim nests, made of more substantial non-woody plant material often survive to be used again. Many species, such as the kittiwakes, compact the nest with mud giving permanency to the nest. Nests of these types are often clearly visible and are often easily counted when the observer is remote from the colony.

Finally, in some species the nest can become a sizeable structure. Such nests usually are the result of use over several years, with each nesting pair adding more material to the top of the nest (e.g., double-crested cormorant, Brandt's cormorant [*P. auritus*], and brown pelican). These nests are easily observed from a distance, are easily counted, and are usually discernible in photographs (Sidle and Ferguson 1982).

Arboreal Nests. Arboreal nests are built at various heights from just a few centimeters to tens of meters. The nest support can vary from bulrushes, willows, and sagebrush to large alders, cottonwoods, or conifers. Nest construction material varies considerably with the large nests of some herons and cormorants, often containing sticks and small branches. Nests are often in full view from the ground or air; however, arboreal nests of some species may be placed in concealed locations, and locating them can be difficult. Nests placed in trees may be fully exposed at the onset of nesting, but are soon concealed by emerging leaves.

POPULATION MEASUREMENT CRITERIA

This section deals with the mechanisms and necessary requirements to design and conduct a survey, monitor, or census program (McCrimmon 1976).

Biologists should remember two important points when working with colonial nesting water birds: (1) that actions can severely affect the study species, and (2) that any program undertaken must be done well. This includes taking steps to ensure the program results are available to present day researchers and to those in the distant future (see McCrimmon 1978b; Herman 1980). Following are the requirements needed before a survey or monitoring and census program can be designed or conducted.

What to Measure: Populations or Habitats

There are two different types of nesting distributions that must be considered. One is the distribution of the study species' colonies over often broad geographic areas of one or more habitat types. The other is the distribution of nests within colonies. The approaches for sampling colonies versus nests are usually different; the sampling program used depends on the program goals. If the goal is general distribution and total numbers of colonies, with imprecise knowledge of species and their numbers, then surveys over large areas are employed. However, if accurate numbers of species at each colony are needed, then censuses of colonies are also required.

Waterbirds (those that commonly nest in colonies) usually concentrate their nests in a few colonies, leaving apparently suitable nesting habitat unused. The colony sizes and species present usually

Nesting double-crested cormorants.

Colorado Division of Wildlife

vary. Sampling a portion of apparently available and suitable habitat to derive values for the number of colonies and individuals per unit area and then extrapolating to the total area are done only with caution. The reliability of derived values is often improved with larger samples, when colony size variation is small, and species composition is constant. To determine the total number of colonies present for any species it is desirable to locate each colony. However, this is not always practical and extrapolations from samples must be considered.

When colonies are censused, the goal is usually to determine the total number of nesting individuals of each species present. The possibilities of accomplishing this depend on the species present, their numbers, the visibility of nests, the resources available, and the limitations imposed by the consequences of disturbance. Preferably, a direct count of each nest in the colony by personnel visiting each nest is most desirable. However, this is often not possible or desirable. In such cases, samples of the colony are obtained and values extrapolated to the total area occupied by the colony. A variety of techniques are available to obtain sample counts (Buckley and Buckley 1978).

Where to Look

The process of locating colonies can take considerable time and resources; therefore, learning as much as possible about the study species' colonies in the study area is needed before field work begins. The time spent reading literature, field notes, and reports, and talking with local observers is usually a good investment. When surveys do begin, the known sites can serve as starting points. Later as more experience is gained through study, other habitats can be searched.

If the habitat occurs as widely scattered patches, as continuous belts, or large expanses, the use of an airplane for observations may be necessary. Depending on the species, colonies may be visible from the air and easily plotted on maps. The use of a boat may be required to locate colonies along rivers, waterways, marshes, and coastlines. For secretive or hard to observe species it may be necessary to closely inspect likely colony sites, on foot or from a boat.

The colonies of some species are not specific to a particular habitat or a few habitats; other colonies are concealed. In both cases, these colonies would be difficult to locate by direct searches. The locations of colonies can be narrowed down to smaller areas by observing where foraging birds are located. Observers can return to these areas and attempt to follow birds to their colonies. It is also possible to determine the locations of colonies by observing where birds emerge from vegetation when leaving

their colonies to forage. Nocturnal species may require systematically checking colony sites at night, a potentially long process. Burrowing species may require the excavation of burrows to determine species composition of colonies.

Once the survey of an area or habitats is completed, observers can return to the located sites and make systematic censuses of the species, their numbers and status. The methods used to locate colonies in the beginning can then be used for monitoring the colonies. Unfortunately there is no one way to survey for the presence of colonies. The methods must be adjusted for the study species, the habitats present, the area covered, the resources available, and the program goals. The researcher must decide the precision needed to cover the target area. Should all the colonies be located, or just a few for later projects? In recent years, there were several programs to locate and count all breeding colonies and species of the North American continental margin (for examples see Blacklock et al. 1978; Clapp et al. 1982a, b; Erwin 1979; Erwin and Korschgen 1979; Korschgen 1979; Nesbitt et al. 1982; Portnoy 1977; Portnoy et al. 1981; Sowls et al. 1978, 1980; and Speich and Wahl 1985).

How to Observe

Counting the number of active nests is an unlikely prospect for many species at many sites, although it can be done under ideal situations. Often, nests are hard to find, and may be concealed in vegetation, or both. Even when nests can be counted, it is unlikely that the status of every nest can be determined. Impacts from disturbance on the study species also need to be considered. In this case, observers must often obtain sample counts and status determinations from portions of the colony and apply correction factors to samples.

High density nesting species, such as white pelicans, successfully reproduce with no social conflict.

If nests cannot be counted, less precise methods must be employed. These include determining the net movements of adults to and from feeding areas, counting adults at feeding areas and, for nocturnal burrowing species, trying to determine numbers from the sounds of adults. Although imprecise, these methods are often the best that can be used.

When to Observe

Equally important to knowing how and what to observe is to know when to observe. Counts of nests or burrows, and adults on nests, are usually made during daylight hours. The time of day observations are made can be important. If adults are counted, it is ideal to count when the adult-to-nest ratio approaches 2:1. When adults might be frightened from their nests, especially if the nests contain eggs and nestlings that would be exposed to overheating, chilling, or predation, a time of day for observations should be chosen when stress is minimal. Ideally, numbers are best determined after the peak of egg laying when most nests at a colony have incubating adults.

MEASUREMENT TECHNIQUES

Counts of All Nests or Adults

Counting every nest is usually practical only in small colonies; larger colonies can be counted when there are sufficient personnel. When making direct counts of burrows, ground nests, or arboreal nests, it is desirable to mark each nest visited and then re-count all nests, marked and unmarked, to derive correction factors. It is useful to partition the colony to ensure a thorough census. Counts from aircraft are necessarily less precise, but often necessary. However, counting nests from aerial photographs, especially through stereo photography, is often a practical way to determine numbers of nesting birds. The counting of all nests, especially by observers in the colony, is limited by the effects of disturbance.

As stated, counts of adults are desirable, but often impractical, especially when nests are difficult to recognize. Counts of adults are usually made from remote vantage points, from aircraft, or through stereo photography. Helicopters are often superior to fixed wing aircraft, as they allow prolonged viewing of the colony from chosen vantage positions above the colony.

Samples of Nests or Adults

Estimates of the total numbers of nesting birds are derived from counts of sample sections in the colony. Sample plots are established through random strip transects, evenly spaced belts, point-centered-quarter, random plots, or other methods suitable

to colony conditions and program goals. Whether the samples are obtained by personnel in the colony, at remote vantage points or in aircraft, or through stereo photography, is decided on a colony-by-colony basis. The sample plots are adjusted as necessary to match the habitat differences within the colony.

If sample counts of adults are required, the procedures are similar to those used to obtain sample counts of nests.

Adult Counts Away from the Colony

When estimates of the numbers of birds nesting in a colony cannot be obtained, counting adults away from the colony is an alternative. One method, flight line counts, counts adult birds as they fly to and from foraging areas. This is accomplished by observing birds from vantage points that offer a clear view of the area surrounding the colony. Numbers derived from net movement counts are affected in several ways. In part these are taken into consideration in calculations to derive total numbers. The total number derived can be affected by (1) the portion of the colony's birds that come by the point of observation, (2) the portion of the adults observed that are actually nesting, and (3) the portion of the birds observed that are from the subject colony and not from other colonies.

Another method is to obtain counts of birds when they are on foraging areas away from the colony. The considerations are the same as for flight line counts. Additionally, for diving birds, at any moment of observation, a portion of the birds may be below the water surface, out of view. Counts of the birds are made directly from vantage points, aircraft, or through stereo photography. The time taken to understand the foraging schedule of the birds is well spent.

Correction Factors

When definitive numbers of birds of any species nesting at any given colony site cannot be obtained, numbers can be approximated through a census program. The number derived is qualified by the date of the census in relation to the nesting stage of the colony. Usually nests, burrows, or adults are counted, but only a proportion of the adults nesting at a colony may be present at the time of the census. Likewise, a count of nests or burrows will contain sites that are not active. And, of the active nests found on any given census, only a portion will be successful, producing fledging young.

Correction factors are applied to counts to bring them more in line with the actual number of adults probably present and nesting at the colony. The usual approach is to correct for the nests or burrows that are not active, and for those missed during a census. The only difference is that generally the correction factors for burrowing species are much harder to obtain, especially for nocturnal species.

If adults are counted, the most important ratio to determine is between adults present and the number of active nests. Thus, counts from the air or from remote observation points are verified by site checks of sample sections in the colony where the ratio is determined (Nisbet 1973; Kadlec and Drury 1968).

Checking Accuracy

Determining the numbers of a species present and nesting in a colony is often elusive because of the known, uncontrollable and usually unquantifiable, variables involved. However, the numbers generated are often good. The accuracy or inaccuracy of numbers obtained may preclude any detailed analysis (Ralph 1981). This and large values may allow statements only when numbers are different by factors of 2, 4, or even orders of magnitude. The application of statistical tests may indicate significant differences or trends in the data, but significant statistical differences may not translate to significant biological differences or be real.

Nevertheless, the accuracy of a survey or census should be checked. There are two main approaches. First, the survey or census can be repeated by the same observers or different observers. Hopefully, all methods are constant and the environmental conditions remain the same. Obtaining the same colony attendance pattern during the repeat of the survey or census is desirable. Repeating a survey or census with different methods could be employed when there is reason to suspect the results of the original survey or census.

Sample Methods and Comparisons

The following examples of methods used to observe and obtain numbers of colonial nesting waterbirds are only a sample; many other methods could be included (Buckley and Buckley 1978). The examples show the results of actual studies from a variety of methods, on several species in different habitats. These examples should help the researcher select the methods needed to satisfy program goals. Studies where different methods are compared are presented in more detail to demonstrate the variability of results and efficiency of methods in specific situations. These examples also show that considerable effort must be extended to obtain data on species and their numbers, nesting in waterbird colonies, and that the inherent difficulties should not be underestimated!

Aerial Photography—Ground Nest Count. On June 2 and 3, 1980, ground counts were conducted and aerial photographs taken of nesting white pelicans on Small Island, Chase Lake National Wildlife Refuge, North Dakota (Sidle and Ferguson 1982). The aerial photography revealed 1,368 pelican nests, and the ground census 1,355 pelican nests, a difference of only 1%.

Ground Nest Counts—Duplications. On May 24, 1980, herring gulls (*L. argentatus*) and lesser black-backed gulls (*L. fuscus*) nests were counted by 10 observers on 10 separate plots in Flat Holm, United Kingdom (Ferns and Mudge 1981). The goal of the observers was to systematically search their respective plots for all nests and place a spray paint mark by each nest found. The observers then switched plots, and counted all marked and unmarked plots, establishing a ratio of the two nest counts. For nine plots the average percentage of nests missed during the first count was 16.9 ± 3.3% (SE). The range for nine plots was 5.0% to 27.3%. In total 2,758 nests were marked and counted, and the corrected total number of nests was 3,651.

Similar results were obtained from duplicating the count and marking the nests in gull colonies in Massachusetts. The error ranged from 4% to 22% on eight sets of counts. Plot totals varied from 27 to 442 nests, on plots of 0.06 to 0.73 ha (0.15 to 1.8 a.) with varied vegetation density (Erwin 1980b). Even in sparsely vegetated small plots, there is considerable error in finding ground nests.

Ground Censuses of Ground Nests. A few of the methods used to determine the numbers of ground nesting species by counting on the ground are presented here. Numbers of ring-billed gulls (*L. delawarensis*) nesting in a colony were determined by dividing the colony into sections and then counting all the nests in each section (Southern and Southern 1981). Total counts of nesting gulls and terns in colonies were obtained by counting and marking all the nests in distinct areas of the colony.

Ronald A. Ryder

Ring-billed gull.

The areas were then counted again and the numbers of marked and unmarked nests were recorded. A Lincoln Index was applied to get the "true" total (Erwin 1980b).

Strip transects were randomly placed through large colonies, and all nests were counted in the transects. These transect counts were continued until 10% to 20% of the colony area was surveyed. The densities obtained were used to calculate the total numbers nesting in the whole colony (Erwin 1980b).

In large wading bird colonies, belt transect counts are a practical way to obtain an idea of the total numbers nesting. Transects are made through the colony and all nests are counted in the belt. These are repeated until 10% of the total colony area is censused. This technique at least obtains order of magnitude counts for a colony (Portnoy 1980). Although this technique may be practical for arboreal or surface ground nesting species, the prospect of obtaining a 10% area sample in a large burrowing species colony is discouraging.

In a burrowing species colony, the nests, in many cases, must be individually examined to identify species and to determine whether the nests are active before correction factors can be calculated (pers. obs.). The point-centered-quarter technique of obtaining samples has been used. Between 8 and 15 samples are taken along an arbitrarily drawn line through a colony. However, the strip transect method is recommended (Erwin 1980b). Total counts of nests are practical only in small colonies (Portnoy 1980) and the accuracy can be quite good (pers. obs.).

Censusing—Helicopter, Airplane, and Ground Nest Counts.

The census results obtained from a helicopter, a fixed wing aircraft, and on the ground, of a mixed species colony of mangrove (*Rhizosphora mangle*) were compared (Kushlan 1979). For large white and dark birds, nesting in the tree tops, the helicopter results had an error 10% to 16% of the ground nest count. The error for fixed wing aircraft compared to ground censuses ranged from 32% to 100% (also see Erwin 1980a).

Census Accuracy—Total Count, Strip Count, and Point-Centered-Quarter.

Three census methods were compared in six gull and three heron colonies (Erwin 1980b). Strip transect and point-centered-quarter methods were compared to known total counts in the colonies. Sample areas were within 10% to 20% of plots for the strip transect method. Between 8 and 15 points were sampled for the fixed point-centered-quarter method. Only the strip transect method showed reasonable accuracy in the field, and the observer error ranged from 3% to

142%. Five samples were below 11%, and one each at 26% and 54%. Point-centered-quarter error rates ranged from 3% to 400%. Most were larger than the corresponding strip transect sample errors. The strip transect method is apparently equally reliable regardless of the spatial distribution of the sample population. Laboratory studies with artificial populations—random, uniform, and patchy—yielded similar results (Erwin 1980b).

Flight Line Count—Ground Count.

Erwin (1981) compared flight line counts and ground nest count results at 13 mixed species wading bird colonies. For three hours in the morning, all birds entering and leaving colonies were counted and identified. Then all nests were counted or belt transects were used to generate the total nests present. Species and colony differences in flight rate were observed. Individual colony size error reached a factor of 2, and the actual populations were predicted with 10% error. Species correction factors to flight line data may be necessary. Hour to hour variation in flight rates can be substantial, and the calculation of a mean rate is suggested. For the use of flight line counts, comparisons with other methods of obtaining the number of nesting birds present, and for diurnal burrowing species, see the discussion in Byrd et al. (1983).

Aerial Visual Estimates, Aerial Photograph Counts, and Transect Sampling.

Portnoy (1980) compared aerial visual estimates, aerial photograph counts, and transect counts in 19 colonies of nesting wading birds. Aerial visual estimates of great egrets (*Casmerodius albus*) at these colonies were greater 4 times and less 15 times than the actual numbers present. Of 33 colonies, mean colony size was 511 nests; the average error of the visual estimates was −4.2% (SD 12.2). Of six snowy egret colonies, mean size was 1,992 nests; the visual error was −8.7% (SD 92.0). For Louisiana heron (*Hydranassa tricolor*) colonies, n = 8; mean size, 3,192 nests; and the visual error was 79.1% (SD 25.1). And in black-crowned night heron colonies, n = 7; mean size, 573 nests; and the visual error was −84.4% (SD 14.7). Clearly, aerial-visual samples of colonial nesting wading birds greatly underestimate numbers of smaller cryptic and concealed nesting species in trees or marsh vegetation (see also Erwin 1980a).

Gull Colony Ground Nest Counts, Aerial Photograph Counts, and Aerial Visual Estimates.

Three methods of determining nesting numbers of gulls at colonies were compared (Kadlec and Drury 1968). Photographs of colonies and visual estimates were made of colonies from helicopters. Double ground counts of gull nests were made in the colonies. On the first ground count, 95% of all nests were found. At some colonies, two additional ground counts were made. The ratios of adults, counted on photographs and from aerial estimates, to ground counts were established for all sites. Ratios tended to be similar within each census, although the ratios varied between censuses. Confidence intervals are given for predicting the number of nests from photograph counts of adults and visual estimates of adults. For regional determinations of gull numbers, visual estimations are a valid approach. More detailed studies within a region require photography. In predicting numbers from visual estimates and photograph counts, errors of 19% to 31% and 26% to 35%, respectively, can be expected. Annual changes of 25% or less may not be detectable with either method.

Belt Transect Sampling and Confidence Limits.

In 1976, gulf coast heronries were sampled with randomly placed ground belt transects, in which all nests were sampled (Portnoy 1980). Transects were run until 10% of the colony area was sampled. The 95% confidence limits generated for nest densities per transect were large: for estimated numbers of nests, n = 16,880; the confidence interval was 2,672 nests; n = 14,938, 3,090; n = 14,279, 1,809; n = 12,600, 1,337; n = 3,240, 810. When dealing with largely inaccessible colonies, i.e., concealed nests, colonies over water, and cryptic species, this is about the best one can expect. When surveying large areas, and a large number of difficult large colonies, economic and personnel limits may not allow better work. In large colonies, order-of-magnitude measurements may be all that can be expected.

Estimating Numbers from Aerial Photographs—An Experiment.

Nine observers were asked to estimate the numbers of birds on 10 different photographs each of 5 consecutive days. The observers were in three groups: inexperienced, past experience, and recent experience. The effects of observer differences, prior experience, training, and numerical magnitude were examined. With no training, experienced observers were more accurate than inexperienced observers. Trends in underestimation were observed. With training, estimates by eight observers were within 10% of the actual number. This study by Erwin (1982) is interesting and suggests that training prior to censuses or surveys is important.

Aerial Photography of Large Colonies of Cliff and Island Top Nesting Species.

Aerial photography was used to determine colony size of nesting common murres (Nettleship 1980). This species can nest in numbers in the 100,000s. It nests on cliff ledges, the flat tops of islands, in boulder fields, and in caves. There is no easy way to census these large colonies. Correction factors for counts from photographs are generated from field counting and counting from photographs, groups of about 200

birds. If photographs cannot be obtained for all areas, then numbers may be estimated for these areas from densities in the known areas. The total "number" may be a composite from photograph counts, area extrapolations, and direct counts or estimates from land or aircraft. Correction factors for flat, accessible island top areas are generated by counting birds on photographs, field counting adults, or both, and then flushing the adults and counting their eggs in distinct areas. For large colonies, this procedure is very time-consuming, taking one observer up to 6 weeks to complete a census. To obtain population samples and detect population trends, numbers are determined in sample plots and extrapolated to known areas of similar habitat. In a large colony, this can take an observer up to 10 days. Several photographs appear in this publication showing birds, habitat, and sampling areas (see also Nettleship 1976).

Aerial Photography of Cliff and Island Top Nesting Species.

Aerial photographs of nesting gannets on ledges, on cliff faces, and on flat ground at the tops of cliffs were used to determine nesting numbers (Nettleship 1975). Overlapping aerial photographs of incubating birds were taken from a fixed-wing aircraft with a 35mm camera, using a 50mm lens and Kodak Plus-X, black-and-white film. The photographs were taken about 600 m (1,980 ft) from the colony. Glossy prints, 7 × 10 in. or 9 × 13 in. were made. It was possible to count the number of birds associated with each nest from the photographs by using hand lenses and 1 × 1 cm (0.4 in.) plastic overlays. This gave a count of nest site holders, not the actual number of birds that build nests and actually lay eggs. The error was thought to be less than 20%. The error largely resulted from the imprecise boundaries on

Common murre and nest in typical cliff ledge site.

photographs and difficulty in counting the nests at the back of broad, flat areas at cliff tops.

Aerial Photograph Counts and Estimates of Ground Nests.
Estimates of the total numbers of ground nests were made from airplanes, and these were corrected with ground counts of nests (Erwin 1980a). Counts of ground-nesting terns and black skimmers (*Runchops niger*) were determined from aerial photographs and then corrected with ground counts of nests (Portnoy 1980).

Aerial Estimates of Arboreal Nests.
Total estimates of all visible arboreal nests were made from an airplane, and the counts were then corrected with "good" data (nest counts, etc.; Erwin 1980a). Large, conspicuous wading birds can be counted in this manner, but the technique is not suitable for determining the numbers of cryptic, and/or concealed, nesting species (Portnoy 1980).

DISTURBANCE

Disturbance includes any activity by an observer that results in any perturbation of the "normal" condition on the colony under observation. The disturbance created ranges from that undetectable by observers to major disruptions of the colony (Table 2). Unless observations are conducted from a position remote and distant to the colony, they will result in disturbance to the colony.

Sources of Disturbance

The nature and magnitude of disturbance often depend on the experience and skill of the observers. The level of disturbance is usually a function of the platform of observation, and the techniques used to make observations. Table 2 lists types and effects of disturbance on several colonial-nesting species, with references to pertinent studies.

Table 2. Types and Effects of Disturbance.

Types of Disturbance	Authors	Species Groups
AIRCRAFT: HELICOPTERS: OBSERVERS IN OR NEAR COLONIES:	Dunnet 1977 Burger 1980 Kushlan 1979 Burger 1981 Robert and Ralph 1975	seabird colonies herring gulls wading bird colonies gulls gulls
Effects of Disturbance		
AGGRESSIVE BEHAVIOR:	Burger 1980, 1981 Robert and Ralph 1975	gulls gulls
THERMAL STRESS: (when adults leave eggs or nestlings unattended)	Bartholomew et al. 1953 Bartholomew and Dawson 1954 Vermeer 1963 Drent et al. 1964 Harris 1964 Drent 1967 Hunt 1972 Anderson and Keith 1980 Dawson and Bennett 1981 Bennett et al. 1981	white pelicans pelicans, gulls, herons glaucous-winged gulls seabird colonies gulls herring gulls herring gulls brown pelicans Western gulls Western gulls
PREDATION:	Drent et al. 1964 Verbeek 1982 Manuwal 1974b Penland 1981	by crows at colonies by crows at colonies by gulls at colonies of Caspian tern eggs
PREDATION FROM OBSERVER-INDUCED DISTURBANCES:	Anderson and Keith 1980 Anderson and Keith 1980 Ellison and Cleary 1978 DesGranges and Reed 1981 Buckley and Buckley 1972 Kury and Gochfeld 1975 Johnson 1938	pelicans by gulls and ravens tern eggs/young by gulls cormorant eggs by gulls eggs/young by gulls tern eggs by gulls cormorant eggs by gulls murre eggs/young by gulls
CHICK MOBILITY: (flushing of young from ground nests)	Robert and Ralph 1975 Penland 1981 Burger 1981	gulls Caspian terns gulls

Table 2. Types and Effects of Disturbance (concluded).

Effects of Disturbance	Authors	Species Groups
NEST AND COLONY ABANDONMENT: (disturbance during nesting)	Werschkul et al. 1976 Manuwal 1978 Anderson and Keith 1980 Jehl 1973 Tremblay and Ellison 1979 Ellison and Cleary 1978 Burger 1981 Penland 1981 Manuwal 1978 Manuwal 1978	great blue herons storm petrels brown pelicans brown pelicans black-crowned night herons double-crested cormorants gulls Caspian terns tufted puffins rhinoceros auklets
DESTRUCTION OF NESTS:	Giles and Marshall 1954	marsh-nesters
CANNIBALISM: (killing of eggs and young by conspecific adults)	Anderson and Keith 1980 Hand 1980 Harris 1964 Hunt and Hunt 1975, 1976 Parson 1971 Patterson 1965 Penland 1981 Robert and Ralph 1975 Vermeer 1963	seabirds Western gulls gulls gulls herring gulls black-headed gulls Caspian terns Western gulls glaucous-winged gulls
REPRODUCTIVE SUCCESS: (additional studies)	Anderson et al. 1976 Ashmole 1963 Brun 1972 Gillett et al. 1975 Kadlec and Drury 1968b Schreiber 1979 Schreiber 1979	seabirds tropical oceanic birds gannet glaucous-winged gulls herring gulls brown pelicans brown pelicans

DISCUSSION AND CONCLUSIONS

A large variety of species of birds are considered colonial nesting waterbirds. They are found in the interior of the continent in association with aquatic systems and in marine environments along the continental margin. The habitat preferences for nest sites vary between species and often within species. Nests range from burrows dug in the soil, ground nests of various sizes and types, floating nests, and arboreal nests. Nests can be completely concealed or easy to see. The feeding methods, positions on food chains, foraging habitats, and feeding schedules are varied, and the sizes of the species range from tens of grams to the low kilograms. These factors are usually important in the design and execution of any program.

The large variance in the breeding biology of colonial nesting waterbirds requires that many different measurement techniques be employed in survey, census, and monitoring programs. The specific measurement techniques depend on the program goals, the resources available to perform the program, the specific characteristics of the placement and visibility of nests and nesting adults, the size of the nesting colonies, the geographic distribution of the colonies, and the effects of disturbance from performing the program. Unfortunately, no one method or few methods can be considered for obtaining quantified information. Each program must be tailor-made and adapted to each species and program goals. It is advisable to be well-prepared before a program begins, but flexibility must be allowed for inevitable adjustments. However, despite all the inherent problems in working with colonial nesting waterbirds, reasonably accurate results can be obtained from measurement programs.

A variety of methods can be employed to measure the numbers of individual species in colonial nesting waterbird colonies. Observations are made in the colony, from the edge of the colony or other remote positions on land, from boats or aircraft, and by stereo photography. Aircraft are efficient when large areas need to be covered quickly. Observations and photographs of colonies are made from aircraft. Helicopters provide stable platforms and can be accurately positioned above colonies for prolonged viewing and photography. Population estimates can be derived from counts of nests or adults. Counts of adults or nests by stereo photography are often efficient. In some situations, every nest or adult in a colony can be counted, but most often, sample counts from plots in the colony are required.

Colonial waterbirds are censused from the ground, at water level, and from the air.

A variety of methods can be useful for partitioning a colony for sample counts. Correction factors should be applied to census numbers to adjust for inactive nests, adults not nesting, adults not present in the colony, when counts of adults are made, etc. Duplicate counting of nests or adults in colony plots generates accuracy correction factors for the percentage of nests or adults missed on the first counting. Additional counts or estimates can be obtained by using a completely different method to check accuracy.

Before colonies can be censused, they first have to be located. This is accomplished first by searching literature, reports, and field notes, and interviewing local observers. This first step can save time and give good indications of the locations of colonies, the species present, and the habitats they occupy. If the goal of the program is to find all colonies, then wide area searches are necessary, with the first effort concentrated in likely habitats or locations. Surveys are conducted on foot and from cars, boats, and aircraft. Once the species, habitats, and geography become familiar, the survey can be refined. If the program goal is the numbers of each species in one or more colonies, then a census is conducted at each colony.

The main factor limiting the methods and ultimately the accuracy of the data obtained from programs, especially censuses of colonies, is the effects of observer-induced disturbance to the nesting birds. Disturbance to colonies in the past has resulted in significant mortality to eggs and nestlings. Every precaution must be taken to ensure that disturbance by observers is kept to a minimum. When working in and near colonies, constant monitoring of the colony is required. The effects of disturbance are not always obvious and immediately evident.

LITERATURE CITED

AINLEY, D.G. and T.J. LEWIS. 1974. The history of the Farallon Island marine bird populations, 1854-1972. Condor 76:432-446.

ANDERSON, D.W. and J.O. KEITH. 1980. The human influence on seabird nesting success: Conservation implications. Biol. Conserv. 18:65-80.

———, J.E. MENDOZA, and J.O. KEITH. 1976. Seabirds in the Gulf of California: A valuable, international resource. Nat. Resour. J. 16:483-505.

ASHMOLE, N.P. 1963. The regulation of numbers of tropical oceanic birds. Ibis 103b:458-473.

BAILEY, V. and M.R. TERMAN. l983. A comparative study of a Great Blue Heron colony in Chase County, Kansas. Trans. Kansas Acad. Sci. 86:81-88.

BARTHOLOMEW, G.A. and W.R. DAWSON. 1954. Temperature regulation in young pelicans, herons, and gulls. Ecol. 35:466-472.

———, ———, and E.J. O'NEILL. 1953. A field study of temperature regulation in young white pelicans, *Pelecanus erythrorynchos*. Ecol. 34:554-560.

BAYER, R.D. and E. MCMAHON. 1981. Colony size and hatching synchrony of Great Blue Herons in coastal Oregon. Murrelet 62:73-79.

BENNETT, A.F., W.R. DAWSON, and R.W. PUTMAN. 1981. Thermal environment and tolerance of embryonic western gulls. Physiological Zoology 54:146-154.

BENT, A.C. 1919. Life histories of North American diving birds. U.S. Natl. Mus. Bull. 107.

———. 1921. Life histories of North American gulls and terns. U.S. Natl. Mus. Bull. 113.

———. 1922. Life histories of North American petrels and pelicans and their allies. U.S. Natl. Mus. Bull. 176.

———. 1927. Life histories of North American marsh birds. U.S. Natl. Mus. Bull. 135.

BIRKHEAD, T.R. 1978. Attendance patterns of Guillemots (*Uria aalge*) at breeding colonies on Skomer Island. Ibis 120:219-229.

BLACKLOCK, G.W., D.R. BLANKINSHIP, S.D. KENNEDY, K.A. KING, R.T. PAUL, R.D. SLACK, J.C. SMITH, and R.C. TELFAIR II, (compilers). 1978. Texas Colonial Waterbird Census, 1973-1976. Texas Park Wildl. Dept., FA Rep. 15.

BRUN, E. 1972. Establishment and population increase of the Gannet (*Sula bassana*) in Norway. Ornis Scand. 3:27-38.

BUCKLEY, F.G. and P.A. BUCKLEY. 1972. The breeding ecology of royal terns, *Sterna (Thalasseus) maxima maxima*. Ibis 114:344-359.

——— and ———. 1980. Habitat selection and marine birds. Pages 69-112 *in* Burger, J., B.L. Olla, and H.E. Winn, eds. Behavior of Marine Animals, Vol. 4. Plenum Publishing Co.

BUCKLEY, P.A. 1978. Guidelines for the protection and management of colonially nesting waterbirds. North Atlantic Regional Office, Natl. Park Serv., Boston, MA.

——— and F.G. BUCKLEY. 1977. Hexagonal packing of royal tern nests. Auk 94:36-43.

BURGER, J. 1976. Daily and seasonal activity patterns in breeding laughing gulls. Auk 93:308-323.

———. 1978. The pattern and mechanism of nesting in mixed-species heronries. Pages 45-58 *in* Sprunt, A.S., IV, J.C. Ogden, and S. Winckler, eds. Wading birds. Natl. Audubon Soc., Res. Rep. 7.

———. 1980. Behavioral responses of herring gulls (*Larus argentatus*) to aircraft noises. Environmental Pollu-

tion 24:177-184.

———. 1981. Effects of human disturbance on colonial species, particularly gulls. Colonial Waterbirds 4:28-36.

BYRD, G.V., R.H. DAY, and E.P. KNUDTSON. 1983. Patterns of colony attendance and censusing of auklets at Buldir Island, Alaska. Condor 85:274-280.

CLAPP, R.B., R.C. BANKS, D. MORGAN-JACOBS, and W.A. HOFFMAN. 1982a. Marine birds of the southeastern United States and Gulf of Mexico. Part I. Gaviiformes through Pelecaniformes. U.S. Dept. Inter., Fish Wildl. Serv., FWS/OBS-82/01.

———, ———, ———, and ———. 1982b. Marine birds of the southeastern United States and Gulf of Mexico. Part II. Anseriformes. U.S. Dept. Inter., Fish Wildl. Serv., Biol. Serv. Prog., FWS/OBS-82/02.

CONOVER, M.R. and D.O. CONOVER. 1981. A documented history of ring-billed gull and California gull colonies in the western United States. Colonial Waterbirds 4:37-43.

——— and D.E. MILLER. 1980. Daily activity patterns of breeding Ring-billed and California Gulls. J. Field Ornith. 51:329-339.

CUSTER, T.W. and R.G. OSBORN. 1978. Feeding habitat use by colonially breeding herons, egrets, and ibises in North Carolina. Auk 95:733-743.

DAWSON, W.R. and A.F. BENNETT. 1981. Field and laboratory studies of the thermal relations of hatching western gulls. Physiological Zoology 54:155-164.

DESGRANGES, J.L. 1979. Abandoned windmill used as a nesting site by great blue herons. Can. Field-Naturalist 93:439-440.

———. 1980. Competition entre le cormoran a aigrettes et Le Grand Heron au moment de la nidification. Naturaliste Can. 107:199-200.

——— and P. LA PORTE. 1979. Second tour of inspection of Quebec heronries, 1978. Can. Wildl. Serv., Prog. Notes 105.

——— and ———. 1981. Third tour of inspection of Quebec heronries, 1979. Can. Wildl. Serv., Prog. Notes 123.

———. and A. REED. 1981. Disturbance and control of selected colonies of double-crested cormorants in Quebec, Colonial Waterbirds 4:12-19.

———, ———, and G. CHAPELAINE. 1979. First tour of inspection of Quebec heronries, 1977. Can. Wildl. Serv., Prog. Notes 93.

DRENT, R.H. 1965. Breeding biology of the pigeon guillemot (*Cepphus columba*). Ardea 53:99-160.

———. 1967. Functional aspects of incubation in the herring gull (*Larus argentatus* Pont.). Behaviour Supplement 17:1-32.

——— and C.J. GUIGUET. 196l. A catalog of British Columbia seabird colonies. Occ. Papers British Columbia Provincial Mus. 12.

———, G.F. VAN TETS, F. TOMPA, and K. VERMEER. 1964. The breeding birds of Mandarte Island, British Columbia. Can. Field-Naturalist 78:208-263.

DUNNET, G.M. 1977. Observations on the effects of low flying aircraft at seabird colonies on the coast of Aberdeenshire, Scotland, Biol. Conserv. 12:55-63.

ELLISON, L.N. and L. CLEARY. 1978. Effects of human disturbance on breeding double-crested cormorants. Auk 95:510-517.

EMLEN, S.T. and N.J. DEMONG. 1975. Adaptive significance of synchronized breeding in a colonial bird: A new hypothesis. Science 188:1029-1031.

ENGLISH, S.M. 1978. Distribution and ecology of Great

Blue Heron colonies on the Willamette River, Oregon. Pages 235-244 *in* Sprunt, A.S., IV, J.C. Ogden, and S. Winckler, eds. Wading birds. Natl. Audubon Soc., Res. Rep. 7.

ERWIN, R.M. 1979. Coastal waterbird colonies: Cape Elizabeth, Maine, to Virginia. U.S. Dept. Inter. Fish Wildl. Serv., Biol. Serv. Prog., FWS/OBS-79/10.

————. 1980a. Censusing colonial waterbirds: Problems and progress. Atlantic Naturalist 33:19-22.

————. 1980b. Censusing waterbird colonies: Some sampling experiments. Trans. Linnaean Soc. New York 9:77-86.

————. 1981. Censusing wading bird colonies: An update on "flight-line" count method. Colonial Waterbirds 4:91-95.

————. 1982. Observer variability in estimating numbers: An experiment. J. Field Ornithol. 53:159-167.1

————, J. GALLI, and J. BURGER. 1981. Colony site dynamics and habitat use in Atlantic coast seabirds. Auk 98:550-561.

———— and C.E. KORSCHGEN. 1979. Coastal waterbird colonies: Maine to Virginia, 1977. U.S. Dept. Inter. Fish Wildl. Serv., Biol. Serv. Prog., FWS/OBS-79/08.

EVANS, R.M. 1982. Flock size and formation in black-billed gulls. Can. J. Zoology 60:1806-1811.

FERNS, P.N. and G.P. MUDGE. 1981. Accuracy of nest counts at a mixed colony of herring and lesser black-backed gulls. Bird Study 28:244-246.

GALUSHA, J.G., Jr. and C.J. AMLANER, Jr. 1978. The effects of diurnal and tidal periodicities in the numbers and activities of herring gulls (*Larus argentatus*) in a colony. Ibis 120:322-328.

GIBSON, J.A. 1950. Methods of determining breeding cliff populations of guillemots and razorbills. British Birds 43:329-331.

GILES, L.W. and D. B. MARSHALL. 1954. A large heron and egret colony on the Stillwater Wildlife Management Area, Nevada, Auk 71:322–325.

GILLET, W.H., J.L. HAYWARD, Jr., AND J.F. STOUT. 1975. Effects of human activity on egg and chick mortality in glaucous-winged gull colony. Condor 77:492-495.

GODFREY, W.E. 1966. The birds of Canada. Nat. Mus. Can., Bull. 203, Biol. Serv. 73.

HAND, J.L. 1980. Human disturbance in western gull (*Larus occidentalis livens*) colonies and possible amplification by intraspecific predation. Biol. Conserv. 18:59-63.

HARRIS, M.P. 1964. Aspects of the breeding biology of the gulls (*Larus argentatus, L. fuscus,* and *L. marinus*). Ibis 106:432-456.

HENNY, C.J. and J.E. KURTZ. 1978. Great blue herons respond to nesting habitat loss. Wildl. Soc. Bull. 6:35-37.

HERMAN, S.G. 1980. The naturalist's field journal: A manual of instruction based on a system established by Joseph Grinnell. Published privately, S.G. Herman, Biol. Dep., The Evergreen State College, Olympia, WA. 200pp.

HUNT, G.L., Jr. 1972. Influence of food distribution and human disturbance on the reproductive success of herring gulls. Ecol. 53:1051-1061.

———— and M.W. HUNT. 1975. Reproductive ecology of the western gull: The importance of nest spacing. Auk 92:270-279.

———— and ————. 1976. Gull chick survival. The significance of growth rates, timing of breeding and territory size. Ecol. 57:62-75.

JEHL, J.R., Jr. 1973. Studies of a declining population of

brown pelicans in northwest Baja, California. Condor 75:69-79.

JOHNSON, R.A. 1938. Predation of gulls in murre colonies. Wilson Bull. 50:161-170.

KADLEC, J.A. and W.H. DRURY. 1968a. Structure of the New England herring gull population. Ecol. 49:644-676.

———— and ————. 1968b. Aerial estimation of the size of gull breeding colonies. J. Wildl. Manage. 32:287-293.

KORSCHGEN, C.E. 1979. Coastal waterbird colonies: Maine. U.S. Dept. Inter., Fish Wildl. Serv., Biol. Serv. Prog., FWS/OBS-70/07.

KREBS, J.R. 1974. Colonial nesting and social feeding as strategies for exploiting food resources in the great blue heron (*Ardea herodias*). Behaviour 51:99-134.

————. 1978. Colonial nesting in birds, with special reference to the Ciconiformes. Pages 299-311 *in* Sprunt, A.S., IV, J.C. Ogden, and S. Winckler, eds. Wading Birds. Natl. Audubon Soc., Res. Rep. 7.

KURY, C.R. and M. GOCHFELD. 1975. Human interference and gull predation in cormorant colonies. Biol. Conserv. 8:23-24.

KUSHLAN, J.A. 1978. Feeding ecology of wading birds. Pages 249-297 *in* Sprunt, A.S., IV, J.C. Ogden, and S. Winckler, eds. Wading Birds. Natl. Audubon Soc., Res. Rep. 7.

————. 1979. Effects of helicopter censuses on wading bird colonies. J. Wildl. Manage. 43:756-760.

LLOYD, C.S. 1972. Attendance at auk colonies during the breeding season. Skokholm Bird Observation Rep. 1972:15-23.

LOWE, F.A. 1954. The heron. Collins, St. James Place, London.

MANUWAL, D.A. 1974a. Effects of territoriality on breeding in a population of Cassin's Auklet. Condor 55:1399-1406.

————. 1974b. The natural history of Cassin's auklet (*Ptychoramphus aleuticus*). Condor 76:421-431.

————. 1978. Effect of man on marine birds: a review. Proc. J.S. Wright Forestry Conf. 4:140-160.

MASSEY, B.W. and J.L. ATWOOD. 1981. Second-wave nesting of the California least tern: Age composition and reproductive success. Auk 98:596-605.

MCCRIMMON, D.A. 1976. A review of some methods and considerations for the assessment of breeding populations of colonial waterbirds. Proc. 4th Ann. Meeting, Texas Fish-Eating Bird Conf. 1976:36-49.

MCCRIMMON, D.A., Jr. 1978a. Nest-site characteristics among five species of herons on the North Carolina coast. Auk 95:267-280.

————. 1978b. The collection, management, and exchange of information on colonially nesting birds. Pages 187-196 *in* Sprunt, A.S., IV. J.C. Ogden, and S. Winckler, eds. Wading Birds, Natl. Audubon Soc., Res. Rep. 7.

MEYERRIECKS, A.J. 1960. Comparative breeding behavior of four species of North American herons. Publ. Nuttal Ornith. Club 2.

NESBITT, S.A., J.C. OGDEN, H.W. KALE, II, B.W. PATTY, and L.A. ROWSE. 1982. Florida atlas of breeding sites for herons and their allies: 1976-78. U.S. Dept. Inter., Fish Wildl. Serv., Biol. Serv. Prog., FWS/OBS-81/49.

NETTLESHIP, D.N. 1975. A recent decline of gannets, *Morus bassanus,* on Bonaventure Island, Quebec. Can. Field-Naturalist 89:125-133.

————. 1976. Census techniques for seabirds of arctic and eastern Canada. Can. Wildl. Serv., Occ. Pap. 25.

————. 1980. Census methods for murres, *Uria* species: A unified approach. Can. Wild. Serv., Occ. Pap. 43.

NISBET, I.C.T. 1973. Terns in Massachusetts: Present numbers and historical changes. Bird-Banding 44:27-55.

OGDEN, J.C. 1978. Recent population trends of colonial wading birds on the Atlantic and Gulf coastal plains. Pages 137-153 in Sprunt, A.S., IV, J.C. Ogden, and S. Winckler, eds. Wading Birds. Natl. Audubon Soc., Res. Rep. 7.

PALMER, R.S. (ed.). 1962. Handbook of North American birds. Vol. 1. Loons through flamingos. Yale Univ. Press., New Haven, CT. 567pp.

PARSON, J. 1971. Cannibalism in herring gulls. British Birds 64:528-537.

PATTERSON, I.J. 1965. Timing and spacing of broods in the black-headed gull, *Larus ridibundus*. Ibis 107:433-459.

PENLAND, S. 1981. Natural history of the Caspian tern in Grays Harbor, Washington. Murrelet 62:66-72.

———. 1982. Distribution and status of the Caspian tern in Washington State. Murrelet 63:73-79.

PORTNOY, J.W. 1977. Nesting colonies of seabirds and wading birds— coastal Louisiana, Mississippi, and Alabama. U.S. Dept. Inter., Fish Wildl. Serv., Biol. Serv. Prog., FWS/OBS-77/07.

———. 1980. Censusing methods for gulf coast waterbirds. Trans. Linnean Soc. New York 9:127-134.

———, R.M. ERWIN, and T.W. CUSTER. 1981. Atlas of gull and tern colonies: North Carolina to Key West, Florida (including pelicans, cormorants, and skimmers). U.S. Dept. Inter., Fish Wildl. Serv., Biol. Serv. Prog., FWS/OBS-80/05.

PRATT, H.M. 1970. Breeding biology of great blue herons and common egrets in central California. Condor 72:407-416.

———. 1972. Nesting success of common egrets and great blue herons in the San Francisco Bay region. Condor 74:447-453.

———. 1973. Breeding attempts by juvenile great blue herons. Auk 90:897-899.

———. 1974. Breeding of great blue herons and great egrets at Audubon Canyon Ranch, California. Western Birds 5:127-136.

———. 1980. Directions and timing of great blue heron foraging flights from a California colony: Implications for social facilitation of food finding. Wilson Bull. 92:489-496.

RALPH, C.J. 1981. Terminology used in estimating numbers of birds. Studies Avian Biol. 6:577-578.

ROBERT, H.C. and C.J. RALPH. 1975. Effects of human disturbance on the breeding success of gulls. Condor 77:495-499.

RODGERS, J.A., Jr. 1978. Display characteristics and frequency of breeding by subadult Little Blue Herons. Pages 35-39 in Sprunt, A.S., IV, J.C. Ogden, and S. Winckler, eds. Wading Birds. Natl. Audubon Soc., Res. Rep. 7.

RYDER, R.A. 1978. Breeding distribution, movements, and mortality of snowy egrets in North America. Pages 197-205 in Sprunt, A.S., IV, J.C. Ogden, and S. Winckler, eds. Wading Birds. Natl. Audubon Soc., Res. Rep. 7.

SCHREIBER, R.W. 1979. Reproductive performance of the eastern brown pelican. Contr. Sci., Natl. Hist. Mus. Los Angeles Co. CA.317:1-43.

——— and E.A. SCHREIBER. 1972. Studies of the brown pelican. Wilson Bull. 84:119-135.

SEALY, S.G. and J. BEDARD. 1973. Breeding biology of the parakeet auklet (*Cyclorrhynchus psittacula*) on St. Lawrence Island, Alaska. Astarte 6:59-68.

SIDLE, J.G. and E.L. FERGUSON. 1982. White pelicans populations at Chase Lake, North Dakota, evaluated by aerial photography. Prairie Naturalist 14:13-26.

SLATER, J.B. 1980. Factors affecting the numbers of guillemots *Uria aalge* present on cliffs. Ornis Scand. 11:155-163.

SOUTHERN, W.F. and L.K. SOUTHERN. 1981. Colony census results as indicators of pre-hatching perturbations. Colonial Waterbirds 4:143-149.

SOWLS, A.L., A.R. DE GANGE, J.W. NELSON, and G.S. LESTER. 1980. Catalog of California seabird colonies. U.S. Dept. Inter., Fish Wildl. Serv., Biol. Serv. Prog., FWS/OBS-80/37.

———, S.M. HATCH, and C.J. LENSINK. 1978. Catalog of Alaskan seabird colonies. U.S. Dept. Inter., Fish Wildl. Serv., Biol. Serv. Prog., FWS/OBS-78/78.

SPEICH, S.M. and D.A. MANUWAL. 1974. Gular pouch development and population structure of Cassin's auklet. Auk 91:291-306.

——— and T.R. WAHL. 1985. Catalog of Washington seabird colonies. U.S. Dept. Inter., Fish Wildl. Serv., Biol. Serv. Prog., FWS/OBS. In press.

STOWE, J.J. 1982. Recent population trends in cliff-breeding seabirds in Britain and Ireland. Ibis 124:502-510.

THOMPSON, B.C. and J.E. TABOR. 1981. Nesting populations and breeding chronologies of gulls, terns, and herons on the upper Columbia River, Oregon and Washington. Northwest Sci. 55:209-218.

THOMPSON, L.S. 1981. Nest-tree sharing by herons and cormorants in Montana. Can. Field-Naturalist 95:257-260.

———. 1982. A 1979 census of Great Blue Heron colonies in Montana. Proc. Montana Acad. Sci. 41:23-27.

THOMPSON, S.P., C.D. LITTLEFIELD, and R.A. RYDER. 1979. Historical review and status of colonial nesting birds on Malheur National Wildlife Refuge, Oregon. Proc. Colonial Waterbird Group 3:156-164.

THORESEN, A.C. 1964. The breeding behavior of the Cassin's auklet. Condor 66:456-476.

TREMBLAY, J. and L.N. ELLISON. 1979. Effects of human disturbance on breeding of black-crowned night herons. Auk 96:364-369.

TUCK, L.K. 1961. The murres. Can. Wildl. Serv. Monogr. 1.

UDVARDY, M.D.F. 1969. Dynamic zoogeography: with special reference to land animals. Van Nostrand Rheinhold Co., New York. 445pp

VAN TETS, G.F. 1965. A comparative study of some social communication patterns in the Pelecaniformes. Am. Ornith. Union, Ornith. Monogr. 2.

VERBEEK, N.A.M. 1982. Egg predation by northwest crows: Its association with human and bald eagle activity. Auk 99:347-352.

VERMEER, K. 1963. The breeding ecology of the glaucous-winged gull (*Larus occidentalis*) on Mandarte Island, B.C. British Columbia Province Mus., Occ. Pap. 13.

WEISE, J.H. 1978. Heron nest-site selection and its ecological effects. Pages 27-34 in Sprunt, A.S., IV, J.C. Ogden, and S. Winckler, eds. Wading Birds. Natl. Audubon Soc., Res. Rep. 7.

WERSCHKUL, D.F., E. MC MAHON, and M. LEITSCHUH. 1976. Some effects of human activities on the great blue heron in Oregon. Wilson Bull. 88:660-662.

———, ———, ———, S. ENGLISH, C. SKIBINSKI, and G. WILLIAMSON. 1977. Observations on the reproductive ecology of the great blue heron (*Ardea herodias*) in western Oregon. Murrelet 58:7-12.

20

Upland Game Birds

Robert L. Eng

Biology Department
Montana State University
Bozeman, MT 59717-0001

Editor's Note: Upland game birds, like other economically important species, have received much attention. And even though most of these species are avidly hunted, in most cases habitat quantity and quality is the factor controlling abundance and distribution. Although much research has been conducted on upland game bird habitat, much of this has focused on species associated with agriculture such as pheasants, rather than on wildland species. For example, the effects of logging, grazing, and recreation on species of grouse are poorly understood. Therefore enlightened management of habitat for these species will require better identification of limiting habitat factors, together with careful inventory and monitoring of habitats and populations.

INTRODUCTION

Usually a reference to upland game birds is an exclusive reference to members of the family Phasianidae: non-migratory, chicken-like birds including the partridge, grouse, turkey, and quail. Recently, increasing mention may be found to migratory upland game birds in reference to members of the family Columbidae, the pigeons and doves.

Emphasis here will be placed on members of the family Phasianidae, primarily because their non-migratory status requires a more labor-intensive inventory and assessment of year-long habitat needs. Also, within this group, emphasis will be placed on those members in the western U.S. that inhabit non-cultivated lands, at least for a major portion of the year.

Although life histories or the biology of each species will not be dealt with here, some basic knowledge of a species' life history is necessary before sound management decisions can be made.

This does not imply the need for an in-depth study of each species. Rather, many species have certain habits similar enough to permit the use of common denominators in monitoring the birds or their habitat. For example, most quail and partridge feed heavily on seeds from a variety of annuals that may show wide year-to-year fluctuations and are often products of an early seral stage. These birds have evolved with a very high reproductive potential, including a high rate of first-year breeding and large clutch sizes, and thus can quickly respond to a bountiful food supply. Conversely, blue grouse (*Dendragapus obscurus*) and sage grouse (*Centrocercus urophasianus*) feed during the winter on the vegetative parts of a few species of dominant plants, a food supply that is produced in a climax or near climax stage, and shows comparatively little annual variation in abundance. These birds have a relatively low reproductive potential with respect to age of consistent first breeding and clutch size; this appears to be in keeping with their more stable food supply. The contrasts in the two facets of life history of these two groups would result in equally contrasting habitats and habitat management concerns.

That there is a close relationship between the quality of a bird's habitat and its welfare (and resulting population status) requires little explanation. The difficulty arises in quantifying the quality of a habitat which for a given species may be found in a continuum from marginal to excellent. Available in the literature are qualitative descriptions of game bird habitats listing food and cover components which may be preferred or required by the species in question. When measurements are taken of the amount and distribution of these components within a unit area, the description assumes a quantitative air. Finally, with the assistance of a series of assumptions, numbers are assigned to the descriptions and measurements, and a numerical rating is assigned placing that particular piece of habitat at a fixed point along the continuum. However, the quality of the overall habitat, which may rate high as a composite, may in reality rate rather low as a result of poor quality of one facet. For example, two areas, one a homogeneous stand of smooth brome and the other 85% smooth brome and 15% forbs, may both be recorded as ungrazed, unmowed pastures of smooth brome. However, the field with a sprinkling of forbs would provide better cover and a greater diversity of insects, making it a superior habitat for brood rearing.

The above is not intended to entirely discredit efforts at measuring the quality of game bird habitats. Certainly, the available descriptions provide land managers with the capability to recognize the general habitat type in which they could expect to find the various species. They could also, with some experience, place an assessment of quality within a broad scale. However, a more realistic measure of the quality can be attained through a measure of the bird's response to its habitat, the home range size, or the population density.

The average size of a home range, whether seasonal or annual, when compared between habitats, will reflect the quality of a given habitat. Birds in high quality, secure habitat tend to have smaller home ranges than those in habitats of lesser quality. Unfortunately, home range determination is time and budget consuming, usually involving trapping, marking, and relocating individual birds.

Census techniques, whereby relative densities can be determined, present a far more workable solution. Most techniques permit only an index to the population; but if conducted by standardized methods, data between areas or time periods provide workable comparisons. For the land managers interested in habitat quality, population density comparisons between areas provide a measure of the various areas to support birds of that species. Similarly, comparable data gathered from a single area over a period of several years may provide a measure of the population trend which in turn could reflect changes in habitat quality.

HABITAT FEATURES CORRELATED WITH SPECIES GROUPS

Major habitat characteristics of the various species are presented in summary form with selected references in Table 1. Supplemental statements to assist in habitat identification are presented in the text.

Gray Partridge (*Perdix perdix*)

The European gray or Hungarian partridge is one of three exotic game birds successfully introduced into the U.S. The others are the ring-necked pheasant (*Phasianus colchicus*) and the chukar (*Alectoris chukar*). The "hun" is native to Europe and Asia although North American stock appears to have originated largely in central Europe.

Although present in a rather wide variety of topographic conditions, the more dense populations of gray partridges are generally associated with flat or moderately rolling land. Stiehl (1984) referred to three geographic populations in North America: western, central, and the Great Lakes.

Gray partridge are frequently associated with a combination of cultivated and non-cultivated lands. Weigand (1980) reported land uses from his study area, in decreasing order of abundance, as small grain and fallow land, rangeland, hayfields, and agriculturally idle areas. Small grain fields and fallow lands were used heavily for feeding (both seeds and green vegetation) during a large part of the year whereas the other types provided an herbaceous cover primarily for loafing, roosting, and nesting. Their affinity for edges probably accounts for their great ability to successfully cope with modern agriculture (Allen 1984).

Weigand (1980) found wheat and barley seeds and leaves a major food component throughout the year; seeds and leaves of such forbs as dandelion (*Taraxacum officinale*), knotweeds (*Polygonum* sp.), mustard (*Brassica kaber*), and white clover (*Trifolium repens*) were prominent at various seasons. He also reported that of 10 nests located, 5 were concealed by grass, the others by forbs.

Table 1. Synopsis of habitat features for species or species groups.

Species or Species Group	Habitat Characteristics (Physical features, vegetation, and species composition)	References
Gray partridge (Perdix perdix)	Agricultural lands, primarily small grains, interspersed with idle areas. Croplands provide major food source and idle areas provide loafing, roosting, and nesting cover. Nesting cover often in grassland/shrub areas—successful nesting efforts dependent on residual cover from the previous year. Seeds from cultivated grains and a variety of forbs and other green succulent vegetation provide primary food.	Johnsgard 1973; Weigand 1980; Smith et al. 1982; Mendel and Peterson 1983; Potts 1984; Stiehl 1984.
Chukar (Alectoris chukar)	Rugged, rocky terrain in arid to semi-arid climates, about equally divided between rocky outcrops and low shrub/grassland. Low winter temperatures are less devastating than persistent snow cover. Water availability may significantly affect summer distribution. Rocky outcrops may provide loafing and roosting cover. Nesting cover similar to shrub/grassland types used for foraging, often on a south facing slope up from creek bottoms. Sagebrush (Artemisia sp.), cheatgrass (Bromus tectorum), and wheatgrass (Agropyron sp.) are common species with cheatgrass seeds and leaves providing a major food source.	Galbreath and Moreland 1953; Bohl 1957; Harper et al. 1958; Christensen 1970; Molini 1976.
Ring-necked pheasant (Phasianus colchicus)	Agricultural land highly interspersed with non-cultivated land (i.e., dense clumps of grasses, forbs, and shrubs). Non-cultivated areas (preferably idle areas such as roadsides, railroad rights-of-way, and temporary wetlands) are necessary for nesting, roosting, and loafing cover, particularly during winter and early spring when crops are removed. Farm crops, primarily waste cereal grains, may account for over 75% of the food with weed seeds associated with cultivation making up another 10-15%.	Hiatt 1947; Yeager et al. 1951; Snyder 1974; Weigand and Janson 1976.
Spruce grouse (Dendragapus canadensis)	Coniferous forests of Canada and northern U.S. A trend toward increased use of upland over lowland areas from eastern to western distribution. Preference shown for coniferous stands that are neither mature nor extremely dense, thus permitting adequate understory for food and cover. Spruce (Picea sp.) and jackpine (Pinus banksiana) in Michigan or lodgepole pine (Pinus contorta) in the mountain west are key to the species. A variety of berries (Vaccinium sp., Symphoricarpus sp., Rubus sp.) are important summer foods whereas coniferous needles (Picea, Pinus, Larix) dominate the winter diet.	Stoneberg 1967; Pendergast and Boag 1970; Robinson 1980; Ratti et al. 1984.
Blue grouse (Dendragapus obscurus)	Coniferous forests of western and coastal mountain ranges. Winter at high elevations in stands of conifers; in spring, found at lower elevations at forest-grassland ecotone, while females with broods may follow brushy draws 2 to 3 miles (3 to 5 km) below conifers. Prefer open, dry sites but near clumps of conifers for escape cover. Structural height of vegetation at least 8 inches (20 cm) preferred in brood rearing areas. Douglas fir (Pseudotsuga menziesii) a key cover and food plant (winter). Berries (Vaccinium sp., Symphoricarpos sp.) and leafy forage (Trifolium sp., Fragaria sp.) are heavily used at other times of the year.	Mussehl 1963; Bendell and Elliott 1966; Martinka 1972.
Ptarmigan Willow (Lagopus lagopus) Rock (Lagopus mutus) White-tailed (Lagopus leucurus)	Willow ptarmigan inhabit open tundra and show a preference for areas with level to moderate terrain, heavily vegetated with grasses, forbs, and shrubs. Rock ptarmigan frequent the open tundra but on more hilly terrain and with less luxuriant vegetation than utilized by the willow ptarmigan. White-tailed ptarmigan occupy alpine tundra, ridges, and steep slopes where vegetation is sparse and dwarfed; rocks provide the structural cover. Willow (Salix sp.) is a regular shrub for all three species, the buds and twigs being dominant food for a large part of the year. Also used are a variety of leaves, flowers, and berries as they become available during a relatively short growing season.	Choate 1963; Weeden 1963, 1965, 1967; Johnsgard 1973.

Table 1. Synopsis of habitat features for species or species groups (continued).

Species or Species Group	Habitat Characteristics (Physical features, vegetation, and species composition)	References
Ruffed grouse (*Bonasa umbellus*)	Deciduous forests or mixed deciduous/coniferous forest edges. In the Mountain West, this species is more prevalent along stream courses or other moist areas. Drumming males prefer areas of high vegetative density (overhead cover important) whereas broods prefer more open stands but with high degrees of herbaceous cover. Aspen (*Populus tremuloides* or *P. grandidentata*) key species in preferred stands. A preference shown for early seral stages of aspen although an interspersion of different age classes desirable for yearlong food source (i.e., aspen buds from mature stands, berries, fruits, and leafy forage from younger stands).	Svoboda and Gullion 1972; Gullion 1977, 1984; Stauffer and Peterson 1985, 1985b; Kubisiak 1985.
Sage grouse (*Centrocercus urophasianus*)	Semi-arid sagebrush or sagebrush/grassland types of the western plains and intermountain basins at elevations from 750 m (2,500 ft) to 2,100 m (7,000 ft). Preference for gentle topography over steep-sided canyons or slopes. Sagebrush is essential to survival with stands of greatest canopy coverage (20-35%) preferred in winter and least (5-10%) in summer. Food is reflected in this seasonal cover preference: sagebrush in winter, a variety of succulent forbs in spring and summer.	Patterson 1952; Eng and Schladweiler 1972; Wallestad 1975; Wallestad et al. 1975.
Greater prairie chicken (*Tympanuchus cupido*)	Arid native grasslands of the Southwest intermixed with shrub or half-shrub component. A portion (5-40%) of an area in cultivation, if well interspersed, may enhance the habitat through increased food source. Shrubs, less than 1 m (3 ft) tall in savannah aspect, are desirable although shrub species may determine preferred shrub density; high densities of sand sagebrush (*Artemisia filifolia*) appear more desirable than high densities of shinnery oak (*Quercus havardii*).	Jones 1963; Crawford and Bolen 1976; Davis et al. 1980; Cannon and Knopf 1981a; Doerr and Guthery 1983.
Sharp-tailed grouse (*Tympanuchus phasianellus*)	Grasslands that have a prominent deciduous shrub or woodland component. Although both western races (*T. p. columbianus* and *jamesi*) inhabit a grassland/shrub/tree complex, the Columbian sharptail is usually found in habitat with a higher overall shrub/tree cover. Columbian sharptails are associated with a variety of shrubs and trees (sagebrush, hawthorne [*Crataegus* sp.], serviceberry [*Amelanchier* sp.], Gambel oak [*Quercus gambellii*], and aspen) which may be used for cover and produce food in the form of berries or winter buds. A similar group of plants exists for the prairie race (juniper [*Juniperus* sp.], buffaloberry [*Shepherdia* sp.]), cottonwood, and aspen.	Miller and Graul 1980; Nielson and Yde 1981.
Wild turkey (*Meleagris gallopavo*)	Open, mature, or nearly mature forests, deciduous but often deciduous-coniferous, particularly in mountainous areas. Mature forests provide a more dependable mast crop and permit greater visibility. Merriam's turkey shows a preference during spring, summer, and fall for ponderosa (*Pinus ponderosa*) forests with an open grassland understory; in winter it often frequents a lower elevation in a mast producing habitat or in the north, grain fields. The Rio Grande race, found in more arid areas to the south, often occupies river bottom habitat, but also oak-grassland interspersions. Scattered openings in forest habitat (10-40% of the total) are highly desirable. Mast producers such as oak (*Quercus* sp.), pinyon pine (*Pinus edulis*), and juniper and seeds and leaves from a variety of grasses are major food sources.	Ligon 1946; Spicer 1959; Hoffman 1962; Jonas 1966; Beasom 1970.
Mearn's quail (*Cyrtonyx montezuma mearnsi*)	Oak-grasslands and pine-oak woodlands ranging from 1,100 to 3,600 m (4,000 to 12,000 ft) in the highlands of the Southwest. Preference is shown for open woodlands with a grass-forb understory. Grass is used commonly for cover; the bulbs and seeds of woodsorrel (*Oxalis*) and flat sedges (*Cyperus*) are prominent foods. During years of scarcity of forbs and sedges, acorns may be a common food.	Leopold and McCabe 1957; Ligon 1961; Bishop and Hungerford 1965; Brown 1979; Brown 1982.

Table 1. Synopsis of habitat features for species or species groups (concluded).

Species or Species Group	Habitat Characteristics (Physical features, vegetation, and species composition)	References
Masked bobwhite (*Colinus virginianus ridgwayi*)	Open desert grasslands at elevations from 300 to 1,200 m (1,000 to 4,000 ft). Although mesquite (*Prosopis* sp.) and catclaw (*Acacia* sp.) are frequently found in the area, this bird seemingly prefers the grassy areas adjacent to shrubs. Coarse grasses (*Sporobolus* sp.) provide cover whereas species of grama (*Bouteloua* sp.) and three-awns (*Aristida* sp.) provide both food and cover.	Tomlinson 1972a, b; Johnsgard 1973.
Scaled quail (*Callipepla squamata*)	Desert grassland, usually below 2,100 m (6,900 ft), composed of low growing grasses, forbs, and shrubs with an overall ground cover between 10 and 50%. Shrubs used for overhead cover with preference shown for those less than 2 m (7 ft). As little as 10% of an area left in clumps of mesquite will provide cover and food (seeds). Major vegetative foods consist of conspicuous forb and shrub seeds such as croton (*Croton* sp.), cycloloma (*Cycloloma atriplicifolium*), snakeweed (*Gutierrezia sarothrae*) and mesquite.	Campbell et al. 1973; Davis et al. 1975; Goodwin and Hungerford 1977; Ault and Stormer 1983.
Gambel's quail (*Callipepla gambelii*)	Desert shrub type usually in habitats below 1,800 m (6,000 ft). Preference is shown for shrub cover of sufficient density to shade 50 to 75% of the ground and where 60 to 80% of the shrubs are taller than 2 m. Mesquite, hackberry (*Celtis reticulata*), wolfberry (*Lycium* sp.), and catclaw provide cover for most of the bird's activities. Many preferred broods are derived from members of the Leguminosae, i.e., mesquite, catclaw, mimosa (*Mimosa* sp.), deervetch (*Lotus* sp.), paloverde (*Cercidium* sp.), and lupine (*Lupinus* sp.)	Gullion 1960; Hungerford 1962; Goodwin and Hungerford 1977.
California quail (*Callipepla californica*)	May occur in desert, rangeland, and dry and irrigated farmland at elevations from sea level to 2,600 m (8,500 ft). Rangeland with the following components are most widely used: clumps of woody vegetation for roosting, shrubs or herbaceous growth for escape cover, and herbaceous cover for nesting. Food habit studies repeatedly show importance of legumes (esp. seeds). Some important legumes include the following: bur clover (*Medicago* sp.), lupines, deervetches, clover (*Trifolium* sp.), and vetches (*Vicia* sp.). Filaree (*Erodium* sp.) leaves and seeds occur frequently in the diet.	Emlen and Glading 1945; Edminster 1954; Shields and Duncan 1966; Johnsgard 1973; Gutierrez 1980.
Band-tailed pigeon Coastal race (*Columba fasciata monilis*) Interior race (*C. f. fasciata*)	The coastal race, although primarily an inhabitant of mountain habitat, can be found from sea level to 4,200 m (13,850 ft). The race may occupy a variety of habitats, but the preferred type consists of large conifers and deciduous trees interspersed with berry and mast producing trees and shrubs. The interior race also shows preference for mountainous areas supporting a mixed conifer-deciduous type and achieves greatest densities in this type at elevations between 1,675 m (5,500 ft) and 2,575 m (8,500 ft). Both races feed heavily on mast produced by species of pine and oak as well as a variety of berries produced by such shrubs as elderberries (*Sambucus* sp.), wild cherries (*Prunus* sp.), huckleberries, and dogwood (*Cornus* sp.). During certain years, both races will move to lower elevations and feed on cultivated grain.	Braun et al. 1975; Jeffrey 1977; Tomlinson 1983.
Mourning dove (*Zenaida macroura*)	The wide breeding distribution of this species almost precludes describing habitat features with precision. It is primarily an inhabitant of woodland-grassland edge. Thus, both clearing of large areas of forest in the East and planting of shelterbelts in the Plains States enhanced mourning dove habitat. Although tree nesting is most common, in the absence of trees or shrubs, the nests are readily placed on the ground. Food supplies for doves have been improved by species that produce more seeds than native grasses.	Keeler 1977; Dunks et al. 1982.

Chukar (*Alectoris chukar*)

The chukar has been widely introduced into the U.S., but was successfully established only in arid areas of the West. Seven species of this genus have been recognized, all of which are native to parts of Europe or Asia. It is believed that the only species that have been successful in the U.S. were those originating in India (Christensen 1970).

Chukars characteristically inhabit very rugged, rocky terrain in arid to semiarid climates. They have been found from sea level to 4,800 m (16,000 ft) in their native Asian habitat and to 3,600 m (12,000 ft) in North America. The Great Basin habitat of the West with its combination of mountain range-valley (basin) floor provides excellent conditions for this exotic species (Christensen 1970).

Chukars frequently use the rugged topography for cover, although they are also found in a shrub-grassland type. The understory may consist of an abundant grass-forb combination of the desert. Sagebrush (*Artemisia tridentata*) is the dominant shrub in chukar habitat in Nevada (Christensen 1970) and probably over most of its range in the U.S. Other structurally similar shrubs such as greasewood (*Sarcobatus* sp.), rabbitbrush (*Chrysothamnus* sp.), and bitterbrush (*Purshia tridentata*) may be found instead of sagebrush in different parts of this bird's U.S. distribution. A food source is largely derived from an understory of grasses and forbs although grasses frequently provide the major portion. Christensen (1970) reported heavy use of seeds and leaves of cheatgrass (*Bromus tectorum*) and believed that the introduction of this exotic grass into the western U.S. may have greatly influenced the later success of the chukar introduction.

Ring-necked Pheasant (*Phasianus colchicus*)

Ring-necked pheasants consist of a group of subspecies from Asia that were successfully introduced into the U.S. in the 1880s. The habitats of this group of birds in Asia were similar to those found in the midwestern and western U.S., and the birds became established in many of these areas as a very popular upland game bird.

The pheasant is closely allied with agricultural lands. In the West, areas placed under irrigation initially created islands of excellent pheasant habitat, where as little as 5% of the area in permanent, well interspersed cover provided adequate nesting, brood rearing, and winter cover (Yeager et al. 1951). As agriculture became more intensive, land use changes (largely the removal of permanent cover) reduced the potential for producing pheasants (Baxter and Wolfe 1972; Snyder 1974; Taylor et al. 1978). Thus,

within and adjacent to agricultural lands, the preservation of grass/forb/shrub cover is frequently the key to maintaining a healthy pheasant population.

Although the pheasant is primarily associated with agricultural lands, a few populations exist in the western U.S. completely removed from cultivation. In such areas, usually a drainage supporting some woody cover, the birds substitute weed seeds and fruits from shrubs such as buffaloberry (*Shepherdia* sp.), rose (*Rosa* sp.), and snowberry (*Symphoricarpos* sp.) for the cultivated grains that usually make up a large part of the diet. In such areas, pheasant densities are much lower than in comparable cover adjacent to agriculture, but the existence of even the low numbers is highly dependent upon the shrubby (protective) cover.

Leonard Lee Rue III

Ring-necked pheasant.

Spruce Grouse (*Dendragapus canadansis*)

The western representative of this small timber grouse, for many years considered a separate species, is presently regarded as a race—the Franklin's spruce grouse. Among the many local names applied to this bird, the most common is undoubtedly the fool hen, a direct result of its lack of fear of man.

Spruce grouse are distributed across the whole of Canada and portions of the northern U.S., closely coinciding with the distribution of the coniferous forest. Robinson (1980), in reviewing literature on habitat for this bird, suggested a trend toward increased use of upland over lowland areas in its distribution from east to west. The most dense forests are seemingly avoided because they do not provide an adequate ground cover and openings large enough for territorial display flights (Stoneberg 1967; Robinson 1980).

Although early descriptions of spruce grouse habitat emphasize the mature coniferous forest with species of spruce being the primary ingredient, more recent studies have shown that habitat often consists of mixed stands of spruces (*Picea* sp.) and jack pine (*Pinus banksiana*) in Michigan (Robinson 1980) and spruces and lodgepole pine (*Pinus contorta*) in western States (Stoneberg 1967; Ratti et al. 1984).

Spruce grouse.

Blue Grouse (*Dendragapus obscurus*)

The blue grouse is the largest of the North American forest grouse, the males commonly weighing 1,200-1,250 g (2.6-2.7 lb) or about twice the weight of spruce or ruffed grouse. The subspecies (*D. fuliquinosus*) inhabiting the coastal mountain ranges is often referred to as the sooty grouse whereas the one in the Rocky Mountain States is often called the dusky grouse.

Blue grouse often participate in a seasonal, altitudinal migration. In winter, they are most frequently found at high elevations in dense stands of coniferous forest. In spring, a downward migration occurs into a forest-grassland ecotone where males establish territories. Females may brood in open meadows at this elevation, or in some parts of their range, will follow small brushy draws out into prairie foothill types. In Montana and Colorado, sharp-tailed grouse (*Tympanuchus phasianellus*), sage grouse, and blue grouse have been observed on common brood-rearing ranges in late summer and early fall (pers. obs.).

Although an inhabitant of forested, mountain areas, blue grouse appear to prefer meadows and grassland adjacent to woody cover (Bendell and Elliott 1966). Breeding habitat is frequently an open, dry site with scattered shrubs but near dense clumps of trees for escape cover (Martinka 1972). Brood

rearing often occurs in meadows or an open stand of timber with a good ground cover of grass and forbs. Mussehl (1963) listed the following basic physical requirements of blue grouse brood range: a relatively high degree of canopy coverage, an effective height of ground cover of about 20 cm (8 in.), which is an important consideration in areas grazed by domestic livestock, diversity of plant life forms, and small amounts of bare ground. Winter habitat, which usually includes a more dense canopy of conifers for a food source, is nonetheless often in a parkland type or along open ridges.

In overall distribution, blue grouse seem closely associated with Douglas fir (*Pseudotsuga menziesii*). Needles from this species are an important winter food source although others (*Larix* sp., *Pinus* sp., and *Abies* sp.) have been reported as common in the winter diet.

Blue grouse.

In breeding and brood rearing habitat, life form is probably as critical as species composition. Martinka (1972) pointed out the importance of Douglas fir thickets as escape cover for males displaying in open logged-over stands of ponderosa pine (*Pinus ponderosa*). Mussehl (1963), in discussing brood habitat, described the bunchgrass-balsamroot openings at the edge of coniferous stands in one study area and in another, a similar grass-forb association in an open stand of mature ponderosa pine. In years when balsamroot was not abundant, broods were found in association with snowberry or large sedges (*Carex* sp.). In late summer, before moving to higher elevations and a conifer diet, blue grouse in the Rocky Mountains feed heavily on berries such as currants (*Ribes* sp.), juneberries (*Amelanchier* sp.), bearberry (*Arctostaphylos* sp.), and huckleberry (*Vaccinium* sp.) (Beer 1943).

Willow Ptarmigan (*Lagopus lagopus*)
Rock Ptarmigan (*L. mutus*)
White-tailed Ptarmigan (*L. leucurus*)

Although considerable overlap exists in the North American geographical distribution of these three species, particularly so with willow and rock ptarmigan, differences in seasonal habitat selection assist in maintaining them as separate species. Because willow (*Salix* sp.) is a shrub group commonly used by all three species, the major difference in habitat characteristics is structural. From willow to rock to white-tailed ptarmigan, the trend is toward shorter and less dense vegetation and increased topographic relief. Thus during the spring and summer, the willow ptarmigan shows a preference for level ground or gentle to moderate slopes, luxuriant plant growth with shrub height usually 1-2.5 m (3-8 ft), and an elevation at the upper edge of timberline among widely scattered trees. The rock ptarmigan shows a preference for moderate slopes in hilly boulder-strewn country, vegetative cover complete but sparse with shrubs (in ravines) 0.3 to 1.4 m (1-4 ft), and most are found at an elevation of 30-300 m (100-1,000 ft) above timberline. The white-tailed ptarmigan prefers steep slopes with rocky outcrops, with plant cover rarely continuous, shrubs sparse and in a dwarf form, and are usually found 150-600 m (500-2,000 ft) above timberline (Weeden 1965).

All three species rely heavily on willow for food. Dominant winter foods eaten by the willow ptarmigan are willow buds and twigs; dwarf birch (*Betula nana*) buds and catkins are second in importance. Rock ptarmigan eat the same species but in reverse order of prominence. During spring, summer, and fall, both species feed commonly on leaves and berries of cranberry and blueberry, horsetail (*Equisetum* sp.) tips, leaves of mountain avens (*Dryas octopetala*), and crowberries (*Empetrum nigrum*) (Weeden 1965). White-tailed ptarmigan in the Rocky Mountain States (primarily Colorado) rely heavily on alpine willows (*Salix nivalis* and *S. arctica*), and the distribution and abundance of these plants dictate the distribution of this ptarmigan (Braun 1970).

Ruffed Grouse (*Bonasa umbellus*)

Ruffed grouse, the most widely distributed grouse in North America, does not have the same popularity as a game bird in the western U.S. that it has in the Lake States and farther east. This distribution of popularity is also reflected by the distribution of ruffed grouse research conducted to date.

Ruffed grouse are closely associated with deciduous forests or mixed deciduous-coniferous forest edges. This permits a more continuous distribution in the Lake States where large expanses of hardwood forest are present. In the mountain West, ruffed grouse are more prevalent along (but not entirely

confined to) stream courses or moist areas where deciduous trees and shrubs are found. During the winter in mountain habitat, the birds prefer a southern exposure and elevations above the stream bottom (Stauffer 1983), both related to higher temperatures, snow melt, and resulting food availability.

The plant most often associated with thriving ruffed grouse populations is quaking aspen (*Populus tremuloides*). Several authors (Svoboda and Gullion 1972; Doerr et al. 1974) have suggested that aspen buds (especially flower buds from mature male aspen) are critical winter and spring foods. Gullion (1977), in discussing forest management for ruffed grouse, pointed out the value of each different age aspen stand to a particular seasonal ruffed grouse requirement. In the West, fire suppression in many areas has probably prevented regeneration of complete stands of aspen, and early seral stages are few or non-existent (Stauffer and Peterson 1985b).

Ruffed grouse.

In many areas of the mountain West, aspen is limited in distribution and seldom in the large continuous stands so common to the Lake States. Under these conditions, ruffed grouse rely on a variety of understory shrubs for food and cover such as willow, serviceberry (*Amelanchier* sp.), blueberry, hawthorne (*Crataegus* sp.), chokecherry (*Prunus* sp.), and snowberry.

Sage Grouse (*Centrocercus urophasianus*)

The sage grouse is decidedly the largest grouse in North America; an adult male may weigh 3,175 g (7 lb), about twice the size of the next largest, the blue grouse. Unlike many other North American grouse, sexual dimorphism is pronounced in the sage grouse in both size and plumage.

Sage grouse are characteristic of the semi-arid sagebrush or sagebrush-grassland types found in the western plains and intermountain basins. Generally following the distribution of the plant genus *Artemisia*, sage grouse can be found at elevations from about 750 m (2,500 ft) in the western Dakotas to over 2,100 m (7,000 ft) in some intermountain basins.

Sagebrush is essential to sage grouse survival. A proper combination of height and canopy of this plant must be available to meet the birds' seasonal needs. Dependency on the plant is greatest during the late fall, winter, and early spring. A sage grouse food habits study in Montana (Wallestad et al. 1975) showed that during 8 months of the year.(October through May), the frequency and volume of big sage leaves found in crops remained above 60% and 90%, respectively. For three of these months (December through February) it was the only food present. Thus for a large part of the year, sage grouse are found in or near stands of sagebrush with a canopy-coverage exceeding 20% (Eng and Schladweiler 1972; Wallestad and Schladweiler 1974). In addition to the sagebrush canopy coverage requirement, winter ranges are frequently on areas with little or no slope (Eng and Schladweiler 1972; Beck 1977), although Beck (1977) reported some use of slopes exceeding 10% and also use of windswept ridges for feeding sites.

During the 4 months of summer and early fall, sage grouse seek out succulent forbs, and frequently leave the dense sage and move to scattered sage distribution with a 1-10 and 10-25% canopy coverage (Wallestad 1975). Sage grouse at this time are often found near seeps, streams, or irrigated fields where succulent forbs are available. By mid September to late September, frequently coinciding with regular heavy frosts, the birds move toward the wintering areas. This movement between summer and winter ranges may be as little as 3-5 km (1.8-3 mi.) (Eng and Schladweiler 1972) or up to 80 km (48 mi.) (Dalke et al. 1963).

Although big sage is the species most frequently associated with sage grouse, several others (*Artemisia cana, A. frigida, A. ludoviciana, A. nova*) have been listed as used for both food and cover (Patterson 1952; Wallestad et al. 1975). Species of forbs that are prominent in the diet of sage grouse are dandelion, prickly lettuce (*Lactuca* sp.), salsify (*Tragopogon* sp.), gumweed (*Grindelia* sp.), yarrow (*Achillea* sp.), and sweet clover (*Melilotus* sp.). Alfalfa (*Medicago* sp.) is frequently heavily used in late summer and early fall.

Prairie Chicken (*Tympanuchus cupido*)

This species, also called the pinnated grouse, was once well represented throughout the central U.S. from the southern prairie provinces of Canada to the Gulf Coast, coinciding closely with the distribution of mid- and tallgrass prairie. The 1957 American Ornithological Union (A.O.U.) checklist recognized the lesser and greater prairie chicken as separate species; the 1983 version lists the two as a superspecies although many consider them to be a single species.

The lesser prairie chicken is characteristic of the more arid grasslands of the Southwest, whereas the greater is associated with the more moist tallgrass prairie of the eastern great plains (Johnsgard 1973). Both races appeared to have benefited from the breaking of the prairies for cultivation, providing winter food in the form of grain, and permitted a northward range extension (Johnsgard and Wood 1968). This extension was relatively short-lived for both races and as the agricultural effort became more intense, distribution receded to the remnant status of today (Johnsgard 1973).

Sage grouse droppings.

Sage grouse at water hole.

A very explicit comparison of habitat for the lesser and greater prairie chickens in Oklahoma was presented by Jones (1963). He stated " ... the habitat of the lesser prairie chicken consisted of small units of shortgrass prairie intermixed with larger units of shrub or half-shrub vegetation; that of the greater prairie chicken consisted of small units of shortgrasses or midgrasses intermixed with larger units of tall grasses." This difference was also shown in day-resting activities with the lesser using primarily half-shrub vegetation whereas the greater favored the edges of tallgrass and midgrass vegetation. Both tended to rear broods in areas of abundant forb growth, at least in part for the insect fauna in association with such areas.

The emphasis of shrub component in the lesser prairie chicken habitat is more pronounced than with the greater prairie chicken. The half-shrub (*Artemisia filifolia*) is common in Oklahoma and New Mexico (Jones 1963). In New Mexico, the shinnery oak (*Quercus havardii*) is heavily used; the habitat consists of a shinnery oak-tallgrass community which included such grasses as sand bluestem (*Andropogon hallii*), little bluestem (*Andropogon scoparius*), three-awn (*Aristida* sp.), dropseed (*Sporobolus* sp.), and hairy grama (*Bouteloua hirsuta*) in addition to a variety of forbs (Davis et al. 1980). However, in Oklahoma, densities of displaying males were negatively correlated with percentage coverage of brush and positively correlated with percentage coverage of grass in a shinnery oak rangeland; the reverse was found on a sand sagebrush rangeland (Cannon and Knopf 1981a).

Sharp-tailed grouse (*Tympanuchus phasianellus*)

Six races of sharp-tailed grouse are recognized (Hamerstrom and Hamerstrom 1961), two of which extend their ranges south of Canada in the western U.S. The Columbian sharptail (*T. p. columbianus*) is found in western Montana and eastern Washington south to Utah and western Colorado. The plains race (*T. p. jamesi*) is the most abundant and widespread of the races in the U.S., being found in eastern Montana, Wyoming, and Colorado, and in western Nebraska and the Dakotas.

Sharp-tailed grouse prefer habitat with structural features intermediate to the early forest stages of ruffed grouse and the tallgrass prairie habitat of the greater prairie chicken. Columbian sharptails currently exist in small isolated populations, with the most viable segments in western Colorado; they associate largely with Kuchler's (1964) sagebrush steppe type (Miller and Graul 1980). The plains race is the most prairie dwelling of the three, and is found in association with patches of shrubs on the prairie.

Both races utilize a combination of trees-shrubs-grasslands but in varying degrees of composition of these structural components. The Columbian sharptail favors rolling hills or benchland with a bunchgrass, forb, and shrub combination. In valleys of western Colorado, this bird overlaps the zones of sagebrush and Gambel oak (*Quercus gambellii*) (Hoffman and Alexander 1980). Frequently agricultural fields are interspersed on the ridgetops or valley floors and may serve as feeding sites in the fall before snow cover.

The plains sharp-tail habitat consists of short to mid-grass prairie, interspersed with shrubby draws and agricultural land. Grazing intensity greatly influences the distribution of grouse in this habitat. Nielson and Yde (1981) noted a uniform use of pastures where grass height averaged 22.8 cm (9.1 in.) compared with those with grass averaging 9-11 cm (3.6-4 in.) where use was more confined to sections where shrubs provided cover.

Robert L. Eng

Sharp-tailed grouse.

Columbia sharptails are most frequently associated with aspen, sagebrush, hawthorne, serviceberry, and rose. In western Colorado, a rather close winter association is frequently seen with Gambel oak which may provide both mast and buds for food. Plains sharptails are linked with such key species as aspen, cottonwood (*Populus* sp.), buffaloberry, juniper (*Juniperus* sp.), snowberry, and rose. Nielson and Yde (1981) indicated a close association with buffaloberry during winters of heavy snow. Swenson (1985) quantified a shift by plains sharptails from feeding in grain stubble to shrubs as snow depth increased beyond 140 mm (5.5 in.).

Wild Turkey (*Meleagris gallopavo*)

Two subspecies of wild turkey, the Merriam's (*M. g. merriami*) and the Rio Grande (*M. g. interme-*

dia), are common in portions of the western U.S. A third, the Mexican or Gould's turkey (*M. g. mexicana*), has limited distribution in the U.S., being confined to a couple of small areas in New Mexico and Arizona (Lee 1959). The Merriam's turkey was originally associated with the mountains of Colorado, New Mexico, and Arizona. However, trapping and transplanting has extended the range to most States west of the Mississippi to the Canadian border. This range expansion is not continuous; rather the distribution consists of discrete populations, many isolated in small islands of mountain habitat. The Rio Grande turkey is found largely in Texas and the northeast corner of New Mexico.

The Merriam's turkey in its original range is a mountain-dwelling bird ranging from 1,800 to 3,000 m (6,000 to 10,000 ft) in elevation in the ponderosa pine-oak forest (Ligon 1946). It frequently has a distinct summer and winter range, moving to lower elevations in the winter to zones producing mast crops, which are more available due to lighter snow conditions. Many of the more successful transplant sites north of its original distribution are characterized by relatively low rainfall (and snowfall), ponderosa pine and grassland areas, and foothill grainfields adjacent to stringers of timber or shrubby draws. Mast producing trees and shrubs are mostly absent from the northern areas and domestic grain is frequently a substitute.

Ponderosa pine forests with open grassland understory characterize Merriam's turkey spring, summer, and fall habitat. In a study in southeastern Montana, Jonas (1966) observed 6,271 turkeys in 468 groups, recording the observations by plant communities. Over a third of the observations, excluding those made during the winter, were in grasslands, but only 9% were more than 100 m (109 yd) from tree or shrub cover. Twenty-seven percent of all observations were in snowberry, but mostly in the brush-grass ecotone and not in pure stands. Much use of snowberry was for cover by young poults—older poults used the forest for cover. Over 20% of all observations were in pine stands and 78% of these were in stands of pole size class. Stands of pole size pine, in contrast to saplings, were open enough to permit growth of a variety of low growing food plants but still provided overhead protection from avian predators. Only in winter did the use of pine forests decrease to less than 20%. During this time, 73% of the observations were in deciduous tree-shrubby draws at the lower elevations where weather was less severe. Beasom (1970) reported on Rio Grande turkeys inhabiting mesquite (*Prosopis juliflora*) and live oak (*Quercus virginiana*) vegetative types in south Texas. Kothmann and Litton (1975) reported that this subspecies extended its range into 14 million ha (3.5 million a.) of shrub mesquite prairie in west Texas.

Ponderosa pine is undoubtedly the single most important plant species in Merriam's turkey habitat. Sapling doghair stands of this species are used for cover (Hoffman 1962), the older more open stands are used for cover and feeding areas, and large mature trees for roost trees and mast producers for winter feed. Other mast producers in the more southern ranges are oak, primarily Gambel oak, pinyon pine (*Pinus edulis*), and alligator juniper (*Juniperus deppeana*) (Ligon 1946).

Because most mast producers do not produce heavy crops annually, other food sources must often be relied upon. This is frequently provided by the grass family, both seed heads and vegetative parts, from a variety of species (Ligon 1946; Spicer 1959; Hoffman 1962; Jonas 1966). In northern extensions of the range, mast crops are even less dependable, and grasses play a greater role in winter foods. Often, waste domestic grains in stubble fields provide supplemental winter foods, particularly when grazing by domestic livestock is excessive and native grass seed production is nil.

Colorado Division of Wildlife

Wild turkeys.

The extension of the Rio Grande turkey beyond its primary range into the relatively treeless area of west Texas was assisted by man-made structures (primarily power lines and poles) for roosting, and available food supplies in the form of grasses, grass seeds, and forbs (Kothmann and Litton 1975). The importance of roost sites to Merriam's turkeys is illustrated by a reported 64% reduction in population following a pinyon-juniper reduction program which isolated roost sites over 300 m (330 yd) from cover (Scott and Boeker 1977).

Mearn's Quail (*Cyrtonyx montezuma mearnsi*)

The largest part of the overall distribution of this quail is in Mexico, although one race, the

Mearn's (*C. m. mearnsi*), is found in westcentral Texas, southwest New Mexico, and southeast Arizona. The male has a striking facial plumage of bluish-black patches mixed with white, hence the common name harlequin quail.

Throughout its range, the Mearn's quail displaces the Gambel's (*Callipepla gambellii*) and scaled quails (*C. squamata*) of the desert grasslands at higher elevations (1,200-3,600 m [4,000-12,000 ft]). In Arizona, Mearn's quail inhabit the oak-grasslands and oak-woodlands (Bishop and Hungerford 1965). In New Mexico, Mearn's quail habitat is typified more by pinyon pine and junipers as well as ponderosa pine (Ligon 1961).

Although this species of quail was considered to be rare in the U.S., Brown (1982) noted that major populations are present in mountain ranges of southeastern Arizona in oak woodland and grassland type, and is common enough to be an important game bird in Arizona (Brown 1979). In the Mexican highlands, Leopold and McCabe (1957) believed that this quail was so closely associated with the pine-oak forest that it could well be considered an avian indicator of the type.

The overstory of pine and oak is not the important habitat component of this species. Rather it signifies a climatic zone harboring a complex of perennial forbs and sedges that provide the food and water source in the form of bulbs (Leopold and McCabe 1957). Although heavy grazing by livestock was believed responsible for a severe reduction in quail food, more recent studies have shown that forage removal > 55% will eliminate a quail population, not because of a short food supply but because of cover removal and subsequent vulnerability of the birds (Brown 1982).

Most food habit studies show that acorns are fairly high in both frequency and volume, particularly in years when some of the other foods may be scarce (Bishop and Hungerford 1965). Thus the various species of scrubby oaks so characteristic of the U.S. range of this quail probably play a dual role as food and cover. Woodsorrel (*Oxalis* sp.) and sedges are both heavily used for food (bulbs and seeds) and only during July through September did these two genera make up less than 50% of the volume of food in a study in Arizona (Bishop and Hungerford 1965).

Masked Bobwhite (*Colinus virginianus ridgwayi*)

The masked bobwhite quail formerly occupied mesquite-grassland areas of southern Arizona and northern Sonora, Mexico. They disappeared from Arizona by 1900, presumably because of cover removal

resulting from a series of droughts coupled with excessive grazing (Tomlinson 1972b).

Descriptions of masked bobwhite habitat have been obtained from studies conducted in Mexico (Tomlinson 1972a, b) or on transplanted birds in Arizona (Goodwin and Hungerford 1977). Masked bobwhite show preference for flat, mesquite-grassland at elevations from 300 to 1,200 m (1,000 to 4,000 ft). This is in contrast to the other quails of the area that exhibit a preference for a more wooded and broken terrain (Tomlinson 1972b). Pen-reared bobwhites released in Arizona also showed a preference for open, grass-forb sites but adjacent to mesquite lined drainages (Goodwin and Hungerford 1977).

Masked bobwhites prefer heavy forb growth in moderate to dense stands of grasses. Grasses common to their Mexican habitat are several species of grama (*Bouteloua* sp.), three-awn, bristlegrass (*Setaria* sp.), and panic grasses (*Panicum* sp.; Tomlinson 1972a). Quail released on Arizona sites were later found in areas with a dense understory of pigweed (*Amaranthus* sp.) and an overstory of mesquite, paloverde (*Cercidium* sp.), and wolfberry (*Lycium* sp.). Like the birds observed in Sonora, a preference was shown for a dense grass-forb complex with adjacent brush or trees (Goodwin and Hungerford 1977). The woody cover was used for cover by the quail during the winter (Tomlinson 1972a).

Scaled Quail (*Callipepla squamata*)

The scaled or blue quail, as it is often called, has a geographic distribution which conforms closely to the Chihuahuan desert and adjacent grasslands (Johnsgard 1973). In New Mexico, it is found over most nonforested sections up to 2,100 m (6,990 ft) (Ligon 1961). Hoffman (1965) described the scaled

Scaled quail.

quail range in Colorado as extremely variable from the flat farmlands at 1,020 m (3,400 ft) to the rocky slopes and canyons adjacent to the Rocky Mountains at 2,100 m (7,000 ft).

In Arizona good scaled quail habitat consists of low-growing grasses, forbs, and shrubs with an overall ground cover between 10 and 50% (Goodwin and Hungerford 1977). In contrast to Gambel's quail (which seemed to prefer taller shrubs—60 to 80% over 2 m [6.6 ft]), scaled quail were found to frequent areas where less than 2% of the shrubs exceeded 2 m (6.6 ft) in height. In the absence of shrubby cover in western Oklahoma, they readily used man-made structures (Schemnitz 1961). In Colorado, scaled quail are most commonly found in sand sagebrush, dense cholla cactus (*Opuntia* sp.), or yucca (soapweed [*Yucca glauca*])-grassland, and pinyon-juniper woodlands (Hoffman 1965).

Species of plants used for cover by scaled quail seemed secondary to structure. Schemnitz (1961) identified habitat use in Oklahoma based on over 2,000 observations in three vegetation types and found 29% in man-made cover (such as buildings and machinery) and 54% in a shrub life-form, primarily skunkbush (*Rhus aromatica*), small soapweed-sandsage, and small soapweed. In New Mexico, prominent shrubs in scaled quail habitat were mesquite, catclaw (*Acacia greggii*), whitehorn (*Acacia constricta*), and snakeweed (*Gutierrezia* sp.) (Campbell et al. 1973).

Based on the analysis of 227 crops collected in the fall and winter in New Mexico, seven foods made up over 75% of the total volume: seeds, leaves, and stems of whitehorn, snakeweed, doveweed (*Croton* sp.), whitemargin euphorbia (*Euphorbia albomarginata*), insects, mesquite, and amaranth (*Amaranthus* sp.) (Campbell et al. 1973).

Gambel's Quail (*Callipepla gambellii*)

Gullion (1960) reported the Gambel's quail as the most promising upland game bird in parts of the Southwest because in many desert areas it is the only resident upland game species in abundance. Although records exist of scattered populations of Gambel's quail occurring at higher elevations, maximum elevations of normal occurrence are more in the 1,220- to 1,830-m (4,000- to 6,000-ft) range. Only marginal populations exist where annual snowfall is greater than 50 cm (20 in.) or where 2.5 cm (1 in.) or more snow is on the ground for more than 40 days each year (Gullion 1960).

A preference for dense stands of desert shrub was clearly evident from Goodwin and Hungerford's (1977) Arizona study. They found this species of quail favoring shrub cover of sufficient density to shade from 50 to 75% of the ground and where 60

to 80% of the shrubs were taller than 2 m (6.5 ft). They suggested that a dense understory was unimportant to Gambel's quail.

Considerable overlap exists in the distribution of scaled and Gambel's quail and although they may be found in the same habitats, their habitat requirements are different. Generally, Gambel's quail are found in the river bottoms and are more associated with dry washes or brushy draws; scaled quail will more likely occur on the surrounding mesas and plains in association with grassy open lands (R.L. Tomlinson pers. commun.).

Mature mesquite, hackberry (*Celtis reticulata*), wolfberry, and catclaw provided cover for feeding, loafing, roosting, nesting, and raising broods in Arizona (Goodwin and Hungerford 1977). Gullion (1960) listed many of the same plants plus other shrubs providing a comparable structure. In addition, he listed a variety of noxious weeds such as redroot amaranth (*Amaranthus retroflexux*), goosefoot (*Chenopodium* sp.), sunflower (*Helianthus annuus*), and white sweetclover (*Melilotus alba*) as low growing forms providing a good food source.

Hungerford (1962), in studying food habits of this quail in Arizona, reported members of the Leguminosae as very important food producers. Six of nine genera listed as important food items were of the legume family including mesquite, catclaw, mimosa (*Mimosa* sp.), deervetch (*Lotus* sp.), paloverde, and lupine.

U.S. Fish and Wildlife Service

Gambel's quail.

California Quail (*Callipepla californica*)

This close relative of the Gambel's quail is distributed along the West Coast. It has also been successfully introduced into the interior in Washington,

Oregon, Idaho, Nevada, and Utah. Although hybridization with Gambel's quail occurs where the two species coexist, ecological differences prevent extensive overlap in distribution (Johnsgard 1973).

With the extensive north-south distribution of this quail, at least eight races are found over a rather wide range of climatic and moisture conditions. In California, this quail can be found from near sea level to 2,550 m (8,500 ft). Although several races occur in California and a wide variety of habitat conditions are utilized, brushy vegetation (stiff-twigged, dense-foliaged trees for night roosting) adjacent to open grassy, weedy types and available water characterize this species' requirements throughout the state (Grinnel and Miller 1944). In comparing habitats of the mountain quail (*Oreortyx pictus*) and California quails, Gutierrez (1980) listed the latter as preferring the open woodland, grassland, and chaparral habitats on less steep hillsides.

California quail habitat reported by Emlen and Glading (1945) includes the following general types: desert, rangeland, dry farming land, and irrigated land. Rangeland is the most extensive and most widely used of the four types. Each type provides for the basic requirements of the quail in various degrees. Water, which is apparently a more critical factor than with Gambel's quail, is usually at a premium on dry-land farms and portions of the desert habitat. Cover (roosting, loafing, and nesting) is often lacking in both irrigated and dry-land farm areas. Deserts and rangelands (particularly the latter) will most often provide the variety of conditions needed for food, water, and various cover components to house the more dense populations (Emlen and Glading 1945).

Like many of the quail that feed on a wide variety of foods (including seeds and leafy parts of plants), species composition of cover is probably far less important than structural or life-form characteristics. This is particularly true of the California quail in light of its very wide distribution through diverse vegetational zones. A variety of food habit studies repeatedly show the importance of legumes, especially the seeds (Edminster 1954; Shields and Duncan 1966; Gutierrez 1980). Important legumes appearing in food include bur clover (*Medicago hispida*) lupines, deervetches (*Lotus* sp.), clover (*Trifolium* sp.), and vetches (*Vicia* sp.). Another herb that appears frequently as food, both as leafage and seeds, is filaree (*Erodium* sp.).

Band-tailed Pigeon (*Columba fasciata*)

The band-tailed pigeon is a large migratory dove similar in size and color to the non-migratory blue-phase domestic pigeon (*Columba livia*). Two races of this bird, the interior race (*C. f. fasciata*) and the coastal race (*C. f. monilis*), have been identified

north of Mexico. The interior race migrates into Mexico for 6 months during the winter; the coastal race winters primarily in southern California (Braun et al. 1975; Tomlinson 1983).

U.S. Fish and Wildlife Service

Band-tailed pigeon.

Both races of band-tailed pigeons are closely associated with forests that provide their major food source in the form of mast, berries, and small fruits. In some areas, when natural forest foods are scarce, usually during migration, grain fields and orchard crops are invaded to a point of human conflict. The coastal race occupies a diverse array of mountain forests from moist coast forests in Washington and Oregon to drier Sierran montane forests further south and east (Jeffrey 1977). The interior race occupies a wide range of habitats ranging from agricultural types near forests to berry-producing forest sites at elevations to 3,300 m (10,900 ft). Habitat is almost always mountain related although occasionally feeding birds will be observed in grassland or desert shrub.

Habitat structure for the coastal race in its northern range consists of forested land, well interspersed with forest openings in early successional stages favoring berry-producing shrubs. California habitat includes mountain forests, woodlands, and chaparral if accompanied by abundant oak. Ranges of the interior race are primarily diverse mountain coniferous forests but most frequently accompanied by a common denominator—a pine-oak combination (Jeffrey 1977). In southern Arizona and New Mexico, breeding habitat may be found in oak communities (Braun et al. 1975).

In the northern habitat of the coastal race, a variety of overstory trees such as western hemlock (*Tsuga heterophylla*), red cedar (*Thuja plicata*), and Douglas fir are dominants, whereas in California the redwood (*Sequoia sempervirens*) predominates in the coastal forest. However, because food supplies appear to control the distribution and abundance of bandtails more than any other single factor, species of understory trees and shrubs are probably most important. Various species of oak are key deciduous trees. Several species of shrubs that are good food producers, and most vigorous and productive in seral stages following logging or fire, are elderberries (*Sambucus* sp.), wild cherries, huckleberries, and dogwood (*Cornus* sp.) (Jeffrey 1977).

The primary winter range of the coastal race is in California. During winter they primarily inhabit the pine-oak woodland and coastal chaparral plant associations, although wintering populations are mobile and may shift areas of concentration from year to year depending on available food sources (Tomlinson 1983).

Although the interior race can be found at elevations supporting Engelmann spruce (*Picea engelmanni*) and alpine fir (*Abies lasiocarpa*), it is most abundant at the lower ponderosa pine/Gambel oak zone. The close association with various species of oak and pine is related to the staple fall and winter foods of acorns and pine nuts.

Mourning Dove (*Zenaida macroura*)

Two races of mourning doves breed in the U.S., *Z. m. carolinensis* in the eastern one-third and *Z. m. marginella* in the western two-thirds. These doves breed in all of the lower 48 States, extending into the Canadian provinces to the north and Mexico to the south. Most mourning doves migrate, spending the winter in the southern U.S., Mexico, Central America, or the West Indies (Keeler 1977).

The mourning dove has probably benefited from or has been able to adapt to man's activities more than most other native bird species. It is primarily a

U.S. Fish and Wildlife Service

Mourning dove.

bird of open woodland or the edge between forest and prairie. Thus, the clearing of large areas of deciduous forest in the East and the planting of trees on the prairie (i.e., shelterbelts for farms and fields, urban tree planting) has enhanced the dove population over large areas. The dove is basically a tree nester but will commonly nest on the ground in the absence of trees or shrubs. Early in the nesting season before deciduous trees leaf out, doves prefer conifers for nest sites. Thus the inclusion of conifers in shelterbelts and urban plantings has also favored this bird. The conversion of large tracts of treeless prairie to domestic grains and farmsteads (trees) has created an excellent combination of food (waste grain) and nesting cover for doves. Intensive grazing on many ranges has encouraged invader plant species that often produce more seeds than native grasses. Also intensive grazing management includes stockdams that provide water in areas where it is at a premium, and often trees and shrubs for nesting and loafing (Dunks et al. 1982).

Population Measurement Techniques

Most techniques for inventorying upland game birds provide direct or indirect data on the presence or absence of the target species within the area being sampled. Such techniques may consist of enumerations of actual sightings or audible responses by the bird to a stimulus (direct) or the observation of droppings, feathers, or tracks (indirect), either of which can provide the manager with at least a basis for initial habitat management decision.

Many techniques, primarily those based on a seasonal activity of the bird (usually breeding activity), show sufficient precision to provide relative abundance data. Thus comparisons can be made between areas or between years on a single area permitting an evaluation of the bird's response to different or changing habitat conditions.

Few if any techniques measure the actual number of birds present. Even on limited areas where a large percentage of the male population may be engaged in a common activity (breeding display), an unknown percentage of the males are not displaying (Dorney et al. 1958; Rippin and Boag 1974).

Although a few upland game census techniques involve complete coverage of a unit, most are based on variations of transect sampling. Likewise, a basic walking transect census, such as the King Census for ruffed grouse originally described by Leopold (1933), has been modified for a variety of species and conditions as pointed out by Hayne (1949) in his examination of the technique. Thus, many methods for determining indexes to upland game bird numbers are derived from a basic technique but modified slightly to accommodate a particular species, habitat type, or season. A very comprehensive and exhaustive coverage of transect sampling was presented by Eberhardt (1978).

All of the techniques listed below will at least indicate presence or absence. The degree of precision and accuracy beyond that will be indicated with each method.

Dropping Counts.

Description. Although this technique (pellet-group counts) has been used extensively with large ungulates, it has been little used with birds. Pyrah (1972) used this method successfully in determining relative use by sage grouse on several study areas subjected to various degrees of herbicide treatment. In areas previously gridded, points were randomly selected on which to establish 30-m (100-ft) transects. At 7.5-m (25-ft) intervals along the transect, 9-m^2 (100-ft^2) circular plots (radius [1.7 m]5.64 ft) were established and searched for droppings. Distinction was made between single droppings and clusters resulting from a night roost.

Accuracy and Precision. No attempt was made to correlate the data with the actual number of birds using the area. However, based on field observations during this rather intensive study, the data reflected relative use by sage grouse among the different areas during the previous winter (D. Pyrah, pers. commun.).

Discussion. This indirect census method has some distinct advantages over many for game birds. Sampling can be conducted throughout the day in contrast to short periods of bird activity. By clearing permanent plots after each count, seasonal use can be measured in a relatively short period of time compared with measuring directly through actual bird observation. Gates (1983) used the same transects and in part the sample plots to determine relative use by sage grouse, pygmy rabbits (*Sylvilagus idahoensis*), black-tailed jack rabbits (*Lepus californicus*), and pronghorn (*Antilocapra americana*).

The method also has some disadvantages: its use is largely restricted to habitats with moderate to light ground cover and to the period after snow melt and before excessive green-up; it is probably restricted to species (several of the grouse) on a diet including adequate roughage to prevent rapid deterioration of the droppings; and until more information on defecation and dropping deterioration rates is available, the method will be restricted to a relative use index.

King Strip Census.

Description. The King Strip census has been modified and discussed many times since first employed on ruffed grouse by King (1973). In its simplest form, a series of parallel transects of known length are walked, and birds observed are recorded including the flushing distance. The average flushing distance is calculated, which when multiplied by the total length of the transects provides the area covered. The total area divided by the number of birds observed provides the density index. A more detailed description of this method is presented by Overton (1971, pp. 420-424).

Accuracy and Precision. Under most conditions this method would denote presence and with adequate samples may indicate distinct trends in the population. One of the longest continuous uses of this method on a single area (Marshall 1954) suggested similar magnitudes in population when compared to grouse numbers with a second index from the same area.

Discussion. This method has some merit in areas or seasons where the use of the other methods are not feasible; it can indicate presence and to a degree, relative abundance of the target species. Because so many variables are potentially present in using such a method, it is imperative that conditions be standardized as much as possible, i.e., time of year (phenologically), time of day, and comparable weather conditions. One advantage of this method is that it forces the biologist onto the ground to systematically walk through the habitat.

This method does not provide usable indexes when used on low density populations—the amount of sampling necessary would be prohibitive.

Roadside Counts.

Description. As the name implies, this method consists of driving along a predetermined route under a prescribed set of conditions and counting the number of birds observed (Kosicky et al. 1952). One should attempt to standardize driving speed, number of observers, season, time of day, and weather conditions (wind speed, temperature, and cloud cover). Thus many of the variables encountered in walking strip counts (King Strip census) would be the same as in roadside counts; the latter permits more extensive coverage in less time.

Accuracy and Precision. Basically the same as for the preceding method.

Discussion. Roadside counts have been used extensively in the Midwest to obtain indexes on pheasants, quail, doves, and cottontails. In the West where game bird densities are frequently lower than in the Midwest, the roadside count is superior to a strip count conducted on foot. In addition to population indexes, roadside counts have also been used to obtain cover or habitat preferences by recording habitat use in relation to availability along the route (Hoffman 1965).

Like the strip census, the greatest drawback to this method is the number of variables that can influence the results. The availability of cottontails for enumeration can vary considerably from day to day as discussed by Newman (1959). The basic problems would be similar for game birds.

Complete Census.

Description. The complete census attempts to tally all birds in a unit of habitat of known size. The procedure can vary from one individual carefully cruising back and forth to one or two persons with well trained dogs, to many individuals essentially in a drive. In all instances care must be exercised to prevent duplication in tally. The distance between lines, whether covered singly or by many, is largely dictated by the type of cover.

Accuracy and Precision. This technique, when properly executed in cover that is not too dense, has been considered to be more accurate and reliable than many others.

Discussion. For most species of game birds, the term complete count would be a misnomer. However, on tracts without heavy cover, with species more prone to flush than run, and with adequate personnel to keep intervals between participants at a minimum, a drive count can be effective in making a large percentage of the birds available for tallying. The results are influenced by many of the same variables mentioned for strip counts, and maximum standardization of the variables is very critical to comparing the results between areas or years.

This method is more manpower-expensive than strip sampling or roadside counts and does not sample as large an area for the effort. One modification that has been employed on a number of game birds, particularly covey species, is to incorporate well-trained pointing dogs into the effort. This can be very effective but all too often simply adds another variable. This method is obviously impractical for use over wide areas (county or state); its application is best confined to areas of intensive study.

Auditory Census.

Description. As used here, this method includes all sounds produced by a bird. Most of the sounds are vocalizations although some, such as those produced by a drumming ruffed grouse, are mechanically produced. The sounds used in obtaining population indexes are associated with the breeding season.

The most basic auditory method is to travel over a predetermined route, stopping and listening at established intervals (listening stops) for a given length of time, during which period the observer records the number of sounds produced or the number of birds that can be heard per stop. Applications or evaluations of this method have been reported for a variety of game bird species: crowing count for pheasants (Kimball 1949), a drumming count for ruffed grouse (Petraborg et al. 1953), mourning dove call-count survey (Armbruster et al. 1978), and woodcock (*Scolopax Minor*) singing ground count (Tautin 1982).

A modification of this method has been used for lekking species; an observer listens for displaying males along a roadside route, plots the locations of arenas, and counts the number of males per arena on subsequent days. The effective width of such a strip is determined by twice the average distance the target species can be heard. A similar effort is often expended in locating all arenas on a block of habitat. Intensive coverage of a block of land with its redundancy through overlap perhaps gives greater assurance of locating all the arenas per unit by using listening stops along a belt.

Still another variation of an auditory census is to employ a recorded sound of the species in question to stimulate a response. This may be a male call to elicit a response by a territorial male as suggested by Kimball (1949) for pheasants; or a female call which may also cause the male to respond as reported by Stirling and Bendell (1966) for blue grouse; and Levy et al. (1966) for Mearn's, Gambel's, and scaled quail. This variation introduces another potential variable—the proportion of the population that responds to the stimulus may vary from year to year depending on changes in cover conditions and population density.

Accuracy and Precision. The auditory census techniques must be used for indexes only, at least under the present methods employed. The data gathered do not permit conversion to actual numbers of birds. Even with the total coverage of a unit for arenas and high counts of males attending, data are available to show the presence in the population of an unknown number of non-participants (Dorney et al. 1958; Rippin and Boag 1974).

Certain of the methods, if conducted properly, will provide trend data of value to the manager (Dorney et al. 1958—ruffed grouse; Smith and Gallizioli 1965—Gambel's quail; Jenni and Hartzler 1978—sage grouse).

Discussion. Auditory counts hold the most promise as a usable technique for the habitat manager. Most calls can be more easily heard than birds can be seen. Consequently, at least presence can be determined. Because most calls are related to a breeding cycle, and this is often an all out seasonal effort, certain variations are avoided. Because a high proportion of the male population usually participates, auditory counts can be used on less dense populations than methods relying on sight observations.

The major disadvantage to auditory counts is that most are restricted to the breeding season and consequently provide only an index to the adult population. Indexes to the adult population are valuable in comparing populations between years or between habitats, but frequently are inadequate for use in predicting a harvestable surplus for the following fall. However, Smith and Gallizioli (1965) suggested that the index they obtained from calling quail reflected both numbers of birds and breeding success, thus providing some predictability of fall numbers and hunter success. Calling counts for mourning and white-winged doves (*Zenaida asiatica*) were believed to be a valid technique for determining spring population levels, but only for mourning doves did the counts provide reasonable predictability for fall hunting success (Brown and Smith 1976).

Lek (Arena) Surveys.

Description. Lekking species (prairie chickens, sharp-tailed grouse, and sage grouse in North America) are those which conduct group breeding display on traditional areas (arenas). The arenas may be located through an auditory census (triangulation), auditory-visual (systematic ground coverage), or visual (aerial coverage). Persistent attendance by some of the males early in the season permits locating the arenas 2 to 3 weeks before the seasonal peak attendance. Peak male attendance on sage grouse arenas occurs in 1 to 3 weeks following peak female attendance (Eng 1963; Jenni and Hartzler 1978). Three to four counts of male sage grouse on each arena during the same period each year will produce the most reliable trend data (Jenni and Hartzler 1978; Emmons and Braun 1984). Counting only the number of arenas (leks) for lesser and greater prairie chickens provides an index to density of displaying males (Cannon and Knopf 1981b).

Accuracy and Precision. Over 90% of the 33 radio-marked male sage grouse attended the display grounds during the period of peak male attendance, indicating that most of the males of an area can be found on the arenas (Emmons and Braun 1984). However, in a sharp-tail population, substantial number of males (about one-half during one year) were non-territorial and non-participants in display (Rippin and Boag 1974).

Discussion. Determining trends in populations of lekking grouse through counts of displaying males is considered an accepted practice. For sage grouse, available data suggest that most of the males will be present if counts are scheduled properly. Sage grouse arenas are very traditional; arenas are less likely to be abandoned or new ones started than with sharp-tailed grouse. Thus for sage grouse, counts of males on arenas is necessary to reflect trend data. Counts of arenas only on a unit area, as recommended for obtaining trend data for prairie chickens (Cannon and Knopf 1981b), may also suffice for sharptails.

DISCUSSION

Wildlife biologists responsible for habitat management on public lands frequently find themselves in the uncomfortable position of having to make recommendations based on scanty data. Furthermore, the size or diversified nature of many areas make it difficult to maintain the intimacy necessary for sound management. Thus an ongoing search is conducted for yardsticks to be used in determining suitability of cover for or the status of a particular population.

Probably as a result of the popular use of key plant species in evaluating big game habitat, game bird habitat has been evaluated in much the same manner. Yet a species of game bird may have a distribution of sufficient breadth that the plant species composition may be very different from one end of the range to the other. It appears, then, that at least with respect to cover, structure of the vegetation is probably a better common denominator throughout the birds' range than plant species composition.

On the other hand, when food requirements are considered, plant species are important. Many of the same plants, at least members of the same genera, are listed as food sources throughout much of the range of Gambel's quail. The entire distribution of the sage grouse is governed by the plant genus *Artemisia*. Although the sage grouse uses *Artemisia* for both food and cover, their dependence on this plant for winter food dictates this inseparable relationship. This plant structure (cover) and plant species (food) relationship has been clearly depicted for marsh birds by Weller (1978).

Studies of upland game populations and of habitat change are often conducted simultaneously. Unfortunately many habitat studies are not initiated until a decided decline in bird numbers has been noted. This situation often results in attempts to evaluate deteriorated habitat from which key ingredients may already be missing.

This sequence should not be totally unexpected because land use (habitat) changes can be very easily overlooked when they occur gradually. Even the occasional conversion of rangeland to cropland may seem somewhat innocuous to a manager of grassland fauna until it is conducted on a scale of some of the recent sod-busting ventures. Thus it is often the consistent, annual, downward trend in numbers of a species of game birds that calls one's attention to the habitat problems. A study is then initiated, and as Robel (1980) pointed out, the population and habitat studies become inseparable.

Knowledge of a game bird's annual home range is of prime importance both in assessing its habitat or determining its presence or relative abundance. With a species like the gray partridge (and many of the quail), the home range is sufficiently small so that most transects established for sampling habitat or birds would be of sufficient length to include areas occupied throughout the year. As such, seasonal timing of the sampling effort would be less critical. Conversely, more mobile species like sage grouse (Berry and Eng 1984), blue grouse (Mussehl 1960), as well as migratory doves, may seasonably occupy habitats somewhat different in type and measurably different in location. Therefore, with such species, timing of the effort within a particular habitat is most critical.

Overton (1971) defined a census index as "a count or ratio which is relative in some sense to the total number of animals in a specified population."

The problem here, of course, is determining how the count or ratio relates to the total number, since the latter figure favors playing the role of the unknown.

Most efforts directed toward measuring the status of a game bird population result in data being compared to similar data collected from the same area in previous years (population trend data), or to similar data gathered from different areas (relative abundance data). Trend data are most frequently used by agencies concerned with annual population status as it applies to harvest recommendations, although long-term trends can also provide information on the status of the habitat. Relative abundance data from different areas are probably of greater use to those agencies primarily concerned with habitat management. Such data enable personnel to assess the role of a given species within a unit of habitat in relation to other potential uses.

In most instances, when target species and season are appropriate, a version of the auditory census will probably provide the best return for the effort. This would be true even for a simple presence or absence determination but especially so if relative abundance data are of concern. As mentioned earlier, the fact that the birds (at least the males) are engaged in a seasonal activity which will have a measurable seasonal and daily peak permits the observer to capitalize on this predictable sequence and thereby reduce considerably the variables encountered. A reduction in variables will provide a more usable measure of the population level.

LITERATURE CITED

ALLEN, A.W. 1984. Habitat suitability index models: gray partridge. U.S. Dep. Inter., Fish and Wildl. Serv. Biol. Rep. 82 (1073). 23pp.

ARMBRUSTER, M.H., T.S. BASKETT, W.R. GOFORTH, and K.C. SADLER. 1978. Evaluating call-count procedures for measuring local mourning dove populations. Trans. Missouri Acad. Sci. 12:75-90.

AULT, S.C. and F.A. STORMER. 1983. Seasonal food selection by scaled quail in northwest Texas. J. Wildl. Manage. 47:222-228.

BAXTER, W.L. and C.W. WOLFE, Jr. 1973. Life history and ecology of the ring-necked pheasant in Nebraska. Nebraska Game and Parks Comm., Lincoln. 58pp.

BEASOM, S.L. 1970. Turkey productivity in two vegetative communities in south Texas. J. Wildl. Manage. 34:166-175.

BECK, T.D.I. 1977. Sage grouse flock characteristics and habitat selection in winter. J. Wildl. Manage. 41:18-26.

BEER, J. 1943. Food habits of the blue grouse. J. Wildl. Manage. 7:32-44.

BENDELL J. and P.W. ELLIOTT. 1966. Habitat selection in blue grouse. Condor. 68:431-446.

BERRY, J.D. and R.L. ENG. 1984. Interseasonal movements and fidelity to seasonal use areas by female sage grouse. J. Wildl. Manage. 49:237-240.

BISHOP, R.A. and C.R. HUNGERFORD. 1965. Seasonal food selection of Arizona Mearn's quail. J. Wildl. Manage. 29:813-819.

BOHL, W.H. 1957. Chukars in New Mexico, 1931-1957. Bull. 6, New Mexico Dep. Game and Fish. Santa Fe. 69pp.

BRAUN, C.E. 1970. Distribution and habitat of white-tailed ptarmigan in Colorado and New Mexico. Abstract of paper presented at 46th Annual Meeting, Southwestern and Rocky Mountain Division, A.A.A.S., Las Vegas, New Mexico.

————, D.E. BROWN, J.C. PETERSON, and T.P. ZAPATKA. 1975. Results of the Four-Corners Cooperative band-tailed pigeon investigation. U.S. Dep. Inter., Fish and Wildl. Serv. Resour. Publ. 126. 20pp.

BROWN, D.E. 1979. Factors influencing reproductive success and population densities in Montezuma quail. J. Wildl. Manage. 43:522-526.

BROWN, D.E. and R.H. SMITH. 1976. Predicting hunter success from call counts of mourning and white-winged doves. J. Wildl. Manage. 40:743-749.

BROWN, R.L. 1982. Effects of livestock grazing on Mearn's quail in southeastern Arizona. J. Range Manage. 35:727-732.

CAMPBELL, H., D.K. MARTIN, P.E. FERKOVICH, and B.K. HARRIS. 1973. Effects of hunting and some other environmental factors on scaled quail in New Mexico. Wildl. Monogr. 34. 49pp.

CANNON, R.W. and F.L. KNOPF. 1981a. Lesser prairie chicken densities on shinnery oak and sand sagebrush rangelands in Oklahoma. J. Wildl. Manage. 45:521-524.

————. 1981b. Lek numbers as a trend index to prairie grouse populations. J. Wildl. Manage. 45:776-778.

CHOATE, T.S. 1963. Habitat and population dynamics of white-tailed ptarmigan in Montana. J. Wildl. Manage. 27:684-699.

CHRISTENSEN, G.C. 1970. The chukar partridge, its introduction, life history, and management. Biol. Bull. 4. Nevada Dep. Fish and Game. Reno. 82pp.

CRAWFORD, J.A. and E.G. BOLEN. 1976. Effects of land-use on lesser prairie chickens in Texas. J. Wildl. Manage. 40:96-104.

DALKE, P.D., D.B. PYRAH, D.C. STANTON, J.E. CRAWFORD, and E.F. SCHLATTERER.1963. Ecology, productivity and management of sage grouse in Idaho. J. Wildl. Manage. 27:811-841.

DAVIS, C.A., R.C. BARKLEY, and W.C. HAUSSAMEN. 1975. Scaled quail foods in southeastern New Mexico. J. Wildl. Manage. 39:496-502.

————, T.Z. RILEY, R.A. SMITH, and M.J. WISDOM. 1980. Spring-summer foods of lesser prairie chickens in New Mexico. Pages 75-80 in Proc. of the Prairie Grouse Symposium. Oklahoma State Univ. Stillwater.

DOERR, P.D., L.B. KEITH, D.H. RAUSCH, and C.A. FISHER. 1974. Characteristics of winter feeding aggregations of ruffed grouse in Alberta. J. Wildl. Manage. 38:601-615.

DOERR, T.B. and F.S. GUTHERY. 1983. Effects of tebuthiuron on lesser prairie-chicken habitat and food. J. Wildl. Manage. 47:1138-1142.

DORNEY, R.S., D.R. THOMPSON, J.B. HALE, and R.F. WENDT. 1958. An evaluation of ruffed grouse drumming counts. J. Wildl. Manage. 22:35-40.

DUNKS, J.H., R.E. TOMLINSON, H.M. DEEVES, D.D. DOLTON, C.E. BRAUN, and T.P. ZAPATKA. 1982. Migration, harvest, and population dynamics of mourning doves banded in the Central Management Unit, 1967-77. U.S. Dep. Inter. Fish and Wildl. Serv. Spec. Sci. Rep.—Wildl. 249. 128pp.

EBERHARDT, L.L. 1978. Transect methods for population studies. J. Wildl. Manage. 42:1-31.

EDMINSTER, F.C. 1954. American game birds of field and forest. Charles Scribner's Sons. New York, NY.

EMLEN, J.T., JR. and B. GLADING. 1945. Increasing valley quail in California. Univ. Calif. Agric. Exp. Sta. Bull. 695.

EMMONS, S.R. and C.E. BRAUN. 1984. Lek attendance of male sage grouse. J. Wildl. Manage. 48:1023-1028.

ENG, R.L. 1963. Observations on the breeding biology of male sage grouse. J. Wildl. Manage. 27:841-846.

———— and P. SCHLADWEILER. 1972. Sage grouse winter movements and habitat use in central Montana. J. Wildl. Manage. 36:141-146.

GALBREATH, D.S. and R. MORELAND. 1953. The Chukar partridge in Washington. Biol. Bull. 11, Washington State Game Dep. 55pp.

GATES, R.J. 1983. Sage grouse, lagamorph and pronghorn use of a sagebrush grassland burn site on the Idaho National Engineering Laboratory. M.S. Thesis, Montana State University, Bozeman. 135pp.

GOODWIN, J.G. and C.R. HUNGERFORD. 1977. Habitat use by native Gambel's and scaled quail and released masked bobwhite quail in southern Arizona. U.S. Dep. Agric. For. Ser. Res. Pap. RM-197. 8pp.

GRINNELL, J.G. and A.H. MILLER. 1944. The distribution of birds of California. Cooper Ornithological Club. Pacific Coast Avifauna 27.

GULLION, G.W. 1960. The ecology of Gambel's quail in Nevada and the arid southwest. Ecology. 41:518-536.

————. 1977. Forest manipulation for ruffed grouse. Trans. North Am. Wildl. Nat. Resour. Conf. 42:449-458.

————. 1984. Ruffed grouse management—where do we stand in the eighties? Pages 169-181 in Robinson,

W.L. ed. Ruffed Grouse Management: State of the Art in the Early 1980s. North Cent. Sect. Wildl. Soc.

GUTIERREZ, R.J. 1980. Comparative ecology of the mountain and California quail in the Carmel Valley, California. The Living Bird. 71-93.

HAMERSTROM, F.N., JR., and F. HAMERSTROM. 1961. Status and problems of North American grouse. Wilson Bull. 73:284-294.

HARPER, H.T., B.H. HARRY, and W.D. BAILEY. 1958. The chukar partridge in California. California Fish and Game. 44(1):5-50.

HAYNE, D.W. 1949. An examination of the strip census method for estimating animal populations. J. Wildl. Manage. 13:145-157.

HIATT, R.W. 1947. The relation of pheasants to agriculture in the Yellowstone and Big Horn River valleys of Montana. Montana Fish and Game Dep., Wildl. Rest. Div., Proj. 1-R. 72pp.

HOFFMAN, D.M. 1962. The wild turkey in eastern Colorado. Colo. Dep. of Game and Fish. Tech. Publ. 12. 47pp.

———. 1965. The scaled quail in Colorado. Colo. Dep. of Game, Fish and Parks Tech. Publ. 18. 47pp.

HOFFMAN, G.R. and R.R. ALEXANDER. 1980. Forest vegetation of the Routt National Forest in northwestern Colorado: a habitat type classification. U.S. Dep. Agric., For. Ser. Res. Pap. RM-221. 41pp.

HUNGERFORD, C.R. 1962. Adaptations shown in selection of food by Gambel's quail. Condor. 64:213-219.

JACOBS, K.F. 1959. Restoration of the greater prairie chicken. Oklahoma Dep. of Wildl. Conserv. Oklahoma City.

JEFFREY, R.G., Chairman. 1977. Band-tailed Pigeon (*Columba fasciata*). Pages 210-245 in Sanderson, G.C. ed. Management of Migratory Shore and Upland Game Birds in North America. International Assoc. of Fish and Wildl. Agencies. Washington, DC. 358pp.

JENNI, D.A. and J.E. HARTZLER. 1978. Attendance at a sage grouse lek: implications for spring census. J. Wildl. Manage. 42:46-52.

JOHNSGARD, P.A. 1973. Grouse and quails of North America. Univ. of Nebraska Press. Lincoln. 553pp.

——— and R.W. WOOD. 1968. Distributional changes and interactions between prairie chickens and sharp-tailed grouse in the Midwest. Wilson Bulletin. 80:173-188.

JONAS, R. 1966. Merriam's turkeys in southeastern Montana. Montana Fish and Game Dep. Tech. Bull. 3. 36pp.

JONES, R.E. 1963. Identification and analysis of lesser and greater prairie chicken habitat. J. Wildl. Manage. 27:757-778.

KEELER, J.E. 1977. Mourning Dove (*Zenaida macroura*). Pages 274-298 in Sanderson, G.C., ed. Management of Migratory Shore and Upland Game Birds in North America. International Assoc. of Fish and Wildl. Agencies. Washington, DC. 358pp.

KIMBALL, J.W. 1949. The crowing count pheasant census. J. Wildl. Manage. 13:101-120.

KING, R.T. 1937. Ruffed grouse management. J. Forestry. 35:523-532.

KOSICKY, E.L., G.O. HENDERSON, P.G. HOMEYER, and E.B. SPEAKER. 1952. The adequacy of the fall roadside pheasant census in Iowa. Trans. North Am. Wildl. Nat. Resour. Conf. 17:293-305.

KOTHMANN, H.G. and G.W. LITTON. 1975. Utilization of man-made roosts by turkey in West Texas. Proc.

Third Natl. Wild Turkey Symp. 159-163.

KUBISIAK, J.F. 1985. Ruffed grouse habitat relationships in aspen and oak forests of central Wisconsin. Tech. Bull. 151. Wisconsin Dep. Nat. Resour. Madison. 22pp.

KUCHLER, A.W. 1964. Potential natural vegetation of the conterminous United States. Am. Geogr. Soc. Spec. Pub. 36. 39pp.

LEE, L. 1959. The present status of the wild turkey in New Mexico. Proc. First. Natl. Wild Turkey Manage. Symp.: 11-18.

LEOPOLD, A. 1933. Game Management. Charles Scribner's Sons. New York, NY. 281pp.

LEOPOLD, A.S. and R.A. MCCABE. 1957. Natural history of the Montezuma quail in Mexico. Condor. 59:3-26.

LEVY, S.H., J.J. LEVY, and R.A. BISHOP. 1966. Use of tape recorded female quail calls during the breeding season. J. Wildl. Manage. 30:426-428.

LIGON, J.S. 1946. History and management of Merriam's wild turkey. New Mexico Game and Fish Dep. 84pp.

———. 1961. New Mexico birds and where to find them. Univ. of New Mexico Press. Albuquerque.

MARSHALL, W.H. 1954. Ruffed grouse and snowshoe hare populations on the Cloquet Experimental Forest, Minnesota. J. Wildl. Manage. 18:109-112.

MARTINKA, R.R. 1972. Structural characteristics of blue grouse territories in southwestern Montana. J. Wildl. Manage. 36:498-510.

MENDEL, G.W. and S.R. PETERSON. 1983. Management implications of gray partridge habitat use on the Palouse Prairie, Idaho. Wildl. Soc. Bull. 11:348-356.

MILLER, G.C. and W.D. GRAUL. 1980. Status of sharp-tailed grouse in North America. Pages 18-28 in Proc. Prairie Grouse Symposium. Oklahoma State University. Stillwater.

MOLINI, W.A. 1976. Chukar partridge species management plan. P-R Proj. W-8-R, W-43-R and W-48-12. Nevada Dep. Fish and Game. Carson City.

MUSSEHL, T.W. 1960. Blue grouse production, movements, and populations in the Bridger Mountains, Montana. J. Wildl. Manage. 24:60-68.

———. 1963. Blue grouse brood cover and land-use implications. J. Wildl. Manage. 27:547-555.

NEWMAN, D.E. 1959. Factors influencing the winter roadside counts of cottontails. J. Wildl. Manage. 23:290-294.

NIELSON, L.S. and C.A. YDE. 1981. The effects of rest-rotation grazing on the distribution of sharp-tailed grouse. Pages 147-165 in Proc. Wildl.—Livestock Relationships Symposium. Univ. of Idaho. Moscow.

OVERTON, W.S. 1971. Estimating the numbers of animals in wildlife populations. Pages 402-455 in Giles, R.H. Jr., ed. Wildlife Management Techniques, Third Edition: Revised. The Wildl. Soc., Washington, DC. 633pp.

PATTERSON, R.L. 1952. The sage grouse in Wyoming. Wyoming Game and Fish Comm., and Sage Books, Inc. Denver, CO. 341pp.

PENDERGAST, B.A. and D.A. BOAG. 1970. Seasonal changes in the diet of spruce grouse in central Alberta. J. Wildl. Manage. 34:605-611.

PETRABORG, W.H., E.G. WELLEIN, and V.E. GUNVALDSON. 1953. Roadside drumming counts a spring census method for ruffed grouse. J. Wildl. Manage. 17:292-295.

POTTS, G.R. 1984. Gray partridge population dynamics: comparisons between Britain and North America.

Pages 7-12 in Dumke, R.T., R.B. Stiehl, and R. Kohl, eds. Proc. of PERDIX III: Gray Partridge/Ring-necked Pheasant Workshop. Wisconsin Dep. Nat. Resour. Madison.

PYRAH, D.B. 1972. Effects of chemical and mechanical sagebrush control on sage grouse. Pages 16-25 in Ecological Effects of Chemical and Mechanical Sagebrush Control. Montana Fish and Game Dep., Job Prog. Rep. W-105-R6. 79pp.

RATTI, J.T., D.L. MACKAY, and J.R. ALDREDGE. 1984. Analysis of spruce grouse habitat in north-central Washington. J. Wildl. Manage. 48:1188-1196.

RIPPIN, A.B. and D.A. BOAG. 1974. Recruitment to populations of male sharp-tailed grouse. J. Wildl. Manage. 38:616-621.

ROBEL, R.J. 1980. Current and future research needs for prairie grouse. Pages 34-41 in Proc. of the Prairie Grouse Symp. Oklahoma State Univ. Stillwater.

ROBINSON, W.L. 1980. Fool hen—the spruce grouse on the Yellow Dog Plains. Univ. of Wisc. Press. Madison. 221pp.

SCHEMNITZ, S.D. 1961. Ecology of the scaled quail in the Oklahoma Panhandle. Wildl. Monogr. 8. 47pp.

SCOTT, V.E. and E.L. BOEKER. 1977. Responses of Merriam's turkey to pinyon-juniper control. J. Range Manage. 30:220-223.

SHIELDS, P.W. and D.A. Duncan. 1966. Fall and winter food of California quail in dry years. California Fish and Game. 52:275-282.

SMITH, L.M., J.W. HUPP, and J.T. RATTI. 1982. Habitat use and home range of gray partridge in eastern North Dakota. J. Wildl. Manage. 46:580-587.

SMITH, R.H. and S. GALLIZIOLI. 1965. Predicting hunter success by means of a spring call count of Gambel's quail. J. Wildl. Manage. 29:806-812.

SNYDER, W.D. 1974. Pheasant use of roadsides for nesting in northeast Colorado. Colo. Div. Wildl. Spec. Rep. 26. 24pp.

SPICER, R.L. 1959. Wild turkey in New Mexico—an evaluation of habitat development. New Mexico Dep. Game and Fish. Bull. 10. 64pp.

STAUFFER, D.F. 1983. Seasonal habitat relationships of ruffed and blue grouse in southeastern Idaho. Ph.D. Dissertation. Univ. of Idaho. Moscow. 108pp.

——— and S.R. PETERSON. 1985a. Ruffed grouse and blue grouse habitat use in southeastern Idaho. J. Wildl. Manage. 49:461-468.

——— and S.R. PETERSON. 1985b. Seasonal micro-habitat relationships of ruffed grouse in southeastern Idaho. J. Wildl. Manage. 49:605-610.

STIEHL, R.B. 1984. Critical habitat components for gray partridge. Pages 129-134 in Dumke, R.T., R.B. Stiehl, and T. Kahl, eds. Proc. of PERDIX III: Gray Partridge/Ring-Necked Pheasant Workshop. Wisconsin Dep. Nat. Resour. Madison.

STIRLING, I. and J.F. BENDELL. 1966. Census of blue grouse with recorded calls of a female. J. Wildl. Manage. 30:184-187.

STONEBERG, R.P. 1967. A preliminary study of the breeding biology of the spruce grouse in northwestern Montana. M.S. Thesis. Univ. of Montana. Missoula. 82pp.

SVOBODA, F.J. and G.W. GULLION. 1972. Preferential use of aspen by ruffed grouse in northern Minnesota. J. Wildl. Manage. 36:1166-1180.

SWENSON, J.E. 1985. Seasonal habitat use by sharp-tailed grouse (Tympanuchus phasianellus) in mixed grass prairie in Montana. Can. Field Nat. 99:40-46.

TAUTIN, J. 1980. Assessment of some important factors affecting the singing-ground survey. Proc. Woodcock Symp. 7:6-11.

TAYLOR, M.W., C.W. WOLFE, and W.L. BAXTER. 1978. Land-use change and ring-necked pheasants in Nebraska. Wildl. Soc. Bull. 6:226-230.

TOMLINSON, R.E. 1972a. Current status of the endangered masked bobwhite quail. Trans. North Am. Wildl. Nat. Resour. Conf. 37:294-311.

———. 1972b. Review of literature on the endangered masked bobwhite. U.S. Dep. Inter. Fish and Wildl. Serv. Res. Pub. 108. Washington, DC.

———. Chairman. 1983. Pacific flyway management plan for the Pacific coast band-tailed pigeon. Pacific Flyway Council. U.S. Dep. Inter., Fish and Wildl. Serv. Portland, OR. 21pp.

TRIPPENSEE, R.E. 1948. Wildlife management. McGraw Hill, New York. 499pp.

WALLESTAD, R. 1975. Life history and habitat requirements of sage grouse in central Montana. Montana Dep. Fish and Game. 66pp.

——— and P. SCHLADWEILER. 1974. Breeding season movements and habitat use of male sage grouse in central Montana. J. Wildl. Manage. 38:634-637.

———, J.G. PETERSON, and R.L. ENG. 1975. Foods of adult sage grouse in central Montana. J. Wildl. Manage. 39:629-630.

WEEDEN, R.B. 1963. Management of ptarmigan in North America. J. Wildl. Manage. 27:673-683.

———. 1965. Grouse and ptarmigan in Alaska: their ecology and management. Mimeo. Alaska Dep. Fish and Game. 110pp.

———. 1967. Seasonal and geographic variation in foods of adult white-tailed ptarmigan. Condor. 69:303-309.

WEIGAND, J.P. 1980. Ecology of the Hungarian partridge in north-central Montana. Wildl. Monogr. 74. 106pp.

——— and R.G. JANSON. 1976. Montana's ring-necked pheasants—history, ecology and management. Game Manage. Div., Montana Dep. of Fish and Game. Helena. 178pp.

WELLER, M.W. 1978. Management of freshwater wetlands for wildlife. Pages 267-284 in Good, R., D. Whigham, and R. Simpson, eds. Freshwater Wetlands. Academic Press. NY. 378pp.

YEAGER, L.E., W.W. SANFORT, and L.J. LYON. 1951. Some problems of pheasant management on irrigated land. Trans. North Am. Wildl. Nat. Resour. Conf. 16:351-367.

21

RODENTS AND INSECTIVORES

Mayo W. Call

P.O. Box 893
Afton, WY 83110

Editor's Note: Although mammalogists have been studying small mammals for years, only recently have management agencies begun to include rodent and insectivore data in their wildlife surveys. These recent attempts have resulted in many inefficient and unproductive efforts. Surveys of rodents and insectivores may be important in land management decisions especially in areas where (1) threatened or endangered populations are or may be present, (2) rodents and insectivores indicate habitat changes, (3) rodents and insectivores are important as a prey base for animals higher on the food chain such as raptors, (4) the larger more economically important species such as beaver and muskrat are involved, and (5) rodents and insectivores are locally important as pest species. These situations usually require careful planning and designing efforts. This chapter provides guidance on planning and designing studies for these diverse groups of species.

INTRODUCTION

Rodents and insectivores (shrews and voles) live in almost every kind of habitat in North America. Some are common and widespread in many kinds of habitats, such as deer mice *(Peromyscus maniculatus),* whereas others live only in certain parts of the country or in specific, limited habitats. For example, beaver *(Castor canadensis)* and muskrats *(Ondatra zibethicus)* are restricted to riparian or other aquatic zones and their associated vegetation.

Most rodents are a major source of food for predators, such as birds of prey, coyotes *(Canis latrans),* badgers *(Taxidea taxus),* and others. Thus, they need to be highly prolific and have some type of defensive, elusive, or other protective behavior to survive. Some of these protective mechanisms complicate efforts to catch them or estimate their numbers.

Before commencing to inventory or monitor any species or population of rodents or insectivores, the biologist should first define his or her objectives for the study. The method used and intensity of the work will be determined by the information that is needed for making the resource management decisions at hand.

Biologists should recognize the kinds of problems they will be faced with as they attempt to estimate numbers and to analyze differences in species or numbers from different habitats (or the same habitat and area) in different seasons or years. Many variables can affect results; even the most intensive studies, using the most sophisticated methods, may not provide as accurate estimates as might be expected because one or more assumptions are not met (Schemnitz 1980).

Some of the models used for estimating rodent numbers require an assumption that the population is "closed," i.e., there is no recruitment or loss of animals to the population during the sampling period (White et al. 1982). This rarely happens in the real world and the complicated procedures required to adjust for probable changes in the population may be difficult to use for most field biologists. Procedures in this chapter will be geared toward simpler methods; references are provided for those who may need to justify more intensive studies.

Populations of many species of rodents and insectivores fluctuate greatly in local areas at various times of the year. High birth rates, high mortality, invasion from surrounding areas, and emigration to other areas must be considered in inventory and monitoring studies. Some small mammal populations are cyclic; they alternately irrupt and subside in a more or less uniform manner between high and low levels of density (Anderson et al. 1977). These population fluctuations sometimes follow a general pattern with respect to time (monthly, seasonal, annual) but other microtine rodents also experience cycles of 3- to 4-, 4- to 7-, and 9- to 10-year intervals, as well as annual fluctuations (Speirs 1939; Elton 1942; Dymond 1947; Keith 1963).

The causal mechanisms of cycles include biotic as well as abiotic factors (Anderson et al. 1977). Biotic factors are inherent in the populations themselves and in the interrelationships of different species. These include disease, predation, food, and physiological mechanisms. Abiotic factors are physical and chemical elements of the environment, including moisture, winds, and solar radiation. An example of the effects of abiotic factors on nocturnal rodents in the Lower Colorado River Valley in Arizona was provided by Anderson et al. (1977). The authors stated that, although there was a general decrease in rodent populations during the entire study period (1974-77), there was significant intraspecific asynchrony among the populations in different vegetation types. There was also a significant degree of interspecific asynchrony in population fluctuations "which renders the task of evaluating habitat difficult and subject to error unless carried out for several years in various vegetation types" (Anderson et al. 1977).

Numerous studies were reviewed by Jorgensen and Smith (1974) relative to estimating the numbers and densities of small mammals in unrestricted populations. They noted that these studies quickly exposed some major difficulties that must be accounted for to produce a single estimate for one restricted location and that "the effort required often challenges the necessity of the data, particularly when one's interest is frequently focused on populations in much larger areas."

Biologists must consider these variables and recognize limitations that may be placed on the data. For example, what might appear to be a simple density calculation, based on a series of parallel trap lines within a designated area of habitat, turns out to be not so simple because one does not know the extent of movement into or out of the trapping area by the various species, factors affecting trappability of individuals or species, times of night of greatest activity of the different species, influences of subtle changes in weather during the trapping period, sizes of home ranges of the different species for that particular habitat, and many other factors.

Monitoring studies should be conducted—

(1) at the same time of year as previous studies;

(2) in the same kind of weather (as nearly as possible) and with approximately the same amount of moonlight;

(3) in the same habitat; and

(4) with the same kind of data collected each time.

There are few situations that require information other than species occurrence and relative density of rodents and insectivores for Federal land management programs. These include—

(1) determination of presence and estimated numbers of rare, endangered, or sensitive species (either Federal or State);

(2) determination of species, estimated numbers (biomass), and trends of small mammals that have been serving as a prey base for raptors or carnivores whose populations are critical or declining;

(3) determination of estimated numbers or trends of a species of economic or scientific importance (such as beaver and muskrat); and

(4) determination of effects of environmental contaminants on either the animals themselves or on dependent predators.

These are only guidelines, however, and the biologist must ultimately decide and justify what information should be obtained to help land managers maintain the ecosystem desired in the area of interest.

In this chapter, I will emphasize a few species that are important in land management programs because of their economic, aesthetic, or scientific values. I will give beaver special attention because they have the ability to modify their habitat more than any other rodent and create changes that affect many other species of wildlife.

HABITAT FEATURES CORRELATED WITH SPECIES GROUPS

Because the species included in this chapter occupy virtually every kind of habitat on the continent, it will not be possible to discuss individual species habitats. I will, however, discuss general habitat types occupied by the different families of rodents and insectivores.

Beaver (Family Castoridae)

Beaver are found in most parts of the U.S. In the West their preferred foods and, therefore, habitat types include aspen (*Populus* sp.), willow (*Salix* sp.), cottonwood (*Populus* sp.), alder (*Alnus* sp.), and other deciduous plants (Call 1970). For short periods of time, beaver may subsist on conifers or some of the less preferred deciduous species, such as hackberry (*Celtis* sp.) and hickory (*Carya* sp.), but they will not thrive on them.

These animals are most often found along low gradient streams where preferred foods are available within about 80 m (80-90 yd). This permits more surface area to be impounded with a given amount of beaver dam construction. Valley grades of 1 to 6% are considered excellent for beaver; those from 7 to 12% are good, and those beyond 12% are questionable for occupation (Rutherford 1964). Beaver are sometimes found occupying small springs, streams, or seeps on timbered mountain slopes (Call 1970).

Muskrat (Family Cricetidae)

Muskrats are found in almost any kind of flowing water or in any kind of impoundment, natural lake, pond, or marsh from sea level to high mountain areas. Their nests may be in holes in stream banks or in piles of vegetation and debris constructed in ponds. Their presence is tied largely to the presence of suitable aquatic vegetation which they use for food and nest construction.

Moles (Family Talpidae)

Moles (*Neurotrichus* sp., *Scapanus* sp., *Parascalops* sp., *Scalopus* sp. and *Condylura* sp.) live most of their lives beneath the ground's surface, usually in the upper dirt layers where digging is easy. Their presence may be detected by the low ridges they push up as they move along just beneath the surface; also, by the earth mounds, each consisting of 0.5 to 2 ft^3 of earth, which they push up from beneath. There is no indication of an entrance to the burrow (Burt and Grossenheider 1964).

Beaver dam.

Beaver lodge.

Shrews (Family Soricidae)

Shrews usually inhabit moist locations, but some species are found in sagebrush areas of arid western States. They are common along most streams and are usually found in moist areas along streams, under logs, and in thick vegetation of seepages.

Squirrels (Family Sciuridae)

Marmots (*Marmota* sp.), ground squirrels (*Spermophilus* sp.), prairie dogs (*Cynomys* sp.), and chipmunks (*Tamias* sp.) nest in burrows in the ground or beneath rocks or logs. Marmots are most often found living in boulder fields on talus slopes but may also live in small rock outcroppings, under isolated boulders on hillsides, in piles of logging debris on hillsides or in gullies, or under abandoned houses or within bridge abutments.

Tree squirrels (*Sciurus* sp.) and flying squirrels (*Glaucomys* sp.) nest in tree cavities or leaf and grass nests in tree canopies. The red squirrel *(Tamiasciurus hudsonicus)* and northern flying squirrel *(G. sabrinus)* are the most common tree squirrels in the West. Red squirrels are found mostly in pine (*Pinus* sp.) and spruce (*Picea* sp.) or mixed hardwood forests and in swamps. The presence of red squirrels in an area is usually noted quickly by an observer who walks through a forested area by either the presence of piles of shucked cones or by the sharp "barking" of the animals when intruders come near.

Chickarees *(T. douglasii)* have habits similar to red squirrels but live almost exclusively in coniferous forests. The Arizona gray squirrel *(S. arizonensis)* is found chiefly in oak (*Quercus* sp.) and pine forests. Tassel-eared squirrels *(S. aberti)* are found mostly in yellow pine *(P. ponderosa)* forests of northern Arizona and New Mexico, southeastern Utah, and southwestern Colorado.

Douglas squirrel

Pocket Gophers (Family Geomyidae)

Pocket gophers (*Thomomys* sp., *Geomys* sp.) are true earth burrowers, seldom seen aboveground. Their presence is easily detected by the mounds of earth they push out as they excavate subterranean tunnels. The mounds are characteristically fan-shaped with an indication of the position of the opening, a round earth plug. The burrow entrance is seldom left open for long. They prefer soil that is slightly moist and easy to work (Burt and Grossenheider 1964).

Pocket Mice, Kangaroo Mice, Kangaroo Rats (Family Heteromyidae)

Pocket mice (*Perognathus* sp.), kangaroo mice (*Microdipodops* sp.), and kangaroo rats (*Dipodomys* sp.) are all adapted for living in arid or semiarid conditions and all burrow into the ground for nest sites. They prefer the more pliable, sandy soils.

Mice, Rats, Voles, and Lemmings (Family Cricetidae)

Mice (*Reithrodontomys* sp., *Peromyscus* sp., *Onychomys* sp., *Sigmodon* sp.), New World rats (*Sigmodon* sp., *Neotoma* sp.), and voles (*Clethrionomys* sp., *Phenacomys* sp., *Microtus* sp., and *Lagurus* sp.) live mostly on the ground, some in rocks, and a few in trees. Grasshopper mice (*Onchomys* sp.) live chiefly on prairies and southwest desert areas. Harvest mice (*Reithrodontomys* sp.) seem to prefer rather dense, low vegetation. White-footed *(P. leucopus)* and deer mice are nocturnal, living in woods, prairies, and around rocks and buildings. Most are ground dwellers, but some nest in trees and are largely arboreal.

red squirrel

Woodrats (*Neotoma* sp.) normally occupy the pinyon-juniper (*Pinus edulus-Juniperus* sp.) plateau region, frequenting rocky places and even cliffs (Hoffmeister and Luis de la Torre 1960), but some forms will be found in Southwest deserts and others in mountain brush of the Northwest.

Woodrats are active mostly at night. They pile sticks and rubbish together for nests in cliff holes or on ledges. In the plains and deserts, they build stick and cactus nests, often 1 to 2 m (4 ft or more) in diameter, in clumps of cactus, yucca, or brush. On the West Coast their nests may be found in live oak trees.

Various species of lemmings (*Synaptomys* sp.) may be found from bogs in the eastern U.S. to arctic and tundra habitats of the far north. The bog lemmings *(S. borealis)* prefer wet bogs and meadows where there is a thick mat of ground vegetation (Burt and Grossenheider 1964).

Deer mouse.

Redback voles (*Clethrionomys* sp.) are small rodents of forested areas in Alaska, Canada, and scattered forested areas of the U.S. Some of the meadow voles and other species may be found in most regions where there is a good grass cover, especially where it is moist. At least one species, the Townsend vole *(Microtus townsendii),* inhabits moist fields and meadows from tidewater up to alpine meadows. The presence of narrow runways, 2.5 to 5.0 cm (1 to 2 in.) wide, through the matted grass usually indicate their presence. In a few places, voles are found among rocks or on forest floors where there is no grass.

Phenacomys sp. may inhabit grassy areas within the cold forested regions of Canada and Alaska, the high mountain tops of western U.S., or dense forested regions of the Northwest. Most are ground-liv-

ing, but the tree *Phenacomys* feed almost entirely on leaves of the tree in which they are living—spruce, hemlock (*Tsuga* sp.), or fir (*Abies* sp.).

Jumping Mice (Family Zapodidae)

Jumping mice (*Zapus* sp. and *Napaeozgapus* sp.) normally inhabit damp meadows and forests and hibernate during the winter.

Porcupines (Family Erethizontidae)

Porcupines *(Erethizon dorsatum)* may be seen lumbering through the forest, along canyon bottoms, or hunched into large dark balls high in trees. They may be found in deciduous or coniferous forests and strangely, sometimes in shrublands or prairies, miles from the nearest trees.

Porcupines sometimes hide in trees by curling into a large dark ball.

Old World Rats and Mice (Family Muridae)

This group includes the Norway rat *(Rattus norvegicus),* black rat *(R. rattus),* and house mouse *(Mus musculus).* None of these animals normally occur far from man-made structures and will not be considered in this chapter.

POPULATION MEASUREMENT TECHNIQUES

With the variety of rodents and insectivores present in most habitats, more than one method is usually required to determine species present, relative density, or estimated numbers. Space is not available here to present the many variations in rodent/insectivore behavior as may apply to sampling techniques. In fact, there remains much to be learned about small mammal home ranges, behavior in different seasons, cycles, responses to traps, and other aspects of their ecology that affect surveys.

Volumes of material have been written about statistical procedures that may be used in sampling wild populations. Depending on their needs for animal population data, biologists must decide if statistical procedures are needed and refer to the Literature Cited section for detailed accounts of the necessary applications. Not every sampling of rodent or insectivore populations needs to be analyzed by elaborate statistical procedures or complicated sampling procedures. Much useful information can be derived on species, relative density, and trends from the raw data itself, together with simple statistics such as means and variances.

General Considerations

Before starting any project, the biologist should—

(1) determine the objective (what kind and how much information is necessary);

(2) determine what kinds of inventory methods or sampling will be required; and

(3) design the study.

For most land management programs, only information on relative density or species trends will be required for rodents and insectivores. At times, however, the biologist may decide that additional data are needed on either a specific species or total populations of several species. Computer programs are available to assist with the more difficult computations (Schultz 1961; Snedecor and Cochran 1967; Sokal and Rohlf 1969; Petrusewicz and MacFayden 1970; Seber 1973; Anderson et al. 1976; Burnham et al. 1980; White et al. 1982).

For most rodents and insectivores, counts of individual animals are a practical impossibility. Therefore, one normally takes a sample from a population and attempts to derive a reasonable estimate of the total population from that sample. The estimate for the total population is then based on the assumption that all animals in the population occur throughout the defined study area in the same ratio as they did within the sampled area.

An index may be employed for monitoring a population. An index is an object (such as a beaver lodge) that is related to the number of animals in the area. The object is usually easier to count than the animal itself. For example, the number of muskrat houses or beaver lodges is an index to the number of animals living in the area. Through intensive trapping, or by using values derived from other researchers in the general area, one can estimate the number of animals in the area by multiplying the number of houses or lodges by the normal number of occupants per house or lodge. One of the problems in using an index is the necessary assumption that the ratio of the index to the population is the same in the several areas or populations being compared (Schemnitz 1980).

The basic premise used in rodent and insectivore monitoring is that a similar proportion of the total population is tabulated each time the same technique is used under similar field conditions with the same species. No statistical procedure will make data collected under different conditions comparable. With all techniques for rodents and insectivores that employ direct counts, the major problem is to conduct counts under sufficiently similar conditions, so that comparison of counts is valid (Schemnitz 1980).

Most populations of rodents and insectivores are not distributed randomly. Each species will tend to be more abundant within small microhabitats that commonly occur within a general habitat type, even when the general habitat appears to be homogeneous. Cover and food are not usually distributed randomly, so neither are the animals. Some burrowing rodents prefer certain soil textures and types for digging their tunnels, and these soils will vary some in what appears to be a fairly homogeneous vegetation type. Thus, using the same transect site for monitoring in subsequent years, or selecting sites for comparative purposes, which are as nearly alike as possible, may reduce variances.

Sampling for Large to Medium-Sized Rodents

Because of the diversity of rodents and insectivores, a number of different survey techniques are required in any given area to determine all species present, their relative density (abundance), or estimated numbers. I will discuss some of the general methods suitable for most species and provide additional references for more sophisticated techniques. In some instances the biologist may need to devise innovative methods to determine presence or estimated numbers of endangered or rare species or animals that are trap-shy or elusive in other ways.

Beaver.

Presence. The presence of beaver along a drainage is determined by looking for beaver dams, lodges, or beaver cuttings (Figure 1). Along desert streams and larger rivers, beaver live in bank dens and do not build dams, but their tree- or shrub-cutting activities will be obvious. Most stream drainages in western mountains that contain aspen, willow, or cottonwood will contain beaver.

Population Estimate. The average number of beaver per colony for the entire U.S. and Canada is about five (Denney 1952). Where beaver trapping occurs over widespread areas, the normal colony composition is disrupted. Although this makes it less precise to use a normal average number for population estimates, the method described will suffice for most management purposes.

The suggested population estimate method is to cruise streams in October or November, counting the active colonies (as evidenced by food caches and repairs on dams and visible lodges) and multiplying the number found by five. Food caches are easily discernible and are the most obvious indication of a wintering beaver colony. The size of the food cache is some indication of the number of beaver in the colony (Figure 2). However, there is no direct relationship between the size of the food cache and the number of beaver in the colony because (1) different colonies may use different kinds of food materials in their caches and (2) some colonies will have much more readily available food (aspen, willow, etc.) adjacent to their primary pond. In a few places, such as western Oregon, beaver may not use food caches but will cut the needed food all winter long. In such areas, the beaver can be surveyed by counting the number of individual cutting areas along the river which should be concentrated near their bank dens (C. Maser, pers. commun.).

Even where colonies do not have a normal makeup because of trapping each year, this method will be satisfactory for most management purposes. A few colonies are usually overlooked and a few bank-dwelling beaver are usually present but not discerned, which will largely make up for a reduction in the average number of beaver per colony caused by trapping.

If the task of determining the number of beaver involves many miles of streams or relatively inaccessible drainages, the best method to use is an aerial survey, either by fixed-wing or helicopter. The terrain will dictate the type of aircraft to use. It is best to fly within 90 to 151 m (300 to 500 ft) of the ground so that all food caches may be seen and counted. Such food caches can be seen on aerial surveys, even when ice has formed on the ponds (Figure 3). This is not difficult in a fixed-wing aircraft along wide valley bottoms with low stream gradients, but becomes more challenging in rough terrain.

Muskrat.

Presence. Muskrats are noted throughout most of their geographical distribution for their conical or dome-shaped houses of vegetation set in marshes or in shallow pond waters. However, in many areas,

Figure 1. A two-lodge beaver pond in southeastern Wyoming. This pond is about 1 acre and was about 20 years old at the time this picture was taken.

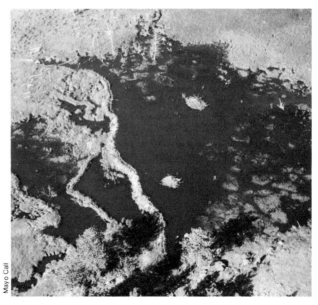

Figure 2. The same beaver pond as shown in Figure 1, as viewed from the air. Food caches, not present in this photograph, are usually built adjacent to dens or lodges, and are easy to discern from this altitude.

Rodents and Insectivores 435

Mayo Call

U.S. Fish and Wildlife Service

Muskrat house.

Figure 3. A relatively large food cache in a beaver primary pond. Eleven beaver were trapped from this colony.

especially along ditches and rivers, they dig bank burrows. Some marshes contain dozens of the dome-shaped houses that leave no doubt as to the occupants, but detecting the presence of muskrats that live along streams is more difficult. Burrow entrances are usually underwater. Their presence in such areas can best be detected by watching for cuttings of cattails, rushes, sedges, small willows, pondweeds, water lilies, and other aquatic and terrestrial plants on which they feed. They are active during the day and may occasionally be seen swimming slowly up or down the stream or sitting quietly on a sandbar, partly submerged tree trunk, or other convenient object where they may sun themselves and still be close to water for a quick escape from danger.

Population Estimate. Estimating numbers of muskrats in an area is very difficult. The number of houses in a marsh is only an index to the number of muskrats.

One method for monitoring trends of these animals is to question local trappers concerning their harvest from local habitats (C. Maser, pers. commun.). For example, if trappers believe they have harvested about 60% of the existing population of a marsh or stream and have taken 70 muskrats, then the population at the beginning of the trapping period would have been about 117 animals. Regardless of trappers' estimated percentage of harvest, trends in the annual harvest would give an indication of trends in the population level. The basic assumption

is that prices and, therefore, interest in trapping, make it worthwhile for trappers to conduct about the same intensity of trapping over the years.

A mark and recapture method, using the Lincoln Index, could be used to estimate the population but would be time-consuming. High mortality from predators could distort the results if too much time were consumed in live trapping and marking a number of animals.

Prairie Dog.

Presence. The black-tailed prairie dog *(Cynomys ludovicianus)* is especially gregarious, i.e., it lives in "towns." Its presence is usually revealed by a group of bare mounds from 8 to 23 m (25 to 75 ft) apart and each mound from 0.03 to 1 m (1 to 3 ft) high (Burt and Grossenheider 1964). Colonies of several hundred animals are not uncommon on some of the dry upland prairies on which they live. Populations may vary from 12 to 85 per ha (5 to 34 per a.) or more.

Some white-tailed prairie dogs *(C. leucurus)* are widely scattered across sagebrush flats and rolling grasslands. For family groups that occur in habitats where they are largely concealed, their presence is often revealed by their danger signal—a two-syllable bark, issued at about 40 per minute.

Utah prairie dogs *(C. parvidens)* have been observed in both dense and scattered colonies. I have counted more than 500 prairie dogs in a pasture of about 4 ha (10 a.) near Cedar City, Utah.

Population Estimate. Prairie dogs live in family groups and exhibit some territoriality around their dens but may use communal feeding areas away from the dens. An estimate of numbers, preferably when their population is somewhat stabilized in the fall, can be obtained by the mark and recapture method using Lincoln Index calculations (see small mammal sampling). However, this procedure is very time-consuming.

I recommend that inventorying and monitoring of these animals be based on the number of active dens, rather than on number of animals observed at any given time. Areas containing prairie dogs should be mapped out and then a grid established over the colony area to facilitate the counting of burrows. Burrows can be plotted on the map for comparison of numbers in future years. Stakes or prominent shrubs can be used as corners of the grid and brightly colored flagging used for easy reference while walking and counting burrows. Additional flagging should be placed along the edges of the colony at intervals of about 10 m (30 yd) along each side to effectively cut the colony area into squares so that burrows can be counted and plotted on a map. Grid square numbering can be done the same as that for the International Bird Plot Census Method, or in any other convenient manner for future comparisons.

Marmots.

Presence. Presence of these animals is usually revealed by their sharp chirps when intruders approach. The den area is rank with the odor of their feces. By sitting near a rockslide in early morning and watching for activity, the observer can usually determine the presence of these animals without doing any trapping. Watching an area of interest for a few hours will generally give the observer a rough idea of how many of the animals are present. Both young and old animals like to sun themselves on rocks or logs near their dens.

Population Estimate. Most colonies of these animals are small. A mark and recapture method can be used for estimating numbers by marking some of the animals with easily visible tags and then spending a period of 3 or 4 days observing the animals and tallying all marked and unmarked animals. Lincoln Index procedures can then be used to estimate total numbers present.

Woodrats.

Presence. Presence is revealed by large stick or cactus houses in clumps of brush, cactus, yucca, or in crevices in cliffs. They may also take over abandoned cabins or other old buildings in foothills and canyons where they build large nests containing rocks, bones, sticks, leaves, and other debris. Nests built on ledges of cliffs or rocky outcroppings are sometimes confused with nests of ravens or birds of

prey. But the inclusion of bones or fragments of human refuse, including pieces of glass or other shiny objects, usually identify it as a woodrat nest. There may be from one to six, or more, rats per nest. The smelly urine stains on rafters or narrow cliff ledges near their nests also reveal the identity of the occupants.

Rocky slopes are home for the yellow-bellied marmot.

Population Estimate. Colonies of woodrats are usually widely scattered. Rough estimates of their abundance may be obtained by walking transects along the desert floor or canyon hillsides while watching for their large stick nests which are often 1.5 to 2 m (4 to 6 ft) in diameter and 1 m (3 ft) tall. When located, they can be checked for tracks and fresh material to determine if they are active. Relative density of this animal can be determined along with other small mammals through the periodic use of trapping transects (see section on small mammal sampling).

Tree Squirrels. The tree squirrels, including the red squirrel, western gray squirrel *(S. griseus),* fox squirrel *(S. niger),* tassel-eared squirrels, and northern flying squirrels, can usually be identified by a combination of region of country where found and the signs which they leave.

Presence. They usually have favorite stumps or racks where shucks from pinecones or nuts may accumulate in piles of a bushel or more. Their nests are either in cavities in trees, on outside branches built of leaves, twigs, and shredded bark, or sometimes in cavities at the bases of trees. Conifer cones and nuts are stored in caches under logs or in cavities in the ground or among tree roots. They are active mostly in daylight hours.

Rodents and Insectivores 437

There are seldom more than two chickarees or red squirrels per ha (per 5.0 a.) of forest, but there may be as many as 10 per 0.4 ha (1 a.; Burt and Grossenheider 1964). Chickarees are fairly quiet during spring and summer while raising their young but become vociferous in fall. Thus, fall is the best time to check for their presence (Maser et al. 1981). Nests may be bulky structures built of twigs, mosses, or lichens, well within the crown of the tree or in hollows of trees.

Northern flying squirrels are strictly nocturnal. They usually nest in tree cavities but may also build outside nests of leaves and twigs. Normally, nests are round balls of material situated in a fork of the trunk of a tree or on a whorl of limbs against the trunk (Maser et al. 1981). In most areas, few people realize how abundant these night-gliders really are. Maser et al. (1981) stated that trappers who trap marten sometimes catch hundreds of these squirrels each winter in traps. These animals are fairly quiet and generally must be detected by observations at night in suspected habitats or caught with traps baited with fresh, raw, or putrid meat, which they seem to relish (Jackson 1961). Much of their diet consists of green vegetation, insects, nuts, seeds, and fruits and they leave few signs of their feeding.

The Arizona gray squirrel (*S. arizonensis*) nests either in tree cavities or in tree branches. It stores nuts and seeds singly in small holes in the ground rather than in large food caches. The squirrels will cling to the opposite sides of trees or lie quietly along a branch and never reveal themselves as long as an intruder is moving near them. Visual observations are the best means for detecting presence of these animals and for estimating numbers. Two persons working together, but a short distance apart, are

effective in locating the animals. Depending on the habitat, there may be from 2 to 20 squirrels per 0.4 ha (1 a.; Burt and Grossenheider 1964).

Tassel-eared squirrels build bulky nests high in the pines. They are usually found from 2,121 to 2,424 m (7,000 to 8,000 ft) in elevation. They may be heard "barking" when excited but are usually quiet. Their presence is best detected by listening for their calls and observing them in appropriate habitats.

Porcupine.

Presence. The presence of porcupines is most often determined by watching for areas of bark removal in coniferous trees and bushes or in winter by finding their waddling trails in the snow. They are often observed at great distances in winter as dark balls in the tops of bushes or deciduous trees as they feed on the bark. Their brownish droppings, consisting of woody materials, are very characteristic. They often have a home den where they may "hole up" during bad weather or before the birth of the single young. The den may be a small cave, crevice in a cliff or among boulders and talus, or in a hollow log. Their feces accumulate in such places and reveal their presence.

Population Estimate. Porcupines seem to be scattered sparsely over most areas. Some estimate of numbers can be obtained by running a 1.6- to 3.2-km (1- to 2-mi.) transect through open forest or mixed deciduous-conifer forest types while watching for signs. Being fairly sparse, they would be easy to miss entirely. Driving unimproved roads through forested areas at night would probably reveal more porcupines than daytime observations. Late one night in the fall of 1950, I counted 21 porcupines along 32 km (20 mi.) of Forest Service road in western Wyoming. I doubt I could have found half as many during daylight hours.

Caution should be used in trying to estimate numbers of porcupines per unit of land area because the animals will sometimes concentrate along canyon bottoms or other desirable habitats.

Sampling for Small Rodents and Insectivores

Inventorying of most small rodent and insectivore species can best be accomplished with trapping transects. Subsequent monitoring of species and populations should be done at the same sites and with the same methods as the original inventory. All trap lines will provide information on species present and relative density; if certain designs are used, one can also calculate an estimate of the populations involved. However, density is a more complicated problem and if such data are needed, the biologist will need to research literature that describes the required field designs and statistical analyses (Smith et al. 1971a; Smith et al. 1972; Smith et al. 1975; O'Farrell et al. 1977; Scott et al. 1978; Burnham et al. 1980; White et al. 1982). The degree of accuracy of either population or density estimates will depend largely on meeting certain assumptions. The following procedures can be used for trapping small mammals to obtain species, relative density, and estimated numbers—but not density.

Species Occurrence and Relative Density. For this information, I suggest following the procedures used by Anderson et al. (1977) and Kepner (1978):

(1) Be sure the vegetation communities are described so that relationships between plant and animal communities can be suggested. Soil types should also be described.

(2) Establish sampling grids within each vegetation community where data are needed. Each grid will consist of snap trap stations placed along two parallel lines of traps 15 m (50 ft) apart (Figure 4). Each line will consist of 15 stations that are also 15 m apart. At each station, set two museum special traps and one Victor rat trap. Bait them with rolled oats and peanut butter with a chemical mixed in, such as dimethyl pthalate, to repel insects (Anderson and Ohmart 1977).

(3) Set the traps in early evening and check them every hour until midnight, if possible. Set them again at midnight and leave until morning, then check them, remove the animals, and leave the traps sprung until evening. Checking the traps every hour before midnight will remove most of the easily caught animals, such as deer mice, and leaving the traps set will increase chances to catch less abundant or more trap-shy animals for the remainder of the night.

(4) Run the trap lines for three consecutive nights. Tabulate all catches by species, sex, and age group (sub-adult and adult). In monitoring a small mammal population, recognize that animals are caught differentially by species, sex, and age, and the catch will depend largely on season of the year. In any future monitoring of the same community, be sure to trap at the same season to obtain comparative results.

(5) Tabulate and analyze your results. Catches will normally be expressed as numbers of each species per 270 trap nights (if the above system is used). If the same type of trapping grid is used in different communities, comparison between species and relative density can be made for different communities. It will soon become obvious which communities are most important in terms of total species and numbers. These communities, however, may not be the ones where rare or indicator species are found that will require special management, and you will need to sample the preferred habitats used by these species.

Live traps suitable for taking medium-sized rodents, such as squirrels and woodrats, may be substituted for the Victor rat trap, if desired (Figure 5). However, if this substitution is made, the animals captured should be removed from the area or kept in captivity until all trapping is completed.

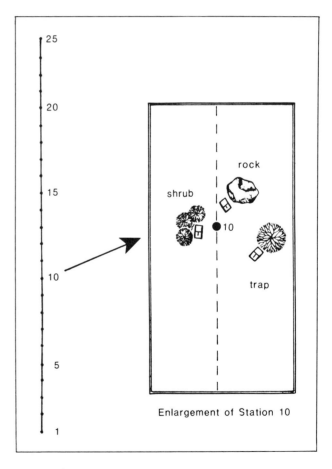

Figure 4. Diagram of a simple linear trap line with an enlarged view of one station (No. 10) to show an example of trap placements.

Figure 5. Live traps are efficient for a wide variety of small mammals. This bushy-tailed woodrat (*Neotoma cinerea*) was captured in western Wyoming using peanut butter as bait.

Trap placement at each station may be biased by placing them in obvious runs, near other rodent signs, or in preferred microhabitats. Small rodents and insectivores have specific microhabitat preferences (e.g., washes, certain kinds of bushes or trees, rocky areas, rotten logs, wet areas). Although all animals move around an area within certain inherent limits or home ranges, it is best to place traps within or adjacent to these preferred sites. The objective is usually to catch as many as possible of each species present in each vegetative community during the predetermined trapping period. Setting traps 2 to 4 m (6 to 13 ft), or more, from the centerline of the transect to improve the chance of taking additional specimens is suggested.

Some species of small mammals, such as squirrels and some mice and voles, are largely arboreal. Consequently, they may not be captured easily in the usual ground surface trap lines. To collect these species, place live or small traps on platforms in trees or fasten them to limbs. Traps may also be placed on the ground around the base of the trees where evidence of the animals is found. Red tree voles *(Arborimus longicaudus)* in Oregon are strictly nocturnal and cannot be trapped. They must be evicted from their arboreal nests, often as high as 15 m (50 ft) above the ground, and captured by hand (Maser et al. 1981). Small mammals observed during the daytime may be shot if the specimens are needed. Special Conibear traps, which catch the animals around the neck or chest, killing them almost instantly, are useful for taking animals ranging in size from squirrels to beaver (Collier 1957).

Gophers and moles are almost entirely fossorial. Gophers may be captured with Macabee gopher traps which are available at many hardware stores. The traps should be set in all gopher tunnels leading from one or more mounds and should be staked down to prevent gophers from pulling them into their burrow complexes. Occasionally, gophers are captured in snap traps on the ground surface.

Moles may be captured with gopher or special mole traps. A gopher trap set upside down in the mole's burrow is often effective (Ingles 1965). Special commercial mole traps consisting of a box-like housing, which opens at the ends and has an impaling device actuated by a trigger mechanism, are also useful in obtaining specimens for identification (Giles 1969).

Shrews and other insectivores are rarely captured with traditional trapping methods for small mammals. Because they are insectivorous, they are often not readily attracted to bait composed of peanut butter or oatmeal. One of the most effective methods for collecting them is to use pitfall or can traps, which are also effective in catching amphibians, reptiles, and other small mammals. For best results, the cans or buckets should hold more than 1 gallon and have a round aperture in the center, which helps reduce the possibility of escape. However, regular ice cream or pickle buckets or cans will also serve the purpose well.

Cans or buckets should be buried in the ground so that the tops are flush with the substrate (Figure 6). For best results, the pitfall traps should be installed and then covered with a lid for about 10 days to allow for accommodation by the resident animals. Maximum trapping success for shrews does not occur until the traps have been in place for about 10 days (S. Cross, pers. commun.). Setting up a trapping array with either three or four arms will capture shrews in moist areas, as well as small mammals and reptiles in arid areas.

The trapping arrays shown in Figure 6 are set so that each can is connected by a drift fence of wire mesh or tin, about 0.3 m (10 in.) high. The drift fence should be set about 3 cm (1 to 2 in.) into the substrate. If the animals are believed to occur in very low densities, the size or number of the sample plots should be expanded and the area of survey increased.

Because shrews move about very rapidly or perhaps because they smell meat (or smell and hear other small animals on which they feed) in the bottom of the pit trap, they frequently drop into the pit and cannot climb back out. If the pitfalls are baited with sardines, earthworms, rodent brains or liver, or other meat, more shrews may be obtained. If you cannot examine the traps on a daily basis, 10 cm (4 in.) of formalin or AFA (Giles 1969), covered by a thin layer of mineral oil, should be placed in each can or bucket to retard decomposition of the specimens. This will also help to prevent the shrews from destroying or eating other trapped animals in the pit. Some trappers fill each bucket about one-third full of water when they are activated to accomplish a similar purpose and to help keep the shrews from jumping out (S. Cross, pers. commun.).

Shrews are frequently found near permanent water sources. Therefore, the biologist should seek out such areas to check for their presence. Shrew sign is not easy to detect, but with some experience, the worker can learn to recognize their runs, burrows, and nests. Leaf litter, matted grass, and moist ground are good habitat signs to look for.

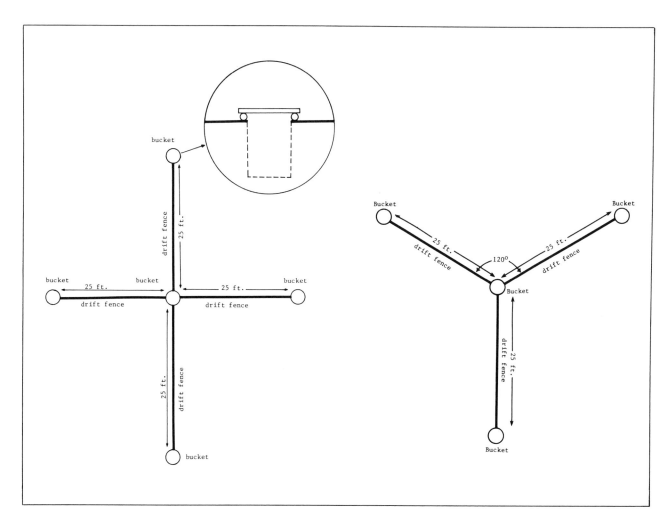

Figure 6. Configuration of pitfalls with associated drift fences to capture small mammals, lizards, and snakes. Arrays with either three or four drift fences are effective. Buckets (insert) are placed flush with the ground surface with a cover supported by rocks to provide cover and protection for the trapped animals.

Another method for capturing shrews is to dig small trenches between the pitfalls, instead of using drift fences (Figure 7). Good success is often achieved by laying out a grid of pitfalls (coffee cans or other suitable containers) adjacent to small streams or other moist areas (Figure 8). Bait is placed in the bottom of the cans and along the trenches; the trenches should be moistened so they are damp. The trap grid should be checked once during the night and again before sunrise. The traps should be closed with plastic lids during the day unless they are going to be visited frequently.

Care should be taken in handling live shrews as some species secrete a toxin in the saliva that can make a bite quite painful. I recommend using gloves when handling them. Unless you intend to retain them as specimens for identification, they should not be kept in captivity longer than about 2 hours.

Most researchers seem to prefer a combination of snap traps and live traps to obtain a representative sample of all species present. Varying results have been reported when only one type of trap (snap vs. live) has been used for sampling. Live traps come in different sizes. Common sizes for small mammals are 3 x 3.5 x 9 in. and 2 x 2.5 x 6 in. Sherman live traps are available from H.B. Sherman Traps, Aenon Creek Industrial Park, Route 4, Box 529 X-2, Tallahassee, Florida 32304; telephone (904) 575-0424.

Permanently molded live traps seem to be preferred to collapsible ones. However, the number to be set and the distance they need to be carried will have a bearing on the type used. Also, rodents are more apt to chew through aluminum live traps and escape than they are with tin traps. Triggers on collapsible traps need to be sensitized each time they are set to be sure they will operate properly.

In-hand examination of small mammals is often required for their identification. Certain members of genera *Dipodomys, Peromyscus, Perognathus,* and *Neotoma* are extremely difficult to identify in the field and may require several individual animals to confirm the identifications. Juveniles are particularly difficult to identify and may require use of comparative skulls and skins. Because of the lack of expertise of most biologists in identifying subspecies (some of which may be endangered or threatened forms), I recommend that arrangements be made to send specimens to qualified museums or universities for identification. If this is done, be sure proper measures are taken to preserve the specimens during shipment so they will be in good condition upon arrival at the institution. Obviously, this will not be necessary if qualified taxonomists are available in-house or with cooperating agencies.

Traps should be checked as early as possible the morning following a night's trapping. Many desert areas heat up rapidly and dead animals will spoil quickly in the heat. When using live traps, consider placing a shingle (or board) on top of the trap with a rock to hold the shingle on. This seems to improve efficiency and provides some shade in early morning heat. Also, I recommend using bedding material such as wool (fleece) in live traps. When sampling for diurnal rodents, set the traps as early in the day as possible. Check them before noon and spring them. Reset them in the afternoon and rerun the line before dark. Remove animals and spring the traps.

The terminal ends of each trap line should be marked with stakes, flagging, or other visible material. Permanent stakes are desirable for future reference; the locations of these markers should be marked on maps so they may be relocated for future monitoring studies. In forested areas or in heavy

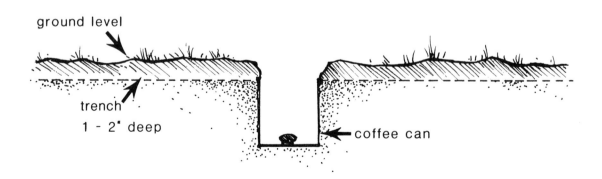

Figure 7. Diagram of pitfall and associated trenches for catching shrews. The trenches should be slightly moistened.

brush, you may wish to run a cord through the habitat and attach tags at appropriate places to facilitate finding the traps. Strips of flagging material may be tied to branches for identifying trapping stations.

Provide a thorough description of the site where the trap line has been placed. Include the following items:

- abundance of trees, shrubs, and grasses

- canopy coverage and height of the plants

- seral stage of the plant community

- litter depth and quantity; disturbance by livestock, fire, or man

- presence of logs, debris, rocky cover

- size of trees and species in forest situations

Include a brief description of topography (e.g., slope, elevation, relation to drainage system, nature of the soil, aspect). For future monitoring studies, photographs of habitat sites are helpful. Describe special microhabitats where traps might have been placed within the general habitat type and note differences in species caught there. Make special note of the weather conditions at the time the traps were in operation and just preceding the trapping effort.

Variability is considerable in the daily and seasonal behavior of rodents and insectivores, including the time species are aboveground and available for trapping. Some hibernate or estivate, whereas others spend parts of the year underground where they are active. Some species spend most or all of their time in tree canopies during spring and summer, then spend time on the forest floor in late fall and winter.

Therefore, determine from the literature or local experts when various species are expected to be most active aboveground and concentrate on trapping during those periods. Trapping for species occurrence and relative density during all four seasons is desirable to obtain a more complete picture of total species using an area.

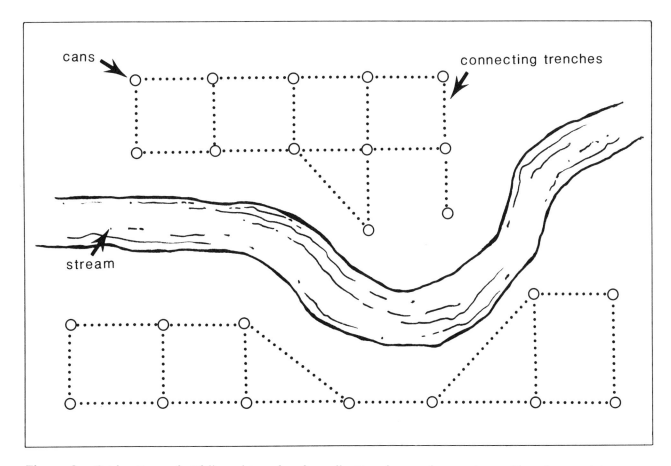

Figure 8. Grid pattern of pitfalls and trenches for collecting shrews along a stream. Trenches are interconnected with pitfalls to guide shrews into the pits.

Obviously, it will be difficult to obtain a true relative density of all species present, from gophers to tree squirrels. They will not have the same trappability nor be taken by the same kind of traps. For example, if you do not set gopher or mole traps where signs of these species are present along the trapping transect, you may not get any in your sample, even though they may be fairly numerous. Special traps or techniques, then, will be necessary if you want a true representation of all species present in a given habitat type.

Population Estimates. Three methods for estimating numbers of animals will be discussed: (1) the strip census, (2) Lincoln Index or mark and recapture, and (3) probability of capture method. Any of these methods will give satisfactory results when used for monitoring the same populations during some future point in time, providing all assumptions are met to the same degree as in the original sampling.

(1) Strip Census. One method for estimating the number of medium-sized rodents, such as tree squirrels or ground squirrels, within a habitat type is to count the number of animals observed within a strip, transect, and then apply the results to the general area. The area censused should be representative of the entire habitat type. Counts of several similar areas or several counts of the same area provide numbers needed for calculation of an estimate of total numbers for the species being surveyed. Detailed versions of the strip census method can be found in Anderson et al. 1976 and Burnham et al. 1980.

The strip census method entails following a straight transect line or series of straight line segments (Anderson et al. 1976), counting the animals observed, and recording the right angle distances from the transect line to the animals observed. The requirement to follow a straight line is usually compromised in the field because of physical obstacles and the near-impossibility of traveling a straight line and searching for animals at the same time. Marking the transect line in some manner will improve the ability to maintain a fairly straight line. This would be done a few days before making a count.

Four assumptions are critical to achieve good results (Anderson et al. 1976):

(1) Animals directly on the line are seen with probability of one (all seen).

(2) Animals are pinpointed at the initial sighting position (they do not move before being sighted) and none are counted twice.

(3) There are no measurement errors (distances are measured exactly).

(4) Animal sightings are independent events.

Obviously, one or more of these assumptions may not be entirely met. Ground squirrels or other burrowing animals may duck into a hole on or near the transect line and not be seen at all, or may run some distance before being observed. Many animals respond to intruders by shying away or running some distance under cover before flushing into the open. This tends to exaggerate the right angle distance from the transect line to the animal when first observed. Some animals run ahead of the observer and, after being counted once, may be counted again if they continue to run ahead. Also, the flushing of one animal is not supposed to cause another animal to flush, but it sometimes does. All these situations tend to violate the assumptions. Nevertheless, if the same procedures are used each time the population is sampled, comparison of results will provide satisfactory information on trends. As in all methods, a replication along the same transect a few days later or in a similar area will add credibility to the results and provide a means to calculate standard deviation and variance.

See Figure 9 for a diagrammatic display of a line transect and the various measurements required.

(2) Lincoln Index or Mark-Recapture Method. The first mark-recapture method for terrestrial animals was known as the Lincoln Index and it is still widely used (Seber 1973). In using the Lincoln Index, part of the animals in a population are live-trapped, marked in some manner, and then released back into the population. Samples are next captured to observe the proportion marked in the entire population, which now consists of a known number of marked animals along with an unknown number of unmarked. An estimate of the total number is computed by dividing the total number marked in the population by the proportion marked in the samples, under the assumption that the samples will estimate closely the proportion marked throughout the entire population.

There are three general methods for marking captured animals: mutilation, tagging, and coloring (Mosby 1963).

Mutilation. Forms of mutilation include toe-clipping, ear-cropping, hole-punching, fur-clipping, tail-notching (beaver), and branding. Any of these forms of marking may receive public criticism in that they maim the animal to some extent and possibly affect its behavior or survival. The main advantages of mutilation are that marks may be readily applied with a minimum of equipment and the marks, in some instances, may be identified at a distance. Systems for marking small mammals by toe-clipping and ear-punching have been described by several workers (Blair 1941; Reynolds 1945; Sanderson 1961). Two methods for numbering systems used in toe-clipping are shown in Figure 10. Toe-clipping is a widely used technique for both small mammals and reptiles. A small pair of sharp scissors or toenail clippers works very efficiently. Only the distal portion of the animal's toe is removed. This is done systematically and recorded as a unique mark to identify a specific animal.

Shearing, clipping, or burning off the tips of the hairs can be used when the hair-base, or underfur, is of a contrasting color, as it often is, such as in newborn mice (Svihla 1934) and chipmunks (*Eutamias* sp.; Yerger 1953). This method is useful only until the next molt but has three advantages: it is easy to apply, painless to the animal, and it constitutes a good mark for field identification. On Norway rats, Chitty and Shorten (1946) used a number drawn on the pelage with a depilatory. Such marks last 2 to 3 weeks, normally long enough for sampling and making population estimates.

In the beaver, the flat, hairless tail has been marked by branding (Bradt 1938) and by cutting

notches. Bradt found straight-line brands on the upper surface of the tail recognizable for at least 4 years. Cuts into the edge of the tail presumably last for life (Mosby 1963).

Tagging. Tagging involves the attachment to the animal of a piece of metal or plastic on which is stamped an individual number. Advantages are that they are easy to affix and to see. The tag should be as light as possible and should be placed so that it does not pinch the animal. It is desirable to place tags low on the ear, where the cartilage is heavy, and on the inner edge where there is greater protection of the tag (Mosby 1963). In some mammals where the ears are very small or there may be high losses of tags through freezing or tearing out, tags may be placed elsewhere.

Muskrats have been tagged by slipping a 5 by 24 mm aluminum tag through two slits in the skin of the back (Errington and Errington 1937) and is most successful with muskrats not over 2 months old, due to the superior regrowth of blood vessels across the strip of skin between the two incisions in young animals (Errington 1944). This method might cause infection if the water they live in is polluted (Takos 1943).

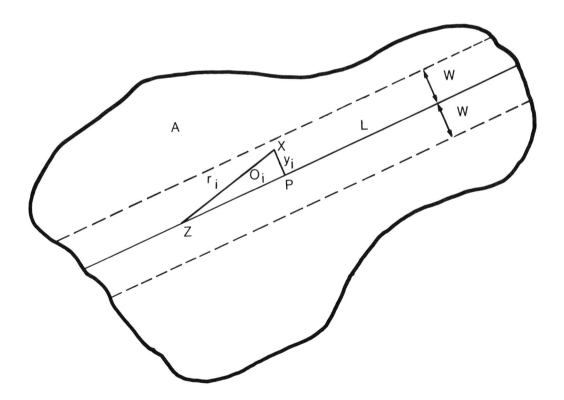

Figure 9. The unit to be censused has area A. The transect length is L and the transect width is 2W. Z is the position of an observer when an animal or object is detected at X. P is the point on the line which is perpendicular to the animal. The sighting distance is r_i, the sighting angle is O_i, and the perpendicular distance from the object to the center line of the transect is y_i. W can be left unspecified or can be a fixed, finite constant (adapted from Anderson et al. 1976).

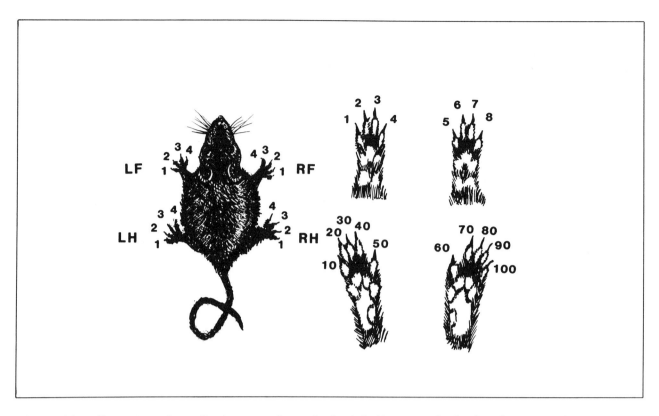

Figure 10. Illustration of toe-clipping procedures. In the left diagram only the first four toes are considered for clipping, counting from the outer toe. A numbering system used in toe-clipping squirrels is shown (from Mosby 1963) in the diagram on the right.

Small bird bands have been used as loose-fitting bracelets around the hind legs of small mammals (Chitty 1937). Use of such bands is more time-consuming than toe-clipping, however, and on some species caused irritation, swelling, skin-puncture, and infection (Takos 1943). Some of these difficulties may be overcome by encircling the band around the Achilles tendon rather than the entire leg. Smaller bands have been clamped loosely around a hind toe on squirrels and are kept in place by the toe pad (Cooley 1948).

A different type of marker, used on muskrats and other medium-sized rodents, consists of a waterproof plastic button, threaded through the loose skin of the back with a flexible steel needle and secured with another button. This plastic marker has the advantage of being visible from a distance on a swimming muskrat (Hensley and Twining 1946; Mosby 1963).

Coloring. Pelage coloring with commercial fur dyes is another successful method of marking animals and lasts until the next molt. Most of these dyes are poisonous and must be used with care. Two common dyes are Nyanzol 4R (reddish-brown) and Nyanzol D (black). Both may be fixed after application with hydrogen peroxide (Evans and Holdenried 1943) or mixed with hydrogen peroxide before application (Fitzwater 1943). Dyes are useful for mammals of light pelage but the range of colors is small. The series can be increased by applying spots to different parts of the body (Mosby 1963). Table 1 shows a few applications of these dyes to small mammals.

(3) Probability of Capture Method (Removal Trapping). Where animals are removed from a population as captured, it is necessary to use a different approach from the mark-recapture method. However, data from the mark and recapture samples may be examined by either the Lincoln Index method or by the removal trapping method, by using only the records for animals trapped the first time.

The number of animals captured during any trapping period may be viewed as the product of two quantities, the first being the probability of capture and the second the number of animals present at the beginning of the period (Hayne 1949a). The probability of capture is assumed to be constant, describing the hazard in which any animal stands in relation to capture in the set of traps during one period. The number of animals present at the beginning of each trapping period is assumed to be the original population minus the number of animals previously captured. Any great departure from these assumptions seems to invalidate this method for estimating the population.

Monitoring Small Mammal Populations

Monitoring small mammals is simply the checking of the status of species, relative density, or numbers at some point before an initial survey or inventory of the population. Baseline information is required to determine how species and numbers are changing over time. The objectives for monitoring small mammals must be determined by the biologist, e.g., to determine trends in populations of endangered, threatened, or sensitive species; to determine trends in species serving as important prey bases; or to determine trends in numbers of other species for economic, scientific, or other reasons. This might involve monitoring only one species, such as beaver, to maintain their numbers within prescribed limits to prevent damage to vegetation or scenic resources, or it might be to monitor several small rodent species that are essential to the continued production of an endangered or sensitive species or raptor. Reasons will vary with locality. Time intervals between checks of species and populations will vary according to productivity, initial status, importance, and possible decimating factors for the species involved. Susceptibility to cycles must also be considered.

DISCUSSION AND SUMMARY

Larger rodents may often be surveyed visually or by their signs, but small mammals, such as mice and shrews, are difficult to observe directly. Nocturnality, protection by overhanging vegetation, and retirement to nest or burrow upon detection of an approaching human contribute to this difficulty of observation. For this reason biologists use a variety of sampling devices and techniques. In previous sections I have discussed general kinds of habitats occupied by different groups of small mammals and some of the methods for determining their presence, relative density, and estimated numbers. Here I will discuss some of the problems involved in rodent and insectivore studies that should be kept in mind when designing an inventory or monitoring study and some of the limitations of the data derived. Anyone can set a trap line, but only a person with some understanding of rodent or insectivore ecology can put the data derived in their proper perspective.

Sampling Assumptions

Species Occurrence and Relative Density. In setting out single trap lines or a series of parallel lines, it might be assumed that most of the individual animals and species within easy travel range of the traps will be equally susceptible to being caught. This is not true. First, using bait in the traps immediately biases the catch. Some species (and probably some individuals) will be attracted to this bait much more quickly than others. Animals, such as deer mice, may be drawn from considerable distance by the smell of the bait, whereas others are only mildly attracted. Therefore, in many localities, a preponderance of deer mice are caught during early evening. In fact, most traps may become occupied by deer mice, excluding other species for the remainder of the night unless the traps are emptied and reset. This is the reason for checking and resetting traps each hour until midnight. By so doing, most of the deer mice or other easily caught species will be caught early and leave the traps ready to capture more secretive, less numerous, or more trap-shy animals. By following this procedure, a more accurate relative density among species can be obtained. Otherwise, the most easily trapped species will appear the most numerous in the

Table 1. Techniques for coloring the pelage of mammals (adapted from Mosby 1963).

Species	Coloring Agent	Special Techniques	Duration of Color	Authority
Pocket gopher	Human black hair dye with oil base: apply equal parts 3% hydrogen peroxide plus granulated soap until liquid is thick.	Recommended for light-pelaged mammals	Until molt	Morejohn and Howard 1956
	Ammonium hydroxide (4%)—1 part to 2 parts 3% hydrogen peroxide plus soap as above.	Recommended for dark-pelaged mammals	Until molt	Morejohn and Howard 1956
Squirrel	Picric acid in 5% formalin.	Use on light pelage		Fitzwater 1943
	Nyanzol A: 20 gm per L of water-hydrogen peroxide mixture in ratio of 2:1.	Ring animal's body in broad bands	Until molt	Fitzwater 1943

composition, whether it is in actuality or not. Regardless of the procedure you use in checking traps, do it the same way each time in order to have comparative information.

When monitoring populations, be sure all environmental conditions and biotic factors are about the same as for prior sampling. For example, species will vary as to time of reproductive peaks, times of greatest seasonal behavior, and months of greatest dispersal. Results may be erroneous if sampling is done before the reproductive peak one year and after the peak when sampling two years later.

In spring and early summer, a preponderance of males of some species may be caught when they are especially active in seeking mates. Times vary with different species. There is always a reason for a preponderance of one sex or age group in a catch. Some knowledge about rodent or insectivore ecology will usually reveal the reason. In making comparisons of numbers or species among years, be aware that many factors may be influencing the results. The reasons may be more important than the numbers themselves.

Of all factors affecting capture probability, time is the most easily controlled. The biologist can select the season of the year when studies are to be conducted, the length of the trapping period, and the time of day when trapping is to be done. The objective is to reduce variation in capture probabilities over time. For usable comparisons equal effort should be expended on each sampling occasion. The number of traps should be the same each time, trapping should be done at the same time of day and, if bait is used, the type and amount should be the same on all occasions.

Weather is an extremely important factor in small mammal trapping (or any kind of sampling). Animals vary greatly in their trappability, behavior, and activity depending on such factors as moonlight, cloudiness, precipitation, high winds, and temperature. Where seasonal weather conditions have produced a poor seed crop, animals will likely be more attracted to baits. It is also important to be aware of possible damage to habitats caused by storms or flooding before the sampling period. Many animals in the study area might have been lost by drowning or emigrated to safer habitat elsewhere. Drought can similarly reduce populations by lowering productivity. On the other hand, unusually good survival conditions may produce much higher than usual numbers during the sampling period. Severe storms and low temperatures or dry conditions that inhibit seed production are among the most important factors to consider when evaluating species changes, relative densities, or population fluctuations.

Relative rather than absolute density has been assumed to suffice for solving many biological problems, but the area factor in density has been ignored. If all procedures are maintained constant, including the time over which samples are taken, it is assumed that the relative densities obtained will suffice for comparing different habitats or the same habitat at different times. However, these relative densities can be misleading. For example, on the trap lines run by the North American Census of Small Mammals from 1948 to 1951, 1,901 male and 1,521 female deer mice were trapped. The conclusion might be that males in these areas were 25% more abundant than females, but this is probably not true. It is more likely that males have a larger home range than do females and, therefore, more males than females are exposed to the trap lines (Stickel 1948).

Similar inaccuracies of assumptions that relative densities are proportionate to true densities also apply to comparisons of the density of different genera or of the same genus in different habitats. Until one knows more about the influence exerted upon home ranges by species, sex, and habitat, it is well to use caution in drawing conclusions from relative densities other than for those densities that concern a single species and sex from different times in the same habitat.

Many small mammal species have home ranges, whereas other species seem to wander continually with no defined center of activity (Calhoun and Casby 1958). When using the Lincoln Index method, one assumes that the marked animals when released into the population will become distributed throughout and that further samples will take these marked animals with no greater or lesser probability of capture than the unmarked animals (Hayne 1949a). If the marked animals return to the use of their original home ranges, they may or may not present a random distribution within the population for subsequent sampling. In fact, White et al. (1982) stated frankly that "there is simply no basis for thinking that samples are drawn randomly in capture studies of animal populations."

Another important assumption is that no significant replacement of the population by unmarked animals will occur between the marking and the sampling periods. Mortality does not present a significant problem, so long as it happens in equal proportion among marked and unmarked animals and does not result in replacement of the dead animals by unmarked individuals from other sources (Hayne 1949a). Movement out of a population is treated the same as mortality; movement into it, as part of recruitment (Schemnitz 1980). If either mortality or recruitment is significant during the initial inventory or monitoring period, subsequent sampling will be difficult to analyze correctly without conducting time-intensive studies (White et al. 1982).

Turnover is rapid in many small mammal populations. Individuals are replaced constantly, either by dispersal with replacement by individuals from adjacent areas or by natural mortality with replacement by younger individuals growing to adult status. If too much time lapses between the preliminary marking period and the subsequent sampling period, an overestimation of the size of the population that was present during the marking period inevitably results. In either this method or methods for estimating density (Scott et al. 1978; O'Farrell et al. 1977; White et al. 1982), the importance of being able to assume no recruitment or mortality is emphasized. It is important not to wait more than a few days between the marking period and the subsequent recapture period.

General Considerations for all Small Mammal Studies.
Sufficient time and money for meaningful studies will continue to be problems facing most biologists. Good judgment must be exercised to obtain the best information possible with limited funding. Most small mammal studies in the past have been classified by Hayne (1976) as "descriptive studies" and discuss animals found at the time and place for each particular study but have little application to other times and areas because they are seldom replicated. Hayne (1976) emphasized that a sample size of even just two is very much better than a sample size of one. He did not imply that a sample size of two is adequate for precision. Obtaining precision in nature can be very costly, but the value of even one replication of a study can shed great light on the results of the first study. Usually, the results of two samples can be lumped or averaged to give a better picture of the real situation. Unreplicated studies can lead to generalizations and unrestrained speculations; even one replication of a sample in a comparable habitat type should put some limitations on how the results are interpreted.

One should not be intimidated by criticism that two studies in the same kind of habitat in different areas cannot be compared because they are not identical habitats. There is no such thing as any two areas being identical; there will always be some differences, but if two similar areas are selected carefully, either for replication of an initial study or for comparison with other years, the results should be valid for comparisons.

The assumption of equal trappability is probably false in most situations, even though it is a necessary assumption in most sophisticated statistical procedures (White et al. 1982). In some studies, a disproportionate number of animals are captured, which had a high probability of capture; these may be termed as "repeaters" or described as having a "trap habit." When using the Lincoln Index method, this

situation will tend to produce underestimates of the population (Hayne 1949a). In other situations animals learn to avoid traps. This may happen to animals that have a toe clipped or have some other unpleasant experience during or after capture in a live trap or after a bare escape from a snap trap. After first capture, an animal's capture probability on subsequent capture occasions changes, often greatly (Getz 1961; Bailey 1969; White et al. 1982). Therefore, marked animals probably do not have the same catchability as previously uncaught animals. Some factors affecting small mammal responses to traps include weather, season, individual inquisitiveness, population density, food availability, type of traps used, social dominance, sex, and activity patterns (Sheppe 1972; Sarrazin and Bider 1973; Summerlin and Wolfe 1973).

Considerable differences occur in the numbers of animals trapped in different types of traps; also, different sizes of the same type of trap may catch different numbers of animals. It would be advisable, therefore, to use the same kind of traps and in the same sequence (live vs. snap traps) for obtaining samples that are to be compared between years, seasons, or habitat types (Schemnitz 1980).

There have been few studies to check population estimates against a known population. Most present-day techniques of estimation have such low precision that only large changes of the population or a large influence of a factor can be detected (Schemnitz 1980). Fortunately, low precision estimates may be adequate for management purposes on small mammals, because even a method of low precision can detect a large effect in a population. However, if better precision is required to meet a specific objective, procedures may be found in the literature (Hayne 1949a; DeLury 1951; Leslie 1952; Fredin 1954; Davis 1956; Nixon et al. 1967; Eberhardt 1969; Burnham 1972; Hansson 1974; Jensen 1975; O'Farrell et al. 1977; Burnham and Overton 1979; Cormack 1981; Seber 1982; White et al. 1982).

In the typical mark-recapture study, a main objective is to estimate the population size (N). Neither the true value of (N) nor the correct assumptions to make about capture probabilities are known (White et al. 1982). Delving into the literature one will find dozens of published estimators. The biologists should select one and proceed with the calculations. However, they rarely can test the assumptions they have made in collecting samples, nor do they take time to estimate the sampling variance of the population estimate. In some instances assumptions hold for one species but not for another living in the same habitat. Unfortunately, the development of the mathematics and statistics has proceeded far more rapidly than has the testing of the assumptions usually used for statistical tests (Schemnitz 1980). The task of testing assumptions about small mammal populations is tremendous and beyond the scope of most investigations. Because there are numerous published estimators, biologists using different estimators can get different estimates with the same data. It is difficult to decide which estimator will give the most accurate results for any given situation. Another difficulty in analyzing differences in species, relative densities, or estimated numbers during monitoring studies over a sequence of years is that of determining whether apparent differences are real or only variations that might be expected among any set of samples.

At times, the biologist may wish to determine an estimate of density of small mammals in a particular habitat type. Density is defined as the number of animals per unit area. Density estimation extends population size estimation to include an estimate of the area to which the population estimate relates. Density estimates are usually derived with the use of a trapping grid. However, density estimation is not as simple as dividing the estimated population of animals by the area of the trapping grid, because of the phenomenon known as edge effect (White et al. 1982). For example, animals at the edge of a grid will not spend all of their time on the grid, because the grid area contains only a part of their home ranges. Thus, the effective area trapped is somewhat larger than the grid area, because the area to which the population estimate applies includes the entire home ranges of such animals.

A boundary strip should be included as part of the area occupied by the population. Dice (1941) suggested that the width of the boundary strip be taken as one-half the average diameter of the home range of the species in question. Other authors have made additional recommendations (Hayne 1949b; Stickel 1954; Tanaka 1972; Otis et al. 1978) but all approaches are subject to difficulties. For example, the estimates depend on trap spacing and numbers of recaptures (White et al. 1982). A second approach involves the use of assessment lines (M.H. Smith et al. 1971; R. Smith et al. 1975; H.D. Smith et al. 1972; Scott et al. 1978; O'Farrell et al. 1977). Although this approach has produced good results, the method can become complex and is heavily dependent on the design of the trap layout. However, it can be demonstrated that the importance of the boundary strip decreases as the size of the grid

increases. Placing traps in a rectangular configuration or in a series of parallel lines reduces this edge effect even when using the simpler methods, such as trap lines set out to determine relative density or species occurrence.

Biologists desiring to calculate densities of one or more species of small mammals should refer to Literature Cited for needed statistical procedures. White et al. (1982) stated that:

"computer programs have become essential in the analysis of capture-recapture and removal studies. The iterative nature of many estimators of population size under closure makes them nearly impossible to compute with a hand calculator, and the testing and model selection procedures are tedious. The notation and algebra for the estimators of open-population parameters are difficult, and recently developed models do not have closed-form estimators. In all cases, rounding errors, especially for the estimates of sampling variances, can be serious on a calculator. Now and in the future, a comprehensive analysis of any set of multiple capture data will require the use of sophisticated computer programs. A good computer system and its accompanying software are now mandatory, if biologists are to benefit from the statistical and theoretical advances made in the past decade. A general, flexible, easy-to-use system will be a great help in future research on biological populations."

The foregoing thoughts have been presented to help the biologist comprehend the magnitude of the factors that influence results of small mammal studies. They are not meant to create doubt but, rather, to create caution in making too broad generalizations based on small samples and to emphasize the need to design all monitoring studies to be comparable with previous studies. Only when the effects of variables discussed in this section are about equal can results of sampling be compared with any confidence from year to year.

Most small mammal surveys for land management purposes are to determine trends in species and numbers, not necessarily to determine densities (Kepner 1978). Even though the Lincoln Index method or Probability of Capture method may provide somewhat crude results, data derived can be effectively used for trends so long as conditions are comparable at each sampling period.

LITERATURE CITED

ANDERSON, B.W., J. DRAKE, and R.D. OHMART. 1977. Population fluctuations in nocturnal rodents in the Lower Colorado River Valley. Pages 183-192 *in* Proc. Symp. on the Importance, Preservation, and Management of the Riparian Habitat. U.S. Dep. Agric., For. Serv. Gen. Tech. Report RM-43.

ANDERSON, D.R., J.L. LAAKE, B.R. CRAIN, and K.P. BURNHAM. 1976. Guidelines for line transect sampling of biological populations. Utah Coop. Wildl. Res. Unit. Logan. 27pp.

―――― and R.D. OHMART. 1977. Rodent bait additive which repels insects. J. Mammal. 58:242.

BAILEY, J.A. 1969. Trap response of wild cottontails. J. Wildl. Manage. 33(1):48-58.

BLAIR, W.F. 1941. Techniques for the study of mammal populations. J. Mammal. 22(2):148-157.

BRADT, G.W. 1938. A study of beaver colonies in Michigan. J. Mammal. 19:139-162.

BURNHAM, K.P. 1972. Estimation of population size in multiple capture-recapture studies when capture probabilities vary among animals. Ph.D. dissertation. Oregon State University, Corvallis.

―――― D.R. ANDERSON, and J.L. LAAKE. 1980. Estimation of density from line transect sampling of biological populations. Wildl. Monogr. 72:1-202.

―――― and W.S. OVERTON. 1979. Robust estimation of population size when capture probabilities vary among animals. Ecology 60(5):927-936.

BURT, W.H. and R.P. GROSSENHEIDER. 1964. A field guide to the mammals. The Riverside Press. Cambridge, MA. 284pp.

CALHOUN, J.B. and J.V. CASBY. 1958. Calculation of home range and density of small mammals. Public Health Service, Public Health Mongr. 55. 24pp.

CALL, M.W. 1970. Beaver pond ecology and beaver-trout relationships in southeastern Wyoming. Ph.D. dissertation. Univ. of Wyoming, Laramie. 319pp.

CHITTY, D. 1937. A ringing technique for small mammals. J. Animal Ecol. 6:36-53.

―――― and M. SHORTEN. 1946. Techniques for the study of the Norway rat (*Rattus norvegicus*). J. Mammal. 27:63-78.

COLLIER, E. 1957. Revolutionary new trap. Outdoor Life. Sept. 1957, p. 38-41, 80, and Oct. 1957, p. 70-73, 80, 82.

COOLEY, M.E. 1948. Improved toe-tag for marking fox squirrels. J. Wildl. Manage. 12:213.

CORMACK, R.M. 1981. Log-linear models for capture-recapture experiments on animal populations. Univ. of Otago. Dunedin, New Zealand.

DAVIS, D.E. 1956. Manual for analysis of rodent populations. Edwards Brothers, Inc. Ann Arbor, MI. 82pp.

DELURY, D.B. 1951. On the planning of experiments for the estimation of fish populations. J. Fish. Res. Board of Canada. 8:281-307.

DENNEY, R.N. 1952. A summary of North American beaver management. Colo. Game and Fish Dep. Current Report 28. Denver, CO. 58pp.

DICE, L.R. 1941. Methods for estimating populations of animals. J. Wildl. Manage. 5(4):398-407.

DYMOND, J.R. 1947. Fluctuations in animal populations with species reference to those of Canada. Trans. Royal Soc. Canada 41(5):1-34.

EBERHARDT, L.L. 1969. Population estimates from recapture frequencies. J. Wildl. Manage. 33(1):28-39.

ELTON, C. 1942. Voles, mice and lemmings. Clarendon Press. Oxford. 496pp.

ERRINGTON, P.L. 1944. Additional studies on tagged young muskrats. J. Wildl. Manage. 8:300-306.

―――― and C.S. ERRINGTON. 1937. Experimental tagging of young muskrats for purposes of study. J. Wildl. Manage. 24:231-260.

EVANS, F.C. and R. HOLDENRIED. 1943. A population study of the Beechey ground squirrel in central California. J. Mammal. 24:231-260.

FITZWATER, W.D., Jr. 1943. Color marking of mammals, with special reference to squirrels. J. Wildl. Manage. 7:190-192.

FREDIN, R.A. 1954. Causes of fluctuations in abundance of Connecticut River shad. U.S. Dep. Inter., Fish and Wildl. Serv. Fishery Bull. 88. Washington, DC.

GETZ, L.L. 1961. Response of small mammals to live-traps and weather conditions. Am. Midl. Nat. 66(1):160-169.

GILES, R.H., ed. 1969. Wildlife management techniques. 3rd ed. The Wildl. Soc. Washington, DC. 623pp.

HANSSON, L. 1974. Influence area of trap stations as a function of number of small mammals exposed per trap. Acta Theriol. 19:19-25.

HAYNE, D.W. 1949a. Two methods for estimating population from trapping records. J. Mammal. 30:399-411.

―――― 1949b. Calculation of size of home range. J. Mammal. 30(1):1-18.

―――― 1976. Experimental designs and statistical analyses in small mammal population studies *in* Populations of Small Mammals Under Natural Conditions. The Pymatuning Symposia in Ecology, Vol. 5. Special Publ. Series, Pymatuning Lab. of Ecology, Univ. of Pittsburgh. Symposia held at the Pymatuning Lab. of Ecology, May 14-16, 1976.

HENSLEY, A.L. and H. TWINING. 1946. Some early summer observations on muskrats in a northeastern California marsh. Calif. Fish and Game 32:171-181.

HOFFMEISTER, D.F. and L. DE LA TORRE. 1960. A revision of the woodrat *Neotoma stephensi*. J. Mammal. 41(4):482.

INGLES, L.G. 1965. Mammals of the Pacific States. Stanford Univ. Press. Stanford, CA. 506pp.

JACKSON, H.H.T. 1961. Mammals of Wisconsin. Univ. Wisconsin Press. Madison. 504pp.

JENSEN, T.S. 1975. Trappability of various functional groups of the forest rodents *Clethrionomys glareolus* and *Apodemus flavicollis*, and its application in density estimations. Oikos 26(2):196-204.

JORGENSEN, C.D. and H.D. SMITH. 1974. Mini-grids and small mammal estimates *in* Proceedings of the Utah Academy of Sciences, Arts, and Letters. Vol. 51, Part I.

KEITH, L.B. 1963. Wildlife's ten-year cycle. Univ. Wisconsin Press. Oxford. 201pp.

KEPNER, W.G. 1978. Small mammals of the Black Canyon and Skull Valley planning units, Maricopa and Yavapai Counties, Arizona. U.S. Dep. Inter., Bur. Land Manage. Tech Note 350. 37pp.

KREFTING, L.W., J.H. STOECKLER, B.J. BRADLE, and W.D. FITZWATER. 1962. Porcupine-timber relationships in the Lake States. J. For. 60:325-330.

LESLIE, P.H. 1952. The estimation of population parameters from data obtained by means of the capture-recapture method: II. The estimation of total numbers. Biometrika 38(3/4):368-388.

———— and D.H.S. DAVIS. 1939. An attempt to determine the absolute number of rats on a given area. J. Anim. Ecol. 8:94-113.

MASER, B.R. MATE, J.F. FRANKLIN, and C.T. DYRNESS. 1981. Natural history of Oregon coast mammals. U.S. Dep. Agric., For. Serv. Gen. Tech. Rep. PNW-133. 496pp.

MOREJOHN, G.V. and W.E. HOWARD. 1956. Moult in the pocket gopher, *Thomomys bottae.* J. Mammal. 37:201-212.

MOSBY, H.S. ed. 1963. Wildlife investigational techniques, 2nd Edition. The Wildl. Soc. Washington, DC. 419pp.

NIXON, C.N., W.R. EDWARDS, and L.L. EBERHARDT. 1967. Estimating squirrel abundance from live trapping data. J. Wildl. Manage. 31(1):96-101.

O'FARRELL, M.J., D.W. KAUFMAN, and D.W. LUNDOHL. 1977. Use of live-trapping with the assessment line method for density estimation. J. Mammal. 58(4):575-582.

OTIS, D.L., K.P. BURNHAM, G.C. WHITE, and D.R. ANDERSON. 1978. Statistical inference from capture data on closed animal populations. Wildl. Monogr. 62:1-135.

PETRUSEWICZ, K. and A. MACFAYDEN. 1970. Productivity of terrestrial animals —principles and methods. Inter. Biol. Prog. Handbook 13. F.A. Davis Co. Philadelphia, PA. l90pp.

REYNOLDS, H.C. 1945. Some aspects of the life history and ecology of the opossum in central Missouri. J. Mammal. 26:361-379.

RUTHERFORD, W.H. 1964. The beaver in Colorado, its biology, ecology, management and economics. Colo. Game, Fish and Parks Dep. Fed. Aid in Wildl. Rest. Proj. W-83-R. Denver, CO. 49pp.

SANDERSON, G.C. 1961. Estimating opossum population by marking young. J.Wildl. Manage. 25:20-27.

SARRAZIN, J.P.R. and J.R. BIDER. 1973. Activity, a neglected parameter in population estimates—the development of a new technique. J. Mammal. 54(2):369-382.

SCHEMNITZ, S.D. ed. 1980. Wildlife management techniques. 4th ed. revised. The Wildl. Soc. Washington, DC. 686pp.

SCHULTZ, V. 1961. An annotated bibliography on the uses of statistics in ecology—a search of 31 periodicals. Publication TID-3908. U.S. Atomic Energy Comm. Office of Tech. Info, Environmental Science Branch, Div. of Bio. and Medicine. Washington, DC. 314pp.

SCOTT, D.T., C.D. JORGENSEN, and H.D. SMITH. 1978. Comparison of live and removal methods to estimate small mammal densities. Acta Therio. 23(8):173-193.

SEBER, G.A.F. 1973. The estimation of animal abundance. Hafner Press, New York, NY. 506pp.

————. 1982. Estimation of animal abundance and related parameters. 2nd. ed. Hafner Press. New York, NY. 654pp.

SHEPPE, W. 1972. The annual cycle of small mammal populations on a Zambian floodplain. J. Mammal. 53(3):445-460.

SMITH, H.D., C D. JORGENSEN, and H.D. TOLLEY. 1972. Estimation of small mammals using recapture methods: partitioning of estimator variables. Acta Therio. 17:57-66.

SMITH, M.H., R. BLESSING, J.G. CHELTON, J.B. GENTRY, G. GOLLEY, and J.T. MCGINNIS. 1971. Determining density for small mammal populations using a grid and assessment lines. Acta Theriol. 16:105-125.

SMITH, R., H. GARDNER, J.B. GENTRY, D.W. DAUFMAN, and M.J. O'FARRELL. 1975. Density estimation of small animal populations, Pages 25-53 *in* F.G. Golley, K. Petrusewicz, and L. Ruszkowski, eds. Small Mammals: Their Production and Population Dynamics, Intern. Biol. Prog. 5. Cambridge Univ. Press, London.

SNEDECOR, G.W. and W.G. COCHRAN. 1967. Statistical methods, 6th ed. Iowa State Univ. Press, Ames. 593pp.

SOKAL, R.R. and F.J. ROHLF. 1969. Biometry: the principles and practice of statistics in biological research. W.H. Freeman and Co. San Francisco, CA. 776pp.

SPEIRS, J.M. 1939. Fluctuations in numbers of birds in the Toronto region. Auk 56:411-419.

STICKEL, L.F. 1948. The trap line as a measure of small mammal populations. J. Wildl. Manage. 12:153-161.

———— 1954. A comparison of certain methods of measuring ranges of small mammals. J. Mammal. 35(1):1-15.

SUMMERLIN, C.T. and J.L. WOLFE. 1973. Social influences on trap response of the cotton rat, *(Sigmodon hispidus).* Ecology 54(5):1156-1159.

SVIHLA, A. 1934. Development and growth of deer mice *(Peromyscus maniculatus artemisiae),* J. Mammal. 15:99-104.

TAKOS, M.J. 1943. Trapping and banding muskrats. J. Wildl. Manage.7:400-407.

TANAKA, R. 1972. Investigation into the edge effect by use of capture-recapture method in a vole population. Res. Pop. Ecol. 12(1):111-125.

WHITE, G.C., D.R. ANDERSON, K.P. BURNHAM, and D.L. OTIS. 1982. Capture-recapture and removal methods for sampling closed populations. Los Alamos National Laboratory. Los Alamos, NM. 235pp.

YERGER, R.W. 1953. Home range, territoriality, and populations of the chipmunk in central New York. J. Mammal. 34:448-458.

22

LAGOMORPHS

Joseph A. Chapman

Utah State University
Logan, UT 84322

Gale R. Willner

The Ecology Center
Utah State University
Logan, UT 84322

Editor's Note: Lagomorphs, among other mid-size mammals, have often been neglected in wildlife surveys. Although often locally important as a game or pest species, they have not received the same amount of attention as other more conspicuous or economically important species. Furthermore, typical inventorying techniques and equipment used for other species are not useful in studying lagomorphs. This chapter identifies some possible techniques that can be used for inventorying and monitoring this often overlooked group of species.

INTRODUCTION

Lagomorphs are important components of the world's ecosystems, particularly in the western U.S. and Alaska where they make the base of many carnivore food chains. In addition, they are important indicators of habitat quality, sport animals, depredators, and models for ecological research.

The order Lagomorpha occurs worldwide and contains two families, Leporidae and Ochotonidae, both found in the U.S. The North American Leporidae includes hares and jackrabbits (*Lepus* sp.), cottontails (*Sylvilagus* sp.), and volcano rabbit (*Romerolagus* sp.), found only in Central Mexico. Five species of *Sylvilagus* and four species of jackrabbits occur in the western half of the U.S. Snowshoe hares (*L. americanus*) are widely distributed in Alaska and the western U.S., but the Alaskan hare (*L. othus*) occurs only in Alaska. The pikas (*Ochotona princeps*) are the only members of the family Ochotonidae and they live on talus slopes throughout most of the higher mountains in the western U.S. and southeastern Alaska.

All Leporidae are adapted for quick movement and flight from danger. Their hind legs are long and adapted to cursorial locomotion. Their ears are large and moveable to permit detection of approaching enemies. Unlike pikas, their eyes are large and suited to their crepuscular and nocturnal habits. These features are most developed in the hares. Many cottontails rely on thick brush or even burrows to avoid predators. Pikas are rodent-like in appearance and are well-suited to living among the rocks and boulders of their talus slope environment.

In general, Lagomorphs are highly fecund and short-lived. Population levels are regulated by mortality (survival) and dispersal. Indirectly, the composition and structure of the plant community within their habitat plays an important part in the survival of these mammals. They are usually associated with disturbed or subclimax plant communities.

The purpose of this chapter is to summarize techniques that are most useful in determining Lagomorph population levels as well as examine habitat features that are important to this order. This should enable the land manager to evaluate the relationship of density and habitat and thus determine the status of Lagomorphs in a given area.

In this chapter, the Lagomorphs are divided into four species groups on the basis of taxonomy, reproductive characteristics, and their most common habitat requirements.

HABITAT FEATURES CORRELATED WITH SPECIES GROUPS

Jackrabbits

Jackrabbits are true hares, primarily associated with arid regions of the 11 western States. They are found at elevations from below sea level in Death Valley to nearly 4,000 m (13,000 ft). Jackrabbits will drink water, but researchers do not consider it a requirement of their habitat.

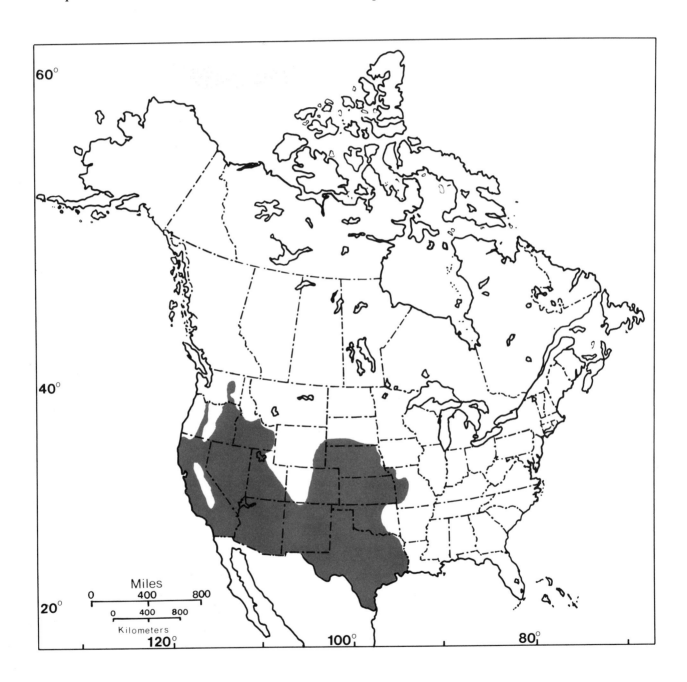

Figure 1. Distribution of the black-tailed jackrabbit in the western United States (adapted from Dunn et al. 1982).

White-tailed jackrabbits are often found in prairies and in open flats and alpine zones above treeline. Black-tailed jackrabbits are the most abundant hare in the western U.S.; white-tailed jackrabbits are locally abundant. The antelope and white-sided jackrabbits are uncommon to rare throughout their rather restricted ranges. (See Figures 1, 2, and 3 for distribution.)

White-tailed jackrabbits usually occur in low-growing scrub, grasslands, or prairie areas. In the western States they are often found at higher elevations, even above treeline where they inhabit tundra-like vegetation (Braun and Streeter 1968). In mountainous regions they also occur in areas vegetated with disjunct clumps of sagebrush. See Tables 1 and 2 for cover and food plants found in areas occupied by jackrabbits.

Black-tailed jackrabbits are often associated with shortgrass-sagebrush areas in arid regions. They also inhabit agricultural areas. White-tailed jackrabbits are also found in sagebrush areas in higher mountain regions, but are most often found in prairie grasslands. Black-tailed jackrabbits appear to displace the white-tailed jackrabbit in disturbed or cultivated areas where the two occur sympatrically.

Although black-tailed jackrabbits seem to prefer diverse plant communities made up of disjunct cover, there are little quantitative data available. Black-tailed jackrabbits are found in a wide array of habitat types, all of which are characterized or dominated by low-growing trees or shrubs and well-drained soils. High populations occur in sagebrush (*Artemisia* sp.) interspersed with sparse grass. In general, only open or semi-open areas are occupied by this species. No area appears to be too open as long as it provides adequate hiding, resting, and birthing sites. Black-tailed jackrabbits are usually associated with vegetation that is no more than about 1 m (3 ft) high.

The antelope jackrabbit occurs exclusively in the lower Sonoran life zone in Arizona where its preferred habitat is grassy slopes. However, it is also found in the cactus belt in areas dominated by mesquite (*Prosopis* sp.), catclaw (*Acacia greggi*), and various grasses. Smaller populations occupy creosote bush (*Larrea* sp.) deserts and valley bottoms (Figure 2). It occurs at elevations from sea level to 1,200 m (3,960 ft) (Vorheis and Taylor 1933). Similarly, the white-sided jackrabbit is found exclusively in the shortgrass habitats of New Mexico (Figure 2). The preferred habitat is composed of 65% or more grasses, 25% or less forbs, and 1% or less shrubs (Bednarz 1977).

Harry Engels

White-tailed jackrabbit.

U.S. Fish and Wildlife Service

Black-tailed jackrabbit.

Kenneth W. Fink

Antelope jackrabbit.

Snowshoe and Alaskan Hares

Alaskan hares are among the least known Lagomorphs in North America. Recent work indicates that *L. othus*, *L. arcticus*, and *L. timidus* are perhaps the same species with a Holarctic distribution (Dixon et al. 1983). There are two distinct ecotypes of Alaskan hares: *L. o. othus*, associated with tundras and alluvial plains, and *L. o. poudromus*, associated with coastal lowland areas of the Aleutian Island chain (Bittner and Rongstand 1982).

Snowshoe hares are found in most higher mountains of the western States, except Arizona, as well as throughout Alaska (Figure 3).

Snowshoe hares inhabit subclimax forests and transition zones adjacent to heavy cover. High densities of snowshoe hares will not be found at distances greater than 200 to 400 m (660 to 1,320 ft) from conifer stands. High densities are unlikely in areas with a solid canopy (Conroy et al. 1979). Throughout their range, these hares appear partial to dense thickets and windfalls where they seek cover. In Alaska, they are found in a mosaic of plant communities that include upland black spruce/ledum/moss, willow-alder thickets, and white spruce/birch/aspen habitat types (Wolff 1978).

Snowshoe hares are also found in dense, second-growth forests, often associated with aspen (*Populus*

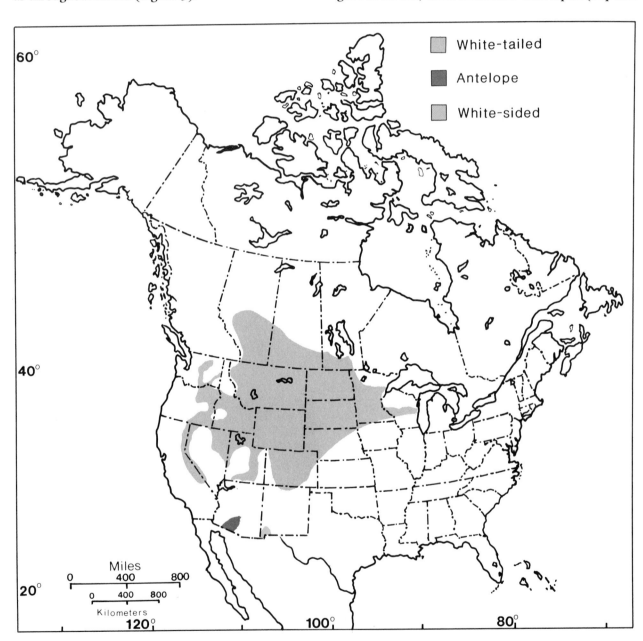

Figure 2. Distribution of the white-tailed, antelope, and white-sided jackrabbits in the western United States (adapted from Dunn et al. 1982.)

tremuloides) thickets and coniferous swamps. In the central Rocky Mountains, snowshoe hares use areas of spruce (*Picea* sp.), fir (*Abies* sp. and *Pseudotsuga* sp.), and lodgepole pine (*Pinus contorta*). In those habitats they prefer conifer stands with dense brushy understories (Dolbeer and Clark 1975). In Utah, prime snowshoe hare habitat occurs in areas with high sapling numbers, high basal area, and dense canopy cover. Optical cover densities of less than 40% above the snowline limit winter use of a habitat by snowshoe hares (Wolff et al. 1982). Snowshoe hare numbers are greatest in areas subjected to periodic burning (Grange 1965).

Little is known about the habitat of the Alaskan hare except that one subspecies prefers tundra or alluvial plain, and the other prefers coastal lowlands (Bittner and Rongstand 1982).

In the western States snowshoe hares are invariably linked with conifers at higher elevations. However they may range away from coniferous timber at high elevations where streams are thickly bordered with vegetation (Dice 1926; Orr 1940). These hares also utilize logged-over areas adjacent to standing conifers. See Tables 1 and 3 for detailed list of cover and food plants found on areas occupied by snowshoe hares.

Figure 3. Distribution of the snowshoe and Alaskan hares in the western United States and Alaska (adapted from Bittner and Rongstand 1982).

Table 1. Some plants occurring in habitats occupied by various Lagomorph species.

Lagomorph and Plant Species	Area
Black-tailed jackrabbit	
Rabbitbrush (*Chrysothamnus* sp.)	California
Sagebrush (*Artemisia tridentata*)	
Saltbush (*Atriplex* sp.)	
Horsebrush (*Tetradymia* sp.)	
Creosotebush (*Larrea tridentata*)	Southern Nevada and southeastern California
Joshua trees (*Yucca brevifolia*)	Southern Utah
Creosotebush	
Brigham tea (*Ephedra* sp.)	
Shadscale (*Atriplex confertifolia*)	Salt deserts of Great Basin
Greasewood (*Scarcobatus vermiculatus*)	
Rabbitbrush	
Sagebrush	
Juniper (*Juniperus* sp.)	
Pinyon pines (*Pinus edulis*)	
Sagebrush	Central and southern Utah
Rabbitbrush	
Mesquite (*Prosopis* sp.)	New Mexico
Snakeweed (*Gutierrezia sarothrae*)	
Soaptree yucca (*Yucca* sp.)	
Agricultural crops—alfalfa hay	
White-tailed jackrabbit	
Juniper (*J. occidentalis*)	California (Lake Tahoe)
Lodgepole pine (*Pinus contorta*)	
Dwarf juniper (*J. communis*)	
Creambush (*Holodiscus discolor*)	
Granite/gilia (*Leptodactylon purges*)	
Sagebrush	Northern Utah
Bitterbrush (*Purshia tridentata*)	
Giant wild rye (*Elymus condensatus*)	
Chokecherry (*Prunus melanocarpa*)	
Snowberry (*Symphoricarpos rotundifolius*)	
Mountain myrtle (*Pachystima myrsinites*)	
Deerbrush (*Ceanothus velotinus*)	Utah and Idaho
Aspen (*Populus tremuloides*)	
Sagebrush	Uintah Basin
Greasewood	
Shadscale	
Saltbush	
Dogwood (*Cornus canadensis*)	
Wild rhubarb (*Polygonum alaskanum*)	
Horsetail (*Equisetum* sp.)	
Audubon's cottontail	
Willow (*Salix* sp.)	California
Buttonwillow (*Cephalanthus occidentalis*)	
Wild grape (*Vitis californica*)	
Arroyo willow (*S. lasiolepis*)	
Brushland (*Adenostoma fasilutatuium*)	
(*Eriodictyeon* sp.)	
(*Eriogonum* sp.)	
Arrow-weed (*Pluchea sericea*)	Southern Nevada
Screw-bean mesquite (*Prosopis pubesans*)	
Catclaw (*Acacia greggii*)	
Joshua trees	Southern Utah
Cactus	

Table 1. Some plants occurring in habitats occupied by various Lagomorph species (continued).

Lagomorph and Plant Species (continued)	Area
Audubon's cottontail (continued)	
Brigham tea Creosotebush Junipers Pinyon Evergreen oaks (*Quercus turbinella*) Gumine bush (*Garrya flaresceni*) Saltbush Rabbitbrush (*Chrysothamnus nauseous*) Snakeweed Winterfat (*Eurotia* sp.)	Western Utah
Nuttall's cottontail	
Sagebrush Rabbitbrush Wild rye (*Elymus condensatus*) Bitterbrush Chokecherry (*Prunus virginiana*)	Northern Utah
Brush rabbit	
Bramble (*Rubus* sp.) Buckbrush (*Ceanothus* sp.) Willows California rosebay (*Rhododendron californicum*) Chaparral broom (*Baccharis pilularis*) Wild rose (*Rosa californica*) Poison oak (*Rhus diversiloba*) Scrub oak (*Q. dumosa*) Snowberry (*Symphoricarpus albus*) Yellow pine (*Pinus ponderosa*) Manzanita (*Arctostaphylos* sp.)	Oregon California
Antelope jackrabbit	
Catsclaw (*Acacia greggi*) Mesquite Grasses (*Graminea*) Creosotebush (*Larrea* sp.)	Arizona
White-sided jackrabbit	
Grasses Grama (*Bouteloua gracilis*) Black grama (*B. eriopoda*) Buffalo grass (*Buchloe dacyloides*) Wolftail (*Lycurus phleoides*)	New Mexico
Snowshoe hares (Continental U.S.)	
Willows Douglas fir (*Pseudotsuga menziesii*) Snowberry Snowbrush Mountain myrtle Mountain ash (*Sorbus scopulina*) Aspen	Northern Utah

Table 1. Some plants occurring in habitats occupied by various Lagomorph species (concluded).

Lagomorph and Plant Species (Concluded)	Area
Snowshoe hares (Continental U.S.) (continued)	
Alpine fir (*Abies*)	Uintah Mountains
Engleman spruce (*P. englemanii*)	of Utah
Lodgepole pine	California
Alder (*Alnus* sp.)	
Willow	
Conifers	
Chaparral (*Ceanothus* sp.)	
Manzanita	
Buckbrush (*C. velutinus*)	Southern California
Douglas fir	
Red cedar (*Thuja plicata*)	
Snowshow hares (Alaska)	
White spruce (*Picea glauca*)	
Black spruce (*P. mariana*)	
Paper birch (*Betula papyrifera*)	
Aspen	
Balsam poplar (*Populus balsamifera*)	
Alder (*Alnus crispa*)	
Dwarf birch (*Betula gladulosa*)	
Willows	
Labrador tea (*Ledum groenlandicum*)	
Blueberry (*Vaccinium uliginosum*)	
Lowbush cranberry (*Vaccinium vitis-idaea*)	
Rose (*Rosa acicularis*)	
Grasses (*Calamagrostis* sp.)	
Fireweed (*Epilobium angustifolium*)	
Pikas	
Rabbitbrush	California
Sagebrush	
Bitterbrush	
Columbine (*Aquilegia pubescens*)	

Sources: (Orr 1940; Janson 1946; Davis et al. 1975; Bednarz 1977; Dice 1926; Wolff 1978; Chapman 1971; Smith 1974a).

Cottontails

Cottontails are widely scattered throughout 11 western States, but are not present in Alaska. The Nuttall's cottontail inhabits the intermountain region, whereas the Audubon's cottontail is found in the arid Southwest and high deserts north to Montana. Ranges of these two species broadly overlap in Colorado, Montana, Utah, and Wyoming (Figure 4). The brush rabbit is confined to the coasts of California and Oregon, whereas the pygmy rabbit is found in the Great Basin with a small disjunct population in eastern Washington (Figure 5). The eastern cottontail occurs primarily from the Midwest east, with the exception of Arizona and New Mexico, which have large eastern cottontail populations. This species occurs peripherally in eastern Colorado, Wyoming, and Montana and has been introduced into Oregon and Washington (Figure 5).

The Audubon's cottontail occurs in the lower Sonoran life zone and often prefers stream bottom vegetation. Shrubs interspersed with pinyon (*Pinus edulis*) and juniper (*Juniperus* sp.) provide excellent cover for this species. Downed trees or shrubs piled 170 to 220 per ha (425 to 1,210 per a.) create excellent habitat for this species (Kundaeli and Reynolds 1972).

The Nuttall's cottontail is found in rocky, wooded, or brushy areas. It is often observed in rocky ravines next to sagebrush-covered hills. When Audubon's and Nuttall's cottontails occupy the same region, the former is found on desert valleys and the latter on higher rocky, sagebrush-covered slopes. Where cover is scarce, Nuttall's cottontails will use burrows dug by badgers (*Taxidea taxus*) or crevices under rocks (Dice 1926; Orr 1940).

Pygmy rabbits are always found in sagebrush. They prefer tall sagebrush (1 to 1.5 m [3 to 5 ft]) often in ravines. They dig their own burrows which are found at the base of sagebrush clumps (Chapman et al. 1982).

The brush rabbit gets its name from its preference for dense, brushy cover. Clumps of brush smaller than 460 m² (14,900 ft²) are probably not permanently occupied (Chapman 1971). Brush rabbits have been reported to use burrows, but they do not dig their own.

In Arizona and New Mexico, eastern cottontails are found in open areas and along stream bottoms or near farm buildings. Where they have been introduced in Washington and Oregon, they have become established on old, overgrown farmsteads, in fence rows, and around buildings. Eastern cottontails in Minnesota have a distinct preference for shrubby vegetation (Swihart and Yahner 1984). They are

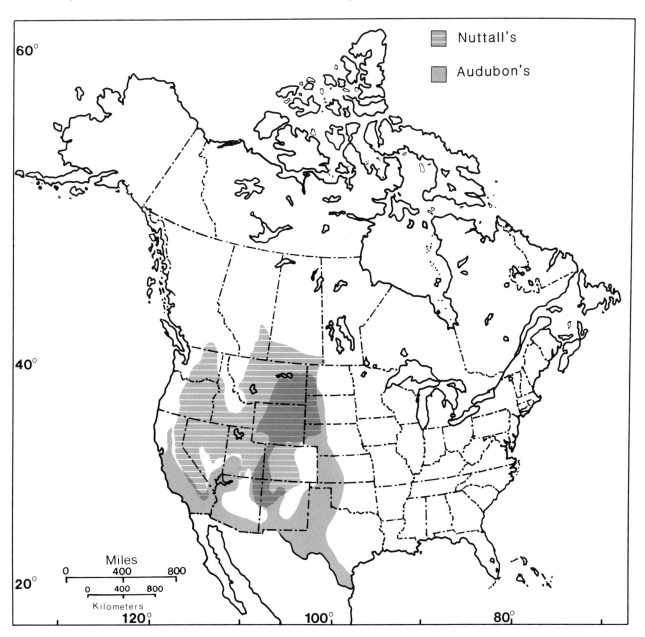

Figure 4. Distribution of the Nuttall's and Audubon's cottontails in the western United States (adapted from Chapman et al. 1982).

most abundant in disturbed successional areas (Chapman et al. 1982). See Tables 1 and 4 for detailed list of cover and food plants found in areas occupied by cottontails.

Pikas

Pikas are guinea-pig-shaped Lagomorphs, having short, rounded ears and no visible tail. Pikas move with a running gait rather than the typical hopping or leaping of other Lagomorphs. They are the only North American Lagomorphs that store or cache food. They are active during the day and are extremely vocal.

Pikas are found throughout the higher mountain ranges of the western States except Arizona and New Mexico. There is also a population of collared pikas in the mountains of southern Alaska (Figure 6).

Pikas inhabit talus slopes where they feed almost exclusively on grasses, forbs, and low bushes adjacent to these talus slopes. Pikas require a boulder-strewn habitat on high mountain slopes with a nearby source of food. Pikas require an abundance of plant species which they can collect and store in "hay" piles for later use in winter. Most often they prefer alpine meadows with abundant grass and low shrubs adjacent to talus slopes.

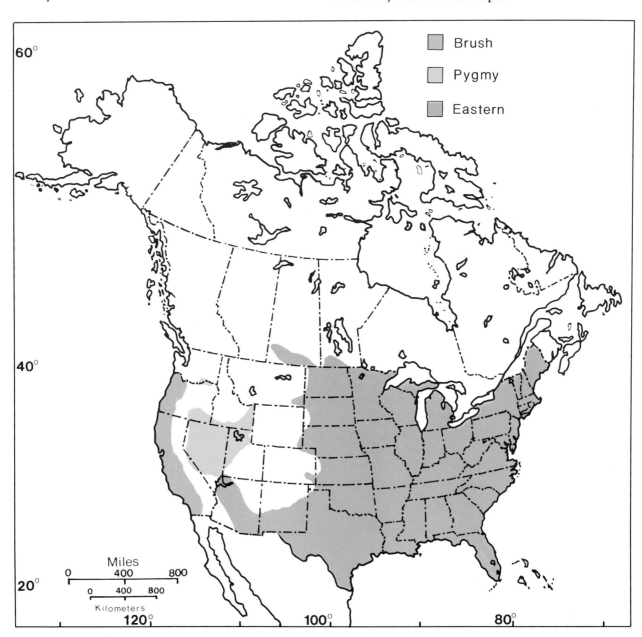

Figure 5. Distribution of the brush rabbit, pygmy rabbit, and eastern cottontail in the western United States (adapted from Chapman et al. 1982).

Pikas are noticeably absent from the Olympic Mountains in Washington even though suitable habitat appears to be available. Researchers attribute this to the lack of talus occurring between the Olympics and the Cascade Range where pikas are abundant (Dalquist 1948). Barriers to dispersal, such as climatic conditions, prevent juveniles from occupying suitable habitats and, therefore, limit population densities (Smith 1974b). Table 1 lists plant species found on areas occupied by pikas.

POPULATION MEASUREMENT TECHNIQUES

Standard census techniques may be applied to Lagomorph populations. Those techniques are summarized in the **Wildlife Management Techniques Manual (Davis and Winstead 1980) and in The Handbook of Census Methods for Terrestrial Vertebrates** (Davis 1982). These census techniques may be divided into three broad categories: (1) presence or absence, (2) relative abundance, and (3) density estimates.

Absolute density and relative abundance are somewhat misleading terms. In reality it is difficult to meet the requirements for estimates of absolute density because of problems associated with delineating boundary areas. Drive counts and mark-recapture techniques are often thought of as measures of absolute density, but it is probably better to consider

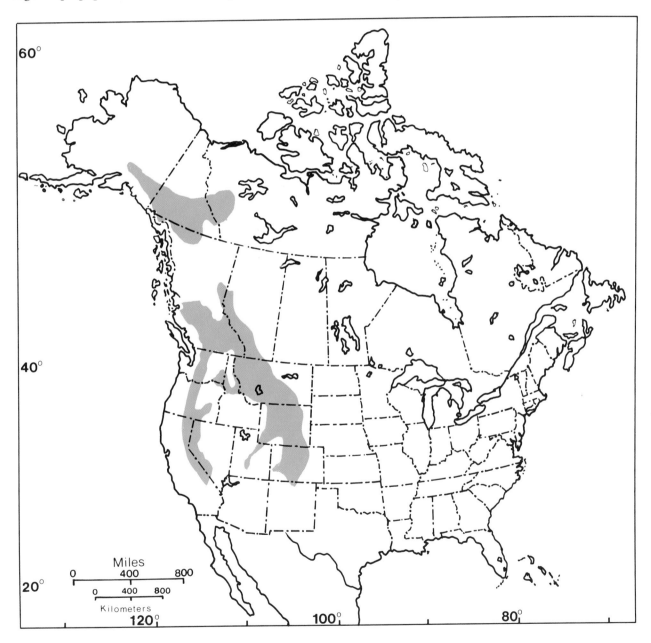

Figure 6. Distribution of the pika in the western United States and Alaska (adapted from Chapman 1979).

Table 2. Food of jackrabbits as reported in the literature.

Black-tailed Jackrabbit	White-tailed Jackrabbit

SHRUBS
    Shadscale
    Fringed sage (*Artemisia frigida*)
    Greasewood
    Sagebrush
    Hopsage (*Grayia spinosa*)
    Four-winged saltbush (*Atriplex
        canescens*)
    Horsebrush
    Snakeweed
    Creosote
	SHRUBS
	    Winterfat

FORBS
    Globemallow (*Sphaeralcea
        coccinia*)
    Winterfat (*Eurotia lanata*)
    Larkspur (*Delphinium* sp.)
    Spiderwort (*Tradescantia* sp.)
    Alfalfa (*Medicago sativa*)
    Mallow plants (*Malvaceae* sp.)
    Curly dock (*Rumex crispu*)
    Yucca (*Yucca glauca*)
    Prickly pear (*Opuntia* sp.)
    Sand dropseed (*Sporobolus
        cyptandrus*)
    Pigweed (*Amaranthus retroflexus*)
    Russian thistle (*Salsola kali*)
    Buffalo burr (*Solanum rostratum*)
    Lily (*Lilium* sp.)
    Sedge (*Carex* sp.)
    Cactus (*Opuntia* sp.)
	FORBS
	    Aster (*Caster* sp.)
	    Vetch (*Astragalus* sp.)
	    Saltbush
	    Indian paintbrush (*Castilleja integra*)
	    Golden aster (*Chrysopsis villosa*)
	    Goosefoot (*Chenopodium* sp.)
	    Corydalis (*Corydalis aurea*)
	    Daisy (*Erigeron* sp.)
	    Gilia (*Gilia aggregate*)
	    Gaura (*Gaura coccinea*)
	    Sunflower (*Helianthus annuus*)
	    Summer cypress (*Kochia* sp.)
	    Blazing star (*Liatris punctata*)
	    Lupine (*Lupinus* sp.)
	    Alfalfa
	    Bluebells (*Mertensia lanceolata*)
	    Four-o'clocks (*Mirabilis linearis*)
	    Musineon (*Musineon divaricatum*)
	    Prickly pear cactus
	    Locoweed (*Oxytropis* sp.)
	    Beardtongue (*Penstemon* sp.)
	    Plaintain (*Plantago purshii*)
	    Cinquefoil (*Potentilla* sp.)
	    Psoralea (*Psoralea tenluiflora*)
	    Rabbitbrush
	    Russian thistle
	    Groundsel (*Senecio* sp.)
	    Scarlet globe mallow (*Sphaeralcea
	        coccinia*)
	    Dandelion (*Taraxacum officinale*)
	    Spreading thermopsis (*Thermopsis
	        divaricarpa*)
	    Verbena (*Verbena bracteata*)
	    Yucca

GRASSES
    Needle-and-thread (*Stipa comata*)
    Downy brome (*Bromus tectorum*)
    Western wheatgrass (*Agropyron
        smithii*)
    Barley (*Hordeum* sp.)
    Buffalo grass (*Buchloe
        dactyloides*)
    Winter wheat (*Triticum aestivum*)
    Blue grama
    Indian ricegrass (*Oryzopsis
        hymenoides*)
    Lovegrass (*Eragrostis* sp.)
	GRASSES
	    Crested wheatgrass (*Agropyron
	        cristatus*)
	    Western wheatgrass
	    Wheatgrass (*A. trachycaulum*)
	    Red three awn (*Aristida longiseta*)
	    Oats (*Avena sativa*)
	    Blue grama
	    Brome (*Bromus anomalus*)
	    Smooth brome (*B. inermis*)
	    Downy brome
	    Sedges
	    Hairgrass (*Deschampsia caespitosa*)

Table 2. Food of jackrabbits as reported in the literature (concluded).

Black-tailed Jackrabbit	White-tailed Jackrabbit

GRASSES
    Barnyard grass (*Echinochloa* sp.)
    Panicum (*Panicum* sp.)
    Dropseed (*Sporobolus* sp.)
    Trichloris (*Trichloris* sp.)
	GRASSES
	    Love grass
	    Arizona fescue (*Festuca arizonica*)
	    Foxtail barley
	    Junegrass (*Koeleria cristada*)
	    Ringgrass
	    Bluegrass (*Poa* sp.)
	    Squirreltail (*Sitanion hystrix*)
	    Sand dropseed
	    Needle-and-thread
	    Letterman needlegrass (*S. lettermanii*)
	    Wheatgrass

White-sided Jackrabbit	Antelope Jackrabbit

GRASSES
    Buffalo grass
    Tabossa grass
    Fiddleneck (*Amsinickia* sp.)
    Wolftail
    Blue grama
    Vine Mesquite (*Pancium obstosum*)
    Ring muhly (*Muhlenbergia torreyi*)
    Wooly Indian wheat (*Plantago purshii*)
    Wright buckwheat (*Eriogonum wrightii*)
	FORBS
	    Cactus (*Echinocactus* sp.)
	
	GRASSES
	    Three awn
	    Grama
	    Love grass
	    Spike grass
	    Sandbar (*Cenchrus* Sp.)
	    Drop Seed
	    Red top (*Agrostis* sp.)
	    Barnyard grass
	    Finger grass (*Chloris* sp.)

Sources: (Hanson and Flinders 1969; Bear and Hansen 1966; Flinders and Hansen 1972; Bednarz 1977; Vorheis and Taylor 1933).

these techniques as being more accurate estimates rather than measures of absolute density.

Presence

The presence of Lagomorphs can be determined by direct observation of the animal or by "activity signs." Activity signs include fecal pellets, active runways and trails, tracks, skeletal remains, and feeding sites (Figure 7). For example, jackrabbits can usually be observed in the field because of their rather large size. Snowshoe hares use runways, especially in the snow. Hay piles along talus slopes are good indicators of pikas. The presence of these signs does not necessarily provide an estimate of numbers of Lagomorphs in a given area, but will help determine sites where they occur or avoid.

Relative Abundance

The most commonly used technique for censusing several species of Leporids is the roadside count. Roadside census of Leporids is best in the evenings

or early morning when Lagomorphs' eyes can be reflected from a spotlight. Jackrabbits and desert cottontails have been censused in the evenings along unpaved roads in shortgrass prairie habitat (Flinders and Hansen 1973). The "eye shine" provided by the spotlight and subsequent "freeze" of the Lagomorphs permitted easy identification of species and counting. Roadside counts may be used as long as factors such as time of day, time of year, and weather conditions remain constant (equal). This type of transect count provides an index to relative abundance but does not give a density estimate (Chapman et al. 1982).

Density Estimates

Density estimates can be obtained by drive counts. Using this method, several people spread equally across an area, walk abreast along parallel transects and count Leporids as they are flushed. Flushing angles and flushing distances should be recorded. The flushing angle is obtained by pinpointing

Table 3. Food of the snowshoe hare in western North America as reported in the literature.

Alaska
Birch
Spruce
Alder
Willow
Viburnum (*Viburnum edule*)
Labrador tea (*Ledum groenlandicum*)
Aspen
Rose
Bramble (*Rubus ideaus*)
Grass
Dogwood (*Cornus canadensis*)
Fireweed
Horsetail
Wild rhubarb

Ontario
Pines (*Pinus strobus* and *P. resinosa*)
Aspen
Alder
Hazel (*Corylus cornuta*)
(*Ostrya virginiana*)
Juneberry (*Amelanchier* sp.)
Willow
Poplar (*P. balsamifera*)
White birch
Grasses

Washington
Spotted catsear (*Hypochoeris radicata*)

Sources: (Radwan and Campbell 1968; Wolff 1978; de Vos 1964).

Snowshoe hare with winter coat.

Colorado Chapter, The Wildlife Society

Joseph A. Chapman

Figure 7. Cottontail fecal pellet group.

the location of the animal and noting its compass direction by using the transect line as a point of reference. The flushing distance is the distance between the center of the transect and point where the Leporid is first observed. Flushing distance and angle will vary according to the density and height of the cover in which the Leporid is living. In general, the greater the density or thickness of the cover, the shorter the flushing distance. The flushing distance and angle will be determining factors in the width of the transect used. The greater the observable flushing distance and angle, the wider the transect will be and, thus, the greater the area censused (Webb 1942).

Behavioral patterns and density of vegetation tend to preclude drive counts as a suitable technique for cottontails and snowshoe hares. Cottontails tend to freeze rather than flee, making a head count difficult.

Snowshoe hares inhabit conifer stands with thick understories, making them difficult to see and count. However, drive counts have been successfully used in jackrabbit studies where sagebrush was the dominant vegetation type (Gross et al. 1974). Biases in census data may result from a change in flushing behavior, observer behavior, and duplicate counting of hares. Gates (1969) used an equation to adjust for flushing behavior changes in jackrabbits due to season and density. Jackrabbits in sagebrush habitat are easily visible and thus can be censused by using the drive count technique (F.H. Wagner, pers. commun.). Broadbooks (1965) successfully used a 30-m (100-ft) wide transect to census pikas on a rock formation.

Lagomorph density can also be estimated by mark-recapture techniques and fecal pellet group counts. Taylor (1930) was one of the first investigators to use fecal pellets as an indicator of Leporid abundance in the West. Pellet counts were also used to evaluate Audubon's cottontail population density in a pinyon-juniper forest in New Mexico (Kundaeli and Reynolds 1972). However, pellet counts are more useful for determining the habitat preference of Lagomorphs than for determining density. The presence of pellets was used to determine the use of montane forest types by snowshoe hares in Utah (Wolff et al. 1982). These methods are useful for comparing Lagomorph populations in different years, different habitat types, and different seasons. When using pellet counts to estimate populations, adjustments for varying defecation rates may be necessary (See Lord 1963).

Mark-recapture techniques involve sampling a segment of a population, marking and releasing them, and at a later date recapturing a percentage of the marked individuals. Mark and recapture techniques are frequently used because they not only give census data but also specific information on factors such as sex and age, survival, and movements of individuals. These techniques have been extensively used to assess Lagomorph population densities.

The **Wildlife Management Techniques Manual** describes several models such as the Lincoln Index (Lincoln 1930) or Jolly Index (Jolly 1963) to estimate the size of a population by the mark-recapture method (Davis and Winstead 1980). Population levels based on mark-recapture techniques often underestimate the actual number of animals present in an area (Eberhardt 1969). Otis et al. (1978) discuss the appropriateness of different models available for estimating the population size from capture and recapture data.

Some problems associated with mark-recapture procedures include the loss of marks or the tendency of some individuals to become "trap-happy" or "trap-shy," all resulting in inaccurate population estimates. Loss of ear tags can result in inflated population estimates. Some problems associated with this technique include variation in recapture rates and the behavioral responses to traps exhibited by individual animals (Otis et al. 1978).

Mark-recapture techniques have been used to census brush rabbits in bush lupine (*Lupinus arbus-*

tus) in Humboldt Bay, California (Shields 1958), Audubon's cottontails in mesquite-grassland habitat associations (Asserson 1967), Nuttall's cottontail in shrub-juniper scrubland in Oregon (McKay and Verts 1978), and jackrabbits in Utah (Clark 1972). Factors affecting the trap responses of eastern cottontails in Oregon included barometric pressure and temperature, but not precipitation (Chapman and Tretheway 1972). Methods to capture, handle, and mark Lagomorphs are outlined in **The Handbook of Census Methods for Terrestrial Vertebrates** (Feist 1982; Smith 1982; and Wolff 1982) and **Wild Mammals of North America** (Chapman and Feldhamer 1982).

Jackrabbits can be captured in winter by using large Havahart traps baited with alfalfa or apples (G. Smith, pers. commun.). Cottontails can be caught in either baited or unbaited wooden box traps (Figure 8; Edwards 1975). Leporids can also be captured from vehicles by using a spotlight and a hand-held net (Labisky 1959, 1968).

Lagomorphs can be marked with size 3 monel ear tags, hair dye, or toe-clipping to identify individuals (Wolff 1982). Depending on the size of the Lagomorph, other types of markers include commercially available colored discs, colored discs cut from surveyors flagging, an alcohol-picric-acid solution, and notching or punching holes in the ears (Figure 9). Approaching and handling Lagomorphs requires care to avoid the flight response and subsequent injury of the rabbit or hare while the animal is still in the trap. Placing the Lagomorph in a cloth bag tends to reduce stress on the animal while handling it for marking or weighing.

Joseph A. Chapman

Figure 8. Typical wooden box trap used for capturing cottontails.

Figure 9. Black-tailed jackrabbit with ear tag in place.

POPULATION LEVELS AND DENSITY

Although there are little specific data on the absolute densities of Lagomorphs associated with specific habitat types, some general guidelines can be obtained from the literature. These guidelines will be useful to the manager because they can compare densities on their study areas with existing information in the literature. Thus, the manager can gain insight into the status of Lagomorph populations in a particular area.

In general, Leporid populations do not reach extremely high densities. There are of course exceptions as noted in localized situations with black-tailed jackrabbits and snowshoe hares. Uniform densities of more than 3 or 4 Leporids per ha (1 to 3 per a.) would be considered high for most North American species.

Population estimates for jackrabbits in the Southwest vary between 0.2 and 1.2 per ha (0.1 to 0.5 per a.); in California they were reported at 3 per ha (1 per a.), and at 35 per ha (14 per a.) in cultivated areas of Kansas (See Dunn et al. 1982 for references).

Audubon's cottontail in shortgrass-prairie regions of Colorado reached densities of 0.02 per ha (0.08 per a.) during the winter. Densities of Nuttall's cottontails in shrub-juniper scrubland in Oregon varied between 0.06 to 2.5 per ha (0.25 to 6.25 per a.). Island populations of eastern cottontails in Maryland reached maximum density levels of 10.2 per ha (25.5 per a.) in December (See Chapman et al. 1982 for references).

Snowshoe hare populations exhibit a marked variation in density levels. During low population cycles, densities may vary from 0.13 to 0.26 per ha (0.32 to 0.65 per a.) to 5.9 to 11.8 per ha (14.7 to 19.5 per a.) in a high cycle in Alberta (Keith and Windberg 1978). Continent-wide, peaks in hare populations have been reported as high as 38.6 per ha (96.5 per a.) to lows of 0.12 per ha (0.3 per a.) (See Bittner and Rongstand 1982 for references).

Pika densities fluctuate greatly, ranging from 2 to 3 per ha (5 to 7 per a.) to as high as 70 to 80 per ha (175 to 200 per a.) (Kawamichi 1984).

Pika.

DISCUSSION

In this chapter we have defined the major plant communities that are associated with the various genera and species of Lagomorphs found in the continental U.S. and Alaska. We have also discussed some of the methods used to estimate Lagomorph population sizes. However, to understand the status of a Lagomorph population in a particular location, season, or year, one must know a considerable amount about the relationship between population size and the habitat.

The relationship between Lagomorphs and their habitats is complex. The factors involved include those inherent in the physiology of the individual species and those edaphic factors external to the species such as weather, topography, and vegetation. The factors which we will consider in this discussion include weather, vegetation, reproduction, food habits, predation, and their interrelations with Lagomorph population dynamics and habitat use.

The population dynamics of Lagomorphs has been the subject of considerable research and numerous publications, particularly for the snowshoe hare (Keith 1979) and eastern cottontail (Edwards et al. 1979). The population dynamics of a species has been defined as "numbers, structural and distributional changes in population with respect to changes in the rate of reproduction, survival, movements, and environmental interactions, which in part determine these rates" (Keith 1979). Much has been written on the cyclic nature of snowshoe hare populations and the random fluctuations in cottontail and jackrabbit populations. We define cyclic as a regular predictable phenomenon, such as the 10-year cycle reported in snowshoe hares at northern latitudes (Keith 1974). Population fluctuations are random sporadic increases and decreases occurring

Table 4. Food of cottontail rabbits (*Sylvilagus*) in Utah.

Audubon's Cottontail	Nuttall's Cottontail
Eastern Utah	Northeastern Utah

Saltgrass (*Distichlis stricta*)
Galleta grass (*Hilaria* sp.)
Indian ricegrass
Sand dropseed
Alkali sacaton (*S. airoides*)
Blue grama
Downy brome
Western wheatgrass
Spike rush (*Eleocharis* sp.)
Sedge
Wire grass (*Juncus balticus*)
Pigweed (*Chenopodium* sp.)
Saltbush (*A. nuttallii*,
   A. corrugata, A. wolfii,
   A. powelli)
Greasewood
Seepweed (*Dondia* sp.)
Russian thistle
Tansymustard (*Descuraiana* sp.)
Yellow cleome (*Cleome lutea*)
Wild rose
Sand bur (*Glycyrrhiza lopidota*)
Globe mallow
Prickly pear
Dogbane (*Apocynum cannabinum*)
Rabbitbrush
Sagebrush
Horsebrush
	Wheat grass
	Willows
	Knotweed (*Polygonum* sp.)
	Spiny hopsage
	Oregon grape (*Berberis repens*)
	Bitterbrush
	Wild rose
	Chokecherry
	Snakeweed
	Rabbitbrush
	Sagebrush

	Pygmy Rabbit
	Northeastern Utah

Western Utah	Rabbitbrush
	Little rabbitbrush (*C.*
	   viscidiflorus)
	Horsebrush
	Russian thistle
	Pigweed
	Smooth wheatgrass (*Agropyron*
	   inerme)
	Spiked wheatgrass (*A. spicatum*)
	Giant wild rye (*Elymus condensatus*)
	Small scale (*Atriplex pusilla*)
	Four-winged saltbush
	Western wheatgrass
	Sagebrush
	Globe mallow
	Snakeweed

Galleta grass Alkali sacaton Saltgrass Four-winged saltbush Mound saltbush Winterfat Finchook bassia (*Bassia* *hyssopifolia*) Pigweed (*Amaranthus* sp.) Purple cleome Snakeweed Sagebrush	

Source: (Janson 1946).

on an irregular basis, caused by man-induced changes in habitat or uncontrolled changes in environmental factors such as weather (Edwards et al. 1979). Fluctuations in Lagomorph population levels may occur annually or seasonally. Several models have been developed to explain the cause of cycles in Lagomorph populations, but most are based on Keith's (1974) model of habitat-hare-predation interaction (Bryant 1979, 1981; Wolff 1980a). Keith's (1974) model is based on regular increases and decreases in population numbers of snowshoe hares with respect to changes in survival, reproduction, and movement of this species (Keith 1979). Similarly, regular cycles have been reported in Utah jackrabbits (Gross et al. 1974).

The effects of environmental factors on Lagomorph populations are difficult to assess and quantify. However, environmental factors such as weather are believed to have an impact on the regularity of Lagomorph population fluctuations. Weather variables such as snowfall and rainfall may have a major impact on the early survival of young cottontails (Applegate and Trout 1976; Havera 1973). In snowshoe hares, the depth of the snowfall can determine the suitability of winter habitat. Optimal habitat for snowshoe hares in the montane forests of northern Utah had an understory cover between 1.0 and 2.5 m (3 and 8.25 ft) high (Wolff et al. 1982).

Temperature and snow depth are correlated with the size of snowshoe hare litters (Meslow and Keith 1971). Similarly, cold, inclement weather affects the onset of reproduction and fetal survival in Leporids (Chapman et al. 1977).

The onset and duration of the breeding season may be regulated by certain weather factors. The length of photoperiod is associated with earlier onset of the breeding season in snowshoe hares (Meslow and Keith 1971) and in cottontails (Bissonnette and Csech 1939). The length of the breeding season for Nuttall's cottontails was shortened when precipitation was reduced. Consequently, population densities were lower in years of low precipitation. Densities in late summer reached a high of 2.54 cottontails per ha (6.35 per a.) when precipitation was 11.54 cm (4.6 in.); in contrast, population levels dropped to 0.66 per ha (1.65 per a.) when precipitation was 5.21 cm (208 in.) the following year (Verts et al. 1984).

Reproduction is an important factor affecting population cycles. Keith's (1974) model attributed decreases in fecundity from small litter sizes, shorter breeding seasons, and lower pregnancy rates, due at least in part to the regulation of hare populations. The onset of the breeding season has been correlated with midwinter photoperiod (Meslow and

Keith 1971). Litter sizes are larger in areas where days are longer; hence latitude is a factor in reproductive output (Keith 1979). Litter sizes were also larger in hares when over-winter weight loss did not occur (Keith and Windberg 1978), pointing to the importance of adequate high quality browse. There is also considerable variation in the size of first and subsequent litters in several species of Leporids (Chapman et al. 1977; Bittner and Rongstand 1982). Leporid litter sizes also vary with latitude (Conaway et al. 1974; Dunn et al. 1982). Similarly, there is a correlation with latitude and length of gestation period in North American rabbits. Those species occurring at more northern latitudes have shorter gestation periods (Chapman 1984).

Lagomorphs are important in many food chains, being prey items for many avian and terrestrial predators (Bittner and Rongstand 1982; Chapman et al. 1982; Dunn et al. 1982). The selection of refugia or escape cover from predators during snowshoe hare population "lows" was considered of major importance in their survival. Refugia for snowshoe hares in Alaska were dense thickets of alder or willow (Wolff 1980a). Hare vulnerability to predation increases as populations rise, forcing individuals to occupy suboptimal areas. In Utah, these areas were generally open, where the vegetation density profile was less then 40% above the snowline (Wolff et al. 1982). Coyote predation on jackrabbits was greatest when jackrabbit densities were at low or moderate levels (Wagner and Stoddart 1972). Even in areas with abundant plant food resources, cover is the most important habitat component (Wolff 1980a). Keith's (1974) model includes predation as a factor in the population regulation of snowshoe hares, particularly in northern latitudes. Thus escape cover is an essential component of Lagomorph habitat.

Lagomorphs eat a wide variety of plants. However, plant resins have been identified as a deterrent in Lagomorph herbivory (Bryant 1979, 1981). These resins have been suggested as a key to hare population regulation (Bryant 1979). This idea is new and requires further verification before it will be widely accepted.

The diameter of the twigs consumed and browsing intensity has been used as an indicator of "food stress" in habitat utilized in excess of carrying capacity (Wolff 1980a). Hares will starve in winter if forced into habitats where the diameter of twigs used for browse was greater than 3 mm (0.12 in.) (Pease et al. 1979). Clark and Wagner (1984) observed that only 20% of a browse plant "brown sage" (*Kochia americana*) was consumed when jackrabbit populations were at their highest level. Heavy grazing by sheep in addition to the limited foraging by hares caused the plants to decline. Food is apparently an important factor in hare population regulation (Keith 1974). As hare densities increase, the biomass of available food is less than that needed by the population, which ultimately leaves a food shortage and thus causes mortality in hare populations.

The relationship of Lagomorph populations to their habitat is evident from studies on snowshoe hares, jackrabbits, cottontails, and pikas. Periods of drought forced jackrabbits to occupy cultivated fields, which provided an abundant food source and supported higher jackrabbit population levels (Bronson and Tiemeier 1959). Similarly, overgrazing by cattle in conjunction with periods of drought created more open, weedy areas, a habitat which also supported higher jackrabbit populations (Taylor et al. 1935). In the Mojave desert, jackrabbit population densities were higher around water sources in winter, declining substantially from spring to summer (Hayden 1966). Thus, changes in jackrabbit populations were affected by food availability and changes in environmental conditions brought on by factors such as drought. Changes in cottontail population levels have also been attributed to changing land-use patterns (Edwards et al. 1979). In pikas, size of territories is determined at least in part by vegetation quality (Smith 1979). Thus, the higher the quality of vegetation, the more pikas an area will support.

Habitat patchiness or the mosaic pattern of vegetation within a Lagomorph's environment plays a key role in the survival of snowshoe hares during a population low (Wolff 1980a). All habitat types from open suboptimal areas to optimal habitat types of dense cover were occupied by snowshoe hares during population highs. However, during lows, the remaining individuals in a population tended to seek refuge in dense thickets of spruce, willow, or alder. In winters of high densities, hares in Alaska utilized more open stands and consumed all of the available browse (Wolff 1979, 1980b).

It is apparent that the inventory of Lagomorph habitat must take into account many factors. Most of these factors are poorly understood or known only for a particular genus or species. This is especially true for the pika and Alaskan hare which remain among the least known Lagomorphs. In addition, there are little quantitative data on habitat variables available for most North American Lagomorphs. This lack of quantitative data makes it difficult to assess changes in Lagomorph abundance in relation to habitat quality.

Table 5. Lagomorph species groups, reproductive characteristics, and common habitat requirements.

Family	Species	Reproductive Characteristics	Habitat
Leporidae	Black-tailed jackrabbit (*Lepus californicus*) White-tailed jackrabbit (*L. townsendii*) Antelope jackrabbit (*L. alleni*) White-sided jackrabbit (*L. callotis*)	Precocial	Desert scrub and dry grasslands
Leporidae	Snowshoe hare (*L. americanus*) Alaskan hare (*L. othus*) (Some workers feel *L. othus* is a synonym for *L. timidus* [Dixon et al. 1983]).	Precocial	Coniferous forests, subalpine and climax forest
Leporidae	Audubon's cottontail (*Sylvilagus audubonii*) Nuttall's cottontail (*S. nuttallii*) Brush rabbit (*S. bachmani*) Eastern cottontail (*S. floridanus*) Pygmy rabbit (*S. idahoenis*) (Some workers consider the pigmy rabbit to be in the genus *Brachylagus* [Chapman et al. 1982]).	Altricial	Disturbed and successional plant communities
Ochotonidae	Southern pika (*Ochotonidae princeps*) (Some workers consider the collared pika [*O. p. collaris*] of Alaska a separate species [Chapman 1979; Hall 1981]).	Altricial	Rocky talus at high altitudes

LITERATURE CITED

ADAMS, L. 1959. An analysis of a population of snowshoe hares in northwestern Montana. Ecol. Monogr. 29:141-170.

APPLEGATE, J.E. and J.R. TROUT. 1976. Weather and the harvest of cottontails in New Jersey. J. Wildl. Manage. 40:658-662.

ASSERSON, W.C. 1967. Upland Game Investigations: Cottontail rabbit investigations. California P-R Rep. W-47-R-15. 12pp.

BEAR, G.D. and R.M. HANSEN. 1966. Food habits, growth, and reproduction of white-tailed jackrabbits in southern Colorado. Colorado State Univ., Agric. Exp. Sta. Tech. Bull. 90. 39pp.

BEDNARZ, J. 1977. The white-sided jackrabbit in New Mexico: distribution, numbers and biology in the grasslands of Hidalgo County. Res. Rep. New Mexico Dep. Game and Fish, Endang. Sp. Program, Santa Fe. 33pp.

BISSONNETTE, T.H. and A.G. CSECH. 1939. Modified sexual periodicity in cottontail rabbits. Biol. Bull. 17:364-367.

BITTNER, S.L. and O.J. RONGSTAND. 1982. Snowshoe hare and allies. Pages 146-163 in Chapman, J.A. and G.A. Feldhamer eds., Wild Mammals of North America. Johns Hopkins Univ. Press. Baltimore, MD. 1147pp.

BRAUN, C.E. and R.G. STREETER. 1968. Observations on the occurrence of the white-tailed jackrabbit in the alpine zone. J. Mammal. 49:160-161.

BROADBOOKS, H.E. 1965. Ecology and distribution of the pikas of Washington and Alaska. Am. Midl. Nature. 73:299-335.

BRONSON, F.H. and O.W. TIEMEIER. 1959. The relationship of precipitation and black-tailed jackrabbit populations in Kansas. Ecology. 40:194-198.

BRYANT, J.P. 1979. The regulation of snowshoe hare feeding behavior during winter by plant antiherbivore chemistry. Pages 720-731 in Proc. World Lagomorph Conf.

——. 1981. Phytochemical deterrence of snowshoe hare browsing by adventitious shoots of four Alaskan trees. Science. 213:889-890.

CHAPMAN, J.A. 1971. Orientation and homing of the brush rabbit (Sylvilagus bachmani). J. Mammal. 52:686-699.

——. 1979. Rabbits, hares, and pikas. Pages 81-98 in Wild Animals of North America. National Geographic Soc., Washington, DC. 406pp.

——. 1984. Latitude and gestation period in New World rabbits (Leporidae: Sylvilagus and Romerolagus). Am. Nature. 124:442-445.

—— and G.A. FELDHAMER eds. 1982. Wild mammals of North America. Johns Hopkins Univ. Press. Baltimore, MD. 1147pp.

—— and D.E.C. TRETHEWAY. 1972. Factors affecting trap responses of introduced eastern cottontail rabbits. J. Wildl. Manage. 36:1221-1226.

——, A.L. HARMAN, and D.E. SAMUEL. 1977. Reproductive and physiological cycles in the cottontail complex in western Maryland and nearby West Virginia. Wildl. Monogr. 56. 73pp.

——, J.G. HOCKMAN, and W.R. EDWARDS. 1982. Cottontails. Pages 83-123 in Chapman, J.A. and G.A. Feldhamer eds., Wild Mammals of North America. Johns Hopkins Univ. Press. Baltimore, MD.

——, ——, and M.M. OJEDA. 1980. Sylvilagus floridanus. Mammalian Species 136:1-8.

CLARK, F.W. 1972. Influence of jackrabbit density on coyote population change. J. Wildl. Manage. 36:343-356.

CLARK, W.R. and F.H. WAGNER. 1984. Role of livestock and black-tailed jackrabbits in changing abundance of Kochia americana. Great Basin Naturalist. 44:635-645.

CONAWAY, C.H., K.C. SADLER, and D.H. HAZELWOOD. 1974. Geographic variation in litter size and onset of breeding in cottontails. J. Wildl. Manage. 38:473-481.

CONROY, M.J., L.W. GYSEL, and G.R. DUDDERAR. 1979. Habitat components of clear-cut areas for snowshoe hares in Michigan. J. Wildl. Manage. 43:680-690.

DALQUIST, W.W. 1948. Mammals of Washington. Univ. of Kansas Publ. Mus. Nat. Hist. 2:1-444.

DAVIS, C.A., J.A. MEDLIN, and J.P. GRIFFING. 1975. Abundance of black-tailed jackrabbits, desert cottontail rabbits, and coyotes in southeastern New Mexico. New Mexico State Univ. Agric. Exp. Sta. Res. Rep. 293.

DAVIS, D.E. ed., 1982. Handbook of census methods for terrestrial vertebrates. CRC Press, Boca Raton, FL. 397pp.

—— and R.L. WINSTEAD. 1980. Estimating the numbers of wildlife populations; pages 221-245 in Schemnitz, S.D. ed., Wildl. Manage. Techniques Manual. Wildl. Soc., Washington, DC.

DE VOS, A. 1964. Food utilization of snowshoe hares on Manitoulin Island, Ontario. J. For. 62:238-244.

DICE, L.R. 1926. Notes of Pacific Coast rabbits and pikas. Occ. Papers Mus. Zool., Univ. of Michigan, Ann Arbor. 166:1-28.

DIXON, K.R., J.A. CHAPMAN, G.R. WILLNER, D.E. WILSON, and W. LOPEZ-FORMENT. 1983. The New World jackrabbits and hares (genus Lepus L. Part 2)—Numerical taxonomic analysis. Acta. Zool. Fenica. 174:53-56.

DOLBEER, R.A. and W.R. CLARK. 1975. Population ecology of snowshoe hares in the central Rocky Mountains. J. Wildl. Manage. 39:535-549.

DOUTT, J.K., C.A. HEPPENSTALL, and J.E. GUILDAY. 1967. Mammals of Pennsylvania. Pennsylvania Game Comm. Harrisburg. 238pp.

DUNN, J.P., J.A. CHAPMAN, and R.E. MARSH. 1982. Jackrabbits. Pages 124-145 in Chapman, J.A. and G.A. Feldhamer eds. Wild Mammals of North America. Johns Hopkins Univ. Press, Baltimore, MD.

EBERHARDT, L.L. 1969. Population estimation from recapture frequencies. J. Wildl. Manage. 33:28-39.

EDWARDS, W.R. 1975. Rabbit Trap. Illinois Nat. Hist. Survey, Urbana, IL. 1pp.

——, S.P. HAVERA, R.F. LABISKY, J.A. EILLES, and R.E. WARNER. 1979. The abundance of cottontails in relation to agriculture land use in Illinois (U.S.A.) 1956-1978, with comments on mechanism and regulation. Pages 761-789 in Proc. World Lagomorph Conf.

FEIST, D.D. 1982. Snowshoe hare (Alaska). Page 139 in Davis, D.E. ed. Handbook of Census Methods for Terrestrial Vertebrates. CRC Press, Boca Raton, FL.

FLINDERS, J.T. and R.M. HANSEN. 1972. Diets and habitats of jackrabbits in northeastern Colorado. Colorado

State Univ., Range Sci. Dep. Sci. Ser., Fort Collins. 12:1-29.

————— and —————. 1973. Abundance and dispersion of leporids within a shortgrass ecosystem. J. Mammal. 54:287-291.

GATES, C.E. 1969. Simulation study of estimates for the line transect sampling method. Biometrics. 25:317-328.

GRANGE, W.B. 1965. Fire and tree growth relationships to snowshoe rabbits. Proc. Tall Timbers Fire Ecol. Conf. 4:111-125.

GROSS, J.E., L.C. STODDART, and F.H. WAGNER. 1974. Demographic analysis of a northern Utah jackrabbit population. Wildl. Monogr. 40. 68pp.

HALL, E.R. 1981. The mammals of North America, Vol. I. John Wiley and Sons, New York, NY. 600pp.

HANSEN, R.M. and J.T. FLINDERS. 1969. Food habits of North American hares. Colorado State Univ., Range Sci. Dep. Sci. Serv. Fort Collins. 31:1-18..

HAVERA, S.P. 1973. The relationship of Illinois weather and agriculture to the eastern cottontail rabbit. Illinois State Water Surv. Tech. Rep. 4. 92pp. (Mimeo.).

HAYDEN, P. 1966. Seasonal occurrence of jackrabbits on Jackass Flat, Nevada. J. Wildl. Manage. 30:835-838.

JANSON, R.G. 1946. A survey of the native rabbits of Utah with reference to their classification, distribution, life histories and ecology. Unpubl. M.S. Thesis, Utah State Agric. College. 103pp.

JOLLY, G.M. 1963. Estimates of population parameters from multiple recapture data with both death and dilution-deterministic model. Biometrika. 50:113-128.

KAWAMICHI, T. 1984. Pikas. Pages 726-727 in Macdonald, D. ed. The Encyclopedia of Mammals. Facts on File Publ. New York, NY.

KEITH, L.B. 1974. Some features of population dynamics in mammals. Proc. Int. Congr. Game Biol. 11:17-58.

—————. 1979. Population dynamics of hares. Pages 395-440 in Proc. World Lagomorph Conf.

————— and L.A. WINDBERG. 1978. A demographic analysis of the snowshoe hare cycle. Wildl. Monogr. 58. 70pp.

KUNDAELI, J.N. and H.G. REYNOLDS. 1972. Desert cottontail use of natural and modified pinyon-juniper woodland. J. Range Manage. 25:116-118.

LABISKY, R.F. 1959. Nightlighting: a technique for capturing birds and mammals. Illinois Nat. History Survey Div. Biol. Notes. 11pp.

—————. 1968. Nightlighting: Its use in capturing pheasants, prairie chickens, bobwhites, and cottontails. Illinois Nat. History Survey Div. Biol. Notes. 62. 12pp.

LINCOLN, F.C. 1930. Calculating waterfowl abundance on the basis of banding returns. U.S. Dep. Agric. Cir. 118:1-4.

LORD, R.D. 1963. The cottontail rabbit in Illinois. Illinois Dep. Conserv. Tech. Bull. 3:1-94.

McKAY, D.O. and B.J. VERTS. 1978. Estimates of some attributes of a population of Nuttall's cottontails. J. Wildl. Manage. 42:159-168.

MESLOW, E.C. and L.B. KEITH. 1971. A correlation analysis of weather versus snowshoe hare population parameters. J. Wildl. Manage. 35:1-14.

ORR, R.T. 1940. The rabbits of California. Occ. Papers California Acad. Sci. 19. 227pp.

OTIS, D.L., K.P. BURNHAM, G.C. WHITE, and D.R. ANDER-
SON. 1978. Statistical inference from capture data on closed animal populations. Wildl. Monogr. 63:1-135.

PEASE, J.L., R.H. VOWLES, and L.B. KEITH. 1979. Interaction of snowshoe hares and woody vegetation. J. Wildl. Manage. 43:43-60.

RADWAN, M.A. and D.L. CAMPBELL. 1968. Snowshoe hare preference for spotted catsear flowers in western Washington. J. Wildl. Manage. 32:104-108.

SHIELDS, P.W. 1958. Ecology and population dynamics of the brush rabbit of the north spit of Humboldt County, California. Unpublished M.S. Thesis. Humboldt State College. 98pp.

SMITH, A.T. 1974a. The distribution and dispersal of pikas: Influences of behavior and climate. Ecology. 55:1368-1376.

—————. 1974b. The distribution and dispersal of pikas: Consequences of insular population structure. Ecology. 55:1112-1119.

—————. 1979. Population dynamics of pikas. Pages 572-586 in Proc. World Lagomorph Conf.

—————. 1982. Pika (Ochotona). Pages 131-133 in Davis, D.E. ed. Handbook of Census Methods for Terrestrial Vertebrates. CRC Press, Boca Raton, FL.

SWIHART, R.K. and R.H. YAHNER. 1984. Winter use of insular habitat patches by the eastern cottontail. Acta Theriologica. 29:45-56.

TAYLOR, W.P. 1930. Methods of determining rodent pressure on the range. Ecology. 11:523-542.

—————, C.T. VORHEIS, and P.B. LISTER. 1935. The relation of jackrabbits to grazing in southern Arizona. J. For. 33:490-498.

VERTS, B.J., S.D. GEHMAN, and K.J. HUNDERTMARK. 1984. Sylvilagus nuttallii: a semiarboreal Lagomorph. J. Mammal. 65(1):131-135.

VORHEIS, C.J. and W.P. TAYLOR. 1933. The life histories and ecology of the jackrabbits (Lepus alleni and L. californicus) in relation to grazing in Arizona. Univ. of Arizona Agric. Exper. Stat. Tech. Bull. 49:1-117.

WAGNER, F.H., and L.C. STODDART. 1972. Influence of coyote predation on black-tailed jackrabbit populations in Utah. J. Wildl. Manage. 25:242-329.

WEBB, W.L. 1942. Notes on a method for censusing snowshoe hare populations. J. Wildl. Manage. 42:159-168.

WOLFF, M.L., N.V. DeBYLE, C.S. WINCHELL, and T.R. McCABE. 1982. Snowshoe hare cover relationships in northern Utah. J. Wildl. Manage. 46:552-670.

WOLFF, J.O. 1978. Food habits of snowshoe hares in interior Alaska. J. Wildl. Manage. 42:148-153.

—————. 1979. Refugia, dispersal, predation, and geographic variation in snowshoe hare cycles. Pages 441-449 in Proc. World Lagomorph Conf.

—————. 1980a. The role of habitat patchiness in the population dynamics of snowshoe hares. Ecol. Monogr. 50:111-130.

—————. 1980b. Moose-snowshoe hare competition during peak hare densities. Proc. N. Amer. Moose Conf. & Workshop. 16:238-254.

—————. 1982. Snowshoe hare. Pages 141-149 in Davis, D.E. ed. Handbook of Census Methods for Terrestrial Vertebrates. CRC Press, Boca Raton, FL.

23

CARNIVORES

Richard A. Spowart[1] **and Fred B. Samson**[2]

Colorado Cooperative Wildlife Research Unit
Colorado State University
Fort Collins, CO 80523

Editor's Note: Carnivores are interesting, elusive, and controversial. They are also one of the most difficult groups to inventory or monitor. Many studies have focused on prey bases for carnivores, but other habitat requirements have not been well defined.

This chapter brings together much of the existing literature on carnivore techniques, and should assist in study design. However, the biologist will find plenty of opportunity for innovation when working with these species.

INTRODUCTION

The order Carnivora is a diverse group of predatory mammals. Trenchant characteristics of the order are found in their dentition, which indicates diet. However, many carnivores are omnivorous or even herbivorous. The variability in diet is reflected by the large array of carnivore habitat types and lifestyles. Some species are habitat and food specialists, distributed within only a few plant communities; others are habitat and food generalists, widely distributed in natural and disturbed ecosystems.

In contrast, the very adaptable and successful coyote (*Canis latrans*) occupies almost every habitat type in North America, whereas the endangered black-footed ferret (*Mustela nigripes*) depends on undisturbed prairie. The smallest living carnivore, the least weasel (*M. nivalis*), weighs about 45 g (1.6 oz); the largest living carnivore, a subspecies of the grizzly or brown bear (*Ursus arctos*), weighs more than 700 kg (1,550 lbs). The hyperactive least weasel feeds almost exclusively on mice and requires about a third of its body weight in food per day; the brown bear, however, is omnivorous and hibernates for about half the year.

Because of the diverse ways carnivores have evolved to exploit their environments, we chose to treat most species separately. When important habitat features are similar for several species, we combined their descriptions. Within these combined descriptions, we attempted to contrast unique habitat preferences of individual species.

We have not attempted to describe all physical features and vegetation types that occur in all habitats of species that are generalists; only habitats that support the densest populations or are considered optimum are discussed. Carnivore species that are rare in western North America, either because they have been extirpated from much of their original range or because their range extends only into the

---

[1]Current Address: Colorado Division of Wildlife, Kremmling, CO 80459
[2]Current Address: U.S. Forest Service, Olympia, WA 98195

periphery of that region, are also not discussed. Certain of these species were excluded largely because of their threatened or endangered status. Species not included are arctic fox (*Alopex lagopus*), black-footed ferret, coati (*Nasua nasua*), jaguar (*Felis onca*), jaguarundi (*F. yagouaroundi*), margay cat (*F. wiedi*), ocelot (*F. pardalis*), polar bear (*Ursus maritimus*), and red wolf (*Canis rufus*).

Peter C. Lent

Arctic fox.

Important considerations in evaluating habitat for any species are food supply, habitat size, and interspecific competition. Food supply, particularly the availability of prey species, often determines the density of carnivore populations. Habitat manipulations can often alter prey population size. Since habitat manipulations indirectly influence the dynamics of carnivore populations, we included a brief description of food habits of each species or species group. Unfortunately, there is little information on food requirements for most carnivores, but when available, we referenced this information. Table 1 summarizes major foods and habitats of carnivores.

Small populations are more likely to become extinct than large populations. A major influence in population size is the availability of habitat. The size or area of habitat must be large enough to support self-sustaining populations of carnivores. The number of prey species in all likelihood will also increase as habitat size increases. This habitat feature is likely most critical to those carnivores that are territorial, have large home ranges, and exploit a patchily distributed food supply.

HABITAT FEATURES CORRELATED WITH SPECIES GROUPS

Canidae

Wolves. Today, substantial populations of gray or timber wolves (*Canis lupus*) occur in wilderness areas and large national parks in Alaska, Canada, and northern Minnesota and Michigan. Here they inhabit

boreal and mixed-hardwood forests and tundra. In all habitats occupied by wolves, either past or present, availability of their principal prey, large ungulates, likely has most influenced wolf distribution and density where wolf control programs have been absent. The primary objective of many studies of wolf ecology in Alaska, Canada, Michigan, and Minnesota has been to determine the interrelationships of wolves and large ungulates (Murie 1944; Mech 1966; Pimlott 1967; Kolenosky 1972; Kuyt 1972; Van Ballenberghe et al. 1975; Peterson 1977; Fuller and Keith 1980; Hollemann and Stephenson 1981; Gasaway et al. 1983). Difficulties in measuring wolf and prey densities and predation rates, as well as the influence of other forms of wolf and prey mortality, have left many questions unanswered. Disparate results have been reported for daily food consumption rates of wolves and, more importantly, the rates at which wolves kill prey (Mech 1966; Pimlott 1967; Kolenosky 1972). In northeastern North America, where simple predator-prey systems exist, wolves are a major mortality factor for prey populations (Mech 1966; Jordan et al. 1967). In addition, declining wolf populations have been attributed primarily to decreasing numbers of their primary prey (Jordan et al. 1967; Mech 1977; Mech and Karns 1977). However, the role wolf predation plays in more complex predator-prey systems in Alaska and the Rocky Mountain national parks of western Canada is unclear (Murie 1944; Cowan 1947; Gasaway et al. 1983).

Inventorying and monitoring habitat in areas of the continental U.S., where wolves have been extirpated, are important to feasibility and evaluation studies of wolf reintroductions. Most attempts to reestablish wolves in areas of their original range have, at best, met limited success (Mech 1966; Henshaw and Stephenson 1974; Henshaw et al. 1975; Weise et al. 1975). Many believe that large areas, having no human habitation, are necessary to reestablish wolves because of their large home ranges and social structure (reviewed by Henshaw 1975; Henshaw et al. 1975; Mech 1975; Brown 1983). However, in Europe and some areas of Alaska, wolves live near humans (Peterson 1975; Pulliainen 1975; Zimen and Boitani 1975; Gasaway et al. 1983). The density of prey populations over a large area may be the most important habitat requisite determining feasibility of reintroduction.

Coyotes. The coyote has survived relentless predator-control programs that extirpated the wolf in most of the continental U.S. Moreover, this ultimate opportunist has expanded its range (Gier 1975; Andrews and Boggess 1978; Berg and Chesness 1978; Hilton 1978). Coyotes evolved in a plains environment and were once most numerous in western grasslands where large ungulate populations were densest. They flourished in the

Table 1. Summary of major foods and habitats for carnivores.

Carnivore Species	Food									Habitat									
	Carrion	Ungulates	Lagomorphs	Rodents	Birds and bird eggs	Reptiles and amphibians	Insects	Seeds, fruits, and berries	Fish	Farmland	Grassland	Sagebrush	Boreal forest	Coniferous forest	Deciduous forest	Tundra	Chaparral	Deserts	Lakes, ponds, and rivers
Wolf	•	•	•										•	•		•			
Coyote	•	•	•	•	•		•	•		•	•	•		•	•		•	•	
Gray fox			•	•	•		•	•							•		•		
Red fox			•	•	•		•	•		•	•		•	•	•	•			
Kit fox			•	•	•													•	
Swift fox			•	•								•						•	
Mountain lion		•												•			•		
Bobcat		•	•	•	•							•		•	•		•	•	
Lynx			•	•	•								•						
Black bear	•						•	•					•	•					
Grizzly bear	•	•		•			•	•			•			•					
Fisher	•		•	•	•	•	•	•						•					
Marten				•	•		•	•						•					
Wolverine	•		•	•	•		•	•						•					
Mink			•	•		•			•										•
River otter					•	•			•										•
Badger			•	•	•		•				•	•							
Raccoon				•	•	•	•	•	•					•	•				•
Ringtail				•			•	•						•	•				
Striped skunk	•		•	•	•	•	•	•		•	•	•	•	•	•				•
Hooded skunk	•		•	•	•	•	•	•						•	•				•
Hognosed skunk	•		•	•	•		•	•			•	•		•	•			•	
Spotted skunk	•		•	•	•	•	•	•		•								•	•
Least weasel			•	•	•		•							•	•				
Short-tailed weasel			•	•	•		•							•					
Long-tailed weasel			•	•	•		•							•					

shortgrass-steppe, semiarid sagebrush (*Artemisia* sp.) grasslands, and deserts. They ranged from deserts and plains to alpine areas of adjacent mountains. Today, range extensions indicate that coyotes can be successful in broken forests, from the tropics of Guatemala to the eastern U.S., up to northern Alaska. Altitude, latitude, and vegetation type do not seem to restrict their survival. Range expansions and population increases were likely caused by elimination of gray wolves, clearing of forests, and agricultural practices (Carbyn 1982).

The coyote's ability to expand its range and adapt to so many habitat types is partly due to its versatile food habits. Coyotes are primarily carnivorous, but their diets depend on the food resources most available. They easily adapt to being omnivorous and, in this respect, their food habits resemble those of foxes (Green and Flinders 1981). An extensive food habits study (Sperry 1941) conducted in 17 western states showed that major diet items were lagomorphs (33%), carrion (25%), rodents (18%), and domestic livestock (13.5%).

Studies conducted locally in the western U.S. revealed large variances in coyote diets from one area to another. Murie (1951) studied coyote food habits on Arizona cattle ranges. The ranges consisted primarily of open grasslands, oak (*Quercus* sp.), juniper (*Juniperus* sp.), prickly pear and cholla (*Opuntia* sp.), and ponderosa pine (*Pinus ponderosa*). In these habitats, coyote diets were complex but contained high percentages of plant material. Juniper berries were particularly important, followed by prickly pear fruits. Berries of manzanita (*Arctostaphylos pungens* and *A. pringlei*) and pods of velvet mesquite (*Prosopsis juliflora*) were rare but preferred foods. Other important diet items were carrion, grasshoppers, and rodents. Lagomorphs were found in only 3% of coyote scats but were rare in this area.

Short (1979) found similar results in another area of Arizona, described as a semidesert, grass-shrub habitat, dominated by velvet mesquite, cholla, and prickly pear. Although coyote food habits were complex, the incidence of some foods in diets followed seasonal patterns. Coyote food habits also exhibited seasonal trends in a ponderosa pine forest of Arizona (Turkowski 1980). In contrast, coyote diets in other western states have been less varied and contained primarily mammals. Clark (1972) reported that coyotes in sagebrush habitat of northeastern Utah and south-central Idaho ate about 90% animal matter; black-tailed jackrabbits (*Lepus californicus*) approached 75% of their year-round diet. This dependence on a single prey species influences coyote density in this region (Clark 1972; Wagner and Stoddart 1972; Johnson and Hansen 1979).

In northeastern California, meadow voles (*Microtus* sp.) occurred in about half of all coyote scats analyzed (Hawthorne 1972). Other important diet items were mule deer and cattle, probably eaten as carrion. Mule deer were also important in coyote diets in two areas of southern Utah (Pederson and Tuckfield 1983). In central Wyoming, mule deer, pronghorn antelope (*Antilocapra americana*), white-tailed jackrabbits (*L. townsendii*), and desert cottontail (*Sylvilagus audubonii*) were present in 63% of coyote scats (Springer and Smith 1981).

Although coyotes are extremely adaptable to whatever foods are available, like most species of carnivores, their populations are regulated largely by food abundance (Clark 1972; Nellis and Keith 1976; Todd and Keith 1983). Population densities of coyotes and their principal prey are strongly correlated. Food availability appears to have a strong influence on litter size and survival but, as yet, the carrying capacity of coyote habitat in terms of prey abundance cannot be evaluated on an absolute basis. Of the few studies conducted to estimate food requirements of coyotes (Clark 1972; Wagner and Stoddart 1972), disparate results have been obtained (reviewed by Gier 1975). Furthermore, the decline in prime habitat may also cause decreases in coyote density (Andelt and Andelt 1981).

Foxes. Like the coyote, the gray fox (*Urocyon cinereoargenteus*) and red fox (*Vulpes vulpes*) have adapted to a wide range of habitat types and foods. Most of the gray fox habitat consists of shrublands and brushy woodlands on hilly, rough, rocky, or broken terrain. In the western U.S., the gray fox

favors chaparral, woodlands of pinyon-juniper (*Pinus-Juniperus* sp.) or oak, along rocky hillsides, mountainsides, and washes. Chaparral vegetation of the foothills of the Pacific states includes ceanothus (*Ceanothus* sp.), chamise (*Adenostoma fasciculatum*), manzanita (*Arctostaphylos* sp.), mountain mahogany (*Cercocarpus* sp.), and oak. Here the gray fox supplements its primary diet of rodents with manzanita berries (Ingles 1965).

In Zion National Park, gray foxes are abundant in blackbrush (*Coleogyne ramosissima*), brushy meadows, open meadows, and pinyon-juniper and ponderosa pine at lower elevations (Trapp and Hallberg 1975). Here the gray fox is more a herbivore, insectivore, or scavenger than a carnivore. Juniper berries are an important food during winter, as is mule deer carrion during late winter and prickly pear fruits during autumn. Similar results were obtained from a food habits study in an Arizona ponderosa pine forest (Turkowski 1980).

The red fox's unspecialized way of life has allowed it to adapt and thrive in many habitat types. While it ranges from deep forests to the most exposed tundra, it prefers a mixture of forest and meadows. In the continental U.S., the red fox is widespread except in the Great Plains and the extreme Southeast and Southwest. One of the densest populations of red foxes in North America inhabits southwestern Wisconsin (Richards and Hine 1953). This country is a patchwork of woodlots, cropland, pasture, and stream bottoms. By following fox trails in the snow, Schofield (1960) found that red foxes in Michigan, at least during winter, preferred lowland brush and oak woods but avoided swamps. Ingles (1965) believed that sheep grazing in meadows adversely affected red fox populations in the western mountains by reducing their rodent food supply. The overall implication is that although the red fox can survive in many habitat types, it prefers those with a mixture of plant communities. Major factors determining habitat selection are probably cover requirements and food availability.

Red foxes are opportunistic feeders, eating foods in proportion to their availability (Errington 1935; Scott 1955). Thus, red fox diets often show seasonal changes in composition (Korschgen 1959). Most red fox food habit studies reviewed by Ables (1975) showed major foods to be small rodents, rabbits (*Sylvilagus* sp.), wild fruits and berries, and insects.

The kit fox (*Vulpes macrotis*) and swift fox (*V. velox*) inhabit the deserts and Great Plains of North America, respectively—areas not occupied by the red fox. An exception is in western Kansas where the red fox is usually found near towns, and the swift fox, in open, often grassland areas. The

Kit fox.

kit fox is the most specialized of the North American canids for desert existence. It prefers open, level, sandy ground with low desert vegetation.

Egoscue (1962) studied kit foxes in a western Utah desert that contained three plant communities: vegetated or stabilized dunes, greasewood (*Sarcobatus vermiculatus*) flats, and shadscale (*Atriplex confertifolia*) flats. Vegetated dunes have a diversified plant cover dominated by desert shrubs, including fourwinged saltbush (*Atriplex canescens*), rabbitbrush (*Chrysothamnus* sp.), greasewood, horsebrush (*Tetradymia* sp.), and shrubby buckwheat (*Eriogonum dubium*). With a single exception, no kit fox dens were discovered in this plant community. Greasewood flats are dominated by widely spaced greasewood shrubs, 1 to 1.5 m (3 to 5 ft) high. Ground cover between shrubs is sparse and consists primarily of grey molly (*Kochia americana*), seepweed (*Suaeda torryana*), and shadscale. Numerous kit fox dens were located in this community, which also was a favorite foraging area. Shadscale flats consist of sparsely growing vegetation averaging ≧60cm (≧24 in.) high. Dominant species were shadscale, inkweed, and grey molly. This community was primarily important as a hunting ground for black-tailed jackrabbits, which composed 90 to 95% of kit fox diets during the pup-rearing season. Although jackrabbit populations were not especially dense in shadscale flats, their numbers did not seem to fluctuate as sharply as in other communities. Thus, this community appeared to provide a stable food source.

The swift fox is considered by some to be a subspecies of the kit fox (Stains 1975). The swift fox, once common and widespread on the high plains of the central U.S. and Canada, now has a much more restricted distribution (Kilgore 1969; Moore and Martin 1980). The original swift fox habitat, the shortgrass plains of the Oklahoma Panhandle, was dominated by buffalograss (*Buchloe dactyloides*) and blue grama (*Bouteloua gracilis*) (Kilgore 1969). Other grass species were bluestem (*Andropogon scoparius*), wiregrass (*Aristida* sp.), and sideoats grama (*B. curtipendula*). Much of this region is now extensively cultivated; as a result, the original vegetation has largely been replaced by grain crops and weeds. In Wyoming, recent records of swift foxes have come from areas of gently rolling, shortgrass prairie, dominated by buffalograss and blue grama (Floyd and Stromberg 1981). In this area, the native shortgrass prairie is interspersed with winter wheat, alfalfa, and fallow fields. This habitat is very similar to that described for swift foxes in the Oklahoma Panhandle by Kilgore (1969).

Felidae

Mountain Lions. In western North America, mountain lions (*Felis concolor*) are generally associated with mountainous terrain, canyons, and rimrock. Here they feed primarily on mule deer (Robinette et al. 1959; Barnes 1960; Spalding and Lesowski 1971; Toweill and Meslow 1977; reviewed by Anderson 1983 and Ackerman et al. 1984).

In southern Utah, mountain lion habitat is vegetatively and topographically diverse (Barnes 1960; Ackerman 1982; Hemker 1982). Desert shrub and sagebrush-grassland communities occur at lower elevations (1,350 to 1,800 m [4,445 to 5,940 ft]). Pinyon-juniper woodlands, oakbrush (*Quercus gambelii*), and ponderosa pine forests dominate mid-elevations (1,800 to 2,700 m [5,940 to 8,910 ft]). Stands of quaking aspen (*Populus tremuloides*), Engelmann spruce (*Picea engelmannii*), and white fir (*Abies concolor*) interspersed with subalpine meadows occur above 2,700 m (8,910 ft). Deep, rocky, vertical-walled river canyons within these communities contain riparian vegetation, including Fremont cottonwood (*P. fremontii*) and willow (*Salix* sp.).

Vegetation and topography of the Idaho Primitive Area, where Hornocker (1969, 1970) and Seidensticker et al. (1973) conducted extensive mountain lion research, are also diverse. Plant communities are interspersed, depending on site characteristics including elevation, slope, and aspect. Engelmann spruce-subalpine fir (*A. lasiocarpa*) and ponderosa pine-Douglas-fir (*Pseudotsuga menziesii*) associations grow at higher elevations and in protected drainages. At lower elevations and on exposed slopes, curlleaf mountain mahogany (*Cerococarpus ledifolius*), bitterbrush (*Purshia tridentata*), and big sagebrush (*A. tridentata*)-bunchgrass associations occur.

In California, mountain lions occur primarily between 600 and 1,800 m (1,980 and 5,940 ft) elevations in mixed conifer and brush habitats (Koford

1977). At higher elevations, in pure stands of conifers, and at lower elevations, in pure stands of chamise brush (*Adenostoma fasciculata*), mountain lions are rare.

Within these western habitats, stream courses and ridgetops are frequently used as travel lanes and hunting routes by mountain lions (Barnes 1960). Riparian vegetation along streams provides cover for lions traveling in open areas, and ridgetops with cover allow undetected surveillance.

From these studies, mountain lions appear to prefer habitats that are vegetatively and topographically complex. This habitat characteristic and prey availability determine the amount of space a resident mountain lion requires. Because of large home ranges, territoriality, and population social structure, large areas of wilderness or remote habitat are essential to sustain viable mountain lion populations (Hornocker 1969, 1970; Koford 1977; Hemker 1982; reviewed by Anderson 1983). Mountain lions wander close to civilization (Barnes 1960), and some populations live near humans (Koford 1977). This is especially true in California, where there is a moratorium on mountain lion hunting. It is questionable, however, whether mountain lion populations can be sustained in this increasingly modified habitat (Figure 1A).

Bobcats. Bobcat (*Felis rufus*) and mountain lion habitat preferences are similar in that both use a variety of habitats. Bobcats still inhabit much of their former range in the eastern and southern U.S. (Figure 1B), where the mountain lion has been extirpated. Western bobcats prefer rocky canyons at elevations between 1,400 and 2,100 m (4,620 and 6,930 ft) with ledges and areas of dense vegetation (Young 1958; Gashwiler et al. 1961; McCord and Cardoza 1982). Common tree and shrub species of western habitats are manzanita, mountain mahogany, pinyon pine, sagebrush, and juniper. In the southwestern and western U.S., bobcats have adapted to living in even the driest deserts (Young 1958; Jones and Smith 1979).

Prey abundance, topography, and vegetation structure affect bobcat social structure and home range size (Bailey 1974; Beason and Moore 1977). In turn, social organization profoundly affects population density and the ways bobcats use their environment. Competitive interaction with coyotes also likely affects bobcat population density and behavior (Linhart and Robinson 1972).

Lynx. Lynx (*F. lynx*) are more restrictive in habitat and food selection than bobcats, making them more vulnerable to a changing environment. Where both these species are sympatric, competition, should it occur, may be more detrimental to the lynx (Parker et al. 1983). Dominant tree species of boreal

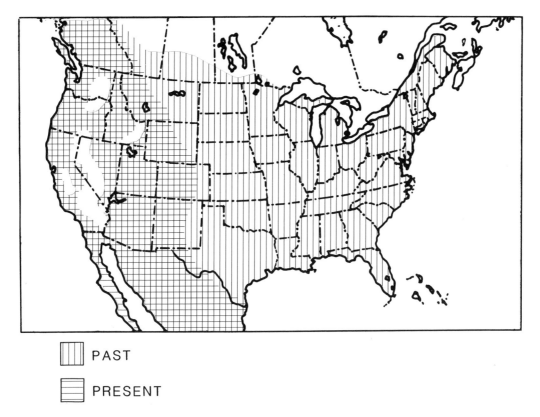

PAST

PRESENT

Figure 1A. Historical distribution of the mountain lion.

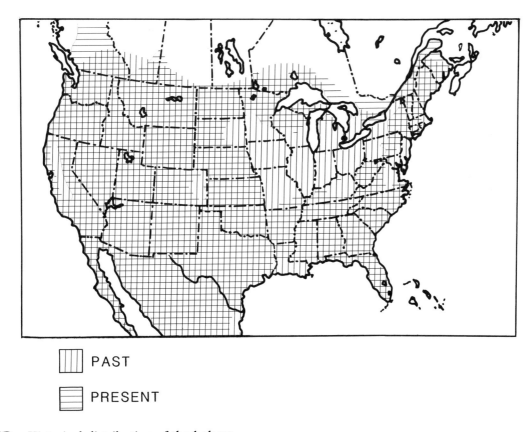

PAST

PRESENT

Figure 1B. Historical distribution of the bobcat.

forests inhabited by lynx are balsam fir
(*A. balsamea*), black spruce (*P. mariana*), white
spruce (*P. glauca*), and paper birch (*Betual
papyrifera*) (Brand et al. 1976; Parker et al. 1983).

In Alberta, lynx inhabit a variety of vegetation
types, ranging from undisturbed forest to 90% cultivated farmland (Nellis and Keith 1968; Nellis et al.
1972). In Montana, lynx preferred dense stands of
lodgepole pine (*P. contorta*) (Koehler et al. 1979).
Snowshoe hares were also most abundant in this
habitat type. Throughout their range, lynx depend
on snowshoe hares for most of their diet (Saunders
1963; van Zyll de Jong 1966; Nellis and Keith 1968;
Nellis et al. 1972; Brand et al. 1976; More 1976;
Koehler et al. 1979; Parker et al. 1983). This dependence is reflected in cyclical fluctuations of lynx
populations with changing snowshoe hare densities
(Figure 2) (Keith 1963; Brand et al. 1976; Brand and
Keith 1979). Because of this phenomenon, forest
management plans that incorporate habitat requirements of snowshoe hares are, in effect, management
plans for lynx (Parker et al. 1983). Clear-cutting
and burning of mature conifer forests are likely to
initially decrease hare and lynx populations, but
in the long term, an increase in food and cover for
hares should increase densities of both hares and
lynx (Koehler et al. 1979; Parker et al. 1983).

Ursidae

Black Bear. Bray and Barnes (1967) noted that
forested environments and food availability were
emphasized in almost all habitat descriptions of black
bear (*Ursus americanus*). Forests provide escape
cover, thermal cover, and den sites. However, in
western North America, black bear habitat ranges
from desert chaparral to closed coniferous forest

(Jonkel and Cowan 1971; Amstrup and Beecham
1976; Lindzey and Meslow 1977; Kelleyhouse 1980;
LeCount 1980; Graber 1982; Novick and Stewart
1982). The physical features and vegetation of black
bear habitat are exceedingly variable, reflecting
differences in latitude, elevation, slope, aspect,
precipitation, and land-use patterns. Because black
bears have adapted to so many habitat types, there is
no clear consensus on which habitat components
are most important (Treadwell 1979). Determining
local habitat use may be needed for sound management of this species.

In whatever ecosystem black bears occur, food
availability greatly influences their abundance and
distribution. Jonkel and Cowan (1971) found that
seasonal food production dictated habitat use by
black bears in spruce-fir (*Picea-Abies*) forests in
northwestern Montana. The spruce-fir/mountain
lover (*Pachistima myrsinites*) association was an
important component of black bear habitat during all
seasons. Other habitat components were important
seasonally: dry meadows in early spring, snowslides
and stream bottoms in early and midsummer, and
spruce-fir/rustyleaf (*Menziesia ferruginea*) and
spruce-fir/beargrass (*Xerophylum tenax*) associations
in fall. Recent clearcuts were avoided. The home
range of bears included the seasonal food sources
and, when a seasonal food was abundant, bears with
adjacent home ranges congregated in these habitats.

Lindzey and Meslow (1977) studied home range
and habitat use by black bears in a western hemlock-
Sitka spruce (*T. heterophylla-P. stichensis*) forest in
southwestern Washington. They found that black
bears used vegetation types disproportionately to
their availability, depending on availability of food

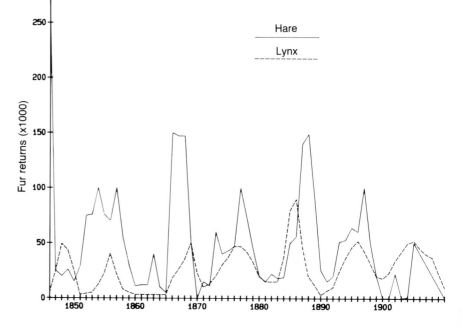

Figure 2. Cyclical fluctuations
in lynx and snowshoe hare
populations, showing
10-year cycle phenomenon.
(after Keith 1963).

and cover. The plant communities that followed clear-cutting provided concentrations of foods, especially huckleberries (*Vaccinium* sp.).

In a mixed coniferous forest of Douglas-fir, ponderosa pine, subalpine fir, and Engelmann spruce in Idaho, seven forage species (wild onions [*Allium* sp.], waterleaf [*Hydrophyllum capitatum*], biscuit root [*Lomatium dissectum*], bitter cherry [*Prunus emarginata*], chokecherry [*P. virginiana*], mountain ash [*Sorbus scopulina*], and huckleberry [*Vaccinium globulare*]) were highly correlated with locations of radio-collared black bears (Amstrup and Beecham 1976). Locations of black bears corresponded to areas of maximum food availability, which depended on phenological stages of these seven key food plants. Researchers in California also correlated habitat use by black bears with seasonal food availability (Piekielek and Burton 1975; Kelleyhouse 1980; Novick et al. 1981; Novick and Stewart 1982; Grenfell and Brody 1983). Habitat types ranged from chaparral, oak woodlands, and coniferous forest.

Grizzly Bears. In contrast to the importance of forested habitats to black bears, the importance of nonforested habitats to grizzly bears has been emphasized by several researchers. Herrero (1972, 1978) hypothesized that grizzly/brown bears evolved to exploit nonforested, periglacial environments. Martinka (1976) stressed the importance of fire in reducing or eliminating forest canopies to improve habitat for grizzlies. He stated that without natural fire, successional advance towards mature forest creates conditions more favorable for black bears than grizzlies. Particularly important open habitats are wet meadows and alluvial plains that supply grizzlies with key forbs and rhizomatous grasses (Singer 1978).

Craighead et al. (1982) included extensive timber cover, as well as open grasslands and meadows, in their descriptions of optimum grizzly habitat in the continental U.S. Grizzly/brown bear populations in Alaska and Canada apparently have no intrinsic need for extensive timber cover, as they thrive in open areas. However, grizzly populations in the continental U.S. may require forested habitat for isolation from human activities. Here a combination of a wide range of vegetation types characterizes prime grizzly bear habitat; mountain parks, grasslands interspersed with timber, alpine meadows, and talus slopes are necessary for feeding and social activities. Alder (*Alnus tenuifolia*) thickets, lodgepole pine "downfalls," and other dense vegetation are preferred bedding sites.

Large geographical areas are needed to provide a variety of alternative foods. Major foods are carrion, ungulates, rodents, insects, berries, pine nuts, green vegetation, bulbs and tubers and, in some

areas, fish (Mealy 1980). Habitat use by grizzlies is greatly influenced by the seasonal availability of these foods. In spring, the location of carcasses of ungulates that died during the winter or individuals that emerged from the winter in poor condition are important (Cole 1972; Houston 1978). In spring and summer, areas with high population densities of rodents or insects, fish-spawning sites, or succulent herbaceous vegetation or bulbs and tubers are important. In fall, berries, pine nuts, and ungulates crippled during hunting seasons are important food sources. Because of the conflict between grizzlies and humans, along with human land uses, wilderness areas are essential to separate them. Grizzly habitat must be isolated from developed areas and should receive only light recreational, logging, and livestock use. Except for humans, the grizzly has no enemies that restrict its use of habitat.

Arboreal, Aquatic, and Terrestrial Furbearers

Fisher, Marten, and Wolverine.

Fisher (*Martes pennanti*). These mustelids are generally associated with climax coniferous forests (de Vos 1952; Hornocker and Hash 1981; Powell 1982; Allen 1982, 1983; Douglass et al. 1983; Spencer et al. 1983; Hargis and McCullough 1984) and have large home range sizes (Koehler and Hornocker 1977; Buck et al. 1978; Powell 1982; Hornocker and Hash 1981). Fishers prefer continuous coniferous and mixed coniferous/deciduous forests with closed canopies (reviewed by Powell 1982; Allen 1983). Dense overhead cover is the one characteristic common to all habitats preferred by fishers. Canopy closure of 80 to 100% is selected and canopy closure of less than 50% is avoided. Within these habitats, fishers eat a variety of foods, including small mammals, carrion, birds and their eggs, insects, reptiles, amphibians, and various fruits and nuts (reviewed by Strickland et al. 1982).

Grinnell et al. (1937) and Schempf and White (1977) reported that fishers in California are most commonly found in Douglas-fir and mixed conifer forests between 610 and 2,440 m (2,000 and 8,000 ft) elevations. Here an unusual but important diet item is false truffles (*Rhizopogon* sp.; Grenfell and Fasenfest 1979).

Marten (*Martes americana*). The effects of fire and timber harvest have generally been considered harmful to fisher and marten habitat (de Vos 1952; reviewed by Powell 1982). However, whether this is true for marten habitat is subject to disagreement, because marten appear to be less dependent than fisher on old growth forest. Marten habitat use varies with the season.

During winter, marten prefer dense overhead cover of mature coniferous forests (Koehler and Hornocker 1977). In Idaho, marten activity was highest in stands having an Engelmann spruce-subalpine fir overstory, 100 years old or more, and a canopy cover greater than 30%; mesic sites also had high marten activity. Similarly, marten in northern California preferred stands of lodgepole pine or red fir (*A. magnifica*) with closed canopies (Spencer et al. 1983). Within both these habitat types, marten selected sites with Douglas squirrel (*Tamiasciurus douglasii*) feeding sign. Old-growth red fir with large snags, stumps, and logs was an especially preferred habitat. In Yosemite National Park, marten selected dense cover less than 3 m (9 ft) above snow level in lodgepole pine and western juniper forests (Hargis and McCullough 1984). Tree trunks allowed access to the subnivean (below the snow surface) zone, and logs served as den sites and hunting areas. Open areas were avoided. Preference for closed canopies may also be due to less snow accumulation, which would permit marten to conserve energy of movement (Raine 1982). Another means to conserve energy is use of red squirrel (*Tamiasciurus hudsonicus*) middens as roosting sites (Buskirk 1984).

Soutiere (1979) hypothesized that prey availability in dense forests rather than density of overhead cover, *per se*, explained winter habitat use by marten. Small mammals, especially the red-backed vole (*Clethrionomys gapperi*), make up the major portion of marten diets during winter (Cowan and MacKay 1959; Weckwerth and Hawley 1962; Soutiere 1979). Red-backed voles are associated with downed logs and mesic conditions of uncut coniferous forests (Koehler and Hornocker 1977).

In summer, effects of timber harvest and fire may be beneficial to marten. In Idaho, Koehler and Hornocker (1977) reported that plant communities created by fire provide marten with important summer foods. Streeter and Braun (1968), working in Colorado, also noted that marten do not require the cover of climax forests during summer. Contrary to these reports, Spencer et al. (1983) found that marten in the northern Sierra Nevada avoided open areas during all seasons. Soutiere (1979) concluded that marten in the Northeast were not limited to climax forests, and partial-cutting methods of timber harvest were compatible with the preservation of marten habitat. In California, Hargis and McCullough (1984) found that mixed-aged forests were important in providing protective cover and subnivean access over a wide range of snow conditions.

Wolverine (*Gulo gulo*). Like marten and fisher, the wolverine is associated with boreal forests. In Montana, wolverines selected subalpine fir cover types throughout the year; this selection was strongest during summer (Hornocker and Hash 1981).

Seral lodgepole pine and western larch (*Larix occidentalis*) sites were also used by wolverines. Large areas of mature timber were preferred, followed by ecotonal areas and rocky areas of timbered benches. Areas of dense, young timber; recent burns; and wet meadows were avoided.

In the Pacific states, wolverines are associated with coniferous forests containing Shasta red fir (*A. magnifica*), lodgepole pine, and western hemlock (*T. heterophylla*); at higher elevations, subalpine fir, Alaska cedar (*P. albicanlis*), and western juniper (*J. occidentalis*) (Ingles 1965). In Canada, wolverines inhabit tundra between the northern tree line and arctic coasts as well as boreal forests (Banfield 1974).

Wilderness is important in protecting wolverine populations because they are highly susceptible to human-caused mortality (van Zyll de Jong 1975). Hornocker and Hash (1981) found no difference in wolverine density between wilderness and nonwilderness areas, but concluded that wilderness was essential as a refuge and reservoir for wolverine populations. Furthermore, large areas of habitat are needed to support wolverine populations because of the wolverine's scavenging life-style, which requires a solitary existence and a large home range. Carrion is a mainstay in wolverine diets, especially during winter (Rausch and Pearson 1972; van Zyll de Jong 1975; Hornocker and Hash 1981). Van Zyll de Jong (1975) hypothesized that wolverine abundance is correlated with biomass and turnover of large ungulate populations.

Mink and River Otter.

Mink (*Mustela vison*). These amphibious mustelids are widespread, but uncommon, and have irregular distributions in western North America. With the exception of otters, mink lead a more aquatic existence than any other mustelid. They are often found near water, where a diet of muskrats (*Ondatra zibethicus*), fish, crayfish, frogs, and aquatic invertebrates are available (Haley 1975; Gilbert and Nancekivell 1982). In Canada and Alaska, habitat types with some of the densest mink populations are tidal flats and ocean beaches (Burns 1964; Banfield 1974). Unlike otters, mink are also common on land where they primarily hunt rodents and lagomorphs. In inland Canada, snowshoe hares are often their principal prey.

River Otter (*Lutra canadensis*). The more aquatic river otter depends on fish for a larger percentage of its diet than does the mink, especially in stream habitats (Melquist et al. 1981). Mink once concentrated on mammals and birds in stream habitats but switched to eating mostly fish at lakes (Gilbert and Nancekivell 1982). River otters, however, ate primarily fish in both habitats. Besides fish, important river otter foods are crayfish, frogs, turtles, and aquatic insects. Muskrat, beaver (*Castor canadensis*), and water birds occur infrequently in river otter diets, but in some areas they may be seasonally important (Greer 1955).

Throughout their range, river otters inhabit streams, rivers, lakes, marshes, and ocean bays where fish populations are dense. In Canada, they occur north beyond the tree line in tundra lakes and streams (Banfield 1974). In west-central Idaho, prey availability had the greatest influence on habitat use by river otters, but adequate shelter was necessary for extensive habitat use (Melquist and Hornocker 1983). Rather than excavate their own dens, river otters use dens constructed by other animals, often those of beavers (Haley 1975; Melquist and Hornocker 1983). They also use natural or man-made structures as dens. Habitat use in Idaho, determined by biotelemetry, indicated that river otters preferred valley to mountain habitats and stream-associated habitats to ponds, lakes, and reservoirs (Melquist and Hornocker 1983). This was believed to be true because stream habitats provided more adequate escape cover and shelter and less human disturbance. However, if food and shelter were adequate, river otters exhibited high tolerance toward human activity.

During winter, habitat use by mink and river otters is complicated by ice-covered waterways (Banfield 1974; Melquist and Hornocker 1983). Habitat is limited to open water during early winter. Outflows from lakes are particularly favored haunts at this time. In late winter, water levels usually drop below ice levels in rivers and lakes, leaving a layer of air that allows mink and river otters to travel and hunt under the ice.

Water quality and quantity are habitat variables that directly and indirectly affect mink and river otters. As secondary or higher-order consumers, these carnivores concentrate water pollutants (Cumbie 1975; Henry et al. 1981). Polluted or inadequate water quantity also adversely affects prey populations, thereby diminishing the carrying capacity of mink and river otter habitat.

Badgers, Raccoons, Ringtails, Skunks, and Weasels. The geographic distribution of most of these small- to medium-sized carnivores overlap broad areas in western North America. Many of these species also have similar food habits. Being opportunists, they eat foods locally or seasonally available and, except for the weasels (*Mustela* sp.), all are omnivorous. Because of these similarities, we have grouped these species so important habitat features can be compared and constructed.

River otters.

Badger (*Taxidea taxus*). Badgers are widespread in the western U.S., occurring in all plant communities except the rain forests of Washington and Oregon. They occur from sea level to alpine meadows and from deserts to dense coniferous forests (Long 1973; Long and Killingley 1983). Consequently, their general food habits are not too surprising. Badgers eat almost any species of vertebrate or invertebrate they can capture, but especially rodents captured underground (Messick and Hornocker 1981; Lampe 1982). They are most numerous in sagebrush-grasslands where pocket gophers (*Thomomys* sp.) and ground squirrels (*Spermophilus* sp.) abound. Their home range size varies dramatically with the season (Sargent and Warner 1972; Lindzey 1978; Lampe and Sovada 1981), being smallest during winter when they can enter a state of torpor and reduce their time aboveground by 93% (Harlow 1981).

Badgers.

Raccoon (*Procyon lotor*). Raccoons are common in forests of the western U.S. at low to middle elevations, where they greatly depend on riparian areas (Lotze and Anderson 1979; Hart 1982). They prefer deciduous stands over coniferous forests, but even inhabit basaltic outcroppings in sagebrush ecosystems. They are absent from deserts, high elevations, and the boreal forests of Canada and Alaska. Their habitat must include den sites; hollow branches are preferred, but hollow trunks and logs, caves or crevices, and attics of abandoned farm buildings are also used (Berner and Gysel 1967; Lynch 1974). Raccoons are probably the most omnivorous native carnivores in the western U.S., feeding on whatever foods are available. They forage extensively in farmyards and wetlands (Ellis 1964; Urban 1970; Fritzell 1978; Greenwood 1982) and have adapted to living in suburban residential communities (Hoffman and Gottschang 1977).

Ringtail (*Bassariscus astutas*). Depending on habitat, ringtails may also be omnivorous. They typically inhabit rocky and brushy canyons and talus area. They are also common in shinnery oak (*Q. harvardii*) woodlands and occur in live oak (*Q. virginiana*) savannas.

In Colorado, ringtails are usually associated with arid canyon and mesa country in the pinyon-juniper vegetation type. However, they have been reported in a wide variety of habitats, including an Engelmann spruce-lodgepole, pine-aspen community (Rutherford 1954). Similarly, in southern Nevada, Bradley and Hansen (1965) reported ringtails in many habitat types. They concluded that ringtails were present in all habitats except the most arid lower deserts.

Skunk (*Conepatus* sp., *Mephitis* sp., *Spilogale* sp.). The striped skunk (*M. mephitis*) occurs in a wider range of habitats and is more omnivorous than the ringtail (Wood 1954; Verts 1967; Ewer 1973; Haley 1975; Schowalter and Gunson 1982). This, the most common mustelid, is absent from colder climes, likely due to its inability to remain dormant for such long winters (Haley 1975). Within its range, the striped skunk flourishes from city parks to wilderness areas because of its generalized habits. Preferred habitats are difficult to delineate for a species so adaptable and widely distributed.

Verts (1967) concluded that relative abundance of striped skunks determined their preferred habitat. Using this criterion, he found that the extent and location of woodlots in farmlands of northeastern Illinois were important habitat factors. Presumably, woodlots provided needed cover and den sites. Contrary to earlier reports, striped skunks were more abundant in intensively cultivated areas than where forest, brushland, and farmland were intermixed (Verts 1967; Smith and Verts 1982). Storm (1972) found that striped skunks used pasture and hay crops more frequently than expected because they were conducive to night foraging and retreats, day or night. Other crops and uncultivated areas were used less than expected. In the open, dry country of Idaho, the importance of riparian growth along streams was deemed important for the same reasons (Larrison and Johnson 1981). Along the Pacific Coast, sand dunes covered with sufficient vegetation to permit digging of dens are excellent habitat (Ingles 1965). Here striped skunks scavenge along beaches at night for washed-up, dead marine animals. Similarly, in the Mississippi Lowland Region of Missouri, available denning habitat determines the distribution and population density of striped skunks (Verts 1967). The high water table makes ground dens unsuitable in many areas of this region.

Life-styles of the hooded skunk (*M. macroura*) and hognosed skunk are similar to those of the striped skunk. The hooded skunk prefers rocky and brushy canyons and riparian areas. Two or more species of hognosed skunks have been recognized (Hall and Kelson 1959) in these areas, but may only be geographical races of the same species (Haley 1975). This skunk inhabits desert valleys, grasslands, and partly wooded mountain foothills.

Spotted skunks (some authors recognize a western species, *S. gracilis,* and an eastern species, *S. putorius*) are less common than the striped skunk and less widely distributed. They generally prefer more open country than striped skunks, but still require some form of cover such as a fence row or gully vegetation between their den and foraging areas (Crabb 1948). In agricultural areas, they often den under old farm buildings or in abandoned ground squirrel burrows. In the southwestern U.S., spotted skunks inhabit rough, broken country below 2,400 m (8,000 ft). They can survive in deserts and drier regions of Nevada, New Mexico, and Arizona, where the striped skunk cannot (Haley 1975). However, they depend on riparian areas in arid country (Larrison and Johnson 1981). Although spotted skunks are highly omnivorous, as are striped skunks, rodents are relatively more important and arthropods correspondingly less so in their diets.

Weasel (*Mustela nivalis, M. frenata, M. erminea*). Unlike the rest of the species in this group, weasels are primarily carnivorous, specializing in killing rodents, lagomorphs, and birds. Like other species in this group, weasels occupy a broad range of habitats including boreal and deciduous forests, shrub-steppe regions, grasslands, and agricultural areas (Hall 1951). Their distributions are not closely linked to those of any certain prey species, but may be limited by competition with other weasel species (Simms 1979).

The least weasel feeds almost entirely on small rodents, primarily *Microtus* sp. (Ewer 1973; Haley 1975), and prefers meadows, brushy areas, and open woods. Ermine or short-tailed weasels are found in habitats similar to those of least weasels, but their distribution extends farther north and south.

Working in southern Ontario, Simms (1979) and King (1983) noted that short-tailed weasels selected early successional communities and avoided forested habitats, whereas long-tailed weasels showed no habitat preferences. Similarly, Larrison and Johnson (1981) reported that the short-tailed weasel in Idaho shuns the more rugged mountains and higher foothill ridges and occupies stream bottoms, rocky slides, fence rows, and shrub growth near water, as well as

Short-tailed weasel.

areas around farmsteads and the edges of urban areas. However, Ingles (1965) reported that short-tailed weasels in California, Oregon, and Washington inhabit high mountain red fir, lodgepole pine, and subalpine forests. Rodents, especially *Microtus* sp., are important in the diet of ermine, but shrews and birds are also eaten (Ewer 1973; Simms 1979).

The long-tailed weasel is more of a generalist in food habits and habitat use than the ermine or least weasel (Ewer 1973; Haley 1975; Gamble 1981). It also has a more southerly distribution than these smaller species. Simms (1979) hypothesized that the northward distribution of the long-tailed weasel is limited by snow cover, while the southward distributions of the two smaller species are limited by interactions with the long-tailed weasel. In the southwestern U.S., it is absent from deserts and desert grasslands.

POPULATION MEASUREMENT TECHNIQUES

Low densities and nonrandom distributions of carnivore populations create sampling problems when estimating population sizes. Carnivores are often distributed in a nonrandom manner because they prefer some specific type of habitat or because of social interactions between individuals or groups. Sampling problems are often compounded by the high mobility and wariness of most carnivore species. No single or best technique has yet been developed that can suitably census all carnivore populations. Basic sampling schemes and census methods indicate either presence or absence of a species, relative abundance, or absolute abundance (reviewed by Lewis 1970; Seber 1973; Sen 1982; Barrett 1983).

How and when a biologist should measure a carnivore population or prey base depends on the type of information needed. If information is required to assess the range or local distribution of the species, then techniques to determine presence are satisfactory. Techniques to obtain relative density estimates should be implemented after strongly declining harvests by trappers and hunters, substantial animal damage, habitat loss, or public concern for the species. Such techniques may require modifications as well as trial and error to achieve the desired results. They can be applied to most species within a reasonable time frame. An estimate of absolute density for most species is virtually impossible. The techniques are extremely time-consuming and expensive but may be appropriate when a carnivore is faced with extinction. These techniques are normally outside the scope of most management agencies.

The need to assess the prey base is most appropriate when carnivores are being censused for absolute density estimates and where knowledge of the prey is crucial to preserving a species (e.g., the prairie dog and black-footed ferret). Often a relative density index can be obtained more readily for prey species than for carnivores. Such estimates are particularly important when data on carnivores reveal areas of low and high abundance. Importantly, many other ecological factors (e.g., denning sites, various aspects of cover, access to subnivially active prey, or interactions with other species) may be of equal or greater importance. Therefore, sampling the prey base may only be appropriate when other ecological factors are also being considered. One also presupposes a knowledge of the principal prey, and relatively few carnivores depend on one or a few species of prey for survival.

Presence

Sightings or sign left by carnivores indicate their presence in a particular area. Yocom (1973, 1974) and Yocom and McCollum (1973) used reports of sightings and sign to indicate the presence and range of wolverine, marten, and fisher in California. Tracks, scats, and landing sites of river otter were used by Melquist and Hornocker (1979) to identify areas frequented by otters. Harvest records indicate geographic areas where species had been present. Responses to man-made stimuli, such as signs left at scent stations or howling by wolves or coyotes to sirens, indicate recent or immediate presence of carnivores.

Some states provide harvest records of carnivores.

Relative Density

Aerial surveys, bounty and harvest records, questionnaires, number of road kills, and indexes developed from counts of sightings, sign, and rate of capture or catch per unit effort data are widely used to estimate relative abundance of carnivore species. These types of data taken over time reveal population trends, are less costly than censuses, and are usually adequate for most management needs. Nellis and Keith (1976) and Parker (1973) used aerial surveys to estimate coyote and wolf densities, respectively. However, this technique is not always reliable for wolves (Miller and Russell 1977).

Cahalane (1964) used responses from mail questionnaires, based mostly on bounty and harvest records, to estimate population trends and relative densities of mountain lion, grizzly bears, and wolves throughout North America. Fuller and Keith (1980) obtained trends in wolf numbers in northeastern Alberta from records of trapping and poisoning. Similarly, coyote densities were estimated from fur and hunter harvest estimates obtained from annual reports and mail and telephone contacts. In Oklahoma, Hatcher and Shaw (1981) obtained slightly over a 50% response rate on 3,000 questionnaires sent to farmers. They compared the results of this mail survey with those of two scent-station surveys to evaluate bobcat, coyote, and gray and red fox populations.

Their results suggested that mail surveys are more effective than scent-station surveys in estimating carnivore populations. Furthermore, mail surveys are more cost-effective. Berg et al. (1983) mailed questionnaires to trappers and mountain lion hunters, outfitters, biologists and foresters, and ranchers and farmers to obtain data on distribution and relative densities of mountain lions in Wyoming.

Allen and Sargent (1975) used sightings of red fox by rural mail carriers as an index of population trends in North Dakota. This technique correlated highly (r = 0.958) with population estimates derived by aerial searches for fox families in the spring. This index appears best-suited to prairie regions, where foxes are relatively conspicuous. Its accuracy, timing, and low cost make this technique especially useful in management programs.

The relative abundance of coyotes has been estimated by scat deposition rates (reviewed by Andelt and Andelt 1984). Scat deposition rates are determined from the number of scats found along a given length of road during a known period. Before coyote density indexes and trends in abundance can be reliably estimated from scat deposition rates, the effect of diet on deposition rates must be determined. Numbers of interstate road-kills have also been used to determine the relative density of wildlife, including the coyote (Case 1978).

Elicited responses to man-made stimuli are often used to estimate relative densities of carnivore populations, especially those of coyotes. Scent-station indexes have recently gained popularity as a means of estimating seasonal and annual trends in relative abundance of carnivores (reviewed by Conner et al. 1983). Richards and Hine (1953) and Wood (1959) originally developed this method for determining the relative abundance of red and gray foxes. Humphrey and Zinn (1982) modified it for river otter and mink. Lindzey and Knowlton (1975) used it extensively for coyotes in 17 western states. Several hundred scent-station lines, each consisting of 50 scent stations located at 0.48-km (0.3-mi.) intervals along a 23.5-km (14.7-mi.) route, were checked for five consecutive days in September. Each station contained a perforated plastic capsule containing a fermented-egg attractant placed in the center of a 1-m (1-yd) circle of sifted dirt. Animal visits (based on tracks) were recorded to provide an index by which coyote population trends could be compared between regions, states, and years. The index of relative abundance was calculated as follows:

$$\text{Index} = 1{,}000 \times \frac{\text{total animal visits}}{\text{total operative station nights}}$$

The presence of many other carnivore species was recorded at scent stations, but because survey lines were located primarily in coyote habitat, these

records are not likely a measure of relative abundance of these species. With modifications, similar scent stations could be used to estimate relative densities of these carnivore species. Lindzey and Meslow (1977) modified this technique to make it more selective for black bears, and Clark and Campbell (1983) modified it for small carnivores. Conner et al. (1983) ran permanent scent-station transects in Florida and evaluated the indexes to determine seasonal and annual trends in abundance of bobcats, raccoons, and gray foxes. They found this technique provided a reliable index of species abundance when compared to estimates based on trapping, radioisotope tagging, and radiotelemetry. Despite the utility of this technique, Roughton and Sweeny (1982) and Conner et al. (1983) recognized it needed to be standardized and verified before between-area comparisons could be made. Furthermore, between-species comparisons of population densities could not be made directly with scent-station indexes because of species-specific visitation rates.

Siren-elicited vocalization has also gained interest as a possible method for estimating relative abundance of coyotes (reviewed by Okoniewski and Chambers 1984). Wenger and Cringan (1978) evaluated the technique in northeastern Colorado by using six radio-instrumented coyotes. Three of the coyotes readily responded to a siren, but the other three rarely responded. These results substantiated the response rate assumed by Alcorn (1971) for coyotes in Nevada. However, further research is needed to determine if an average response rate exists for all areas. With yearly sampling on a given area, this technique should provide good indexes of locally specific, annual coyote fluctuations. Andrews and Boggess (1978) reported two advantages of using this technique for coyotes over the more popular scent-station survey: (1) coyote and dog vocalizations are more easily distinguished than coyote and dog tracks and (2) the elicited-vocalization technique is not complicated by regional variation in coyote use or avoidance of roadways. Okoniewski and Chambers (1984) considered the advantages of the elicited-vocalization technique to be especially

important in areas where dog densities are high and habitat types diverse. On the other hand, specialized equipment is needed, and a substantial amount of field effort and time is required.

Catch per unit effort has also been used to estimate the relative densities of coyotes (Clark 1972; Knowlton 1972). Clark (1972) used the success of a summer trapping program, expressed as coyotes captured per 1,000 trap days, as one relative index of a postbreeding coyote population. Knowlton (1972) used humane "coyote-getters," set in standard lines, as a similar technique to quantify relative coyote abundance. Live-trapping techniques can also be used to estimate carnivore relative densities. Simms (1979) live-trapped species of weasels to determine their habitat preferences and population densities. Trapping success was measured as the number of captures per 100 trap days. A trap day was 24 hours, from one morning check to the next.

Barrett (1983) used smoked aluminum tracking stations to sample carnivores in California. The advantages of the technique are the ease in transporting and the ability to identify tracks. The major disadvantage is similar to that of other bait-based techniques (variation in attractability of many species).

Absolute Density

Direct counts and capture-recapture techniques are most commonly used to determine absolute density of wildlife species. The term "direct count" refers to counting each animal rather than its tracks,

den, or other sign. A complete count of all individuals in a population is a census in the true meaning of the word. This is very difficult for most carnivore populations. An exception may be locating wolf packs by radiotelemetry and then counting entire packs from aircraft (Fuller 1982). However, counting packs of wolves may not account for the number of transients, which in wolves make up 8 to 20% of the population (Mech and Frenzel 1971).

The Lincoln or Petersen Index method is a capture-recapture technique commonly used to estimate population sizes of many species of wildlife, including carnivores (Lewis 1970; Seber 1973; Davis and Winstead 1980). The word "index" is a misnomer because this technique provides an estimate of total population. Accuracy of this technique depends on the proportion of the population sampled. The Schnabel Method is a variation of the Lincoln Index. With this method, samples are taken over time so population estimates can be averaged. With the Lincoln or Petersen Index method, M individuals from a population are caught, marked, and released. On a second occasion, a sample of n individuals is captured. If m is the number of marked animals in this sample, an estimate $\hat{N}_2$ of the population size N and an estimate $v(\hat{N}_2)$ of its variance are calculated as follows:

$$\hat{N}_2 = \frac{n(M)}{m}$$

$$v(\hat{N}_2) = \frac{\hat{N}_2{}^2 (\hat{N}_2 - M)(\hat{N}_2 - n)}{Mn(\hat{N}_2 - 1)}$$

Sign left by carnivores has also been used to determine absolute density. Brand et al. (1976) believed the number of lynx and their movements could be accurately determined on a study area by track observations. After snowfalls, they drove along all roads in their study areas each day and recorded lynx tracks across roads until conditions prevented identifying recent tracks.

Koford (1977) derived estimates of mountain lion populations for several study areas in California, based on the number of different sets of tracks detected per 160 km (100 mi.) of road and trail tracking. By comparing these results with the total number of mountain lions detected by intensive searches of each study area, track counts were calibrated to indicate numbers of mountain lions per 260 km^2 (100 mi.^{2}). Koford (1977) and Shaw (1979) believed all mountain lions on a study area could be distinguished by the shape and size of their footprints. Both authors reported that the width of track heel pads was the most useful measurement to be taken.

Sightings of fox dens from the ground (Scott and Selko 1939) and from the air (Sargent et al. 1975) have been used to census red fox populations in Iowa and North Dakota, respectively. Sargent et al. (1975) flew systematic aerial searches to locate red foxes and their dens. The number of individual fox families was used as a census of the population.

DISCUSSION

Carnivores are a diverse group of mammals. Their respective habitats and food requirements vary greatly (Table 1). However, to accurately relate habitat to any species or animal community, biologists must be able to identify environmental features that accurately reflect a species' or community's requirements. Moreover, changes in these environmental features should allow biologists to make accurate predictions of a species' response to habitat alteration (Anderson 1982), either directly or indirectly, through a change in prey base. Usually dominant soils, plant species, and landforms have been listed and qualitatively described. Although these descriptions convey much information about an individual habitat type, they do not allow correlations between specific environmental features and a species' requirements. Quantitatively measuring many habitat features allows statistical correlation between specific habitat components and presence and abundance of a wildlife species.

Habitat requirements or preferences of carnivore species can be quantified with current technology. Soil, vegetation, and landforms can be quantitatively evaluated on the ground by techniques of Nudds (1977) and Hays et al. (1981) and those reviewed by Anderson (1982). Large-scale aerial photography (Aldrich 1979; Ulliman et al. 1979) and satellite imagery (Varney 1973; Brabander and Barclay 1977; Aldrich 1979; Cannon et al. 1982; Craighead et al. 1982) can be used to classify, inventory, and monitor general vegetative cover types (e.g., alpine meadows, forest, grassland, shrubland). Development of these remote-sensing techniques to evaluate vegetation types and land uses has greatly reduced the logistical effort and the cost of surveying and monitoring extensive areas by conventional methods.

LITERATURE CITED

ABLES, E.D. 1975. Ecology of the red fox in America. Pages 216-236 in Fox, M.W. ed. The Wild Canids. Van Nostrand Reinhold Co. New York, NY.

ACKERMAN, B.B. 1982. Cougar predation and ecological energetics in southern Utah. M.S. Thesis. Utah State Univ., Logan. 103pp.

———, F.G. LINDZEY, and T.P. HEMKER. 1984. Cougar food habits in southern Utah. J. Wildl. Manage. 48:147-155.

ALCORN, J.R. 1971. A discussion of coyote censusing techniques. U.S. Bur. Sport Fish. and Wildl., Div. Wildl. Serv. 8pp.

ALDRICH, R.C. 1979. Remote sensing of wildland resources: A state-of-the-art review. U.S. Dep. Agric., For. Serv. Gen Tech. Rep. RM-71. 56pp.

ALLEN, A.W. 1982. Habitat suitability index models: Marten. U.S. Dep. Inter., Fish and Wildl. Serv. FWS/OBS-82/10.11. 9pp.

———. 1983. Habitat suitability index models: Fisher. U.S. Dep. Inter., Fish and Wildl. Serv. FWS/OBS-82/0.45. 20pp.

ALLEN, S.H. and A.B. SARGENT. 1975. A rural mail-carrier index of North Dakota red foxes. Wildl. Soc. Bull. 3:74-77.

AMSTRUP, S.C. and J. BEECHAM. 1976. Activity patterns of radio-collared black bears in Idaho. J. Wildl. Manage. 40:340-348.

ANDELT, W.F. and S.H. ANDELT. 1981. Habitat use by coyote in southeastern Nebraska. J. Wildl. Manage. 45(4):1001-1005.

——— and ———. 1984. Diet bias in scat deposition-rate surveys of coyote density. Wildl. Soc. Bull. 12:74-77.

ANDERSON, A.E. 1983. A critical review of literature on puma (Felis concolor). Colo. Div. Wildl. Spec. Rep. 54. 91pp.

ANDERSON, S.H. 1982. Comments on measurement of habitat. Pages 278-280 in Davis, D.E. ed. CRC Handbook of Census Methods for Terrestrial Vertebrates. CRC Press, Inc. Boca Raton, FL.

ANDREWS, R.D. and E.K. BOGGESS. 1978. Ecology of coyotes in Iowa. Pages 249-265 in Bekoff, M. ed. Coyotes Biology, Behavior and Management. Academic Press. New York, NY.

BAILEY, T.N. 1974. Social organization in a bobcat population. J. Wildl. Manage. 38:435-445.

BANFIELD, A.W.F. 1974. The Mammals of Canada. Univ. Toronto Press, Toronto. 438pp.

BARNES, C.T. 1960. The cougar or mountain lion. The Ralton Co. Salt Lake City, UT. 176pp.

BARRETT, R.H. 1983. Smoked aluminum track plots for determining furbearer distribution and relative abundance. California Fish and Game 69:188-190.

BEASON, S.L. and R.A. MOORE. 1977. Bobcat food habit response to a change in prey abundance. Southwest. Nat. 21:451-457.

BERG, R.L., L.L. MCDONALD, and M.D. STRICKLAND. 1983. Distribution of mountain lions in Wyoming as determined by mail questionnaire. Wildl. Soc. Bull. 11:265-268.

BERG, W.E. and R.A. CHESNESS. 1978. Ecology of coyotes in northern Minnesota. Pages 229-247 in Bekoff, M. ed. Coyotes Biology, Behavior and Management. Academic Press. New York, NY.

BERNER, A. and L.W. GYSEL. 1967. Raccoon use of large tree cavities and ground burrows. J. Wildl. Manage. 31:706-714.

BRABANDER, J.J. and J.S. BARCLAY. 1977. A practical application of satellite imagery to wildlife habitat evaluation. Proc. Ann. Conf. Southeast Assoc. Fish Wildl. Agencies 31:300-306.

BRADLEY, W.G. and C.G. HANSEN. 1965. Observations on the distribution of the ring-tailed cat in southern Nevada. Southwest. Nat. 10:310-311.

BRAND, C.J. and L.B. KEITH. 1979. Lynx demography during a snowshoe hare decline in Alberta. J. Wildl. Manage. 40:416-428.

———, L.B. KEITH, and C.A. FISCHER. 1976. Lynx response to changing snowshoe hare densities in central Alberta. J. Wildl. Manage. 40:416-428.

BRAY, O.E. and V.G. BARNES. 1967. A literature review on black bear populations and activities. U.S. Dep. Inter., Natl. Park Serv., and Colo. Coop. Wildl. Res. Unit. 34pp.

BROWN, D.E. 1983. The wolf in the Southwest. Univ. Arizona Press, Tucson. 195pp.

BUCK, S., C. MULLIS, and A. MOSSMAN. 1978. A radio telemetry study of fishers in northwestern California. Cal.-Nev. Wildl. Trans. 1979:166-172.

BURNS, J.J. 1964. Comparisons of two populations of mink from Alaska. Can. J. Zool. 42:1071-1079.

BUSKIRK, S.W. 1984. Seasonal use of resting sites by marten in south-central Alaska. J. Wildl. Manage. 48:950-953.

CAHALANE, V.H. 1964. A preliminary study of distribution and numbers of cougar, grizzly and wolf in North America. NY. Zool. Soc. 12pp.

CANNON, R.W., F.L. KNOPF, and L.R. PETTINGER. 1982. Use of landsat data to evaluate lesser prairie chicken habitats in western Oklahoma. J. Wildl. Manage. 46:915-922.

CARBYN, L.N. 1982. Coyote population fluctuations and spatial distribution in relation to wolf territories in Riding Mountain National Park. Can. Field-Nat. 96:176-183.

CASE, R.M. 1978. Interstate highway road-killed animals, a data source for biologists. Wildl. Soc. Bull. 6:8-13.

CLARK, F.W. 1972. Influence of jackrabbit density on coyote population change. J. Wildl. Manage. 36:343-356.

CLARK, T.W. and T.M. CAMPBELL 1983. A small carnivore survey technique. Great Basin Nat. 43:438-440.

COLE, G.F. 1972. Grizzly bear-elk relationships in Yellowstone National Park. J. Wildl. Manage. 36:556-561.

CONNER, M.C., R.F. LABISKY, and D.R. PROGULSKE, Jr. 1983. Scent-station indices as measures of population abundance for bobcats, raccoons, gray foxes, and opossums. Wildl. Soc. Bull. 11:146-152.

COWAN, I. McT. 1947. The timber wolf in the Rocky Mountain National Parks of Canada. Can. J. Res. 25:139-174.

——— and R.H. MACKAY. 1959. Food habits of marten (Martes americana) in the Rocky Mountain region of Canada. Can. Field-Nat. 64:100-104.

CRABB, W.G. 1948. The ecology and management of the prairie spotted skunk in Iowa. Ecol. Monogr. 18:201-233.

CRAIGHEAD, J.J., J.S. SUMMER, and G.B. SCAGGS. 1982. A definitive system for analysis of grizzly bear habitat and other wilderness resources utilizing LANDSAT multispectral imagery and computer technology.

Wildlife-Wildlands Inst. Monogr. 1, Univ. Montana Foundation, Missoula.

CUMBIE, P.M. 1975. Mercury levels in Georgia otter, mink and freshwater fish. Environ. Contam. Toxicol. 14:193-196.

DAVIS, D.E. and R.L. WINSTEAD. 1980. Estimating the number of wildlife populations. Pages 221-246 in Giles, R.H. ed. Wildlife Management Techniques Manual. The Wildl. Soc. Washington, DC.

DE VOS, A. 1952. Ecology and management of fisher and marten in Ontario. Tech. Bull. Ontario Dep. Lands and Forests.

DOUGLASS, R.J., L.G. FISHER, and M. MAIR. 1983. Habitat selection and food habits of marten, Martes americana, in the Northwest Territories. Can. Field-Nat. 97:71-74.

EGOSCUE, H.J. 1962. Ecology and life history of the kit fox in Tooele County, Utah. Ecology 43:481-497.

ELLIS, R.J. 1964. Tracking raccoons by radio. J. Wildl. Manage. 28:363-368.

ERRINGTON, P.L. 1935. Food habits of mid-west foxes. J. Mammal. 16:192-200.

EWER, R.F. 1973. The Carnivores. Cornell Univ. Press. Ithaca, NY. 494pp.

FLOYD, B.L. and M.R. STROMBERG. 1981. New records of the swift fox (Vulpes velox) in Wyoming. J. Mammal. 62:650-651.

FRITZELL, E.K. 1978. Habitat use by prairie raccoons during the waterfowl breeding season. J. Wildl. Manage. 42:118-127.

FULLER, T.K. 1982. Wolves. Pages 225-226 in Davis, D.E. ed. CRC Handbook of Census Methods for Terrestrial Vertebrates. CRC Press, Inc. Boca Raton, FL.

——— and L.B. KEITH. 1980. Wolf population dynamics and prey relationships in northeastern Alberta. J. Wildl. Manage. 44:583-602.

GAMBLE, R.L. 1981. Distribution in Manitoba of Mustela Frenata Longicauda, the long-tailed weasel, and the interrelation of distribution and habitat selection in Manitoba, Saskatchewan and Alberta. Can. J. Zool. 59:1036-1039.

GASAWAY, W.C., R.O. STEPHENSON, J.L. DAVIS, P.E.K. SHEPHERD, and O.E. BURRIS. 1983. Interrelationships of wolves, prey, and man in interior Alaska. Wildl. Monogr. 84. 50pp.

GASHWILER, J., W.L. ROBINETTE, and O.W. MORRIS. 1961. Breeding habits of bobcats in Utah. J. Mammal. 42:76-84.

GIER, H.T. 1975. Ecology and behavior of the coyote (Canis latrans). Pages 246-262 in Fox, M.W. ed. The Wild Canids. Van Nostrand Reinhold Co. New York, NY.

GILBERT, F.F. and E.G. NANCEKIVELL. 1982. Food habits of mink (Mustelavison) and otter (Lutra canadensis) in northeastern Alberta Canada. Can. J. Zool. 60:1282-1288.

GRABER, D.M. 1982. Ecology and management of black bear in Yosemite National Park. Cooperative National Park Resources Study Unit. Univ. of California at Davis. Tech. Rep. 5.

GREEN, J.S. and J.T. FLINDERS. 1981. Diets of sympatric red foxes and coyotes in southeastern Idaho. Great Basin Nat. 41:251-254.

GREENWOOD, R.J. 1982. Nocturnal activity and foraging of prairie raccoons in North Dakota. Am. Midl. Nat. 107:238-243.

GREER, K.R. 1955. Yearly food habits of the river otter in the Thompson Lakes region, northwestern Montana, as indicated by scat analysis. Am. Midl. Nat. 54:299-313.

GRENFELL, W.E. and A.J. BRODY. 1983. Seasonal foods of black bears in Tahoe National Forest, California. Calif. Fish and Game 69:132-150.

——— and M. FASENFEST. 1979. Winter food habits of fishers, Martes pennanti, in northwestern California. Calif. Fish Game 65:186-189.

GRINNELL, J., J.S. DIXON, and J.M. LINSDALE. 1937. Fur-bearing mammals of California, Vol. I. Univ. Calif. Press, Berkeley. 375pp.

HALEY, D. 1975. Sleek and savage: North America's weasel family. Pacific Search. Seattle, WA. 298pp.

HALL, E.R. 1951. Weasels. Univ. Kansas Publ. Mus. Nat. Hist. No. 4.

——— and K.R. KELSON. 1959. The mammals of North America, Vol. II. The Ronald Press. New York, NY.

HARGIS, C.D. and D.R. McCULLOUGH. 1984. Winter diet and habitat selection of marten in Yosemite National Park. J. Wildl. Manage. 48:140-146.

HARLOW, H.J. 1981. Torpor and other physiological adaptations of the badger (Taxidea taxus) to cold environments. Physiol. Zool. 54:267-276.

HART, E.B. 1982. The raccoon (Procyon lotor) in Wyoming. Great Basin Nat. 42:599-600.

HATCHER, R.T. and J.H. SHAW. 1981. A comparison of three indices to furbearer populations. Wildl. Soc. Bull. 9:153-156.

HAWTHORNE, V.M. 1972. Coyote food habits in Sagehen Creek basin, northeastern California. Calif. Fish and Game 58:4-12.

HAYS, R.L., C. SUMMERS, and W. SEITZ. 1981. Estimating wildlife habitat variables. U.S. Dep. Inter., Fish and Wildl. Serv. FWS/OBS-81/47. Washington, DC. 111pp.

HEMKER, T.P. 1982. Population characteristics and movement patterns of cougars in southern Utah. M.S. Thesis. Utah State Univ., Logan. 59pp.

HENRY, C.J., L.J. BLUS, S.V. GREGORY, and C.J. STAFFORD. 1981. PCBs and organochlorine pesticides in wild mink and river otters from Oregon. Pages 1763-1789 in Chapman, J.A. and Pursley, D. eds. Worldwide Furbearer Conf. Proc. 1980. Frostburg, MD.

HENSHAW, R.E. 1975. Reintroduction of wolves into the wild. Pages 420-444 in Klinghammer, E. ed. The Behavior and Ecology of Wolves. Symp. Proc. Garland STPM Press. New York, NY.

———, R. LOCKWOOD, R. SHIDELER, and R.O. STEPHENSON. 1975. Experimental release of captive wolves. Pages 319-345 in Klinghammer, E. ed. The Behavior and Ecology of Wolves. Symp. Proc. Garland STPM Press, New York, NY.

——— and R.O. STEPHENSON. 1974. Homing in the gray wolf (Canis lupus). J. Mammal. 55:234-237.

HERRERO, S. 1972. Aspects of evolution and adaptation in American black bears (Ursus americanus Pallus) and brown and grizzly bears (U. asctos Linne) of North America. Pages 221-231 in Herrero, S. ed. Bears—Their Biology and Management. New Series 23, International Union for Conservation of Nature. Morges, Switzerland.

———. 1978. A comparison of some features of the evolution, ecology and behavior of black and grizzly/brown bears. Carnivore 1:7-17.

HILTON, H. 1978. Systematics and ecology of the eastern coyote. Pages 209-228 in Bekoff, M. ed. Coyotes Biology, Behavior and Management. Academic Press.

New York, NY.

HOFFMAN, C.O. and J.L. GOTTSCHANG. 1977. Numbers, distribution, and movements of a raccoon population in a suburban residential community. J. Mammal. 58:623-636.

HOLLEMANN, D.F. and R.O. STEPHENSON. 1981. Prey selection and consumption by Alaskan wolves in winter. J. Wildl. Manage. 45:620-628.

HORNOCKER, M.G. 1969. Winter territoriality in mountain lions. J. Wildl. Manage. 33:457-464.

———. 1970. An analysis of mountain lion predation upon mule deer and elk in the Idaho Primitive Area. Wildl. Monogr. 21. 39pp.

——— and H.S. HASH. 1981. Ecology of the wolverine in northwestern Montana. Can. J. Zool. 59:1286-1301.

HOUSTON, D.B. 1978. Elk as winter-spring food for carnivores in northern Yellowstone National Park. J. Appl. Ecol. 15:653-662.

HUMPHREY, S.R. and T.L. ZINN. 1982. Seasonal habitat use by river otters and Everglades mink in Florida. J. Wildl. Manage. 46:375-381.

INGLES, L.G. 1965. Mammals of the Pacific States. Stanford Univ. Press, Stanford, CA. 506pp.

JOHNSON, M.K. and R.M. HANSEN. 1979. Coyote food habits on the Idaho Natural Engineering Laboratory. J. Wildl. Manage. 43:951-955.

JONES, J.H. and N.S. SMITH. 1979. Bobcat density and prey selection in central Arizona. J. Wildl. Manage. 43:666-672.

JONKEL, J. and I. McT. COWAN. 1971. The black bear in the spruce-fir forest. Wildl. Monogr. 27.

JORDAN, P.A., P.C. SHELTON, and D.L. ALLEN. 1967. Numbers, turnover, and social structure of the Isle Royale wolf population. Am. Zool. 7:233-252.

KEITH, L.B. 1963. Wildlife's ten-year cycle. Univ. Wisconsin Press, Madison. 201pp.

KELLEYHOUSE, D.G. 1980. Habitat utilization by black bears in northern California. Pages 221-228 in Martinka, C.J. and K.L. McArthur eds. Bears—Their Biology and Management. Bear Biol. Assoc. Ser. 4.

KILGORE, D.L., Jr. 1969. An ecological study of the swift fox (Vulpes velox) in the Oklahoma Panhandle. Am. Midl. Nat. 81:512-534.

KING, C.M. 1983. Mustela erminea. Mammalian Species 195. 8pp.

KNOWLTON, F.F. 1972. Preliminary interpretation of coyote population mechanics with some management implications. J. Wildl. Manage. 36:369-382.

KOEHLER, G.M. and M.G. HORNOCKER. 1977. Fire effects on marten habitat in the Selway-Bitterroot Wilderness. J. Wildl. Manage. 41:500-505.

———, ———, and H.S. HASH. 1979. Lynx movements and habitat use in Montana. Can. Field-Nat. 93:441-442.

KOFORD, C.B. 1977. Status and welfare of the puma (Felis concolor) in California, 1973-1976. Final Rep. Defenders of Wildlife and the National Audubon Society. Mus. Vert. Zool. Univ. Calif., Berkeley. 57pp.

KOLENOSKY, G.B. 1972. Wolf predation on wintering deer in east-central Ontario. J. Wildl. Manage. 36:257-369.

KORSCHGEN, L.J. 1959. Food habits of the red fox in Missouri. J. Wildl. Manage. 23:168-176.

KUYT, E. 1972. Food habits and ecology of wolves on barren-ground caribou range in the Northwest Territories. Can. Wildl. Serv. Rep. Ser. 21. 36pp.

LAMPE, R.P. 1982. Food habits of badgers in east-central Minnesota. J. Wildl. Manage. 46:790-795.

——— and M. SOVADA. 1981. Seasonal variation in home range of a female badger (Taxidea taxus). Prairie Nat. 13:55-58.

LARRISON, E.J. and D.R. JOHNSON. 1981. Mammals of Idaho. Univ. Idaho Press, Moscow. 166pp.

LECOUNT, A.L. 1980. Some aspects of black bear ecology in the Arizona chaparral. Pages 175-180 in Martinka, C.J. and K.L. McArthur eds. Bears—Their Biology and Management. Bear Biol. Assoc. Ser. 4.

LEWIS, J.C. 1970. Wildlife census methods: A resume. J. Wildl. Dis. 6:356-364.

LINDZEY, F.G. 1978. Movement patterns of badgers in northwestern Utah. J. Wildl. Manage. 42:418-422.

——— and F.F. KNOWLTON. 1975. Determining the relative abundance of coyotes by scent station lines. Wildl. Soc. Bull. 3:119-124.

——— and E.C. MESLOW. 1977. Home range and habitat use by black bears in southwestern Washington. J. Wildl. Manage. 41:408-415.

LINHART, S.B. and W.B. ROBINSON. 1972. Some relative carnivore densities in areas under sustained coyote control. J. Mammal. 53:880-884.

LONG, C.A. 1973. Taxidea taxus. Mammalian Species 26. The Amer. Soc. of Mammal. Lawrence, KS. 4pp.

——— and C.A. KILLINGLEY. 1983. The badgers of the world. Charles C. Thomas, Publisher. Springfield, IL. 404pp.

LOTZE, J.H. and S. ANDERSON. 1979. Procyon lotor. Mammalian Species 119. The Amer. Soc. of Mammal. Lawrence, KS. 8pp.

LYNCH, G.M. 1974. Some den sites of Manitoba raccoons. Can. Field-Nat. 88:494-495.

MARTINKA, C.J. 1976. Ecological role and management of grizzly bears in Glacier National Park, Montana. Pages 147-156 in Pelton, M.R., J.W. Lentfer, and G.E. Folk eds. Bears—Their Biology and Management. IUCN Publ. New Ser. 40. Morges, Switzerland.

McCORD, C.M. and J.E. CARDOZA. 1982. Bobcat and lynx. Pages 728-766 in Chapman, J.A. and G.A. Feldhamer eds. Wild Mammals of North America: Biology, Management and Economics. John Hopkins Univ. Press. Baltimore, MD.

MEALY, S.P. 1980. The natural food habits of grizzly bears in Yellowstone National Park, 1973-74. Pages 281-292 in Martinka, C.J. and K.L. McArthur eds. Bears—Their Biology and Management. Bear Biol. Assoc. Ser. 4.

MECH, L.D. 1966. The wolves of Isle Royale. U.S. Dep. Inter., Natl. Park Serv. Fauna Ser. 7. Washington, DC. 210pp.

———. 1975. Some considerations in re-establishing wolves in the wild. Pages 445-457 in Klinghammer, E. ed. The Behavior and Ecology of Wolves. Symp. Proc. Garland STPM Press. New York, NY.

———. 1977. Productivity, mortality, and population trends of wolves in northeastern Minnesota. J. Mammal. 58:559-574.

——— and L.D. FRENZEL. 1971. Ecological studies of the timber wolf in northeastern Minnesota. U.S. Dep. Agric., For. Serv. Res. Pap. NC-52. 62pp.

——— and P.D. KARNS. 1977. Role of the wolf in deer decline in the Superior National Forest. U.S. Dep. Agric., For. Serv. Res. Pap. NC-51. 62pp.

MELQUIST, W.E. and M.G. HORNOCKER. 1979. Methods and techniques for studying and censusing river otter populations. Univ. Idaho For. Wildl. and Range Exp. Sta. Tech. Rep. 8. 17pp.

————— and —————. 1983. Ecology of river otters in west-central Idaho. Wildl. Monogr. 83. 60pp.

—————, J.S. WHITMAN, and M.G. HORNOCKER. 1981. Resource partitioning and coexistence of sympatric mink and river otter populations. Pages 187-220 *in* Chapman, J.A. and D. Pursley eds. Worldwide Fur-bearer Conf., Vol. 1. Frostburg, MD.

MESSICK, J.P. and M.G. HORNOCKER. 1981. Ecology of the badger. *Taxidea taxus* in southeastern Idaho. Wildl. Monogr. 76. 53pp.

MILLER, F.L. and R.H. RUSSELL. 1977. Unreliability of strip aerial surveys for estimating numbers of wolves on western Queen Elizabeth Islands, Northwest Territories. Can. Field-Nat. 91:77-82.

MOORE, R.E. and N.S. MARTIN. 1980. A recent record of the swift fox (*Vulpes velox*) in Montana. J. Mammal. 61:161.

MORE, G. 1976. Some winter food habits of lynx (*Felix lynx*) in the southern Mackenzie district, Northwest Territories. Can. Field-Nat. 90:499-500.

MURIE, A. 1944. The wolves of Mount McKinley. U.S. Dep. Inter., Natl. Park Serv. Fauna Ser. 5. 238pp.

—————. 1951. Coyote food habits on a southwestern cattle range. J. Mammal. 32:291-295.

NELLIS, C.H. and L.B. KEITH. 1968. Hunting activities and success of lynx in Alberta. J. Wildl. Manage. 32:718-722.

————— and —————. 1976. Population dynamics of coyotes in central Alberta, 1964-68. J. Wildl. Manage. 40:389-399.

—————, S.P. WETMORE, and L.B. KEITH. 1972. Lynx-prey interactions in central Alberta. J. Wildl. Manage. 36:320-329.

NOVICK, H.J., J.M. SIPEREK, and G.R. STEWART. 1981. Denning characteristics of black bears (*Ursus americanus*) in the San Bernardino mountains of southern California. Calif. Fish and Game 67:52-61.

————— and G.R. STEWART. 1982. Home range and habitat preferences of black bears (*Ursus americanus*) in the San Bernardino Mountains of southern California, U.S.A. Calif. Fish and Game 68:21-35.

NUDDS, T.D. 1977. Quantifying the vegetative structure of wildlife cover. Wildl. Soc. Bull. 5:113-117.

OKONIEWSKI, J.C. and R.E. CHAMBERS. 1984. Coyote vocal response to an electronic siren and human howling. J. Wildl. Manage. 48:217-221.

PARKER, G.R. 1973. Distribution and densities of wolves within barren-ground caribou range in northern mainland Canada. J. Mammal. 54:341-346.

—————, J.W. MAXWELL, L.D. MORTON, and E.J. SMITH. 1983. The ecology of the lynx (*Lynx canadensis*) on Cape Breton Island. Can. J. Zool. 61:770-786.

PEDERSON, J.C. and R.C. TUCKFIELD. 1983. A comparative study of coyote food habits on two Utah deer herds. Great Basin Nat. 43:432-437.

PETERSON, R.O. 1975. The wolves of Isle Royale: New developments. Pages 3-18 *in* Klinghammer, E. ed. The Behavior and Ecology of Wolves. Symp. Proc. Garland STPM Press. New York, NY.

—————. 1977. Wolf ecology and prey relationships on Isle Royale. U.S. Dep. Inter., Natl. Park Serv. Sci. Monogr. Ser. 11. 210pp.

PIEKIELEK, W. and T. BURTON. 1975. A black bear population study in northern California. Calif. Fish and Game 61:4-25.

PIMLOTT, D.H. 1967. Wolf predation and ungulate populations. Am. Zool. 7:267-278.

POWELL, R.A. 1982. The fisher, life history, ecology, and behavior. Univ. Minnesota Press, Minneapolis. 217pp.

PULLIAINEN, E. 1975. Ecology of the wolf in the settled areas of Finland. Pages 84-92 *in* Klinghammer, E. ed. The Behavior and Ecology of Wolves. Symp. Proc. Garland STPM Press. New York, NY.

RAINE, R.M. 1982. Ranges of juvenile fisher (*Martes pennanti*) and marten, (*Martes americana*) in southeastern Manitoba. Can. Field-Nat. 96:431-438.

RAUSCH, R.A. and A.M. PEARSON. 1972. Notes on the wolverine in Alaska and the Yukon Territory. J. Wildl. Manage. 36:249-268.

RICHARDS, S.H. and R.L. HINE. 1953. Wisconsin fox populations. Tech. Wildl. Bull. 6. Wisconsin Conserv. Dep., Madison.

ROBINETTE, W.L., J.S. GASHWILER, and O.W. MORRIS. 1959. Food habits of the cougar in Utah and Nevada. J. Wildl. Manage. 23:261-273.

ROUGHTON, R.D. and M.W. SWEENY. 1982. Refinements in scent-station methodology for assessing trends in carnivore populations. J. Wildl. Manage. 46:217-229.

RUTHERFORD, W.H. 1954. A record of the ringtail (*Bassaricus astutus*) in Colorado. J. Mammal. 35:442-443.

SARGENT, A.B., W.K. PFEIFER, and S.H. ALLEN. 1975. A spring aerial census of red foxes in North Dakota. J. Wildl. Manage. 39:30-39.

————— and D.W. WARNER. 1972. Movements and denning habits of a badger. J. Mammal. 53:207-210.

SAUNDERS, J.K., Jr. 1963. Food habits of the lynx in Newfoundland. J. Wildl. Manage. 27:384-390.

SCHEMPF, P.F. and M. WHITE. 1977. Status of six furbearers in the mountains of northern California. U.S. Dep. Agric., For. Serv. Calif. Reg. 51pp.

SCHOFIELD, R.D. 1960. A thousand miles of fox trails in Michigan's ruffed grouse range. J. Wildl. Manage. 24:432-434.

SCHOWALTER, D.B. and J.R. GUNSON. 1982. Parameters of populations and seasonal activity of striped skunks, *Mephitis mephitis*, in Alberta and Saskatchewan. Can. Field-Nat. 96:409-420.

SCOTT, T.G. 1955. Dietary patterns of red and gray foxes. Ecology 36:366-367.

————— and L.F. SELKO. 1939. A census of red foxes and striped skunks in Clay and Boone counties, Iowa. J. Wildl. Manage. 3:92-98.

SEBER, G.A.F. 1973. The estimation of animal abundance. Griffin. London. 506pp.

SEIDENSTICKER, J.C., M.G. HORNOCKER, W.V. WILES, and J.P. MESSICK. 1973. Mountain lion social organization in the Idaho Primitive Area. Wildl. Monogr. 35. 60pp.

SEN, A.R. 1982. A review of some important techniques in sampling wildlife. Can. Wildl. Serv., Occ. Paper 49. 17pp.

SHAW, H.G. 1979. A mountain lion field guide. Arizona Game and Fish Dep. Spec. Rep. 9, Phoenix. 27pp.

SHORT, H.L. 1979. Food habits of coyotes in a semidesert grass-shrub habitat. U.S. Dep. Agric., For. Serv. Res. Note RM-364. 4pp.

SIMMS, D.A. 1979. North American weasels resource utilization and distribution. Can. J. Zool. 57:504-520.

SINGER, F.J. 1978. Seasonal concentrations of grizzly bears, North Fork of the Flathead River, Montana. Can. Field-Nat. 92:283-286.

SMITH, J.W. and B.J. VERTS. 1982. *Mephitis mephitis*. Mammalian Species 173. The Amer. Soc. of Mammal. Lawrence, KS. 7pp.

SOUTIERE, E.C. 1979. Effects of timber harvesting on marten in Maine. J. Wildl. Manage. 43:850-860.

SPALDING, D.J. and J. LESOWSKI. 1971. Winter food of the cougar in south-central British Columbia. J. Wildl. Manage. 35:378-381.

SPENCER, W.D., R.H. BARRETT, and W.J. ZIELINSKI. 1983. Marten habitat preferences in the northern Sierra Nevada. J. Wildl. Manage. 47:1181-1186.

SPERRY, C.C. 1941. Food habits of the coyote. U.S. Dep. Inter., Fish and Wildl. Serv. Res. Bull. 4. 70pp.

SPRINGER, J.T. and J.S. SMITH. 1981. Summer food habits of coyotes in central Wyoming. Great Basin Nat. 41:449-456.

STAINS, H.J. 1975. Distribution and taxonomy of the canidae. Pages 3-26 in Vox, M.W. ed. The Wild Canids. Van Nostrand Reinhold Co. New York, NY.

STORM, G.L. 1972. Daytime retreats and movements of skunks on farmlands of Illinois. J. Wildl. Manage. 36:31-45.

STREETER, R.G. and C.E. BRAUN. 1968. Occurrence of pine marten (Martes americana) in Colorado alpine areas. Southwest. Nat. 13:449-451.

STRICKLAND, M.A., C.W. DOUGLAS, M. NOVAK, and N.P. HUNZIGER. 1982. Martin. Pages 599-612 in Chapman, J. and G. Feldhamer eds. Wild Mammals of North America: Their Biology, Management and Economics. The John Hopkins Univ. Press. Baltimore, MD.

TODD, A.W. and L.B. KEITH. 1983. Coyote demography during a snowshoe hare decline in Alberta. J. Wildl. Manage. 47:394-404.

TOWEILL, D.E. and E.C. MESLOW. 1977. Food habits of cougars in Oregon. J. Wildl. Manage. 41:576-578.

TRAPP, G. and D.L. HALLBERG. 1975. Ecology of the gray fox (Urocyon cinereoargenteus): a review. Pages 164-178 in Fox, M.W. ed. The Wild Canids: Their Systematics, Behavioral Ecology and Evolution. Van Nostrand Reinhold Co. New York, NY.

TREADWELL, B.D. 1979. A provisional framework for defining black bear habitat. Pages 319-330 in LeCount, A. ed. First Western Black Bear Workshop. Ariz. Game and Fish Dep., Phoenix.

TURKOWSKI, F.J. 1980. Carnivora food habits and habitat use in ponderosa pine forests. U.S. Dep. Agric., For. Serv. Res. Pap. RM-215. 9pp.

ULLIMAN, J.J., E.O. GARTON, and J.A. KEAY. 1979. Wildlife habitat classification using large-scale aerial photography. Pages 414-422 in Frayer, W.F. ed. Forest Resource Inventories, Vol. 1. Colo. State Univ., Ft. Collins.

URBAN, D. 1970. Raccoon populations, movement patterns, and predation of a managed waterfowl marsh. J. Wildl. Manage. 34:372-382.

VAN BALLENBERGHE, V., A.W. ERICKSON, and D. BYMAN. 1975. Ecology of the timber wolf in northeastern Minnesota. Wildl. Monogr. 43. 43pp.

VAN ZYLL DE JONG, C.G. 1966. Food habits of the lynx in Alberta and the Mackenzie District, N.W.T. Can. Field-Nat. 80:18-23.

———. 1975. The distribution and abundance of the wolverine (Gulo gulo) in Canada. Can. Field-Nat. 89:431-437.

VARNEY, J.R. 1973. An evaluation of the use of ERTS-1 satellite imagery for grizzly bear habitat analysis. NASA Prog. Rep., Mont. Coop. Wildl. Res. Unit. Univ. Montana, Missoula.

VERTS, B.J. 1967. The biology of the striped skunk. Univ. Illinois Press, Urbana. 218pp.

WAGNER, F.H. and L.C. STODDART. 1972. Influence of coyote predation on black-tailed jackrabbit populations in Utah. J. Wildl. Manage. 36:329-342.

WECKWERTH, R.P. and V.D. HAWLEY. 1962. Marten food habits and population fluctuations in Montana. J. Wildl. Manage. 27(1):5574.

WEISE, T.F., W.L. ROBINSON, R.A. HOOK, and L.D. MECH. 1975. An experimental translocation of the eastern timber wolf. Pages 19-42 in Klinghammer, E. ed. The Behavior and Ecology of Wolves. Symp. Proc. Garland STPM Press. New York, NY.

WENGER, C.R. and A.T. CRINGAN. 1978. Siren-elicited coyote vocalizations: an evaluation of a census technique. Wildl. Soc. Bull. 6:73-76.

WOOD, J.E. 1954. Food habits of furbearers of the upland post oak region in Texas. J. Mammal. 35:406-415.

———. 1959. Relative estimates of fox population levels. J. Wildl. Manage. 23:53-63.

YOCOM, C.F. 1973. Wolverine records in the Pacific coastal states and new records for northern California. Calif. Fish and Game 59:207-209.

———. 1974. Status of marten in northern California, Oregon, and Washington. Calif. Fish and Game 60:54-57.

——— and M.T. McCOLLUM. 1973. Status of the fisher in northern California, Oregon, and Washington. Calif. Fish and Game 59:305-309.

YOUNG, S.P. 1958. The bobcat of North America. The Stackpole Co. Harrisburg, PA. and The Wildlife Management Inst. Washington, DC.

ZIMEN, E. and L. BOITANI. 1975. Status of the wolf in Europe and the possibilities of conservation and reintroduction. Pages 43-83 in Klinghammer, E. ed. The Behavior and Ecology of Wolves. Symp. Proc. Garland STPM Press. New York, NY.

24

BATS

Stephen P. Cross

Department of Biology
Southern Oregon State College
Ashland, OR 97520

Editor's Note: Most biologists have little experience with bats, and therefore tend to exclude them from inventories or monitoring studies. Bats, however, are an important resource and are often locally abundant.

The study of bats is a specialized discipline that requires the use of distinctive techniques. This chapter provides a summary of bat study methods and suggests appropriate circumstances for their use.

INTRODUCTION

Bats are often a neglected segment of wildlife inventories; they are difficult to sample, they are mobile and have secretive nocturnal habits, and they are considered by many people to be a mysterious and unlikable group of wildlife. However, bats play important roles in many ecosystems and they certainly deserve attention in wildlife habitat and population inventories.

Roughly 40 species of bats exist in North America north of Mexico (Jones et al. 1982; Hall 1981). In some habitats the number of bat species exceeds that of all other mammal species combined, and some species can occur in very large numbers if conditions are favorable. Bats have many distinctive morphological, physiological, and behavioral adaptations that are associated with some unique uses of habitat. Consequently, methods of inventory and monitoring of habitat and populations also tend to be unique. Only methods most suitable for application to the bats of temperate North America will be considered here.

A knowledge of basic behavioral characteristics, especially daily and seasonal activity patterns, is essential when contemplating any study of bats. Because bats are extremely mobile, some habitat inventory and monitoring techniques are similar to those for birds. Unlike most birds, however, bats are active at night and are not easily detected or distinguished by direct observation or unaided audition. Further, the local distribution of bats is usually patchy and uneven. This is caused by variation in the distribution of essential habitat resources and seasonally variable tendencies of bats to congregate at specific and often unique resting, breeding, feeding, and watering places. Consequently, although population measurements and determination of species presence may be accomplished by censusing at such congregation sites, determination of absolute density is virtually impossible.

Daily and seasonal activity patterns are important aspects of behavior that are directly related to inventory of populations and analysis of habitat associations. During the summer a typical daily activity pattern for North American bats begins with emer-

Pat Brown

Pallid bat.

gence from a daytime shelter (roost) during evening twilight or after dark. A roost is any site where a bat lands when it voluntarily ceases flying. By convention, roosts usually include resting sites where food may be devoured and digested but exclude sites where a bat lands to capture prey. Some species ordinarily congregate in large numbers whereas others roost singly.

Bats may begin feeding immediately after leaving the day roost or they may fly several miles before reaching a foraging site. Most North American species feed on flying insects. After feeding, they may fly to a drinking site or, alternatively, a night roost. A night roost is generally not at the same site as a day roost. Night roosts are occupied for various lengths of time depending upon the species and purpose for which the roost is being used. Some night roosts may be used simultaneously by several species that do not normally share a day roost.

The active-inactive pattern may be repeated one or two times during the night after which the bats return to their original day roost. This daily pattern

varies depending on the species, geographic location, season, and environmental conditions. Water requirements and drinking activity vary with the temperature and humidity. During late spring or early summer the females of many species congregate to form colonies at maternity roost sites where parturition and maturation of the young take place. During this period, water requirements may be elevated due to lactation and high environmental temperatures, and the bats may begin their nocturnal activity with a trip to a drinking site. While females congregate in maternity colonies, males of some species may form separate bachelor colonies.

Some night roosts are used primarily in the late summer and fall, presumably for breeding. Congregation at such sites is often referred to as swarming. For some species that are usually found solitary or sexually segregated, late summer and fall is a time when individuals come together, thus facilitating mating and reducing the probability of inbreeding.

Roosts used during the winter for dormancy are called hibernacula. Such roosts may be at different elevations or in different geographic regions than those of summer roosts. Often these are the same sites visited during swarming earlier in the year. Those species that do not hibernate may undertake extensive latitudinal migration to find suitable conditions during different periods of the year. It becomes evident that several different types of roosts, each with distinct characteristics, are required throughout the year for many species.

Although techniques are not standardized, there is a logical sequence of procedures that may be followed when investigating bat populations and their habitat relationships at a local level. The first step is to compile a list of species potentially in the area of concern by reviewing publications on mammal distribution in North America (e.g., Hall 1981), one that deals specifically with the distribution of bats (e.g., Barbour and Davis 1969), or one that deals with the distribution of mammals or bats in a more specific region (e.g., Maser et al. 1981). The known habitat affinities may also be determined by consulting general publications on bats, especially Barbour and Davis (1969), or on regional natural history. For many regions in North America, one may consult the very specific descriptions of wildlife-habitat associations and distribution that have been compiled in recent years (e.g., Thomas 1979).

The next phase of study depends on the question(s) being asked. One question may be simply whether a given species or group of different species is present in an area or habitat. Techniques for verifying the presence of predicted species should be selected with the habits of the species in mind. For some species an investigation of potential roost sites is appropriate. For species whose roost sites are inaccessible or little known, a technique such as mist-netting at water holes or foraging areas may be best. Even more specialized techniques, such as the use of ultrasonic detectors, may be appropriate for some species. These techniques may complement one another depending on the objectives of the study (e.g., see Paige et al. 1985). The important point is that many species or groups of species have distinctive behaviors that must be taken into consideration when attempting to verify presence.

Questions related to the use of specific habitat features are sometimes difficult to answer. Determining whether bats use a given cave as a roost site is relatively simple, but the investigator must be aware that just because bats or their sign are not found at one time of a day or year does not necessarily mean that they do not use the site at another time. Because some roost areas, such as cliffs and trees, are often inaccessible, it is very difficult to establish habitat relationships.

Questions regarding population size also require consideration of both general and specific behaviors.

Although measurement of absolute density is not a feasible objective, an estimation of population size utilizing a specific area or habitat feature is possible for those species whose members congregate at specific locations. For many species these congregation sites are the summer day roosts, especially maternity colonies, or winter hibernacula. Even though there may be a great distance between such sites, most bats seem to exhibit loyalty to them—at least on a seasonal basis. This fidelity makes it possible to compare population size at a given site during the same time from year to year. Other species may use a particular site year around. In any event, knowledge of such species-specific behavior is imperative when framing questions about the importance of a habitat feature or change that might influence population size.

For species that do not congregate at accessible daytime roosts or hibernacula, it may be possible to obtain rough estimates of population size by capturing them in other areas of concentration. Although drinking sites are often difficult places to estimate species population sizes, they may be the best places to assess bat community structure. Whereas many species segregate for day roosting and dormancy, they may come together at common drinking sites during the summer. To a lesser extent this may also be true for night roosts during the fall. However, both drinking places and night roosts may have characteristics that are differentially attractive to various species so one must not assume that samples taken at those sites are necessarily representative of local community structure.

When population estimates are compared spatially or temporally, the techniques need to be identical. In contrast, to determine bat community composition in a particular area, as many sampling techniques as possible should be employed. Relative density of the entire community may not be easily measured, but it is possible to measure the portion of the community using a common local resource, and the data obtained need only be qualified as such to be useful for descriptive or comparative purposes.

HABITAT FEATURES CORRELATED WITH BATS

Many bats are closely tied to specific habitat features. The primary activities associated with such features are drinking, feeding, and roosting. Drinking is obviously associated with physical features, particularly the presence of a suitable source of water, whereas feeding often shows some association with vegetative features. Because roosting behavior may be associated with both physical and vegetative features, a brief consideration of the general physical attributes of the various functional categories or roosts follows.

Day roosts are generally inaccessible to predators and have relatively stable microclimatic conditions thus providing safe and physiologically efficient places to spend most of the inactive time. Much less is known about night roosts but they seem essential for bat survival. They are often located much closer to foraging and drinking sites than day roosts and provide a relatively safe place to rest, eat and digest food, and groom. The physical structure of night roosts is often distinctly different from that of day roosts. For example, many bats that roost in crevices during the day select caves or other relatively open sites as night roosts.

The largest congregations of bats occur in maternity roosts. Even some bats that are solitary during most of the year may congregate in small colonies for birthing purposes. This indicates either that sites with the proper conditions for birthing are scarce or that the presence of large numbers of bats is necessary to create the proper roost conditions. Maternity roosts are warmer than other roosts—a condition which increases the growth rate of young during gestation and afterbirth (McNab 1982).

Maternity colony of the Yuma Myotis in a man-made structure.

Conditions in bat hibernacula that are crucial for survival include relatively stable temperatures that are low enough to foster the reduced metabolic activity necessary to conserve energy, but not so low as to be lethal. For a comprehensive treatment of current knowledge of bat roosting ecology, see Kunz (1982).

Physical Features

Compared with other wildlife, bats exhibit a relatively strong association with prominent physical features of their habitat. Most of these physical features fall into the category that Maser et al. (1979) refer to as "unique" habitats. These sites make up a very small percentage of the total land base but are often disproportionately important as habitat. Distribution and abundance of bats are often directly related to the availability of these habitat features, which may be natural or man-made structures.

There are two principal activities associated directly with the use of physical habitat features. The first, roosting, occurs in a variety of natural and man-made structures. The second, drinking, usually requires an open water source. Specific structural features are described under these two functional headings.

Roosting sites. Physical features that serve as roosting sites may be categorized in a number of ways. The following list is not intended to be comprehensive but does include the structures used most often for roosts. Bats appear to choose these structures on the basis of their specific and relatively constant microclimatic conditions and lack of disturbance.

Caves and Cave-like Structures. Caves are utilized by bats more than by any other group of wildlife. Caves provide shelter from adverse weather, a relatively stable environment, darkness, and protection from predators. Bats may roost in caves singly or in large congregations. As many as 25 million Brazilian free-tailed bats (*Tadarida brasiliensis*) have been found in single caves in the southwestern United States in the summer (Cockrum 1969; Davis et al. 1962). Some species use caves or cave-like structures for all roosting activities whereas others use them only for one type of roosting behavior. For example, Townsend's big-eared bat (*Plecotus townsendii*) and the gray myotis (*Myotis grisescens*) seem restricted to cave-like roosts, whereas the long-eared myotis (*M. evotis*) and long-legged myotis (*M. volans*) ordinarily use caves only as night roosts (Barbour and Davis 1969).

Many caves are unsuitable as bat roosts and some are used regularly for only a portion of the year. The important characteristics of a cave are temperature, humidity, light, size, and interior configuration and surface texture. Caves that offer the most optimal range of all of these features are those most likely to be used by the greatest number of individuals and species. Caves with large spacious chambers are more likely to house large aggregations. Cold and damp caves are more suitable as hibernacula or as summer night roosts. Warm caves are more suitable for maternity roosts or for species that are active year-round. Total darkness does not seem to be an absolute requirement for most cave dwelling bats, although they may select the darkest portion of a particular cave. Caves used as day roosts are often more likely to be occupied simultaneously by fewer species than those used as night roosts.

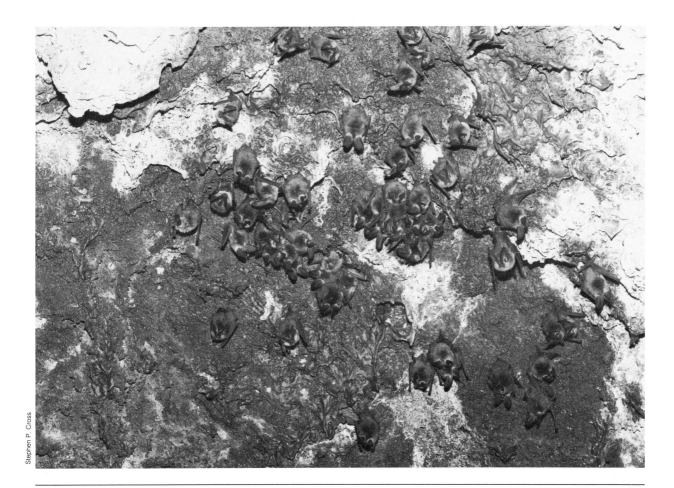

Stephen P. Cross

A group of Townsend's big-eared bats roosting on the ceiling of a lava tube at Lava Beds National Monument.

Many types of man-made cave-like structures have access to the surface. Tunnels and mines are the most obvious. Although not usually as structurally diverse as natural caves, they may be used by bats for all types of roosting. Generally they are easier for humans to find and access than natural caves because of habitat modifications related to excavation. Not only are the locations more visible but they are often recorded on legal or topographic maps. Old mine shafts and tunnels are often very dangerous—great care should be exercised when investigating such abandoned excavations.

Cliffs, Crevices, and Talus Slopes. Cliffs provide some roosting structures—especially crevices—favored by many bat species. Rock crevices in cliffs may have more suitable temperature and moisture conditions for bats than rock crevices elsewhere because of their vertical exposure and large mass associated with large heat-retaining capacity. Further, cliffs provide a safer refuge from predators than roost structures more accessible to flat terrain.

The largest and smallest species of bats in the U.S. are cliff-crevice dwellers. The greater mastiff bat (*Eumops perotis*), roosting in small groups, occupies large crevices with downward facing openings at least twice as wide as its body (Vaughan 1959). The western pipestrelle (*Pipistrellus hesperus*) usually roosts singly in small, up to 2.5 cm (1 in.) wide, vertical rock crevices (Cross 1965). A few other species have been found in intermediate situations but, as Kunz (1982) pointed out, little is known about the ecology of crevice-dwelling bats because of the difficulty of finding them in these relatively inaccessible places.

In general, those cliffs with greatest fracturing are more likely to provide a diversity of rock crevices from which bats may choose roosting sites. Orientation of cliff faces with respect to the sun may be important for determining the temperature conditions of the associated crevices or other cavities. Occupied cliff crevice roosts offer some thermal buffering and a variety of thermal choices (O'Shea and Vaughan 1977; Hayward and Cross 1979).

Talus is the accumulation of broken rocks at the base of cliffs or other steep slopes. Talus creates a variety of crevices, cavities, and even small caves, depending on the size of the breakdown debris. Bats roosting in such habitat are more susceptible to natural predation than in caves or cliffs.

Man-Made Structures. Many species of North American bats readily use certain man-made structures as roost sites. These structures appear to supply suitable substitutes for "natural" roost sites. Some species, such as the big brown bat (*Eptesicus fuscus*), the little brown bat (*Myotis lucifugus*), and the Yuma myotis (*M. yumanensis*), show a great dependency upon these roosts, especially as maternity sites (Barbour and Davis 1969). There is evidence to indicate that both ranges and population sizes of some species have increased as a result of using man-made structures for roosts (see Kunz 1982). A great variety of man-made structures are used by bats. In addition to the cave-like structures mentioned above, the other structures may be grouped into three categories: buildings, bridges, and miscellaneous structures.

Buildings offer an endless variety of roosting sites that environmentally resemble natural crevices, caves, or cavities. For example, spaces under roofing or siding provide crevice-like structures. Attics, basements, and abandoned buildings provide cave-like conditions. Intermediate-sized spaces may resemble natural rock or tree cavities. Many semi-open structures such as carports, porches, or woodsheds serve as temporary night roosts. Some structures have been built specifically to attract roosting bats (see Greenhall and Paradiso 1968; Greenhall 1982).

Bridges also provide a variety of roosting sites, sometimes in remote areas otherwise having relatively featureless terrain (Davis and Cockrum 1963). Some concrete bridges have cave-like chambers in the ends. Several types of crevices are available, especially in older style bridges. Modern bridges tend to have fewer protected roosting sites but some are still useful as night roosts and, in some instances, could be modified to serve as day roosts.

Other potentially useful man-made structures include dams, windmill support structures, storm sewers, and any structures that provide cavities, crevices, or cave-like areas with suitable temperature, humidity, light, and protection.

Drinking Sites. The availability of open water is crucial to the survival of most bats, and therefore greatly influences their distribution and abundance. Most bats drink while flying, which means that the surface area of the open water must be sufficiently large to accommodate this behavior. Rapid flyers,

Highway bridge.

Crevices formed between wooden planks of bridge.

Bats roosting in one of the crevices.

such as members of the family *Molossidae* (free-tailed bats), need a very large surface area from which to drink whereas some of the highly agile flyers, such as several small *Myotis,* can drink from a pool only a few centimeters in diameter while still in flight. Because free water is an essential requirement for most species, seasonal fluctuations in the amount and distribution of open water greatly influence the local distribution of bats, especially in arid regions where water is scarce.

Man has inadvertently made many otherwise un-inhabitable regions useful to bats by providing water in the form of seasonal storage reservoirs, ponds and watering devices for livestock, heliponds, some types of wildlife water catchment devices (guzzlers), and swimming pools. Any habitat modification that results in the availability of open water during dry periods may result in greater use of the areas by bats if other requirements are available.

Vegetation Features

Little information is available regarding bat-vegetation associations. It appears that most North American bats respond to major structural differences in vegetation rather than to vegetation species differences. Roosting and feeding are two prominent activities that are often associated with vegetative features. Because bats are very mobile, these two activities may occur in widely separated and vegetatively distinct areas.

Roosting Sites. Some North American bats roost on vegetation but relatively little is known about specific requirements. Most known vegetative roosts are daytime retreats, but some evidence exists that bats may also use trees and shrubs as night roosts (Kunz 1982). Vegetative day roosts are most prominently associated with living trees or snags and logs.

A few North American species regularly roost in the foliage of trees. These include the hoary bat (*Lasiurus cinereus*), red bat (*L. borealis*), northern yellow bat (*L. intermedius*), seminole bat (*L. seminolus*), and probably the silver-haired bat (*Lasionycteris noctivagans*). Some species, such as the big brown bat and the pallid bat (*Antrozous pallidus*), may use tree cavities or crevices. Species such as Keen's myotis (*M. keenii*) and long-eared myotis have been found in tree crevices or under exfoliating bark, primarily in standing trees (Barbour and Davis 1969). Many other species are also thought to use these sites because of their close association with forested habitats.

Feeding Relationships. Three species with limited distribution in the southwestern U.S. use plants directly for food. The long-tongued bat (*Choeronyc-* *teris mexicana*) feeds on nectar. The Mexican long-nosed bat (*Leptonycteris nivalis*) and the other long-nosed bat (*L. yerbabuenae* or *sanborni*) feed on nectar but also utilize pollen and fruit.

Insectivorous species may be more numerous near areas such as marshes and agricultural lands where the vegetation supports high insect populations. Often in such places, chemical insecticides are used to control the insects and there is evidence that these accumulate secondarily in the tissues of some bats and may be harmful to their populations (Geluso et al. 1976; Henny et al. 1982). Some forest dwelling bats respond to tree density on the basis of foraging style. Those that are strong flyers and catch their insect prey in flight need open forests whereas those that are very agile or glean their food from the vegetation can utilize more densely vegetated areas.

Discussion

Because bats are closely associated with distinctive habitat features, their occupancy of a particular area may be predicted to some extent on the basis

Stephen P. Cross

Conifer snag with hole and exfoliating bark—creating roosting sites for bats.

of the presence or absence of these features. The best places to look for bats or signs of their presence are in and around essential habitat features. Any geographic area of interest should first be surveyed for potential roost and drinking sites. In addition to the presence or absence of essential habitat features, their proximity to other features is also important. For example, the absence of open water within a few miles of potential roosting or feeding sites will limit some species. The available surface of open water will limit others. The types of roost sites available will also limit some species. Cave and crevice dwellers are often restricted to just those specific roost structures.

Apparent or potential roost structures should be investigated first. If bats are present, it is possible to obtain samples for species identification and estimates of population size. However, because bats are only associated with some roosts seasonally, absence from a potential roost site may not mean it is not used. If bat guano or other sign, such as urine stains or remains of chewed insects are found, the roost should be visited at other times for sampling. In some instances, bats may use a roost structure without leaving obvious evidence of their visits. This is true at some night roosts where several hundred bats may use a site without leaving much sign. If such a situation seems possible based on other types of evidence of bats presence in the area, the investigator must visit the roost at different times to ascertain usage.

Potential water sources should be investigated. If water is limited, bats may be highly concentrated at available sources. The presence of bats in an area may sometimes be determined easily by simple observation at an isolated water source during the evening activity period. Observations should be scheduled on partially moon-lit nights or may be aided by a low intensity light, such as a gas lantern, to enhance observation after dark.

In addition to drinking places, bats may also be seen in their foraging areas, especially those species that begin their activities during the twilight period. Some species can be identified by their characteristic flight but this often requires considerable experience. Even if species are not identified, the relative number of bats associated with different habitat features may be estimated.

POPULATION MEASUREMENT

Measuring populations of nocturnal flying mammals presents some unusual problems. It is virtually impossible or impractical to achieve accurate measurements of absolute density. However, because many North American bat species tend to congregate at preferred roosting sites or at isolated water sources, it is often feasible to determine presence and broad habitat associations. In addition, the population features of size, relative density, and age structure of bats using the congregation sites may often be obtained.

Presence

Presence may often be determined by simple observation. Bats are sometimes readily observed while feeding, drinking, or roosting. Counts may be made but species identification usually involves capturing some of the animals. There are three practical capture methods: hand capture, mist netting, and trapping. These capture techniques all involve similar handling methods associated with species identification, sexing, aging, and marking. Handling techniques are described in association with the first sampling method. For more detailed and complete accounts, see "Bats and Bat Banding" by Greenhall and Paradiso (1968) or "Behavioral and Ecological Methods for the Study of Bats," T.H. Kunz, editor (in press).

Hand Capture. Opportunities to capture bats directly with the hand are rare. Such instances usually come about when bats are in a torpid state, such as when hibernating or when a bat is sick or injured and partially immobilized. Bats should be handled only if absolutely necessary and gloves should be worn. Arousal from torpor may cause serious depletion of stored energy that might lead to death at a later time. Handling or disturbance of some species can force them to abandon a preferred roost for one that is less favorable for survival.

Hand-capture techniques also include those involving some implement manipulated by hand. It is common to encounter bats that are out of normal reach or grasp, often in crevices or flying in a confined space such as a cave or building. There are two implements that are particularly valuable aids for capturing such bats. Long-nose scissor forceps (bottle forceps) are useful for reaching into cracks, crevices, and corners where a hand will not fit or cannot be extended. The tips of the forceps should be padded by covering them with rubber tubing, plastic rubber, or some substance that will reduce chances of injury. Another useful capture tool is a wide-mouth insect net, preferably with an adjustable-length handle. The net can be used to capture bats in flight, especially in confined spaces, or may be placed over a small roost opening or over bats that are roosting in the open but are out of reach. For capturing bats in flight, sweeping from behind may be more effective and have less chance of causing injury than a head-on sweep. Both of these equipment items may be purchased from biological supply companies (see Dowler and Genoways 1976) and are relatively inexpensive. No special training is required for their use. Efficient use of both of these capture implements will usually be aided by a hand-held flashlight or, preferably, a head lamp.

Handling Techniques. Whether captured by hand or by some other method, it is often necessary to handle individual bats. Handling may be necessary to identify species, determine sex and age, or mark the bats for population estimates. Handling bats should be done with care to avoid injuring the animals or being bitten. Like most wild mammals, bats will attempt to defend themselves by biting. They are capable of carrying rabies. Although the incidence of rabies is not unusually high (estimated at less than 1% in natural populations), some precautions should be taken such as wearing gloves and, where there is unusually high risk of bites, acquiring protection from rabies by pre-exposure immunization. Information regarding pre-exposure immunization may be obtained from a physician or local public health service agency. In most instances a pair of pliable leather gloves will provide adequate protection against bites and allow enough feeling for sensitive manipulation of the bat.

Care should be taken not to apply too much pressure to a bat during handling because their wing (finger) bones are easily broken and some species are easily suffocated or may go into shock. Placing the thumb or forefinger under the chin of the bat while cradling the body in the palm of the hand allows immobilization without excessive pressure (Figure 1). Alternatively, a bat may be held with its two

wings open by grasping each wing with the thumb and forefinger at the distal end of the bat's forearm near the clawed thumb. Using this method requires that measurements and marking be done by a second worker. Although the bat's head (and teeth) are farther from the handler's fingers, many bats will struggle violently in this position and there is often a greater chance of either being bitten or injuring the bat. Considering these problems and the difficulty in grabbing a bat in this position to start with, it seems more sensible to use the finger-under-the-chin

A long-eared Myotis handled by grasping wings near the wrist.

Figure 1. An effective and relatively safe way to hold a bat without being bitten or injuring the bat. The worker's forefinger or thumb is placed under the bat's lower jaw while the remaining fingers restrain the body and wings. This leaves the other hand free for manipulation, marking, or measuring.

A big brown bat held with the wings extended. When holding by the wings, take care to avoid grasping the delicate finger (wing) bones.

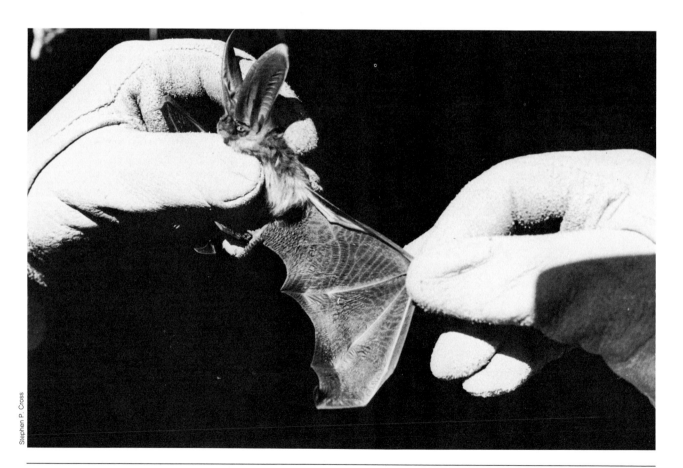

Grasping this Townsend's big-eared bat with thumb and forefinger of one hand allows for manipulation with the other hand.

method of immobilization. The most difficult part of this method is the initial seizure of the animal, which is most easily accomplished by pinning it against something solid.

It is often necessary to retain some individual bats temporarily. For small numbers a cloth sack is adequate as a holding container. For larger numbers additional sacks or some type of cage-like container may be necessary. Greenhall and Paradiso (1968) described a number of such holding cages. If a cage is deemed necessary, it should be constructed to fit the specific conditions under which it is likely to be used.

The first task of inspection is species identification. This is relatively simple for some species but difficult for others. A good place to start is with a key to the bat species of North America such as that found in Barbour and Davis (1969). There have been some taxonomic revisions since that work was published, so it would be wise to check a more recent publication, perhaps one that is focused on the specific region of work. For some species there is no foolproof method of identification in the field, such as distinguishing the Yuma myotis from the little brown myotis in areas where they occur together. Some other species of *Myotis* are particularly difficult to identify without experience. Time spent with a regional key and collection, such as one might find at a local college or university, may be helpful.

It is often necessary to determine sex, and sometimes age, of individuals so that the type of aggregation (breeding, maternity, or bachelor) may be ascertained. The sex of bats is generally easy to determine. The males have an obvious penis and the clitoris of the females is not enlarged. Testes of males and mammary nipples of females are seasonably obvious. Aging is difficult after the juvenile period. Juveniles less than 4-5 months old can be recognized by the cartilaginous areas in the finger joints. The joints are lighter in color and relatively smooth compared with the darker, knobby appearance of the adult joints. Tooth wear can only give a general impression of age; canines and premolars become obviously round in very old individuals.

After inspection, bats may be released by carefully launching them into flight such as one might pitch a horseshoe, or by quickly releasing the grip and allowing them to take off on their own. The launching method is preferred for fast flying species that need some initial speed to gain flight and may be used for all species unless holding time is prolonged. Some species become progressively more lethargic the longer they are held in captivity, especially under cold conditions, and they should not be launched or dropped. The best release method in this situation is to simply place the bat as high as possible above the ground on a solid substrate such as a rock, wall, or tree. As soon as the bat warms up it will fly off on its own. Bats released from grasp in this fashion will often attempt to bite if the restraining hold is gradually reduced. Those released by launching or rapid relaxation of the grip usually make no attempt to bite.

Marking Techniques. Bats are often marked to aid in determining movements or to identify them as previously captured individuals for population estimates. A variety of marking techniques are available, but two—banding and punch-marking—are most useful for studying populations related to habitat inventories. For details of other techniques, see Barclay (in press).

Banding involves placing a small plastic band around the distal end of the forearm where the leading edge of the wing membrane is very narrow. For the North American species being considered here, use of lipped or flanged plastic bands applied loosely so they slide freely along the forearm will reduce injuries to the bats (Stebbings 1978).

Banding with aluminum bands should be avoided because identification numbers may be lost as a result of chewing by the bats. The use of plastic bands with large embossed numbers or color codes will solve this problem (Bonaccorso et al. 1976). For local studies of abundance and movements, the colored plastic bands are easily coded to represent date and location of banding. Bands may be purchased from A.C. Hughes, 1 High St., Hampton Hill, Middlesex, Eng. TW121WA (colored plastic); Gey Band and Tag Co., Box 363, Norristown, PA 19404; National Band and Tag Co., 721 York St., Newport, KY 41071; and Ball Chain Mfg. Co., Inc., 741 South Fulton Ave., Mt. Vernon, NY 10550.

Stephen P. Cross

Aluminum band on the forearm of a long-legged Myotis.

A second method of marking bats is punch-marking (Bonaccorso and Smythe 1972). The technique consists of punching small holes in the form of numbers through the outstretched wing membrane. This is accomplished with a tattoo instrument normally used to mark domestic livestock. These instruments may be purchased from veterinary supply companies or some livestock supply stores, and they come in at least two sizes, for large and small animals. With care, the large animal tattoo marker can be used for all species of North American bats. It has the advantage of larger perforations (both size of numbers and size of holes) that are more legible and longer lasting than those made by the small animal instrument. Although initially touted as a suitable substitute for banding, it was quickly learned that punch-marking had the drawback of being short-lived (Bonaccorso et al. 1976). Punch marks remain legible for only about 5 months. Nevertheless, the advantages are numerous and the technique is suitable for short-term population inventories related to habitat monitoring.

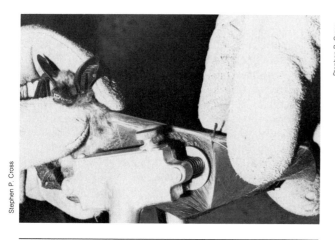

Punch-marking a long-eared Myotis with a large animal tattoo device.

Each individual bat may be marked with a distinct number but this is usually unnecessary. A simpler and adequate approach for population census and local movement studies is to use a distinctive numerical sequence (letters may be included) for each marking episode at each location. If necessary, additional punch marks may be made in the same wing or opposite wing on subsequent encounters.

Mist-Netting. The mist net was developed by the Japanese to capture birds and is still used extensively for that purpose. Because mist-netting is the most commonly used capture method in bird research, it has received a great deal of attention from ornithologists (see review by Keyes and Grue 1982). The basic technique and many of the recent innovations developed by bird netters are readily applicable to bats.

Several publications are available that describe the technique in considerable detail. See Bleitz (1984) and Keyes and Grue (1982) for general procedure and review of history and techniques. See Greenhall and Paradiso (1968) and Kunz (in press) for application of the techniques to bats. A general description of the technique will be given here with emphasis on those areas that are important or unique with respect to bats. This information should allow an investigator to determine if the technique is suitable for a given bat sampling situation. The proper use of mist nets requires experience and is

A Yuma Myotis with punch-marked wing.

greatly facilitated by field training. If instruction is not available from someone working with bats, the best alternative is to work with a knowledgeable bird netter. Names and addresses of such individuals may be obtained from a regional bird banding association (see Bleitz 1984). Attempts to "start from scratch" may result in injury or stress to the bats, damage to the nets, and frustration to the investigator.

Basic Technique. The basic technique consists of placing a large rectangular net, having several tiers made of fine hairnet-like material, in a position where it will be in the pathway of flying bats. For best results, these nets are placed where bats are concentrated such as near their unique habitat features or drinking sites. Bats attempting to enter or leave a roost site, drink water from an open water source, or forage in a relatively confined area are vulnerable to capture with mist nets. Bats are captured when they strike the netting and fall into hammock-like pouches at the lower side of each shelf of the net (Figure 2). Entangled bats are removed from the net by hand.

Equipment. Mist nets are available in a variety of colors, sizes, and construction material. A list of suppliers may be found in Dowler and Genoways

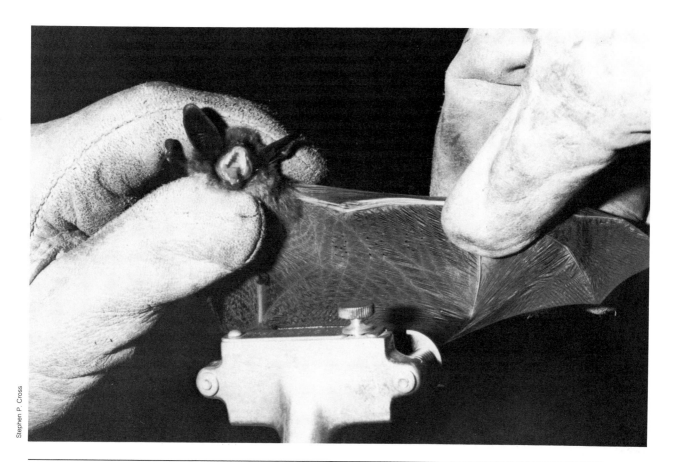

Stephen P. Cross

The wing of a long-eared Myotis with perforations resulting from the punch-marking process. The tattoo device used for making the marks is shown below the wing.

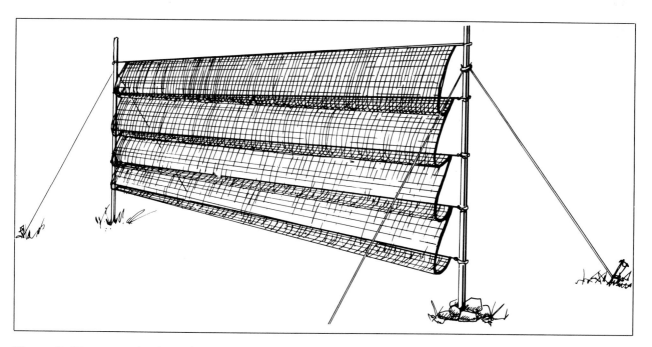

Figure 2. Diagrammatic view of a mist net setup. The net has five cross lines forming four tiers and associated pockets where the bats are usually entrapped.

(1976). The capture location, situation, and size of bats to be captured should be considered when determining the most suitable net characteristics. Black nets are suitable for bats because most capturing is done at night and the color does not contrast with the background.

Net sizes vary in length, height, number of tiers, and mesh. All sizes for nets are given in the fully-stretched position. The most common sizes used for bat netting are about 5 m (18 ft), 9 m (30 ft), and 13 m (42 ft). Nets longer than 13 m (42 ft) are difficult to operate without some sort of center support or heavy guying. Short-length nets are useful for roost entrances, small ponds, or foraging pathways in heavy vegetation. The 9-m (30-ft) net is very useful for netting over small ponds or in foraging areas with larger open spaces. Most nets used for capturing bats are about 2 m (7 ft) high and have four tiers (also referred to as shelves or pockets). The working height becomes less than 2 m (6.6 ft) when the cross lines (trammels) are compressed to form the pockets. Nets with two or five shelves are also commercially available. Other widths (heights) may be obtained by removing shelves of the standard nets or by stacking nets to cover a greater vertical distance.

Mesh sizes (designated by the diagonal of each square) useful for netting North American bats range from 3.8 cm (1.5 in.) for small species to 6.4 cm (2.5 in.) for large species. Because many regions support a combination of large and small species, it is safest to use a relatively small mesh size.

Nylon and terylene are common construction materials; terylene is stronger but less pliable. Strength is determined by the "ply" (number of strands per thread) and "denier" (a weight measurement). Nets for capturing bats are usually 2 ply and range from 50 to 110 denier (d), are black color, nylon, 70 d, 2 ply, 3.8-cm (1.5-in.) mesh, 4 tiers, 2 m (7 ft) high, and 9 m (30 ft) long.

Many types of poles may be used to hold the ends of a mist net in place. Electrical conduit, which may be cut into portable sections that can be coupled in the field, is very commonly used for this purpose. Keyes and Grue (1982) described many of the available alternatives. Because deployment conditions usually vary, sometimes greatly between sites, it is advisable to have versatile equipment.

Nylon cord is an essential item for guying the tops of any pole setup. Other useful items include a headlamp, so both hands are free for removing bats from the net; gloves; cloth holding sacks that are easily carried under the belt; and insect repellent. When netting over water, hip boots or chest waders are often necessary to facilitate removing bats from the net. Another alternative in such situations is to use a boat or raft. Some items that appear to be luxuries,

such as a comfortable chair and warm clothing, often become necessities as a night of netting wears on.

Operation. Nets should be set up well before dark but the cross lines should be bunched until bats are seen flying or when fully dark. This prevents capturing birds that are active during the daylight or twilight periods. Position of the nets is often critical and influences capture success. If possible, the nets should be set so they are perpendicular to the direction that the bats are most likely to fly. This is relatively easy to determine at roost sites but often involves experience with the particular situation at drinking and foraging sites (Figure 3). If possible, several nets should be set up in such situations so as to find the most efficient positions. Generally, when nets are set over somewhat rectangular bodies of water they should be positioned perpendicular to the long axis of the pond. Other features such as obstructions to flight should also be considered and the nets placed where there is the least interference with the bats' flight patterns. In open areas where there are no criteria for orientation of a single net, several nets may be set at different angles. Common configurations are V, L, and triangles. Vertical stacking of nets to achieve greater height is a variation particularly useful in foraging areas.

Nets should be checked regularly—at least every 15 minutes. Bats captured in a net should be removed as quickly as possible to avoid confounding entanglements and holes in the net resulting from the bats chewing or the netter having to break the strands to free the bats. A captured bat should be removed from the side of the net from which it entered a pocket. A good sequence for untangling is head, one wing, other wing, and body.

When removing a bat from a net, the bat may be grasped in such a way as to immobilize the mouth, as described previously, or by using a cloth baffle on the opposite side of the net for support and to provide something the bat can get its teeth into. The cloth baffle is also useful as a backing to get an initial hold on the bat. Inducing a bat to release its bite on the baffle or other object (such as a finger) may be achieved by mild pulling pressure, by touching the back of the bat's head, by blowing on the animal, or by a combination of these strategies. After removal from the net, the bats may be held in a cloth sack or holding cage, or marked and released immediately. Bats flying nearby may be attracted to the calls of captives held near a net or trap site.

The duration and timing of netting depends upon the objectives of the investigator. It is relatively easy to determine when the evening emergence flight of bats from a day roost is finished. In contrast, the period of greatest bat activity at night roosts may be difficult to predict and may occur during the middle of the night. Netting at foraging sites

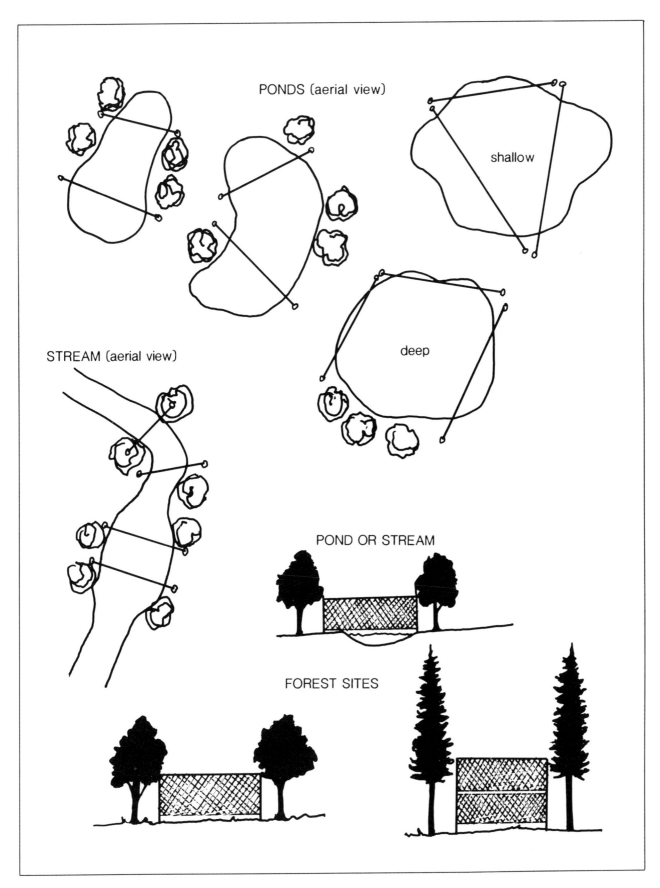

Figure 3. Some possible placements for mist nets to capture bats.

A bat entrapped in the pocket of a mist net. Captured bats should be removed as soon as possible to avoid confounding entanglements. Bats will also chew the netting which results in holes (pictured).

in places where there are extremely high concentrations of bats. For example, at the entrance of some cave roosting sites, the captured bats cannot be untangled quickly enough to avoid bat injury or damaged nets. Windy conditions greatly diminish netting success because of reduced bat activity or decreased net effectiveness.

Trapping. An alternative to mist-netting is trapping, first developed by Constantine (1958). He used a so-called "harp trap" which is designed to capture and hold bats. Like a mist net, a trap is placed where it is likely to intercept passing bats. Unlike the mist net, it does not require constant attention and can be used where the density of flying bats is very high and where space is restricted.

Basic Technique. The basic technique consists of placing a metal frame, strung with vertical strands of wire or nylon, directly in the path of flying bats (Figure 4). The strands of the trap are closely spaced and kept taut so that when a bat strikes them it will lose control of its flight and slide to the bottom of the frame. A sack-like container is suspended from the bottom of the frame to serve as a retaining structure or as a funnel to direct the bats into a holding container. Bats captured in such a device may be handled immediately or left until a more convenient time for the investigator.

Equipment. Bat traps are not readily available commercially but are fairly easy to build. Information presented here will give a rough idea of design; details of construction are given in the references cited below.

The original design (Constantine 1958; see also Greenhall and Paradiso 1968), commonly referred to as the Constantine trap, consists of a single rectangular aluminum frame with vertically arranged taut steel wires spaced 1 in. (2.5 cm) apart. Bats stopped in flight slide down the wire and are directed through a large funnel-shaped plastic catchment into an escape-proof cage. Constantine later modified his original design by varying the size and collapsibility of the trap to conform to specific spatial needs and logistical constraints.

Tuttle (1974) further modified the harp trap and provided detailed construction plans. Tuttle's trap uses two adjacent frames, 157.5 cm (62 in.) square, spaced about 8 cm (3 in.) apart. The tautness of the vertical strings is adjustable as is the distance between frames. These adjustments allow for differences in conditions, and size and flight characteristics of different species of bats. The strings may consist of 0.20-mm (0.008-in.) stainless spring-steel wire or 6- to 20-lb (3- to 9-kg) test monofilament nylon line. Ideally, bats hitting the strings should not bounce off but slide down the first bank of strings or pass into the space between frames and then slide

or at drinking sites is usually most productive within 2 to 3 hours after sunset. However, it appears that different species have different peak periods for feeding and drinking so it is desirable to sample for as long as possible for species presence and to sample for a constant period when attempting to estimate population size for comparative purposes.

Upon completion of a sampling episode the nets should be dried, if necessary, and all debris removed. Each net should be folded in such a manner that it can be easily unfolded for the next use (e.g., see Greenhall and Paradiso 1968). Proper care at the end of one session, including tying lines so they stay in order and making notations regarding the condition of the net, will greatly facilitate setup at the next session.

Although mist-netting is a versatile and fairly efficient method of capturing bats, it has some limitations. Netting is most efficient under very specific circumstances, e.g., in areas where bats concentrate to forage or drink and where there is sufficient space to deploy the net. Mist nets are often inappropriate

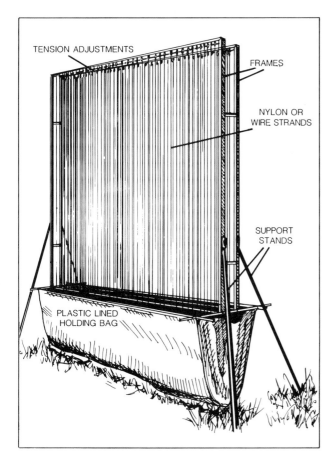

Figure 4. Harp-type bat trap with major part labeled (after Tuttle 1974).

down. The canvas holding bag is lined with plastic that is attached at the top but hangs free at the bottom. The bats slide in easily but instead of crawling up the outer slick plastic surface, they crawl up the cloth sides, under the plastic to a blind ending. Here, unless large numbers are present, they usually remain quiet until harvested by the trapper. The width of the opening of the holding bag is adjustable to accommodate different sized species. The trap also has adjustable legs to allow for changes in height.

The Tuttle harp trap is designed to be portable but field assembly requires about 45 minutes. If sample sites are relatively accessible and the frames can be transported without dismantling, assembly time may be reduced. In fact, permanent non-collapsible frames may be practical in most situations where the sample sites are accessible and have limited physical variation.

Tidemann and Woodside (1978) gave design and construction details for a light-weight collapsible version of the harp trap. By using telescoping sections of aluminum tubing, the trap becomes a relatively portable package 95 cm (37.4 in.) long and 15 cm (5.9 in.) in diameter, weighing 7 kg (15 lb).

They maintain that the trap may be assembled in about 5 minutes. If potential sample sites are inaccessible or if transport of a fully assembled trap is not possible, this construction option should be considered.

Operation. Typically, bat traps have much less capture surface area than mist nets. Consequently, they are particularly appropriate where bats are flying in rather confined spaces such as cave entrances, small heavily-canopied streams, small isolated pools of water, building openings, and along narrow pathways in thickly-vegetated areas. In many situations, the open area around the trap may be blocked off to direct the bats into the trap. When necessary, several traps may be used simultaneously because the bats are retained without harm until it is convenient for the investigator to deal with them. In most instances it is necessary to check a trap at least every hour to ensure that the holding bag is not overloaded and to release bats as soon as possible so they can resume their normal activity.

<u>Other Techniques.</u> Some other techniques are occasionally useful for determining presence of bats. Generally these techniques are used under more specialized circumstances than those described above and, therefore, will not be treated in the same detail.

Stephen P. Cross

Bat trap set up in cave opening. Bats slide down vertical strands into holding bag.

Bat trap set up over open area of small stream.

Detection of Echolocation Calls. Flying bats produce high frequency sounds for communication, orientation, and prey capture (see Fenton 1982). Most such calls are above the range of unaided human detection and are referred to as "ultrasonic." In recent years, equipment has become available that allows detection of these ultrasonic calls in the field. Echolocation calls, especially those used for pursuit and capture of prey, are often recognizable as species-specific (Fenton 1982).

The technique has several features that are useful for wildlife management applications. Species presence in a general area or specific habitats may often be determined without actually handling the animals or interfering with their normal activity. Unlike mist-netting and trapping, this technique is not restricted to sites with very specific capture conditions. It may be especially useful in areas where congregation sites are unknown, inaccessible, or not conducive to sampling by conventional methods. The technique may also be useful in conjunction with more conventional methods. For example, an ultrasonic detector may be a valuable tool in determining optimal habitats and time intervals for successful deployment of mist nets (Kunz and Brock 1975). In other instances, a detector may be used to monitor degree of activity or to aid in counting the number of bats at a specific place after some of the bats have been captured to determine or verify species identity.

The technique does have some limitations. Some bat species are not easily detected and some are not easily distinguished from others. It cannot be used to determine population density because calls of specific individuals cannot be identified. However, it can sometimes be used to count the number of individuals passing by a restricted area in one direction, such as a roost opening.

Ultrasonic detection equipment varies in complexity, cost, and availability (Simmons et al. 1979; Fenton in press). The cost of some sophisticated units is beyond the reach of local management units. In addition, equipment operation and data interpretation often require extensive training and experience. If information that is only obtainable with this method is deemed essential for a land management decision, it may be desirable to contract specialists for its collection rather than to attempt to acquire the equipment and training at the local level. However, some inexpensive, easy-to-build, and relatively easy-to-use systems are becoming available (e.g., see Paige et al. 1985) and may provide some valuable information useful for management purposes.

Observation. The presence of bats in general and a few species in particular can be determined by direct observation. This is best done in the evening twilight period. Bats may also be seen during morning twilight although they are not usually as numerous as in the evening. It is often possible to view bats around attractive habitat features such as roosting, drinking, and foraging sites, with the aid of low-intensity artificial red light. Enhancement of vision is also possible through the use of a night-vision scope, sometimes aided by an infrared light source, but the value of this instrument is somewhat limited because of its relatively small field of view. Such an instrument is best used where areas of bat flight are restricted, to determine population size of known species with a minimum of disturbance (e.g., see Bagley and Jacobs 1985). For further details concerning observational techniques, see Barclay (in press).

Advertising. One method of finding concentrations of bats, especially roosting sites in areas frequented by humans, is to advertise. Most local newspapers will run stories about bats that include a request for information concerning their whereabouts. Some radio stations, especially public service types, will do the same. Finally, posters may be printed and distributed in the area of concern. Most responses obtained from these methods are from people wanting to know how to get rid of bats in man-made structures. This provides the opportunity for some conservation education in addition to locating local populations of bats.

Shooting. Because many bats emerge from their daytime roosts during the twilight period, it is often possible to collect them by shooting. This may be done with a standard shotgun using shells loaded with very small shot (No. 9 or higher). A small-gauge light-weight shotgun with light loads is usually most efficient for hitting erratically flying bats in dim light. A pistol or small-bore rifle loaded with shot shells may be used in the same manner, but the shot pattern produced is smaller and less uniform than that of a shotgun.

Killing an animal forecloses the option of subsequent release, and shooting should only be used if absolutely necessary. If roost sites are unknown or inaccessible and other techniques are not applicable in an area where bats are known to occur, this option might be justified to establish presence. If possible, all specimens collected in this fashion should be prepared as study skins or preserved in alcohol and deposited in a regional museum for future reference. Such specimens may be necessary for species identification or may serve as vouchers to verify the presence of species in an area.

The drawbacks of the technique are obvious. Whereas only one or two specimens may be necessary for species identification or to serve as vouchers, many more may be killed needlessly while trying to collect specific species. Shooting at twilight is dangerous and illegal in some areas without special permission. The technique should only be used as a last resort when other more selective and less destructive methods are not applicable.

Relative Density

Relative density values of bats may be computed from data obtained by some of the techniques described above. It is important to realize that all such density values are biased to some degree because of selectivity for certain species. The degree of technique selectivity and the intended use of the relative density values should be considered when collecting and analyzing data. There are two primary, but not exclusive, uses of relative density values. First, relative densities of temporally or spatially separated populations may be compared to detect possible differences in community composition. Second, relative density values may be viewed as valid indicators of bat community structure. Considering the built-in biases and possible uses, some specific sampling situations can be described to illustrate possible applications.

Capture at day roosts is often highly species-selective and therefore of little value for calculating relative density that reflects overall bat community structure. However, day roosts that are used by more than one species may yield relative density values that are useful for evaluating changes over time at a particular site. Site-to-site comparisons are usually not possible because different physical features make it impossible to sample in an identical manner. Some night roosts such as caves or tunnels may be used by several species at once and therefore yield data that may be used to calculate relative densities. Again, these values are best used for temporal comparisons related to habitat or seasonal changes at a given site. They are not good indicators of total bat community structure because not all bats in an area are likely to use the same type of night roost. They

may, however, indicate the community of species that is utilizing a particular habitat feature.

Sampling at foraging sites is also selective and, therefore, not a good measure of total community structure. Sampling at communal drinking sites offers perhaps the best opportunity to collect relative density data that reflect community structure. This is particularly true where water sources are scarce and the site is large enough to accommodate all species potentially in an area. Data obtained at such sites may also be used to calculate species diversity values that may be useful for comparative and descriptive purposes.

To determine species richness for a habitat or area, one should use as many forms of capture and detection as are available.

Absolute Density

It is very difficult, if not impossible, to determine the absolute density of bat populations. There are two basic problems: (1) samples are taken at points of concentration rather that at random, and (2) it is extremely difficult to determine the total area used by individuals in the sample. A few attempts have been made to estimate density of bats (see Gaisler 1979) but there are no standard techniques similar to those used for other small mammals or birds.

Whereas measurement of absolute density is not a feasible objective, it is often possible to measure population size at the places where bats congregate. The values thus derived may be compared, at least temporally, to look for trends (seasonal or annual) or the effects of environmental alterations. Several methods have been used to estimate the size of selected bat concentrations (see Laval in press). Often, with small colonies in roosting sites, it is possible to simply count the bats present. This is especially applicable to hibernacula where the bats are extremely immobile and not easily disturbed if care is taken by the investigator. In large aggregations, where it is impossible to count every individual, the number of bats in several sample areas of known size may be counted and the estimate made by extrapolation from the total area covered. Photographic analysis may be used in the same manner and may also be used to estimate population size by taking pictures of bats emerging from day roosts (Altenbach et al. 1979; Warden 1980). The number of flying bats can be counted in each sample picture leading to the estimate of bats per unit of time. If the total time of the emergence flight is also known then population size may be estimated.

Population estimates may also be made from capture-recapture data. However, it appears that most capture methods cause some alienation to a particular site and chances of recapture are diminished. Nevertheless, if such estimates are obtained in a consistent manner from place to place and time to time, they can provide a quantitative value that is useful for comparison. Such values are usually overestimates of the real population because animals are more likely to become capture-shy rather than capture-prone. With consideration of these weaknesses, a simple Lincoln/Peterson estimator, or some modification, such as that of Gaisler (1979), will yield adequate estimates.

DISCUSSION

The problems of monitoring bat populations and their habitats are challenging. To address these problems, one must be aware of the peculiarities of bat behavior and the limitations of the specialized techniques associated with their study.

Two characteristics of many bat species make their populations particularly susceptible to sharp population declines. First, their tendency to congregate often makes them especially vulnerable to density-independent mortality factors. These factors include both natural events and human-caused death and disturbance. A few thoughtless or misguided people can cause severe population reductions either by direct killing, vandalizing roosts, or disturbing the bats during critical periods. Bats disturbed during hibernation may use essential energy reserves during the arousal process and those disturbed at maternity sites may lose contact with their young.

Second, bats have a very low reproductive rate; the females of most species only produce one young per year. This low reproductive potential makes recovery from sudden increases in mortality relatively slow. Reduction of populations of North American bats during recent years has been documented for several species (Harvey 1976).

Little doubt exists that bats fill important niches and the impact of their insectivorous habits in temperate ecosystems should not be underestimated. It is important to acknowledge this vital role and attempt to inventory and monitor bat habitat and populations to facilitate their effective management and conservation.

LITERATURE CITED

ALTENBACH, J.S., K.N. GELUSO, and D.E. WILSON. 1979. Population size of *Tadarida brasiliensis* at Carlsbad Caverns in 1973. Pages 341-348 in Genoways, H.H. and Baker, R.J. eds. Biological Investigation in the Guadalupe Mountains National Park, Texas. Natl. Park Serv. Proc. and Trans. Ser. 4.

BAGLEY, F. and J. JACOBS. 1985. Census technique for endangered big-eared bats proving successful. Endang. Species Tech. Bull. 3:5-7.

BARBOUR, R.W. and W.H. DAVIS. 1969. Bats of America. University Press of Kentucky, Lexington. 286pp.

BARCLAY, R.M.R. (In press). Marking and observational techniques. *in* Kunz, T.H. ed. Behavioral and Ecological Methods for the Study of Bats. Smithsonian Institution Press. Washington, DC.

BLEITZ, D. 1984. Mist nets and their use. Bleitz Wildlife Foundation, 5334 Hollywood Blvd., Hollywood, CA. 18pp.

BONACCORSO, F.J. and N. SMYTHE. 1972. Punch-marking: an alternative to banding. J. Mammal. 53:389-390.

———, ———, and S.R. HUMPHREY. 1976. Improved techniques for marking bats. J. Mammal. 57:181-182.

COCKRUM, E.L. 1969. Migration in the guano bat, *Tadarida brasiliensis*. Pages 303-336 *in* Jones, J.K., Jr. ed. Contributions in Mammalogy. Misc. Publ. 51. Univ. Kansas, Lawrence

CONSTANTINE, D.G. 1958. An automatic bat-collecting device. J. Wildl. Manage. 22:17-22.

CROSS, S.P. 1965. Roosting habits of *Pipistrellus hesperus*. J. Mammal. 46:270-279.

DAVIS, R.B., C.F. HERREID II, and H.L. SHORT. 1962. Mexican free-tailed bats in Texas. Ecol. Monogr. 32:311-346.

DAVIS, R.P. and E.L. COCKRUM. 1963. Bridges utilized as day roosts by bats. J. Mammal. 44:428-430.

DOWLER, R.C. and H.H. GENOWAYS. 1976. Museology: supplies and suppliers for vertebrate collections. Texas Tech Press. Lubbock. 83pp.

FENTON, M.B. 1982. Echolocation, insect hearing, and feeding ecology of insectivorous bats. Pages 261-28 *in* Kunz, T.H. ed. Ecology of Bats. Plenum Publ. Corp. New York, NY.

———. (In press). Detecting, recording, and analyzing the vocalizations of bats. *in* Kunz, T.H. ed. Behavioral and Ecological Methods for the Study of Bats. Smithsonian Institution Press. Washington, DC.

GAISLER, J. 1979. Ecology of bats. Pages 281-342 *in* Stoddard, D.M. ed. Ecology of Small Mammals. Chapman and Hall, London.

GELUSO, K.N., J.S. ALTENBACH, and D.E. WILSON. 1976. Bat mortality: pesticide poisoning and migratory stress. Science 194:184-186.

GREENHALL, A.M. 1982. House bat management. U.S. Dep. Inter., Fish and Wildl. Serv. Resour. Publ. 143. 53pp.

——— and J.L. PARADISO. 1968. Bats and bat banding. U.S. Dep. Inter., Bur. Sport Fish. and Wildl. 72. 48pp.

HALL, E.R. 1981. The mammals of North America. 2nd Ed. John Wiley & Sons. New York, NY. 1181pp.

HARVEY, M.J. 1976. Endangered Chiroptera of the southeastern United States. Proc. Annu. Conf. Southeast. Assoc. Game Fish Comm. 29:429-433.

HAYWARD, B.J. and S.P. CROSS. 1979. The natural history of *Pipistrellus hesperus* (Chiroptera: Vespertilionidae). Office Res. West. New Mexico Univ., Silver City. 3:1-36.

HENNY, C.J., C. MASER, J.O. WHITAKER, and T.E. KAISER. 1982. Organochlorine residues in bats after forest spraying with DDT. Northw. Sci. 56:329-337.

JONES, J.K. Jr., D.C. CARTER, and H.H. GENPWAUS. 1982. Revised checklist of North American mammals north of Mexico. Occ. Pap. 62. Mus. Texas Tech. Univ., Lubbock.

KEYES, B.E. and C.E. GRUE. 1982. Capturing birds with mist nets: a review. N. Am. Bird Bander. 6:1-14.

KUNZ, T.H. 1982. Roosting ecology. Pages 1-46 *in* Kunz, T.H. ed. Ecology of Bats. Plenum Publ. Corp. New York, NY.

———, ed. (In press). Behavioral and ecological methods for the study of bats. Smithsonian Institution Press. Washington, DC.

——— and C.E. BROCK. 1975. A comparison of mist nets and ultrasonic detectors for monitoring flight activity of bats. J. Mammal. 56:907-911.

LAVAL, R.K. (In press). Census techniques. *in* Kunz, T.H., ed. Behavioral and Ecological Methods for the Study of Bats. Smithsonian Institution Press. Washington, DC.

MASER, C., J.E. RODIEK, and J.W. THOMAS. 1979. Cliffs, talus, and caves. Pages 96-103 *in* Thomas, J.W. tech. ed. Wildlife Habitats in Managed Forests. U.S. Dep. Agric. For. Serv. Agric. Handbook 553.

———, B.R. MATE, J.F. FRANKLIN, and C.T. DYRNESS. 1981. Natural history of Oregon coast mammals. U.S. Dep. Agric., For. Serv. Gen. Tech. Rep. PNW-133. 496pp.

MENAB, B.K. 1982. Evolutionary alternatives in the physiological ecology of bats. Pages 151-200 *in* Kunz, T.H. ed. Ecology of Bats. Plenum Publ. Corp. New York, NY.

O'SHEA, T.J. and T.A. VAUGHAN. 1977. Nocturnal and seasonal activities of the pallid bat, *Antrozous pallidus*. J. Mammal. 58:269-284.

PAIGE, K.N., L.A. MINK, and V.R. McDANIEL. 1985. A broadband ultrasonic field detector for monitoring bat cries. J. Wildl. Manage. 49:11-13.

SIMMONS, J.A., M.B. FENTON, W.R. FERGUSON, M. JUTTING, and J. PALIN. 1979. Apparatus for research on animal ultrasonic signals. Life Sci. Misc. Publ. Royal Ontario Mus. 31pp.

STEBBINGS, R.E. 1978. Marking bats. Pages 81-94 *in* Stonehouse, R. ed. Animal Marking. Univ. Park Press, Baltimore, MD.

THOMAS, J.W. tech ed. 1979. Wildlife habitats in managed forests: the Blue Mountains of Oregon and Washington. U.S. Dep. Agric., For. Serv. Agric. Handbook 553. 512pp.

TIDEMANN, C.R. and D.P. WOODSIDE. 1978. A collapsible bat-trap and comparison of results obtained with the trap and with mist nets. Australian Wildl. Res. 5:355-362.

TUTTLE, M.D. 1974. An improved trap for bats. J. Mammal. 55:475-477.

VAUGHAN, T.A. 1959. Functional morphology of three bats: *Eumops, Myotis, Macrotus*. Publ. Mus. Nat. Hist. Univ. Kansas, Lawrence. 12:1-153.

WARDEN, T. 1980. Notes on the determination of bat populations using photographic measurements. Nat. Speol. Soc. Bulletin. 42:70-71.

25

Ungulates

Raymond J. Boyd and Allen Y. Cooperrider

U.S. Bureau of Land Management
Service Center
Denver, CO 80225

Peter C. Lent

U.S. Bureau of Land Management
920 Valley Road
Reno, NV 89512

James A. Bailey

Colorado State University
Fort Collins, CO 80523

"All animals are created equal, but some are created more equal than others."

—George Orwell, *Animal Farm*

Editor's Note: Ungulates occupy a great diversity of habitats in North America and have life-history strategies uniquely adapted to these habitats. Yet, many inventory and monitoring techniques are similar for each of the species. Ungulates are extremely important because of their recreational hunting and viewing values; they also can compete with livestock for forage and cause damage to various agricultural crops.

Many common ungulates in North America, such as elk and antelope, were once quite rare and extirpated from many parts of their historical range. This suggests that given adequate public support, cooperation, and funding, ungulates can be maintained or increased in natural habitats with adequate food, cover, and water. Intensive efforts in studying, inventorying, and monitoring such habitat factors have been largely responsible for the successful increase in North American ungulate numbers. These efforts have been detailed in much literature over the past 50 years. This chapter, therefore, only introduces and provides an overview of this knowledge base. A biologist working with ungulates will need to review the sources listed in the chapter for more detailed information.

INTRODUCTION

Wild ungulates are among the most prized wildlife groups, and management of their habitat is an important task of wildlife biologists. Most areas of North America contain habitat or potential habitat for one or more ungulate species. These animals are highly valued for aesthetic reasons, and public hunting of wild ungulates is an important cultural heritage. Recreational hunting is an important source of revenue for local economies and for manufacturers of hunting-related equipment. License sales for these animals provide a primary source of funding for state wildlife agencies.

On the other hand, wild ungulates can cause obvious, short-term habitat alterations through grazing and browsing. They can damage agricultural crops, directly compete for forage with livestock, as well as degrade their own habitat.

Inventory and monitoring of habitat for wild ungulates is thus one of the most important tasks of wildlife biologists; it is also difficult, challenging, and interesting work. Although biologists have studied and attempted to manage wild ungulate habitat more intensively than most other species habitats, our understanding and ability to manage it is still primitive.

In particular, biologists often have difficulty predicting how ungulate populations will respond to habitat changes. Because ungulates are adaptable, a

Colorado Division of Wildlife

Haystack damage by elk.

species such as white-tailed deer (*Odocoileus virginianus*) may live in habitats ranging from tropical Florida swamps to hot Arizona deserts, or northern coniferous forests of British Columbia. Furthermore, since the Pleistocene epoch, the number of ungulate species in North America has been quite limited, consisting of "generalists" (as opposed to some of the highly specialized forms found in Africa). In adapting to different habitats, ungulate populations acquire distinct patterns of forage selection, habitat use, and population dynamics. Therefore, generalizing about the species from study of an individual population is not only risky, but may increase or perpetuate misinformation.

Ungulates are highly intelligent animals. For example, choice of migration routes for species such as bighorn sheep results not from random selection among appropriate alternative routes, but rather selection learned from travel with other individuals during previous migrations. Such learned behaviors greatly affect how the animals use habitat and respond to habitat changes. Such use and response to management cannot always be determined by looking at the habitat.

Because ungulates are relatively long-lived, responses to habitat changes may not be apparent for many years. Such time lags make assessing the effects of management difficult unless careful, well-planned records are kept for many years.

Finally, habitat suitability often is not the sole factor limiting ungulate populations. Predation, disease, or hunting may limit a population. Each of these factors can, of course, be related to habitat conditions or interact with habitat factors. However, there are well-documented cases where changes in predation, disease, or hunting, in the absence of any change in habitat, have caused significant changes in ungulate populations.

Because ungulates have been studied so extensively, this chapter only provides a broad overview. It is intended for biologists having limited experience with ungulates and for those wanting guidance on finding additional information in the literature. In the following sections we describe general habitat requirements of ungulates and methods for measuring population variables. We then describe specific requirements and techniques for individual North American species. These accounts are necessarily brief, but should assist the reader in finding more detailed information in the literature.

HABITAT REQUIREMENTS

Habitat requirements of ungulates are analyzed in terms of their needs for food, water, cover, and reproduction as well as the way they must be arranged in space and time.

Food

Forage supply often limits ungulate populations, either by itself or in conjunction with some other factor such as cover. Food is almost always a qualitative rather than a quantitative problem with ungulates. By this we mean that the quality of available food rather than the total amount of food limits a population. Ungulates have died of malnutrition with their stomachs full of food. Thus, the habitat biologist must consider not only the amount of food available, but its nutritional content. Furthermore, forage availability and nutritional quality of available plants vary seasonally due to phenology of plants, utilization by other wild and domestic animals, and weather conditions that may make plants unavailable (e.g., deep snow) or alter phenology or nutritional quality (Figures 1 and 2). Thus, analyzing the adequacy of the forage supply for an ungulate is complex. Biologists have tried to simplify the problem by identifying measurable limiting factors among the vast number of forage-related factors. This approach has been quite successful in local areas, but unsuccessful when knowledge of limiting factors from one region has been blindly used as the basis for evaluating forage supply in another. As background for understanding methods of analyzing forage supply for ungulates, we describe the annual forage cycle, patterns of forage preference and food habits, potential limiting factors, and mineral licks.

Annual Forage Cycle. Since ungulates may eat many plant species in different regions and different seasons, biologists need to classify forage species according to similar nutritional and/or phenological characteristics. Wildlife biologists and range managers have found it convenient to classify forage as grasses, forbs, and browse (Table 1). This classification is based primarily on structure and phenology of the plants, but also correlates well with seasonal

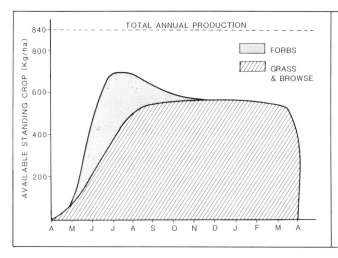

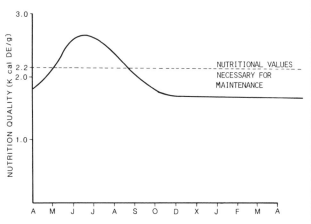

Figure 1. Typical annual cycle of available standing crop of forage (from Cooperrider and Bailey 1984).

Figure 2. Typical annual cycle of average nutritional value of forage on temperate ranges (modified from Cooperrider and Bailey 1984).

Table 1. Classification of ungulate forages.

Class	Description	Taxonomy	Notes
Grass and grass-like plants	True grass and grass-like sedges and rushes	Family Gramineae and grass-like Cyperaceae and Juncaceae	This category often is abbreviated to grass, but still includes sedges and rushes.
Forbs	All herbaceous plants other than grass and grass-like plants	Most monocots other than three families listed above; herbaceous dicots	Since classification of forbs and browse is not based on taxonomy, classification of some semi-woody species is somewhat arbitrary.
Browse	All woody plants	Woody dicots	

nutritional qualities, making it a basis for describing such an annual cycle. The nutritional quality of a given plant species varies with parts of a plant, individual plants, ecotypes, subspecies, regions, and physical characteristics of the site.

A general picture of the forage cycle can be provided by considering a typical pattern of production, availability, and forage quality of grasses, forbs, and browse in temperate and arctic areas. Forbs are mostly available for a short time in the spring and summer (Figure 1); during this time they are generally highly nutritious as measured by digestible energy content or similar measures (Figure 2). Grasses, on the other hand, are available year-round but are most nutritious during the spring and early summer when they are green. They also often begin growing earlier than any other forages (Figures 1 and 3). Dry dormant grass, on the other hand, has limited nutritional value. Browse, by contrast, is available year-round with relatively similar nutritional value among seasons (Figure 3). Significant variations may occur because of species differences,

annual versus perennial grasses, local weather patterns, deciduous versus evergreen browse species, etc. However, understanding this basic model along with local variations should help in understanding food habits and forage preferences of a specific ungulate herd and thus in identifying potential limiting factors related to forage.

Forage Preference and Food Habits. All North American ungulates are generalist herbivores, choosing opportunistically among hundreds of local plant species. A typical ungulate will eat over 100 plant species during the course of a year. However, due to availability and preference, less than a dozen plants usually constitute over 75% of the animal's seasonal diet. These are the species that should be the initial concern of management.

Forage cycles can be used to help interpret food habits of the various ungulate species. Beginning in spring, ungulates will turn to plants that are actively growing. For instance, the food habits of pronghorn

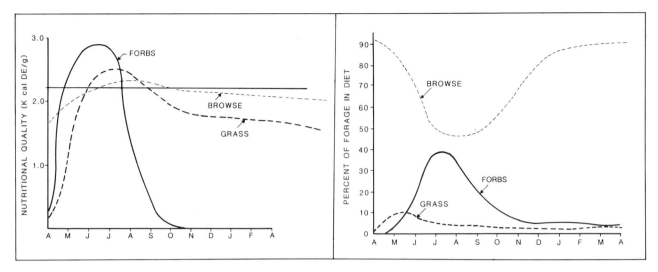

Figure 3. Typical annual cycle of nutritional quality of grass, forbs, and browse.

Figure 4. Food habits of pronghorn antelope on Trickle Mountain, Colorado (from Bailey and Cooperrider 1982).

shown in Figure 4 can be, to a large extent, explained by the pattern of forage production availability and nutritional value shown in Figures 1 and 3. Typically, the actively growing plant species are first grasses, then forbs. As the season progresses and forbs become less nutritious or available, ungulates turn more to browse or grass, depending on the species and its habitat and forage preference. During winter, most ungulates depend on dry grass or browse to maintain themselves. Ungulates reduce their forage intake during this period and typically lose weight over winter.

Although North American ungulates are opportunistic, significant differences in forage preferences are presumably a reflection of their ability to gather and digest different forage classes. Most notable of these differences is the distinction between grass eaters and browse eaters. All North American ungulates eat grass or browse when it is green, succulent, and nutritious. However, when grass or browse is dry or dormant, some ungulates prefer one over the other. In general, grass has poorer nutritional quality at this time, but is usually available in greater concentrations, favoring animals that can gather greater quantities in a short period of time. Browse, on the other hand, is usually more nutritious, but an animal needs to be more selective and therefore take more time to gather the same quantity. In general, the smaller ungulates (pronghorn antelope [*Antilocapra americana*], mule [*Odocoileus hemionus*] and white-tailed deer [*O. virginianus*]) tend toward browse at this time, while the larger species (bison [*Bison bison*] and muskox [*Ovibos moschatus*]) prefer grasses.

Habitat preferences and evolutionary history also play a role. The North American bovids (bighorn [*Ovis canadensis*] and Dall's sheep [*O. dalli*],

muskox, bison, and mountain goat [*Oreamnos americana*]) are generally animals of open country (grasslands) and are capable of surviving on dry grass in winter. On the other hand, North American cervids (mule and white-tailed deer, elk [*Cervus elaphus*], moose [*Alces alces*]) tend to be forest or forest-edge animals or have evolved from forest-dwelling ancestors; all can survive on dormant browse. Caribou (*Rangifer tarandus*), an apparent exception, survive on lichens during winter over much of their range. Caribou probably evolved as forest animals, eating arboreal lichens but some learned to move out into the tundra to eat lichens on the ground. Some North American ungulates seem capable of surviving either way, most notably elk; although less well-studied, mountain goats appear to have the same capability.

Food habits are foods that an animal actually eats, based on forage availability and preference. Measurement or observation of food habits can be an important tool toward understanding limiting factors related to forage quality and quantity. If observed food habits differ significantly from typical or expected food habits, it may suggest a problem or limiting factor. For example, if deer are eating significant quantities of dry grass during winter (an atypical pattern), it could suggest that their winter range lacks suitable browse species. This could be confirmed by observing or measuring plant species composition on that range. Similarly, if antelope are eating small quantities of forbs in spring, it could suggest that the range is lacking good quality forbs.

Food habits must always be interpreted in terms of local conditions and the ungulate species under consideration. For example, the food habit pattern for mule deer shown in Figure 5 would appear, at first glance, to be atypical of the species as a whole. However, it can easily be explained by recognizing that these deer live in California in a Mediterranean climate where winters are mild and all precipitation comes in fall, winter, and spring. Therefore, grass is green and nutritious during winter but dry and unpalatable during summer.

Analysis of Limiting Forage Factors. Several methods have been developed to analyze limiting factors related to forage supply. In order of increasing complexity, these are the—

(1) Foraging area approach,

(2) Key species approach,

(3) Carrying-capacity approach, and

(4) Nutritional approach.

Items 2 and 3 have been used in one form or another for over 50 years in North America. The foraging area approach, however, has only been formalized in recent years in response to land management needs. Similarly, the nutritional approach has only recently been developed and formalized, although earlier attempts were made to incorporate nutritional considerations into analysis methods.

Shrubland Diet

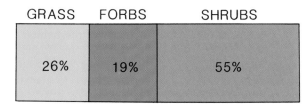

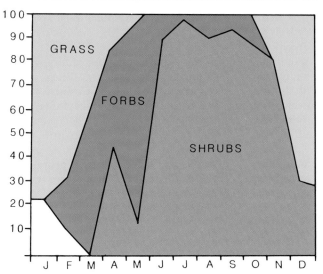

Figure 5. Food habits of mule deer in California chaparral (from Taber and Dasmann 1958).

Foraging Area Approach. The foraging area approach is a landscape-based analysis system. With this approach, the biologist identifies the aspects of topography, vegetation structure, and other physical features required to provide suitable foraging areas for ungulate species. For example, suitable winter foraging areas for bighorn sheep in northern Colorado might be considered to be south-facing, grass-covered slopes below 2,400 m (7,920 ft) elevation, within 400 m (1,320 ft) of suitable rocky escape cover. The biologist then analyzes the range to determine if it contains an adequate acreage or distribution of foraging areas. This analysis does not result in a quantitative estimation of carrying capacity. The foraging area approach was developed for elk and mule deer in the Blue Mountains of eastern Oregon by Black et al. (1976) and Thomas et al. (1979). The technique has the advantage of requiring only limited data collection, with data frequently obtained from existing sources such as aerial photographs, topographic maps, etc. The technique is limited in that forage quality is not considered in terms of plant species composition, range condition, total forage weight, browse species condition, or nutritional value. However, it is a good way to begin an analysis of ungulate range and may serve as the basis for more detailed analyses if these are required later.

Key Species Approach. The key species approach is based on the assumption that a biologist can identify the critical (limiting) range of the animal and also the critical or key forage species on that range. It was developed primarily for mule and white-tailed deer in northern areas of the U.S. and Canada. In winter, these deer typically concentrate on traditional winter ranges and subsist on one or more species of palatable browse. The browse species on these ranges are assumed to be the factors limiting these herds. By concentrating on key browse species on key areas, the biologist can simplify a complex situation. The condition, trend, and production of the key species can be measured and monitored; if total production is estimated, it can lead to a carrying-capacity determination.

The utility of this technique depends entirely on two factors: (1) the degree to which ungulates depend on key species and range and (2) the biologists' ability to correctly identify these key species and ranges. Recent research has demonstrated the importance of all seasonal ranges in determining the health of deer and other ungulate herds (Mautz 1978). For many years, biologists concentrated on winter ranges because this was when deer and other ungulates lost weight; furthermore, losses from starvation typically were observed during late winter and early spring while deer were still on winter ranges. However, recent field studies and nutritional research have demonstrated that the condition of ungulates before winter may be as important or more important than the condition of the winter food supply in determining overwinter survival. Therefore, biologists have begun to pay more attention to spring, summer, and fall range conditions.

The key species approach has provided and will continue to provide a useful way of analyzing ungulate forage supplies. However, blind adherence to this approach has caused much misinformation and inefficient use of limited habitat management funds. In extreme cases, dogmatic belief in key forages as limiting factors has caused biologists to overlook limiting factors such as predation, hunting, or disease. Biologists should use the key species approach with caution.

Carrying-Capacity Approach. When discussing carrying capacity, biologists tend to bog down in semantics; for the purpose of this discussion, carrying capacity is the number of animals that can be supported on a range with a given amount of forage production without adversely affecting the long-term productivity of the forage supply. For a more detailed discussion of the concept, its use and misuse, see Bailey (1984:280-288) or Caughley (1979).

To use the carrying-capacity approach, a biologist must measure or estimate the total amount of forage available on a year-round or seasonal range, determine the amount of forage that can be used without damaging future productivity, and then calculate the number of animals this amount of usable forage can sustain. Although seemingly simple, the approach is difficult at each stage. Measuring total forage is expensive and complex in itself. Furthermore, determining the amount of forage that can be used without damage is more of an art than a science (Skiles et al. 1980). Finally, calculating the number of animals that can be sustained requires making assumptions or estimates on the quality or condition of the animals, sex and age ratios, etc. Furthermore, it may require information on intake rates or food habits that are not available or can only be obtained at great expense.

To alleviate these problems, biologists tend to make simplifying assumptions and use "rules of thumb" in making the calculations. For example, the 50% or "graze half/leave half" rule developed by range managers is commonly used to determine the percentage of total forage that can be consumed. Similarly, many agencies have developed tables of forage intake rates for both domestic and wild ungulates.

Calculating carrying capacity is thus a very crude measure of the capability of the habitat to support ungulates on a sustained basis. Nonetheless, it has been useful and will continue to be used. It is especially useful where more than one wild or domestic ungulate is found on the same range. In particular, when livestock are grazing areas used by

Winter-killed mule deer under overbrowsed juniper.

wild ungulates, land managers must determine the amount of forage to be allocated for livestock and the amount to be reserved for wild animals. Forage allocation requires a carrying-capacity approach, and several systems have been developed for formalizing these calculations (MacPherson et al. 1982; Cooperrider and Bailey 1984; Nelson 1984).

Calculating carrying capacity, therefore, requires a great deal of information which may be costly to obtain, and the final measure may only be a very crude determination of the ability of the habitat to provide forage for the animals. Furthermore, most carrying-capacity approaches do not consider information on the nutritional requirements of animals nor the nutritional content of plants.

Nutritional Approach. The nutritional approach attempts to consider both the quality and quantity of forage in a carrying-capacity model. When considering the nutritional value of forage, many factors can be measured. For many years, wildlife biologists used proximate analyses (Table 1) to evaluate forages. These analyses were developed by livestock nutritionists and proved to have some value in evaluating wildlife forages. Crude protein was found to be especially useful since it was easy and cheap to measure, and levels of crude protein in most plants seemed to correlate with their palatability to wild ungulates. There were some notable exceptions, however, including arid land browse species plants such as big sagebrush (*Artemisia tridentata*) and conifers such as Douglas fir (*Pseudotsuga menziesii*). These types of plants typically contained high levels of crude protein but were frequently far less palatable or digestible than other plants with similar levels of crude protein. Understanding wildlife nutrition was greatly enhanced by the discovery of essential oils in plants, which inhibited ruminant digestion and made the plants unpalatable (Nagy et al. 1964; Longhurst et al. 1968). Although some plants can have relatively high levels of certain key nutrients, these nutrients are unavailable to the animal because of the presence of other non-nutritive substances.

This discovery and other developments stimulated the search for new measures of nutritional quality. Two such measures are commonly used now: digestible protein (DP) and digestible energy (DE). Both effectively measure the overall quality of a forage for ungulates, although they can be expensive to obtain. Furthermore, these measures tend to be highly correlated with each other and with certain other measurements such as concentration of certain vitamins. Since the basic requirements for maintenance, reproduction, lactation, etc. have been developed for animals in terms of digestible energy, animal requirements can be related directly to intake.

Nutritional approaches to carrying capacity require biologists to limit analyses to a very few possible nutrients or nutritional measurement. Everything from trace minerals to vitamins has been suggested as factors limiting ungulate populations, and such substances may be important in local situations. However, the biologist is well-advised to begin a nutritional investigation or analysis by measuring the more obvious and basic parameters such as crude protein, digestible protein, or digestible energy.

Systems for integrating nutritional measurements such as DP and DE into carrying-capacity determinations have been developed and described by Mautz (1978), Robbins (1973), Wallmo et al. (1977), Hobbs et al. (1982), Cooperrider and Bailey (1984), and others.

Nutritional approaches to determining carrying capacity require much sophisticated information on nutritional requirements of animals and nutrient content of forages. In addition, much data are required for traditional carrying-capacity models. Selecting appropriate measurement(s) of nutritional quality is critical both in terms of costs and predictive power; nutritional approaches should only be used when ungulate populations and management issues warrant the high cost in money and personnel. Not surprisingly, we do not know of any situations where a nutritional approach is being used in an operational mode by land- or wildlife-management agencies.

Mineral Licks. On some ranges, ungulates are attracted seasonally to mineral licks. While these areas may certainly affect animal distribution, the effect on herd productivity has not yet been demonstrated. Mountain sheep, mountain goats, and moose may be an exception as discussed later in this chapter, although the effects have only been hypothesized.

Biologists once provided salt on ungulate ranges as livestock operators do on cattle ranges. This practice, however, does not seem to affect animal productivity, survival, or abundance.

Water

Free Water. Although some desert species such as bighorn sheep can survive for extended periods without free water or with free water in plants, all North American ungulates need to have water sources in their habitat for survival. The biologist must determine the spacing or density of water sources: what is minimal for a given species and what is optimal. In most northern areas of the continent, water is abundant and relatively well-distributed. As a result, lack of water as a limiting factor has rarely been suggested or studied. In the southwestern desert areas, however, lack of water has been identified as an important factor limiting bighorn sheep (Turner and Weaver 1980), pronghorn antelope (Yoakum 1980), and mule deer (Wood et al. 1970). For desert bighorn, minimal spacing of water sources has been estimated at 10 km (6 mi.) and optimal spacing as 2 km (1.2 mi.) (Turner and Weaver 1980). Optimal spacing of water has been estimated at 4 to 5 km (2.5 to 3 mi.) for mule deer (Wood et al. 1970) and 5 to 7 km (3 to 4 mi.) for pronghorn (Yoakum 1978). Without further study, a biologist may conclude that distribution of free-water sources (streams, lakes, or perennial springs) every 2 to 5 km (1 to 3 mi.) is an optimal free-water supply for ungulates in North America.

Water Quality. Water quality requirements for wild ungulates have seldom been investigated. However, biologists have documented that waters high in total dissolved solids (TDS) or with a high pH will not be used by some species. Sundstrom (1968) noted that pronghorn antelope avoid waters with TDS in excess of 5,000 mg/l or pH higher than 9.2. In general, biologists need not worry about water quality for ungulates unless there is evidence that some waters are being avoided. In these cases, water quality measurements should be considered, particularly if water quality can potentially be improved through management actions.

Snow. The presence or absence of snow packs is such an obvious determinant of habitat suitability for ungulates in the northern areas of this continent that it is frequently omitted from elementary discussions on the subject. However, more than one novice biologist has seriously misjudged habitat suitability by examining a range during summer without understanding conditions of the range in midwinter. More seriously, some agencies have formalized procedures that calculate carrying capacities based on forage production without considering snow depths on the range. By using such systems, forage may be considered available to wild ungulates even though it is under l0 feet of snow during the time of year they need it.

On the basis of much observation and measurements, snow depth has two important effects on ungulates: it covers up and eventually makes ground forage unavailable or unlocatable, and it reduces mobility. However, these effects are quite species-specific and, even then, conventional wisdom or "rules of thumb" may be misleading.

Most ungulates, even those that are not particularly adapted to living in snowy areas, will paw through a light snow cover of up to 10 cm (3 in.) and forage without difficulty. Snow covers over 10 cm (3 in.) may inhibit foraging on the ground for some species, although others such as caribou can locate by smell and paw for food through depths of approximately 15 to 18 cm (6 to 7 in.) (Bergerud 1978). Elk have been reported to shift from herbaceous forage to browse when depths exceeded 61 cm (24 in.) (Skovlin 1982).

Effects of snow on mobility are partly caused by depth but also by snow density and crusting. As a general rule, most ungulates can travel through snow that reaches up to their bellies without great difficulty. Some species, such as caribou, have wide hooves that help them walk on snow rather than through it. Kelsall (1969) suggested that snow depths from 36 to 43 cm (14 to 17 in.) would restrict white-tailed deer mobility. Similarly, snow depths greater than 76 cm (30 in.) seriously curtail movement of elk (Skovlin 1982). Sweeney and Steinhoff (1976) suggested that depths over 71 cm (28 in.) usually prohibited use by elk.

Many ungulates move to areas with lighter snow cover during winter. This may require long migrations, movement to lower altitudes, or more limited shifts in use of particular cover types or areas with special topographic features. In mountainous areas, south-facing slopes generally have lower snow depths, and many ungulates such as mule deer and elk will concentrate there. However, some ungulates such as mountain goats use windswept ridges at high elevations.

Snow cover can easily be measured. However, obtaining enough samples throughout a range during winter would be exceedingly difficult and of questionable value unless conditions were uniform throughout the range from year to year. Mountainous areas that are likely to remain relatively snow-free can be predicted to a limited extent from knowledge of elevation, slope, and aspect. Such areas can be delineated simply and easily through direct observation, or through direct observation combined with use of low-level aerial photographs taken at appropriate times during winter.

Ray Boyd

Elk tracks and pawing craters in snow.

Cover

Cover, for purposes of this discussion, is defined as any structural feature of the environment that is used for protection from the environment (e.g., thermal cover) or from predators (e.g., security cover). As Bailey (1984:110) pointed out, cover has connoted vegetation cover in the past. However, for an ungulate that relies on sight to detect predators and on open country for escape, absence of vegetation may serve the same function as presence of vegetation does for a hiding species. For example, bighorn sheep rely on sight to detect predators and avoid areas of dense vegetation; escape cover for bighorn sheep consists of steep, open, rugged areas (Bailey 1984:112).

For many years, cover for wildlife species was described in terms of the habitat they favored, without distinguishing the many biological functions such cover was providing. Biologists have begun to identify the purposes that a given type of cover serves. Black et al. (1976) distinguished between thermal and hiding cover; the former is defined as overstories that give protection from the weather and sun and the latter, as vegetation used for escape and protection from predators and humans. This is a useful distinction, but will be used here to include all structural features, rather than just vegetation, and will be termed shelter or security cover. In some cases, both functions may be served by the same physical structure, but frequently this is not the case. Shelter and security, however, are the two most commonly recognized year-round cover needs. As with many other wildlife species, cover requirements for reproduction (birthing and early rearing) of ungulates are quite specific and will be discussed separately. Some species also have special cover requirements and these are mentioned.

Escape cover for bighorn sheep.

Shelter. Ungulates use shelter to escape the extreme conditions of weather, particularly extreme heat or cold or rain, hail, or snow. Most forest or forest-edge species use tree or brush overstories for this purpose. During winter, conifer or other evergreen species are obviously most effective. Open country animals such as bighorn sheep, pronghorn antelope, and bison may appear at first to survive without using shelter cover. However, many field biologists have noted that these species will use minor topographic features as shelter from weather. On cold, windy, winter days, pronghorn antelope will frequently be found in swales where wind speed and chill factor are substantially less. Similarly, bighorn sheep will often take advantage of overhanging cliffs to provide thermal cover in winter and shade in summer; desert bighorn have even been observed using caves during the summer. To our knowledge, no system for quantitatively identifying such topographic cover features has been devised or published. There are, however, many guidelines on what constitutes suitable shelter or thermal cover in terms of vegetation by animal species. For example, Witmer et al. (1985) define thermal cover for elk as a "stand of evergreen coniferous trees over 40 ft tall with crown closure over 70% with an optimum size of 30 to 50 acres."

Security. Security cover is used for protection from predators or humans. North American ungulates have several distinct strategies for avoiding predation. **Hiders** such as the white-tailed deer rely on suitable vegetation cover to conceal them from predators; they can also usually run effectively through dense vegetation to escape predators. Many quantitative definitions are available for what constitutes hiding cover for an individual ungulate species. For example, Thomas et al. (1979) has defined hiding cover for elk as "vegetation capable of hiding an elk from view at 200 ft or less with an optimum size of 30 to 50 acres."

Watchers such as pronghorn antelope live in open country and rely on observation to protect them from predators. Some watchers can effectively outrun their predators in open country, which may be level terrain in the case of the pronghorns or rocky slopes in the case of bighorn and Dall's sheep. Other watchers rely on group defense (e.g., muskoxen) or individual defense (e.g., moose) as protection. Watchers tend to congregate into groups ranging from small family units to large herds (over 100 animals). For these ungulates, security cover consists of suitable open habitat. Pronghorn antelope, for example, prefer habitat with a mean height vegetation of 37.5 cm (15 in.); areas with vegetation over 60 cm (24 in.) are less preferred and those over 75 cm (30 in.) are rarely used (Yoakum 1980). This preference can be attributed to security cover since suitable forage is often more abundant in areas with taller vegetation.

Many ungulates use more than one strategy. For example, mule deer tend to hide; yet on many ranges they will congregate into large herds in open areas, such as for feeding in late winter and early spring, and use a watcher strategy. Often this feeding takes place near rocky terrain or more thickly vegetated areas where deer can more effectively outrun predators.

Ungulates may also use different strategies in different parts of their zoogeographic range or even from one range to another. Elk, for example, tend to use coniferous forests for hiding cover in much of the West; however, in recent years they have naturally colonized shrub-steppe regions of Washington, which are devoid of trees, and also sagebrush steppes of Wyoming, where they use tall shrubs for security cover. Similarly, animals may use different strategies against different predators. Bighorn sheep, for example, will run from wolves, but they may turn and defend themselves from coyotes.

Because of the different strategies and the diversity of security cover that ungulates may use, a biologist must be cautious in assessing what is suitable security cover. First-hand knowledge of the range being analyzed and of the behavior of the animals that use it are necessary.

Special Cover. Some ungulates use special areas for cover from other forces. For example, caribou may seek windy areas in summer where they are more protected from biting and stinging insects.

Relationship between Cover Preference and Requirements. Preference for a cover type does not necessarily indicate that the type is required for survival or that its absence will limit the herd (Allen 1977; Peek et al. 1982). For example, bighorn sheep have evolved a predator-evasion strategy and use rocky terrain as escape cover from wolves. Bighorn sheep continue to use such habitats even in areas where wolves have been extirpated for over 50 years. Do they need it or merely prefer it? Such questions are difficult to answer and raise questions of value (e.g., should we be managing for "natural" animals; when does a wild animal become domesticated?). These questions are, for the most part, beyond the scope of this publication. However, the subject of cover deserves some cautionary notes.

If an animal has evolved a strong preference for using a certain type of security or shelter cover and this cover is available within its range, then that preference will effectively determine which portion of the range the animal will use. For example, bighorn sheep often deplete forage on small areas of suitable open, rugged terrain to the detriment of the herd, even though vast expanses of coniferous forest with suitable forage surround such areas. Under these conditions, the question of preference or requirement is moot. Biologists should be cautious in assuming they understand better than the animal what it needs. If an animal has evolved or learned a strong preference for a given type of cover, it is probably adaptive, even though the reasons may not be obvious to the biologist.

Birthing Areas. Many ungulate species use special birthing areas. The lambing areas of wild sheep (Geist 1971a) and calving grounds of caribou (Lent 1974a) are well-known examples. Birthing habitat requirements of species such as pronghorn (Fichter 1974) have been of management concern. Such special areas are frequently identified in the development of land-use plans, habitat management plans, and environmental impact assessments. For those species in which clear birthing habitat descriptions are available, the wildlife biologist should be alert to identify areas meeting these specifications. Documenting early infant mortality rates in ungulates is extremely difficult, however, and data to describe the demographic consequences of loss or alteration of birthing areas are not available. Most examples are anecdotal and relate to direct human disturbance (Kurt 1968; Lent 1974a).

Special habitat requirements for cover may be anticipated, especially for hider species (Lent 1974a) that depend on predator defense to isolate the parturient female from others of the species and subsequently isolate the newborn for long periods of the day. Such antipredator strategy may be significant for up to 2 months after birth, like in mule deer (Geist 1971a, 1981).

Migration and Movements

Most North American ungulate populations show predictable patterns of movements over the course of a year, periodically returning to some original locality. Nomadic movements are those in which such a fixed, recurrent locality seems to be absent. The more general term "movements" is used in the literature, particularly in reference to migrations of relatively short distance or when the type of movement is not clear.

Even white-tailed deer, generally considered to be relatively sedentary, may make seasonal migrations of 20 to 100 km (12 to 60 mi.). They occupy more restricted home ranges (X = 44 ha [110 a.]) in winter, larger ones in summer (100 to 500 ha [250 to 1,250 a.]) (Nelson 1979; Nelson and Mech 1981). This illustrates the phenomenon of seasonal home range prevalent in many temperate and boreal populations. That is, there are relatively localized seasonal use areas where movements are over short distances, connected by corridors of longer distances traversed relatively quickly. Moose in Wyoming represent another well-documented example (Houston 1974).

The biologist must be particularly alert for situations where resident (relatively sedentary) and migratory populations of the same species may overlap during certain seasons. This has been reported for white-tailed deer (Nelson and Mech 1981), caribou (NPR-A Task Force 1978, 1979; Cameron and Whitten 1979), and moose (LeResche 1974). Such overlaps, which often require marking or telemetry programs to identify and understand, have obvious implications for management. Whether one needs to estimate seasonal carrying capacities, regulate harvest by establishing zones or seasons, or assess impacts of proposed developments, one needs to be able to discriminate between such resident and migratory populations.

POPULATION MEASUREMENT TECHNIQUES

Measuring ungulate population attributes is one of the most important, yet most difficult and expensive, aspects of ungulate management. Mule deer have been studied, measured, and censused for over 50 years in the West, yet Connolly (1981:226) wrote—

"No reliable estimate of mule ... deer numbers exists for any state or province. The only available estimates are speculative and often they are no more than guesses by the best-qualified persons."

Determining numbers or density of ungulates and trends for these measurements are extremely important not only as a measure of the effectiveness of habitat management actions, but also as a basis for setting harvest quotas or goals. Biologists have studied this problem extensively, and a vast body of literature has accumulated. Some state agencies are making substantial progress in improving methodology (Gill et al. 1983). There are many disagreements on the subject, however, and much work needs to be done.

Because so much work has been done on this subject, this section only serves as a brief overview to literature on the subject. Biologists will need to consult original references for detailed information on methodology and extended discussions of advantages and limitations of specific techniques.

Ray Boyd

Neck-banded cow elk in summer range herd.

Because state wildlife agencies are responsible for managing resident ungulate species, they are usually more active in developing and implementing techniques for gathering population data on ungulates. Biologists in land-managing agencies, who require population data, should consult with state agencies to determine whether such data are available and can be obtained from them or through a cooperative effort. Ungulate surveys are expensive; publicly funded wildlife programs cannot afford duplications.

Presence/Absence

Evidence of presence or absence of an ungulate species in a given area can be determined by directly observing animals or tracks, droppings, or other signs. Tracks of most North American ungulates are relatively distinct (Murie 1954). Droppings may be more difficult to distinguish; droppings of mule and white-tailed deer, pronghorn antelope, bighorn sheep, and mountain goat overlap in size, shape, and appearance. However, a biologist may be able to rule out all except one of these species through knowledge of habitat requirements and geographic distribution.

Although data on presence/absence are relatively easy to collect, they are of limited value for ungulates. Management agencies and the public are more concerned with numbers, density, or relative density. Presence information is most useful in determining geographic distribution or use of a range. The geographic distribution of North American ungulates is well-known on a continental or regional basis; however, local patterns of distribution are often poorly understood. For example, only in the past 35 years has the distribution of bighorn sheep in North America been described in enough detail to indicate whether a given mountain range supported sheep populations. Furthermore, much of this information has only been gathered in the past 15 years; some states still do not have this information. Finally, detailed information on habitat use, seasonal ranges, lambing areas, etc. is lacking for most of these herds, and much of the information obtained in the past needs to be updated. Some ungulates such as moose are expanding their range; other species are being locally extirpated and many herds are abandoning or no longer using parts of their range. Knowledge of seasonal ranges including migration corridors and birthing areas is essential for good habitat management. This is basic and very important information and often can be obtained with equipment no more sophisticated than a field notebook, topographic maps, field glasses, and a stout pair of hiking boots.

Relative Density or Relative Abundance

Relative density or relative abundance are commonly used to measure the effectiveness of habitat management actions. Collecting this data provides an index of population abundance, such as deer observed per square mile or antelope counted per mile of highway. Many such indexes have been developed; some require directly observing animals, whereas others use indirect signs, such as tracks and fecal pellets. Indexes can then be compared from year to year or from area to area. Population indexes do not usually require the biologist to make the same sort of assumptions as required with population estimation methods. Furthermore, they are easier and cheaper to obtain and, for measuring population trends or comparing areas, they may be adequate.

The major problem with indexes is ensuring observations or counts are replicated as nearly as possible. Factors that may need to be standardized include routes, flying or driving conditions, weather, experience of personnel, training, protocol for such things as counting an animal in or out of an area, time of day, etc. The value of indexes for measuring year-to-year changes in abundance significantly decreases and becomes useless if the techniques or protocol for collecting the information is periodically changed.

One technique, the pellet group count, needs further explanation. Biologists have attempted with varying success to use this technique for quite different purposes for over 50 years (Neff 1968). As a method for determining presence, it is sound. As a method for population density estimation, it has significant problems (Neff 1968). As a method for determining relative density, it is useful for comparing years or large areas, but may be misleading if used to compare habitat use between or among small adjacent areas. The problem is that defecation does not correlate well with habitat use. Elk, for example, often defecate while traveling (40% of all defecations), yet this activity consumes only about 5% of their day (Collins and Urness 1979). Using such a technique within the home range of an elk herd would erroneously suggest that areas used for travel were heavily used. On the other hand, if the technique is used to compare average relative densities on areas large enough to contain the daily home ranges of animals, then such factors are of negligible importance.

Density

Estimating density or total numbers in a herd is difficult and expensive, yet if done carefully, it can provide very useful information. The many techniques available fall into four general categories: total counts (census), sample counts, ratio methods, and indirect methods.

Total Counts. Total counts are most successful with diurnal ungulates on open country, such as

pronghorn antelope. Observers on foot often try to totally count small isolated herds that are concentrated, such as on a winter range or at waterholes in summer. Such counts usually require good planning and coordination to ensure that all animals are observed and are not counted more than once.

Various methods have been devised to correct or adjust for these problems, but none are entirely satisfactory. For this reason, information from many such efforts are used as indexes rather than total counts.

Total counts are often attempted from helicopters or fixed-wing aircraft, although more often some form of sampling is used. The practical problems are similar, but sampling schemes make the calculations more complex.

Sample Counts. Sample counts are of two general types, strip samples and plot samples. Strip samples have been used effectively to count ungulates from airplanes, motor vehicles, or on foot (Riney 1982:78-84). Many different types of strip samples are available; Robinette et al. (1974) tested many of these and Burnham et al. (1980) summarized assumptions and statistical analyses.

Plot counts have been used less frequently, especially from airplanes. However, a helicopter quadrat system (Kufeld et al. 1980) is being used in Colorado and initial results and tests appear promising (Gill et al. 1983).

Ratio Methods. Ratio methods, including mark-recapture methods, are based on knowing the number of marked animals in a population or removed from a population at some point. These methods generally require animals to be marked or tagged—expensive and time-consuming with ungulates. Many variations on the basic capture/recapture models have been developed. Refer to Riney (1982:42-74) for practical aspects of capturing and marking animals, to Bailey (1984:311-315) and Gilbert (1979:302-304) for a general discussion of ratio methods, and to White et al. (1982) for a discussion of detailed statistical treatment.

Indirect Methods. Indirect methods correlate animal density with some measurable and observable sign left by the animals. With ungulates, the indirect method used most frequently is the pellet group density measurement (Freddy and Bowden 1983a,b; Neff 1968).

General Cautions. Gill et al. (1983) suggested that biologists obtain reliable estimates of ungulate population density to track changes over time. This is certainly laudable and biologists with agencies responsible for population management would be well-advised to pursue it. However, because such estimates are expensive and difficult to obtain and the results often debatable, many biologists and managers prefer to use indexes. Furthermore, although many techniques have serious disadvantages when used to count and estimate populations, most of these disadvantages disappear when they are used as indexes (Riney 1982:85). The biologists charged with habitat management or working for a habitat management agency should consider whether a population or condition index will be adequate for their purposes.

Animal Condition

Condition indexes have been developed and used experimentally for many years to measure ungulate health, but few have been used operationally by management agencies. Generally, condition measurements or observations are collected on individual animals and then averaged to derive an index of the condition of the herd or population. Animal condition indexes can be considered a function of the habitat and the number of animals. Thus, unlike most other population measurements, they reflect ecological density or the number of animals relative to the quantity and quality of habitat available (Bailey 1984:318). Indeed, many measures of population structure, such as doe to fawn ratios (a measure of productivity) or behavioral indexes, can be considered special types of population condition indexes (Bailey 1984:318-324; Hanks 1981).

Population Structure and Productivity

With most North American ungulates, sex and a limited number of age classes (young of the year, yearling, adult) can be distinguished in the field. In addition, more detailed age information can be obtained from dead or harvested animals using tooth eruption characteristics, dental cementum annuli, or horn growth rings. Biologists have collected much data on sex and age structures of ungulate populations and expended much effort in developing and refining methods to analyze such data (Caughley 1977; Riney 1982; Fowler and Smith 1981). This type of information is now commonly used in population models that can simulate the dynamics of herd numbers and structure over time (Conley 1978). The models are now used routinely by several western state game agencies as a source of information to be used with other sources in making recommendations about harvest goals and quotas for big game species (Pojar and Strickland 1979).

Some very good work has been done with population structure measurements. However, management biologists must keep in mind the original reasons for collecting population structure data and avoid getting bogged down in the complexities of population modeling. For management purposes, the simplest and directly observable measures, such as cow to calf ratios, have often proven to be the most useful.

Behavioral Indicators

Interest in the use of behavioral attributes as indexes of population and habitat condition is increasing. Hanks (1981:61) reported that several studies of population condition correlate declines in physiological condition or demographic vigor with certain behavioral attributes of the population. He recommended considering these attributes as a possible early warning system of adverse population trends: (1) rate and quality of social interaction, (2) population density, and (3) feeding strategy. As an example, Horejsi (1976) concluded that duration of suckling and total time spent suckling could be related to population and habitat quality in bighorn sheep.

MAJOR SPECIES

The following descriptions treat each major ungulate species or species group separately because of the importance of these animals. Because many of these species are similar in many ways, the sections emphasize aspects of the biology and management that are unique to the species.

Many books and monographs are available on North American ungulates. Some of the more recent, major publications about population or habitat meas-

Colorado Division of Wildlife

Jaw board used as aging reference at big game check stations.

Table 2. Major recent references on North American ungulates that cover habitat and population measurements.[1]

Species	Periodicals	Books/Monographs Bibliographies
General		Schmidt and Gilbert (1978)
Individual Species		
Collared peccary		Sowls (1984)
Elk	Proceedings of Western States Elk Workshop	Thomas and Toweill (1982)
Mule deer		Wallmo (1981) Kerr (1979)
White-tailed deer		Halls (1984)
Moose	Alces (Proceedings of North American Moose Conference and Workshop	
Caribou	Proceedings of International Reindeer and Caribou Symposiums	
Pronghorn	Proceedings of Pronghorn Antelope Workshop	Yoakum (1980) Autenrieth (1978)
Bison[2]		
Mountain goat	Proceedings of Biennial Symposium of the Northern Sheep and Goat Council	Samuel and MacGregor (1977)
Muskox	Proceedings of International Muskox Symposiums	Klein et al. (1984)
Bighorn sheep	Proceedings of Desert Bighorn Council	Monson and Sumner (1980) Trefethen (1975)
and		
Dall's Sheep	Proceedings of Biennial Symposiums of Northern Sheep and Goat Council	Krausman et al. (1984)

[1]Only references since 1975 are cited.
[2]No recent general references available.

urements are listed in Table 2; others are cited in specific species subsections.

Collared Peccary

Of all large game animals in North America, the collared peccary (*Tayassu tajacu*) has been the last to get the attention of wildlife biologists. In many places it was considered vermin or a pest to livestock operators. In the past 30 years, however, the peccary has become a protected big game species in Arizona, New Mexico, and Texas. Careful censuses and regulated harvests now ensure its survival if habitats can be preserved. The most serious limiting factor to the future survival of this animal is habitat loss. Areas of unspoiled habitats need to be set aside to ensure their future existence (Sowls 1984). Predation levels are thought to be low, although hard

Collared peccary.

data are not available on the effects of predation on population levels (Sowls 1984). Although the collared peccary could have both ecto- and endoparasites, they do not seem to cause significant population losses (Sowls 1984).

The species is not long-lived (mean length of life is about 4 years), but the high reproductive rate and its ability to withstand severe food and water shortages for short periods enables the species to maintain good, young animal populations.

Habitat Requirements and Analysis. In the Southwest, collared peccaries occupy a variety of habitats. Habitat types occupied by peccaries in Arizona have been described by Knipe (1957), Neal (1959), and Eddy (1961). Arizona populations are found primarily in the southeastern quarter of the state and are generally contiguous with populations in New Mexico (Bissonette 1982). The Arizona populations inhabit areas of low desert-scrub vegetation where the principal plants are saguaro (*Carnegia gigantea*), mesquite (*Prosopis* sp.), paloverde (*Cercidium* sp.), and many species of cactus. The oak-woodland, chaparral, and lower areas of ponderosa pine (*Pinus ponderosa*) forests are occupied during the summer, but can be too cold for peccaries in the winter. Peccaries can inhabit desert environments because they make full use of microclimates, and during very hot summer periods, they move only at night.

Peccaries in New Mexico occupy two types of vegetation cover. One is the oak-juniper association between elevations of 1,500 and 1,940 m (5,000 and 6,400 ft) just below the ponderosa pine belt. The other cover type is mesquite, beginning at elevations about 1,303 m (4,300 ft) and extending to about 1,879 m (6,200 ft) on some exposures (Donaldson 1967). Other protective cover includes caves and mine shafts, natural crevices, rock overhangs, and undercut arroyo banks.

Habitats occupied by peccaries in Texas vary from dry deserts in the west to lush chaparral and deciduous brushlands in the east. Peccaries occupy about 260,000 km^2 (100,000 mi.^{2}) in this state in areas having rainfall varying from 40 cm (16 in.) per year in the west to 75 cm (27 to 30 in.) per year in the east (Jennings and Harris 1953; Low 1970; Bissonette 1976; Ellisor and Harwell 1979).

Food and water are supplied by succulent food (Sowls 1978). The prickly pear cactus is the preferred food of the peccary in Arizona (Knipe 1957), but tubers, bulbs, and rhizomes are also important. In Texas, good peccary habitat consists of heavy brush with an abundance of prickly pear (Ellisor and Harwell 1979). In New Mexico, major food items include oak (*Quercus* sp.) mast, juniper (*Juniperus deppeana* and *J. monosperma*), pinyon (*Pinus edulis*), mesquite beans, leaves and fruits of Engelmann prickly pear (*Opuntia engelmanni*), and mescal (*Lophophora williamsii*) or Palmer agave (*Agave palmeri*) (Donaldson 1967).

Peccaries do not depend entirely on free water, but use it if it is available. Peccaries can usually obtain ample amounts of water from prickly pear, the basal ends of mescal, and underground bulbs (Donaldson 1967). Thus they can withstand long dry periods without ill effects.

Since prickly pear cactus seems to be the most common of all peccary foods, habitat measurements should include determination of abundance of prickly pear. Because the greatest threat to peccary populations is habitat loss (Sowls 1978), the vegetation trend of peccary habitat should be monitored, particularly that of prickly pear.

Population Measurements. Compared with more common big game animals, peccaries present new problems to researchers trying to gather and interpret biological data. The principal problem is that peccaries have a year-round breeding season. This, coupled with the female's ability to become pregnant within a few days after giving birth, gives the species a very high breeding potential. Because of these factors, these animals do not fit as easily into age classes or cohorts like elk, deer, and other big game animals (Sowls 1984). Life tables have been constructed from ages of hunter-killed animals, but problems, primarily unequal birth and survival rates, make use of these analytical techniques suspect (Low 1970).

In Texas, aerial surveys, road censuses by ground vehicles, and track counts have been tried for inventorying these animals. These census methods, however, are not feasible in brushy country. In Arizona, extensive testing of peccary census methods involved track counts, counts at waterholes, helicopter counts, surveys by biologists on foot, and questioning hunters about numbers of animals seen. Results indicated that helicopter counts were too expensive and variable, and track counts were too variable. The Arizona Game and Fish Department found that deer hunter counts of peccaries, obtained right after a hunt, were more accurate than sightings reported later in questionnaires. They also reported that data from deer hunters compared well with data obtained by biologists surveying on foot (Sowls 1978). Thus, the most promising method seems to be questioning hunters in peccary range immediately after hunting seasons for other species, particularly deer. Combined with foot or horseback observations by biologists, this method gives good indications of population number and trend. Roadblocks and established hunter checking stations also provide important data on peccary populations, and data on productivity can be obtained by estimating ages of harvested animals.

Discussion. The most important management consideration is maintaining as much suitable peccary habitat as possible. The collared peccary has high reproductive potential and is remarkably adaptable. For these reasons, healthy and productive populations of this unique animal can be effectively managed throughout its range. Although habitat factors limiting peccary populations are not well-known, evidence suggests that density of prickly pear is very important and should be a high priority for inventory and monitoring.

Elk

At one time, the American elk (*Cervus elaphus*) was the most widely distributed member of the deer family in North America. It was found from the Atlantic to Pacific coasts and from Mexico to northern Alberta, except the southern coastal plains and Great Basin (Hall and Kelson 1959). However, as people moved westward, elk disappeared from settled regions until they virtually vanished from most of their historic ranges. Remnant herds were scattered in the Rocky Mountain region and parts of the Pacific Northwest and Canada. In the past 50 years, elk have expanded their range and been reintroduced so that they are fairly widespread throughout the mountainous areas of the West.

Habitat Requirements and Analysis. Much of the work in recent years on elk habitat has concentrated on (1) identifying areas used for foraging, cover, and other needs, and the necessary spatial relationships of these areas using the Thomas et al. (1979) landscape approach, and (2) determining the effects of logging, roads, fire, livestock grazing, and other human disturbance on habitat suitability for elk.

Thomas et al. (1979) defined optimum elk habitat for the Blue Mountains of Oregon and Washington in terms of a proper mixture of foraging and cover areas. They further subdivided cover into hiding cover and thermal cover. This landscape approach has been modified for use in many other areas of the West. For example, Witmer et al. (1985) have used this approach for the elk in the coastal forests of Oregon and Washington, and Wisdom et al. (1986) have formalized this into a habitat evaluation model.

The greatest limitation of such a landscape approach is that the quantity, quality, or availability of forage in "foraging areas" is not considered. Elk consume more forage per animal than most of the other common North American ungulates, and their forage preferences are similar to those of domestic cattle (Cooperrider 1982). Therefore, where elk are reaching carrying capacity or where they occupy common range with cattle, forage quantity and quality can be a problem.

For a current and more thorough review of elk habitat requirements and evaluations, see Skovlin (1982).

Population Measurements. Enumerating various components (age structure, sex and age ratios, and total population) of an elk population is difficult, but important. These data tell the biologist or manager much about the dynamics and general health of the herd, and with adequate sample sizes, they provide the information needed for proper elk population management.

Age Structure. Two methods are used to determine age structure. The first involves examining tooth wear and replacement in elk killed by hunters. Aging by this method is based on the sequence of tooth eruption and wear. Several good aging guidelines are available, but techniques developed by Quimby and Gaab (1957) are used by most wildlife researchers and managers. One problem associated with this method, however, is obtaining a large enough sample to enable the manager to make an accurate estimate of the herd's age structure.

To increase samples, hunters are invited to remove the lower jaws from their kills and bring them to check stations. However, ages obtained by this method do not necessarily represent a herd's age composition. If a wildlife management agency is willing to spend the time and money, rather large sample sizes of jaws can be gathered by setting up several check stations around one herd area. This method is effective for special research areas or extremely important herds, but is not satisfactory for statewide age-structure estimations.

The second method is the dental cementum-aging procedure, which requires only an incisor

Cross-section of an incisor from an unknown age elk killed in October; age estimated at six years by cementum annuli count.

tooth from a harvested elk (Keiss 1969). By using this method, age samples from all elk herds in a state can be greatly increased. The tooth is sectioned with a special sectioning saw, put through various staining procedures, and then examined through a microscope for cementum annuli which can be counted in a manner similar to counting rings in a tree stump. By sending every hunter, or a statistically reliable sample of hunters, a small postage-paid envelope in which to collect and mail an incisor, sample sizes can be increased substantially. A hunter can more easily remove and carry an incisor than a whole jaw.

Sex and Age Ratios. Ground counts and aerial counts are two general methods used to estimate sex and age ratios. Ground counts are useful in areas where elk congregate in large numbers, such as feeding grounds or winter ranges. Ground sex and age classifications can be considerably biased, however, because larger bulls tend to winter away from the cow/calf/young bull groups. Ground sex and age classifications are generally only possible from December through February, when elk are congregated on their winter ranges. This means that some mortality has occurred after the hunting season so that ratios are not exactly the posthunt ratios needed for some population formulas. In addition, large samples of prehunt sex and age ratios can rarely be obtained by ground-count methods. While the total number of

elk on winter ranges can be satisfactorily estimated from a fixed-wing aircraft, sex and age ratio counts cannot. Low and slow-flying helicopters are needed to accurately determine these ratios.

Prehunt sex and age ratio counts should be made in mid-September at the peak of the rut when the largest percentage of bulls can be observed. Elk can be classified as spike bulls; young bulls (typical antler conformation, but with light beams and usually four or five points); mature bulls (typical antler conformation, but with heavy beams); cows; and calves. Calves can be distinguished from yearling cows primarily from the face or nose conformation, but color, relative thickness of the neck, and comparative size are other criteria (Boyd 1970, 1978).

Biologists can facilitate classifications by using tape recorders to tally various categories and later extract the data. This method allows them to watch the elk continually while recording the sex or age of each animal.

Sex and age ratio counts can be made in early December, before the larger bulls have moved to high and isolated wintering areas away from the main herd, to estimate changes caused by fall hunting. Techniques and criteria of posthunt counts are not different from prehunt counts.

Calves are distinguished from yearling cows primarily on the basis of nose or face conformation (a calf has a short, blunt nose). The neck on a calf appears to be shorter and heavier than that of a mature cow. A calf has a fuzzy, rounded patch on its forehead and in general has a "puppylike" appearance.

Total Population. To properly manage an elk population, the wildlife manager must estimate the total elk population on a given range. Several censusing methods can be used to make these estimates.

Elk on winter ranges have been aerially counted since about 1946. These sample counts, for the most part, are accomplished by using fixed-wing aircraft but do not encompass all elk in a survey area. In Colorado, the percentages of deer or elk observed from the air were compared with the total population present for several years. Only about 37% of the elk present on a sagebrush-oakbrush-serviceberry (*Artemesia-Quercus-Amelanchier* sp.) wintering area actually were seen by aerial observers (Boyd 1958). However, winter counts are used by many wildlife management agencies to evaluate the population trends and to set annual hunting seasons and regulations.

Indirect census methods have been used successfully by several management agencies by contrasting prehunt and posthunt sex ratio counts and harvest estimates (Boyd 1970). Among the many references concerning these methods, one excellent review applicable to elk is by Hanson (1963), which provides a discussion on calculating abundance of vertebrates from sex-age ratios.

While population figures resulting from these methods are extremely valuable, they do not tell the entire story of elk herd dynamics. Missing data include estimates of nonhunting mortality and formulas to calculate the consequences of past and future management on elk populations.

A wildlife manager also needs to set management goals and priorities for managing wildlife populations. Obtaining reliable information on which to base these objectives, however, is difficult. Without

Mature bull elk.

tools or methods to assist in gathering and analyzing data, management often ignored many elk population factors when setting harvest limits, regulations, and management priorities. Now, with the development of the computer, these factors can be considered (Gross 1970; Pojar 1981). All factors that contribute to the life cycle of an elk population (i.e., sex-age ratios, cow-calf ratios, harvest by sex and age, wounding loss) are needed to conduct a simulation (Boyd et al. 1975).

One new approach to censusing elk involves the use of mark-recapture techniques to estimate numbers of elk (Bear and Green 1980). Individual elk in a wintering area are randomly trapped and marked with colored ear tags. An attempt is made to capture about 10% of the estimated herd. The recapture effort is accomplished by surveying the entire winter range with a helicopter as soon after trapping as possible. All ear-tagged individuals are counted to determine the ratio of marked to unmarked animals. Three or four recapture flights are made each year. This system is quite precise (SE ± 5%). Accuracy is unknown, but the estimates agree very well with life-table analyses, other aerial counts, and estimates from biologists familiar with the area (Gill et al. 1983).

Discussion. The major concerns of managing elk habitat focus on the effects of competing land uses, particularly logging, grazing, and other human disturbance. Logging especially is a concern because it physically alters the habitat through cutting trees, piling slash, and other forestry-related activities. In addition to the immediate disturbance from such activity, habitat is also subsequently disturbed from roads built as part of the logging job. Not only do elk tend to avoid well-used roads, such roads also provide increased hunter access. The effects of logging, roads, and other human disturbances are described by Lyon et al. (1985), Lyon and Ward (1982), and Heib (1976).

Grazing is another concern because elk compete with livestock for forage. The competition is most severe with elk and cattle because they occupy many common ranges, their diets are similar, and both species consume large amounts of forage (Cooperrider 1982).

Mule and White-tailed Deer

The mule deer (*Odocoileus hemionus*) ranges over most of temperate North America between the Pacific Coast and the 100th Meridian. The white-tailed deer (*O. virginianus*) is the most popular and widespread big game animal in North America, found in almost all the contiguous 48 states. It thrives in a wide range of climatic and habitat conditions and adapts quickly to changes.

Mule and white-tailed deer are often victims of automobile accidents, diseases, parasites, predation, starvation, wounds, fence entanglements, poaching and, of course, legal hunting. A primary limiting factor for these species would be habitat degradation caused by urban development, deteriorating forest habitat, and agricultural development. Of all these limiting factors, the primary management concern is habitat loss.

Habitat Requirements and Analysis. Mule deer and white-tailed deer have been intensively studied for many years. However, because they occupy such diverse habitats, generalizations about habitat requirements are extremely difficult to make. A biologist should, therefore, consult the literature on a particular region for specific habitat requirements. Wallmo (1981) and Halls (1982) provide extensive reviews of habitat evaluation and management for mule and white-tailed deer, respectively.

Because mule deer are adaptable, they may be found in all major climatic and vegetational zones of the western U.S. except the arctic, tropics, and extreme deserts. Generally, mule deer inhabit semiarid, open forest, brush, and shrublands found in conjunction with steep, broken, or otherwise rough terrain. However, extensive populations are also found in prairie habitats along the eastern limits of their distribution and in semidesert shrub habitats of the Southwest (Mackie et al. 1982). Black-tailed deer, which consist of two mule deer subspecies, are found in temperate, coniferous forests along the Pacific Coast from central California, north to southeastern Alaska. Populations can also be found in adjacent woodland-chaparral areas of the coastal ranges of California.

In general, the white-tailed deer does best in subclimax habitat (Hesselton and Hesselton 1982), particularly cut over forests. This is particularly true

in the eastern U.S. However, west of the 100th Meridian, white-tailed deer are often associated with riparian areas along major river drainages. Many of these areas consist of forested stands of cottonwoods (*Populus* sp.), willows (*Salix* sp.), and other tree species. Although white-tailed deer have not been studied as extensively in the West, the evidence suggests that these habitats are very important if not essential for many white-tailed deer herds.

The same caution applies to mule deer. Whereas early research and writing emphasized the importance of early successional habitat, recent research suggests that, in some areas, climax forest is the most important of the available or potential habitat types for maintaining high year-round carrying capacity (Wallmo and Schoen 1981). This is particularly true of black-tailed deer at the northern areas of their geographic range.

Both mule and white-tailed deer require a diversity of plant species as food at any one time and during an entire year. Diverse vegetation is also required for hiding, escape, and thermal cover. Because of this, interspersion of several individual forage and habitat types may be more important than the occurrence of individual types.

Population Measurements.

Direct Counts. Four basic methods are used to count mule and white-tailed deer: aerial counts, drives or "complete" surveys, flushing counts, and automobile counts. For direct counts, aerial census is probably the only method to be considered. These counts are usually conducted during the winter when there is a good counting background, deciduous trees have shed their leaves, and deer are concentrated on limited winter ranges.

Note differences in antler conformation between the white-tailed deer buck (left photo) with the points coming off the main beam and the mule deer buck (right photo) with dichotomous branching.

Aerial counts from fixed-wing aircraft are generally limited to total counts of entire herds or total counts on trend areas, flown annually. As stated for elk, sex and age ratio data cannot usually be obtained with the use of fixed-wing aircraft. The use of aerial censusing has been revolutionized by the helicopter, however. Sex, age, and area data can now be obtained that were not possible from fixed-wing aircraft. Helicopter counts are more expensive, but better quality data can be obtained.

Present-day aerial census has moved from total counts to sample-based estimates of population size (Gill et al. 1983). A helicopter-quadrat system of censusing deer has been developed in Colorado (Bartmann 1974; Kufeld et al. 1980) that consists of 1.6-km^2 (1-mi.^{2}) quadrats, randomly located in winter range areas and permanently marked so the same areas can be flown each year. The accuracy, precision, frequency, and resolution of the quadrat census method are currently being studied (Gill et al. 1983).

Indirect Counts. The primary indirect census method is the pellet counts. Pellet counts are best used in wintering areas. This technique is based on assumptions of the number of pellet groups deposited every 24 hours by an individual deer. A winter range is censused for pellet groups after the deer leave an area. All pellet groups within a series of statistically designed plots are then counted. The number of pellet groups per hectare (acre) is multiplied by the number of hectares (acres) per habitat type, resulting in an estimate of the total number of pellet groups per habitat type. Another factor that must be closely estimated is the number of days that deer have been on the area sampled. Knowing this, the number of pellet groups per hectare (acre) for each habitat type and the daily defecation rate, results in an estimate of the number of deer using the area (Neff 1968; Ryel 1971; Anderson et al. 1972).

A review of research on methods to estimate total populations of mule and white-tailed deer over large areas revealed that the helicopter quadrat and pellet group count methods mentioned above were conceptually feasible for implementation on large areas of the western U.S. No single system can apply to all areas of the western U.S. Topography, weather, and vegetation composition are primary items that dictate the system to be used at different localities.

Helicopter aerial surveys appear to be the method of choice wherever possible, because they require less time, are more accurate than fixed-wing aircraft counts, and provide direct estimates of population size. Aerial censuses cannot be used, however, in areas of turbulent winds or where combinations of topography and mottled snow background preclude accurate, consistent counts.

Research in Colorado revealed that pellet group counts on permanently marked plots and on temporary plots yielded comparable estimates of population size. Seemingly, temporary plots are more practical because they are easier to implement and are less costly (Freddy and Bowden 1983a).

Discussion. Because habitat and population measurements are so similar for mule and white-tailed deer, the species were combined in this section to save repeating much of the information. Some of the problems encountered while inventorying and monitoring deer include a lack of accurate and precise census methods, extreme difficulty in determining carrying capacity on seasonal ranges, and the fact that some populations inhabit areas of the western U.S. where winters are so mild that winter range concentrations are unknown and year-round ranges are normal.

Factors limiting deer populations in the short term are still not well understood. For example, available evidence indicates that mule deer declined substantially over most of the species' range from the early 1960s to around 1976, then began to increase with no generally accepted explanation for either the decline or recovery. Connolly (1981:243) wrote—

"It reveals how little control biologists and managers have over the deer they purport to manage. Just as they were powerless to halt the decline, the biologists and managers now are unable to show in any scientifically acceptable way that improved management put the herds on the road to recovery."

In spite of the problems, a wealth of information on techniques can be used as is or modified slightly to fit site-specific situations. The brief writeups and literature cited in this section should give guidance on where to obtain additional information for either the biologist with no or limited experience or the experienced biologist who has need for more detailed information.

Moose

The moose (*Alces alces*) is a valued trophy and game animal throughout most of its range. In many areas (Isle Royale, Denali National Park, Kenai Moose Range), it is also important as a large, impressive, and relatively photogenic focus for tourists and photographers.

Female reproductive performance in moose populations varies, apparently reflecting levels of nutrition which, in turn, can be related to habitat characteristics. Yearling pregnancy rates are especially variable, ranging from 0 to 62% according to various studies. Adult pregnancy rates are somewhat less variable, but the twinning rate among adult females in a population may be an especially good indicator of habitat quality (Franzmann 1978).

Such reproductive performance indicators should relate to quite specific habitat areas, because moose generally have small home ranges (3 to 6 km^2 [1.8 to 3.6 mi.^{2}]). In some cases, however, these are seasonal home ranges, separated by migration corridors of up to 50 km (30 mi.) (LeResche 1974; Franzmann 1978).

Moose are widely distributed in North America, extending from coastal areas bordering the Arctic Ocean to the mixed deciduous/coniferous forests of Minnesota and Maine and as far south as Utah in the western montane forests. Dramatic expansions in the Rocky Mountains have occurred in this century, as have apparent expansions and increases in tundra areas of western and northern Alaska. Climatic changes and a large increase in the proportion of fire-seral communities are two reasons most frequently cited for these distributional dynamics (Kelsall and Telfer 1974).

Average adult body weights for females are 414 kg (920 lb) in Alberta and 445 kg (980 lb) in Alaska; males attain weights of up to 585 kg (1,300 lb) (Franzmann 1978). From their size, moose are clearly an ungulate species requiring large amounts of forage. Adult energy requirements vary, but average around 14,000 kcal per day (Belovsky 1978). Although moose have large bite sizes, they have relatively low bite rates. In a study in Alberta, Renecker and Hudson (1986) estimated that consumption rates ranged from 23 g/min (0.8 oz/min) in July to 11 g/min (0.4 oz/min) in January.

In Alaska, calves grow from birth weights of 11.2-13.5 kg (25-30 lb) to weights of 180 kg (400 lb) in 5 months. Their size suggests that forage abundance and quality are critical factors for moose. Indeed, Belovsky (1978) presents convincing evidence that moose almost always forage to maintain energy input. They have little room for error if they are to achieve positive energy balances.

Habitat Requirements and Analysis. Because of the high forage demand of moose, habitat evaluation for the species has concentrated on identifying foraging areas and measuring forage quantity and quality.

Browse comprises 75 to 80% of the moose diets in winter but becomes less important by varying degrees in summer. Moose can break off large stems and branches and exploit the canopy up to 3 m (10 ft) above ground level. Throughout the range of the species, willows (*Salix* sp.) are used out of proportion to their abundance. Other highly palatable and apparently preferred plants include birch (*Betula* sp.), aspen (*Populus tremuloides*), and cottonwood (*Populus* sp.). When snow is not too deep, low shrubs (such as *Vaccinium* sp.) or sedges (*Carex* sp. and *Equisetum* sp.) may also be used.

Brassard et al. (1974) examined several variables potentially useful in measuring relative habitat value and winter carrying capacity in Quebec. They found a direct relationship between degree of occupation and quantity of available deciduous stems. Later work (Polequin et al. 1977) has shown that in late winter, cover and reduced exposure from wind may be as important as forage availability in the selection of sites.

In most parts of their range, moose make significant use of aquatic plants in summer. Much of this use is concentrated at a time when twigs and leaves of browse species have peak nutritional value. In terms of energy needs, there is no obvious advantage for moose switching to aquatics. However, Jordan et al. (1973) and Fraser et al. (1984) concluded that sodium content is being selected since winter browse may have been insufficient.

Similarly, natural mineral licks are also important sources of sodium for moose (Tankersley and Gasaway 1983). Although nothing directly links aquatic forage and mineral licks to moose reproductive dynamics, such links can be hypothesized, at least physiologically. Thus, habitat managers should identify and maintain such features.

For many populations, riparian and floodplain communities are also preferred habitats, apparently of importance far beyond their relatively restricted occurrence. This is certainly true of Shiras moose (*A. a. shirasi*) in the Rocky Mountains (Peek 1974) and of populations that extend into tundra areas (Mould 1977, 1979).

Mature bull moose.

Browse quality has been determined by many measurement techniques (Oldemeyer 1977a). On the Kenai Pensinsula, Alaska, deteriorating range quality has been circumstantially linked with declining moose numbers (Oldemeyer et al. 1977a). Animal physiological factors, such as hair and blood chemistry, have also been used in measuring habitat quality (LeResche et al. 1974; Franzmann et al. 1975). LaPerriere et al. (1980) used Landsat images and cluster analysis techniques to map moose habitat classes and features in interior Alaska. Through these techniques, large areas could be mapped with high accuracy and little field checking.

A model has been developed to evaluate moose habitat suitability and quality in Alaska. The model allows quality to be estimated quantitatively, based primarily on data from studies in south-central and interior Alaska. A handbook is available that would help a biologist apply the model (Konkel 1980, as cited in Mule 1982). However, Mule (1982) compared the habitat quality ratings generated by the model with those derived by a team of experts, and he concluded that the model-based ratings were unacceptably inaccurate. A revision of the model is described but not fully tested (Mule 1982).

Population Measurements. Techniques for accurately censusing moose need to be perfected. In spite of their large size, their habitats and frequent use of forested cover make them difficult to see from aircraft, even helicopters. Even though at some times of the year some populations move into more open terrain, moose are not sufficiently consistent in such behavior. Furthermore, seasonal aggregations, when they do occur, do not involve large segments of the population.

Despite these problems, most census techniques still involve aerial surveys, using either transects or intensive complete counts of small blocks of habitat. Transects have been discontinued in some areas because of their extremely low accuracy (Timmermann 1974); in other areas, they are used only as indexes of relative abundance. In the most intensive tests of aerial counts to date, conducted over enclosures with known numbers of animals, LeResche and Rausch (1974) found that only about 68% of the adults were observed under ideal conditions, with inexperienced observers seeing only 43%. Both precision and accuracy were low. Recent experience with conditions similar to the test area, along with planning and attention to details, was found to be essential in obtaining valid trend indicators. Similarly, Gasaway et al. (1985) described significant and widely variable biases in summer aerial surveys of moose where even the direction of population trend, except very large changes, could not be reliably detected.

Helicopter surveys, before bulls drop their antlers in the fall, are useful in obtaining adult sex ratios. Yearling bulls may also be reliably identified from the air, but yearling females are difficult to reliably identify (LeResche and Rausch 1974). After males have shed their antlers, adult females may be correctly distinguished from the ground by their white vulvar markings (Lent 1974b). More detailed information on the age structure of populations can only be obtained by sectioning teeth and reading cementum annuli from hunter kills or other dead animals (Sergeant and Pimlott 1959).

Timmermann (1974) reviewed other tried techniques in assessing relative population levels of moose, ranging from track-and-fecal dropping counts to infrared scanning devices. All these techniques had factors that severely limited their usefulness.

Discussion. Because moose generally prefer early successional vegetation, carrying capacity can be improved by manipulating selected habitats. These manipulations may include mechanical rehabilitation (Oldemeyer 1977b), prescribed burns, and special logging practices (Telfer 1974). But Peek (1974) advised caution and careful planning of such manipulations, particularly in areas where more than one large herbivore species may be present.

Perhaps the most critical management need for moose is the development of truly accurate and useful census techniques. Until this happens, biologists will have difficulty assessing the value of various management practices, including habitat manipulations.

Caribou

Populations of caribou (*Rangifer tarandus*) roam a variety of northern boreal habitats in North America, from the barren polar deserts of the Canadian Arctic Archipelago southward, occupying much of Alaska and extending into woodland and alpine areas of southern Canada. A small remnant population moves into the contiguous 48 states in the area of the Idaho Panhandle during part of the year. The species is typically divided into two groups of subspecies: the tundra (*cylindricornis*) group and the woodland (*compressicornis*) group (Banfield 1962). Ecologically, however, at least four categories should be considered:

(1) Small groups that remain in tundra habitats throughout the year;

(2) Large migratory populations, some portions of which typically use taiga habitats in the winter months;

Caribou.

(3) Mountain caribou that make marked altitudinal migrations seasonally;

(4) Woodland caribou that generally make only short annual movements.

Generally the woodland populations are small, showing one of the latter two strategies. There are exceptions however. In Labrador, populations of woodland caribou have reached nearly 200,000 animals and migrate over 200,000 km^2 (80,000 mi.^{2}) of tundra and taiga (Juniper 1980; Parker 1981).

Reindeer, domesticated members of the same species, have been introduced into North America, primarily from Siberia. Herds exist in Alaska and in the Mackenzie River Delta of Canada. Management as domesticated stock continues in some areas to varying degrees. In other areas, reindeer are now feral, and some have mixed and interbred with native subspecies.

Habitat Requirements and Analysis. Surprisingly, few biologists agree on the habitat requirements of caribou, despite an extraordinary amount of research and management concern over the past decades. Much controversy in recent years has focused on the importance and need of lichens in the winter diet of caribou. Populations of the high arctic polar desert and some introduced populations make little use

of lichens and yet they thrive. Klein (1982) argued that these exceptions in no way excluded or refuted the possibility that the species' evolution may be closely linked to a lichen-based niche, unexploited by other herbivores. Lichens, as winter forage, are low in protein but high in digestible carbohydrates.

Late winter-spring fat deposition may occur on high-quality lichen ranges. But clearly, caribou, like other northern ungulates, adapt to long periods of low-quality forage in winter and indeed do not normally maintain body weight in winter even on a relatively high-protein diet (McEwan and Whitehead 1970, 1975). However, actual examples of starvation or extreme malnutrition among adult caribou in winter or spring are rare, although it has occurred in some arctic island populations. Bergerud (1978:98) points out that—

"It has not been demonstrated that an absolute shortage of food has caused caribou declines .... I do not know of any studies where it could be shown that birth and death rates were altered due to an absolute shortage of food."

However, the massive declines and die-offs that have occurred in insular populations demonstrate that, under certain circumstances, forage can be absolutely limiting (Klein 1968).

Thing and Clausen (1980) attributed a high mortality among calves in Greenland to overuse and depletion of lichens on winter ranges. Leader-Williams (1980) also attributed alterations in reproductive performance to habitat overutilization. Bergerud's analysis (1978), emphasizing hunting and predation as the key mortality factors in caribou population dynamics, tended to ignore the possible role of habitat quality and nutrition in mediating mortality factors.

Most specialists have stressed the importance of identifying and protecting the calving grounds of migratory caribou populations. Nevertheless, there has again been no agreement as to what critical habitat requirements are linked with such calving grounds. Isolation from human centers (Lent 1966) and phenological characteristics (Kuropat and Bryant 1980; Lent 1980) have been suggested as important. Kelsall (1968) believed that most Canadian calving grounds were extremely harsh with poor forage, and stressed the low density of predators as a factor. Reimers et al. (1983) showed that females on early greened calving grounds had less weight loss during lactation than those still on winter forage at calving time.

As noted above, specific habitat requirements of caribou are controversial issues, particularly in winter ranges and calving areas. In addition, many now believe that the quality of winter forage and, within broad limits, quantity of winter forage are of relatively little consequence in terms of caribou demography. In contrast, managers of domestic reindeer continue to be concerned about winter range condition techniques for evaluating these ranges (Eriksson 1980). Workers with woodland caribou have also developed techniques for assessing arboreal lichen abundance (Van Daele and Johnson 1983). The relative availability of forage, as influenced by patterns of snow cover and ice accumulation, have also been of great interest in terms of wild and domestic populations. These techniques are described in Chapter 8, Tundra.

A broad concensus has developed that *Rangifer* habitat quality is presently best measured by examining population attributes. Parker (1981) measured both physical and reproductive characteristics in females, consistent with an expanding population. Reimers et al. (1983) noted several attributes they believe highly correlate with spring-summer range quality.

Population Measurements. The first aerial censuses of caribou relied primarily on winter and spring transect data. Bergerud (1963) presented one of the best early treatments of such aerial censuses, their problems and uses. He noted, as did Lent (1966), that a low but continuous, unbroken snow cover is essential for accurate winter counts. Bergerud provided many other recommendations on census design and execution. Siniff and Skoog (1964) reported on the use of stratified random sampling with aerial transects.

In the early 1960s, specialized aerial census techniques for estimating the size of migratory caribou populations were developed in Alaska. These techniques take advantage of specific behavioral attributes of migratory caribou: their use of calving grounds at relatively fixed locations, where almost all adult females converge for a brief calving season, and the typical concentration of these females and other individuals into extremely dense aggregations during an even briefer post-calving period.

Skoog (1962) pioneered the calving-ground count method and Lent (1966) first described the post-calving aerial photography method. Because adult males are largely segregated from cows and widely dispersed at these times, both methods require later samples to obtain adult sex ratios needed to determine total population estimates. Thus, the current technique has commonly been referred to as the "aerial photo-direct count extrapolation" method. Such ratios are best obtained from samples at several locations during the rutting season.

Modern refinements and analyses of these basic methods have been described in several Pittman-Robertson (Federal Aid) reports of the Alaska Department of Fish and Game (Pegau and Hemming 1972). These reports are discussed in detail by Doerr (1979).

Canadian workers have continued to make more use of winter and spring censuses (Parker 1975). Aside from using such censuses for total population estimates, they are universally important in determining relative use of winter ranges; estimating relative mortality rates (Davis and Valkenberg 1979); and assessing vulnerability to hunting pressure, much of which occurs on winter ranges.

Calef and Heard (1980) used aerial transects to sample and derive population estimates for three caribou populations. They used a 25% correction factor for animals overlooked, citing empirical evidence for a similar correction factor of 29%. They were able to compare the transect estimate with an estimated calving ground count for the same population. The two estimates were 17,225 and 15,884, respectively, for the Lorillard herd.

Discussion. Many census techniques have been developed for obtaining good numeric and composition data for caribou populations, particularly for those inhabiting tundra and open woodland environments. The ability to meaningfully relate habitat quality and trend to population dynamics of *Rangifer* continues to be marred by a general lack of agreement. Sampling of reproductive and physiological attributes of individual animals holds the most promise for monitoring populations and, indirectly, the status of their seasonal ranges.

Pronghorn

Pronghorn antelope (*Antilocapra americana*) symbolize the wide open rangelands of the West. The range of pronghorn during the early 1800s included most of the Great Plains, the high sagebrush steppes and grass valleys of the Great Basin states, and parts of south-central Canada and northern Mexico (Einarsen 1948). By the 1920s, however, the former densely populated ranges had been drastically reduced. Ranges occupied by pronghorn today are virtually identical to historical ranges except areas along the Mississippi River. Reintroductions since the 1920s are largely responsible for increased populations of this swift ungulate.

Limiting factors for pronghorn herds include predation; severe winters with deep snow; fences that preclude seasonal movements; and neonatal mortality, possibly caused by a lack of adequate nutrition for pregnant does during the last 3 months of pregnancy. Disease does not appear to be a significant mortality factor in pronghorn (Yoakum 1978:107). Management concerns about pronghorn are related to limiting factors and include coyote and bobcat predation on newborn fawns; road kills on high-speed roads; wire fences constructed in ways that preclude pronghorn movements, especially in winter; and decreasing availability of diversified vegetative ranges.

Habitat Requirements. Pronghorn typically occupy habitats characterized by low, rolling, wide-open, expansive terrain. Sites with sparse stands of conifers may be used at certain times if understory vegetation allows distant visibility and rapid mobility (Yoakum 1978).

Habitat requirements for pronghorn are described in detail in Autenrieth (1978), Yoakum (1980), Kindschy et al. (1982), and Allen et al. (1984).

Free-standing water, available year-round, appears necessary for producing and maintaining high pronghorn densities. This water should be available every 1.6 to 8.0 km (1 to 5 mi.). Studies by Sundstrom (1968) in Wyoming indicated that 95% of the observed pronghorn were within a 4.8 to 6.4 km (3 to 4 mi.) radius of water. Highest densities of pronghorn occur in habitats averaging 25 to 38 cm (10 to 15 in.) of precipitation per year. Where pronghorn have been transplanted to areas of higher precipitation, production and survival rates declined.

Mature pronghorn buck.

Pronghorn also occur in areas of lower precipitation, but population densities are less (Yoakum 1978).

Most pronghorn ranges receive some snow; however, when snow accumulations exceed 25 to 30 cm (10 to 12 in.), pronghorns have trouble finding forage. Prolonged winters with deep snow are especially harmful when combined with factors such as—

(1) Low quantities or qualities of forage,

(2) Excessive wind, and

(3) Man-made obstacles that impede or restrict free movement to areas with less snow cover.

Temperatures do not seem to be a significant limiting factor, as pronghorns can adapt to hot deserts or alpine plateau conditions.

Quality and quantity of vegetation appear to be the major factors affecting pronghorn population densities. In the sagebrush-grassland areas of the Great Basin states, the following vegetative characteristics are found on ranges preferred by pronghorn (from Kindschy et al. 1982):

- ground cover averaging 50% living vegetation;

- general range composition of 40 to 60% grass, 10 to 30% forbs, and 5 to 20% browse;

- a variety of species, within a vegetative community, including 5 to 10 species of grasses, 20 to 40 species of forbs, and 5 to 10 species of shrubs;

- succulent plants, available in spring and wet summers;

- open, rolling rangelands having a variety of vegetative types rather than monotypic vegetative communities;

- low vegetation structure averaging 38 to 61cm (15 to 24 in.) in height.

Most of these preferred habitat qualities would also apply to pronghorn ranges east of the Continental Divide.

West of the 100th Meridian, pronghorn typically inhabit ranges characterized by low rolling, expansive terrain and are almost never observed for more than a few minutes at a time where their view was restricted by terrain or other natural features (Allen et al. 1984). Kindschy et al. (1982) indicate that areas with slopes less than 5% were best for pronghorn in this region.

Microhabitats provided by topographic relief in this region apparently increase habitat quality during winter by providing lower wind velocities, less snow, and less dense snow. During the fall and winter, pronghorn spent more time in basins less than 1.6 km (1 mi.) in diameter than at any other time of the year (Prenzlow et al. 1968).

Pronghorn typically forage heavily on browse and forbs and only eat grass when it is green and succulent. Thus, pronghorn food habits do not generally overlap those of horses and cattle. However, pronghorn food habits are similar to those of domestic sheep, and pronghorn may compete with sheep for available forage.

Wheat (*Triticum aestivum*) is a major portion of the diet of pronghorn living near winter wheat fields in Colorado (Hoover et al. 1959). Heavy use of wheat by pronghorn has also been reported from Kansas, Montana, and Alberta (Allen et al. 1984). Winter wheat near or interspersed with rangeland is assumed to improve the winter food value for pronghorn if shrubs are present at densities of 75% or less (Allen et al. 1984).

Fences on pronghorn ranges west of the 100th Meridian may restrict movements and cause direct injury or mortality (Allen et al. 1984). Fences may cause significant adverse impacts when constructed across migration routes or where they interfere with daily movements to and from water.

Population Measurements. Most pronghorn are counted from the air, although some ground counts are used on sparsely inhabited ranges. Ground surveys are time-consuming and expensive, but they provide accurate data on fawn survival.

Aerial counts, usually by fixed-wing aircraft, cover larger areas in less time. Aerial surveys are conducted during the summer and fall in some states, and during the winter in others. Winter counts are usually flown to obtain total numbers, as fawns are hard to distinguish from yearlings in win-

Twin pronghorn fawns.

ter, and most bucks have shed their horn sheaths by the time winter aerial counts are made.

If sex and age ratio data are needed, counts are made in late summer or early fall. Flight patterns should be either sample strips (usually 0.8 km [0.5 mi.] on each side of the aircraft and 1.6 km [1 mi.] apart) or in randomly located (1.6 km^2 [1 mi.^{2}]) quadrats. Most flying for pronghorn census should be approximately 46 to 91 m (150 to 300 ft.) aboveground with speeds of about 112 to 128 km (70 to 80 mi.) per hour. Usually 30% of the area is sampled by a strip census while 10% is sampled by quadrats. The quadrat sample method usually takes twice as long as the strip census (T.M. Pojar, pers. commun.).

Discussion. The pronghorn is unique in that it is easy to observe during all seasons in all its preferred habitats; therefore, censuses are relatively easy. Census techniques vary, however, from Great Plains grassland habitats to Great Basin sagebrush habitats. Inventory and monitoring of pronghorn habitats is also relatively easy since their habitat requirements are relatively similar throughout their range, have been well-described, and can be measured easily.

Bison

The American bison (*Bison bison*) today is being raised in predominantly domestic situations. With few exceptions, free-ranging herds of bison are no longer found. Only in the vicinity of Wood Buffalo National Park in Canada and in Yellowstone National Park in Wyoming can free-ranging bison populations be found that are neither cropped nor hunted. Free-ranging herds in Utah and Alaska are intensively managed and cropped. In recent years, the commercial value of bison has increased. Numerous private herds are managed as livestock, with

American bison (bull, cow, and calf).

meat being sold as a specialty item, and hides, heads, and other parts finding a ready market.

Natural limiting habitat factors for the American bison are not of great concern because most of today's herds are intensively managed, which includes disease control and selective culling. Historically, the grizzly bear and the wolf were probably the only natural predators that affected bison (Meagher 1978). Because of the present-day, low population levels of these two large predators, they no longer significantly threaten free-ranging bison herds.

Large-scale mortality from adverse winter weather has been reported historically. Today, only the herds in Yellowstone National Park suffer any significant winter losses (Meagher 1978). Winterkill usually results from the combined effects of forage availability, climatic stress, and physical condition of individual animals. These losses usually occur in late winter and early spring after prolonged severe winters. Some calf mortality has been reported during severe spring weather.

Habitat Requirements and Analysis. The primary habitat requirements for bison on public lands are adequate forage, water, and space.

Bison are primarily grazers. Grasses furnish most of their food over the year; however, sedges make up a large portion of their diet in both Wood Buffalo and Yellowstone National Parks. Bison seem quite similar to cattle in their forage preferences and, as a result, these two animals often directly compete with each other. Peden et al. (1974) compared the diets of bison and domestic cattle in a short-grass plains area and found that bison prefer warm-season grasses, feed in different areas, and are less selective. Bison appear to be able to digest low-protein, low-quality forage and apparently can eat more of this

type of forage. Bison appear to need water every day.

If bison are to be maintained as free-ranging animals, they will need large areas to roam. However, they can also be successfully kept in small pastures as semidomestic animals.

When available, bison use forested areas for shade and to escape insects (Meagher 1978). These areas also furnish forage in deep, crusted snow because snow is more loosely packed in forested areas. During severe weather, forest areas and some topographical features furnish cover (Meagher 1973, 1976).

The bison can thrive in places where no other large ungulate can. This includes open valleys covered with deep snow and subject to frequent, severe wind and blizzard conditions, lasting up to 6 months (Meagher 1976).

Population Measurements. Bison population levels are best determined by aerial censuses rather than sample estimates (Meagher 1978). These counts are most effective when flown during the winter. Herd and calf production were successfully counted through the use of aerial photography in Wood Buffalo National Park (Stelfox 1976).

Discussion. Free-ranging American bison are found on only a few areas of public domain land (Utah and Alaska). Present-day herds are small, easily located and tracked, and easily censused. Any standard vegetation measurement technique can be used to determine range use and to monitor condition and trend of bison ranges.

This species is important from a historical and aesthetic standpoint. Free-ranging populations will never be large, but proper management of present-day, free-ranging herds should not be neglected.

Mountain Goat

The mountain goat (*Oreamnos americanus*) is one of the least understood of native North American ungulates. Relatively few studies have been conducted on mountain goats because of their limited geographic range and comparatively low economic importance. Further, the species has been difficult to study because its habitats are severe and often remote.

Most studies of mountain goats are recent. A large portion of literature on the goat can be found in the proceedings of a special symposium (Samuel and MacGregor 1977) and the Biennial Symposium of the Northern Wild Sheep and Goat Council (Hebert and Nation 1978; Hickey 1980; Bailey and Schoonveld 1982).

Rocky Mountain goat; mature billy.

Habitat Requirements and Analysis. The basic habitat requirements of mountain goats are—

- suitable topography for predator evasion along with a sufficient microclimate,
- forages for all seasons,
- salt, and
- water.

For management purposes, winter ranges, summer ranges, kidding areas, salt licks, and migration corridors need to be identified.

Mountain goat winter ranges are characterized by their lack of persistent or melt-crusted snow along cliffs and steep terrain interspersed with vegetation. Suitable winter ranges may be (1) at lower elevations (Rideout 1974; Smith 1977), including coastal areas (Hjeljord 1973; Hebert and Turnbull 1977; Fox and Taber 1981) where snow is less abundant and persistent, or (2) on relatively unforested, steep, mostly south-facing slopes where snow sheds rapidly (Brandborg 1955; Hjeljord 1973). Mountain goats mostly use those portions of winter ranges that are on slopes exceeding 40° (Smith 1977; Smith and

Raedeke 1982). Usually, these slopes face south, although Adams and Bailey (1980) described some goats in a southern population wintering on north aspects. Overhanging ledges, caves, and abandoned mine entrances may provide additional shelter for wintering goats (Richardson 1971; Smith 1977).

In winter, goats become sedentary on traditionally used winter ranges (Smith 1976; Adams and Bailey 1980; Chadwick 1983), with forages on ledges or benches within cliff areas or on windswept ridges. One small population of goats in a forested area rarely foraged more than 50 m (165 ft) from escape terrain (Smith 1982). This may have been an exception, related to the small numbers of goats, the poor visibility in their forested habitat, and the presence of large predators. In contrast, Fox and Taber (1981) observed that wintering goats made little use of areas more than 300 m (990 ft) from steep broken terrain; Schoen and Kirchoff (1981) reported over 90% of observed goats were within 400 m (1,320 ft) of cliffs.

At low elevations, particularly near the Pacific Coast, a conifer canopy may benefit wintering mountain goats by intercepting and redistributing snow and by providing forage, including arboreal lichens. In contrast, goats wintering on interior ranges, where snowfall is great, tend to avoid dense stands of conifers that accumulate snow (Adams and Bailey 1980).

When snow is not an overriding problem, habitat selection is most often determined by needs for security from predation and for abundant, nutritious forage. Security is probably a function of distance from escape terrain, visibility afforded by the habitat, and group size (Adams et al. 1982a; Risenhoover and Bailey 1985a). Thompson (1980) noted the average distance of goats from escape terrain on his study area was 75 m (248 ft). Schoen and Kirchoff (1981) found that distance to cliffs was the most important factor determining goat distribution and that summering goats made little use of foraging areas over 400 m (1,320 ft) from cliffs. McFetridge (1977) also noted that most foraging by nursery bands was within 400 m (1,320 ft) of escape terrain. Risenhoover and Bailey (1985a) suggest that nanny goats form large nursery bands on alpine tundra, where visibility is excellent. This may be a strategy for reducing the risk of predation while exploiting forages far from escape terrain. This strategy is only effective where goat populations are relatively large and wolves are absent.

Goats will exploit phenological differences among habitats to obtain the most nutritious forage. They often move to lower elevations in spring, seek green forage at higher elevations in summer, and feed on north aspects in late summer (Brandborg 1955; Rideout 1974; Smith 1976; Bailey and Johnson 1977). On some ranges, moist meadows below cirques or snowfields are attractive foraging sites in late summer.

Visibility of surroundings seems important to mountain goats (Chadwick 1983). This may limit their use of dense stands of conifers far from escape terrain. In contrast, goats often use sparse stands of conifers (Smith 1976; Adams and Bailey 1980) and have used conifers for avoiding people (Singer 1975). The value of conifers on summer range is unclear, but may involve associated forage, available water or salt, or an attractive thermal regime.

Kids are born on the steepest, most rugged areas of a goat range. Based on a few reports, kidding areas are usually within winter ranges and used year after year (Smith 1976; Adams 1981).

Judging by the frequency and tenacity with which goats use licks, these areas seem to be very important habitat resources. Peak use of licks occurs in spring and early summer (Singer 1975). The principal attractant at licks probably is sodium (Hebert and Turnbull 1977). On a Colorado study area, goat movements seemed limited by licks occurring at only one end of the area. These summer movements

expanded after a new salt lick was established at the other end of the area (Bailey, J.A., unpubl. data).

Migration corridors are used between winter and summer ranges and when goats are visiting salt licks. When crossing forested areas without escape terrain, goats repeatedly use the same trails (Singer 1975). Presumably the risk of unexpected predator attack can be great in these areas, since visibility may be poor and the frequent occurrence of goats may attract predators. If this is correct, reducing conifer cover to enhance visibility could improve goat habitat on migration corridors.

Water is not believed to be a limiting factor on most mountain goat ranges as these are either in moist climates or in areas with persistent snowfields. However, water availability may restrict goat movements and habitat selection in southern ranges where the species has been introduced.

Food habits of mountain goats have been reviewed by Hibbs (1966), Wigal and Coggins (1982), and Adams and Bailey (1983). Dailey et al. (1984) used tame animals to evaluate forage preference. Mountain goats are such adaptable feeders that literature on their food habits allows few generalizations. Reported diets have varied depending on locations and habitats, season, and snow conditions. Grasses and sedges, forbs, and browse have each been reported as abundant in the diet or as preferred in both winter and summer studies. Conifers or mosses and lichens have been important winter forages.

The ability of mountain goats to exploit a wide variety of forages may be an adaptation compensating for their narrow habitat preferences, especially during winter (Adams et al. 1982b). By using all available forages, goats are able to exist in small groups on small, snow-shedding areas where they are protected from predators. Wintering goats seem to choose areas on the basis of a sedentary life-style rather than for abundant forage. In contrast, during summer when nutritional demands for growth and lactation are high, goats benefit by choosing lush stands of quality herbaceous forage in alpine grasslands and meadows (Risenhoover and Bailey 1985a).

Habitat types used or preferred by mountain goats on winter and summer ranges have been described in several studies in diverse locations (Smith 1976; Adams and Bailey 1980; Fox and Taber 1981; Schoen and Kirchoff 1981). In these studies, habitat classifications have involved overstory vegetation, understory vegetation, and terrain characteristics (aspect, steepness, brokenness). While goats use a variety of vegetation types, their habitat selection has been most consistently related to steep terrain.

Fox et al. (1982) developed a model for predicting presence/absence of mountain goats in a coastal range of southeast Alaska. The principal predictor was distance to cliffs. This model apparently has not been tested in other areas. Useful models of goat habitat quality, yet to be developed, will probably depend on the following factors, in order of importance:

(1) Distance to cliffs or slope characteristics;

(2) Elevation and aspect, including available ranges of these variables; and

(3) Vegetation type.

The influences of these factors vary among areas within the geographic range of the species. Another important factor may be presence and location of salt licks. While such a model may predict the quantity and quality of seasonal goat ranges, additional consideration may be needed to identify migration corridors.

Population Measurements.

Relative Density. Trend counts, especially from aircraft, are the most commonly used methods for monitoring mountain goat populations. In repeated counts, more goats have been observed from helicopters than from fixed-wing aircraft (Ballard 1977; Nichols 1980).

Trend counts provide more than annual population indexes. They provide herd productivity (age ratios) and minimum population size indexes that may be used as bases for conservative harvest strategies. However, the precision of trend counts has not been evaluated. Many successive surveys of one population in one season still need to be done. Without measuring precision, the significance of a difference between trend counts over 2 years cannot be evaluated. Likewise, the probability of detecting a significant change in population size from trend counts in consecutive years is uncertain.

A subjective appraisal of Nichols' (1980) data from replicated aerial counts of local populations, from July to mid-September and with consistent weather conditions, suggests that the 90% confidence limits for a single count from a fixed-wing aircraft might vary by ±18% of the count. If this is correct, there is only a 25% probability of detecting, with 90% confidence, an 18% change in population size, based on trend counts from consecutive years. This statement must be used with caution because Nichols' (1980) study was not designed to measure precision in this way, and precision may vary greatly among local populations. However, Nichols' data illustrate that aerial trend counts of mountain goats may not be sensitive to fairly significant changes

in goat abundance, even when flying and observing conditions are selected for consistency. The possibility that ground-based counts will be equally imprecise should be evaluated.

In mostly forested areas, early spring counts of goats on winter ranges have been favored (Smith 1976; Bone 1978). Counts are best made after most snow has melted and goats are easier to observe, but before the animals leave their winter ranges. Successive trend counts may be difficult within this short period.

Midsummer has been preferred for trend counts in areas where goats form large bands on alpine tundra (Ballard 1977; Hall 1977; Nichols 1980). Large bands may develop after the kidding season and can more easily be observed after most snowfields have melted. Nichols (1980) preferred overcast skies, soft light, and no turbulence for these aerial counts. Adult male goats, which are more solitary than other sex-age classes, may be under-represented in counts taken in midsummer (Risenhoover and Bailey 1982a; Foster 1982).

Census. A known minimum population of mountain goats may be determined by using the largest number of goats seen in several successive counts. If animals are classified, the cohort-completion method may provide a larger known minimum population. With this method, the largest number of goats seen in each age class (rarely, sex-age class) is determined and the numbers summed (Smith 1976). Known minimum populations are used as bases for conservative harvest strategies.

Use of the highest count from several successive counts within a season may enhance precision for detecting among-years trends in goat numbers (year-to-year variation among highest counts may be less than among single counts made each year). In practice, the precision of the annual highest count method has been evaluated subjectively. Accuracy is unknown, but actual populations must be underestimated in almost every case.

Adams and Bailey (1982) used marked goats and the Peterson Estimator to census a Colorado herd. With this method, accuracy will be enhanced if animals from all herd segments are marked. Adult males and females should be marked proportionally to their occurrence in the herd (Risenhoover and Bailey 1982a). The possibility of marking goats in more than one geographic segment of the herd should also be considered. The second sample used to estimate the proportion of marked goats in the herd should be based on observations throughout the study area.

Marking a large proportion of a goat herd will seldom be possible. Consequently, the precision of a population estimate will be poor and confidence limits (Bailey 1951) high whenever a single second sample is used. Precision can be enhanced indefinitely by using numerous second samples, resulting in replicated population estimates. With replications, the population is estimated by the mean of successive estimates, and confidence limits are based on the number and variance of the estimates, using common t-statistics.

Animal Condition. Foster (1978) reviewed the concepts of animal condition and population quality in relation to mountain goats. Presumably, measures of animal condition commonly used for ungulates, such as body size, growth rates, skeletal ratios, and measures of fat reserves, can be applied to goats. However, these methods have seldom been used, partly because large samples of goat carcasses have seldom been available. It would be useful to obtain and report such data so that inter- and intrapopulation variation can be evaluated.

Foster (1978) evaluated horn dimensions as possibly useful measurements of population quality in mountain goats. Results were largely inconclusive. The most useful horn dimension measurements may be (1) horn growth in the first 2 years of life (which can be measured in goats over 2 years old because the second horn annulus is distinct) and (2) a ratio of horn length to ear length for kids and yearlings, when data are collected in the same month each year. For 2-year old goats, at least, horn lengths are different between sexes. Thus, populations should be compared by using data from one sex for each comparison. Lastly, intrapopulation variation of horn growth may be so large that the horn measurements for comparing populations will be invalid.

Population Structure. Mountain goat females are not expected to breed before they are 2½ years old, nor kid before they are 3 years old. Consequently, classification by sex and by four age classes is desirable, especially if a ratio of kids to breeding nannies is to provide an index of current production. However, such detailed classification is practical only in intensive, local studies. Not only are yearlings and, especially, 2-year olds difficult to distinguish in some situations, but a lack of strong sexual dimorphism further complicates classification. Nichols (1980), Chadwick (1983), and Smith (unpubl. ms.) have provided descriptions of the eight sex-age classes of goats and Foster (1978) illustrated their horn characteristics.

The difficulty in distinguishing age classes of goats varies with season and with the distance and duration of observation. Often, midsummer is best for distinguishing kids and yearlings from older goats. Kids usually become more visible in July, and yearlings are especially easily distinguished by size alone until about September. Adult males may be distinguished by their advanced molt in midsummer (Nichols 1980) but may be under-represented in samples taken during this time (Foster 1982; Risenhoover and Bailey 1982a).

Small, randomly taken samples from a goat herd will provide highly variable estimates of age structure. Thus, biologists should not rely on classification data unless a large proportion of the herd can be classified.

When data are limited, the simplest age ratio is the kid to older goat ratio (where older goats include yearlings, 2-year olds, and adults of both sexes). This ratio is not a precise indicator of current reproductive success since variation in the sex ratio and in the numbers of nonbreeding older goats will distort the ratio. However, this ratio has reflected herd age (recently transplanted herds having higher ratios) and winter weather (Bailey and Johnson 1977; Adams and Bailey 1982). The ratio has also been used to estimate numbers of kids in estimated herd sizes (Adams and Bailey 1982).

With more detailed classifications of goats in local herds, population models may be constructed. Nichols (1980) used aerial surveys in spring to estimate the proportion of yearlings and aerial surveys in summer to estimate herd size and the proportions of kids and adult males. He then used data from successive years to simulate herd dynamics. Simulations provided estimates of the numbers of 2-year olds in a herd each year. By subtraction, the number of breeding-age females was estimated, and a kid to breeding-age nanny ratio determined. Nichols suggested this ratio will be correlated with population trend. The accuracy of this approach was untested.

Rocky Mountain goat; nanny and kid.

Behavioral Indexes. Petocz (1973) suggested that conflicts (agonistic behavior) among mountain goats may indicate the degree of resource deprivation. Risenhoover and Bailey (1985a) speculated that average group size may be correlated with forage abundance and continuity.

Discussion. A primary management concern is overharvest of mountain goats when access to their habitats has been improved by new roads (Foster 1977; Kuck 1977a,b; Adams and Bailey 1982; Chadwick 1983). Appropriate levels of harvest could be achieved if (1) annual data on population size and productivity are known, (2) harvest levels can be regulated on a local basis, and (3) illegal kill can be controlled. However, these requirements are often impractical.

The effects of removing vegetation from mountain goat habitat, such as by logging or fire, are unclear. In addition, the effects may differ between coastal and interior ranges (Hebert and Turnbull 1977), especially on winter ranges, where detrimental effects would most likely occur. Near the Pacific Coast, for example, forest removal may be detrimental to winter ranges.

Interior winter ranges often support sparse stands of trees or shrubs that are used for forage. The steep slopes of these winter ranges are often used by mountain goats for their snow-shedding characteristics (Kuck 1977a; Adams and Bailey 1980). Removing forage in these areas may affect forage resources, shelter, or snow-shedding characteristics.

Some goat populations are small and isolated (Smith and Raedeke 1982; Smith 1982), and gene flow among such populations seems infrequent. Any human activities (e.g., harvest, habitat alteration) may inhibit goat movements, especially among males, thus increasing possibilities for inbreeding.

Mountain goats are known to travel long distances to visit natural licks or artificially established salt licks (Singer 1975; Hebert and Turnbull 1977; Thompson and Guenzel 1978; Adams et al. 1982). The possibility that a sparse distribution of licks may limit the distribution or productivity of goats has not been tested.

Muskox

The muskox (*Ovibos moschatus*) is a boreal species whose numbers and distribution were greatly reduced in the 1800s and early 1900s. Since then, the management of muskoxen has been a conservation success story. Hunting prohibitions and successful transplants have restored populations to the point where limited harvests are now possible in Alaska, Canada, and Greenland. The species has also been a focus of study in efforts to produce a new domestic animal for rural economies of circumpolar nations (Lent 1971, 1978; Coady and Hinman 1984; Wilkinson and Teal 1984).

Muskoxen live 20 years or more and were once thought to have extremely low reproductive rates. New evidence demonstrates that while rates are relatively low compared with ungulates that may produce twins or triplets, they are considerably higher than was once thought (Lent 1978).

Habitat Requirements and Analysis. The native range of muskoxen is primarily in the high arctic, a zone distinguished by very low precipitation, shallow snow cover, and patchy distribution of snow from winds. Many areas where muskoxen have been introduced are subject to much greater winter snow accumulation or maritime climates, having icing conditions in winter or spring (Lono 1960; Spencer and Lensink 1970; Lent 1974b, 1978). Thus identification, monitoring, and protection of suitable winter habitat have been important and will be increasingly important as introduced populations expand.

Riparian areas with shrubs are preferred summer habitats in Alaska (Lent 1978; Robus 1984). Wet habitats with sedges (*Carex* sp.) also receive heavy use in summer. Both Parker and Ross (1976) and Thing (1984) contend that such meadows are important to this species for weight gain and development of fat reserves in summer. In general, caribou and muskoxen rarely compete in areas where they occur together (Wilkinson et al. 1976; Thomas and Edmonds 1984).

Peter C. Lent

Musk-ox herd on tundra.

Few measurements of muskox habitat have conclusively related to habitat quality. The importance of wet meadows and riparian strips has already been referred to. In the arctic, remote sensing techniques provided opportunities to map such features on a large scale (U.S. Department of the Interior, Fish and Wildlife Service 1983). Home ranges that provide a variety of habitats in summer seem important because muskoxen can take advantage of successive peaks in forage quality.

In winter, forage availability is the key habitat requirement. Regions with low precipitation and low and stable temperature regimes are crucial. Methods for monitoring and mapping tundra vegetation and for mapping and measuring snow-cover features have been treated in Chapter 8, Tundra.

Population Measurements. Since the early studies by Vibe (1958, 1967) and Tener (1965), through the work of Spencer and Lensink (1970), up to the most recent censuses (Lassen 1984), the total count method has been generally used in obtaining muskox population estimates. The reasons for this are several: muskoxen occur in relatively low numbers; they are large and conspicuous in typically treeless habitats; and in winter, they are highly clumped in their distribution and comparatively sedentary. In a few cases, sampling on transects has been used to estimate populations (Gunn et al. 1984).

Total counts provide little opportunity to assess sample error except through successive counts over short periods. Spencer and Lensink (1970), working from snow machines on Nunivak Island where snow conditions lead to extreme clumping of the population, believed they counted essentially the entire population.

Such ground counts and even low-level aerial surveys, especially with helicopters, are also useful in obtaining sex and age composition data. After some training, an observer can accurately identify the sex of all animals, 1 year and older, and determine, by year, the age of animals up to 4 years old (Allen 1913; Smith 1976). Low-level aerial photography has also been used for this purpose (U.S. Department of the Interior, Fish and Wildlife Service 1983).

Sex and age structure of groups may be determined in the field by experienced observers. This is done by referencing horn development with the sexual dimorphism associated with horn boss and curvature. Adults may be aged up to the fifth year. Line drawings in Smith (1976) and photographs in Pohle (1981) serve as useful points of reference. Calf and yearling counts can generally be obtained with ease, although tight bunching behavior may be a problem when observing young calves.

Cementum annuli in incisors have been used to determine age at death. Lent (1974c) concluded that this technique was fairly reliable. However, Gronquist and Dinneford (1984), working with 18 known-age specimens, half of which were from animals raised in captivity, concluded that the technique underestimated true age and had low reliability. Lent (1974c) and Parker et al. (1975) have used femur marrow lipid analyses to assess levels of malnutrition and starvation in populations.

Discussion. The most important management consideration for muskoxen is the identification and protection of suitable winter habitat. This must be accomplished before muskoxen are transplanted. Protection of such areas of stable winter conditions and forage availability is crucial to long-term management success (Thomas et al. 1981).

Mountain Sheep

The mountain sheep comprise two species, *Ovis canadensis* and *O. dalli*, the bighorn and thinhorn sheep, respectively (Geist 1971a). Mountain sheep are distributed in mountains and rugged terrain from Mexico to Alaska. Their recent research and management is reported in the annual proceedings of the Desert Bighorn Council and the Biennial Symposium of the Northern Wild Sheep and Goat Council.

Habitat Requirements and Analysis. The evolutionary history, anatomy, and behavior of mountain sheep, especially bighorn sheep, suggest that they are best adapted to living in moderately large social groups in open habitats, on or near steep, rugged terrain. Specific habitat resources for mountain sheep are—

- forage of adequate quality and of adequate density and continuity to support a large group;
- water;
- salt licks;
- good visibility for predator detection and for visual communication;
- steep, usually rocky, escape terrain; and
- a suitable thermal environment.

Favorable combinations of these resources exist in a patchy distribution. Consequently, the annual ranges of mountain sheep populations tend to consist of up to seven or more seasonal ranges (Geist 1971a) and their connecting migration corridors (Ough and deVos 1984). Commonly, an annual range includes separate winter, spring (green-up), and summer ranges for rams and ewe-juvenile groups, and a lambing area. Seasonally critical areas, generally within these ranges, provide salt licks or, in arid country, water sources. When seasonal ranges are large and dispersed over a large range of elevation, sheep have options for avoiding harassment and for selecting elevations and aspects to improve their foraging and thermal environments.

Mountain sheep are adaptable foragers. Their food habits vary greatly among regions and seasons (Todd 1972; Browning and Monson 1980; Cooperrider et al. 1980). In northern areas, grasses tend to dominate sheep diets, especially during spring, summer, and fall, and modest amounts of browse are eaten in winter when snow inhibits use of herbs. By contrast, desert bighorn, and Rocky Mountain bighorn at low elevations, may browse abundantly on twigs or leaves in any season. While species compositions of mountain sheep diets are inconsistent, three characteristics are common to quality forage resources: abundance, continuous distribution, and low stature. Forage abundance and continuity are needed to support at least modest group sizes; to allow individuals within groups to be dispersed, thus alleviating social interference with foraging and enhancing predator detection; and to allow efficient rates of forage intake (Dale and Bailey 1982). Low-growing forage does not interfere with vision, thus allowing for predator detection and visual communication among sheep. Grasses are the epitome of abundant, continuous, low-growing forage, but dense stands of forbs or low shrubs may also be excellent forage.

Water and mineral licks are seasonally critical resources. Sodium and magnesium seem to be key components of licks used by ungulates, especially during plant growth season in moist climates (Jones and Hanson 1985). Water sources and mineral licks can be created and maintained in sheep management. Mountain sheep are especially favored when these sources are located in open areas near escape terrain, when human activity is kept at a distance and livestock are fenced from the site.

The predator-evasion strategy of mountain sheep requires visibility and escape terrain (Risenhoover and Bailey 1985b). These habitat characteristics are especially important to ewes with lambs. Rams are more prone to use areas lacking these security factors. In addition, sheep may forego security to use critical water sources, salt licks, or necessary migration corridors. Visibility and escape terrain have compensating effects on security. Poor visibility is acceptable on steep terrain; sheep will forage farther from escape terrain when visibility is good.

Lambing areas are usually the largest areas of rugged, steep terrain within the annual range of a population. They are often near water.

In both hot and cold climates, mountain sheep will avoid extreme temperatures and wind chills by varying their daily activity pattern and by selecting favorable environments. They may use elevation, aspect, terrain wind-shadow, tree shade (especially in open forests near or on steep terrain), and rock overhangs or caves to advantage (Simmons 1969). Often, selection of elevation or aspect provides advantages of forage quality or snow scarcity, as well as thermal advantages (Hebert 1973; Shannon et al. 1975).

Land areas are evaluated as habitat for mountain sheep when ranges are not occupied by sheep, but are candidates for a transplanted herd or candidates for habitat improvement to encourage range expansion by an established herd. Land areas can also be evaluated when ranges are occupied by sheep if range condition and trend are to be monitored or the qualities of ranges are to be compared so disruptive developments or habitat degradations can be directed toward less valuable sheep range.

If the seasonal ranges, water sources, mineral licks, lambing areas, and migration corridors for an existing herd are unknown, first consideration should be given to a telemetry study for locating these areas. This information will be needed if range condition is to be monitored. It will also be needed if good range condition is to be maintained or protected from development or habitat manipulation.

Range Assessments. Hansen (1980), Grunigen (1980), and Holl (1982) published methods for evaluating land areas as habitat for bighorn sheep. These methods have not been verified with test applications outside the areas where they were developed. In these methods, habitat components indicating high value as sheep range include—

(1) Abundance of steep escape terrain;

(2) Abundance of certain vegetation types that are low-growing or open and known to provide sheep forage, especially where these types are on or near escape terrain;

(3) Abundance of southerly aspects (this may duplicate information from vegetation types);

(4) Annual precipitation and presence of reliable water sources in arid areas;

(5) Absence of livestock and other human activities and development that would threaten sheep or sheep habitat.

Ratings of such habitat components would not likely be combined in a simple additive model. Absence of a key factor, such as escape terrain or water, may severely limit the value of a range, regardless of high ratings for other factors.

Desert bighorn sheep on escape terrain.

When the objective of range assessment is to monitor habitat condition and trend, data on habitat condition should be obtained primarily from—

(1) Areas known to be used by sheep;

(2) Areas on or within 250 m (825 ft) of steep, rocky terrain;

(3) The most likely migration corridors between seasonal ranges (shortest routes, with good visibility, over escape terrain or along ridges); and

(4) Areas including potential water sources or mineral licks.

Habitat Component Assessments. Escape terrain is the most consistent feature of mountain sheep habitat. However, most biologists have identified escape terrain subjectively, usually describing it as steep (> 80% slope), broken, or rocky terrain, usually including cliffs. Beasom et al. (1983) offered a method for quantifying land ruggedness. McCollough et al. (1980) found the minimum height and length of cliffs used as escape terrain were 8 m (26 ft) and 220 m (726 ft), respectively. Lambing areas are steeper and larger than other acceptable escape terrain. The value of escape terrain will be diminished by visibility-obstructing vegetation or by accumulation of snow on north aspects.

The most important habitats for mountain sheep are on or near escape terrain. Rams, rather than ewes and juveniles, and sheep in large groups, rather than small, will use areas farther from escape terrain. However, out of 13 studies of bighorn sheep surveyed, only one showed more than 10% of the observed groups of sheep over 250 m (825 ft) from escape terrain (Wakelyn 1984). This review indicates that sheep are more restricted to escape terrain than suggested by Van Dyke et al. (1983). Until more definitive studies are reported, range assessment should emphasize areas on or within 250 m (825 ft) of escape terrain.

Visibility is an important habitat component for mountain sheep. It allows for predator detection, visual communication among sheep, and efficient foraging. In addition, open habitats with good visibility may provide abundant forage. In assessing condition and trend of sheep habitats, some measurement or index of visibility should be monitored. However, few objective methods for measuring visibility have been applied to sheep habitat, and no standards for acceptable levels of visibility have been developed. Most often, visibility has been evaluated by rating vegetation types or tree or shrub crown cover (with the more open types or overstories rated as better sheep habitat). Risenhoover and Bailey (1985b) estimated visibility as the percentage of the compass over which an object, 1 m (3.3 ft) tall, could be seen at 40 m (132 ft). A more objective, but more expensive, method would involve using a density board (Gysel and Lyon 1980).

In arid ranges, the distribution of water may limit bighorn habitat. Best water sources are near escape terrain in areas allowing good visibility, located or fenced so livestock competition or human activity did not discourage use by sheep. In dry seasons, most desert bighorn have been observed within 1.6 to 2.4 km (0.96 to 1.4 mi.) of water (Leslie and Douglas 1979; Elenowitz 1984).

Forage resources for mountain sheep have been evaluated at two levels. In the simplest approach, vegetation types have been numerically rated as forage resources, based on local experience (Hansen 1980; Van Dyke et al. 1983). These ratings may be influenced not only by forage values, but also by expected visibility and proximity to escape terrain for each vegetation type.

At a higher level of resolution, forage resources may be evaluated by measuring abundance, species composition, and plant use on selected areas. Interpretation of species composition data will require a classification of forage species based on local studies of sheep food habits and preferences. In the western U.S., monitoring forage condition and trend on critical ranges of wild ungulates in this way has been traditional. These detailed measurements of forage condition and trend can be useful in managing sheep when the numbers and productivity of sheep are limited by forage resources and forage conditions are determined by manageable factors (either the density of foraging ungulates or plant succession). In contrast, sheep populations may be controlled by factors such as predation, disease, or accidents and forage conditions may be controlled largely by the density-independent influences of weather. Expensive systems for detailed measurement of forage condition and trend should not be established without considering the potential value of the information to be obtained.

Population Measurements.

Relative Density. Trends in sheep populations have long been evaluated by counting animals on key areas (winter ranges, at water holes) or along transects observed from aircraft, vehicles, or on foot. Resulting data provide minimum population sizes and estimates of population sex-age structure. On key areas or with small herds, counts of animals may include nearly the entire population, though this assumption is best tested with marked animals.

Trend counts have not usually been considered for year-to-year population monitoring. Repeated

Ram, ewe, and lamb herd.

counts within years will be needed to evaluate sampling variations (measure the standard count deviations) so trends occurring over a few years can be detected. Repeated counts should be taken several days apart to allow for independence. Selection of standard weather conditions for making counts may reduce variation among counts and improve the ability to detect trends. Without repeated counts within years, only long-term trends may be evaluated statistically (Harris 1986).

Trend counts may be biased if changes in animal-observability are correlated with population trend. This could occur if some animals alter their habitat selection or their distribution in relation to counting areas, in response to changing population size.

Census. On key areas, repeated classifications of sheep may be used to produce a known, minimum population size. Since sheep may be counted by several sex-age classes, the cohort-completion method (summing the maximum unduplicated count for each class) may be advantageous. Largest counts are obtained when several key areas, such as lambing areas, winter ranges or rutting areas, or waterholes, are well-known for the herd.

With a known number of marked sheep in the population, a herd may be estimated by a Petersen estimate or a similar method (Furlow et al. 1981). Unless a large proportion of the herd can be marked, the precision of a Petersen estimate is best controlled by using several second samples of the marked to unmarked ratio. Variances among several resulting estimates may be used to calculate confidence limits. Limits will become narrower as the number of second samples increases.

Most often, all sex-age classes of sheep cannot be marked at random nor in proportion to their numbers in the herd. Consequently, the accuracy of a Petersen estimate will depend on representative second samples. These samples must be distributed over the entire area used by the herd. For many herds, rams and ewes may not be equally sampled except during the rutting or winter seasons. An alternative solution may be to estimate the number of ewes by the Petersen method and to estimate the numbers of lambs, yearlings, and rams by lamb to yearling to ewe and ram to ewe ratios obtained during seasons when unbiased ratios are most likely (as during the rut).

Holl and Bleich (1983) used a variation of the Petersen Estimator requiring concurrent ground-based and helicopter-based counts of sheep to identify duplicate sightings. With this variation, many ground-based counters were necessary.

Population Structure. Mountain sheep may be classified by eight sex-age categories: lambs, yearling males, yearling females, ewes, and four classes of rams based on ¾ curl horn increments. However, yearlings, especially yearling females, may be difficult to distinguish from ewes when they are viewed from a distance or from aircraft. Desert bighorns have relatively asynchronous lambing, and yearling females may vary by 4, 6, or more months. The oldest of these yearling females will be difficult to distinguish from ewes. Consequently, in desert sheep literature, many reported lamb to ewe ratios are based on ewe classes, including nonparous yearlings with ewes. In contrast, lamb to yearling to ewe ratios are routinely reported for northern mountain sheep.

Mountain sheep are social animals even though rams and ewe-juvenile groups use separate ranges during most seasons. This creates special problems in obtaining a representative sample of population sex-age structure. Ram to ewe ratios are best obtained during rutting or perhaps on winter ranges or near water sources in dry seasons, when the distributions of rams and ewes are usually less independent. Sampling the population requires at least one seasonally used range to be well-known. Due to the social patterns of mountain sheep, individuals are unlikely to be classified at random. Consequently, either the social group or all sheep seen on a census route or area should be the sampling unit (Bowden et al. 1984). Whenever a few large groups of sheep have been classified, efforts should continue to find smaller, peripheral groups having differing sex-age structures. If a large proportion of a herd is classified, confidence limits for the resulting sex-age ratios may be narrowed by using statistical methods appropriate for finite populations.

Goodson (1978) reviewed 23 studies of Rocky Mountain bighorn, seeking a correlation between population age structure and population trend. Lamb to ewe ratios showed no correlation, but yearling to ewe ratios were loosely correlated. Yearling to ewe ratios (mean, range/100 ewes) were 9 (0-20) for decreasing herds; 28 (15-56) for stable herds; 31 (20-43) for slightly increasing herds; and 52 (41-61) for strongly increasing herds. Since mortality rates are seldom known, these generalizations must be used with caution.

Discussion. Habitat loss from expanding human activities is the most widespread threat to mountain sheep. In the past, impacts of habitat degradation and expanding human activity have rarely been mitigated. There may be frequent opportunities to mitigate for habitat impacts by scheduling threatening activities to avoid critical periods (e.g., lambing) or by improving and expanding off-site habitat. Mitigation, however, remains largely untested. Furthermore, with habitat impacts, opportunities for poaching are often increased and cannot be mitigated.

Bighorn sheep in open habitat.

Harvest of mountain sheep is usually conservative, with only older rams being legal. However, Heimer et al. (1984) and Geist (1971b) questioned the harvest of rams smaller than full curl.

Disease is a common problem with bighorn sheep. Rocky Mountain and California bighorn have suffered spectacular all-age dieoffs from pneumonia (Stelfox 1971; Feuerstein et al. 1980; Foreyt and Jessup 1982; Spraker et al. 1984; Onderka and Wishart 1984); scabies caused an all-age dieoff in desert bighorn (Lange et al. 1980). Chronic lamb mortality is common in Rocky Mountain and desert bighorn (Spraker and Hibler 1977, 1982; DeForge et al. 1982). Chronic sinusitis and contagious ecthyma are additional problems (Bunch et al. 1978; Samuel et al. 1975; Lance et al. 1981). Factors predisposing sheep to diseases have been proximity to livestock, especially domestic sheep (Goodson 1982), and various stressors resulting from habitat loss, concentration of animals, and harassment from human activities in critical areas or small ranges. In addition, mountain sheep may not have had a long evolutionary history with many diseases they now face, especially in southern latitudes and where livestock or exotic ungulates have been introduced (Geist 1985).

Lack of water is another limiting factor for desert bighorn herds and may also influence the distribution of Rocky Mountain bighorn at low elevations. Development of artificial water sources is prominent in desert bighorn management (Graf 1980).

In the forested ranges of Rocky Mountain bighorn, succession has gradually degraded many bighorn ranges (Wakelyn 1984; Risenhoover and Bailey 1985). Encroachment by trees, combined with man-made habitat losses, has reduced the sizes of seasonal ranges, interrupted migration corridors, and isolated herds. The result has been many small sedentary herds with few options to move in response to weather or human activity. Such small isolated herds may also suffer from inbreeding and depression of reproduction and survival (Soule and Wilcox 1980; Sausman 1982). In forested regions, there should be abundant opportunities to expand sheep ranges and to mitigate for habitat losses by vegetation management, especially with prescribed fire.

Much effort is expended trapping and transplanting bighorn into historic ranges from which they have been extirpated (Schmidt et al. 1978; Wilson et al. 1980; Dodd 1983; Fuller 1984; Bates et al. 1985). Rocky Mountain bighorn are also baited and treated for lungworms (Schmidt et al. 1979). However, long-term effects of these management activities have not always been monitored.

Lamb/ewe group.

LITERATURE CITED

ADAMS, L. 1981. Ecology and population dynamics of mountain goats, Sheep Mountain-Gladstone Ridge, Colorado. M.S. thesis, Colorado State Univ., Fort Collins. 189pp.

ADAMS, L.G. and J.A. BAILEY. 1980. Winter habitat selection and group size of mountain goats, Sheep Mountain-Gladstone Ridge, Colorado. Pages 465-481 *in* Hickey, W.O., ed. Proc. Biennial Symp., Northern Wild Sheep and Goat Council. Salmon, ID.

———— and ————. 1982. Population dynamics of mountain goats in the Sawatch Range, Colorado. J. Wildl. Manage. 46:1003-1009.

———— and ————. 1983. Winter forages of mountain goats in central Colorado. J. Wildl. Manage. 46:1237-1243.

————, M.A. MASTELLER, and J.A. BAILEY. 1982a. Movements and home range of mountain goats, Sheep Mountain-Gladstone Ridge, Colorado. Pages 391-405 *in* Bailey, J.A. and G.G. Schoonveld, eds. Proc. Third Biennial Symp., Northern Wild Sheep and Goat Council. Fort Collins, CO.

————, K.L. RISENHOOVER, and J.A. BAILEY. 1982b. Ecological relationships of mountain goats and Rocky Mountain bighorn sheep. Pages 9-22 *in* Bailey, J.A. and G.G. Schooneld, eds. Proc. Third Biennial Symp., Northern Wild Sheep and Goat Council. Fort Collins, CO.

ALLEN, A.W., J.G. COOK, and M.J. ARMBRUSTER. 1984. Habitat suitability index models: Pronghorn. U.S. Dep. Inter., Fish and Wildl. Serv. FWS/OBS-82/10.65. WELUT, Fort Collins, CO. 23pp.

ALLEN, E.O. 1977. A new perspective for elk habitat management. Proc. Western Assoc. Fish and Game Comm. 195-205.

ALLEN, J.A. 1913. Ontogenetic and other variations in muskoxen with a systematic review of the muskox group, recent and extinct. Memoirs Am. Mus. Nat. Hist., Vol. 1, Part IV:103-226.

ANDERSON, A.E., D.E. MEDIN, and D.C. BOWDEN. 1972. Mule deer numbers and shrub-yield-utilization on winter range. J. Wildl. Manage. 36:571-578.

AUTENRIETH, R., ed. 1978. Guidelines for the management of pronghorn antelope. Pages 472-526 *in* Barrett, M.W., ed. Proc. Eighth Biennial Pronghorn Antelope Workshop. Alberta Recreation, Parks, and Wildlife, Fish and Wildlife Division.

BAILEY, J.A. 1984. Principles of wildlife management. John Wiley and Sons, New York, NY. 373pp.

———— and A.Y. COOPERRIDER. 1982. Final Report: Trickle Mountain Research Study. U.S. Dep. Inter., Bur. Land Manage., Denver Service Center, Denver, CO. 137pp.

———— and B.K. JOHNSON. 1977. Status of introduced mountain goats in the Sawatch Range of Colorado. Pages 54-63 *in* Samuel, W. and W.G. MacGregor, eds. Proc. First Int. Mountain Goat Symp. Kalispell, MT.

———— and G.G. SCHOONVELD, eds. 1982. Northern wild sheep and goat council. Proc. Third Biennial Symp. Fort Collins, CO. 405pp.

BAILEY, N.T.J. 1951. On estimating the size of mobile populations from recapture data. Biometrika 38:293-306.

BALLARD, W. 1977. Status and management of the mountain goat in Alaska. Pages 15-23 *in* Samuel, W. and W.G. MacGregor, eds. Proc. First Int. Mountain Goat Symp. Kalispell, MT. 243pp.

BANFIELD, A.W.F. 1962. A revision of the reindeer and caribou, Genus *Rangifer*. Natl. Mus. Canada Bull. 177. Ottawa. 137pp.

BARTMANN, R.M. 1974. Piceance deer study—population density and structure. Colorado Div. Wildl. Game Res. Rep., July. Part 2:363-380.

BATES, J.W., Jr., J.W. BATES, and J.G. GUYMON. 1985. Comparison of drive nets and darting for capture of desert bighorn sheep. Wildl. Soc. Bull. 13:73-76.

BEAR, G.D. and R.A. GREEN. 1980. Elk population and ecology studies. Colorado Div. Wildl., Wildl. Res. Rep., July. Part 2:221-313.

BEASOM, S.L., E.P. WIGGERS, and J.R. GIARDINO. 1983. A technique for assessing land surface ruggedness. J. Wildl. Manage. 47:1163-1166.

BELOVSKY, G.E. 1978. Diet optimization in a generalist herbivore: The moose. Theoretical Population Biol. 14:105-134.

BERGERUD, A.T. 1963. Aerial winter census of caribou. J. Wildl. Manage. 27:438-449.

————. 1978. Caribou. Pages 83-101 *in* Schmidt, J.L. and D.L. Gilbert, eds. Big Game of North America: Ecology and Management. The Wildl. Manage. Inst., Washington, DC. and Stackpole Books, Harrisburg, PA.

————. 1979. Caribou. Pages 83-102 *in* Schmidt, J.L. and D.L. Gilbert, eds. Big Game of North America: Ecology and Management. Stackpole Books, New York, NY. 494pp.

BISSONETTE, J.A. 1976. The relationship of resource quality and availability to social behavior and organization in the collared peccary. PhD dissertation, Univ. Michigan, Ann Arbor. 137pp.

————. 1982. Collared peccary. Pages 841-850 *in* Chapman, J.A. and G.A. Feldhamer, eds. Wild Mammals of North America. The Johns Hopkins Univ. Press, Baltimore, MD.

BLACK, H., R.J. SCHERZINGER, and J.W. THOMAS. 1976. Relationships of Rocky Mountain elk and Rocky Mountain mule deer habitat to timber management in the Blue Mountains of Oregon and Washington. Proc. Elk-Logging-Roads Symp. Univ. Idaho, Moscow:11-31.

BONE, J.N. 1978. Status of the mountain goat (*Oreamnos americanus*) of the Similkameen River, British Columbia. Biennial Symp., Northern Wild Sheep and Goat Council 1:123-130.

BOWDEN, D.C., A.E. ANDERSON, and D.E. MEDIN. 1984. Sampling plans for mule deer sex and age ratios. J. Wildl. Manage. 48:500-509.

BOYD, R.J. 1958. Comparison of air and ground deer and elk counts. Colorado Dep. Game and Fish Quarterly Progress Rep. Oct:145-146.

————. 1970. Elk of the White River Plateau, Colorado. Colorado Game, Fish, and Parks Dep. Tech. Publ. 25. 126pp.

————. 1978. American elk. Pages 10-29 *in* Schmidt, J.L. and D.L. Gilbert, eds. Big Game of North America: Ecology and Management. The Wildl. Manage. Inst., Washington, DC. and Stackpole Books, Harrisburg, PA.

————, T.M. POJAR, and B.D. BAKER. 1975. Deer and elk management study. Colorado Div. Wildl. Game Res. Rep., July. Part 2:365-412.

BRANDBORG, S.M. 1955. Life history and management of the mountain goat in Idaho. Idaho Dep. Fish and Game Wildl. Bull. 2. 142pp.

BRASSARD, J.M., E. AUDY, M. CRETE, and P. GRENIER. 1974. Distribution and winter habitat of moose in Quebec. Naturaliste Canadien 101:67-80.

BROWNING, B.M. and G. MONSON. 1980. Food. Pages 80-99 *in* Monson, G. and L. Sumner, eds. The Desert Bighorn. Univ. Arizona Press, Tucson. 370pp.

BUNCH, T.D., S.R. PAUL, and H.E. McCUTCHEN. 1978. Chronic sinusitis in desert bighorn sheep (*Ovis canadensis nelsoni*). Trans. Desert Bighorn Council 22:16-20.

BURNHAM, K.P., D.R. ANDERSON, and J.L. LAAKE. 1980. Estimation of density from line transect sampling of biological populations. Wildl. Monogr. 72. 202pp.

CALEF, G. and D.C. HEARD. 1980. The status of three tundra wintering caribou herds in northeastern mainland Northwest Territories. Pages 582-594 *in* Reimers, E., E. Gaare, and S. Skjenneberg, eds. Proc. Second Int. Reindeer/Caribou Symp. Dir. for Vilt og Ferskvannsfisk, Trondheim.

CAMERON, R.D. and K.R. WHITTEN. 1979. Seasonal movements and sexual segregation of caribou determined by aerial survey. J. Wildl. Manage. 43:626-633.

CAUGHLEY, G. 1977. Analysis of vertebrate populations. John Wiley and Sons, New York, NY. 234pp.

———. 1979. "What is this thing called carrying capacity?" Pages 2-8 *in* Boyce, M.S. and L.D. Hayden-Wing, eds. North American Elk: Ecology, Behavior, and Management. Univ. Wyoming, Laramie. 294pp.

CHADWICK, D.H. 1983. A beast the color of winter. Sierra Club, San Francisco, CA. 208pp.

COADY, J.W. and R.A. HINMAN. 1984. Management of muskoxen in Alaska. Pages 47-51 *in* Klein, D.R., R.G. White, and S. Keller, eds. Proc. First Int. Muskox Symp. Spec. Rep., Biol. Pap. Univ. Alaska, Fairbanks.

COLLINS, W.B. and P.J. URNESS. 1979. Elk pellet group distributions and rates of deposition in aspen and lodgepole pine habitats. Pages 140-144 *in* Boyce, M.S., and L.D. Hayden-Wing, eds. North American Elk: Ecology, Behavior, and Management. Univ. Wyoming, Laramie. 294pp.

CONLEY, W. 1978. Population modeling. Pages 305-320 *in* Schmidt, J.L. and D.L. Gilbert, eds. Big Game of North America: Ecology and Management. Stackpole Books, New York, NY. 494pp.

CONNOLLY, G.E. 1981. Trends in populations and harvests. Pages 225-243 *in* Wallmo, O.C., ed. Mule and Black-tailed Deer of North America. Univ. Nebraska Press, Lincoln. 605pp.

COOPERRIDER, A.Y. 1982. Forage allocation for elk and cattle. Pages 142-149 *in* Britt, T.L., and D.P. Theobald, eds., Proc. Western States Elk Workshop, February 22-24, 1982. Flagstaff, AZ. 166pp.

——— and J.A. BAILEY. 1984. A simulation approach to forage allocation. Pages 525-559 *in* Developing Strategies for Rangeland Management. Rep. prepared by the Committee on Developing Strategies for Rangeland Manage. Natl. Res. Council/Natl. Acad. Sciences. Westview Press, Boulder, CO. 2022pp.

———, S.A. McCOLLOUGH, and J.A. BAILEY. 1980. Variation in bighorn sheep food habits as measured by fecal analysis. Biennial Symp., Northern Wild Sheep and Goat Council. Salmon, ID. 2:29-41.

DAILEY, T.V., N.T. HOBBS, and T.N. WOODARD. 1984. Experimental comparisons of diet selection by mountain goats and mountain sheep in Colorado. J. Wildl. Manage. 48:799-806.

DALE, A.R. and J.A. BAILEY. 1982. Application of optimal foraging theory for bighorn sheep habitat evaluation. Biennial Symp., Northern Wild Sheep and Goat Council 3:254-261.

DAVIS, J.L. and P. VALKENBERG. 1979. Caribou distribution, population characteristics, mortality and responses to disturbance in northwest Alaska. Chapter 2 *in* Lent, P.C., ed. Studies of Selected Wildlife and Fish Populations on and adjacent to the National Petroleum Reserve, Alaska. U.S. Dep. Inter., Fish and Wildl. Serv., Anchorage, AK. 226pp.

DeFORGE, J.R., D.A. JESSUP, C.W. JENNER, and J.E. SCOTT. 1982. Disease investigations into high lamb mortality of desert bighorn sheep in the Santa Rosa Mountains, California. Desert Bighorn Council Trans. 65-76.

DODD, N.L. 1983. Ideas and recommendations for maximizing desert bighorn transplant efforts. Desert Bighorn Council Trans. 12-16.

DOERR, J. 1979. Population analysis and modeling of the western arctic herd with comparisons to other Alaskan *Rangifer* populations. Unpubl. M.S. thesis, Univ. Alaska, Fairbanks. 341pp.

DONALDSON, B. 1967. Javelina. Pages 88-94 *in* New Mexico Wildlife Management. New Mexico Dep. Game and Fish, Santa Fe.

EDDY, T.A. 1961. Food and feeding patterns of the collared peccary in southern Arizona. J. Wildl. Manage. 25(3):248-257.

EINARSEN, A.S. 1948. The pronghorn antelope and its management. Stackpole Books, Harrisburg, PA. 235pp.

ELENOWITZ, A. 1984. Group dynamics and habitat use of transplanted desert bighorn sheep in the Peloncillo Mountains, New Mexico. Desert Bighorn Council 28:1-8.

ELLISOR, J.E. and W.F. HARWELL. 1979. Ecology and management of javelina in south Texas. F.A. Rep., Series 16. Texas Parks and Wildl. Dep., Austin. 25pp.

ERIKSSON, O. 1980. A method for range appraisal using small aircraft for sampling of vegetation data. Pages 41-46 *in* Reimers, E., E. Gaare, and S. Skjenneberg, eds. Proc. Second Int. Reindeer/Caribou Symp. Dir. for Vilt og Ferskvannsfisk, Trondheim.

FEUERSTEIN, V., R.L. SCHMIDT, C.P. HIBLER, and W.H. RUTHERFORD. 1980. Bighorn sheep mortality in the Taylor River-Almont Triangle Area, 1978-1979. A case study. Colorado Div. Wildl. Spec. Rep. 48. 19pp.

FICHTER, E. 1974. On the bedding behaviour of pronghorn fawns. Pages 352-355 *in* Geist, V. and F. Walther, eds. The Behaviour of Ungulates and Its Relation to Management. IUCN Publ. New Series 24. 941pp.

FOREYT, W.J. and D.A. JESSUP. 1982. Fatal pneumonia of bighorn sheep following association with domestic sheep. J. Wildl. Diseases 18:163-168.

FOSTER, B.R. 1977. Historical patterns of mountain goat harvest in British Columbia. Pages 147-159 *in* Samuel, W. and W. MacGregor, eds. Proc. First Int. Mountain Goat Symp. Kalispell, MT.

———. 1978. Horn growth and quality management for mountain goats. Pages 200-226 *in* Hebert, D.M. and M. Nation, eds. Proc. 1978 Northern Wild Sheep and Goat Conf. Penticton, British Columbia.

———. 1982. Observability and habitat characteristics of the mountain goat in west-central British Columbia. M.S. thesis, Univ. British Columbia, Vancouver. 134pp.

FOWLER, C.W. and T.D. SMITH, eds. 1981. Dynamics of large mammal populations. John Wiley and Sons, New

York, NY. 477pp.

FOX, J.L. and R.D. TABER. 1981. Site selection by mountain goats wintering in forest habitat. U.S. Dep. Agric., For. Serv., Pacific Northwest For. and Range Experiment Sta., Juneau, AK. 55pp.

———, K.J. RAEDEKE, and C.A. SMITH. 1982. Mountain goat ecology on Cleveland Peninsula, Alaska, 1980-1982. U.S. Dep. Agric., For. Serv., Pacific Northwest For. and Range Experiment Sta., Juneau, AK. 41pp.

FRANZMANN, A.W. 1978. Moose. Pages 67-82 in Schmidt, J.L. and D.L. Gilbert, eds. Big Game of North America. Stackpole Books, Harrisburg, PA.

———, A. FLYNN, and P.D. ARNESON. 1975. Levels of some mineral elements in Alaskan moose hair. J. Wildl. Manage. 39:374-378.

———, R.E. LeRESCHE, R.A. RAUSCH, and J.L. OLDEMEYER. 1978. Alaskan moose measurements and weights and measurement-weight relationships. Canadian J. Zoology 56:298-306.

FRASER, D., E.R. CHAVEZ, and J.L. PALOHEIMO. 1984. Aquatic feeding by moose: Selection of plant species and feeding areas in relation to plant chemical composition and characteristics of lakes. Canadian J. Zoology 62:80-87.

FREDDY, D.J. and D.C. BOWDEN. 1983a. Efficacy of permanent and temporary pellet plots in juniper-pinyon woodland. J. Wildl. Manage. 47:512-516.

——— and ———. 1983b. Sampling mule deer pellet-group densities in juniper-pinyon woodland. J. Wildl. Manage. 47:476-485.

FULLER, A.F. 1984. Drop net capture of bighorn sheep in Arizona. Desert Bighorn Council Trans. 28:39-40.

FURLOW, R.C., M. HADERLIE, and R. VAN DEN BERGE. 1981. Estimating a bighorn population by mark-recapture. Desert Bighorn Council Trans. 25:31-33.

GASAWAY, W.D., S.D. DUBOIS, and S. HARBO. 1985. Biases in aerial transect surveys for moose during May and June. J. Wildl. Manage. 49:777-784.

GEIST, V. 1971a. Mountain sheep: A study in behavior and evolution. Univ. Chicago Press, IL. 383pp.

———. 1971b. Bighorn sheep biology. The Wildl. Soc. News 136:61.

———. 1981. Behavior—adaptive strategies in mule deer. Pages 157-224 in Wallmo, O.C., ed. Mule and Black-tailed Deer of North America. Univ. Nebraska Press, Lincoln. 605pp.

———. 1985. Pleistocene bighorn sheep: Some problems of adaptation, and relevance to today's American megafauna. Wildl. Soc. Bull. 13:351-359.

GILBERT, J.R. 1978. Estimating population characteristics. Pages 297-304 in Schmidt, J.L. and D.L. Gilbert, eds. Big Game of North America: Ecology and Management. Stackpole Books, New York, NY. 494pp.

GILL, R.B., L.H. CARPENTER, and D.C. BOWDEN. 1983. Monitoring large animal populations—the Colorado experience. Trans. North Am. Wildl. and Nat. Res. Conf. 48:330-341.

GOODSON, N.J. 1978. Status of bighorn sheep in Rocky Mountain National Park. M.S. thesis, Colorado State Univ., Fort Collins. 190pp.

———. 1982. Effects of domestic sheep grazing on bighorn sheep populations: A review. Biennial Symp., Northern Wild Sheep and Goat Council 3:287-313.

GRAF, W. 1980. Habitat protection and improvement. Pages 310-319 in Monson, G. and L. Sumner, eds. The Desert Bighorn. Univ. Arizona Press, Tucson. 370pp.

GRONQUIST, R.M. and W.B. DINNEFORD. 1984. Age determination of muskoxen from dental cementum annuli. Pages 67-68 in Klein, D.R., R.G. White, and S. Keller, eds. Proc. First Int. Muskox Symp. Spec. Rep., Biol. Pap. Univ. Alaska, Fairbanks.

GROSS, J.E. 1970. Program ANPOP. A simulation modeling exercise of the Wichita Mountains National Wildlife Refuge. Colorado Coop. Wildl. Res. Unit Prog. Rep. Colorado State Univ., Fort Collins. 133pp.

GRUNIGEN, R.E. 1980. A system for evaluating potential bighorn sheep transplant sites in northern New Mexico. Biennial Symp., Northern Wild Sheep and Goat Council 2:211-228.

GUNN, A., R. DECKER, and T.W. BARRY. 1984. Pages 67-68 in Klein, D.R., R.G. White, and S. Keller, eds. Proc. First Int. Muskox Symp. Spec. Rep., Biol. Pap. Univ. Alaska, Fairbanks.

GYSEL, L.W. and L.J. LYON. 1980. Habitat analysis and evaluation. Pages 305-327 in Schemnitz, S.D., ed. Wildlife Management Techniques Manual. The Wildl. Soc., Washington, DC. 686pp.

HALL, E.R. and K.R. KELSON. 1959. The mammals of North America. Vol. II:547-1083. The Ronald Press, New York, NY.

HALL, W.K. 1977. Status and management of the Rocky Mountain goat, Oreamnos americanus, in the province of Alberta. Pages 8-14 in Samuel, W. and W.G. MacGregor, eds. Proc. First Int. Mountain Goat Symp. Kalispell, MT. 243pp.

HALLS, L.K. 1984. White-tailed deer: Ecology and Management. Stackpole Books, Harrisburg, PA. 870pp.

HANKS, J. 1981. Characterization of population condition. Pages 47-74 in Fowler, C.W. and T.D. Smith, eds. Dynamics of Large Mammal Populations. John Wiley and Sons, New York, NY. 477 pp.

HANSEN, C.G. 1980a. Habitat. Pages 64-79 in Monson, G. and L. Sumner, eds. The Desert Bighorn—Its Life History, Ecology, and Management. Univ. Arizona Press, Tucson. 370pp.

———. 1980b. Habitat evaluation. Pages 320-335 in Monson, G. and L. Sumner, eds. The Desert Bighorn—Its Life History, Ecology, and Management. Univ. Arizona Press, Tucson. 370pp.

HANSON, W.R. 1963. Calculation of productivity, survival and abundance of selected vertebrates from sex and age ratios. Wildl. Monogr. 9. 60pp.

HARRIS, R.B. 1986. Reliability of trend lines obtained from variable counts. J. Wild. Manage. 50:165-171.

HEBERT, D.M. 1973. Altitudinal migration as a factor in the nutrition of bighorn sheep. PhD dissertation, Univ. British Columbia, Vancouver. 355pp.

——— and M. NATION, eds. 1978. Proceedings of the 1978 northern wild sheep and goat conference. Penticton, British Columbia. 412pp.

——— and W.G. TURNBULL. 1977. A description of southern interior and coastal mountain goat types of British Columbia. Pages 126-159 in Proc. First Inter. Mountain Goat Symp. Kalispell, MT.

HEIB, S.R., ed. 1976. Proceedings of the elk-logging-roads symposium. Univ. Idaho, Moscow. 142pp.

HEIMER, W.E., S.M. WATSON, and T.C. SMITH. 1984. Excess ram mortality in a heavily hunted Dall's sheep population. Biennial Symp., Northern Wild Sheep and Goat Council 4:425-432.

HESSELTON, W.T. and R.M. HESSELTON. 1982. White-tailed deer. Pages 878-901 in Chapman, J.A. and G.A. Feldhamer, eds. Wild Mammals of North America. The Johns Hopkins Univ. Press, Baltimore, MD.

HIBBS, L.D. 1966. A literature review on mountain goat ecology. Colorado Dep. Game, Fish, and Parks Spec. Rep. 8. 23pp.

HICKEY, W.O., ed. 1980. Proceedings of the biennial symposium of the northern wild sheep and goat council. Salmon, ID. 668pp.

HJELJORD, O. 1973. Mountain goat forage and habitat preference in Alaska. J. Wildl. Manage. 37(3):353-362.

HOBBS, N.T., D.L. BAKER, J.E. ELLIS, D.M. SWIFT, and R.A. GREEN. 1982. Energy- and nitrogen-based estimates of elk winter-range carrying capacity. J. Wildl. Manage. 46:12-21.

HOLL, S.A. 1982. Evaluation of bighorn sheep habitat. Desert Bighorn Council Trans. 24:47-49.

——— and V.C. BLEICH. 1983. San Gabriel mountain sheep: Biological and management considerations. U.S. Dep. Agric., For. Serv., San Bernardino National Forest, San Bernardino, CA.

HOOVER, R.L., C.E. TILL, and S. OGILVIE. 1959. The antelope of Colorado. Colorado Dep. of Game and Fish Tech. Bull. 4. Denver, CO. 110pp.

HOREJSI, B.L. 1976. Suckling and feeding behavior in relation to lamb survival in bighorn sheep (Ovis canadensis canadensis Shaw). Unpubl. PhD dissertation, Univ. Calgary. 265pp.

HOUSTON, D.B. 1974. Aspects of the social organization of moose. Pages 690-696 in Geist, V. and F. Walther, eds. The Behaviour of Ungulates and Its Relation to Management. IUCN Publ. New Series 24. 941pp.

JENNINGS, W.S. and J.T. HARRIS. 1953. The collared peccary in Texas. Texas Game and Fish Comm. F.A. Rep. Series 12. 31pp.

JONES, R.L. and H.C. HANSON. 1985. Mineral licks, geophagy, and biogeochemistry of North American ungulates. Iowa State Univ. Press. 302pp.

JORDAN, P.A., D.B. BOTKIN, A.S. DOMINSKI, H.S. LOWENDORF, and G.E. BELOVSKY. 1973. Sodium as a critical nutrient for the moose of Isle Royale. North Am. Moose Conf. 9:13-42.

JUNIPER, I. 1980. Problems in managing an irrupting caribou herd. Pages 722-724 in Reimers, E., E. Gaare, and S. Skjenneberg, eds. Proc. Second Int. Reindeer/Caribou Symp. Dir. for Vilt og Ferskvannsfisk, Trondheim.

KEISS, R.E. 1969. Comparison of eruption-wear patterns and cementum annuli as age criteria in elk. J. Wildl. Manage. 33(1)175-180.

KELSALL, J.P. 1965. The migratory barren-ground caribou of Canada. Dep. of Indian Affairs and Northern Development. Canadian Wildl. Serv., Ottawa. 339pp.

———. 1968. The migratory barren-ground caribou of Canada. Canadian Wildl. Serv. Monogr. 3. Ottawa, Ontario. 340pp.

———. 1969. Structural adaptation of moose and deer for snow. J. Mammal. 50:302-310.

——— and E.S. TELFER. 1974. Biogeography of moose with particular reference to western North America. Naturaliste Canadien 101:117-130.

KERR, R. 1979. Mule deer habitat guidelines. U.S. Dep. Inter., Bur. Land Manage. Tech. Note 366. Service Center, Denver, CO.

KINDSCHY, R.R., C. SUNDSTROM, and J.D. YOAKUM. 1982. Wildlife habitats in managed rangelands—the Great Basin of southeastern Oregon. U.S. Dep. Agric., For. Serv., Pacific Northwest For. and Range Experiment Sta. Gen. Tech. Rep. 145. 18pp.

KLEIN, D.R. 1968. The introduction, increase and crash of reindeer on St. Matthew Island. J. Wildl. Manage. 32:350-367.

———. 1982. Fire, lichens and caribou. J. Range Manage. 35:390-395.

———, R.G. WHITE, and S. KELLER, eds. 1984. Proceedings of first international muskox symposium. Biol. Pap. Univ. Alaska, Fairbanks.

KNIPE, T. 1957. The javelina in Arizona. Arizona Game and Fish Dep. Wildl. Bull. 2.

KONKEL, G.W., ed. 1980. Terrestrial habitat evaluation criteria handbook—Alaska. Div. Ecol. Serv., U.S. Dep. Inter., Fish and Wildl. Serv., Anchorage, AK. (Original not seen; cited and partially reproduced in Mule 1982).

KRAUSMAN, P.R., J.R. MORGART, and M. CHILELLI. 1984. Annotated bibliography of desert bighorn sheep literature, 1897-1983. Southwest Nat. Hist. Assoc., Phoenix, AZ. 204pp.

KUCK, L. 1977a. Status and management of the mountain goat in Idaho. Pages 37-40 in Samuel, W. and W.O. MacGregor, eds. Proc. First Int. Mountain Goat Symp. Kalispell, MT.

———. 1977b. The impact of hunting on Idaho's Pahsimeroi mountain goat herd. Pages 114-125 in Samuel, W. and W.O. MacGregor, eds. Proc. First Int. Mountain Goat Symp. Kalispell, MT.

KUFELD, R.C., J.H. OLTERMAN, and D.C. BOWDEN. 1980. A helicopter quadrat census for mule deer on Uncompahgre Plateau, Colorado. J. Wildl. Manage. 44:632-639.

KUROPAT, P. and J.P. BRYANT. 1980. Foraging behavior of cow caribou on the Utukok calving grounds in Northwestern Alaska. Pages 64-70 in Reimers, E., E. Garre, and S. Skjenneberg, eds. Proc. Second Int. Reindeer/Caribou Symp. Dir. for Vilt og Ferskvannsfisk, Trondheim.

KURT, F. 1968. Das Socialverhalten des Rehes. Eines Feldstudie. P. Parey-Verlag, Berlin. 102pp.

LANCE, W., W. ADRIAN, and B. WIDHALM. 1981. An epizootic of contagious ecthyma in Rocky Mountain bighorn sheep in Colorado. J. Wildl. Diseases 17:601-603.

LANGE, R.E., A. SANDOVAL, and W.P. MELANEY. 1980. Psoroptic scabies in bighorn sheep in New Mexico. J. Wildl. Diseases 16:77-82.

LaPERRIERE, A.J., P.C. LENT, W.C. GASAWAY, and F.A. NODLER. 1980. Use of Landsat data for moose-habitat analyses in Alaska. J. Wildl. Manage. 44:881-887.

LASSEN, P. 1984. Muskox distribution and population structure in Jameson Land, northeast Greenland, 1981-1983. Pages 19-24 in Klein, D.R., R.G. White, and S. Keller, eds. Proc. First Int. Muskox Symp. Spec. Rep., Biol. Pap. Univ. Alaska, Fairbanks.

LEADER-WILLIAMS, N. 1980. Population ecology of reindeer on South Georgia. Pages 664-676 in Reimers, E., E. Gaare, and S. Skjenneberg, eds. Proc. Second Int. Reindeer/Caribou Symp. Dir. for Vilt og Ferskvannsfisk, Trondheim.

LENT, P.C. 1966. The caribou of northwestern Alaska. Pages 481-517 in Reimers, E., E. Gaare, and S. Skjenneberg, eds. Proc. Second Int. Reindeer/Caribou Symp. Dir. for Vilt og Ferskvannsfisk, Trondheim.

———. 1971. Muskox management controversies in North America. Biol. Conserv. 3:255-263.

———. 1974a. Mother-infant relationships in ungulates. Pages 14-55 in Geist, V. and F. Walthers, eds. The Behavior of Ungulates and Its Relation to Management.

Vol. I, IUCN Publ. New Series 24. Morges, Switzerland. 940pp.

———. 1974b. A review of rutting behavior in moose. Naturaliste Canadien 101:307-323.

———. 1974c. Ecological and behavioral study of the Nunivak Island muskox population. Unpubl. Rep. U.S. Dep. Inter., Fish and Wildl. Serv., Anchorage and Bethel, AK. 90pp.

———. 1978. Muskox. Pages 135-147 *in* Schmidt, J.L. and D.L. Gilbert, eds. Big Game of North America: Ecology and Management. The Wildl. Manage. Inst., Washington, DC. and Stackpole Books, Harrisburg, PA.

———. 1980. Synoptic snowmelt patterns in arctic Alaska in relation to caribou habitat use. Pages 71-83 *in* Reimers, E., E. Gaare, and S. Skjenneberg, eds. Proc. Second Int. Reindeer/Caribou Symp. Dir. for Vilt og Ferskvannsfisk, Trondheim.

LeRESCHE, R.E. 1974. Moose migrations in North America. Naturaliste Canadien 101:393-415.

——— and A. RAUSCH. 1974. Accuracy and precision of aerial moose censusing. J. Wildl. Manage. 38:175-182.

———, U.S. SEAL, P.D. KARNS, and A.W. FRANZMANN. 1974. A review of blood chemistry of moose and other Cervidae with emphasis on nutritional assessments. Naturaliste Canadien 101:263-290.

LESLIE, D.M., Jr. and C.L. DOUGLAS. 1979. Desert bighorn sheep of the River Mountains, Nevada. Wildl. Monogr. 66:1-56.

LONGHURST, W.M., H.K. OH, M.B. JONES, and R.E. KEPNER. 1968. A basis for the palatability of deer forage plants. Trans. North Am. Wildl. and Nat. Resour. Conf. 33:181-189.

LONO, O. 1960. Transplantation of the muskox in Europe and North America. Meddel. Norsk Polarinst. 84:3-25.

LOW, W.A. 1970. The influence of aridity on reproduction of the collared peccary (*Dicotyles tajacu* [Linn]) in Texas. PhD dissertation, Univ. British Columbia, Vancouver. 170pp.

LYON, L.J., T.N. LONNER, J.P. WEIGAND, C.L. MARCUM, W.D. EDGE, J.D. JONES, D.W. McCLEEREY, and L.L. HICKS. 1985. Coordinating elk and timber management. Final Rep. Montana Coop. Elk-Logging Study, 1970-1985. Montana Dep. Fish, Wildlife, and Parks, Helena.

——— and A.L. WARD. 1982. Elk and land management. Pages 443-478 *in* Thomas, J.W. and D.E. Toweill, eds. Elk of North America: Ecology and Management. Stackpole Books, Harrisburg, PA, 698pp.

MACKIE, R.J., K.L. HAMLIN, and D.F. PAC. 1982. Mule deer. Pages 862-877 *in* Chapman, J.A. and G.A. Feldhamer, eds. Wild Mammals of North America. The Johns Hopkins Univ. Press, Baltimore, MD.

MacPHERSON, S., F.K. MARTINSON, and A.Y. COOPERRIDER. 1982. Forage allocation between big game and domestic livestock—new approaches. Proc. Western Assoc. Fish and Wildl. Agencies 62:120-129.

MAUTZ, W.W. 1978. Nutrition and carrying capacity. Pages 321-348 *in* Schmidt, J.L. and D.L. Gilbert, eds. Big Game of North America: Ecology and Management. The Wildl. Manage. Inst., Washington, DC. and Stackpole Books, Harrisburg, PA.

McCOLLOUGH, S.A. 1982. Impact of cattle grazing on bighorn sheep, Trickle Mountain, Colorado. M.S. thesis, Colorado State Univ., Fort Collins. 119pp.

———., A.Y. COOPERRIDER, and J.A. BAILEY. 1980. Impact of cattle grazing on bighorn sheep at Trickle Mountain, Colorado. Biennial Symp., Northern Wild Sheep and Goat Council 2:42-58.

McEWAN, E.H. and P.E. WHITEHEAD. 1970. Seasonal changes in the energy and nitrogen intake in reindeer and caribou. Canadian J. Zoology 48:905-913.

McFETRIDGE, R.J. 1977. Strategy of resource use by mountain goats nursery groups. Pages 169-173 *in* Samuel, W. and W.G. MacGregor, eds. Proc. First Int. Mountain Goat Symp. Kalispell, MT.

MEAGHER, M.M. 1973. The bison of Yellowstone National Park. U.S. Dep. Inter., Natl. Park Serv. Sci. Monogr. 1. 161pp.

———. 1976. Winter weather as a population regulating influence on free-ranging bison in Yellowstone National Park. Pages 29-38 *in* Research in the Parks. Trans. Natl. Park Centennial Symp., AAAS, December 28-29, 1971. Series 1. U.S. Govt. Printing Office. 232pp.

———. 1978. Bison. Pages 123-133 *in* Schmidt, J.L. and D.L. Gilbert, eds. Big Game of North America: Ecology and Management. The Wildl. Manage. Inst., Washington, DC. and Stackpole Books, Harrisburg, PA. 494pp.

MONSON, G. and L. SUMNER, eds. 1980. The desert bighorn. Univ. Arizona Press, Tucson. 370pp.

MOULD, E. 1977. Habitat relationships of moose in northern Alaska. North Am. Moose Conf. 13:144-156.

———. 1979. Seasonal movements related to habitat of moose along the Colville River, Alaska. Murrelet 60:6-11.

MULE, R.S. 1982. An assessment of a wildlife habitat evaluation methodology for Alaska. M.S. thesis, Univ. Alaska, Fairbanks. 215pp.

MURIE, O.J. 1954. A field guide to animal tracks. Houghton Mifflin Co., Boston, MA. 375pp.

NAGY, J.G., H.W. STEINHOFF, and G.M. WARD. 1964. Effects of essential oils of sagebrush on deer rumen microbial function. J. Wildl. Manage. 28:785-790.

NEAL, B.J. 1959. A contribution on the life history of the collared peccary in Arizona. Am. Midl. Nat. 61:177-190.

NEFF, D.J. 1968. The pellet group count technique for big game trend, census, and distribution: A review. J. Wildl. Manage. 32:597-614.

NELSON, J.R. 1984. A modeling approach to large herbivore competition. Pages 491-524 *in* Developing Strategies for Rangeland Management. Rep. prepared by the Committee on Developing Strategies for Rangeland Manage., Natl. Res. Council/Natl. Acad. Sciences. Westview Press, Boulder, CO. 2022pp.

NELSON, M.E. 1979. Home range location of white-tailed deer. U.S. Dep. Agric., For. Serv. Res. Pap. NC-173. 10pp.

——— and L.C. MECH. 1981. Deer social organization and wolf predation in northeastern Minnesota. Wildl. Monogr. 77. 53pp.

NICHOLS, L., Jr. 1980. Aerial census and classification of mountain goats in Alaska. Pages 523-589 *in* Hickey, W.O., ed. Proc. Biennial Symp., Northern Wild Sheep and Goat Council. Salmon, ID.

NPR-A (NATIONAL PETROLEUM RESERVE—ALASKA) TASK FORCE. 1978. Fish and wildlife resources. Values and Resource Analysis, Section 6, Vol. 3, Study Rep. 2. U.S. Dep. Inter. 224pp.

———. 1979. Ecological profile. National Petroleum Reserve in Alaska. Study 25, Rep. 4. U.S. Dep. Inter.

OLDEMEYER, J.L. 1977a. Nutritive value of moose forage. Naturaliste Canadien 101:217-226.

———. 1977b. Impact of LeTourneau tree crushers on

moose habitat on the Kenai National Moose Range. Proc. 28th Annual Conf., Northwest Sections. The Wildl. Soc., Kalispell, MT.

————, W.J. BARMORE, and D.L. GILBERT. 1971. Winter ecology of bighorn sheep in Yellowstone National Park. J. Wildl. Manage. 35:257-269.

————, A.W. FRANZMANN, A.L. BRUNDAGE, P.D. ARNESON, and A. FLYNN. 1977. Browse quality and the Kenai moose population. J. Wildl. Manage. 41:533-542.

ONDERKA, D.K. and W.D. WISHART. 1984. A major bighorn sheep die-off from pneumonia in southern Alberta. Biennial Symp., Northern Wild Sheep and Goat Council. Salmon, ID. 4:356-363.

OUGH, W.D. and J.C. DE VOS, Jr. 1984. Intermountain travel corridors and their management implications for bighorn sheep. Desert Bighorn Council Trans. 32-36.

PARKER, G.R. 1975. A review of aerial surveys used for estimating the numbers of barren-ground caribou in northern Canada. Polar Record 17:627-638.

————. 1981. Physical and reproductive characteristics of an expanding woodland caribou population in northern Labrador. Canadian J. Zoology 59:1929-1940.

———— and R.K. ROSS. 1976. Summer habitat use by muskoxen (*Ovibos moschatus*) and Peary caribou (*Rangifer tarandus pearyi*) in the Canadian High Arctic. Polarforschung 46:12-25.

————, D.C. THOMAS, E. BROUGHTON, and D.R. GRAY. 1975. Crashes of muskox and Peary caribou populations in 1973-74 on the Parry Island, Arctic Canada. Canadian Wild. Serv. Progress Note 56:1-10.

PEDEN, D.G., G.M. VAN DYNE, R.W. RICE, and R.M. HANSEN. 1974. The trophic ecology of *Bison bison L.* on shortgrass plains. J. Applied Ecol. 11:489-498.

PEEK, J.M. 1974. On the nature of winter habitats of Shiras moose. Naturaliste Canadien 101:131-141.

————, M.D. SCOTT, L.J. NELSON, and D.J. PIERCE. 1982. Role of cover in habitat management for big game in northwestern United States. Trans. North Am. Wildl. Nat. Resour. Conf. 47:363-373.

PEGAU, R.E. and J.E. HEMMING. 1970. Caribou report. Alaska Dep. of Fish and Game, Federal Aid in Wildl. Restoration Project Rep., Vol. 12. Juneau. 224pp.

PETOCZ, R.G. 1973. The effect of snow cover on the social behaviour of bighorn rams and mountain goats. Canadian J. Zoology 51:987-993.

POHLE, C. 1981. Trergartnerische Beobachtungen bei der Haltung und Zucht von Moschusochsen in Tierpark Berlin. Zool. Gart. 51:289-322.

POJAR, T.M. 1981. A management perspective of population modeling. Pages 241-261 in Fowler, C.W. and T.D. Smith, eds. Dynamics of Large Mammal Populations. John Wiley and Sons, New York, NY. 477pp.

———— and D. STRICKLAND, eds. 1979. A workshop on the status and application of big game population modeling. Colorado Div. Wildl., Fort Collins. 53pp.

POLEQUIN, A., B. SCHERRER, and R. JOYAL. 1977. Characteristics of winter browsing areas of moose in western Quebec as determined by multivariate analysis. North Am. Moose Conf. 13:128-143.

PRENZLOW, E.J., D.L. GILBERT, and F.A. GLOVER. 1968. Some behavior patterns of the pronghorn. Colorado Dep. Game, Fish, and Parks Spec. Rep. 17. 16pp.

QUIMBY, D.C. and J.E. GAAB. 1957. Mandibular dentition as an age indicator in Rocky Mountain elk. J. Wildl. Manage. 21(4):435-451.

REIMERS, E., D.R. KLEIN, and R. SORUMGORD. 1983. Calving time, growth rate and body size of Norwegian reindeer on different ranges. Arctic and Alpine Res. 15:107-118.

RENECKER, L.A. and R.J. HUDSON. 1986. Seasonal foraging rates of free-ranging moose. J. Wildl. Manage. 50:143-147.

RICHARDSON, A.H. 1971. The Rocky Mountain goat in the Black Hills. South Dakota Dep. Game, Fish, and Parks Bull. 2. 25pp.

RIDEOUT, C.B. 1974. A radio telemetry study of the ecology and behavior of the Rocky Mountain goat in western Montana. PhD thesis, Univ. Kansas, Lawrence. 146pp.

RINEY, T. 1982. Study and management of large mammals. John Wiley and Sons, New York, NY. 552pp.

RISENHOOVER, K.L. and J.A. BAILEY. 1982. Social dynamics of mountain goats in summer: Implications for age ratios. Pages 364-373 in Bailey, J.A. and G.G. Schoonveld, eds. Proc. Third Biennial Symp., Northern Wild Sheep and Goat Council. Fort Collins, CO.

———— and ————. 1985a. Relationships between group size, feeding time, and agonistic behavior of mountain goats. Canadian J. Zoology 63:2501-2506.

———— and ————. 1985b. Foraging ecology of mountain sheep: Implications for habitat management. J. Wildl. Manage. 49:797-804.

ROBBINS, C.T. 1973. The biological basis for the determination of carrying capacity. PhD dissertation, Cornell Univ., Ithaca, NY. 239pp.

ROBINETTE, W.L., C.M. LOVELESS, and D.A. JONES. 1974. Field tests of strip census methods. J. Wildl. Manage. 38:81-96.

ROBUS, M. 1984. Summer food habits of muskoxen in northeastern Alaska. Pages 81-85 in Klein, D.R., R.G. White, and S. Keller, eds. Proc. First Int. Muskox Symp. Spec. Rep., Biol. Pap. Univ. Alaska, Fairbanks.

RYEL, L.A. 1971. Evaluation of pellet group surveys for estimating deer populations in Michigan. PhD dissertation, Michigan State Univ., Lansing. 237pp.

SAMUEL, W., G.A. CHALMERS, J.G. STELLOX, A. LOWEN, and J.J. THOMSEN. 1975. Contagious ecthyma in bighorn sheep and mountain goat in western Canada. J. Wildl. Diseases 11:26-31.

———— and W. MacGREGOR, eds. 1977. Proceedings of the first international mountain goat symposium. Kalispell, MT.

SAUSMAN, K. 1982. Survival of captive-born *Ovis canadensis* in North American zoos. Desert Bighorn Council Trans. 26-31.

SCHMIDT, J.L. and D.L. GILBERT. 1978. Big game of North America: Ecology and Management. The Wildl. Manage. Inst., Washington, DC and Stackpole Books, Harrisburg, PA. 494pp.

SCHMIDT, R.L., C.P. HIBLER, T.R. SPRAKER, and W.H. RUTHERFORD. 1979. An evaluation of drug treatment for lungworm in bighorn sheep. J. Wildl. Manage. 43:461-467.

————, W.H. RUTHERFORD, and F.M. BODENHAM. 1978. Colorado bighorn sheep-trapping techniques. Wildl. Soc. Bull. 6:159-163.

SCHOEN, J.W. and M.D. KIRCHOFF. 1981. Habitat use by mountain goats in southeast Alaska. Alaska Dep. Fish and Game, P-R Project Rep. W-17-10, 11 and W-21-1, 2. 67pp.

SERGEANT, D.E. and D.H. PIMLOTT. 1959. Age determination in moose from sectioned incisor teeth. J. Wildl.

Manage. 23:315-321.

SHANNON, N.H., R.J. HUDSON, V.C. BRINK, and W.D. KITTS. 1975. Determinants of spatial distribution of Rocky Mountain bighorn sheep. J. Wildl. Manage. 39:387-401.

SIMMONS, N.M. 1969. Heat stress and bighorn behavior in the Cabeza Prieta Game Range, Arizona. Desert Bighorn Council Trans. 13:55-63.

SINGER, F.J. 1975. Behavior of mountain goats, elk and other wildlife in relation to U.S. Highway 2, Glacier National Park. Completion Rep. U.S. Dep. Inter., Natl. Park Serv., West Glacier, MT. 98pp.

SINIFF, D.B. and R.O. SKOOG. 1964. Aerial censusing of caribou using stratified random sampling. J. Wildl. Manage. 28:39-40.

SKILES J.W., P.T. KORTOPATES, and G.M. VAN DYNE. 1980. Optimization models for forage allocation to combinations of large herbivores for grazing land situations: A critical use of proper use factors. Rep. to U.S. Dep. Inter., Bur. Land Manage. 86pp.

SKOOG, R.O. 1962. Method for estimating caribou herds. Alaska Dep. of Fish and Game Information Leaflet 20., Juneau. 6pp.

SKOVLIN, J.M. 1982. Habitat requirements and evaluations. Pages 368-413 in Thomas, J.W. and D.E. Toweill, eds. Elk of North America: Ecology and Management. Stackpole Books, Harrisburg, PA. 698pp.

SMITH, B.L. 1976. Ecology of Rocky Mountain goats in the Bitterroot Mountains, Montana. M.S. thesis, Univ. Montana. 203pp.

———. 1977. Influence of snow conditions on winter distribution, habitat use, and group size of mountain goats. Pages 174-189 in Samuel, W. and W.G. MacGregor, eds. Proc. First Int. Mountain Goat Symp. Kalispell, MT.

SMITH, C.A. and K.J. RAEDEKE. 1982. Group size and movements of a dispersed, low density goat population, with comments on inbreeding and human impacts. Pages 54-67 in Bailey, J.A. and G.G. Schoonveld, eds. Proc. Third Biennial Symp., Northern Wild Sheep and Goat Council. Fort Collins, CO.

SMITH, K.G. 1982. Winter studies of forest-dwelling mountain goats of Pinto Creek, Alberta. Pages 374-390 in Bailey, J.A. and G.G. Schoonveld, eds. Proc. Third Biennial Symp., Northern Wild Sheep and Goat Council. Fort Collins, CO.

SMITH, T.E. 1976. Reproductive behavior and related social organization of the muskox on Nunivak Island. M.S. thesis, Univ. Alaska, Fairbanks. 138pp.

SOULE, M.E. and B.A. WILCOX, eds. 1980. Conservation biology, an evolutionary-ecological perspective. Sinauer Assoc., Sunderland, MA. 395pp.

SOWLS, L.K. 1978. Collared peccary. Pages 191-205 in Schmidt, J.L. and D.L. Gilbert, eds. Big Game of North America: Ecology and Management. The Wildl. Manage. Inst., Washington, DC. and Stackpole Books. Harrisburg, PA.

———. 1984. The peccaries. Univ. Arizona Press, Tucson. 251pp.

SPENCER, D.L. and C. LENSINK. 1970. The muskox of Nunivak Island. J. Wildl. Manage. 34:1-15.

SPRAKER, T.R. and C.P. HIBLER. 1977. Summer lamb mortality of Rocky Mountain bighorn sheep. Desert Bighorn Council Trans. 21:11-12.

——— and ———. 1982. An overview of the clinical signs, gross and histological lesions of the pneumonia complex of bighorn sheep. Proc. Biennial Symp.,

Northern Wild Sheep and Goat Council. Fort Collins, CO. 3:163-172.

———, G.G. SCHOONVELD, and W.S. ADNEY. 1984. Pathologic changes and microorganisms found in bighorn sheep during a stress-related die-off. J. Wildl. Diseases 20:319-327.

STELFOX, J.G. 1971. Bighorn sheep in the Canadian Rockies: A history 1800-1970. Canadian Field-Naturalist 85:101-122.

———. 1976. Wood Buffalo National Park, bison research 1972-76. Section A-I in 1976 Annual Report. Canadian Wildl. Serv. and Parks, Ottawa.

SUNDSTROM, C. 1968. Water consumption by pronghorn antelope and distribution related to water in Wyoming's Red Desert. Proc. Biennial Antelope States Workshop 3:39-46.

SWEENEY, J.M. and H.W. STEINHOFF. 1976. Elk movements and calving as related to snow cover. Pages 415-436 in Steinhoff, H.W. and J.D. Ives, eds. Ecological Impacts of Snowpack Augmentation in the San Juan Mountains, Colorado. Colorado State Univ., Fort Collins.

TABER, R.D. and R.F. DASMANN. 1958. The black-tailed deer of the chaparral—its life history and management in the North Coast Range of California. California Dep. Fish and Game, Game Bull. 8. 163pp.

TANKERSLEY, N.G. and W.C. GASAWAY. 1983. Mineral lick use by moose in Alaska. Canadian J. Zoology 61:2242-2249.

TELFER, E.S. 1974. Logging as a factor in wildlife ecology in the boreal forest. Forest Chronical 50:186-190.

TENER, J.S. 1965. Muskoxen in Canada. Canadian Wildl. Monogr. Series 2. Dep. Northern Affairs and Nat. Resour. Queens Printer, Ottawa. 166pp.

THING, H. 1984. Food and habitat selection by muskoxen in Jameson Land, Northeast Greenland: A preliminary report. Pages 69-74 in Klein, D.R., R.G. White, and S. Keller, eds. Proc. First Int. Muskox Symp. Spec. Rep., Biol. Pap. Univ. Alaska, Fairbanks.

——— and B. CLAUSEN. 1980. Summer mortality among caribou calves in Greenland. Pages 434-437 in Reimers, E., E. Gaare, and S. Skjenneberg, eds. Proc. Second Int. Reindeer/Caribou Symp. Dir. for Vilt og Ferskvannsfisk, Trondheim.

THOMAS, D.C. and J. EDMONDS. 1984. Pages 93-100 in Klein, D.R., R.G. White, and S. Keller, eds. Proc. First Int. Muskox Symp. Spec. Rep., Biol. Pap. Univ. Alaska, Fairbanks.

———, F.L. MILLER, R.H. RUSSELL, and G.R. PARKER. 1981. The Bailey Point Region and other muskox refugia in the Canadian Arctic: A short review. Arctic 34:34-36.

THOMAS, J.W., H. BLACK, Jr., R.J. SCHERZINGER, and R.J. PEDERSEN. 1979. Deer and elk. Pages 104-127 in Thomas, J.W., ed. Wildlife Habitats in Managed Forests: The Blue Mountains of Oregon and Washington. U.S. Dep. Agric., For. Serv. Handbook 553. Washington, DC.

——— and D.E. TOWEILL. 1982. Elk of North America: Ecology and Management. Stackpole Books, Harrisburg, PA. 698pp.

THOMPSON, R.W. 1980. Population dynamics, habitat utilization, recreational impacts and trapping of introduced Rocky Mountain goats in the Eagles Nest Wilderness Area, Colorado. Pages 459-464 in Hickey, W.O., ed. Proc. 1980 Biennial Symp., Northern Wild Sheep and Goat Council. Salmon, ID. 668pp.

————— and R.J. GUENZEL. 1978. Status of the introduced mountain goats in the Eagles Nest Wilderness Area, Colorado. Pages 175-197 *in* Hebert, D.M. and M. Nation, eds. Proc. 1978 Biennial Symp. Northern Wild Sheep and Goat Conf. Penticton, British Columbia.

TIMMERMANN, H.R. 1974. Moose inventory methods: A review. Naturaliste Canadien 101:615-629.

TODD, J.W. 1972. A literature review on bighorn sheep food habits. Colorado Div. Game, Fish, and Parks Spec. Rep. 27. 21pp.

TREFETHEN, J.B., ed. 1975. The wild sheep in modern North America. Winchester Press, New York, NY. 302pp.

—————. 1975. The Wild Sheep in Modern North America. Proc. Workshop on the Manage. Biol. North American Wild Sheep. Univ. Montana, Missoula, June 18-20, 1974. Boone and Crockett Club and the Winchester Press, New York, NY. 302pp.

TURNER, J.C. and R.A. WEAVER. 1980. Water. Pages 100-112 *in* Monson, G. and L. Sumner, eds. The Desert Bighorn—Its Life History, Ecology, and Management. Univ. Arizona Press, Tucson.

U.S. DEPARTMENT OF THE INTERIOR, FISH AND WILDLIFE SERVICE. 1983. Initial report, baseline study of the fish, wildlife and their habitats. Arctic Natl. Wildl. Refuge Coastal Plain Resour. Assessment. U.S. Dep. Inter., Fish and Wild. Serv., Anchorage, AK. 507pp.

VAN DAELE, L.J. and D.R. JOHNSON. 1983. Estimation of arboreal lichen biomass available to caribou. J. Wildl. Manage. 47:888-890.

VAN DYKE, W.A., A. SANDS, J. YOAKUM, A. POLENZ, AND J. BLAISDELL. 1983. Wildlife habitats in managed rangelands, the Great Basin of southeastern Oregon: Bighorn sheep. U.S. Dep. Agric., For. Serv., Pacific Northwest Experiment Sta., Gen. Tech. Rep. PNW-159. 37pp.

VIBE, C. 1958. The muskox in east Greenland. Mammalia 22:168-174.

—————. 1967. Arctic animals in relation to climatic fluctuations. Meddel om Gronland 171:1-227.

WAKELYN, L.A. 1984. Analysis and comparison of existing and historic bighorn sheep ranges in Colorado. M.S. thesis, Colorado State Univ., Fort Collins. 274pp.

WALLMO, O.C., ed. 1981. Mule and black-tailed deer of North America. Univ. Nebraska Press, Lincoln. 605pp.

—————. 1981. Mule and black-tailed deer distribution and habitats. Pages 1-25 *in* Wallmo, O.C., ed. Mule and Black-tailed Deer of North America. Univ. Nebraska Press, Lincoln.

—————, L.C. CARPENTER, W.L. REGELIN, R.B. GILL, and D.B. BAKER. 1977. Evaluation of deer habitat on a nutritional basis. J. Range Manage. 30:122-127.

—————, R.B. GILL, L.H. CARPENTER, and D.W. REICHERT. 1973. Accuracy of field estimates of deer food habits. J. Wildl. Manage. 37:556-562.

—————- and J.W. SCHOEN. 1981. Forest management for deer. Pages 434-448 *in* Wallmo, O.C., ed. Mule and Black-tailed Deer of North America. Univ. Nebraska Press, Lincoln. 605pp.

WHITE, G.C., D.R. ANDERSON, K.P. BURNHAM, and D.L. OTIS. 1982. Capture-recapture and removal methods for sampling closed populations. Los Alamos Natl. Laboratory, Los Alamos, NM. 235pp.

WIGAL, R.A. and V.L. COGGINS. 1982. Mountain goat. Pages 1008-1020 *in* Chapman, J.A. and G.A. Feldhamer, eds. Wild Mammals of North America. Johns Hopkins Univ. Press, Baltimore, MD. 1147pp.

WILKINSON, P.F., C.C. SHANK, and D.E. PENNER. 1976. Muskox-caribou summer range on Banks Island, Northwest Territories. J. Wildl. Manage. 40:151-162.

—————- and P.N. TEAL. 1984. The muskox domestication project: An overview and evaluation. Pages 162-166 *in* Klein, D.R., R.G. White, and S. Keller, eds. Proc. First Int. Muskox Symp. Spec. Rep., Biol. Pap. Univ. Alaska, Fairbanks.

WILSON, L.W., J. BLAISDELL, G. WELSH, R. WEAVER, R. BRIGHAM, W. KELLY, J. YOAKUM, M. HINKS, J. TURNER, and J. DeFORGE. 1980. Desert bighorn habitat requirements and management recommendations. Trans. Desert Bighorn Council 24:1-7.

WISDOM, M.J., L.R. BRIGHT, C.G. CAREY, W.W. HINES, R.J. PEDERSEN, D.A. SMITHEY, J.W. THOMAS, and F.W. WITMER. 1986. A model to evaluate elk habitat in western Oregon. U.S. Dep. Agric., For. Serv., Pacific Northwest Region. 36pp.

WITMER, G.W., M. WISDOM, E.P. HARSHMAN, R.J. ANDERSON, C. CAREY, M.P. KUTTEL, I.D. LUMAN, J.A. ROCHELLE, R.W. SCHARPF, and D. SMITHEY. 1985. Deer and elk. Pages 231-258 *in* Brown, E.R., ed. Management of Wildlife and Fish Habitats in Forests of Western Oregon and Washington. U.S. Dep. Agric., For. Serv. Pub. R6-F&WL-192-1985. Portland, OR.

WOOD, J.E., T.S. BICKLE, W. EVANS, J.C. GERMANY, and V.W. HOWARD, Jr. 1970. The Fort Stanton mule deer herd (some ecological and life history characteristics with special emphasis on the use of water). New Mexico State Univ., Agric. Experiment Sta. Bull. 567. 32pp.

YOAKUM, J.D. 1978. Pronghorn. Pages 103-122 *in* Schmidt, J.L. and D.L. Gilbert, eds. Big Game of North America: Ecology and Management. The Wildl. Manage. Inst., Washington, DC. and Stackpole Books, Harrisburg, PA. 494pp.

—————. 1980. Habitat management guides for the American pronghorn antelope. U.S. Dep. Inter., Bur. Land Manage. Tech. Note 347. Denver Federal Center, Denver, CO. 77pp.

IV HABITAT MEASUREMENTS

Shirley McCulloch 1987

26

SOILS

James E. Stone

U.S. Bureau of Land Management
Washington, DC 20240

"... there is a remarkable correlation between game supply and soil fertility throughout North America."

— Aldo Leopold, from *Game Management*

Editor's Note: Aldo Leopold noted the relationship between soils and wildlife populations. Since then, many wildlife biologists and soil scientists have observed the linkage between soils, vegetation, and wildlife populations.

While the concept of relating soils to vegetation and wildlife is well established, the predictive relationships are not. This chapter brings together information available on these relationships.

INTRODUCTION

Soil is a vital part of wildlife habitat. Indirectly, soil affects animals through its influence on the composition, amount, palatability, and nutritive value of vegetation. In addition, soil properties directly affect such things as the ease of digging, burrow stability and depth, maintenance of body temperature and moisture levels, availability of suitable reproductive and resting sites, mobility, and body coloration.

Until recently, the consideration of soils on wildlands has been hampered by the lack of available soil information, but this situation is rapidly changing. Millions of acres of lands administered by the U.S. Bureau of Land Management and the U.S. Forest Service have now been surveyed, and ongoing programs are in place. Acquiring the soil information, however, is only the beginning. Putting this information to use is the ultimate goal.

Several years ago, Klemmedson (1970) wrote of the communication gap between those who make soil surveys and those who could and should be using the information. Although progress has been made, the problem still exists. Effective application of soils data in habitat management requires a cooperative effort on the part of both soil scientists and wildlife biologists. Soil scientists must recognize the needs of other disciplines and tailor surveys and associated soil interpretations to meet those needs. Wildlife biologists in turn must acquire at least a working knowledge of soil terminology, kinds and sources of soil information, and soil-animal relationships so as to fairly assess application opportunities as well as constraints.

The intent of this chapter is to provide a working-level discussion of the use of soil information in habitat characterization and management.

SOIL DESCRIPTION

Soil is a mixture of solids and pores. The solid fraction consists of mineral particles from the weathering of rocks and organic material from the deposition and decay of plant and animal tissue. The intervening pore spaces contain either air or an aqueous solution with substances either dissolved or in suspension. The nature and relative amounts of these constituents are described according to specific standards set forth in the Soil Survey Manual (U.S. Soil Conservation Service 1981). A representative soil description is given in Figure 1; descriptive terminology and standards are summarized below for selected soil characteristics.

Parent Material

Parent material is the unconsolidated and more or less chemically weathered mineral material from which soils develop. Parent materials may have been formed in place or transported by water, wind, ice, or gravity. In any event, parent material exerts a strong influence on soil development and associated plant and animal communities. For example, soils derived from serpentine parent materials are generally low or lacking in several essential plant nutrients and are therefore highly selective for native plant species (Kruckeberg 1969). Notable plant-soil relationships are also evident on other parent materials (Marchand 1973). In addition, the nature of the parent rock itself influences the availability of specialized habitats such as caves, lava tubes, and talus (Maser et al. 1979).

Kech series

DEPTH, DRAINAGE

PARENT MATERIAL

The Kech series consists of shallow, well-drained soils that formed in place and from locally transported sediment from sandstone and interbedded shale. Kech soils are on upland hills and ridges. Slopes range from 3 to 40%. Average annual precipitation is about 14 inches, and average annual air temperature is about 44°F.

⟩ SETTING

Kech soils are similar to Progresso and Potts soils and are near Scholle, Mesa, and Agua Fria soils. Progresso soils have sandstone bedrock at a depth of 20 to 40 inches. Potts, Scholle, Mesa, and Agua Fria soils are more than 60 inches deep. Mesa soils are dry. Agua Fria soils have more than 35 percent clay in the B horizon.

⟩ ASSOCIATED SOILS

Typical pedon of Kech loam, in an area of Kech-Progresso loams, 3 to 15 percent slopes, SW1/4 Sec. 13, T. 15 S., R. 93 W., in Delta County:

⟩ TYPE LOCATION

HORIZONATION

ROOTS

A1—0 to 4 inches; brown (7.5YR 5/2) loam, dark brown (7.5YR 4/2) moist; moderate very fine granular structure; soft, friable, slightly sticky and slightly plastic; few fine and medium roots; 5 to 15% sandstone channers; neutral; clear smooth boundary. (3 to 5 inches thick).

TEXTURE

STRUCTURE

ROCK CONTENT

B2t—4 to 12 inches; brown (7.5YR 5/4) clay loam, dark brown (7.5YR 4/4) moist; moderate medium subangular blocky structure parting to moderate fine subangular blocky; hard, friable, sticky and plastic; few fine and very fine roots; moderate continuous clay films on peds; 5 to 10% sandstone channers; noncareous; mildly alkaline; clear wavy boundary. (4 to 9 inches thick).

⟩ PROFILE DESCRIPTION

COLOR

CONSISTENCE

REACTION (pH)

B3ca—12 to 19 inches; pinkish white (7.5YR 8/2) channery loam, pink (7.5YR 7/4) moist; weak medium subangular blocky structure parting to weak fine subangular blocky; hard, firm, slightly sticky and slightly plastic; 25 to 30% sandstone channers; few thin patchy clay films; soft masses of secondary lime; mildy alkaline; clear irregular boundary (4 to 8 inches thick)
R—19 inches; partially weathered calcareous sandstone.

The A horizon has value of 4 to 6 dry and 3 to 5 moist and has chroma of 2 or 3 dry and moist. The B horizon has hue of 7.5YR or 10YR, value of 5 or 6 dry and 4 or 5 moist, and chroma of 3 or 4 dry and moist. Texture of the B horizon is clay loam. Clay content ranges from 27 to 35% in this horizon, and sandstone channers range from 0 to 15%. Reaction is neutral or mildly alkaline. The B3 horizon contains visible secondary lime and has as much as 30% sandstone channers. Weathered sandstone bedrock is at a depth of 10 to 20 inches.

⟩ RANGE OF CHARACTERISTICS

Figure 1. Soil description.

Horizonation

Vertical sections through the soil (soil profile) often reveal the presence of distinct layers or horizons (Figure 2). The nature, arrangement, and thickness of horizons (or their absence) are important for differentiating soils and for interpreting soil behavior. Each soil horizon, designated by a particular symbol (e.g., A1—0 to 4 in.), is described separately.

Figure 2. Soil horizonation.

Texture

Texture refers to the size distribution of mineral particles within the soil. Those particles smaller than 2 mm (0.08 in.) in diameter, termed the fine earth fraction, are described separately from larger rock fragments. Soils are assigned textural class names (e.g., sandy loam, silty clay) based on the amounts of sand-, silt-, and clay-sized particles in the fine earth fraction (Figure 3).

Small ground-dwelling animals often show an affinity for particular soil textures. Stuart (1932) related the distribution of several lizard species to soil texture; Hardy (1945) observed a varying de-

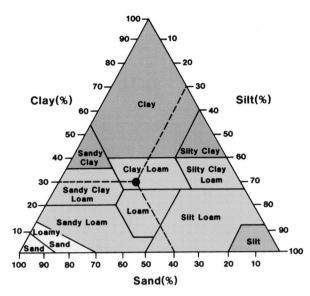

Figure 3. Soil texture.

pendence upon soil texture of 18 races of rodents. Feldhamer (1979) reported a direct relationship between the population density of pocket mice *(Perognathus parvus)* and the percentage of sand in the soil; an inverse relationship existed with the percentage of clay.

Mojave fringed-toe lizard. Completely restricted to fine, loose, windblown sand.

Rock Fragments

Rock fragments, those mineral particles greater than 2 mm (0.08 in.) in diameter, are described according to their size and shape (Figure 4). The adjective form of a rock fragment class is often used to modify the textural class name (e.g., channery loam). Rock content in the profile is described as a percentage by volume.

Rock fragments in the soil profile reduce moisture storage as well as the volume of soil material

Fragment	Centimeters		Inches
	Diameter	Length	
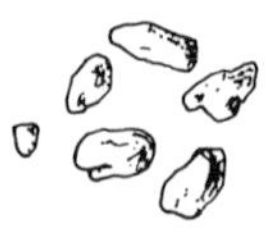 Gravel[a]	0.2–7.6		0.1–3
 Cobble	7.6–25		3–10
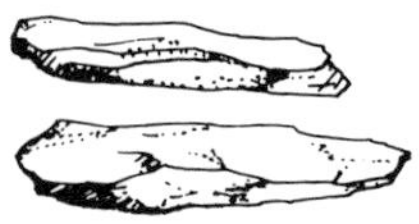 Channer (flat)		0.2–15	0.1–6
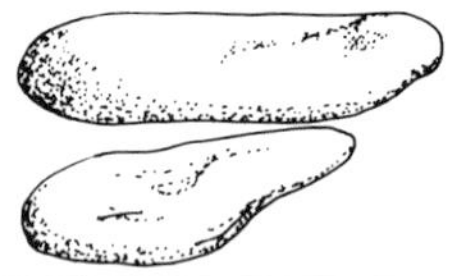 Flagstone (flat)		15–38	6–15
 Stone	25–60		10–24
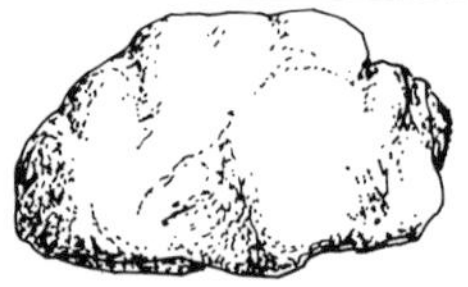 Boulder	60		24

[a]A single fragment of this size is called a "pebble."

Figure 4. Rock fragments.

that plant roots and animals can occupy. Fragments on the surface can provide specialized habitats for animals in areas that might otherwise be unsuitable.

Structure

Soil structure refers to the organization of individual mineral particles into clumps or aggregates. Some soils, such as loose sands, are structureless. Structured soils are described by the stability, size, and shape of the aggregates (e.g., moderate, medium, subangular blocky structure [Figure 5]). Structure affects the size of pores and the total amount of pore space in the soil, thus influencing air and water relations. Unlike texture, soil structure can be altered rapidly by use and management practices, thereby altering habitat suitability for some animals.

Consistence

Soil consistence characterizes the cohesion among soil particles and the adhesion between soil and other substances. One element of consistence is soil strength, the degree of resistance to breaking or crushing when force is applied. The standard terms used to describe soil strength are specific to moisture condition (Table 1).

Soil strength is important when considering habitat suitability for small burrowing animals. For example, Feldhamer (1979) found a direct correlation between the population density of chipmunks (*Eutamias minimus*) and soil strength.

Color

Soil color is described by comparison with standard Munsell color charts (Munsell 1975). The Munsell System uses three elements (hue, value, chroma) to make up a specific color notation. For example, 7.5 YR 8/2 is the hue and value/chroma notation for pinkish white (Figure 6). Colors of both moist and dry soil are commonly recorded in the soil description.

Structural Type		General Connotation
	Granular	Found in surface horizons; formation promoted by organic matter; encourages air and water transmission.
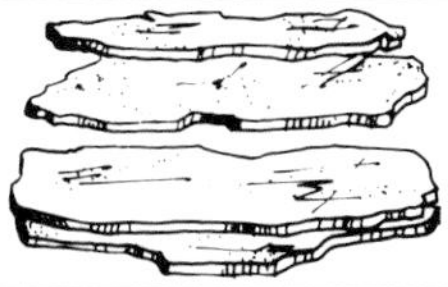	Platy	Found in surface and subsurface horizons; severely restricts air and water transmission.
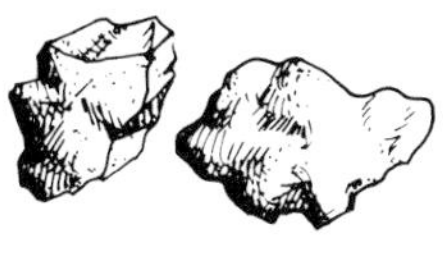	Blocky	Found in fine-textured subsurface horizons; most common in humid climates; restricts air and water transmission.
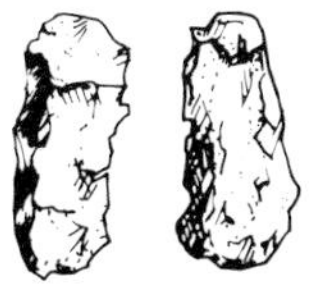	Prismatic	Found in fine-textured subsurface horizons; most common in arid and semiarid climates; restricts air and water transmission.
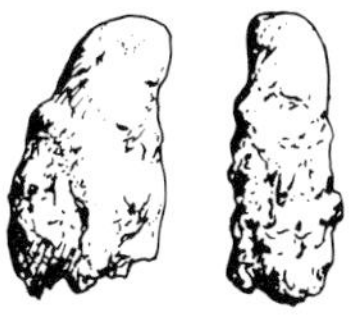	Columnar	Found in fine-textured subsurface horizons; most common in arid and semiarid climates; often indicates high sodium levels; restricts air and water transmission.

Figure 5. Soil structure.

Table 1. Soil consistence (U.S. Soil Conservation Service 1981, Chap. 4).

Descriptive Term (by moisture condition)		Connotation
Air Dry	*Field Capacity (moist)*	
Loose	Loose	No specimen can be obtained.[1]
Soft	Very friable	Crushes or breaks under slight force applied by thumb and forefinger.[2]
Slightly hard	Friable	Crushes or breaks under moderate force by thumb and forefinger.
Slightly hard	Firm	Crushes or breaks under moderate force by thumb and forefinger.
Hard	Very firm	Crushes or breaks under strong force by thumb and forefinger.
Very hard	Extremely firm	Cannot be crushed or broken by thumb and forefinger; can be broken by squeezing slowly between hands.
Extremely hard	Extremely hard	Cannot be crushed or broken in hands; can be crushed or broken underfoot.

[1]A specimen for testing strength is normally a cube approximately 1 cm on a side.
[2]Under laboratory conditions, strength classes are defined quantitatively by measured force in newtons.

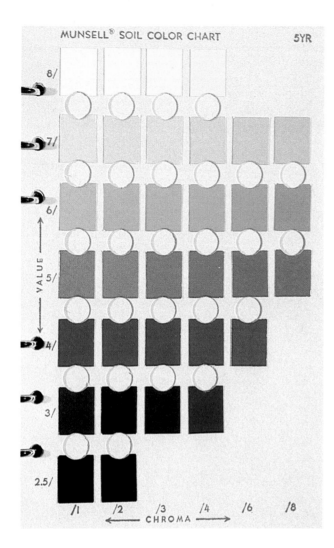

Figure 6. Soil color.

Chipmunk.

Depth Class		Centimeters	Inches
	Very shallow	< 25	< 10
	Shallow	25-50	10-20
	Moderately deep	50-100	20-40
	Deep	100-150	40-60
	Very deep	> 150	> 60

Figure 7. Soil depth.

Several researchers have found a distinct relationship between soil color and the pelage coloration of various mammals (Dice and Blossom 1937; Hardy 1945). For woodrats (*Neotoma* sp.) and chipmunks (*Eutamias* sp.) in the South Dakota badlands, the color relationship was strongest on sites largely devoid of vegetative cover (Stebler 1939). Soil color can also exert a strong influence over surface temperatures.

Depth

Soil depth is measured from the surface to a restricting or contrasting layer. The nature of the layer in question is generally specified (e.g., depth to hardpan). Where the nature of the layer is not given, it is understood to be consolidated bedrock. Standard classes for depth are given in Figure 7.

Soil depth and soil texture influence the size and distribution of pocket gophers (*Thomomys* sp., *Geomys* sp.) in the western U.S. (Davis 1938; Davis et al. 1938). Hardy (1945) contrasted the soil depth requirements of two species of kangaroo rats (*Dipodomys* sp.). Additionally, soil depth can affect animals indirectly through its influence on the kind and amount of vegetation (McColley and Hodgkinson 1970; Passey et al. 1982).

Ord's kangaroo rat.

Table 2. Root quantity and size classes (U.S. Soil Conservative Service 1981, Chap. 4).

Root Quantity	Descriptive Term
< 1 per unit area[1] 1–5 per unit area > 5 per unit area	Few Common Many
Root Size	
(diameter) < 1 mm 1–2 mm 2–5 mm > 5 mm	Very Fine Fine Medium Coarse

[1]Unit area for very fine and fine roots is 1 square centimeter; unit area for medium and coarse roots is 1 square decimeter.

Roots and Animal Traces

The quantity and size of plant roots in each soil layer are routinely recorded in soil descriptions (Table 2). Evidences of animal activity are also described when apparent, although no specific descriptive standards have been developed. Such evidences range from surface features (e.g., ant mounds, burrow openings) to actual structures within the soil (e.g., tunnels, krotovinas). Krotovinas are irregular, tubular streaks or spots in the soil caused when abandoned animal tunnels become filled with contrasting materials.

The presence or absence of roots and animal traces is useful for assessing habitat suitability for plants and animals. Root abundance can be used to make inferences about soil moisture conditions as well as aeration and temperature (Weaver 1977; Lunt et al. 1973; Daubenmire 1972). The abrupt termination of roots at a particular level generally defines a physical or chemical barrier. That which restricts root growth will likely inhibit many burrowing animals and other biological activity.

Drainage

The times and depths at which a soil is wet exerts a strong influence on biological activities as well as chemical processes. Soil drainage classes (Table 3) serve to summarize soil wetness. As generally defined, however, drainage classes reflect an agricultural and a geographic (humid-temperate) bias. Local refinements are often necessary to adapt the drainage class concept to other climates and land uses. Drainage is a product of climate, slope, and landscape position along with soil characteristics.

Reaction

Soil reaction is expressed as pH. The pH influences the presence of toxic ions in the soil as well as nutrient availability to plants. Plants growing in soils with a pH less than 5.2 are likely to be affected by aluminum toxicity. Soils with a pH greater than 8.5 often have excessive amounts of sodium which can destroy soil structure and thereby reduce soil moisture and aeration. In addition, sodium can be toxic to some plants.

Table 3. Soil drainage classes (adapted from U.S. Soil Conservation Service 1981, Chap. 4).

Descriptive Term	General Connotation
Excessively drained, somewhat excessively drained	These soils have high to very high rates of water transmission and retain little moisture for plant use.
Well-drained	These soils have intermediate water transmission rates and retention capacities.
Moderately well-drained, somewhat poorly drained	These soils are commonly wet near the surface for at least a portion of the year.
Poorly drained, very poorly drained	These soils are commonly wet at or near the surface for a considerable part of the year.

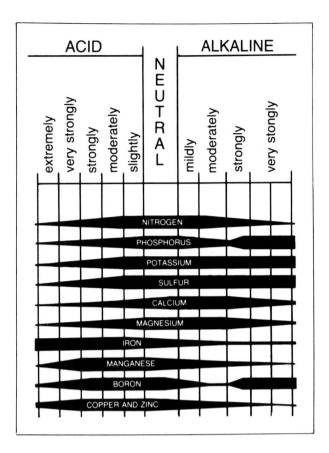

Figure 8. Soil reaction and nutrient availability.

Several essential nutrients become less available to plants as the pH decreases below about 6 or increases above about 7 (Figure 8). This effect can indirectly affect wildlife through the forage they consume. For example, many arid soils of the West have pH values between 7 and 8.4. Within this range, phosphorus availability is reduced through the formation of insoluble calcium phosphates. Short (1979) suggested that declines in herds of mule deer (*Odocoileus hemionus*) in the southwestern U.S. might be caused in part by the low available phosphorus levels in the soils.

Soil pH and associated potassium levels partially account for variation in peak densities in *Microtus pennsylvanicus* (Krebs et al. 1971). The distribution of several species of salamanders has also been related to soil pH (Mushinsky and Brodie, Jr. 1975; Batson 1965).

Other Soil Characteristics

Additional soil properties and characteristics, although not specifically stated in a standard soil description, are nevertheless commonly determined during the course of a soil survey. Many of these characteristics are not directly observed on a soil profile, but can be inferred from other properties or measured through laboratory analyses of soil samples.

Available Water Capacity. Within the plant-rooting zone, the amount of water that can be held between 1/3 bar and 15 bars of tension (1 bar = 0.99 atm) is the water retention difference. The amount of moisture at 1/3 bar, termed the field capacity, approximates the moisture that would remain in the soil after natural drainage occurred in response to gravity alone. At this point, the larger soil pores would be empty while the smaller pores would be filled with water. Soil water held at tensions of more than 15 bars (wilting point) is unavailable to many plants; hence, the moisture content between 1/3 and 15 bars is commonly referred to as the available water capacity (AWC). Some plants, however, most notably greasewood, saltbush, shadscale, and other salt desert species, can extract soil moisture at tensions far exceeding 15 bars.

The available water capacity varies with soil texture, structure, rock fragment content, and other soil properties. In general, however, fine-textured soils such as clays, clay loams, or silt loams have a high AWC whereas coarse-textured soils such as sands or sandy loams have a low AWC. The AWC does not reflect actual soil moisture content, but rather the potential to retain moisture within the defined tension limits. Thus, a sandy loam in New Mexico and New York might well have similar available water capacities, yet contain vastly different amounts of moisture at any given time due to different precipitation regimes. Nevertheless, the AWC can be useful in evaluating wildlife habitat on a local basis (Figure 9).

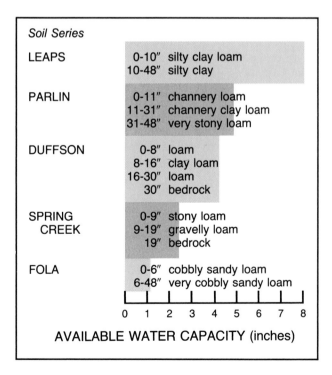

Figure 9. The potential of selected soils to retain moisture.

Seasonal Water Table. A seasonal water table is marked by the upper limit of the soil that is saturated with water for a specified period during most years. For example, a particular soil may be characterized as having a seasonally high water table at a depth of 2 feet, commonly during May and June. The presence or absence of a seasonally high water table can alter the suitability of a site for burrowing animals. It can also affect the vertical distribution within the soil of certain animals such as salamanders (Taub 1961).

Hydrologic Soil Group. The hydrologic soil group provides an interpretation of soil behavior in terms of water infiltration, transmission, and runoff. Infiltration is the rate at which water enters the soil surface, transmission is the rate of water movement within the soil, and runoff is the amount of water that moves over the surface to depressions or defined channels without entering the soil. For standardized conditions of bare soil after prolonged wetting, individual soils are assigned to one of four hydrologic soil groups, A, B, C, or D (Figure 10).

Group	Water Infiltration	Water Transmission	Water Runoff
A	(HIGH)	(HIGH)	(LOW)
B			
C			
D	(LOW)	(LOW)	(HIGH)

Figure 10. Hydrologic soil groups.

Soils in Group A with low runoff potential and correspondingly high infiltration rates consist chiefly of deep, well to excessively drained sands and gravels. In contrast, soils in Group D, having high runoff potential and low infiltration, are often clayey, have a permanent high water table, or are shallow over impervious or nearly impervious material.

Salinity. Salinity refers to the amount of salts in the soil, the standard measure of which is the electrical conductivity (EC) of an extract of the soil solution. In many situations, however, salinity is inferred and expressed as salinity classes covering a range of EC values.

Soil salinity exerts a strong influence over vegetation; as might be expected, the higher the salinity, the greater the effect (Table 4). Salts in the soil can also affect certain animals directly. Hardy (1945) noted the lack of digging activity on sites thought to

be suitable for the Merriam kangaroo rat (*Dipodomys merriami*). He speculated that this was due to a salt-derived surface crust.

Sodium Adsorption Ratio. The sodium adsorption ratio (SAR) relates the amount of sodium in the soil to the amount of calcium and magnesium. As noted earlier, high sodium can be toxic to plants as well as harmful to the physical condition of the soil. The SAR is particularly useful in assessing reclamation potential of mined lands or other severely disturbed areas. Most State and Federal reclamation guidelines for topsoil and overburden suitability include the SAR as an evaluation factor. In general, SAR values of 12 or more suggest unsuitability or at least severe limitations for successful reclamation (Fisher and Deutsch 1983).

Erodibility. Soil erosion is influenced by several non-soil factors such as slope, precipitation, wind velocity, and vegetative cover. Nevertheless, some soils erode more readily than others even when all other factors are the same.

The soil erodibility factor (K) reflects this inherent susceptibility of a soil to erode under the action of raindrop impact and water flowing over the surface (sheet and rill erosion). The wind erodibility group (WEG) reflects the susceptibility of a soil to erode under wind action. Although inherent soil erodibility varies with several different soil properties, a rough relationship exists between soil texture and both the K factor and the WEG (Figure 11).

Erosion presents dual problems in habitat management. First, soil loss can result in reduced forage production because of the removal of fertile topsoil. Second, soil lost from one site is eventually deposited elsewhere. During transport, suspended soil particles and attached ions can degrade water quality. Upon deposition, eroded soil material can further affect aquatic habitats. For example, the distribution of two species of frogs (*Rana* sp.) varied with soil texture, apparently due to different erodibilities and associated sediment burdens in adjacent streams (Lynch 1978).

Soil Fertility. Soil fertility is the inherent capability of a soil to supply nutrients to plants in adequate amounts and in suitable proportions (Buckman and Brady 1969). As discussed earlier, soil pH serves as an indicator of nutrient availability. Soil fertility is more specifically characterized through laboratory analyses of extractable bases (e.g., Ca, Mg, Na, K), phosphorus, nitrogen, and determinations of cation exchange capacity, and percentage-base saturation (see Sources of Soil Information section).

Soil fertility has long been known to influence the palatability of plants. For example, the volatile oil

Table 4. Soil salinity classes (U.S. Soil Conservation Service 1983, Part 603).

Electrical Conductivity (millimhos/cm)	Salinity Class	Connotation[1]
0–2	Nonsaline	No effect on plants.
2–4	Very slightly saline	Effect on plants is mostly negligible; only most sensitive plants affected adversely.
4–8	Slightly saline	Many plants are adversely affected but diversity of adapted species is quite high (e.g., four-wing saltbush, winterfat, galleta).
8–16	Moderately saline	Plant communities are dominated by salt-tolerant species (e.g., greasewood, mat saltbush, western wheatgrass).
> 16	Strongly saline	Few plants are adapted (e.g., shadscale, iodine bush, alkali sacaton).

[1]U.S. Salinity Laboratory Staff 1954; McArthur et al. 1978; Thornburg 1982.

content of sagebrush leaves seems to vary with soil depth and fertility among other non-soil factors (Powell 1970; Nagy 1966). This is of particular importance because high volatile oil content inhibits the activity of rumen microorganisms (Nagy et al. 1964). Some of the more dramatic palatability effects are observed when commercial fertilizers are added to nutrient deficient soils. Gessel and Orians (1967) observed that certain rodents selectively fed on nitrogen-fertilized trees while avoiding adjacent unfertilized trees or those fertilized with potassium.

In a series of studies spanning several years in Missouri, the abundance, distribution, health, and size of several animals including wild turkeys, rabbits, raccoons, muskrats, opossums, and squirrels were linked to soil fertility (Denny 1944; Crawford 1950; Albrecht 1957). Low soil fertility, particularly levels of nitrogen and phosphorus, has previously been noted as a possible cause of the decline in herds of mule deer in the Southwest (Short 1979).

Relationships between animals and soil fertility are not always predictable. For example, a pocket gopher *(Thomomys bottae)* has been found in abundance on serpentine-derived soils in contrast to adjacent non-serpentine soils (Proctor and Whitten 1971). As noted previously, serpentine-derived soils are generally low or lacking in several essential plant nutrients. This apparent anomaly was explained by the presence of *Brodiaca* sp., a serpentine-tolerant plant whose corm serves as a primary food source for the gophers.

SOIL CLASSIFICATION

Soil taxonomy, although foreign to most biologists, is as much a scientific necessity as the taxonomic systems used to classify plants and animals. The soil taxonomic system used in the U.S. groups soils according to measurable characteristics such as depth, texture, temperature and moisture regimes, and chemical properties. Like botanical and zoological systems, soil taxonomy provides a uniform means to identify a particular soil and facilitates the transfer of both soils information and that which can be related to soils.

The system is hierarchical, consisting of six levels or categories including order, suborder, great group, subgroup, family, and series. At the highest or most general level there are 10 soil orders. At the lowest and most specific level, over 12,000 series have been identified in the U.S. alone, and the number is increasing annually. Table 5 shows the classification at all levels for one particular soil. The nomenclature applied conveys progressively more information from the order through the family level. Each term is specifically defined in a handbook outlining soil taxonomy (Soil Survey Staff 1975). At the lowest level, the series name itself has no specific technical meaning, often being derived from a place or local landmark near where the soil was first described. A series description, however, refines family attributes by further narrowing the allowable range of individual soil properties (Figure 1).

Soil taxonomy is useful in making habitat generalizations. For example, Kantrud and Kologiski

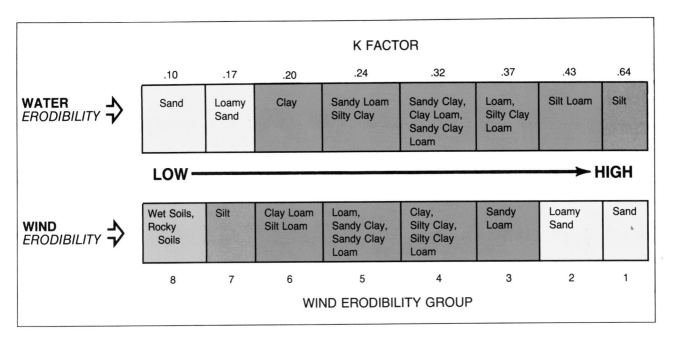

Figure 11. Soil erodibility.

Table 5. Taxonomic system for soil classification (Soil Survey Staff 1975).

Taxonomic Category	Number in System[1]	Example						
Order	10							Aridisol
Suborder	45							Argid
Great Group	187							Haplargid
Subgroup	990					Lithic	Ustollic	Haplargid
Family	5,603		Loamy,	mixed,	mesic,	Lithic	Ustollic	Haplargid
Series	12,002							

< 35% clay in zone of clay accumulation

mixed mineralogy (40% of any one mineral other than quartz)

mean annual soil temp. between 8° and 15° C (at 50 cm or bedrock, whichever shallower)

depth to bedrock is < 50 cm (20 in.)

is wetter and has more organic matter than normal for the great group

has no cemented pan or high sodium content

has a horizon of silicate clay accumulation

is dry in plant-root zone for at least half of growing season

[1]as of October 1980

(1982) found that average bird density and species richness were slightly higher on soils of the order Mollisol than on soils of the order Aridisol. Within the order Mollisol, significantly different species densities were found at the soil subgroup level. In another study, Leopold and Dalke (1941) found that a single soil series supported over 90% of the wild turkey population in Missouri.

SOIL MAPPING

Soil surveys are designed and conducted at different intensities to meet different needs. Accordingly, not all surveys provide information at the same level of detail nor of equal applicability in habitat management. Failure to recognize this fact can and has led to the misuse of soil survey information. Potential users of soil information should be involved in the design of soil surveys. Where soil surveys are already completed, users of the data should be sufficiently knowledgeable to recognize both the strengths and the limitations of the soil map.

Mapping Variables

Four main variables, map unit components, kinds of map units, field procedures, and map scales, are used in designing soil surveys. The same variables are useful in assessing the applicability of existing soil survey information.

Map unit components are bodies of soil that can be identified as being a member of some class (taxon) in soil taxonomy or bodies of nonsoil that can be identified as any of 22 types of miscellaneous areas (e.g., rock outcrop, badland, riverwash; U.S. Soil Conservation Service 1981). In practice, soil taxons and miscellaneous areas are often further refined by one or more phase modifiers. Phases reflect various use-related soil and nonsoil attributes such as surface texture and slope (see examples in Figure 12).

The kind of map unit depends on the number and arrangement of the individual components on the landscape (Figure 12). Single-component map units, termed consociations, are dominated by one soil taxon or miscellaneous area. Multicomponent map units, termed either associations or complexes, contain two or more dominant taxons or miscellaneous areas. In an association, the named components generally lie in a regular geographic pattern and can be located in the field by visible landscape features (e.g., hill slopes vs. valley bottoms, north slopes vs. south slopes). In contrast, the named components in a complex either lie in a very intricate pattern that cannot be determined by visible landscape features or are simply too small to be separated. The choice of map unit depends on the soil itself as well as the purpose of the survey and the level of detail needed. Regardless of the map unit, however, there will always be some areas of soil or nonsoil material that do not conform to the named components. Such areas, termed inclusions, occur because of map scale limitations or errors in the placement of map unit boundaries. As a general rule, inclusions that would differ significantly in use and management from the named components should not exceed 15% of the map unit.

The initial step in a soil survey is often to develop a preliminary soil map based on ancillary data (e.g., geology, landform, adjacent soil maps) and a knowledge of soil formation and its relationship to other landscape features. These preliminary map units are then field checked and revised as necessary. The specific procedures used in the field work determine the precision with which map unit components are identified and described, and the accuracy of map unit boundaries. Common field procedures include explicit soil sampling schemes, observations of exposed soils (e.g., roadcut), landscape features on the ground, and interpretations of aerial photographs or other remotely sensed images.

Map scale determines the smallest sized unit that can be practically delineated on a map. Generally this is a 1/4 x 1/4 in. square or a circular area of about 1/16 square inch. By using these guidelines, the smallest unit that can be delineated at a scale of 1:24,000 (7 1/2′min quadrangle) is about 6 acres (Table 6). Smaller areas, if important, can be shown by spot symbols. Such a practice should be used to indicate special habitat features such as small ponds, or wet depressions, springs, and escarpments.

Table 6. Guide to map scales and corresponding minimum size delineations (U.S. Soil Conservation Service 1981, Chap. 2).

Scale	Inches/Mile	Minimum Delineation (acres)
1:7,920	8.0	0.6
1:15,840	4.0	2.5
1:24,000	2.6	6.0
1:31,680	2.0	10.0
1:63,360	1.0	40.0
1:126,720	0.5	160.0

Mapping Intensity

Based on the four variables above, soil surveys can be grouped by levels of intensity and general application. Five such levels are commonly recognized ranging from Order 1 surveys, the most intensive, to Order 5 surveys, the least intensive. Any given survey, however, need not be of a single intensity. In fact, a mixture of intensities will often best meet user needs most economically. Soil surveys on BLM-administered lands often contain elements of Order 2, 3, and 4 mapping intensities. Figure 13 shows how a single area might differ when mapped at each of these intensity levels.

SOURCES OF SOIL INFORMATION

Perhaps the most obvious source of soils information is a soil scientist. Currently, the Bureau of Land Management employs about 75 soil scientists distributed among its various field offices, the BLM Service Center, and the Headquarters Office in Washington, DC.

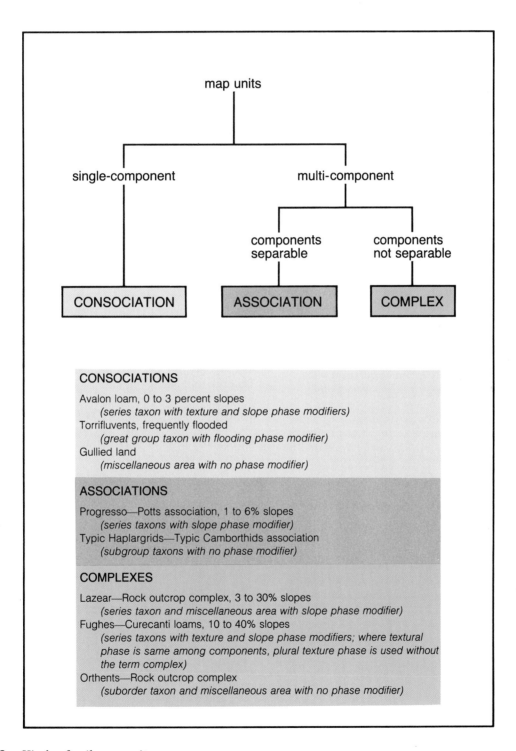

Figure 12. Kinds of soil-map units.

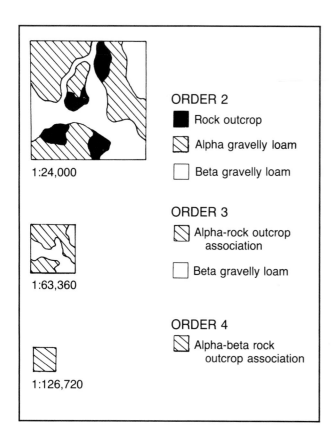

ORDER 2
- ■ Rock outcrop
- ▨ Alpha gravelly loam
- ☐ Beta gravelly loam

1:24,000

ORDER 3
- ▨ Alpha-rock outcrop association
- ☐ Beta gravelly loam

1:63,360

ORDER 4
- ▨ Alpha-beta rock outcrop association

1:126,720

Figure 13. Soil mapping intensity.

Published soils information is concentrated in soil survey reports. Such reports are generally published by the U.S. Soil Conservation Service (SCS) as part of a formal series, often in cooperation with State Agricultural Experiment Stations and other State and Federal agencies. These reports have a standardized format, the primary elements of which are listed in Table 7. A nationwide list of published soil surveys is prepared and periodically updated by the SCS (U.S. Soil Conservation Service 1982).

Interim reports, of variable content and formality, are often prepared before formal publication. This is true on much of the public land administered by the BLM where field mapping is still in progress or only recently completed. These reports are available in the respective District or Resource Area Offices. Special purpose surveys, often of limited areal extent (e.g., mining and mineral exploration tracts, research areas), may also be available through private companies, universities, or other Federal agencies.

Soil laboratory data in much greater detail than that commonly found in soil survey reports are published as Soil Survey Investigations Reports (SSIR). They have been issued for many individual States and groups of States (U.S. Soil Conservation Service 1972). Similar information is also published by State Agricultural Experiment Stations in various forms

(e.g., Science Monographs, Miscellaneous Reports, Special Resource Series).

APPLICATION OF SOIL INFORMATION

A knowledge of soils and their variability across the landscape can aid in delineating habitat units, in assessing habitat suitability, and in developing and evaluating habitat management alternatives.

Habitat Delineation

An initial objective in wildlife inventory is to delineate land units with the same environmental attributes. The "habitat site" constitutes this unit in the BLM's Integrated Habitat Inventory and Classification System (IHICS; U.S. Bureau of Land Management 1982). Once delineated, similar although not necessarily adjacent habitat sites are aggregated into so-called standard habitat sites (SHS). Data on animal occurrence from a few representative habitat sites are then extrapolated to characterize an entire SHS. The reliability of this procedure rests on the assumption that any given habitat site is uniform in terms of those site factors that influence animal occurrence.

By definition, a habitat site is an area of homogeneous (present) vegetation, landform, soils, and climate (U.S. Bureau of Land Management 1982). In practice, however, habitat sites and standard habitat sites are often delineated almost exclusively on the present vegetation. This approach can result in non-homogeneous sites which in turn can lead to erroneous conclusions on animal occurrence and distribution. For example, overgrazing or other land-use practices can produce relatively uniform vegetation over broad areas. With vegetation as the main habitat criterion, the illusion of habitat uniformity exists even though the underlying soils may be variable. For animals sensitive to soil variability, subsequent habitat characterizations are incomplete at best.

In most instances, neither soils nor vegetation (nor any other single factor) can adequately describe habitat. When all relevant factors are considered together, however, they are complementary and provide an added dimension to the understanding of the habitat unit.

Habitat Suitability

The suitability of a standard habitat site for a particular wildlife species depends on whether existing habitat features meet the needs of the animal. When soil information is used in the delineation and aggregation of habitat sites, suitability assessments

Table 7. Major sections of a soil survey report (U.S. Soil Conservation Service 1983, Part 605).

Section	General Content
General nature of the survey area	Commonly contains a discussion of the history, climate, physiography, drainage, and natural resources of the survey area.
General soil map and map unit description	Includes a general soil map (common scale of 1:250,000 or smaller) and associated map unit descriptions; narrative descriptions commonly give a brief characterization of the included soils, their relative proportions, and major inclusions, along with information on elevation, landform, topography, average precipitation and air temperature, plant communities, and dominant use and management considerations.
Use and management	Provides interpretive information, mainly in tabular form, on soil productive capability, potential plant communities, and suitability and/or limitations for major land uses and practices.
Soil properties	Commonly includes tabular data on soil texture, rock content, water retention difference, pH, salinity, wind and water erosion factors, hydrologic soil group, and other features.
Classification of soils	Gives the taxonomic classification for each soil.
Soil series and morphology	Contains the detailed descriptions for each soil series (or other category if applicable); Figure 1 was taken from this section of a soil survey report.

can be strengthened. To do so, relationships between animals and soils must be characterized. More specifically, the soil-related affinities and tolerances must be identified for individual animal species or groups of species.

Applicable information on soil-animal relationships does exist, although it is widely scattered and poorly developed for actual application. The results of a limited literature review are shown in Table 8. The task of accumulating and arraying such information in a usable form should be a joint effort between soil scientists and wildlife biologists. The logical first step would be an exhaustive review of pertinent literature. The next step would be to develop a data format to enable practical application. A sample format patterned after traditional soil interpretations is shown in Table 9. Once identified, relationships between soil properties and animals can be used to interpret soil map units or components of map units. For example, the Kech loam, 3 to 15% slopes, is a soil map unit whose primary component is the Kech soil series. If the Kech series exhibits properties that are suited to a particular animal species, all areas mapped as such could be considered at least potentially suitable for that species. In conjunction with the evaluation of other factors (e.g., vegetation), such analyses can be useful in predicting animal presence or absence, determining probable ranges, and selecting optimum sampling sites for supporting studies.

Even when relationships between soils and animals are unknown, there are opportunities to make use of existing soils information. For example, where estimates of wildlife occurrence have been established through previous sampling or other studies, presumed distribution patterns can be superimposed on soil maps. The objective is to identify any apparent associations between wildlife distribution and soil map units. At this level of analysis, it is not necessary to know the exact nature of the relationship, but simply that a relationship is probable. This knowledge alone can aid in extrapolating data from sampled to unsampled areas.

For certain animal species, particularly large ungulates with broad ranges, habitat suitability may be closely related to the intermingling of various soils and associated vegetation producing so-called edge effects or ecotones. Wertz (1966) provided an example of such an analysis from Wisconsin. Individual soils were characterized by vegetation type and cover. Natural edge conditions were identified where contrasting soils occurred together on the landscape. Ratings based on the number of miles of soil-associated natural edge were then used to assess the suitability of different management areas for various wildlife species.

Searching for soil-animal relationships by analyzing several layers of data is a tedious job. This, in part, accounts for the general lack of species-specific soil interpretations for wildlife habitat management. With the increasing availability of computerized soils and vegetational data bases along with the analytic capabilities of geographic information systems (GIS), such analyses should be greatly facilitated.

Table 8. Relationships between soils and wildlife.

Soil Property	Wildlife Characteristic	Wildlife Species	Reference
Texture	Distribution	Kangaroo rats (*Dipodomys sp.*)	Dale 1939
Texture	Distribution	Pocket mice (*Perognathus sp.*)	Hardy 1945
Texture	Distribution	Deer mouse (*Peromyscus maniculatus*)	Hardy 1945
Texture	Distribution	S. grasshopper mouse (*Unchomys torridus*)	Hardy 1945
Texture	Distribution	Various lizard species	Stuart 1932
Texture	Population density	G. Basin pocket mouse (*Perognathus parvus*)	Feldhamer 1979
Texture	Population density	Least chipmunk (*Tamias minimus*)	Feldhamer 1979
Texture	Dust-bathing behavior	Bobwhite quail (*Colinus virginianus*)	Borchelt and Overmann 1974
Texture	Denning habits	Red fox (*Vulpes vulpes*)	Sheldon 1950
Texture	Burrow location	Woodchuck (*Marmota monax*)	Moss 1940
Texture & erodibility	Distribution	Leopard frogs (*Rana sp.*)	Lynch 1978
Texture & depth	Distribution, animal size	Pocket gophers (*Thomomys sp.*)	Davis 1938
Texture & depth	Distribution, animal size	Pocket gophers (*Geomys sp.*)	Davis et al. 1938
Depth	Distribution	Kangaroo rats (*Dipodomys sp.*)	Hardy 1945
Depth	Distribution	W. harvest mouse (*Reithrodontomys megalotis*)	Hardy 1945
Depth & strength	Population density	Least chipmunk (*Tamius minimus*)	Feldhamer 1979
Strength		Various desert rodents	Rosenzweig and Winakur 1969
Drainage	Burrowing habits	Black-tailed prairie dog (*Cynomys ludovicianus*)	Sheets et al. 1971
Water table depth	Vertical distribution	Red-backed salamander (*Plethodon cinereus*)	Taub 1961
Moisture	Distribution	Voles (*Microtus sp.*)	Hodgson 1972
Moisture	Distribution	Sagebrush vole (*Lagurus curtatus*)	O'Farrell 1972
Moisture	Distribution	Ground squirrels (*Spermophilus sp.*)	Turner 1972
Moisture	Distribution	Kangaroo rats (*Dipodomys sp.*)	Bienek and Grundmann 1971
Moisture	Rehydration (water balance)	Various salamander species	Spight 1967
Color	Pelage coloration	Various small mammals	Dice and Blossom 1937
Color	Pelage coloration	Various small mammals	Stebler 1939
Reaction (pH)	Substrate preference	Various salamander species	Mushinsky & Brodie, Jr. 1975
Reaction (pH)	Population density	Meadow vole (*Microtus pennsylvanicus*)	Krebs et al. 1971
Nitrogen level	Feeding habits	Red-backed vole (*Clethrionmys sp.*)	Gessel and Orians 1967
Available phosphorus	Fawn recruitment	Mule deer (*docoileus hemionus*)	Short 1979
Sodium level	Lick preference	Mountain goat (*Oreamnos americanus*)	Stockstad et al. 1953
Sodium level	Lick preference	Elk (*Cervus elaphus*)	Stockstad et al. 1953
Sodium level	Lick preference	Mule deer (*Odocoileus hemionus*)	Stockstad et al. 1953
Sodium level	Lick preference	White-tailed deer (*Odocoileus virginianus*)	Stockstad et al. 1953
Sodium level	Peak population density	Microtine rodents	Aumann 1965
Calcium availability	Feeding habits	Ring-necked pheasant (*Phasianus colchicus*)	Harper and Labisky 1964
Overall fertility	Distribution, animal weight	Raccoon (*Procyon lotor*)	Crawford 1950
Overall fertility	Pelt size and quality	Opossum (*Didelphis virginianus*)	Crawford 1950
Overall fertility	Animal weight, bone strength	E. cottontail (*Sylvilagus floridanus*)	Crawford 1950
Overall fertility	Fecundity	E. cottontail (*Sylvilagus floridanus*)	Williams and Caskey 1965
Overall fertility	Litter size	E. cottontail (*Sylvilagus floridanus*)	Hill 1972
Overall fertility	Breeding potential	White-tailed deer (*Odocoileus virginianus*)	Crawford 1953
Parent material (Serpentine)	Distribution	Botta's pocket gopher (*Thomomys bottaie*)	Proctor and Whitten 1971
Soil classification series	Distribution	Turkey (*Meleagris gallopavo*)	Leopold and Dalke 1943
Soil classification series	Forage preference	Black-tailed deer (*Odocoileus Hemionus columbianus*)	Whitaker 1965
Subgroup	Species richness	Various bird species	Kantrud and Kologiski 1982

Table 9. Sample format for soil interpretations of habitat suitability for a particular animal species.

Soil Property or Soil-Related Habitat Feature	HABITAT SUITABILITY		
	Optimum	*Marginal*	*Unsuitable*
Texture	Loamy sand, Sandy loam, Sandy clay loam, Loam	Silt loam, Silt, Silty clay loam, Clay loam	Clay, Silty clay, Sandy clay, Sand
Depth (inches)	>40	20–40	<20
Drainage	Well-drained	Moderately well-drained, Somewhat poorly drained	Poorly drained, Very poorly drained, Excessively drained, Somewhat excessively drained
Consistence (moist)	Very friable, Friable	Firm	Loose, Very firm, Extremely firm, Extremely hard
Salinity (mmhos/cm)	0–4	4–8	>8
Depth to high water table (ft)	—	—	<2
Rock fragments 3 in. (wt. %)	>15	—	—
Hydrologic soil group	B	C	A, D
Salt-derived surface crust	—	—	Present

Habitat Management

Habitat managers are naturally concerned with existing habitat conditions. Management objectives, however, may well call for more than maintenance of the status quo. Effective management often necessitates change and with it the need to predict the likelihood of success, risks involved, and any special practices that may be desirable. This requires a knowledge of the present, but equally important, a knowledge of habitat capability. Habitat capability as embodied in the concepts of habitat type (Daubenmire 1968; Dyksterhuis 1983), and ecological (range) site (U.S. Soil Conservation Service 1976; Society for Range Management 1983) is expressed as the potential plant community. Where sites have been subjected to little disturbance, potential can often be described directly or deduced from the existing plant community. As a result of past land use, however, present vegetation may bear little resemblance to the potential. In such situations, soils may provide the only identifiable link between present and potential (Munn et al. 1978; Passey et al. 1982). With soil as the common denominator, knowledge of potential plant communities can be extrapolated from a few relict sites to numerous disturbed or altered sites. In addition, arraying vegetational data from several sites on the same or similar soils reveals the variety of developmental stages, presumably leading to the same potential plant community. Comparison of the present with the potential provides a valuable clue as to site responsiveness and thereby aids in evaluating opportunities and choosing among various management alternatives.

The concept of site capability goes beyond an interest in potential plant communities. Equally important are soil-related limitations in the selection of habitat improvement methods and materials and in the establishment of reasonable use restrictions to prevent habitat degradation. Some soils have few limitations. They are often deep, flat-lying, well-drained, and are free of surface stones or boulders. Other soils may have yearlong or perhaps seasonal limitations due to wetness. Surface stones may preclude the use of certain types of seeding equipment and brush choppers. Hardpans and soils shallow to bedrock can obviously affect projects requiring excavation. Failure to observe such limitations can damage equipment, increase construction and maintenance costs, reduce the effective life of an improvement, and result in unnecessary habitat degradation.

Soil survey reports commonly rate soils for shallow excavations (e.g., pipelines), pond and reservoir areas, embankments, and as sources of construction materials (e.g., sand, gravel, topsoil). Many other interpretations applicable to habitat management are being developed although there has been insufficient testing and validation to warrant widespread use. Examples include soil limitations for rangeland equipment (e.g., drills, discs), tree planting, fencing, prescribed burning, and the use of off-road vehicles. A strong commitment to testing and refining interpretations is essential if they are to be applied with confidence.

LITERATURE CITED

ALBRECHT, W.A. 1957. Soil fertility and biotic geography. Geog. Rev. 47(1):86-105.

AUMANN, G.D. 1965. Microtine abundance and soil sodium levels. J. Mammal. 46(4):594-604.

BATSON, J.D. 1965. Some comparative behavior studies on three genera of salamanders. Trans. Ky. Acad. Sci. 25:120-128.

BIENEK, G.K. and A.W. GRUNDMANN. 1971. Burrowing habits of two subspecies of *Dipodomys merriami* in California and Utah. Great Basin Nat. 31(3):190-192.

BORCHELT, P.L. and S.R. OVERMANN. 1974. Development of dust-bathing in bobwhite quail: I. Effects of age, experience, texture of dust, and social facilitation. Dev. Psychobiol. 7(4):305-313.

BUCKMAN, H.O. and N.C. BRADY. 1969. The nature and properties of soils. The Macmillian Company. New York, NY. 567pp.

CRAWFORD, W.T. 1950. Some specific relationships between soils and wildlife. J. Wildl. Manage. 14(2):115-123.

———. 1953. Relationships of soils and wildlife. Pages 10-18 *in* Nagel, W.O. ed. Wildlife and the Soil. Missouri Conservation Commission, Jefferson City, MO.

DALE, F.H. 1939. Variability and environmental responses of the kangaroo rat, *Dipodomys heermanni saxatilis.* Amer. Midl. Nat. 22:703-731.

DAUBENMIRE, R. 1968. Plant communities: A textbook of plant synecology. Harper and Row. New York, NY. 300pp.

———. 1972. Annual cycles of soil moisture and temperature as related to grass development in the steppe of eastern Washington. Ecol. 53(3):419-424.

DAVIS, W.B. 1938. Relation of size of pocket gophers to soil and altitude. J. Mammal 19:338-342.

———, R.R. RAMSEY, and J.M. ARENDALE. 1938. Distribution of pocket gophers *(Geomys breviceps)* in relation to soils. J. Mammal. 19:412-418.

DENNY, A.H. 1944. Wildlife relationships to soil types. Trans. N. Am. Wildl. Conf. 9:316-322.

DICE, L.R. and P.M. BLOSSOM. 1937. Studies of mammalian ecology in southwestern North America with special attention to the colors of desert mammals. Carnegie Inst. Wash. Publ. No. 485:1-129.

DYKSTERHUIS, E.J. 1983. Habitat-type: A review. Rangelands 5(6):270-271.

FELDHAMER, G.A. 1979. Vegetative and edaphic factors affecting the abundance and distribution of small mammals in southeast Oregon. Great Basin Nat. 39(3):207-218.

FISHER, S. and P. DEUTSCH. 1983. The soil resource: Its importance in the West and its role in coal development and reclamation *in* Coal Development: Collected Papers. Papers presented at Coal Development Workshops in Grand Junction, Colorado, and Casper, Wyoming. Sponsored by U.S. Dep. Inter., Bur. Land Manage. Vol. II:845-984.

GESSEL, S.P. and G.H. ORIANS. 1967. Rodent damage to fertilized silver fir in western Washington. Ecol. 48(4):694-697.

HARDY, R. 1945. The influence of types of soil upon the local distribution of small mammals in southwestern Utah. Ecol. Monog. 15(1):71-108.

HARPER, J.A. and R.F. LABISKY. 1964. The influence of calcium on the distribution of pheasants in Illinois. J. Wildl. Manage. 28:722-731.

HILL, E.P., III. 1972. Litter size in Alabama cottontails as influenced by soil fertility. J. Wildl. Manage. 36:1199-1209.

HODGSON, J.R. 1972. Local distribution of *Microtus montanus* and *M. pennsylvanicus* in southwestern Montana. J. Mammal. 53(3):487-499.

KANTRUD, H.A. and R.L. KOLOGISKI. 1982. Effects of soils and grazing on breeding birds of uncultivated upland grasslands of the Northern Great Plains. U.S. Dep. Inter., Fish and Wildl. Serv. Wildl. Res. Rep. 15. Washington, DC. 33pp.

KLEMMEDSON, J.O. 1970. Needs for soil information in the management of range resources. J. Range Manage. 23(2):139-143.

KREBS, C.J., B.L. KELLER, and J.H. MYERS. 1971. *Microtus* population densities and soil nutrients in southern Indiana grasslands. Ecol. 52(4):660-663.

KRUCKEBERG, A.R. 1969. Soil diversity and the distribution of plants with examples from western North America. Madrono 20:129-154.

LEOPOLD, A.S. and P.D. DALKE. 1943. The 1942 status of wild turkeys in Missouri. J. Forest. 41(6):428-435.

LUNT, O.R., J. LETEY, and S.B. CLARK. 1973. Oxygen requirements for root growth in three species of desert shrubs. Ecol. 54(6):1356-1362.

LYNCH, J.D. 1978. The distribution of leopard frogs (*Rana blairi* and *R. pipiens*) (Amphibia, Anura, Ranadae) in Nebraska. J. Herpetol. 12(2):157-162.

MARCHAND, D.E. 1973. Edaphic control of plant distribution in the White Mountains, eastern California. Ecol. 54(2):233-250.

MASER, C., J.M. GEIST, D.M. CONCANNON, R. ANDERSON, and B. LOVELL. 1979. Wildlife habitat in managed rangelands—the Great Basin of southeastern Oregon: geomorphic and edaphic habitats. U.S. Dep. Agric., For. Serv. Gen. Tech. Rep. PNW-99. Portland, OR. 84pp.

MCARTHUR, E.D., A.P. PLUMMER, and J.N. DAVIS. 1978. Rehabilitation of game range in the salt desert. Pages 23-50 *in* Wyoming Shrublands, Proc. Seventh Wyoming Shrub Ecology Workshop, Rock Springs, WY. Range Manage. Div., Univ. WY. Laramie.

MCCOLLEY, P.D. and H.S. HODGKINSON. 1970. Effect of soil depth on plant production. J. Range Manage. 23(3):189-192.

MOSS, A.E. 1940. The woodchuck as a soil expert. J. Wildl. Manage. 4:441-443.

MUNN, L.C., G.A. NIELSEN, and W.F. MUEGGLER. 1978. Relationships of soils to mountain and foothill range habitat types and production in western Montana. Soil Sci. Soc. Amer. J. 42:135-139.

MUNSELL COLOR. 1975. Munsell Soil Color Charts. Macbeth Division, Kollmorgen Corp. Baltimore, MD. 21218.

MUSHINSKY, H.R. and E.D. BRODIE, Jr. 1975. Selection of substrate pH by salamanders. Amer. Midl. Nat. 93(2):440-443.

NAGY, J.G. 1966. Volatile oils and antibiosis of *Artemisia.* PhD. dissertation. Colorado State Univ. Ft. Collins. 73pp.

———, H.W. STEINHOFF, and G.W. WARD. 1964. Effects of essential oils of sagebrush on deer rumen microbial function. J. Wildl. Manage. 28:785-790.

O'FARRELL, T.P. 1972. Ecological distribution of sage-brush voles, *Lagurus curtatus,* in south-central Washington. J. Mammal. 53(3):632-636.

PASSEY, H.B., V.K. HUGIE, E.W. WILLIAMS, and D.E. BALL. 1982. Relationships between soil, plant community, and climate on rangelands of the Intermountain West. U.S. Dep. Agric., Soil Conserv. Serv. Tech. Bull. 1669. 123pp.

POWELL, J. 1970. Site factor relationships with volatile oils in big sagebrush. J. Range Manage. 23(1):42-46.

PROCTOR, J. and K. WHITTEN. 1971. A population of the valley pocket gopher *(Thomomys bottae)* on a serpentine soil. Amer. Midl. Nat. 85(2):517-521.

ROSENZWEIG, M.L. and J. Winakur. 1969. Population ecology of desert rodent communities: Habitats and environmental complexity. Ecol. 50(4):558-572.

SHEETS, R.G., R.L. LINDER, and R.B. DAHLGREN. 1971. Burrow systems of prairie dogs in South Dakota. J. Mammal. 52(2):451-453.

SHELDON, W.G. 1950. Denning habits and home range of red foxes in New York State. J. Wildl. Manage. 14:33-42.

SHORT, H.L. 1979. Deer in Arizona and New Mexico: Their ecology and a theory explaining recent population decreases. U.S. Dep. Agric., For. Serv. Gen. Tech. Rep. RM-70. 25pp.

SOCIETY FOR RANGE MANAGEMENT. 1983. Guidelines and terminology for range inventories and monitoring. Report of the Range Inventory Standardization Committee (RISC). 13pp.

SOIL SURVEY STAFF. 1975. Soil taxonomy: A basic system of soil classification for making and interpreting soil surveys. U.S. Dep. Agric., Soil Conserv. Serv., Agric. Handb. 436. 754pp.

SPIGHT, T. M. 1967. The water economy of salamanders: Exchange of water with the soil. Biol. Bull. 132(1):126-132.

STEBLER, A.M. 1939. An ecological study of the mammals of the Badlands and the Black Hills of South Dakota and Wyoming. Ecol. 20:382-393.

STOCKSTAD, D.S., M.S. MORRIS, and E.C. LORY. 1953. Chemical characteristics of natural licks used by big game animals in western Montana. Trans. N. Am. Wildl. Conf. 18:247-257.

STUART, L.C. 1932. The lizards of the middle Pahvant Valley, Utah: Materials for a study in saurian distribution. Occ. Papers Mus. Zool., Univ. Mich. 244:1-33.

TAUB, F.B. 1961. The distribution of the red-backed salamander, *Plethodon C. cinereus,* within the soil. Ecol. 42(4):681-698.

THORNBURG, A.A. 1982. Plant materials for use on surface-mined lands in arid and semiarid regions. U.S. Dep. Agric., Soil Conserv. Serv. SCS-TP-157. 88pp.

TURNER, L.W. 1972. Habitat differences between *Spermophilus beldingi* and *Spermophilus columbianus* in Oregon. J. Mammal. 53(4):914-917.

U.S. BUREAU OF LAND MANAGEMENT. 1982. Integrated Habitat Inventory and Classification System. U.S. Dep. Inter., Bur. Land Manage. Manual 6602. Washington, DC.

U.S. SALINITY LABORATORY STAFF. 1954. Diagnosis and improvement of saline and alkali soils. U.S. Dep. Agric., Agric. Handb. 60. Washington, DC. 160pp.

U.S. SOIL CONSERVATION SERVICE. 1972. Soil Survey Laboratory Methods and Procedures for Collecting Soil Samples. Soil Survey Investigation Report (SSIR) No. 1. U.S. Dep. Agric., Soil Conserv. Serv. Washington, DC. 20013.

Additional reports, containing soil survey laboratory data for specific states include:

    SSIR No.   7 Montana
    SSIR No.   8 Wyoming
    SSIR No. 10 Colorado
    SSIR No. 11 Oklahoma
    SSIR No. 22 Alabama and Florida
    SSIR No. 23 Nevada
    SSIR No. 24 California
    SSIR No. 28 Arizona

————. 1976. National range handbook. NRH-1. U.S. Dep. Agric., Soil Conserv. Serv. Washington, DC. 20013.

————. 1981. Soil survey manual SSM-430-V. U.S. Dep. Agric., Soil Conserv. Serv. Washington, DC. 20013.

————. 1982. List of published soil surveys: January 1982. U.S. Dep. Agric., Soil Conserv. Serv. Washington, DC. 20013.

————. 1983. National soils handbook. NSH-430-VI. U.S. Dep. Agric., Soil Conserv. Serv. Washington, DC. 20013.

WEAVER, T. 1977. Root distribution and soil water regimes in nine habitat types of the northern Rocky Mountains. Marshall, J. ed. The Below Ground Ecosystem. Range Sci. Dep. Sci. Series 26. Colorado State Univ., Fort Collins. 351pp.

WERTZ, W.A. 1966. Interpretation of soil surveys for wildlife management. Amer. Midl. Nat. 75(1):211-224.

WHITAKER, G.A. 1965. Deer-soil relationships in the oak-grasslands. M.S. Thesis, Humboldt State College. Arcata, CA. 87pp.

WILLIAMS, C.E. and A.L. CASKEY. 1965. Soil fertility and cottontail fecundity in southeastern Missouri. Amer. Mid. Nat. 74(1):211-224.

27

TERRESTRIAL PHYSICAL FEATURES

Allen Cooperrider

U.S. Bureau of Land Management
Service Center
Denver, CO 80225

"With a broad awareness and understanding of particular physiographic features, one begins to appreciate them as wildlife habitat, their relationship to land mangement, and the need to account for them in land-use planning."

—Chris Maser et al., *Geomorphic and Edaphic Habitats*

Editor's Note: The wildlife biologist instinctively recognizes the importance of physical features for wildlife—the nesting cliff for falcons, the talus slope for marmots, the south-facing, snow-free winter range for mule deer. However, habitat inventories and evaluations often concentrate exclusively on vegetation and ignore these important habitat components and attributes. Formal systems for classifying and naming such features as wildlife habitat are virtually non-existent for terrestrial features. This chapter covers the classification and measurement of terrestrial features.

INTRODUCTION

Physical features of the environment are just as important as vegetation in determining animal abundance and distribution. Many wildlife species have adapted to using certain physical features of the environment to the point where they cannot survive and reproduce without them. Consider such obligate relationships as use of cliffs for breeding by prairie falcons and many other raptors, or use of steep, rugged topography for escape cover by bighorn sheep (*Ovis canadensis*).

Biologists and naturalists have long recognized these dependencies and use of physical features by individual species. However, little work has been done to develop general methodology for categorizing or quantifying the features themselves. Several reasons account for this neglect. First, some of the most important attributes of physical features are spatial or geographic. For example, the most important attribute about a feature, such as a seep in a limestone outcropping, is its location. If biologists have marked the location on a map, they have recorded the data needed to predict, for instance, that a species of salamander may be present. Measurements of height, slope, etc., may be quite irrelevant. Even with features such as cliffs, where attributes such as height are important, broad categories, such as "10 to 30 m" (33 to 99 ft) and "over 30 m" (99 ft), are adequate for most purposes.

Second, most biologists only work with a limited number of species and they know from experience what a suitable physical feature looks like. For example, bighorn sheep biologists know that "steep, rugged, rocky terrain" is an essential component of sheep habitat. However, since they easily recognize such habitat, few bother to attempt to quantify "steep," "rugged," or "rocky." This lack of quantification of terrestrial physical features sharply contrasts with aquatic features, for which well-developed measurement systems have been in use for years.

However, the need for more quantification or at least more standardized categorization has become evident. Biologists must deal with many more species than in the past, and it is useful to have quantitative measures or standard categories of physical features that they can use with unfamiliar species. Furthermore, biologists must document their work more thoroughly. The subjective judgment that "it looks like bighorn habitat to me" is being replaced or corroborated by simple measurements that can be compared to a standard description to confirm such judgment.

The limited literature on terrestrial physical features is confusing due to slightly different terminology and varying approaches in determining physical features from biological ones. Is a snag, for example, physical or biological? A concrete dam is certainly a man-made physical feature, but what is a beaver dam? Similarly, physical structures, such as playas, are sometimes considered landforms (Peterson 1981) and other times considered geomorphic features (Maser et al. 1979a).

Much of this confusion is caused by biologists borrowing terms and definitions from other fields such as soil science and geology. These definitions have been developed for quite different purposes. For the purposes of wildlife biology, how a feature is classified (e.g., landform or geomorphic feature) is probably not too important, as long as biologists understand what the terms mean and know how to use such features to predict species occurrence. If biologists understand what a playa is and what animal species depend on such a feature, it does not matter if they call it a landform because of its large size or a geomorphic feature because it is a small, distinct, localized habitat.

For the purposes of this chapter, terrestrial physical features are all features of the terrestrial environment, including man-made, that are not composed of living vegetation, but are useful in predicting animal abundance and distribution. Therefore, this chapter identifies those features that are commonly termed landforms (Peterson 1981), geomorphic and edaphic habitats (Maser et al. 1979a), special habitat features (Hamilton et al. 1983), man-made habitats (Maser et al. 1979b), and features derived from vegetation as snags and litter. Soils also fall into this category. However, because of the importance of soils in determining both plant and animal distribution, an entire chapter in this publication has been devoted to this relationship (Chapter 26). Soils are only briefly discussed in this chapter. This chapter emphasizes "wildland" environments, those habitats that are not used for urban, suburban, or agricultural purposes, but which may be managed for forestry, livestock production, or other purposes.

The dearth of literature on the subject has been mentioned. Several publications are available, however, that must be considered as pioneering efforts in the field, and they will be cited and quoted frequently in the following discussions. The biologist who is seriously involved in measuring terrestrial physical features should obtain copies of these publications.

The paper by Maser et al. (1979a) on "Geomorphic and Edaphic Habitats" is one of the first attempts to list, categorize, and quantify these habitats. Although it focuses on the Great Basin of southeastern Oregon, much of the information and suggested approaches can apply to different regions. Similarly, the paper by Maser et al. (1979b) on "Man-Made Habitats" published in the same series may have widespread application. Biologists have been aware for years of the benefits of man-made habitat features such as nest boxes and gallinaceous guzzlers that were developed specifically for wildlife. In the latter paper, the importance to many species of wildlife of certain man-made features, such as mine shafts, abandoned buildings, and telephone poles, that were developed for quite different reasons, is also described.

A paper by Short and Burnham (1982) represents one of the first attempts to systematically define structural components of habitat that are used for feeding and breeding. They use both physical strata and vegetation structure for this purpose. The former provides one of the first systematic efforts to provide a comprehensive listing of physical features used by vertebrate species.

Finally, Hays et al. (1981) have provided a comprehensive and systematic listing of measurement techniques for habitat variables. Many procedures, such as estimating height, can be applied to a variety of habitat features, such as cliffs, trees, power poles, etc. I refer to this publication frequently for guidance on making these measurements or estimates, and for information on considerations such as precision, accuracy, cost, efficiency, equipment, and training associated with different sampling techniques.

FEATURES AND THEIR MEASUREMENT

Physical features are discussed here under seven general categories: (1) landforms, (2) geomorphic habitats, (3) soils, (4) edaphic habitats, (5) vegetation-derived features, (6) animal-made features, and (7) man-made features. These categories represent a convenient grouping based primarily on two factors: (1) derivation of the feature and (2) size of the feature. Some features such as a beaver dam, can fall easily into two categories: vegetation derived and animal made. It may be classified as either one or both depending on the purpose of the investigation. Where authors have categorized or defined features slightly differently, I point out such differences.

Landforms

A landform is "a three-dimensional part of the land surface, formed of soil, sediment, or rock, that is distinctive because of its shape, that is significant for land use or to landscape genesis, that repeats in various landscapes, and that also has fairly consistent position relative to surrounding landforms" (Peterson 1981). Alluvial fans and rock pediment are examples of landforms. Landforms are the basic building blocks of the landscape and, thus, have a dominating influence on the soils, vegetation, and animal life that develop on their surfaces. For this reason, landform is quite useful in predicting animal occurrence.

The following two aspects of landforms are usually considered:

Classification. Classification of landforms is the process of delineating an area on a map as a landform type. A landform is thus always something with area; this contrasts with most other physical features used, which tend to be small and localized and typically treated as points on maps. Landform can usually be classified by simple visual observation or by interpretation of appropriate aerial photography by a biologist who is familiar with the concept and the local landforms. Unfortunately, few if any landform classifications have been developed for use by wildlife biologists. In fact, landform classifications for any purpose are not available for most areas. Therefore, in many cases, classifications will have to be developed.

Peterson (1981) developed a landform classification for the Basin and Range Province for purposes of soil surveys (Table 1), and this has been used by many range conservationists, botanists, and wildlife biologists for their own purposes. This is a hierarchical classification in which major landforms are broken down into component landforms, landform elements, and slope components. A biologist not wanting to use all levels of the classification may find the lower levels of classification (landform elements, slope components) useful in predicting animal occurrence. However, Peterson's classification should be useful in developing classifications for other areas.

The U.S. Department of Interior, Bureau of Land Management's (BLM's) Integrated Habitat Inventory and Classification System (IHICS) (1982) lists landforms used by biologists; these represent *ad hoc* definitions, and new categories are being added continuously. However, most of the initial definitions came from Peterson (1981).

Attributes. Biologists frequently find that attributes of landforms, such as slope and aspect, are useful in predicting animal occurrence. These types of measurements can be made anywhere and treated as point measurements (i.e., a characteristic of an exact location). Since measurements such as slope are usually averaged and used to categorize a landform or some other area of land, they are treated here as landform attributes. The three most common such measurements are slope, aspect, and elevation. Hays et al. (1981) describe the first two measurements.

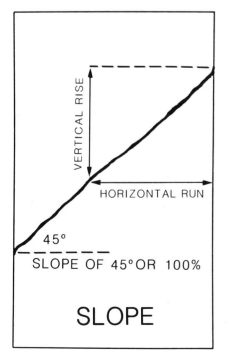

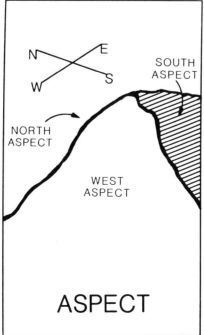

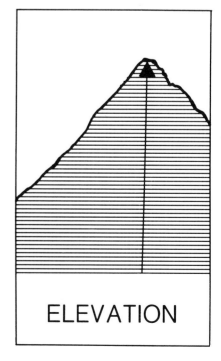

Table 1. Landform Classification System for the Basin and Range Province (from Peterson 1981).

Landforms			Parts of Landforms	
I Major Physiographic Part	II Major Landform	III Component Landform	IV Landform Element	V Slope Component
Bounding mountains	(not defined)			
Piedmont slope	Mountain-valley fan	Erosional fan remnant	Summit Sideslope ---------	 Shoulder Backslope Footslope
			Partial ballena-----	Crest Shoulder Backslope Footslope
		Inset fan	Channel Channel	
	Rock pediment	Rock-pediment remnant	Summit or--------- sideslope ---------	Crest Shoulder Backslope
			Channel	Footslope
	Ballena	--------------------	--------------------	Crest Shoulder Backslope Footslope
		Inset fan	Channel Channel	
	Alluvial fan	Fan collar Erosional fan remnant	Channel Summit Sideslope ---------	 Shoulder Backslope Footslope
			Partial ballena-----	Crest Shoulder Backslope Footslope
		Inset fan	Channel Channel	
	Fan pediment	Erosional fan remnant	Summit Sideslope ---------	 Shoulder Backslope Footslope
			Partial ballena-----	Crest Shoulder Backslope
		Inset fan Fan apron Nonburied fan remnant Beach terrace	Channel Channel Channel Channel	
	Pediment	Pediment remnant	Summit Sideslope ---------	 Shoulder Backslope Footslope
			Channel	
	Fan skirt	-------------------- Beach terrace	Channel	

Table 1. Landform Classification System for the Basin and Range Province (concluded).

Landforms			Parts of Landforms	
I Major Physiographic Part	II Major Landform	III Component Landform	IV Landform Element	V Slope Component
Basin floor (Bolsom or semi-Bolsom floor)	Alluvial flat	Relict alluvial flat Recent alluvial flat	Channel Channel	
	Alluvial plain			
	Sand sheet	Sand dune (Parna dune)	Interdune flat	
	Beach plain (Bolson floor only)	Offshore bar Barrier bar Lagoon	Channel	
	Lake plain (Bolson floor only)	Lake-plain terrace	Channel	
	Playa (Bolson floor only)	Floodplain playa	Channel	
	Axial-stream flood-plain	Floodplain playa Stream terrace	Channel Summit Sideslope ---------	Shoulder Backslope Footslope

Slope is the angle between the horizontal and the plane of the ground surface. It is usually expressed in either angle degrees or percent. In the latter case, percent is the vertical rise per horizontal run. Thus, a 45-degree angle would be 100% so that slopes of over 100% can occur. Slope can be measured using a clinometer (Hays et al. 1981:87). Usually an area will vary quite a bit in slope due to microtopography. Since a biologist is usually interested in the average slope of the entire area, many slope measurements are usually taken and then averaged. Certain types of "badland" areas may have very steep slopes even though there is little net slope in any direction from one boundary of the area to another. In such cases, average slope would be close to zero and thus meaningless. However, the variance of slope measurements may be a useful measure of the ruggedness of the topography.

Aspect is the downhill direction of a slope or the direction a slope faces. It is usually measured in conjunction with slope by using a compass (Hays et al. 1981:87). As with slope, average aspect for an area, rather than a point measurement, is usually determined. On flat or relatively flat areas of little measurable slope, aspect is of negligible interest and is often not measured.

Elevation is the height above sea level. Although elevation can be measured with an altimeter, since most areas in the lower 48 states have already been surveyed, the elevation can be read from a topographic map.

Slope, aspect, and elevation are extremely important determinants of animal distribution. For example, in northern areas, south-facing slopes are substantially warmer in winter and contain less snow; therefore, animals congregate in these areas. Similarly, the distribution of many animal species is limited by elevation. However, if one has topographic maps, measurement of these attributes is not necessary since they can be read (elevation) or measured (slope and aspect) from such maps (Hays et al. 1981:85). Furthermore, if information is being stored in a geographic information system (GIS), then digitized topographic information for many areas is available on tapes. This information can be purchased from the National Cartographic Information Center (NCIC) of the U.S. Geological Survey. Most GIS software has commands for making such calculations, so the biologist does not need to do the process manually.

Soils

Soils provide a substrate for vegetation to grow and are a major determinant of the type and abundance of vegetation that can grow on a site. However, soil also provides habitat for many species of fossorial animals such as moles, ground squirrels, pocket gophers, badgers, and many species of amphibians and reptiles. Soils provide habitat for—

• feeding (e.g., American woodcock [*Scolopax minor*], starnose mole [*Condylura cristata*], California legless lizard [*Aniella pulchra*]);

- breeding or nesting (e.g., desert tortoise [*Gopherus agassizii*], white-tailed prairie dog [*Cynomys leucurus*], burrowing owl [*Athene cunicularia*]);

- cover (e.g., California ground squirrel [*Spermophilus beecheyi*], Coachella Valley fringe-toed lizard [*Uma notata*]).

The type, texture, and other properties of the soil will all determine the suitability of an area for animals such as those mentioned above. For more information see Soils, Chapter 26 in this book; for further reading, see Bailey (1984:68–78) and Robinson and Bolen (1984:125–146).

Edaphic Habitats

An edaphic habitat is one in which existing or potential vegetation is determined primarily by soils rather than climate. To a certain extent, this is true of all habitats. Thus, Odum (1959) states that for a given region it is convenient to recognize (1) a single climatic climax, which is in equilibrium with the general climate, and (2) a varying number of edaphic climaxes, which are modified by the local conditions of the substrate. Theoretically, given enough time, the edaphic climaxes would converge upon the climatic climax. In practice, however, biologists work with edaphic climaxes in terms of identifying potential natural vegetation. Thus the concept of edaphic habitat is used commonly in vegetation and wildlife habitat classifications.

Edaphic habitats have been used in a more restrictive sense, however, by Maser et al. (1979b). They considered edaphic features (1979a:2) as "local distinctive soils that, along with their vegetation,

contrast markedly with the surrounding area." They described one edaphic habitat that supports a desert shrub community of saltbush (*Atriplex* sp.), sagebrush (*Artemisia* sp.), and rabbitbrush (*Chrysothamnus* sp.). Although they recognize that edaphic habitats have universal occurrence, they stated that it is of special interest in the northern Great Basin because it is the primary habitat of the white-tailed antelope squirrel (*Ammospermophilus leucurus*) and the only habitat of several native endemic plants.

Edaphic habitats form the basis for many wildlife habitat classifications. As such, no particular measurements are required but rather edaphic habitats are identified as either areas or points on maps and classified accordingly.

Geomorphic Habitat Features

Geomorphic habitat features are products of geologic or geomorphic processes and include cliffs, caves, talus, lava flows, sand dunes, and playas. There is some overlap between what some consider a landform and a geomorphic feature. For example, a playa is considered a geomorphic feature by Maser et al. (1979a) and a landform by Peterson (1981). In general, however, geomorphic features represent parts of the larger landform and do not necessarily occur in a predictable position relative to surrounding landforms or geomorphic features. For example, low cliffs may be scattered throughout a larger landform such as a fan piedmont. They do not necessarily bear any consistent relationship to each other or to other landforms. Similarly, geomorphic features such as caves are often relatively small and localized and treated as points on maps rather than features with areas. Landforms, on the other hand, always have area.

Sand dunes are examples of geomorphic habitats.

Playas are considered either a geomorphic feature or a landform.

Maser et al. (1979a) described six geomorphic features of particular use in predicting the occurrence of vertebrate species in the Great Basin of eastern Oregon: cliffs, caves, talus, lava flows, sand dunes, and playas. Other geomorphic features are used in the BLM IHICS efforts. In both systems, most of these features are treated as point data, that is, the only information recorded during an inventory is the location. The area of a rock shelter, for example, is considered to be negligible. Others are treated as point data or an area depending on size. For example, a cliff that is very localized and occupies less than a hectare (2.5 a.), may be conveniently treated as a point on a map, whereas in other situations, where a series of cliffs are found for many kilometers along a river system, they are more usefully recorded on the map as polygons with area.

Most descriptions of geomorphic features for purposes of wildlife habitat surveys are limited to mere notation of occurrence. However, systems of classification or measurement have been developed for several of these features. These systems are described below.

Cliffs. Maser et al. (1979a) described features of igneous rock cliffs such as facial cracks or joints, ledges and occasional caves, and the shelflike features and holes or pockets in sedimentary rock cliffs as being very important for wildlife species in the Great Basin. Cliffs are equally important in other regions.

In addition to noting presence and possibly area, cliffs can be classified according to parent rock and resistance (Table 2) and according to structural characteristics of height class, length class, joint spacing, and joint width (Table 3). Any of these variables such as height can be measured according to methods described in Hays et al. (1981).

Table 2. General resistance of cliffs to weathering in Great Basin Region of southwestern Oregon (from Maser et al. 1979a).

Parent Rock	Group	
	I	II
Basalt	●	
Rhyolite	●	
Andesite	●	
Nonwelded tuff		○
Welded tuff	●	
Sedimentary rock (weakly consolidated)		○

● = more resistant   ○ = less resistant

Caves. Caves are extremely important for many species of vertebrates because they provide shelter from weather extremes, stable environments, darkness, and seclusion. Generally caves are recorded as points on maps. Like cliffs, they can be

Igneous rock cliffs are important to wildlife because they have long-lived features such as cracks, ledges, and deep caves.

Caves in igneous rock are more important to cave dwelling animals than sedimentary rock cliffs because they are usually deeper and more resistant to weathering.

classified according to the type of parent rock, type of formation (Figure 1), as well as by structural characteristics such as diameter of opening and horizontal depth (Table 4).

Talus. Talus is the accumulation of rocks on or at the base of steep slopes, usually cliffs. Talus affords protection for reproduction and hibernation and includes a stable environment. Talus slopes are frequently recorded as point locations, although Maser et al. (1979a) indicate that length and width of deposits as well as depth are important determinants of animal use. A slope can be noted as a point location, while measurements are recorded as attributes. In addition, talus can be classified by structural characteristics such as type and size classes of rocks (Table 5 and Figure 2).

Lava Flows. Lava flows have been classified into two general categories, "old" and "new," by Maser et al. (1979a). New flows are distinguished from old flows by the lack of soil and vegetation development. Lava flows, particularly old flows, create areas of rock rubble of a size similar to talus and would afford the same advantages to various wildlife species as talus areas.

Sand Dunes. Sand dunes form unique habitats for many species of vertebrates. Because the habitat is usually unique and dunes tend to be rather localized and few in number, many threatened, endangered, and sensitive species of vertebrates as well as plants and invertebrates occur on sand dunes. They are usually mapped out. In addition, Maser et al. (1979a) distinguish between active and stabilized dunes.

Playas. Playas are shallow desert basins into which water drains after snow melt or rain storms. They do not have natural drainageways and water is accumulated seasonally. These areas that contain water are important feeding and nesting habitat for some water bird species. They also form important resting areas for migrating waterfowl in the spring (Maser et al. 1979a). Because of salts left after evaporation, playas have distinctive vegetation communities. Playas are usually mapped as intermittent water areas on maps and labeled as playas.

Vegetation-Derived Habitat Features

Vegetation-derived habitat features refer here to any habitat feature that is composed of dead vegetation. For convenience, these features are frequently measured or located during the course of vegetation surveys. For example, density of snag trees can usually be measured during the course of a timber inventory without much additional effort. Similarly,

Table 3. Classification of structural characteristics of cliffs that produce habitat attributes that can be exploited by adapted species of wildlife (from Maser et al. 1979a).

Structural Characteristic	Size Class or Description
Height class	3 m (10 ft) 3–10 m (10–33 ft) 10–30 m (33–100 ft) 30 m (100 ft)
Length class	30 m (100 ft) 30–100 m (100–330 ft) 100–500 m (330–1,640 ft) 500–1,500 m (1,640–4,920 ft) 1,500 m (4,920 ft)
Joint spacing	0.3 m (1 ft) (called netted jointing—fine network of small cracks) 0.3–1.5 m (1.5 ft) 1.5–7.5 m (5–25 ft) 7.5–30 m (25–100 ft) 30 m (100 ft)
Joint width (opening size)	0.15 m (0.5 ft) 0.15–0.30 m (0.5 ft) 0.3–0.6 m (1–2 ft) 0.6–1.5 m (2.5 ft) 1.5 m (5 ft)

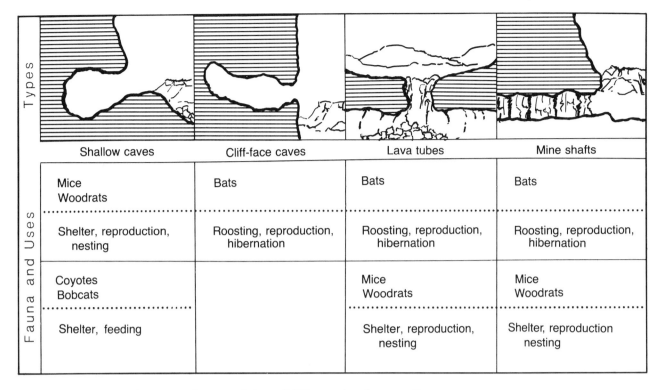

Types	Shallow caves	Cliff-face caves	Lava tubes	Mine shafts
Fauna and Uses	Mice Woodrats	Bats	Bats	Bats
	Shelter, reproduction, nesting	Roosting, reproduction, hibernation	Roosting, reproduction, hibernation	Roosting, reproduction, hibernation
	Coyotes Bobcats		Mice Woodrats	Mice Woodrats
	Shelter, feeding		Shelter, reproduction, nesting	Shelter, reproduction nesting

Figure 1. Types of caves and some of the wildlife species that use them.

Table 4. Structural characteristics of caves that produce habitat attributes which can be exploited by adapted species of wildlife (from Maser et al. 1979a).

Structural Characteristic	Size Class or Description
Opening (diameter)	0.3 m (1 ft) 0.3–1 m (1–3.3 ft) 1 m (3.3 ft)
Depth of cave (horizontal)	1 m (3.3 ft) 1–3 m (3.3–10 ft) 3 m (10 ft)
Origin	Natural Man-made —abandoned mine shaft —abandoned railroad tunnel

Table 5. Talus class, based on the predominant or most common rock size in the talus field (from Maser et al. 1979a).

Talus Class	Rock Size (Diameter)
I	0.5 m (< 1.6 ft)
II	0.5–1 m (1.6–3.3 ft)
III	1–2 m (3.3–6.5 ft)
IV	2 m (< 6.5 ft)

density or thickness of litter is often estimated during range surveys. The features are described here because they are sometimes omitted from vegetation surveys; those conducting such surveys are primarily concerned with live vegetation and often do not understand the importance of dead material to wildlife.

Dead vegetation as a habitat feature is extremely important to many species. Furthermore, many vegetation management practices such as livestock grazing, timber harvesting, fire management, and firewood cutting and collecting are done in a manner that tends to minimize the amount of dead vegetation left in the habitat. The quantity and quality of vegetation-derived habitat features may thus change drastically in a few years. By contrast, physical features such as cliffs, caves, and other geomorphic habitats are largely unaffected by human activities and are primarily quantified during inventories but rarely monitored. Measurement of dead vegetation should not be overlooked or dismissed in inventorying or monitoring habitat features.

There are literally thousands of habitat features formed by dead vegetation that are relevant to individual vertebrate species. Three major categories are discussed here: (1) litter and mulch, (2) dead and down woody material, and (3) snags.

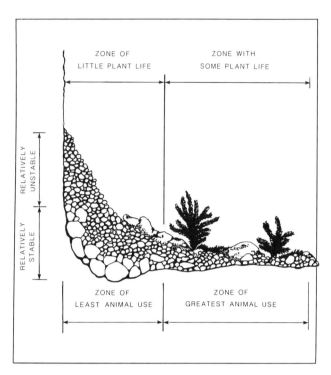

ZONE OF
LITTLE PLANT LIFE

ZONE WITH
SOME PLANT LIFE

RELATIVELY UNSTABLE

RELATIVELY STABLE

ZONE OF
LEAST ANIMAL USE

ZONE OF
GREATEST ANIMAL USE

Figure 2. Structure of a talus field and its use by wildlife.

Litter and Mulch. Litter or mulch is the dead material from herbaceous or woody plants, primarily grasses, forbs, and shrubs. Range conservationists make the distinction between persistent and non-persistent litter. Persistent litter is defined as "undecomposed organic debris on or near the soil surface with expected decomposition rates exceeding 2 years" (U.S. Department of the Interior, Bureau of Land Management 1985).

Non-persistent litter is "undecomposed organic debris on or near the soil surface with expected decomposition rates of 2 years or less" (U.S. Department of the Interior, Bureau of Land Management 1985). It is composed primarily of herbaceous material.

Litter is commonly measured during range vegetation surveys through step-point transects or other techniques. It is usually expressed as percent cover. In certain areas, particularly the Mediterranean, annual grasslands of California, and deciduous riparian habitats, litter is so abundant and important that thickness is important and is measured. The term mulch is often used for this type of litter in annual grasslands.

Litter is an important habitat component for many species of small mammals, reptiles, and amphibians. It provides habitat for many invertebrates that are food sources for vertebrates, and it provides thermal and hiding cover for many of these species.

Dead and Down Woody Material. Dead and down woody material refers to fallen trees in various stages of decay. The importance of such material as wildlife habitat in forests has received considerable attention in recent years (Maser et al. 1979c; Maser and Trappe 1984), because many management practices, such as chipping and slash-burning, tend to reduce the amount of such material.

Biologists have rarely measured amounts of dead and down woody material. However, Maser et al. (1979c) have suggested several approaches that might be useful and practical. The number of dead and down logs in an area can be sampled and expressed as number per unit area without any measurements of characteristics of individual logs. In addition, if a more refined approach is desired, they have suggested classifying of logs in terms of their stage of decomposition, which is relevant to their value for wildlife species (Table 6).

Snags. A snag has been defined for wildlife purposes as "any dead or partly dead tree at least 10.2 cm (4 in.) in diameter at breast height (DBH) and at least 1.8 m (6 ft) tall" (Thomas et al. 1979). This definition is based on the minimum diameter and height of trees for cavity nesting birds. Snags are important for many species of wildlife not only for nest or den sites but for many other biological functions such as feeding and roosting (Davis et al. 1983; Thomas et al. 1979).

Snags in an area are generally counted or estimated by using a standard sampling procedure and expressed as a density (i.e., the number of snags per hectare or acre). Thomas et al. (1979) have suggested that snags may be usefully classified as hard or soft, depending on the degree of decay and deterioration. Hard and soft snags can be classified in the field by striking them with an axe (Gale 1973). If the axe sinks in with difficulty, the snag is hard, whereas if it penetrates the wood easily, the snag is soft. Hard snags usually have many dead branches and an intact top, whereas soft snags usually have broken tops and few limbs (Gale et al. 1973).

Snags can be further classified based on DBH. The U.S. Fish and Wildlife Service uses many variations of snag measurements in their habitat suitability index (HSI) models.

Animal-Made and Man-Made Features

In many cases, animals create distinctive features in a habitat which are then used by the same or other species. Many of these are small and localized, such as the tree cavities created by woodpeckers that may subsequently be used by birds lacking

Table 6. A classification of decomposed logs (from Maser et al. 1979c).

Decomposition Class	Log Characteristic					
	Bark	Twigs 3 cm (1.18 in.)	Texture	Shape	Color of Wood	Portion of Log on Ground
1	Intact	Present	Intact	Round	Original color	Log elevated on support points
2	Intact	Absent	Intact to partly soft	Round	Original color	Original log elevated on support points but sagging slightly
3	Trace	Absent	Hard, large pieces	Round	Original color to faded	Log is sagging near ground
4	Absent	Absent	Small, soft, blocky pieces	Round to oval	Light brown to faded brown or yellowish	All of log on ground
5	Absent	Absent	Soft and powdery	Oval	Faded to light yellow or gray	All of log on ground

D.D. Bradshaw

Decaying logs furnish cover for many species of wildlife.

U.S. Forest Service

Snags are used by many species of cavity using animals.

the ability to excavate a cavity. However, some animal-made features are large and important enough to be noted during habitat surveys. Examples of these types of features are beaver dams and elk wallows. These are usually noted as present or absent without any measurement or further categorization of the feature.

The importance of man-made features for wildlife has received increased recognition. Wildlife managers have developed structures such as guzzlers and nesting platforms for wildlife for many years and their value to wildlife is understood. In recent years, the value of structures built for other purposes has received attention. These include features such as bridges and culverts used for nesting by swallows and other birds, mine shafts used by many bat species, and rock walls used by many species of reptiles and small mammals. However, rarely has a man-made feature been solely responsible for the occurrence of a species in an area.

On the other hand, many man-made features such as roads, powerlines, and pipelines, have obvious detrimental effects on wildlife. These detrimental features need to be recorded during wildlife habitat inventories as they are also an important component of the habitat. Maser et al. (1979b) describes in detail important man-made features for the Great Basin of eastern Oregon. However, few features in other regions have been described.

Both animal- and man-made features are generally not measured but simply recorded as being present in habitat inventories. Since these types of features change very slowly over time, monitoring them is rarely a high priority.

SPECIAL HABITAT FEATURES AND THEIR USE

The above description of terrestrial physical features categorizes habitat components according to their origin in a series, ranging from those caused by geological processes to those created by humans. Although useful in subdividing a large set of components, in practice, the origin of a habitat feature is probably of little concern to the animals that use them. If the environmental conditions are otherwise similar, an abandoned mine shaft is equally acceptable as a natural cave to a roosting bat. Thus a biologist conducting an inventory of such features does not need to be overly concerned with categorizing origin.

The BLM's IHICS makes extensive use of "special habitat features," including any of the above categories (geomorphic, edaphic, soils, vegetation-derived, animal-made, man-made). In most cases, these are habitat features that are too small to be mapped as units with area, i.e., that are mapped as points on maps. In addition, these features include small patches of vegetation that are too small to be mapped as separate vegetation types, such as a small stand of trees around a desert spring (Table 7).

Since the number of special habitat features is almost unlimited, time and money do not permit a complete inventory of them. Thus, the biologist must choose those that are relevant to wildlife management. BLM biologists have found this approach of recording terrestrial physical features to be quite useful.

The special habitat features listed in Table 7 for IHICS are those that were in use as of July 1985. However, these are not fixed. Biologists may add other features as required. Undoubtedly features listed in Table 7 that are used in other systems or described in other publications, will be added as necessary. As with all habitat components, the biologist must determine which ones are most useful based on the objectives of the inventory or monitoring effort.

DISCUSSION

Wildlife use physical features in many different ways with varying degrees of dependence. First, some species in an area increase their abundance through the presence or addition of a feature. For example, many lizard populations will increase through the addition of a wooden fence, but the populations do not depend on fences for survival. Most species respond to man-made features of this type.

Second, some species that are mobile will use a site if a necessary feature is there, but the feature may not be limiting the population. For example, many cliff-nesting raptors use a limited number of appropriate cliff sites; presence of an appropriate site may determine local use, but may not limit population density or productivity in the region. If the site is destroyed, the birds simply use alternative nest sites with no detrimental effects on the population. Unfortunately, many man-made structures, including some that have been constructed deliberately for wildlife, fall into this category. For example, many gallinaceous guzzlers have been constructed for quail and chukars in desert areas that were already fairly well-watered. Although quail will concentrate around such waters during dry periods and drink from them, there is no evidence that they increase population densities in such areas.

Table 7. Special habitat features used in the Bureau of Land Management's Integrated Habitat Inventory and Classification System (IHICS).

Natural Features	Man-Made Features
Avalanche-slide area	Bridge
Cave	Fence
Cave ice	Underpass
Cave lava	Salting area
Cliff	Goose nesting platforms
Cone, volcanic	Artificial nesting boxes
Dike, volcanic	Small seedlings
Dune, sand	Buffer strip
Insect mounds	Building
Overhang	Bird ramp
Salting area	Berm
Seep	Culvert
Cold spring	Dock
Sinkhole	Dredged area
Snag or group of snags	Exclosure, study
Talus slope	Fish migration barrier
Talus field	Gauging station, water
Elk wallow	Mining activity
Waterfall	Poles, electrical/telephone
Wasteland	Perches
Island (too small to be typed as habitat site)	Road
Log jam	Trail
Downed timber	Stream improvement structure
Bluff	Railroad
Beaver dam	Stream crossing
Muskrat house	Shelter (overnight)
Cataracts (stream)	Recreation area
Barren lands	Feeding stations
Hot springs	Fire break
Blowouts	Seismographic trail
Mudflow	Oil sump pit
Temporary pond	Windmill
Small natural pond	Irrigation diversion or ditch
Small grp trees or shrubs	Water gap
Small grp trees or riparian	Stock water pond
Dry meadow (not typed as vegetation type)	Corral or loading chute
Dry wash	Artificial wildlife water
Stream bank gravel	Domestic water source
Raptor nest tree	Artesian well
Buffalo wallow	Oil well
Boulder or rock outcrop	Gas well
Rodent colony	Pipeline
Beaver lodge	Material site
Otter slide	Airfield
Perennial snowfield	Breakwater
Rocky crags	Dam
Alpine fell field	Wilderness camp
Pingo	Winter trail
Gravel bar	Burn
Sand bar	Mine shaft
Ocean cliff	Mine tunnel
Stack	Stock water tank
Glacier	Disposal site (active)
Spit	Disposal site (inactive)
Barren	Wrecked ships
Burn	Abandoned homesites
Booming, dancing, or strutting ground	Relay stations
Wet meadow (not typed as vegetation type)	Pump jack
Brushy openings (too small to be typed as habitat site)	Brush pile/rows

Table 7. Special habitat features used in the Bureau of Land Management's Integrated Habitat Inventory and Classification System (IHICS) (concluded).

Natural Features	Man-Made Features
Snake den	Oxidation ponds (oxidation ponds and evaporation playa)
Roost	Spring, wildlife (developed & useable by wildlife only)
Kipuka	Spring, livestock (developed & useable by livestock only)
Stream (too small to be mapped as habitat site)	
Mineral spring	Spring, wildlife/livestock (developed & useable by wildlife & livestock)
Rock formation raptor nests	
Raptor cliff nest-stick	Exclosure (vegetation protection for wildlife)
Raptor cliff nest-scrape (no nest material)	Vegetation Manipulation (for wildlife; too small to be typed as a habitat site)
Raptor cliff perch	
Raptor nest on pinnacle (rock or earthen)	Artificial catchment
Raptor nest (ground or hillside)	Reservoir
Raptor nest (shrub)	Gallinaceous guzzler
Raptor nest (ground burrow)	Rain gauge
Rookery	Raptor nest (artificial)
	Raptor nest (earth cut)

A third category involves species that are totally dependent on a feature within an area. Examples of this relationship are species of salamanders found only at limestone seeps and the many desert fishes found at isolated desert springs. Most of these species are sedentary, such as amphibians and reptiles. Many species are remnant or relict species from earlier ages when conditions favorable to their existence were more widespread. Desert pupfish (*Cyprinodon* sp.) are good examples of such a situation.

Biologists should consider these three types of relationships when planning and setting priorities to inventory or measure physical features. Priority should normally be given to inventory features in the third category and subsequently verify species presence around them. The second category requires that the biologist determine the extent to which the features are limiting and at what level (site, regional, statewide, etc.). Returning to the raptor example, the biologist must determine if suitable nest sites are a factor limiting the population at the state or regional level. If it is not, then attention to inventory and management of such sites is not warranted un-less the management objective is to attract birds to the local site. Special features of the first type are not normally a high priority for inventory or management, unless they increase the abundance of high priority species, such as threatened, endangered, or game species.

SUMMARY

Physical features are important habitat components for many wildlife species. These include landforms, geomorphic and edaphic features, soils, vegetation-derived features, animal-made features, and man-made features. Formal systems for inventorying and describing such features have not been developed to the same degree as systems for surveying vegetation. In many cases, simply noting or mapping their presence is adequate. For some special features, measurements may be required; for others, classifying them by size or other characteristics is useful. The biologist must determine which physical features to inventory, describe, or measure depending on the objectives of the project.

LITERATURE CITED

BAILEY, J.A. 1984. Principles of wildlife management. John Wiley & Sons. New York, NY 373pp.

DAVIS, J.W., G.A. Goodwin, and R.A. Ockenfels, tech. coords. 1983. Snag habitat management: Proceedings at the symposium. U.S. Dep. Agric., For. Serv., Gen. Tech. Rep. RM-99. 226pp.

GALE, R.M. 1973. Snags, chainsaws and wildlife: One aspect of habitat management. Pages 97-112 *in* Yoakum, J. ed. Cal-Neva Wildlife 1973, Transactions. Reno

———, W.F. KELLEY, and J.A. LORENZANA. 1973. Snag management: Coordination guidelines for wildlife habitat. U.S. Dep. Agric., For. Serv., California Region. 13pp.

HAMILTON, C.K., R.M. KERR, and L.A. PETERSON. 1983. IHICS, the Bureau of Land Management's habitat inventory system. Presented at National Workshop on Computer Uses in Fish and Wildlife Programs—a State of the Art Review. Virginia Polytechnic Institute and State University, Blacksburg, VA. 13pp.

HAYS, R.L., C. SUMMERS, and W. SEITZ. 1981. Estimating wildlife habitat variables. U.S. Dep. Inter., Fish and Wildl. Serv., FWS/OBS-81/47. 111pp.

MASER, C., R.G. ANDERSON, K. CROMACK, Jr., J.T. WILLIAMS, and R.E. MARTIN. 1979c. Dead and down woody material. Pages 78–95 *in* Thomas, J.W. ed. Wildlife Habitats in Managed Forests—The Blue Mountains of Oregon and Washington. U.S. Dep. Agric., For. Serv., Agric. Handbook 553. 512pp.

———, J.M. GEIST, D.M. CONCANNON, R. ANDERSON, and B. LOVELL. 1979a. Wildlife habitats in managed rangelands—The Great Basin of Southeastern Oregon—Geomorphic and edaphic habitats. U.S. Dep. Agric., For. Serv., Gen. Tech. Rep. PNW-99. 84pp.

———, J.W. THOMAS, I.D. LUMAN, and R. ANDERSON. 1979b. Wildlife habitats in managed rangelands—The Great Basin of southeastern Oregon—man-made habitats. U.S. Dep. Agric., For. Serv., Gen. Tech. Rep. PNW-86. 84pp.

——— and J.M. TRAPPE, eds. 1984. The seen and unseen world of the fallen tree. U.S. Dep. Agric., For. Serv., Gen. Tech. Rep. PNW-164. 56pp.

ODUM, E.P. 1959. Fundamentals of ecology. 2nd Edition, W.B. Saunders Co., Philadelphia, PA. 546pp.

PETERSON, F.F. 1981. Landforms of the Basin and Range Province. University of Nevada, Tech. Bull. 28, Reno. 52pp.

ROBINSON, W.L. and E.G. BOLEN. 1984. Wildlife ecology and management. MacMillan Publishing Co., New York, NY. 478pp.

SHORT, H.L. and K.P. BURNHAM. 1982. Techniques for structuring wildlife guilds to evaluate impacts on wildlife communities. U.S. Dep. Inter., Fish and Wildl. Serv., Spec. Sci. Rep.—Wildlife 244. 34pp.

THOMAS, J.W., R.G. ANDERSON, C. MASER, and E. BULL. 1979. Snags. Pages 60-77 *in* Thomas, J.W. ed. Wildlife Habitats in Managed Forests—the Blue Mountains of Oregon and Washington. U.S. Dep. Agric., For. Serv., Agric. Handbook 553. 512pp.

U.S. DEPARTMENT OF THE INTERIOR, BUREAU OF LAND MANAGEMENT. 1982. Integrated habitat inventory and classification system. U.S. Dep. Inter., Bur. Land Manage., Manual 6602, unnumbered.

U.S. DEPARTMENT OF THE INTERIOR, BUREAU OF LAND MANAGEMENT. 1985. Rangeland monitoring—analysis, interpretation, and evaluation. U.S. Dep. Inter., Bur. Land Manage., Tech. Reference 4400–7. 69pp.

28

AQUATIC PHYSICAL FEATURES

Paul Cuplin

U.S. Bureau of Land Management
Service Center
Denver, CO 80225

Editor's Note: Although biologists have done little to develop standardized methods or measurements for terrestrial physical features, there has been more work with aquatic systems. Fisheries biologists and limnologists have long recognized the importance of physical features of streams such as streamflow, stream gradient, and water temperature. Whereas the terrestrial biologist must, for the most part, develop ad hoc systems for quantifying physical features, the aquatic biologist has some reasonably well-developed measurements and classification systems for aquatic systems. This chapter describes physical features that are important determinants or predictors of the quality of the aquatic habitat for fish and other vertebrates, and systems for measuring or classifying such features.

INTRODUCTION

Aquatic biologists have collected many types of data to describe aquatic habitat—sometimes with uncertainty as to their value. Accuracy, precision, and bias were not generally considered; usually the ease of data collection was most important. More attention is now being directed toward repeatable results, recognizing fewer variables that can be measured with higher precision and accuracy. Examples of these variables are water temperature, stream width, stream depth, lake depth, surface acreage, stream gradient, and turbidity. Examples of variables that cannot be measured with high precision are pool quality, stream channel stability, streambank stability, and the amount of various-sized particles in the streambed.

HABITAT FEATURES AND MEASUREMENT TECHNIQUES

The variables that are most important for describing stream and lake habitat are discussed in this chapter, regardless of the precision with which they can be measured.

Precision and accuracy of measurements of aquatic physical features vary considerably. Platts (1981) rates the precision that can be applied to variables related to stream habitat (Table 1). Hamilton and Bergersen (1984) discuss precision and accuracy of many of these variables.

Streamflow Pattern

Characterization of streamflow pattern as perennial, intermittent, or ephemeral streamflow can be determined by observing the stream and measuring streamflow during high and low precipitation periods. It can also be determined from U.S. Geological

Survey (USGS) topographic maps as different symbols are used for perennial, intermittent, and ephemeral stream reaches.

Streamflow

Streamflow is measured to determine stream size for baseline information. Streamflow volume relates to the amount of living space available for fish and aquatic life.

Historic records of streamflow (mean, record high and low, etc.) can be obtained from the U.S. Geological Survey.

Streamflow can be measured by using the formula R = WDCV (Robins and Crawford 1954):

where R = flow in cubic feet per second (cfs)
W = average width of stream in feet
D = average depth of stream in feet
C = a constant for stream bottom
0.8 - rough bottom
0.9 - smooth bottom
V = velocity in feet/second

Two people are generally required to make these measurements at each sampling station. Approximately half an hour is required to measure stream depths, widths, and velocities which are needed to calculate streamflow in cubic feet per second. Measurement of each of these is described separately. The minimum equipment required is a watch with second hand, yardstick or meter stick, float stick, and 100-foot measuring tape.

Installing a streamflow measuring gauge.

Table 1. The average expected repeatability, precision, and confidence intervals of water column and streambank measurement means from six selected streams in Idaho and Nevada. Confidence intervals are at the 95% level and expressed as percent of the mean (from Platts 1981).

Measurement	Confidence Interval	Precision	Repeatability over Time
Water Column			
Stream width	5.4	◒	◒ ●
Stream depth	8.2	◒	◒ - ◒
Streamside water depth	16.6	⊖	○
Pool (percent)	10.3	◒	
Pool (quality)	8.0	◒	○ - ◒
Riffle (percent)	12.5	◒	◒
Sun arc angle	1.1	●	◒
Bank to bank width	Very wide	○	○
High water stream width	Very wide	○	○
Streambank			
Soil alteration	12.3	◒	◒ - ◒
Vegetative stability	3.1	●	◒ - ◒
Undercut	18.5	◒	◒
Angle	4.4	●	◒
Rock content	Very wide	○	○

● = Excellent   ◒ = Good   ⊖ = Fair   ○ = Poor

Stream Velocity. Stream velocity can be measured in numerous ways. The simplest method, and the one commonly used in conjunction with streamflow measurement, is the float method.

A straight section of stream, 100 feet long, is measured. A 6-inch wooden stick or table tennis ball is used as a float. Some people recommend using an object with the specific gravity of water (1.0), such as an orange or water-filled prescription bottle.

Streamflow velocity is more precisely measured by using a flow meter to determine feet-per-second flow. A minimum of 20 measurements are taken across a stream transect and averaged.

For a more detailed discussion of velocity and its measurement, see Hamilton and Bergersen (1984).

Stream Width. Stream width is the average distance between water's edges transversely across the stream. On smaller streams, measurements can be made with a tape or estimated. Several measurements should be taken and the average calculated for a given stream reach.

For larger streams, an optical range finder can be used in the field and a map measurer can be useful in making these measurements in the office. Hays et al. (1981) describe use of these techniques.

Stream Depth. Water depth is the vertical distance from the surface to the bottom. Water depth measurements may be required for either streams or lakes; however, the techniques used are often different.

In addition to its use in streamflow calculations, measuring the depth of a body of water provides a check on siltation rate and a basis for classifying and typing lakes and reservoirs.

For streams, water depth can be measured with a calibrated rod. Several depth recordings are used to calculate average stream depth.

Lakes, ponds, and reservoirs and larger streams or rivers can be sounded with a weighted line or recorded with depth-sounding equipment from a boat. A sounding line, marked in 5-foot increments, will provide adequate depth information for cross sections and verification and correction of topographic maps for small lakes and reservoirs.

A depth recorder, with the transducer mounted on the boat keel, provides an accurate timesaving depth-measuring tool. The recorder should be calibrated in feet or meters and equipped with a recording tape. A minimum of four depth-sounding cross

sections are located on the topographic map—a transect from the backwater to the outlet in the center of the lake and three or four transects perpendicular to the backwater-outlet transect. Irregularly shaped reservoirs and lakes will require additional transect soundings. The depth-sounding tapes keyed to the topographic map can be processed by an engineer to develop a new or current topographic map.

Hamilton and Bergersen (1984) provide a detailed description of techniques for measuring water depth.

Instream Flow Needs

The amount of water needed to maintain stream habitat on a year-round basis is termed "instream flow needs." Instream flow needs are assessed to identify streamflow requirements for resident aquatic life and identify the amount of habitat loss that would occur at reduced rates of streamflow.

Instream flow needs can be determined by several methods as summarized by Cuplin et al. (1979). Where detailed, precise, legally defensible information is required, the multiple transect—incremental flow method—is recommended. This method is described in detail in Bovee and Milhous (1978).

For rapid assessment, a single transect method is available (Cuplin et al. 1979). This technique requires less time for field work and data analysis but it produces less precise results than the incremental flow methods.

Computer programs have been developed for analyzing stream channel cross-section survey data collected in conjunction with instream flow assessments (Parsons and Hudson 1985). A single transect method can be used for rapid assessment using ADP programs. A computer analysis program is available for U.S. Bureau of Land Management offices through the Denver Service Center, Division of Resources (Parsons and Hudson 1985).

Streambank and Shoreline Stability

Streambank and shoreline stability refers to the resistance of bank materials to erosion from flowing water. Streambank and shoreline stability measurements are used to classify stream/riparian habitat quality and to monitor changes in stability caused by the land use.

Streambank stability can be classified into four condition classes from excellent to poor (Table 2). This classification is designed for addressing stability as a function of livestock grazing. Other land-use impacts can also be assessed by ocular surveys. All

Table 2. Condition classes for streambanks and shorelines (U.S. Department of the Interior, Bureau of Land Management 1979).

Category	Rating	Description
I	●	No negligible use/damage; well-rooted vegetation, primarily grasses, sedges, and forbs; sod intact; very little if any erosion from vegetation areas; less than 5% bare soil showing along shoreline.
II	◐	Some use/damage; vegetation generally well-rooted; sod mostly intact; soil showing in places, 6 to 15% bare soil showing overall; some surface erosion evident.
III	⊖	Use or damage close to sod; vegetation shallowly rooted; moderate surface erosion, 16 to 25% bare soil showing overall.
IV	○	Heavy to severe use/damage; vegetation generally grazed down to the soil; considerable soil showing, over 25% with serious sod damage; active surface erosion is a serious problem.

● = Excellent   ◐ = Good   ⊖ = Fair   ○ = Poor

estimates are subjective and thus the accuracy of this method depends on the ability and experience of the surveyor.

Stream Channel Stability

Stream channel stability is rated as part of the overall stream habitat condition. Existing natural conditions and land use govern stream channel stability.

Stream channel stability is evaluated by ocular classification. One method that can be used classifies channel stability in four categories—excellent, good, fair, and poor (Table 3). This method has limited application to desert streams that are generally erosional in nature.

Pfankuch (1975) and Duff and Cooper (1978) describe a very detailed channel stability evaluation procedure. This method requires visually categorizing numerous bank and bottom attributes individually and then assigning them a point value (Figure 1). An overall score is determined by summing scores for individual attributes. This system works best for timbered mountainous streams; I have had poor results trying to apply it to arid land sedimentary streams. For the latter, the simpler visual system (Table 3) works better.

Stream Gradient

Stream gradient is a general slope or rate of change in vertical elevation per unit of horizontal distance of water surface of a flowing stream. Stream gradient can be measured in the field using a clinometer or Abney level or calculated in the office from measurements on topographic maps.

In the field, gradient is estimated by measuring the angle from the horizontal on two selected points on the ground with a clinometer or Abney level. Use a rod with a mark at the same height as the measuring crew member's eye level to measure angle from the horizontal. One crew member holds the marked rod at one of the sample points and the other measures the angle of the target from the horizontal using the clinometer. One person can complete the required measurements, but it is more efficient with two. Hays et al. (1981:87-90) describe this technique in detail.

In the office, gradient can be calculated off USGS topographic maps using the following formula:

$$G = \frac{Em \text{ (map scale fraction)}}{d}$$

where G = gradient (in percent)
E = difference (in feet) in elevation on ground between two points
m = the map scale, decimal fraction
d = distance (in inches) on the map between the two points

Hays et al. (1981:85–87) describe this technique in detail.

If digital elevation model tapes are available and a stream course has been digitized, then gradient can be calculated automatically for any stream reach using a geographic information system (GIS).

Table 3. Stream channel stability (from Cuplin 1978).

Category	Rating	Description
I	●	None or negligible lateral channel movement and bank erosion (cutting) (5% or less), scour, or changing channels.
II	◑	Some lateral channel movement and bank erosion (5 to 10%); minor channel scour or changing channel within streambed.
III	⊖	Frequent lateral channel movement (10 to 15%); moderate channel scour or channel change within streambed.
IV	○	More than 20% lateral channel movement and bank cutting; changing channels and severe scour evident; source of extreme sedimentation.

● = Excellent   ◑ = Good   ⊖ = Fair   ○ = Poor

Pool Quality

Pools are the deeper, slow-moving sections of streams which provide resting areas for fish. A variety of pool classes will provide the greatest diversity and fulfill the requirements for various stages of fish life.

Pool quality is an estimate of the pool's capability to provide habitat for the various life stages of fishes. A method of rating pools has been developed that considers pool size, depth, and cover ratings (Table 4). By using these measurements, pools are categorized into five pool classes of which one is the best. Nevertheless, pools with low ratings may have some value. For example, a pool that receives a low rating of 1 for depth and 1 for size may still provide essential habitat for the survival of young fish. Hamilton and Bergersen (1984) describe pool rating systems in detail.

Riffles

Riffles are the steeper gradient, higher velocity stream sections. They generally consist of coarse gravel, rubble, or larger substrate. Riffles are used for spawning and also produce macroinvertebrates—a primary source of fish food. Headwater streams are often primarily composed of riffles with few pools.

Riffles are not usually rated the way pools are. However, riffle length and width can be measured with a tape or ocular estimate. Pool-to-riffle ratio is often used as an indicator of stream habitat condition.

Streambed

Streambed material can be classified by particle size according to Table 5. A stream transect or cross

Meandering, low-gradient stream.

Steeper gradient, as indicated by riffles.

Table 4. Pool quality rating system (after Hamilton and Bergersen 1984).

Category	Rating[1]	Description
Pool size	3 2 1	Pool larger or wider than average width of stream Pool as wide or long as average width of stream Pool shorter or narrower than average width of stream
Depth First through Fourth Order streams Fifth Order streams or larger	 3 2 1 3 2 1	 Over 3 feet deep 2–3 feet deep Under 2 feet deep Depth 20% of average stream width or greater Depth 10–20% of average stream width Depth less than 10% of average stream width
Cover	3 2 1	Abundant cover Partial cover Exposed

[1]Pool size, depth, and cover ratings are summed to provide an overall pool rating according to the following scheme:

Total Ratings	Pool Class
8–9	1
7	2
5–6[2]	3
4–5	4
3	5

[2]Sum of 5 must include 2 for depth and 2 for cover.

An electronic depth finder.

Table 5. Classification of streambed material (from Duff and Cooper 1978).

Material	Particle Size
Bedrock	Exposed solid rock
Boulder	+ 12 in. (305 mm)
Large rubble	6–12 in. (152–305 mm)
Small rubble	3–6 in. (76–152 mm)
Coarse gravel	1–3 in. (25–76 mm)
Fine gravel	0.1–1.0 in. (2.5–25 mm)
Sand	(0.074–2.5 mm)
Clay	(0.074 mm)
Organic muck (sapropel)	Decomposed organic matter
Organic debris (detritus)	Undecomposed organic matter

Stability Indicator by Classes

Item Rated	EXCELLENT		GOOD		FAIR		POOR	
UPPER BANKS								
Landform slope	Bank slope gradient 30%.	2	Bank slope gradient 30–40%.	4	Bank slope gradient 40–60%.	6	Bank slope gradient 60%+.	8
Mass wasting Existing and potential	No evidence of past or potential for future mass wasting into channels.	3	Infrequent and/or very small. Mostly healed over. Low future potential.	6	Moderate frequency & size, with some raw spots eroded by water during high flows.	9	Frequent or large, causing sediment nearly yearlong or imminent danger of same.	12
Debris jam potential Floatable objects	Essentially absent from immediate channel area.	2	Present but mostly small twigs and limbs.	4	Present, volume and size are both increasing.	6	Moderate to heavy amounts, predominantly larger sizes.	8
Bank protection from vegetation	90%+ plant density. Vigor and variety suggests a deep, dense root mass.	3	70–90% density. Fewer plant species or lower vigor suggests a less dense or deep root mass.	6	50–70% density. Lower vigor and still fewer species form a somewhat shallow and discontinuous root mass.	9	<50% density plus fewer species & less vigor indicate poor, discontinuous, and shallow root mass.	12
LOWER BANKS								
Channel capacity	Ample for present plus some increases. Peak flows contained. (W/D) ratio < 7.	1	Adequate. Overbank flows rare. (W/D) ratio 8:15.	2	Barely contains present peaks. Occasional overbank floods. W/D ratio 15:25.	3	Inadequate. Overbank flows common. W/D ratio 25.	4
Bank rock content	65%+ with large, angular boulders 12"+ numerous.	2	40–65%, mostly small boulders to cobble 6–12".	4	20–40% with most in the 3–6" diameter class.	6	<20% rock fragments of gravel sizes, 1–3" or less.	8
Obstructions Flow deflectors Sediment traps	Rocks, old logs firmly embedded. Flow pattern of pool & riffles stable without cutting or deposition.	2	Some present, causing erosive cross currents and minor pool filling. Obstructions and deflectors newer and less firm.	4	Moderately frequent, moderately unstable obstructions & deflectors move with high water causing bank cutting and filling of pools.	6	Frequent obstructions and deflectors cause bank erosion yearly. Sediment traps full; channel migration occurring.	8
Cutting	Little or none evident. Infrequent raw banks less than 6" high generally.	4	Some, intermittently at outcurves & constrictions. Raw banks may be up to 12".	8	Significant. Cuts 12–24" high. Root mat overhangs and sloughing evident.	12	Almost continuous cuts, some over 24" high. Failure of overhangs frequent.	16
Deposition	Little or no enlargement of channel or point bars.	4	Some new increases in bar formation, mostly from coarse gravels.	8	Moderate deposition of new gravel & coarse sand on old and some new bars.	12	Extensive deposits of predominantly fine particles. Accelerated bar development.	16
BOTTOM								
Rock angularity	Sharp edges and corners; plane surfaces roughened.	1	Rounded corners & edges; surfaces smooth & flat.	2	Corners & wedges well-rounded in two dimensions.	3	Well-rounded in all dimensions; surfaces smooth.	4
Brightness	Surfaces, dull, darkened, or stained. Generally not "bright."	1	Mostly dull but may have up to 35% bright surfaces.	2	Mixture, 50–50% dull and bright, ± 15%, i.e., 35–65%.	3	Predominantly bright, 65%+ exposed or scoured surfaces.	4
Consolidation or particle packing	Assorted sizes tightly packed and/or overlapping.	2	Moderately packed with some overlapping.	4	Mostly a loose assortment with no apparent overlap.	6	No packing evident. Loose assortment; easily moved.	8
Bottom size distribution Percent stable material	No change in sizes evident. Stable materials 80–100%.	4	Distribution shift slight. Stable materials 50–80%.	8	Moderate change in sizes. Stable materials 20–50%.	12	Marked distribution change. Stable materials 0–20%.	16
Scouring and deposition	Less than 5% of the bottom affected by scouring and deposition.	6	5–30% affected. Scour at constrictions and where grades steepen. Some deposition in pools.	12	30–50% affected. Deposits & scour at obstructions, constrictions, and bends. Some filling of pools.	18	More than 50% of the bottom in a state of flux or change nearly yearlong.	24
Clinging aquatic vegetation, moss, and algae	Abundant. Growth largely moss-like, dark green, perennial. In swift water too.	1	Common. Algal forms in low velocity & pool areas. Moss here too and swifter waters.	2	Present but spotty, mostly in backwater areas. Seasonal blooms make rock slick.	3	Perennial types scarce or absent. Yellow-green, short-term bloom may be present.	4
COLUMN TOTALS		—		—		—		—

Record the values in each column for a total reach score. (E.___ +G.___ +F.___ +P.___ = ___)

Reach score of: 38 = Excellent, 39–76 = Good, 77–114 = Fair, 115+ = Poor.

Figure 1. Stream Channel Stability Field Evaluation Form (from Duff and Cooper 1976).

section can be inventoried for particle size by percent of the total cross section, and the transect site marked by steel stakes for future monitoring (Duff and Cooper 1978). The amount of the various particle sizes is estimated by ocular estimates. Estimates are not reproducible to a high degree of accuracy even by the same stream surveyor. This variable does not have a high degree of precision from one biologist to another or from one year to the next. However, it is valuable to describe existing habitat conditions on the date of the survey, which can be used for general trend comparisons on a continuing inventory basis. Hamilton and Bergersen (1984) describe substrate sampling in detail.

Surface Acreage

Surface acreage can be determined from a map or aerial photograph using an acreage dot grid or a polar planimeter. An average of three readings from the map or photograph should be used for acreage computation. The 256-dots-per-square-inch dot grid should be adequate for lake and reservoir measurement. Increased precision can be achieved by using the microdot grid with 1,024 dots per square inch. Hamilton and Bergersen (1984) describe this technique and others for calculating acreage.

Shoreline Miles

The number of shoreline miles can also be determined using a planimeter. This measurement is used to calculate an index of shoreline development described below.

Shore Development

Shore (or shoreline) development is a measure of the convolution of the shoreline. An irregular shoreline provides more littoral zones for the production of aquatic fish food organisms and more spawning and nursing areas for fish. An index to shoreline development can be calculated using the ratio of actual shoreline length to shoreline length of a circular lake of the same acreage, as follows:

$$\text{shore development} = \frac{S}{2\sqrt{A}}$$

where S equals the length of shoreline and A equals the surface area of the lake in acres.

Water Temperature

Water temperature can be accurately recorded by a pocket thermometer, maximum-minimum thermometer, or thermograph. The temperature variable

A surface scatter turbidimeter being used to monitor stream turbidity during a controlled reservoir release designed to flush fine sediments from the stream bed.

Table 6. Average turbidities found to be fatal to fish (from Federal Water Pollution Control Administration 1968).

Species	Length of Exposure (days)	Turbidity (mg/l)
Largemouth bass (*Micropterus salmoides*)	7.6	101,000
Pumpkin seed sunfish (*Lepomis gibliosus*)	13.0	69,000
Channel catfish (*Ictalurus punctatus*)	9.3	85,000
Black bullhead (*I. melas*)	17.0	222,000
Golden shiner (*Notemigonus crysoleucas*)	7.1	166,000

is reproducible with a high degree of accuracy when instruments are accurately calibrated. Hamilton and Bergersen (1984) describe temperature measurements in greater detail.

Turbidity

Turbidity is an expression of the optical property of a sample of water which causes light to be scattered and absorbed rather than transmitted in straight lines through a sample (Federal Water Pollution Control Administration 1968). Turbidity is caused by the presence of suspended material such as clay, silt, finely divided organic matter, plankton, and other microscopic organisms. Turbidity is measured by turbidimeters in Jackson Turbidity Units (JTUs) or Nephelometric Turbidity Units (NTUs).

Turbidity of not more than 25 JTUs (25 NTUs) is recommended for cold-water streams and not more than 50 JTUs (50 NTUs) for warm-water streams. High turbidities can cause fish mortality as shown in Table 6. The examples given are unusually high for extended periods of time. Instream activity such as dredging and placer mining can cause high turbidities that may not kill fish directly but cause other detrimental effects such as streambed siltation. Mining can cause high turbidities that may not kill fish but may cover the streambed and suffocate fish eggs and macroinvertebrates.

Hamilton and Bergersen (1984) discuss turbidity in detail.

SUMMARY

Inventory and monitoring should be directed to the variables that have the greatest possibility of repeated results by various workers. The variables that can be measured with the greatest accuracy (i.e., water temperature, stream width, stream depth, lake depth, surface acreage, stream gradient, and turbidity) should be used in monitoring change in habitat conditions related to specific land-use actions. Inventory and monitoring should measure those variables that limit distribution and abundance of aquatic organisms. Measured variables should serve as indicators of effectiveness of management practice. The ultimate measure of the effectiveness or impact of management should be productivity of the fish or other aquatic species.

LITERATURE CITED

ARMOUR, C.L., K.P. BURNHAM, and W.S. PLATTS. 1983. Field methods and statistical analysis for monitoring small salmonid streams. U.S. Dep. Inter., Fish and Wildl. Serv. FWS/OBS-83/33. 200pp.

BOVEE, K.D. and R. MILHOUS. 1978. Hydraulic simulation in instream flow studies: Theory and techniques. IFIP 5, Cooperative Instream Flow Serv. Group, U.S. Dep. Inter., Fish and Wildl. Serv., Ft. Collins, CO. 130pp.

CUPLIN, P. 1978. The use of large scale color infrared photography for stream habitat inventory. U.S. Dep. Inter., Bur. Land Manage. Tech. Note TN-325. Denver, CO. 11pp.

———, R. BOROVICKA, J. ERDMANN, B. VAN HAVEREN, L. LEE, R. MCQUISTEN, and M. WHITTINGTON. 1979. Instream flow guidelines. U.S. Dep. Inter., Bur. Land Manage., Service Center. Denver, CO. 57pp.

DUFF, D.A. and J.L. COOPER. 1978. Techniques for conducting stream habitat surveys on National Resource Land. U.S. Dep. Inter., Bur. Land Manage., Tech. Note TN-283. 72pp.

FEDERAL WATER POLLUTION CONTROL ADMINISTRATION. 1968. Water quality criteria. Washington, DC. 234pp.

HAMILTON, K. and E.P. BERGERSEN. 1984. Methods to estimate aquatic habitat variables. Colorado Coop. Fishery Res. Unit. Colorado State Univ., Fort Collins.

HAYS, R.L., C. SUMMERS, and W. SEITZ. 1981. Estimating wildlife habitat variables. U.S. Dep. Inter., Fish and Wildl. Serv. FWS/OBS-81-47. 111pp.

PARSONS, S.C. and S. HUDSON. 1985. Stream channel cross-section surveys and data analysis. U.S. Dep. Inter., Bur. Land Manage. TR-4341-1. Denver, CO. 48pp.

PFANKUCH, D.J. 1975. Stream reach inventory and channel stability evaluation. U.S. Dep. Agric., For. Serv. Northern Region. R1-75-002. 26pp.

PLATTS, W.S. 1981. Stream inventory: Acquisition and utilization of aquatic habitat inventory information. Pages 75–84 in Proc. Symp. Western Div. Am. Fish. Soc., Portland, Oregon, October 1981.

———, W.F. MEGAHAN, and G.W. MINSHALL. 1983. Methods for evaluating stream, riparian, and biotic conditions. U.S. Dep. Agric. For. Serv. Gen. Tech. Rep. INT-138. 70pp.

ROBINS, C.R. and R.W. CRAWFORD. 1954. A short accurate method for estimating the volume of streamflow. J. Wildl. Manage. 18:366–369.

U.S. DEPARTMENT OF THE INTERIOR, BUREAU OF LAND MANAGEMENT. 1979. Wetland-riparian area protection and management. Manual 6740. Washington, DC. 16pp.

29

HYDROLOGIC PROPERTIES

Bruce Van Haveren

U.S. Bureau of Land Management
Service Center
Denver, CO 80225

Editor's Note: Biologists know that animals do not exist in isolation and that the habitat in which they live—the ecosystem of which they are a part—must be understood. This interrelationship is frequently the first principle ignored by students as they eagerly pursue a narrow disciplinary approach. Water is the single most important life requirement for all plant and animal life. Thus, the movement and properties of water in an animal's habitat should be of concern to the biologists conducting a habitat inventory and monitoring effort, particularly in the arid western United States. Yet hydrology, the study of water in the natural environment, is virtually ignored by many biologists. This chapter describes some of the common measurements of hydrologic properties useful to the biologist.

INTRODUCTION

Water, one of the vital wildlife habitat elements on public lands, is the lifeblood of all ecosystems, terrestrial as well as aquatic. Its natural occurrence and circulation are especially vital to the functioning and vigor of wetland and riparian systems. Biologists must remember that all terrestrial and aquatic ecosystems are tied to hydrologic and geomorphic systems. For example, to manage riparian habitat, one must consider the surface and groundwater systems that are hydrologically related.

Fishery and wildlife biologists should understand that subtle changes in land use can produce not-so-subtle alterations in hydrologic conditions, which can directly influence fish and wildife habitat. Furthermore, hydrologic changes may occur several miles from the habitat site that is or could be affected.

This chapter focuses on the measurement and use of certain hydrologic properties important to wildlife habitat. The hydrologic properties of both lentic (lakes, ponds, bogs, meadows) and lotic (rivers, streams, springs) habitats are discussed in terms of measurement techniques and data applications.

Hydrologic Terminology

Biologists should be familiar with common terms used in land-use hydrology to facilitate communication with their hydrologist colleagues. Precipitation, evaporation, runoff, soil water storage, and sediment transport are all examples of hydrologic processes. Hydrologic variables, such as instantaneous stream discharge, monthly groundwater levels, or daily lake evaporation, quantitatively describe hydrologic processes. Hydrologic variables are nearly always continuous in time and, therefore, must be observed or measured at given intervals to convert them to discrete variables. When discrete variables are described statistically, they are called hydrologic parameters. Mean annual precipitation, the 100-year peak river discharge, and the coefficient of variation of monthly suspended sediment are all examples of hydrologic parameters.

The era of the Environmental Impact Statement (EIS) has brought with it a new vocabulary. In the field of hydrology, terms such as hydrologic changes, effects, and impacts are all used in environmental reports, often interchangeably. However, used correctly, hydrologic change refers to the increase or decrease (statistically at a given level of probability) in a hydrologic variable or parameter. For example, a 100-mg/L increase (significant at the 0.80 level of probability) in mean daily suspended sediment represents a hydrologic change.

The term hydrologic effect invokes a cause and effect relationship. A significant hydrologic effect would be road construction causing the 100-mg/L increase in mean daily suspended sediment.

Finally, a distinction must be made between effects and impacts. From a hydrologic or water resources standpoint, an impact occurs only when the value of that resource diminishes (negative impact) or increases (positive impact). Referring back to our suspended sediment example, the 100-mg/L increase due to road construction cannot be called an impact unless the effect has resulted in a change in a related resource value.

Watershed Stability: The Concept

Watershed stability has an inherent relationship to the stability and productivity of wildlife habitat. Watershed stability includes the following elements: soil productivity, hydrologic response to precipitation, quality of surface and shallow groundwater, movement of nutrients by water, and structure and function of wetland-riparian systems.

These may be viewed as components as well as partial indexes of watershed stability. They are highly interrelated and directly influence habitat variables.

If a simple equation could be used for measuring the present watershed stability, it would look like this:

Watershed stability = watershed constants + climate variables + present watershed condition + land-use variables.

The watershed constants that influence stability include geology, soils, latitude and elevation, topography (relief, slope, and aspect), and vegetation type,

both present and potential. These factors are static over time and easily determined.

Watershed condition and trend are determined semi-quantitatively by evaluating soil erodibility (see Soils chapter), mass wasting potential (potential for mass slope failures), stream channel stability (see section on Stream Channel Stability and Sediment Transport, this chapter), and watershed infiltration-storage capacity.

The climate factors important to watershed stability are limited to the frequency and intensity of runoff-producing precipitation, seasonality of precipitation, and the frequency and duration of drought.

Land use refers to past and present land-use factors that influence watershed stability, such as road construction, timber harvesting, excessive livestock trampling, overutilization of forage, mining, and mineral or energy exploration activities. Also included would be natural events that may affect watershed stability such as storms, wildfires, floods, and insect or disease attacks on vegetation.

All of these factors are evaluated in the present, assigned an appropriate weight, and then combined into an overall watershed stability rating. Trend in watershed stability can be inferred by comparing past and present watershed stability ratings and by considering present and near-future land-use activities that influence watershed stability.

Watershed stability ratings are subjective. Rating systems are nearly always tailored to fit specific locales and applications. For this reason, information on watershed stability is generally not available from other sources and must be obtained directly from field surveys. Before field work, the area in question must be stratified on the basis of hydrologic response units (homogeneous areas that respond similarly to a given hydrologic event).

Because land management activities can affect stability, the specialist must determine and present to management the acceptable versus unacceptable levels of watershed stability. The consequences of unacceptable watershed stability must be thoroughly explained in terms of impact magnitude and probability of occurrence.

PRECIPITATION, SNOW, AND EVAPORATION

Wildlife biologists may on occasion have need for hydrometeorological data such as precipitation, evaporation, and snow depth. Precipitation and evaporation have an indirect influence on habitat through the fluctuations of lake and pond levels and the water balance of wetland ecosystems. Snow, in terms of depth and areal distribution, affects animal movement and food availability, and thus the health of many wildlife species.

Measurement of Precipitation

Precipitation includes rain, snow, and all other forms of precipitated atmospheric water. The biologist should first ascertain the type and quality of data needed. Are data needed on a year-round basis or just seasonally? What is the desired frequency of the data: monthly, daily, hourly? Will snowfall data be needed as well as rainfall data? These questions must first be answered before a gage and sample schedule are selected. For most wildlife applications, monthly precipitation totals collected year-round would suffice, particularly for U.S. Bureau of Land Management (BLM) special wildlife management areas where water supply is a concern. Many national wildlife refuges, for example, routinely collect this type of precipitation data.

Cumulative rain is measured in a storage can having an orifice diameter of at least 20.3 cm (8 in.). Many rain gages are available that will store up to a year's accumulation of precipitation. Lightweight oil is added to retard evaporation.

Recording gages are necessary if one needs to know rainfall intensity or the time of occurrence of rainfall. There are several commercial types available. Agricultural Handbook 224 (Brakensiek et al. 1979) includes a good discussion on precipitation recording and characteristics of various gage types.

Measurement of precipitation falling as snow is much more difficult. Most precipitation gages used currently in the U.S. underestimate snowfall. Efficiency of catch depends on the size of orifice, gage siting, and whether or not the gage has a windshield (Figure 1). The efficiency of catch of snowfall at this site has been at least 90%. Catch efficiency is checked by measuring the water content of snow on the ground at the gage and comparing this to the gage catch for the same period of time.

Measurement of Evaporation

Evaporation is also a difficult variable to measure. Lake or pond evaporation is usually inferred from measurements of pan evaporation. The National Weather Service's 1.2-m (4-ft) diameter class A evaporation pan (Figure 2) is the standard instrument for evaporation measurements in the U.S. The U.S. Agriculture Handbook 224 contains a good discussion on siting and operation of a class A pan.

Figure 2. Class A evaporation pan.

Measurement of Snow on the Ground

Depth of snow on the ground is important because it may limit access to food and make movement difficult for big game animals. Depth of snow is measured with a yardstick or graduated rod. Snow depth, because of its extreme variability, must be sampled carefully and systematically. Stratified sampling, considering elevation, vegetation type, and slope aspect strata, is recommended.

Figure 1. A precipitation storage gage with an "alter shield" at an ideal gage site in a forest clearing.

Measurement of the water content of snow is of interest for calculating water balances; these data may also supplement or verify winter precipitation gage catch. The U.S. Soil Conservation Service (SCS), for example, operates a Westwide network of snow surveys used for forecasting spring and summer runoff for irrigators, reservoir operators, and hydropower companies. There is no reason why the same techniques could not be used to forecast wildlife water supplies in certain situations.

The standard federal snow sampler is used for measuring both depth and water content in mountain snowpacks (Figure 3). Agriculture Handbook 224 gives a brief description of snow surveying. The SCS State snow survey supervisor (located in the SCS State Office of each western State except California) can be contacted for more information and assistance.

Snow density, the ratio of snow water content to snow depth, can be computed directly from the measurements data taken with the federal snow sampler. Snow density is a good indicator of the maturity or ripeness of a seasonal snowpack. New snow densities vary between 0.07 and 0.25 g/cm^3. Late season snowpacks range between 0.30 and 0.45 g/cm^3. As snowpack density approaches 0.50 g/cm^3, the snowpack is said to be "ripe" and is ready for snowmelt release.

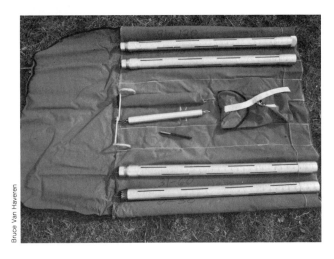

Bruce Van Haveren

Figure 3. A standard federal snow sampler kit for measuring snow depth and water content.

Sources of Published Data

Published precipitation, evaporation, and snow data are available for the more populated areas in the West. Sources of precipitation and evaporation data include the National Weather Service (NWS), State agricultural experiment stations, reservoir oper-

ators, U.S. Forest Service, and Agricultural Research Service experiment stations. Snow data are available for selected NWS stations and from the SCS.

Hydrometeorological data are scarce for public lands in general. The State climatologist is generally a good source of information about data availability for specific areas within the State. The State climatologist can also assist with data extrapolation and interpretation.

STREAMFLOW MEASUREMENT AND CHARACTERISTICS

Wildlife biologists, and particularly fishery biologists, occasionally need streamflow data. The anticipated use of these data will determine the data type and desired accuracy. For example, for some purposes such as water quality grab-sampling, an instantaneous discharge measurement will suffice (and should always accompany a water quality sample). For long-term characterization of streamflow, discharge data continuously recorded over several years are necessary. To characterize flow and channel hydraulic conditions for a given channel reach, one would need only a few discharge measurements. The BLM Instream Flow Guidelines (Cuplin and Van Haveren 1979) should be consulted for advice on the measurement of stream discharge in instream flow studies.

A decision on the desired accuracy of these data is important because it directly relates to the measurement method chosen and corresponding cost. Eight streamflow measurement methods can be used for typical small stream applications:

(1) Float method
(2) Volumetric measurements
(3) Current-meter and velocity-head measurements
(4) Portable weirs and flumes
(5) Dye-dilution method
(6) Continuous streamflow recording—natural control
(7) Continuous streamflow recording—artificial control
(8) Indirect methods

Float Method

The float method is the least expensive, but least accurate, of the available methods. A partially submerged float (water-logged stick, orange, piece of ice, or half-full beer can) is timed through a measured reach to estimate average water velocity (the average of several runs is computed). A cross section of the wetted portion of the channel is then measured. The stream discharge is therefore the product of the average velocity and the cross section. If a good estimate of velocity is obtained, the method is accurate within ±10%. Under conditions where velocity cannot be estimated adequately, the error could be ±25%.

Volumetric Measurements

Volumetric measurements are taken whenever the flow is sufficiently small and is concentrated or can be concentrated so that all of it may be caught in a container. Time required to fill a known volume is measured with a stopwatch. The method is fairly accurate, with the error averaging ±2 to 3% or less. Volumetric measurements can often be made at culverts by using a 19-L or 38-L (5-gal. or 10-gal.) bucket for small flows or a 208-L (55-gal.) drum for larger flows. I have often carried a piece of thin sheet metal in my vehicle for forming temporary flumes to facilitate volumetric measurements.

At culvert sites where the flow is too large for a volumetric measurement, the float method may be used with reasonable accuracy.

Current-Meter and Velocity-Head Measurements

Although several types of current meters are in use at this time, the Price AA and pygmy vertical-axis meters (Figure 4) are used most commonly by the U.S. Geological Survey, Water Resources Division. Because current meters measure velocity at a point, several velocity measurements are taken at a stream cross section. The number of measurements in the vertical direction is chosen according to the accuracy desired. The one-point procedure, where a single velocity measurement is taken (for each horizontal point on the cross section) at 18.3-cm (0.6-ft) depth below the surface, is most commonly used for small streams. In larger streams and where more accuracy is desired, velocity measurements are taken at the 6.1- and 24.4-cm (0.2- and 0.8-ft) depths below the surface. The gain in accuracy is about one percentage point. Additional accuracy may be obtained with the three-point method at 6-, 18-, and 24-cm (0.2-, 0.6-, and 0.8-ft) depths where stream depths exceed 76.2 cm (2.5 ft). Spacing of measurement points across the channel depends on the width of the stream. Normal spacing is within 0.6 or

Bruce Van Haveren

Figure 4. Price AA and pygmy current meters for measuring stream velocity.

1.5 m (2 or 5 ft); however, the points should be spaced so that no subsection has more than 10% of the total discharge.

Selection of a suitable site for current meter measurements should follow these criteria (see Figure 5):

(1) Cross section lies within a straight reach and flow lines are parallel.

(2) Velocities exceed 15 cm/sec (0.5 ft/sec) and maximum depths exceed 15.2 cm (0.5 ft).

(3) Streambed is relatively uniform, free of large boulders, organic debris, and aquatic growth.

(4) Flow is uniform, free of eddies, slack water, and excessive turbulence.

(5) The stream can be waded from bank to bank.

If a stream is too deep or velocities too high for wading, a suitable bridge site must be located. In this situation, a suspension cable is substituted for the wading rod. Procedures for taking current meter measurements from bridges are covered in detail by Rantz (1982).

A standard discharge measurement form used by the U.S. Geological Survey for all stream discharge measurements is shown in Figure 6. The "midsection method" (Buchanan and Somers 1969; Rantz 1982) is used to compute stream discharge from this form.

Accuracy of the current meter method depends on flow and channel conditions, number of velocity measurements taken in the vertical direction, spacing of measurements across the channel, condition and calibration of current meter, and operator error. U.S. Geological Survey provides the following accuracy limits:

Overall Rating of Measurement	Error
Excellent	± 2%
Good	± 5%
Fair	± 8%
Poor	>8%

In spite of their lower cost and ease of operation, velocity-head rods (Figure 7) have not achieved the same popularity as current meters for gaging streams. The rod consists of a broad edge at least 2.5

Bruce Van Haveren

Figure 5. A good location for a current meter measurement.

cm (1 in.) wide and a sharp edge opposed 180° to the broad edge. Constructed of hardwood or aluminum, the rod is scaled in English or metric units. To measure the velocity head, the sharp edge of the rod is pointed upstream and the water elevation read from the rod. The rod is then revolved 180° so the broad edge is perpendicular to the flow lines. The water elevation is again read, and the difference between readings computed. The resulting number is the velocity head expressed in feet or meters. Velocity m/sec (ft/sec) is found by the equation—

$$V = 2gh$$

where g = acceleration due to gravity (ft/sec/sec) and h the velocity head (ft).

Under very good channel conditions, the velocity-head rod will give discharge readings within a few percentage points of the true value (Wilm and Storey 1944). It is comparable in accuracy to the one-point method using current meters. Heede (1974) recommended use of the velocity-head rod only if channel bottoms are fairly smooth and channels are approximately prismatic. This precludes their use in boulder-strewn mountain streams with highly turbulent flows, unless the gaged section can be modified to fit the above criteria.

Because of the surging nature of flow in natural streams, the precision of head measurements is around ± 0.01 m (± 0.05 ft). Heede (1974) recommended reading the water elevation that occurs most frequently, rather than the average elevation.

Portable Weirs and Flumes

Portable weir plates and pre-calibrated flumes can be used to accurately measure small flows. Both rectangular and triangular (30°, 60°, 90° or 120° notches) weirs are used; the specific design is based on the most probable range of expected flows (Van Haveren 1986).

Parshall flumes are the most common pre-calibrated, portable flumes in use (Figure 8). They are commercially available in a variety of sizes and are easily installed at most locations (see Rantz 1982).

Dye-Dilution Method

The dye-dilution method is fairly sophisticated and requires moderately expensive sampling equipment. A known quantity of tracer dye is injected at the upstream end of the reach being measured, allowed to mix thoroughly through natural stream turbulence, and the resulting concentration measured at a downstream point. The technique has definite advantages in very turbulent mountain streams where more traditional stream gaging techniques are

not possible. Intensive training is required to effectively use the technique. Refer to Rantz (1982) for a complete discussion of this technique.

Continuous Streamflow Measurement— Natural Control

Continuous measurement of streamflow generally involves more expense and expertise than the methods discussed above. The method involves direct sampling of water level (stage) and the establishment of a stage-discharge relationship from which streamflow is computed. This method is expensive in terms of labor and equipment. As in all stream gaging methods, site selection is critical. Where an artificial control (e.g., bridge, culvert, flume, bank revetment) is not used, a suitable natural control must be found. Rantz (1982) listed criteria to be used in selecting a gage site with a natural control. Water level is recorded continuously with a stage recorder. Stream discharge is related to stage height by periodically making discharge measurements at known stages. A stage-discharge rating curve is established from these measurements, taken at a wide range of stage heights. The rating curve is checked and modified, usually annually. The stage-discharge curve will remain stable at sites having good natural channel control and no net sediment accumulation or channel erosion.

Continuous Streamflow Recording— Artificial Control

Artificial controls are installed where a good natural control cannot be found, or when a very high degree of accuracy is desired. Artificial controls include weirs; flumes; and concrete, rock, or treated wood control structures that maintain a stable channel geometry. Further discussion of the types of artificial controls available, including their advantages and disadvantages, is beyond the scope of this chapter. Brakensiek et al. (1979) and Rantz (1982) provided good discussions of weirs and flumes. Some weirs and flumes are available with known calibrations, precluding the need for field development of the stage-discharge rating curve.

Discharge measurements can also be made in reservoirs where presumably all inflow is contained in the structure with negligible leakage. A water level recorder is used to measure water depth, which is related to inflow volume through a reservoir stage-capacity curve.

Indirect Methods

Indirect methods of streamflow measurement include channel geometry relationships and the Mannings equation.

**UNITED STATES
DEPARTMENT OF THE INTERIOR
GEOLOGICAL SURVEY**

WATER RESOURCES DIVISION

DISCHARGE MEASUREMENT NOTES

Meas. No. ---------------

Comp. by ---------------

Checked by ------------

Sta. No. ------------------

_____

Date _____, 19_____ Party _____

Width _____ Area _____ Vel. _____ G. H. _____ Disch. _____

Method _____ No. secs. _____ G. H. change _____ in _____ hrs. Susp. _____

Method coef. _____ Hor. angle coef. _____ Susp. coef. _____ Meter No. _____

GAGE READINGS				
Time		Recorder	Inside	Outside
--------	----	--------	--------	---------
--------	----	--------	--------	---------
--------	----	--------	--------	---------
--------	----	--------	--------	---------
--------	----	--------	--------	---------
--------	----	--------	--------	---------
--------	----	--------	--------	---------
--------	----	--------	--------	---------
--------	----	--------	--------	---------
Weighted M. G. H.____				
G. H. correction_____				
Correct M. G. H._____				

Date rated _____ Used rating

for rod _____ susp. Meter _____ ft.

above bottom of wt. Tags checked _____

Spin before meas. _____ after _____

Meas. plots _____% diff. from _____ rating

Wading, cable, ice, boat, upstr., downstr., side

bridge _____ feet, mile, above, below

gage, and _____

Check-bar, chain found _____

changed to _____ at _____

Correct _____

Levels obtained _____

Measurement rated excellent (2%), good (5%), fair (8%), poor (over 8%), based on following

conditions: Cross section _____

Flow _____ Weather _____

Other _____ Air _____°F@ _____

Gage _____ Water _____°F@ _____

_____ Record removed _____ Intake flushed U L_____

Observer _____

_____

Control _____

_____

Remarks _____

_____

_____

G. H. of zero flow _____ ft.

☆ GPO : 1963—O–688360

Figure 6. Standard discharge measurement form used by the U.S. Geological Survey.

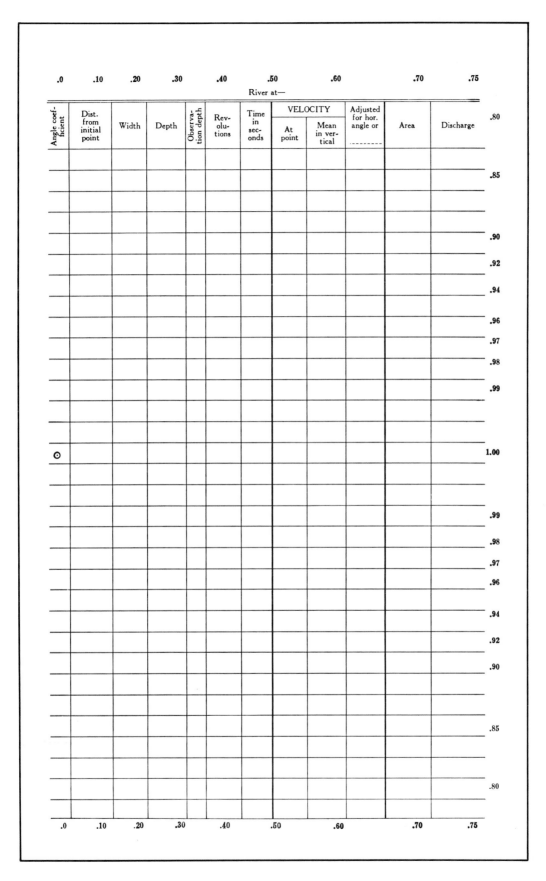

Figure 6. Standard discharge measurement form used by the U.S. Geological Survey (concluded).

The Manning equation can be used to estimate flows in natural channels:

$$Q = \frac{1.486 \, AR^{2/3} S^{1/2}}{n}$$

where A is the cross section of the channel, R the hydraulic radius, S the slope of the energy line (usually approximated by the water-surface slope), and n the roughness coefficient. All the independent variables can be measured in the field except n, which must be estimated. This technique is often used for estimating flood peaks if sufficient high-water marks can be found. A minimum error of 10% can be expected even if the roughness coefficient chosen is within ± 0.005 of the true value.

Channel geometry can be used to estimate mean annual streamflow and flood peaks of various frequencies. Using only active-channel width, Hedman and Osterkamp (1982) constructed equations for predicting the 2-, 5-, 10-, 25-, 50-, and 100-yr flood discharges and the mean annual runoff for four regions in the western U.S. State-specific channel geometry relations have been established for most States by the respective Water Resources Division District Office of the U.S. Geological Survey.

Field measurement of active-channel width requires very little equipment and effort. Training is required in order to properly identify the active channel elevation.

Figure 7. A velocity-head rod for measuring stream velocity.

Figure 8. A Parshall flume for the continuous measurement of streamflow.

Also, annual, monthly, or even daily streamflow can be estimated by using index techniques. A gaged stream with characteristics similar to the ungaged stream of interest can be used to index or predict some streamflow variables. This is accomplished by first expressing the streamflow data on a "per square mile" basis. Adjustments in certain streamflow variables should then be made, based on differences in elevation, exposure, geology, or other appropriate hydrophysiographic factors. This procedure is highly subjective and should be done in consultation with an experienced hydrologist.

Sources of Streamflow Data

Published streamflow data are available from the U.S. Geological Survey, Water Resources Division, on many larger streams and rivers in the nation. Data for small watersheds in remote areas in the West are more difficult to acquire. Figure 9 is taken from Water Resources Data for Colorado, 1985 (U.S. Geological Survey 1985). This is a standardized streamflow data format used in every State. Maps, available from the Water Resource Division Offices, show locations of streamflow gaging stations.

The State Engineer's Office is another potential source of streamflow data. The local U.S Forest Service hydrologist should also be consulted if national forest lands are involved or are close to the area in question.

Interpretation of Streamflow Data

Analysis and interpretation of streamflow data depend on the intended use of these data. Discrete values of streamflow (hourly, daily, monthly) can be plotted as a "hydrograph" for visual analysis purposes. Figure 10 is an example of an annual hydrograph based on monthly streamflow data. Low-flow statistics, such as the minimum 7-day mean flow, can be computed easily from daily flow data. For U.S. Geological Survey continuous streamflow data, a number of different streamflow statistics are available through the WATSTORE data bank, accessible through any U.S. Geological Survey Water Resources Division.

Streamflow data for other than general interest should be interpreted by an experienced hydrologist. The wildlife biologist must tell the hydrologist the specific objectives or intended uses of these data.

Flow data are usually expressed in units of volume per unit time, for example cubic feet per second or cfs. Table 1 contains a set of factors for converting different streamflow measurement units.

HYDROLOGY OF LAKES, PONDS, AND RESERVOIRS

The hydrologic factors that relate to wildlife habitat characteristics of standing water bodies include inflow and outflow rates, volume (or capacity), mean and maximum depths, basin shape, precipitation-evaporation balance, drainage basin area, and groundwater interaction (both physical and chemical).

Before undertaking a field inventory of a lake, pond, or reservoir, an attempt should be made to characterize the water body on the basis of origin, geology, morphometric and physiographic properties (which can be obtained from maps), drainage basin characteristics, trophic state, and hydrologic setting. Winter (1977) discussed hydrologic classification and characterization of lakes.

Inflow and outflow characteristics (including quantity and quality of the water) directly influence lakes, ponds, and reservoirs. The measurement of inflow or outflow usually involves stream gaging. Refer to "Streamflow Measurement and Characteristics."

For water balance and certain limnological studies, lake volume often needs to be determined. As a rough estimate, the lake surface area can be measured from a map, the basin shape assumed, and the volume computed from mensuration formulas. A few common lake basin shapes and their volume formulas are given in Figure 11.

More accurate volume determinations are made from detailed surveys and soundings of lake depths. Depths are best measured in winter when a standard land survey can be conducted on the frozen surface. Depths are easily measured through holes augered in the ice.

Water level often directly relates to habitat quality. Periodic, visual readings of water level can be taken inexpensively with staff gages (Figure 12). Continuous recording of water level requires the installation of a water level recorder, as in continuous streamflow measurement.

The precipitation-evaporation ratio is important in determining lake characteristics (Winter 1977). The ratio should be calculated on an average annual basis from reliable data. Precipitation data are usually obtained from NWS. Evaporation data may also be available from NWS or from a nearby reservoir operator. Pan evaporation data should be adjusted to represent free-water evaporation.

GREEN RIVER BASIN

09241000 ELK RIVER AT CLARK, CO

LOCATION.--Lat 40°43'03", long 106°54'55", in NW¼NW¼ sec.27, T.9 N., R.85 W., Routt County, Hydrologic
Unit 14050001, on left bank 30 ft downstream from bridge on State Highway 129, 0.8 mi north of Clark, and
2.0 mi upstream from Cottonwood Gulch.

DRAINAGE AREA.--206 mi².

PERIOD OF RECORD.--May 1910 to September 1922 (published as "near Clark"), April 1930 to current year. Monthly
discharge only for some periods, published in WSP 1313.

REVISED RECORDS.--WSP 1733: 1956.

GAGE.--Water-stage recorder. Datum of gage is 7,267.75 ft, (State Highway Department bench mark). May 1910 to
September 1922, nonrecording gage at site 30 ft upstream at datum 0.15 ft lower. Apr. 23, 1930, to Sept. 27,
1934, water-stage recorder at present site at datum 0.15 ft lower.

REMARKS.--Estimated daily discharges: Nov. 20 to Apr. 7. Records good except for estimated daily discharges,
which are poor. Diversions above station for irrigation of about 230 acres above and about 460 acres below
station. Natural flow of stream affected by storage in Lester Creek Reservoir (known also as Pearl Lake),
capacity, 5,660 acre-ft since 1963 and Steamboat Lake, capacity, 23,060 acre-ft since 1968. Several
observations of specific conductance and water temperature were obtained and are published elsewhere in this
report.

AVERAGE DISCHARGE.--67 years, 339 ft³/s; 245,600 acre-ft/yr.

EXTREMES FOR PERIOD OF RECORD.--Maximum discharge, 4,910 ft³/s, May 23, 1984, gage height, 6.12 ft; minimum
daily determined, 22 ft³/s, Dec. 12, 1963, but a lesser discharge may have occurred during periods of no
gage-height record prior to 1939.

EXTREMES FOR CURRENT YEAR.--Peak discharges above base of 1,900 ft³/s, and maximum (*):

Date	Time	Discharge (ft³/s)	Gage height (ft)	Date	Time	Discharge (ft³/s)	Gage height (ft)
May 10	1900	2,000	4.44	June 8	2300	*3,180	*5.36
May 28	2200	2,300	4.68				

Minimum daily discharge, 40 ft³/s, Feb. 20 to Mar. 2.

DISCHARGE, IN CUBIC FEET PER SECOND, WATER YEAR OCTOBER 1984 TO SEPTEMBER 1985
MEAN   VALUES

DAY	OCT	NOV	DEC	JAN	FEB	MAR	APR	MAY	JUN	JUL	AUG	SEP
1	121	104	72	100	60	40	226	1030	1200	527	226	72
2	126	98	66	100	60	40	226	1210	1180	501	221	75
3	118	107	70	98	60	42	225	1380	1220	491	211	97
4	115	95	72	100	60	45	223	1500	1290	483	194	86
5	124	92	74	100	60	47	223	1630	1330	463	185	78
6	131	104	74	98	60	50	223	1500	1350	437	179	72
7	123	97	76	98	58	56	223	1410	1710	398	170	70
8	113	97	78	98	56	60	224	1580	2280	381	161	75
9	108	93	80	96	54	64	262	1640	2410	377	167	71
10	104	104	80	96	50	66	258	1720	2080	343	156	68
11	106	109	80	96	45	68	258	1620	1630	329	149	67
12	104	100	82	96	45	68	329	1300	1410	358	181	86
13	108	102	82	96	42	70	411	1120	1440	343	148	72
14	111	105	84	96	42	70	500	1000	1470	298	135	67
15	100	92	86	94	42	70	675	1030	1530	266	126	64
16	97	100	88	94	42	70	817	1110	1570	251	119	65
17	96	106	90	94	42	70	893	1160	1520	233	114	62
18	111	87	92	94	42	72	1090	1150	1370	390	112	62
19	110	89	92	94	42	74	1240	1140	1280	715	115	73
20	112	90	92	90	40	76	1100	1170	1220	560	107	68
21	111	90	90	86	40	78	1060	1280	1210	409	101	70
22	103	80	88	84	40	80	987	1310	1090	374	99	73
23	108	80	86	82	40	80	964	1340	968	364	94	77
24	108	80	88	82	40	80	953	1500	892	408	89	72
25	97	80	94	80	40	82	789	1700	1120	322	85	71
26	105	80	94	74	40	84	574	1860	1000	302	83	71
27	106	80	92	70	40	86	569	1930	738	288	82	79
28	103	78	92	66	40	88	708	2000	631	251	83	92
29	108	76	94	62	---	90	832	1760	583	301	81	84
30	105	74	96	60	---	100	890	1590	565	273	77	68
31	106	---	98	60	---	105	---	1320	---	248	73	---
TOTAL	3398	2769	2622	2734	1322	2171	17952	43990	39287	11684	4123	2207
MEAN	110	92.3	84.6	88.2	47.2	70.0	598	1419	1310	377	133	73.6
MAX	131	109	98	100	60	105	1240	2000	2410	715	226	97
MIN	96	74	66	60	40	40	223	1000	565	233	73	62
AC-FT	6740	5490	5200	5420	2620	4310	35610	87250	77930	23180	8180	4380

CAL YR 1984	TOTAL	183267	MEAN	501	MAX	4090	MIN	53	AC-FT	363500
WTR YR 1985	TOTAL	134259	MEAN	368	MAX	2410	MIN	40	AC-FT	266300

Figure 9. An annual summary of daily streamflow data collected and published by the U.S. Geological Survey
(1985).

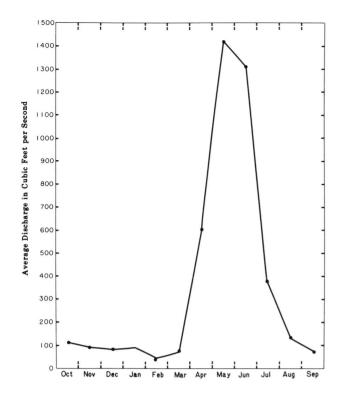

Figure 10. An example of an annual hydrograph based on mean monthly streamflow data, Elk River at Clark, CO, Station 09241000 (U.S. Geological Survey 1985).

Figure 12. A staff gage for measuring water level.

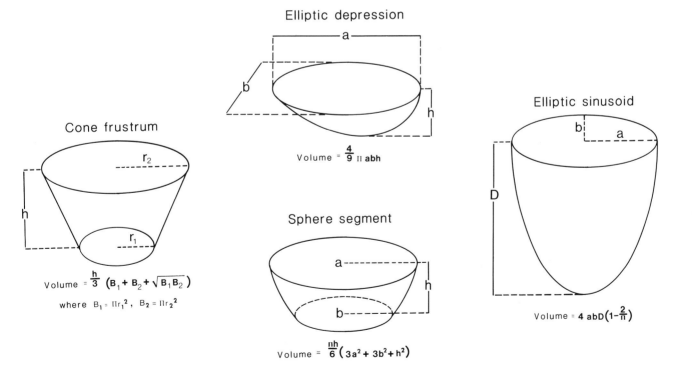

Figure 11. Common lake basin shapes and their corresponding volume formulas.

Table 1. Streamflow unit conversions.

To convert from	Multiply by	To find
acre-ft/day	0.504167	cfs
acre-ft/day	0.123349	ha-m/day
acre-ft/day	0.325851	million gal./day
acre-ft/mo (28-day)	0.018006	cfs
acre-ft/mo (29-day)	0.017385	cfs
acre-ft/mo (30-day)	0.016806	cfs
acre-ft/mo (31-day)	0.016263	cfs
acre-ft/yr	0.001370	acre-in./hr
acre-in./hr	2	acre-ft/day
acre-in./hr	1.008333	cfs
acre-in./hr	1.027906	ha-cm/hr
cfs	1.98347	acre-ft/day
cfs	55.53719	acre-ft/mo (28-day)
cfs	57.52066	acre-ft/mo (29-day)
cfs	59.50413	acre-ft/mo (30-day)
cfs	61.48760	acre-ft/mo (31-day)
cfs	723.96694	acre-ft/yr
cfs	725.95041	acre-ft/leap year
cfs	0.99174	acre-in./hr
cfs	60.45620/area (a.)	cm/day
cfs	2.51901/area (a.)	cm/hr
cfs	1.69901	m^3/min
cfs	0.02832	m^3/sec
cfs	0.00021424	mi^3/yr
cfs	6.66667	yd^3/min
cfs	448.83117	gal./min
cfs	538168.7	Imp. gal./day
cfs	373.73	Imp. gal./min
cfs	23.80165/area (a.)	in./day
cfs	0.99174/area (a.)	in./hr
cfs	28.31685	L/sec
cfs	0.64632	million gal./day
cfs	50	miner's inches (ID, KS, NE, SD, ND, NM, UT, WA, S. CA)
cfs	40	miner's inches (AZ, MT, OR, NV, N. CA)
cfs	38	miner's inches (CO)
cfs	2696.082	tons of water (50°F)/day
m^3/sec	864/area (ha)	cm/day
m^3/sec	315360/area (ha)	cm/yr
m^3/sec	35.31467	ft^3/sec (cfs)
m^3/sec	8.640	ha-m/day
m^3/sec	3153.60	ha-m/yr
m^3/sec	3162.24	ha-m/leap yr
m^3/sec	86400010	L/day
m^3/sec	60000	L/min
m^3/sec	1000.00012	L/sec
cm/day	0.01654 × area (a.)	cfs
cm/day	0.00116 × area (ha)	m^3/sec
cm/hr	0.39698 × area (a.)	cfs
cm/yr	3.171E-06 × area (ha)	m^3/sec

Table 1. Streamflow unit conversions (concluded).

To convert from	Multiply by	To find
gal./day	0.00112	acre-ft/yr
gal./min	0.00442	acre-ft/day
gal./min	1.61301	acre-ft/yr
gal./min	0.00223	cfs
gal./min	0.00006309	m^3/sec
gal./min	0.06309	L/sec
Imp. gal./min	0.00268	cfs
million gal./day	3.06888	acre-ft/day
million gal./day	1.54723	cfs
ha-m/day	8.10710	acre-ft/day
ha-m/day	0.11574	m^3/sec
ha-m/day	115.74075	L/sec
ha-m/yr	8.10710	acre-ft/yr
ha-m/yr	3.17E-04	m^3/sec
ha-m/yr	0.31710	L/sec
in./day	0.04201 × area (a.)	cfs
in./hr	1.00833 × area (a.)	cfs
in./yr	0.000115 × area (a.)	cfs
L/sec	0.864/area (ha)	cm/day
L/sec	0.036/area (ha)	cm/hr
L/sec	315.36/area (ha)	cm/yr
L/sec	0.03531	cfs
L/sec	0.001	m^3/sec
L/sec	15.85032	gal./min.
miner's inches (ID, KS, NE, SD, ND, NM, UT, WA, S. CA)	0.020	cfs
miner's inches (AZ, MT, OR, NV, N. CA)	0.025	cfs
miner's inches (CO)	0.026	cfs
acre-ft	504.17	Kft^3/sec-days
acre-ft/$mi.^2$	0.04763	cm over watershed
acre-ft/$mi.^2$	0.04763	ha-m/km^2
acre-ft/$mi.^2$	0.01875	in. over watershed
cm over watershed	20.99738	acre-ft/mi^2
cfs/mi^2	0.01093	m^3/sec/km^2
cfs/mi^2	1.04132	in./mo (28 days)
cfs/mi^2	1.07851	in./mo (29 days)
cfs/mi^2	1.11570	in./mo (30 days)
cfs/mi^2	1.15289	in./mo (31 days)
cfs/mi^2	13.57438	in./yr (365 days)
cfs/mi^2	13.61157	in./yr (366 days)
cfs/mi^2	0.03719	in./day
cfs/mi^2	10.93320	L/sec/km^2
m^3/sec/km^2	91.46457	ft^3/sec/mi^2
ha-m/km^2	20.99729	acre-ft/mi^2
in. over watershed	53.33333	acre-ft/mi^2
in. over watershed	0.02689	Kft^3/sec-days/mi^2
Kft^3/sec-days/mi^2	37.19008	in. over watershed
Kft^3/sec-days	0.00198	acre-ft
L/sec/km^2	0.09146	ft^3/sec/mi^2

GROUNDWATER FEATURES AND THEIR RELATIONSHIP TO WILDLIFE HABITAT

I have taken the liberty in this section to discuss springs, seeps, and related water features in an overall groundwater context, even though many classify springs as surface water features. Springs and seeps are usually an expression of the local groundwater system.

Wildlife biologists may be concerned about the reliability of wildlife water supplies from springs and seep areas. Spatial distribution as well as discharge of individual springs or seeps would be of interest for inventory purposes. Measurement of spring discharge is done by the same basic techniques covered in "Streamflow Measurement and Characteristics" and will depend on size and physical setting of the spring.

Groundwater levels may be of interest to the wildlife biologist, particularly where wildlife water supplies are obtained from pumping wells or artesian wells. The Water Resources Division of the U.S. Geological Survey operates a network of observation wells around the U.S. That agency should be contacted for data on water levels and water quality. Nearly all completed water wells may be used for measuring water levels. However, the well log should be consulted to determine the depth of the well, whether or not packers were included during well construction, and any other construction details.

STREAM CHANNEL STABILITY AND SEDIMENT TRANSPORT

A very good overview of stream dynamics, from a hydrologic and geomorphic point of view, has been prepared by Dr. Burchard Heede of the U.S. Forest Service (Heede 1980). This is highly recommended reading for the biologist planning to engage in stream channel stability or sediment transport investigations, or riparian improvement projects.

Stream Channel Stability

The channel stability evaluation procedure used most often by land management agencies is that presented by Pfankuch (1978). An evaluation form for this method is presented in Figure 13. Field training is required before using this procedure because of its subjectivity. Furthermore, the summary numerical rating system may need adjusting to fit the general region of interest.

The interpretation of the results depends somewhat on the use of the ratings; it is not an aquatic habitat evaluation. It can be used as an index to sediment delivery because poor stability usually indicates high levels of sediment transport and good to excellent stability correlates with low sediment transport.

Standard statistical sampling guidelines should be used to determine sample stratification and sample size (Platts et al. 1983).

Suspended Sediment and Bedload

Sediment transport and deposition in streams directly influence riparian systems. For example, aquatic habitat condition deteriorates with increasing suspended sediment.

Field sampling of suspended sediment is a relatively easy exercise in wadable streams. Williams and Thomas (1984) discuss the collection and analysis of sediment data from a land management perspective. Grab samples should be taken with a DH-48 sampler (Figure 14). Streamflow must be measured at the time of sediment sampling to facilitate meaningful interpretation of these data.

Continuous sediment sampling is both difficult and expensive and should be left to experienced hydrologic technicians.

Total sediment in a stream is composed of both suspended and bedload fractions. Accurate bedload sampling is a difficult procedure. Fortunately, the wildlife biologist seldom has need for such data. Guy and Norman (1970) discuss bedload sampling procedures.

MONITORING HYDROLOGIC VARIABLES

Water in nature is highly transient in time and space. Monitoring of hydrologic variables thus requires some special considerations. Ponce (1980a, 1980b) and Jackson et al. (1985) provide excellent guidance for hydrologic monitoring in land management situations. Those references should be consulted prior to engaging in any monitoring involving water quantity or quality.

R-1 STREAM REACH INVENTORY and CHANNEL STABILITY EVALUATION

REACH LOCATION: Survey Date_____ Time_____ Obs._____

Forest_____ Rgr. Dist._____
                                  P.W.I.
Stream_____ W/S No. __-__-__-__-__-__-__-__
Reach Description &
Other Identification_____

Key #	Stability Indicators by Classes (Fair and Poor on reverse side)			
	EXCELLENT		GOOD	
1	Bank slope gradient <30%.	(2)	Bank slope gradient 30-40%.	(4)
2	No evidence of past or any potential for future mass wasting into channel.	(3)	Infrequent and/or very small. Mostly healed over. Low future potential.	(6)
3	Essentially absent from immediate channel area.	(2)	Present but mostly small twigs and limbs.	(4)
4	90%+ plant density. Vigor and variety suggests a deep, dense, soil binding, root mass.	(3)	70-90% density. Fewer plant species or lower vigor suggests a less dense or deep root mass.	(6)
5	Ample for present plus some increases. Peak flows contained. W/D ratio <7.	(1)	Adequate. Overbank flows rare. Width to Depth (W/D) ratio 8 to 15.	(2)
6	65%+ with large, angular boulders 12"+ numerous.	(2)	40 to 65%, mostly small boulders to cobbles 6-12".	(4)
7	Rocks and old logs firmly embedded. Flow pattern without cutting or deposition. Pools and riffles stable.	(2)	Some present, causing erosive cross currents and minor pool filling. Obstructions and deflectors newer and less firm.	(4)
8	Little or none evident. Infrequent raw banks less than 6" high generally.	(4)	Some, intermittently at outcurves and constrictions. Raw banks may be up to 12".	(8)
9	Little or no enlargement of channel or point bars.	(4)	Some new increase in bar formation, mostly from coarse gravels.	(8)
10	Sharp edges and corners, plane surfaces roughened.	(1)	Rounded corners and edges, surfaces smooth and flat.	(2)
11	Surfaces dull, darkened, or stained, Gen. not "bright".	(1)	Mostly dull, but may have up to 35% bright surfaces.	(2)
12	Assorted sizes tightly packed and/or overlapping.	(2)	Moderately packed with some overlapping.	(4)
13	No change in sizes evident. Stable materials 80-100%.	(4)	Distribution shift slight. Stable materials 50-80%.	(8)
14	Less than 5% of the bottom affected by scouring and deposition.	(6)	5-30% affected. Scour at constrictions and where grades steepen. Some deposition in pools.	(12)
15	Abundant. Growth largely moss-like, dark green, perennial. In swift water too.	(1)	Common. Algal forms in low velocity & pool areas. Moss here too and swifter waters.	(2)
	EXCELLENT COLUMN TOTAL →		GOOD COLUMN TOTAL →	

(Upper Banks: rows 1-4; Lower Banks: rows 5-9; Bottom: rows 10-15)

Add values in each column and record in spaces below. Add column scores.
    E.___ + G.___ + F.___ + P.___ = _____ Total Reach Score.
Adjective ratings:<38=Excellent, 39-76=Good, 77-114=Fair, 115+=Poor*
*(Scores above may be locally adjusted by Forest Hydrologist)

R1-Form 2500-5A Rev.1-75   Side 1.

Figure 13. Stream channel stability evaluation form used with the evaluation procedure presented by Pfankuch (1978).

INVENTORY DATA: (observed or measured on this date)   Side 2

Stream Width____ft.X Ave.Depth____ft.X Ave.Velocity____f/s=____Flow cfs
Reach   Stream   Turbidity   Stream   Sinuosity
Gradient____%, Order____,   Level_____,   Stage_____,   Ratio_____,
Temperature
  °F or °C of: Air____Water____, Others_____

	Key #	Stability Indicators by Classes			
		FAIR		POOR	
Upper Banks	1	Bank slope gradient 40-60%.	(6)	Bank slope gradient 60%+.	(8)
	2	Moderate frequency & size, with some raw spots eroded by water during high flows.	(9)	Frequent or large, causing sediment nearly yearlong OR imminent danger of same.	(12)
	3	Present, volume and size are both increasing.	(6)	Moderate to heavy amounts, predominantly larger sizes.	(8)
	4	50-70% density. Lower vigor and still fewer species form a somewhat shallow and discontinuous root mass.	(9)	<50% density plus fewer species & less vigor indicate poor, discontinuous, and shallow root mass.	(12)
Lower Banks	5	Barely contains present peaks. Occassional overbank floods. W/D ratio 15 to 25.	(3)	Inadequate. Overbank flows common. W/D ratio > 25.	(4)
	6	20 to 40%, with most in the 3-6" diameter class.	(6)	< 20% rock fragments of gravel sizes, 1-3" or less.	(8)
	7	Moderately frequent, moderately unstable obstructions & deflectors move with high water causing bank cutting and filling of pools.	(6)	Frequent obstructions and deflectors cause bank erosion yearlong. Sediment traps full, channel migration occurring.	(8)
	8	Significant. Cuts 12"-24" high. Root mat overhangs and sloughing evident.	(12)	Almost continuous cuts, some over 24" high. Failure of overhangs frequent.	(16)
	9	Moderate deposition of new gravel & coarse sand on old and some new bars.	(12)	Extensive deposits of predominantly fine particles. Accelerated bar development.	(16)
Bottom	10	Corners & edges well rounded in two dimensions.	(3)	Well rounded in all dimensions, surfaces smooth.	(4)
	11	Mixture, 50-50% dull and bright, ± 15% ie. 35-65%	(3)	Predominantely bright, 65%+, exposed or scoured surfaces.	(4)
	12	Mostly a loose assortment with no apparent overlap.	(6)	No packing evident. Loose assortment, easily moved.	(8)
	13	Moderate change in sizes. Stable materials 20-50%.	(12)	Marked distribution change. Stable materials 0-20%.	(16)
	14	30-50% affected. Deposits & scour at obstructions, constrictions, and bends. Some filling of pools.	(18)	More than 50% of the bottom in a state of flux or change nearly yearlong.	(24)
	15	Present but spotty, mostly in backwater areas. Seasonal blooms make rocks slick.	(3)	Perennial types scarce or absent. Yellow-green, short term bloom may be present.	(4)
		FAIR COLUMN TOTAL →	[ ]	POOR COLUMN TOTAL →	[ ]

Size Composition of Bottom Materials (Total to 100%)

1. Exposed bedrock............____%   5. Small rubble, 3"-6".....____%
2. Large boulders, 3'+ Dia....____%   6. Coarse gravel, 1"-3"....____%
3. Small boulders, 1-3'.......____%   7. Fine gravel, 0.1-1".....____%
4. Large rubble, 6"-12".......____%   8. Sand, silt, clay, muck..____%

Figure 13. Stream channel stability evaluation form used with the evaluation procedure presented by Pfankuch (1978) (concluded).

Figure 14. Model DH-48 suspended-sediment sampler.

LITERATURE CITED

BRAKENSIEK, D.L., H.B. OSBORN, and W.J. RAWLS, coords. 1979. Field manual for research in agricultural hydrology. Agriculture Handbook 224. U.S. Dep. Agric. 550pp.

BUCHANAN, T.J. and W.P. SOMERS. 1969. Discharge measurements at gaging stations. Techniques of Water-Resources Investigations, Book 3, Chapter A8. U.S. Dep. Inter., Geol. Surv. 65pp.

CUPLIN, P. and B.P. VAN HAVEREN, eds. 1979. Instream flow guidelines. U.S. Dep. Inter., Bur. Land Manage. 57pp.

GUY, H.P. and V.W. NORMAN. 1970. Field methods for measurement of fluvial sediment. Techniques of Water-Resources Investigations, Book 3, Chapter C2. U.S. Dep. Inter., Geol. Surv. 59pp.

HEDMAN, E.R. and W.R. OSTERKAMP. 1982. Streamflow characteristics related to channel geometry of streams in western United States. U.S. Dep. Inter., Geol. Surv. Water-Supply Pap. 2193. 17pp.

HEEDE, B.H. 1974. Velocity-head rod and current meter use in boulder-strewn mountain streams. U.S. Dep. Agric., For. Serv. Res. Note RM-271. 4pp.

———. 1980. Stream dynamics: An overview for land managers. U.S. Dep. Agric., For. Serv. Gen. Tech. Rep. RM-72. 26pp.

JACKSON, W.L., S. HUDSON, and K. GEBHARDT. 1985. Consideration in rangeland watershed monitoring. U.S. Dep. Inter., Bur. Land Manage. Tech. Note 369. Denver, CO. 25pp.

PFANKUCH, D.J. 1978. Stream reach inventory and channel stability evaluation. U.S. Dep. Agric., For. Serv., Northern Region, Missoula, MT. 26pp.

PLATTS, W.S., W.F. MEGAHAN, and G.W. MINSHALL. 1983. Methods for evaluating stream, riparian, and biotic conditions. U.S. Dep. Agric., For. Serv. Gen. Tech. Rep. INT-138. 70pp.

PONCE, S.L. 1980a. Statistical methods commonly used in water quality data analysis. U.S. Dep. Agric., For. Serv., Watershed Systems Development Group, Tech. Pap. WSDG-TP-001. 144pp.

———. 1980b. Water quality monitoring programs. U.S. Dep. Agric., For. Serv., Watershed Systems Development Group, Tech. Pap. WSDG-TP-002. 68pp.

RANTZ, S.E. 1982. Measurement and computation of streamflow: Volumes 1 and 2. U.S. Dep. Inter., Geol. Surv. Water-Supply Pap. 2175. 631pp.

U.S. GEOLOGICAL SURVEY. 1985. Water resources data for Colorado, Part I—Colorado River Basin. U.S. Dep. Inter., Geol. Surv.

VAN HAVEREN, B.P. 1986. Water resource measurements: A handbook for hydrologists and engineers. American Water Works Assoc., Denver, CO. 132pp.

WILLIAMS, O. and R.B. THOMAS. 1984. Guidelines for collection and analysis of sediment data. Draft report, U.S. Dep. Agric., For. Serv., Watershed Systems Development Group, Fort Collins, CO. 108pp.

WILM, H.G. and H.C. STOREY. 1944. Velocity-head rod calibrated for measuring stream flow. Civil Engineering. 14(11):475-476.

WINTER, T.C. 1977. Classification of the hydrologic settings of lakes in the north-central United States. Water Res. 13(4):753-767.

30

WATER QUALITY

Paul Cuplin

U.S. Bureau of Land Management
Service Center
Denver, CO 80225

Editor's Note: Water quality, the purity of water, is a concern from many perspectives—public health, aesthetics, agriculture, and as habitat for aquatic life. This chapter focuses on water quality requirements for fishes and other aquatic vertebrates, and field methods to measure or monitor these requirements.

INTRODUCTION

Water availability is critical to almost every renewable natural resource including wildlife and vegetation. Therefore, information on all of the water that occurs on desert, forest, stream, lake, and wetland on public lands is of importance to land management. Water found on public lands represents all of the major water systems, i.e., marine, estuarine, riverine, lacustrine, palustrine, perennial ice or snow, and terrestrial systems. The chemical and physical properties of water, as they affect "water" as a habitat for aquatic organisms and as a substance for consumption by wildlife and domestic livestock, are the concerns of this chapter.

LAND-USE ACTIVITIES THAT AFFECT WATER QUALITY

Human activities can alter baseline water chemistry, resulting in detrimental effects on aquatic and terrestrial organisms that drink or dwell in water. Land-use activities such as grazing, mining, timber harvest, and recreation may increase sediment production and therefore affect water quality. Mining can also produce "acid mine waste," making the pH of water too acidic for any organism to survive. Herbicide or pesticide spraying or the dumping of toxic materials can significantly alter water quality and cause high mortality rates in sensitive aquatic life. To protect aquatic habitats and water quality, the U.S. Environmental Protection Agency (EPA) established standards for the introduction of toxic materials into water, which were published in "Quality Criteria for Water" (U.S. Environmental Protection Agency 1976).

The Water Quality Act of 1965 required States to set standards for releasing materials into streams and lakes. The Federal Water Pollution Control Act and Amendments of 1972 (Public Law 92-500; 86 Stat. 816), as amended by the Clean Water Act of 1977 (Public Law 95-217; 91 Stat. 1566), are also pertinent. See 33 U.S.C., Chapter 23:

[Section 208 directs that the Administrator of the Environmental Protection Agency shall promulgate comprehensive regulations intended to control water pollution sources, including nonpoint sources. Under the regulations which have been promulgated, the use of permits is required for any continuing pollution sources. *The Federal land management practices are designed to prevent degradation of streams and lakes on the lands under their jurisdiction.*]

(author's emphasis)

[Section 404 authorizes the Army Corps of Engineers to issue permits for activities which result in earth disturbances contributing to stream sedimentation or which will result in decreased stream flows because of water impoundment.]

UNIQUE PROPERTIES OF WATER

Water, a universal solvent, dissolves many substances, resulting in the alteration of water quality. Water is the only known substance which allows the solid state (ice) to float on the liquid state. If this process were not possible, lakes would freeze from the bottom up, eliminating aquatic life annually. Some deep lakes would remain frozen forever. The greatest water density is reached at 4°C (39.6°F), allowing aquatic life to survive in an ice-covered lake unless light penetration is prevented for long periods. Then the available oxygen may be completely consumed, resulting in a "winter kill" of fish.

WATER QUALITY DATA SOURCES

Many sources provide water quality information. The U.S. Geological Survey (USGS) annually publishes surface water reports, by State, that contain streamflow and chemical analysis data for major streams where sampling stations have been established. The U.S. Environmental Protection Agency maintains two computerized data bases: (STORET) for chemical water information and (BIOSTORET) for biological information on aquatic life. Data are stored geographically by latitude and longitude.

State water quality control commissions and State fish and wildlife agencies are also sources of chemical and biological information on water quality.

WATER SAMPLING

If animals become distressed from being in or drinking from polluted waters on public lands, then water sampling and analysis become urgent matters in determining the cause and solution to the problem. Reduced oxygen or introduced toxic materials are common causes. Dissolved oxygen (DO) can be readily analyzed in the field with a field DO kit. If the dissolved oxygen is 5 mg/l or higher, the problem is more likely to be a toxic material problem than a lack of oxygen.

At least a 1-gallon water sample is collected and carefully labeled as to time, date, location, and site conditions. Water chemical analysis is then done by a qualified chemist. The chemist must be informed of the most likely substance causing the problem, as the chemist cannot conduct a thorough analysis on all elements which might be present in the water sample.

Preferably, water quality should be monitored on site since many parameters, e.g. temperature, DO, and pH, will be altered during transportation to the laboratory. If monitoring is done in the field, samples need only be collected for the more detailed analyses such as trace metals.

Beyond the crisis situation described above, what chemical and physical characteristics of water are useful for land management? The list is short: pH, DO, temperature, alkalinity, conductivity, and nutrients. These variables aid in describing habitat conditions suitable for specific aquatic organisms. In addition to these variables, others may be of interest or importance. The most important are listed with references where more detailed information can be found.

Water samples to be analyzed by a chemist (or placed in storage) should contain identifying information such as sample or station number; name of water, stream, lake or reservoir; time and date of collection; collector's name and agency; and a report about the chemical analysis done at the collection site. Because storage of water samples in certain containers for extended periods may alter water chemistry, inquiries as to sampling procedures and containers should be made from local and regional water quality analysts or by consulting "Standard Methods for the Examination of Water and Wastewater" (American Public Health Association 1976) and "Methods for Chemical Analysis of Water and Wastes" (U.S. Environmental Protection Agency 1979). The Federal Register, Vol. 44, No. 244, pp. 75028-75052, December 18, 1979, describes approved test procedures, containers, and preservation and holding times.

Sampling Procedures

Water sampling analysis describes the water qualities for a particular location on a special date, at a designated time. This is sometimes called a "grab sample" which may be more meaningful if the same site is sampled over a period of time.

Water can be analyzed with a field chemical kit at the sampling site or transported to a chemical laboratory for more detailed analyses. The field chemical kit can be used to analyze temperature, turbidity, pH, hardness, alkalinity, sulfate, ammonia, phosphate, nitrate, some metals, and dissolved gases.

In fact, dissolved gases, such as oxygen, carbon dioxide, and hydrogen sulfide, must be analyzed at the site. (Special care is required to avoid altering the levels of dissolved gases by aeration.) All measurements should be recorded carefully in a field notebook or on appropriate forms.

Water Quality Criteria

Water quality criteria specify concentrations of water constituents for various uses, e.g., fish, wildlife, recreation, domestic water sources, and agriculture (irrigation and livestock). Typically, fish and wildlife criteria are the most sensitive. Criteria, derived from scientific research and observation, are established by each State and may vary regionally as well as among States.

Water quality criteria are listed alphabetically in "Quality Criteria for Water" (U.S. Environmental Protection Agency 1976) with comments by the American Fisheries Society (Thurston et al. 1979). The issue of water quality criteria is unsettled. In most cases, establishing water quality criteria is not desirable or feasible at the local level. The State water quality criteria should therefore be used where applicable. Additional guidance can be obtained from the literature.

Water Measurement Terms

Some common terms used in water quality analysis are described below.

mg/l = milligrams of a chemical per liter of water; a way to express the concentration of chemicals; equivalent to parts per million (ppm) or micrograms per gram ($\mu g/g$) or milligrams per kilogram (mg/kg).

$\mu g/l$ = micrograms of chemical per liter of water; equivalent to parts per billion (ppb) or nanograms per gram (ng/g) or micrograms per kilogram ($\mu g/kg$).

LC = lethal concentration; usually expressed as a concentration of a toxicant that is lethal (fatal) to a fixed percentage of the organisms in a specified time. Thus a 96-hour LC_{50} will be lethal to 50% of the organisms within 96 hours.

Water quality criteria are generally listed as dissolved (d) or total (t) depending on the application. This is particularly important for metals where the dissolved (ionic) forms can be quite toxic, whereas the precipitated, bound forms are relatively nontoxic.

Quality Criteria for Selected Substances

The following are criteria and wildlife and fishery considerations for some of the more important substances, considering that water quality changes among sites, seasons, and even days. "EPA criteria" refer to criteria listed in "Quality Criteria for Water" (U.S. Environmental Protection Agency 1976).

Alkalinity. Alkalinity is the sum total of the components in the water that tend to elevate the pH of water above a value of about 4.5. It is measured by titration with standardized acid to a pH value of about 4.5 and expressed as mg/l of calcium carbonate. Alkalinity is therefore a measure of the buffering capacity of water. The EPA criteria for alkalinity is 20 mg/l or more as $CaCO_3$ for freshwater aquatic life except where natural concentrations are less. Thurston et al. (1979:3) say the EPA criteria of 20 mg/l are not valid. Controversy exists in all stated criteria because of the great variability in regional water quality and the aquatic species that inhabit the waters.

Cadmium. The EPA criteria for cadmium are—

Soft Water
0.4 $\mu g/l$ for cladocerans and salmonid fishes
4.0 $\mu g/l$ for other, less sensitive aquatic life

Hard Water
2.0 $\mu g/l$ for cladocerans and salmonid fishes
12.0 $\mu g/l$ for other, less sensitive aquatic life

Thurston et al. (1979:51) indicate that "Toxicological data would suggest criteria for five levels of hardness: 0-35, 35-75, 75-150, 150-300, and 300 mg/l $CaCO_3$."

Chlorine. The EPA criteria for total residual chlorine are—

2.0 $\mu g/l$ for salmonid fish
10.0 $\mu g/l$ for other fresh-water and marine organisms

Thurston et al. (1979:67-72) feel these criteria are not acceptable and state, "A single criterion of 3-5 mg/l (measured by amperometric titration in conjunction with polarograph) is more appropriate for the protection of fresh-water organisms."

Chromium. The EPA criterion is 100 $\mu g/l$ for fresh-water aquatic organisms.

Thurston et al. (1979) recommend that in no case should the criterion be higher than 50 $\mu g/l$ for any aquatic organisms.

Conductivity. Conductivity is a numerical expression of the ability of an aqueous solution to carry electric current, expressed in μmhos/cm (micromhos/cm) at 25° C. Conductivity can be used to approximate total dissolved solids in water by using the formula: Specific conductance × (0.65 ± 0.05) = mg/l dissolved solids. The formula should be verified by comparing specific conductance in μmhos with the total dissolved solids determined empirically by filter-evaporation procedures.

Copper. The EPA criteria for fresh-water and marine aquatic life, 0.1 × a 96-hr LC_{50} value, is determined through nonaerated bioassay using sensitive aquatic (resident) species.

Thurston et al. (1979:100) do not agree with this criterion (which is 10 times higher—0.01 to 0.1—than the previous criterion); however, they do not suggest another criterion.

Cyanide. The EPA criterion is 5 μg/l for fresh-water and marine aquatic life and wildlife.

Thurston et al. (1979:100) suggest that—

"The criterion for cyanide, presumably an upper limit of total cyanide concentration at any time or place, is unacceptable. A limit of the concentration of free cyanide (HCN and CN⁻) or of molecular hydrogen cyanide (HCN), with the same numerical value (5 μg/l) can be accepted as a reasonable water quality criterion for general application with some reservations. However, the . . . criterion evidently is a limit for total cyanide . . . Such a criterion can leave no sound toxicological basis, because only free and not complexed cyanide has been shown to be toxic at concentrations less than 1 mg/l (1,000 μg/l). Moreover, very low levels of molecular HCN can now be reliably determined by any of several proven methods . . ."

Hardness. Hardness is reported as an equivalent concentration of calcium carbonate ($CaCO_3$).

Concentration of $CaCO_3$ (mg/l)	Description
0-75	soft water
75-150	moderately hard water
150-300	hard water
300 and up	very hard water

The EPA (1976) suggests that the effects of hardness on fresh-water fish and other aquatic life are related to the ions causing the hardness rather than hardness itself.

Iron. The EPA criterion is 1 mg/l for fresh-water aquatic life.

Thurston et al. (1979) suggest the criterion for iron is too high. Lethality for aquatic insects has been observed at 320 μg/l.

Lead. The EPA criterion is 0.01 times the 96-hour LC_{50} value, using the receiving or comparable water as the diluent and soluble lead measurement (nonfilterable lead using 0.45 micron filter), for sensitive fresh-water resident fish.

Mercury. The EPA criterion is 0.05 μg/l for fresh-water aquatic and marine aquatic organisms.

Nickel. The EPA criterion is 0.01 of the 96-hour LC_{50} value, for fresh-water marine aquatic organisms.

Nitrates and Nitrites. The nitrogen compounds in natural waters are derived from the fixation of atmospheric nitrogen or from pollution sources. These compounds are available for absorption by bacteria, which produce ammonia, nitrite, and nitrate. Inorganic forms of nitrogen are rapidly absorbed and concentrated by phytoplankton. Little plant growth occurs if nitrate nitrogen is below 0.3 mg/l.

The EPA (1976) states—

"It is concluded that: (1) levels of nitrate nitrogen at or below 90 mg/l would have no adverse effects on warm-water fish . . . (2) nitrite nitrogen at or below 5 mg/l should be protective of most warm-water fish . . . and (3) nitrite nitrogen at or below 0.06 mg/l should be protective of salmonid fishes . . . These levels either are not known to occur or would be likely to occur in natural surface waters. Recognizing that concentrations of nitrate or nitrite that would exhibit toxic effects on warm or cold water fish could rarely occur in nature, restrictive criteria are not recommended."

Oil and Grease. The EPA (1976) suggests, for aquatic life, that levels of individual petrochemicals in the water should not exceed 0.01 of the lowest continuous flow 96-hour LC_{50} value, since each species has demonstrated high susceptibility to oils and petrochemicals.

Oxygen, Dissolved. The EPA criteria for dissolved oxygen (DO) for fresh-water aquatic life is 5 mg/l. The amount of oxygen that will dissolve in water is affected by temperature, elevation, and total dissolved solids, although certain desert fishes such as pupfish can survive low oxygen tension, e.g., 0.1 to 0.4 mg/l.

pH. The abbreviation "pH" is a measure of the hydrogen-ion activity in a water sample. It is mathematically related to hydrogen-ion activity according to the expression: $pH = -\log_{10}[H^+]$, where $[H^+]$ is the hydrogen-ion activity. Stream water in areas not influenced by pollution generally has a pH range between 6.5 and 8.5, which is acceptable for fish. The EPA criterion is 6.5 to 9.0 for fresh-water aquatic life.

Acid rain, the product of fossil fuel combustion, produces sulfur dioxide and other oxides which combine with water to form acids. Water bodies with low buffering capacity (i.e., low alkalinity) cannot counteract acid rain, and the pH level lowers to a lethal level of less than 4.

Low pH caused by acid precipitation has eliminated fish populations in many lakes in the Adirondack Mountains of New York, the LaCloche Mountains of Ontario, and the lakes and streams of southern Norway and western Sweden (Fritz 1980).

Phosphates. Phosphates occur in water as a result of leaching from minerals or as one of the stabilized products of decomposition of organic matter. Phosphorus also occurs as orthophosphate from land agricultural application and is essential to the growth of organisms. It can be the nutrient that limits productivity of a water body. The EPA (1976) discusses effects of phosphorus concentrations on aquatic life but does not set any criteria for fresh-water fish or aquatic life.

Polychlorinated Biphenyls (PCB). The EPA criterion is 0.001 μg/l for fresh-water and marine life and for the consumers thereof.

Selenium. The EPA criterion is 0.01 mg/l of the 96-hour LC_{50} value, as determined by bioassay using sensitive resident species for marine and fresh-water aquatic life.

Silver. The EPA criterion is 0.01 mg/l of the 96-hour LC_{50} value, as determined by bioassay using sensitive resident species for marine and fresh-water aquatic life.

Solids (suspended, settleable) and Turbidity. Suspended or settleable solids include both inorganic and organic materials. Turbidity is an expression of the optical property that causes light to be scattered and absorbed rather than transmitted in straight lines through water. The EPA criterion for both solids (suspended, settleable) and turbidity for fresh-water fish and other aquatic life is that "settleable and suspended solids should not reduce the depth of the compensation point for photosynthetic activity by

more than 10 percent from the seasonally established norm for aquatic life."

Thurston et al. (1979) disagree with this criterion because "the criterion treats solids and turbidity as synonymous, which they are not." They recommend two sets of criteria: residue (solids) measured in mg/l and turbidity measured in Nephelometric Turbidity Units (NTU's). Both sets of measurements are to be done in accordance with "Standard Methods for the Examination of Water and Wastewater (American Public Health Association et al. 1976).

Commercial turbidimeters measure light transmitted in NTU's. Turbidity criteria vary regionally and may depend on the type of fishery of concern, i.e. warm- or cold-water.

Sulfide (Hydrogen Sulfide). The EPA criterion is 2 μg/l undissociated H_2S for fish and aquatic life.

Tainting Substances. Tainting substances can produce undesirable flavor in the edible portions of fish or other aquatic vertebrates. Diesel oil in very small amounts will taint fish flesh.

WATER QUALITY BASELINE DATA COLLECTION—PROJECT PLANNING

Land-use projects having major impacts on water quality require special attention in establishing baseline pre-project water quality. An example of gathering water quality data before surface mining is displayed in Table 1 (Harris et al. 1983). The field and laboratory analyses are divided logically. Baseline physical and chemical data will provide a basis for water quality monitoring during the lifetime of the land-use project.

WATER QUALITY MONITORING PROGRAMS

Water quality monitoring can be related to management objectives on a long-term basis. Methods for testing the statistical significance of change in water data collected over a period of time are outlined in several publications. Two publications providing statistical analysis procedures for field use are "Water Quality Monitoring Programs" (Ponce 1980) and "Stream Monitoring Techniques" (Armour et al. 1983).

Table 1. Water quality and bottom-sediment parameters measured in the Tyro Creek watershed, September 1981 through September 1982 (from Harris et al. 1983).

Field Determinations[1]	Laboratory Analyses[1]	Bottom Sediments
Discharge (cfs) Temperature (°C) pH (as units) Alkalinity (as HCO$_3$) Specific conductance (μmhos/cm) Color (Pt-Co) Turbidity (JTU) Dissolved oxygen	Suspended sediment Calcium (Ca) Chloride (Cl) Fluoride (F) Potassium (K) Magnesium (Mg) Sodium (Na) Nitrate (N) (dissolved) Nitrate (NO$_3$) Silica (SiO$_2$) Sulfate (SO$_4$) Trace metals (μg/l) Arsenic (As) Cadmium (Cd) Chromium (Cr) Cobalt (Co) Copper (Cu) Iron (Fe) Lead (Pb) Vanadium (V) Manganese (Mg) Mercury (Hg) Selenium (Se) Strontium (Sr) Zinc (Zn)	Sieve analyses Trace metals and nutrients (mg/kg) Arsenic (As) Cadmium (Cd) Chromium (Cr) Cobalt (Co) Copper (Cu) Iron (Fe) Lead (Pb) Mercury (Hg) Selenium (Se) Strontium (Sr) Vanadium (V) Zinc (Zn) Chloride (Cl) Phosphate (PO$_4$) Nitrate (NO$_3$) pH (as units)

[1] All measurements should be taken in mg/l unless otherwise indicated.

LITERATURE CITED

AMERICAN PUBLIC HEALTH ASSOCIATION. 1976. Standard methods for the examination of water and wastewater, 15th edition. Am. Public Health Assoc. New York, NY. 1134pp.

ARMOUR, C.L., K.P. BURNHAN, and W.S. PLATTS. 1983. Field methods and statistical analysis for monitoring small salmonid streams. U.S. Dep. Inter., Fish and Wildl. Serv. FWS/OBS-83/33. 200pp.

FRITZ, E.S. 1980. Potential impacts of low pH on fish and fish populations. U.S. Dep. Inter., Fish and Wildl. Serv., Biological Services Program, National Power Plant Team, FWS/OSS-80/40.2. 14pp.

HARRIS, C.H., P.E. O'NEIL, R.V. CHANDLER, M.F. METEE, and E.J. MCCULLOUGH. 1983. Biological and hydrological impacts of surface mining for federal minerals on the Tyro Creek Watershed, Alabama, Phase 1. Premining-aquatic baseline information. Contract performed for U.S. Dep. Inter., Bur. Land Manage. 98pp.

PONCE, S.L. 1980. Water quality monitoring programs. U.S. Dep. Agric., For. Serv., 3825 E. Mulberry St., Ft. Collins, CO 80524. 66pp.

THURSTON, R.V., R.C. RUSSON, C.M. FETTEROLF, Jr., T.A. EDSALL, and Y.M. BARBER, Jr. 1979. A review of the EPA Red Book: Quality Criteria for Water. Am. Fish. Soc. Bethesda, MD. 313pp.

U.S. ENVIRONMENTAL PROTECTION AGENCY. 1976. Quality criteria for water. U.S. Environmental Protection Agency, Washington, DC 20460. 50lpp.

———. 1979. Methods for chemical analysis of water and wastes. EPA-600/4-79-020. Washington, DC.

31

VEGETATION

Bertin W. Anderson and Robert D. Ohmart

Center for Environmental Studies
Arizona State University
Tempe, AZ 85287

Editor's Note: Although vegetation is widely recognized as one of the most important determinants of wildlife abundance and distribution, most systems for measuring and classifying vegetation have been developed for other purposes. Development of vegetation measurements for wildlife purposes has mostly focused on measuring forage supplies for big game and other herbivores. Such techniques are well-described in the literature and are discussed briefly in Chapter 25, Ungulates.

This chapter focuses on vegetation measurement techniques that have been found useful for (1) evaluating habitat for vertebrate communities, (2) predicting presence or abundance of individual species for a wide variety of vertebrates, and (3) predicting species richness of habitat areas. Because of the diversity of possible approaches, the authors have not attempted to provide a thorough review of all techniques and their relative strengths. Rather, they have described one system that is reasonably efficient and has worked well for them. Biologists will undoubtedly need to modify systems to meet the needs of their inventory or monitoring programs. Nevertheless, the attributes described in this chapter should be useful predictors of wildlife habitat quality in a wide variety of habitats, and the measurement techniques described should be usable or modifiable for a diversity of problems.

INTRODUCTION

This chapter describes attributes of plant communities that we found useful in evaluating habitat for vertebrate wildlife. We describe methods for measuring these attributes and show how these measurements may be useful in predicting species presence or absence, species abundance, and wildlife species richness in various communities. We developed these primarily for riparian habitat, but the general procedures should be applicable to other habitats. This is not intended to be an exhaustive catalogue of all or even a majority of the methods available, nor a critical review of the numerous methods for quantifying vegetation attributes. Reviews of methods for measuring vegetation can be found in U.S. Department of the Interior, Bureau of Land Management (1985); Daubenmire (1968); Mueller-Dombois and Ellenberg (1974); and other standard texts.

One of the fundamental reasons for measuring attributes of a plant community is to classify the stand under consideration. Classification facilitates communication by reducing the verbage required to provide someone with a clear and, hopefully, unambiguous mental picture of the community being considered. We think classifying and describing plant communities are virtually synonymous.

In our experience, time and personnel for measuring vegetation are always limited. Therefore, we have developed a reasonably small number of field methods that can be done relatively quickly and, from which, other plant community descriptors can be generated. For example, we measure foliage density in the field and, from this, calculate patchiness in the horizontal dimension, foliage height diversity, and foliage density at various vertical layers (i.e., ground, shrub, canopy). We describe these methods in this chapter. Other sets of more traditional methods can lead to the accumulation of data equally useful in describing a vegetation community, but their use will probably be more costly in terms of time and personnel.

In classifying (describing) vegetation communities, a two- or three-dimensional approach should be considered. In general, the physiognomy or structure of the vegetation represents two dimensions. For example, a given stand of vegetation varies in vertical and horizontal space. Variation in the vertical dimension, whether single or multilayered, is particularly useful in describing the stand. Similarly, the floristics, i.e., species composition of a stand, is often invaluable in describing that stand. If structure and floristics can be relatively quickly and easily quantified, limits of a vegetation type can be clearly defined. Standard texts describing methods in synecology (Daubenmire 1968) or in mapping vegetation (Kuchler 1967) should be consulted for more details on quantifying vegetation variables and classifying vegetation.

The same characteristics used in quantitatively describing a stand of vegetation can be used in developing predictive capabilities relative to the resident wildlife. We describe reasonably fast and accurate field methods for quantitatively classifying vegetation and correlating wildlife associations with various attributes of vegetation communities.

VEGETATION ATTRIBUTES

Simple Basic Variables

We refer to foliage density, plant species composition, and fruit production as simple, basic variables because they are usually quantified in the field.

Foliage Density. Foliage density refers to the amount of green foliage present or to the amount of leaf-bearing stems and leaves per unit area. (Foliage density should not be confused with "plant density" or "density," which is the number of plants per unit area.) Usually foliage density is measured at various vertical levels (e.g., every yard or 0.1 yard [meter or 0.1 meter]). Foliage density measurements taken in summer may be useful in describing the foliage density in winter, in terms of the relative amounts of

leaf-bearing stems and leaves present, thus negating the need for remeasurements in winter. This procedure is most valid in areas dominated by trees or annuals.

Species Composition. This can be easily determined by counting individuals of each tree/shrub species present. This is not as simple as it sounds; size classes must be considered. Even then, two trees of the same height and species can be quite different. The general health of a tree or tree density can affect general structure. Thus some thought must be given to what will actually be counted.

Fruit Production. In stands of vegetation that produce fruit, especially fruits that are sought by wildlife, it may be useful to obtain some idea of the total fruit produced. We have done this when the correlation between number of trees present and fruit production is rather poor. For example, mistletoe (*Phoradendron californicum*) along the Colorado River parasitizes honey mesquite (*Prosopis glandulosa*) more frequently than other tree species. However, the proportion of trees parasitized varies widely from stand to stand. We therefore obtained estimates of the number of mistletoe clumps in a given stand. Similarly, pod production by individual honey mesquite trees varies widely between stands; thus, there is a poor correlation between number of trees present and production of pods. This is also true of pod production by screwbean mesquite (*P. pubescens*). At higher elevations, some shrub species may be important for berry or seed production for wildlife. These shrub species should be noted and given important management concern.

Composite or Derived Variables

From these foliage density and species composition measurements, a host of other variables can be derived. Foliage height diversity (FHD) is calculated from the foliage density measurements taken at various vertical planes. Horizontal foliage diversity (patchiness) can be determined by considering foliage density variation in the horizontal plane. In vertically complex (i.e., multilayered) communities, it may be desirable to calculate patchiness for each of the vertical layers, with total patchiness equal to the sum of patchiness in the vertical layers. The number of vertical layers recognized is an arbitrary matter, as is the size of the area being called a patch. The concept of FHD is depicted in Figure 1 and patchiness in Figure 2.

Tree density estimates can be expressed as the number of each species per unit area or as the proportion of the total tree species present. When measuring foliage density, one may record the plant

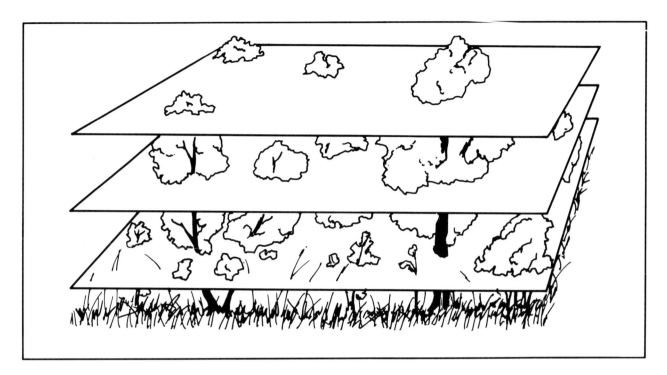

Figure 1. Diagram of foliage diversity in the vertical plane. The stand depicts an area of at least 25 a. (10 ha).

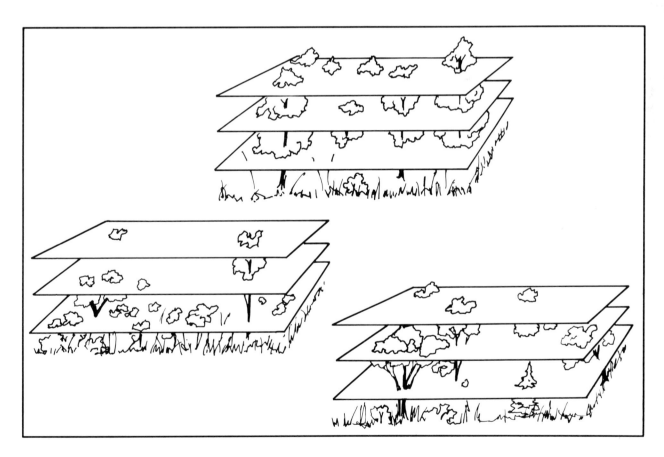

Figure 2. Diagram of foliage diversity (patchiness) in the horizontal plane at each of three vertical layers. The blocks represent patches of roughly 5 a. (2 ha).

species contributing to the foliage density at each point where measurements are taken. The density of each tree/shrub species can then be given for each vertical layer or in terms of the total foliage density for the entire area.

Usefulness of the Variables

We found that the counts of tree/shrub species were particularly useful in predicting the presence and densities of many rodent and bird species (Anderson and Ohmart 1984a, in press-b; Rice et al. 1983, 1984). We found that patchiness and FHD have useful predictive value, but are not as good a predictor as tree/shrub counts (Anderson and Ohmart 1984a, in press-b; Rice et al. 1983, 1984). Mistletoe counts were associated with the presence of frugivorous birds (Anderson and Ohmart 1978). In general, foliage density at low levels had a high association with lizards (Anderson and Ohmart 1982) and also some rodents and birds (Anderson and Ohmart, in press-b). At various times and places, desert mule deer (*Odocoileus hemionus*) were associated with screwbean and honey mesquite, but foliage density and diversity were also important in explaining their habitat selection (Haywood et al. 1984).

From this brief discussion, it seems that all of the vegetation variables given may be important to at least some species of wildlife. We found considerable seasonal variation in habitat selection within a group, i.e., birds (Anderson and Ohmart 1984a). Rodents used the vegetation differently in any given season than the majority of bird species. The point is, there is no *a priori* means of selecting a single attribute, or even a few vegetation attributes, that will be adequate for predicting wildlife use of a habitat.

Findings from our research lead us to offer a precautionary note to others planning habitat studies, particularly studies of avian habitat use. From most literature sources, we would have been led to de-emphasize tree species measurements completely. We have found many habitat attributes to be crucial to the prediction of habitat selection of at least some bird species. Had only a small set of attributes been collected, analyses would have been successful enough that one would have been tempted to conclude erroneously that the important habitat attributes and selection processes for the entire community had been captured in the study.

Studies of habitat use should be designed to sample the annual, seasonal, and spatial variation in habitat use of the animal community. Within the limits of biological reality, biologists should measure as comprehensive a set of attributes as time and money allow and should avoid measuring only a few attributes based on knowledge of a few species, data

from other areas, or information from the literature. Studies providing data for environmental management plans, especially habitat modification projects with impacts on substantial portions of the animal communities, should be based on data sets adequate for a thorough description of the system. If we had studied selected subsets of our species, transects, time periods, or habitat attributes, we could have undoubtedly produced results supporting quite a wide range of invalid proposals. Such actions are not ecologically wise nor do they lead to effective management.

MEASURING VEGETATION ATTRIBUTES

Establishing Study Sites

Lines or transects are established by cutting swaths 3 ft (1 m) wide through the middle of stands encompassing at least 25 a. (10 ha), with dimensions of at least 2,461 ft (750 m) long by 164 ft (50 m) wide. Small patches (2.5 a. [1 ha]) of vegetation, differing in species composition or structure from the major type in the stand, should be bisected by the transect at right angles whenever possible. In no case should a transect be situated so that vegetation differing from the stand as a whole is paralleled by the transect at a distance closer than 49 ft (15 m). When vegetation is very much unlike the stand as a whole, it has an unduly large effect on the vegetation analysis and on estimates of bird and rodent densities.

Semipermanent markers should be placed at the beginning and end of each transect. A stake with the distance from the beginning of the transect inscribed on it can be driven into the ground at intervals every 492 ft (150 m), which can represent a patch size. The size of a patch will depend on the species being studied. Patches 492 ft (150 m) long × 656 ft (200 m) wide represent average territory size for bird species in southwestern riparian vegetation. A transect 2,461 ft (750 m) long has five subplots or patches, each 492 ft (150 m) long on each side, for a total of 10 subplots. Vegetation data should be collected within each subplot. Each transect can be numbered, and the number and directional orientation recorded on a map. A typical transect is illustrated in Figure 3.

Vegetation Measurements

In each subplot (patch), tree counts and foliage density measurements are made. Tree counts are made only once on each transect unless the area is later affected by some major disturbance. Counting is unaffected by amount of foliage present and can be done any time. Individuals of each species of tree or shrub within 49 ft (15 m) of the transect are

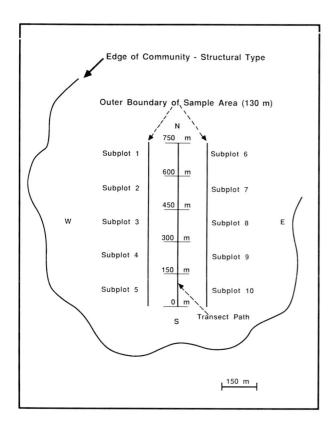

Figure 3. Typical transect through a relatively homogeneous stand of vegetation, showing individual subplots (patches) and outer boundaries.

counted in each 492 ft (150 m) subplot. Each individual tree is categorized by height (e.g., > or < 10 ft [> or < 3 m]), by presence or absence of mistletoe, and by its condition (alive or dead).

Sometimes shrubs or trees grow in densities so great that it is not feasible or possible to count individuals. Often densely packed individuals provide no more ground cover than trees in less dense areas. For example, 20 trees in one area could equate, in terms of ground cover, to 200 trees in another area. To circumvent this problem, measure the height and north-south crown diameter of 30 or more individuals of each tree species growing at various heights in uncrowded conditions. From these measurements, develop regression equations to determine the ground cover by an individual tree (shrub) of a given height (Figure 4). Thus, when a dense patch of trees or shrubs is encountered, measure the area of the patch and obtain the average height of the trees in it. Then, divide the area of the patch by the area occupied by the average single tree of the same height growing in uncrowded conditions to obtain the equivalent number of trees or shrubs growing under uncrowded conditions. This method may be applied to all trees and shrubs to obtain a rough estimate of the number of full-sized equivalents of a given plant species in an area.

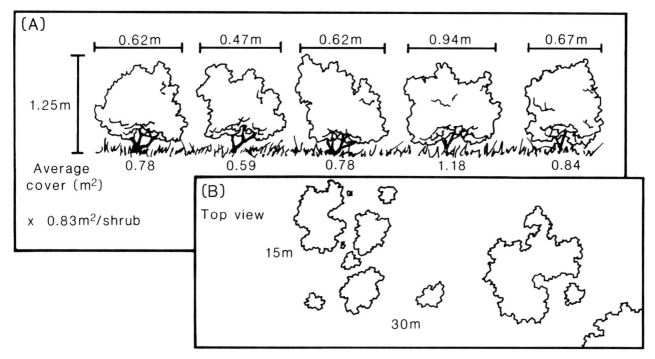

Figure 4. (A) Reference sample of quail bush. (B) Sample area with approximately 30% cover by quail bush or 1,435 ft^2 (135 m^2). Since one shrub occupies 9 ft^2 (0.83 m^2), the area has approximately 163 individual shrubs. The area occupied by each patch of quail bush was measured to determine the ground cover by quail bush.

Foliage density estimates are made in all stands annually between May and July; stands undergoing succession (i.e., burned and regenerated areas) can be measured again in September or October or even more frequently if desired. Relative foliage density estimates are made using a cover board technique (MacArthur and MacArthur 1961). Sampling is done on each side of a transect at three points (49 ft [15 m], 246 ft [75 m], and 432 ft [135 m]) from the beginning of each subplot (patch). Thus on a 2,461 ft (750 m) transect, there are 15 points per side for a total of 30 points (Figure 5).

At each sample point, one observer paces one step perpendicular to the transect. A second observer holds a board (approximately 8 × 16 in. [20 × 40 cm]) at a given height behind the nearest green, leafy vegetation on the appropriate side of the transect. The first observer directs the second observer to stop when green foliage covers half the board. Distance from observer to board is measured with a tape measure or range finder (Figure 6). Foliage density measurements are recorded in feet because of the scaling of the equipment we used; also, all vegetation calculations were based on the English system of measures. All of this could just as easily be done in metric units.

Round all measurements to the nearest foot (0.3 m), except the first. In the first foot (0.3 m), a distance of 2 in. (5 cm) represents very dense vegetation, but zero means that foliage is absent. Thus, any distance > 0 but < 1 ft (< 0.3 m) should be regarded as 1 ft (0.3 m). Often it is difficult to obtain agreement between two observers for distances < 1 ft (< 0.3 m), yet the difference in, for example,

the foliage density estimate between 1 in. (2.5 cm) and 2 in. (5 cm) is large. Rounding to 1 ft (0.3 m) results in a conservative estimate of foliage density in very dense places, but yields reproducible results. Vertical foliage density determinations can be made at, for example, 0.5 ft (0.15 m), 2 ft (0.6 m), 5 ft (1.5 m), 10 ft (3 m), 15 ft (4.5 m), 20 ft (6 m), 25 ft (7.5 m), 30 ft (9 m), and every 10 ft (3 m) thereafter, until no vegetation is present. Where measurements are taken is up to the judgment of those in charge of the project. Theoretically, one should use a ladder to make measurements at higher levels. This is impractical. We use a range finder to locate a point, for example, at 26 ft (8 m), then estimate as carefully as possible the distance to a second point where leaves would cover half the board.

Distances are measured with a tape measure to the nearest foot within the first 10 feet (3 meters), because the foliage density index is more sensitive to vegetation located nearby. Measurements beyond this are estimated with the aid of a range finder. In sparse areas, the distance to the few tall trees and prominent shrubs with foliage should be measured from only one sample point within a subplot—the point to which they are closest. These data should be recorded; many suitable ways are imaginable.

Frequency of Measurements. It is important to take as many measurements as necessary to obtain a reasonably accurate reflection of the true foliage density and diversity of a stand. In general, the more measurements that are taken, the greater the precision; however, for most field workers, time and personnel are restraining factors. Beyond some number, additional measurements increase labor

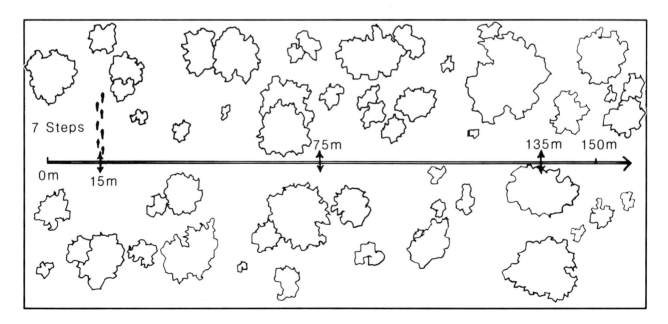

Figure 5. Sampling points for foliage density measurements within each subplot along the length of a transect.

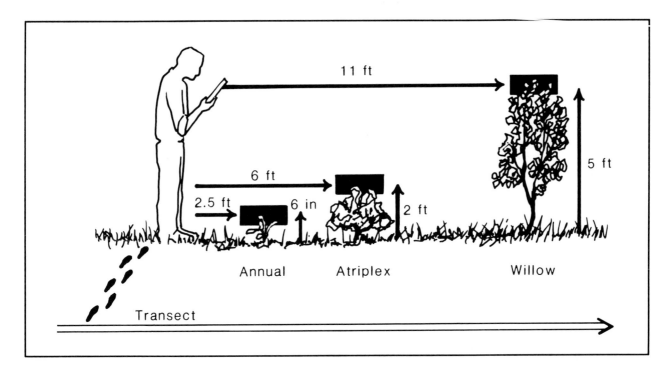

Figure 6. Selection of vegetation for foliage density measurements.

requirements more than can be justified when the increase in precision is very small.

In identifying the effort required to obtain reasonably precise data, we made foliage density measurements at 1, 2, 3, 4, 5, 9, and 12 points within each subplot on each side of 7 transects, which involved 104 subplots. Foliage density calculations were made using one measurement from each subplot, then two measurements, and so on, until five separate sets of calculations were made. This was repeated using 9 and 12 measurements per subplot. We assumed that 12 measurements per subplot yielded results as close to reality as could possibly be obtained with our methods. The foliage density and diversity results obtained for each set of measurements were expressed as percentage deviation from the results obtained with 12 measurements per subplot. The mean percentage difference and standard deviation decreases as the number of measurement points increases (Figure 7), until five measurements were included per subplot. Precision did not increase with nine measurements per subplot. We ultimately chose to make three measurements per subplot. Making five measurements decreases the error rate by only 1%, but increases the work by 67%. In our judgment, the additional precision is not warranted by the effort to obtain it.

Repeatability. Work encompassing a large area (100,000 a. [40,000 ha]) will probably require several individuals to collect data. Thus, all personnel must be carefully trained and the similarity of data collected from the same stand by

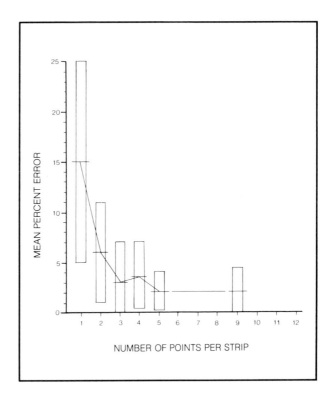

Figure 7. Mean percentage error associated with foliage density and diversity measurements when measurements were made at various numbers of points in each subplot. The values obtained from 12 measurements per subplot were assumed to accurately represent the true values. This standard was used for comparing values obtained with smaller numbers of measurements per subplot.

different observers, determined. In general, we found least agreement in data from stands with tall vegetation (> 33 ft [> 10 m]). Space precludes an exhaustive presentation of our data; however, we describe where discrepancies among observer teams were greatest. For a more thorough presentation, see Anderson and Hunter (1983).

Foliage measurements were taken by four teams in a relatively dense stand encompassing about 25 a. (10 ha) and containing trees to 64 ft (20 m) tall. It was assumed that some observer estimates would be too high and some would be too low; thus the average for the teams would approximate the "correct" estimate for each foliage variable. The deviation from the average was then considered to be the error rate for a team. The error divided by the "correct" value yielded the percentage of error. This procedure indicated, for all variables, a mean error of 8%. The greatest difficulty was in assessing vegetation density at the highest levels; the average error at 26 ft (8 m) was 33% (Table 1). The mean error was lowest for FHD (2%) and total patchiness (4%). Since the error rates for foliage density estimates were higher than hoped, we examined the results in greater detail.

Although foliage density estimates had a mean error rate of 15%, the profiles of vertical foliage distribution derived from the estimates were nearly identical in three of the four cases in the first test and, in all four cases, the vegetation would be classified the same. In the second test, two of the three profiles would have led to the same classification. This is of major importance because the fact that all four teams in the first set obtained results that led to

classifying the stand in the same way, should minimize the importance of the observed variation in data obtained by different teams. FHD and patchiness estimates obtained by different teams for a given stand were always similar.

Overall, we are satisfied that these methods accurately and consistently differentiated areas of high, intermediate, and low foliage density and diversity in the vertical and horizontal planes. However, stands differing slightly in foliage density probably cannot be reliably separated.

Training Personnel. All personnel should be thoroughly trained in field techniques before collecting data on their own. More experienced personnel should accompany less experienced personnel in the field. Having people with experience with the technique is not essential, but having dedicated, conscientious personnel is.

Need for Preliminary Studies

In any study where discovery of relationships between animals and environmental variables is a goal, there is a need for preliminary studies (Green 1979; Platts 1981; Platts et al. 1983). Such studies are essential because they allow investigators to test to see if their methods satisfactorily produce the desired kinds of information. Preliminary studies also offer an opportunity to become thoroughly familiar with the study area before beginning the study and provide a training period for field personnel. In addition, preliminary studies allow the investigators to determine differences between experimental and control areas prior to treating the experimental area.

Table 1. Average error associated with various vegetation variables collected by four different teams from the same stand. (The mean measurements by all four teams were the standards with which comparisons were made.)

Team	Foliage Density at Various Heights						Patchiness				
	0.0–0.6 m (0–2 ft)	0.6–4.5 m (2–15 ft)	4.5–7.5 m (15–25 ft)	≥7.5 m (≥25 ft)	Total	FHD	0.0–0.6 m (0–2 ft)	0.6–4.5 m (2–15 ft)	4.5–7.5 m (15–25 ft)	≥7.5 m (≥25 ft)	Total
TEST I											
1	20.5	3.4	20.8	74.2	31.6	1.1	0.9	0.8	0.9	11.6	1.8
2	12.6	13.9	5.9	21.0	1.7	4.1	5.2	3.7	8.7	6.1	6.7
3	16.8	6.1	14.8	27.0	17.3	0.9	2.0	1.4	1.5	6.9	3.7
4	16.2	4.3	11.7	26.3	15.9	2.0	2.3	1.3	1.5	10.7	5.0
TEST II											
1	8.5	3.2	1.0	13.5	2.4	2.8	1.5	0.2	2.4	0.0	2.8
2	4.6	7.3	10.2	42.0	1.3	2.8	1.3	0.9	0.3	2.0	2.8
3	12.7	10.5	11.0	28.0	1.6	0.1	1.6	2.1	1.2	0.6	0.1
Mean	13.3	7.0	10.8	33.1	10.3	2.0	2.1	1.5	2.4	5.4	3.3
SD	4.9	4.0	6.3	20.0	11.7	1.4	1.4	1.1	2.9	4.7	2.1

For example, if the objective is to determine the impact of light grazing on an area in terms of changes in wildlife densities and diversities, it is critically important to establish plots where all variables, except the one being tested, are controlled. This means that the vegetation and wildlife use must be analyzed in the control and experimental areas before grazing. Impacts can only be evaluated after internal variation, before the impact, is known.

The argument is often heard that such preliminary studies are too time-consuming and expensive to carry out. This is fallacy; preliminary studies can save time and money and are the only way of obtaining scientifically valid results (Green 1979). Without them, results obtained after an impact cannot be determined because the lack of knowledge of the variation before the impact was unknown. In other words, as Platts (1981) correctly pointed out, the notion that collection of inventory "garbage" (i.e., data without preliminary studies) leads to reliable analyses is purely mythical. Unfortunately, it is a pervasive myth. If preliminary studies cannot be done, the study should not be undertaken or undertaken with the realization that conclusions based on the findings are not well-founded scientifically.

ANALYTICAL METHODS

Foliage Density

Each plant distance measurement is converted to surface area per cubic unit of space (i.e., foliage density) according to the following formula:

$$K = \frac{\log_e 2}{D} = \frac{0.693}{D}$$

Where: K = the foliage density and D = the measured distance.

Foliage density per subplot is the sum of the average of the three measurements taken at each vertical plane. For example, foliage density at 5 ft (1.5 m) in one subplot, for which the distances were 9, 15, and 2 ft (2.7, 4.5, and 0.6 m), respectively, would be calculated as follows:

$$\left(\frac{0.693}{9} + \frac{0.693}{15} + \frac{0.693}{2} \right) \div 3 = 0.1556$$

Foliage density at 10 ft (3 m) for distances of 1, 2, and 3 ft (0.3, 0.6, 0.9 m), respectively, would be—

$$\left(\frac{0.693}{1} + \frac{0.693}{2} + \frac{0.693}{3} \right) \div 3 = 0.4217$$

The density for the two vertical planes is 0.1556 + 0.4217 = 0.5773. If no green foliage occurred at a particular point, a zero is used in the calculations.

These measurements will produce a table of density measurements such as in Table 2, which can be used for subsequent calculations of derived variables such as vertical and horizontal diversity.

Table 2. Sample foliage density estimates (ft^2/ft^3) used for calculating patchiness and foliage height diversity.

Plot	0.15 m (0.5 ft)	0.6 m (2 ft)	1.5 m (5 ft)	3 m (10 ft)	4.6 m (15 ft)
1	0.16	0.20	0.29	0.10	0.01
2	0.12	0.15	0.23	0.06	—
3	0.08	0.09	0.27	0.09	0.01
4	0.28	0.15	0.09	0.01	0.00
5	0.19	0.22	0.09	0.02	0.00
6	0.18	0.34	0.29	0.10	0.02
7	0.07	0.31	0.31	0.03	0.01
8	0.08	0.18	0.31	0.02	—
9	0.15	0.16	0.32	0.03	—
10	0.23	0.15	0.13	0.01	—

Vertical Diversity (Foliage Height Diversity)

Vertical or foliage height diversity (FHD) for each transect is calculated according to the information theory (Shannon and Weaver 1949):

$$FHD = -\sum_{i}^{n} (p_i)(\log_n p_i)$$

Where: p_i is the proportion of total foliage density contributed by the density at level i. (Sample calculations are shown in Table 3.)

Many stands of vegetation include a shrubby layer up to about 3 ft (1 m). We chose foliage density estimates from 0.5 ft (0.15 m) and 2 ft (0.6 m) to represent this vertical layer. Foliage density in this layer is the sum of the density at 0.5 ft (0.15 m) and 2 ft (0.6 m). Most stands will probably have another layer extending, for example, from 2 to 15 ft (0.6 to 4.5 m). Foliage density estimates at 5 ft (1.5 m) and 10 ft (3 m) could be used to represent this layer. Many stands have a third layer, usually poorly developed, extending above the second layer for an additional 7 to 10 ft (2 to 3 m) or more, depending on locality. We chose foliage density estimates at 15 ft (4.5 m) and 20 ft (6 m) to represent this layer. Foliage < 7.5 m (< 25 ft) could represent a fourth layer. The concept of FHD with four vertical layers is depicted in Figure 1.

Table 3. Example of calculation of foliage height diversity from data in Table 2.

Item	Height Class				
	0.15–0.6 m (0.5–2 ft)	1.5–3.0 m (5–10 ft)	4.6–6.0 m (15–20 ft)	> 7.5 m (> 25 ft)	*Total*
Mean total density	0.35	0.28	0.00	0	0.63
Proportion (p$_i$)	0.55	0.44	0.01	0	
log$_{10}$p$_i$	−0.26	−0.36	−2.20	0	
p$_i$log$_{10}$p$_i$	−0.14	−0.16	−0.01	0	
	FHD $= -\sum_{i}^{n}(p_i)(\log_{10}p_i) = -[(-0.14) + (0.16) + (0.01) + (0)]$ $= 0.31$				

Horizontal Diversity (Patchiness)

Horizontal diversity (or patchiness) is a structural feature of a habitat describing the regularity of vegetation as it is distributed in the horizontal plane (Figure 2). A citrus orchard with roughly equally sized and evenly spaced trees has little horizontal diversity. Patchiness or diversity is greater in a honey mesquite-quail bush (*Atriplex lentiformis*) habitat with irregularly spaced trees and shrubs of different heights. Diversity in the horizontal plane can be calculated for any vertical layer from which foliage density estimates are made.

The variance associated with the mean total foliage density for each vertical plane across all subplots can be used as a measure of horizontal diversity. For example, the summed and averaged foliage densities for 0.5 ft (0.15 m) and 2 ft (0.6 m) in each plot (Table 4) yields the mean foliage density for the layer 0 to 2 ft (0.0 to 0.6 m), in this case, 0.35. Horizontal diversity is the variance associated with mean total foliage density, in this case, 0.01. Variance or standard deviation squared (s^2) is defined as—

$$\text{HDI} = s^2 = \frac{\sum_{i=1}^{n}(k_i - \bar{K})^2}{n\text{-}1}$$

It can be calculated more easily using the formula—

$$\text{HDI} = s^2 = \frac{\sum_{i=1}^{n}k_i^2 - \frac{(\Sigma k_i)^2}{n}}{n\text{-}1}$$

Where: k_i = the foliage density of the ith sample
$\bar{K}$ = the mean foliage density for the sample
n = sample size
HDI = Horizontal Diversity Index

This variance is calculated for each vertical layer. Total horizontal diversity is the sum of the variances for all layers.

In calculating horizontal diversity, we are assessing the variance between subplots. Therefore, if horizontal diversity is thought of as patchiness, we are defining a patch as a unit 492 ft (150 m) long and as wide as the distance from the transect to the edge of the stand under study, usually 420 ft (128 m). Choice of this patch size was based on evidence that many common birds in the area use patches of about this size (Conine 1982). It is possible that an area that rated very patchy on a smaller scale could be rated homogeneous using this particular scale.

Since 0.00 and 0.69 represent minimum and maximum foliage density values, respectively, maximum horizontal diversity or patchiness for a given layer is 0.238. Since there are four layers, maximum horizontal plane diversity is 4 × 0.238 or 0.952. Since this is close to 1, the sum of the diversity for the four layers closely represents the percentage of maximum diversity possible for an area.

Another method for calculating FHD and patchiness is to simply record the presence or absence of vegetation at various vertical positions. This could be done with a long pole and/or a range finder. More stops would have to be made, but FHD, relative density values, and patchiness estimates could be made on the basis of the proportion of total points at which foliage occurred. This method may be quicker, could reduce the amount of calculation, and might be equally accurate.

CLASSIFYING VEGETATION

If the goal of a field project is to determine habitat associations for a wildlife group, such as birds, over a relatively large area (e.g.,100,000 a. [40,000 ha]), the area must be sampled with sufficient intensity so all habitats are represented by at least one

Table 4. Example of calculation of horizontal diversity index (HDI) from data in Table 2.

Item	Height Class				
	0.15–0.6 m (0.5–2 ft)	1.5–3.0 m (5–10 ft)	4.6–6.0 m (15–20 ft)	> 7.5 m (> 25 ft)	Total
Sum of k_i	3.49	2.80	0.05	—	
Sum of squares k_i^2	1.3073	0.8967	0.0007	—	
Sum squared $(\Sigma k_i)^2$	12.1801	7.8400	0.0025	—	
n	10	10	10	—	

$$\text{HDI} = s^2 = \frac{\Sigma k_i^2 - \frac{(\Sigma k_i)^2}{n}}{n-1} = 0.01 \qquad + \quad 0.01 \qquad + \quad 0.00 \qquad + \quad - \qquad = 0.02$$

sample plot (transected area). Of course, replication is desirable. If this sampling is random, then the number of transects per habitat will be proportional to the abundance of that habitat in the study area. All transects should be about the same length and should be within a relatively homogeneous stand. At this point, some arbitrary decisions may have to be made because of the ambiguity associated with the term "relatively homogeneous."

In general, experience and common sense will be immeasurably helpful. A field biologist relatively familiar with an area will generally know when (s)he leaves one habitat type and enters another. It would be poor judgment to establish a transect in a mixed cottonwood (*Populus fremontii*) and willow (*Salix* sp.) habitat and have the transect cross 990 ft (300 m) of honey mesquite habitat. Having such a transect cross a small group of 10 or 15 honey mesquite trees might not be inappropriate. A general familiarity with what is available will usefully serve as a guide. If the decision is made to include one or more small patches of honey mesquite in the cottonwood-willow habitat, this will add heterogeneity to the data. Vegetation often varies considerably over small areas; thus, some heterogeneity is not necessarily bad and is probably inevitable.

The next step is to cluster transects that are similar in, for example, vertical diversity. This can be done by calculating the overlap in vertical foliage diversity. One way to do this is to use Horn's (1966) equation for overlap:

$$R_o = \frac{\Sigma(x_i + y_i)\log(x_i + y_i) - \Sigma x_i \log x_i - \Sigma y_i \log y_i}{(X + Y)\log(X + Y) - X\log Y - Y\log Y}$$

Where: x_i and y_i = proportion of total foliage density occurring at vertical band i for stand X and stand Y.

X,Y = the total foliage density for stand X and stand Y. X and Y represent total foliage density.

Although this equation appears formidable, it is actually very simple. The calculations are laborious but in this age of computers, large numbers of overlaps can be calculated in minutes. The biologist must, of course, grasp the fundamental arithmetic process. Biologically, high overlaps simply represent a mathematical expression of a high degree of similarity in vertical configuration. Once this is understood, the computer can take care of the tedium.

From a matrix of overlap values, including all possible two-way comparisons between stands (transects), a dendrogram, such as that in Figure 8, can be constructed using the following relationship:

$$C, AB = \frac{CA + CB}{2}$$

Where: C, AB = the overlap of stand C with stands A and B

CA = the overlap between stand C and stand A

CB = the overlap between stand C and stand B

Simply stated, the overlap in the vertical distribution of foliage in stand C with stands A and B is equal to the average overlap of C with A and C with B (Cody 1974). The dendrogram (Figure 8) was interpreted as revealing six categories, based on vertical configuration without consideration of dominant vegetation. Each transected stand within a category (designated I-VI) has a vertical configuration more similar to other intracategory stands than to any stand within

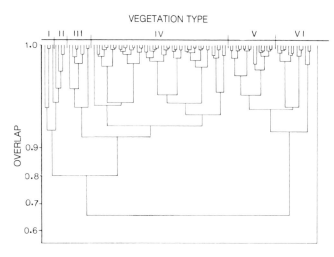

Figure 8. Dendrogram showing similarities in vertical profile between transects, based on overlap in vertical distribution of foliage.

any other category. This determination is based on proportional distribution of the foliage in the vertical dimension. These categories can now be subdivided according to the dominant vegetation present (honey mesquite, salt cedar [*Tamarix chinensis*], screwbean-mesquite mix, quaking aspen (*Populus tremuloides*), sycamore, etc.). Criteria used to arrive at these divisions is up to the investigator. As a

guideline, consider that each habitat should be represented by at least two transected stands and that the number of recognized habitats should not be unwieldy. Stress similarities rather than differences in attempting to reduce the overall number.

The categories could be subdivided again on the basis of foliage density. For example, if we found a stand dominated by willow to 20 ft (6 m) containing 1,250 trees/a. (500/ha) and another stand with the same vertical configuration but only half as many trees, we might want to recognize these stands as distinct habitats. Ordinarily, this situation does not arise because the sparser (more open) area would have a more highly developed layer of vegetation (shrubs, annuals) and would, therefore, have a different vertical configuration.

The vertical classification we arrived at for riparian vegetation is depicted in Figure 9. From this information, a quick and easy-to-use key to the various habitats can be developed (Table 5).

Habitat Heterogeneity

Including several transects in one habitat can increase within-habitat variation considerably. The advantage of using the habitat concept is that habitats can be mapped, data are less cumbersome to

Table 5. User's guide to classifying vegetation by dominant tree or shrub species present.

(1) A. Stand in which virtually 100% of the trees present are of one species or virtually 100% arrowweed .... **Go to 2**	
B. Trees within stand, clearly of mixed species. The different species may occur as mixed individuals or as small clumps .... **Go to 3**	
(2) A. Stand in which trees are composed of nearly 100% of some species (may be occasional, widely scattered individuals of one or more species). Many large stands have arrowweed in patches encompassing 5 a. (2 ha) or more. Honey mesquite stands in addition to or instead of arrowweed may have quail bush, four-winged salt bush, wolfberry, or inkweed .... **Salt Cedar I-IV or Honey Mesquite III–IV**	
B. Stand composed of nearly 100% arrowweed; may be an occasional tree or widely scattered clump of some other shrub .... **Arrowweed**	
(3) A. Stand of vegetation is structural type I and trees are primarily salt cedar, cottonwood and/or willow with occasional widely scattered screwbean or honey mesquite tree or clumps of trees. Arrowweed or some other shrub may occur in relatively widely scattered clumps .... **Salt Cedar-Cottonwood Willow mix**	
B. Vegetation not structural type I .... **Go to 4**	
(4) A. Stand of vegetation is structural type II or III .... **Go to 5**	
B. Stand not structural type II or III .... **Go to 6**	

Table 5. User's guide to classifying vegetation by dominant tree or shrub species present (concluded).

(5) A. Stand in which trees are salt cedar with large numbers of cottonwood and/or willow present; may be widely scattered individuals or clumps of screwbean or honey mesquite .... **Salt Cedar-Cottonwood/Willow mix**

   B. Stand in which trees are mainly salt cedar and screwbean mesquite; may be an occasional, widely scattered clump or individual cottonwood and/or willow or honey mesquite .... **Salt Cedar-Screwbean Mesquite mix**

(6) A. Stand of vegetation in structural type IV .... **Go to 7**

   B. Stand not structural type IV .... **Go to 8**

(7) A. Stand composed mainly of salt cedar but with significant numbers of cottonwood and/or willow present; may be widely scattered individuals or clumps of screwbean or honey mesquite. Shrubs, mainly arrowweed, abundant and occurring in moderate to relatively large patches, sometimes encompassing 5 a. (2 ha) or more .... **Salt Cedar-Cottonwood/Willow mix**

   B. Stand much as above but with screwbean mesquite or honey mesquite instead of cottonwood and/or willow .... **Salt Cedar-Screwbean Mesquite mix or Salt Cedar-Honey Mesquite mix**

(8) A. Stand of vegetation is structural types V or VI .... **Go to 9**

   B. Stand not structural type V or VI .... **Go to 3**

(9) A. Stand composed mainly of salt cedar, but with significant numbers of cottonwood and/or willow occurring as scattered individuals or clumps. Arrowweed is usually abundant (occasionally some other shrub species such as quail bush also present) and occurring in patches encompassing several a. (ha) .... **Salt Cedar-Cottonwood/Willow mix**

   B. Stand composed primarily of salt cedar but with significant numbers of individuals or clumps of screwbean or honey mesquite. May be widely scattered individuals or clumps of screwbean or honey mesquite. Arrowweed present as in (9)A. .... **Salt Cedar-Screwbean Mesquite mix or Salt Cedar-Honey Mesquite mix**

NOTE: This key can be used to classify about 95% of the riparian vegetation found along the lower Colorado River. By applying the same general principles used to construct the key and a little imagination, rare vegetation types can also be classified.

work with, and habitats can be communicated easier than transects. Furthermore, habitat is usually managed as a concept. However, if microhabitat variation is marked, it will be a matter of concern to many biologists. Use of the habitat concept should occur after one is thoroughly familiar with the variation that will be concealed and its meaning when interpreting subsequent data analyses.

Foliage Density. In separating transects into structural types, having various structural types different from one another at a statistically significant ($P < 0.05$) level for at least one of the recognized vertical layers could be desirable. Adjacent structural types may overlap, but as long as some statistical differences exist, one can legitimately maintain that they represent different habitats. Data from our studies (Anderson and Ohmart 1984b; Anderson and Hunter 1983) are shown for foliage density in Figure 10 and the proportion of foliage in each of three vertical layers in Figure 11. These figures illustrate the range of variation found among transects falling into each category; they also show the mean and two standard errors of the mean for each type. Note that when using foliage density measurements, types V and VI differed little from each other, but when the proportion of the total foliage found in each of three layers was considered, type VI had a significantly greater proportion of its total foliage in the lower layer and significantly less in the middle layer (Figure 11).

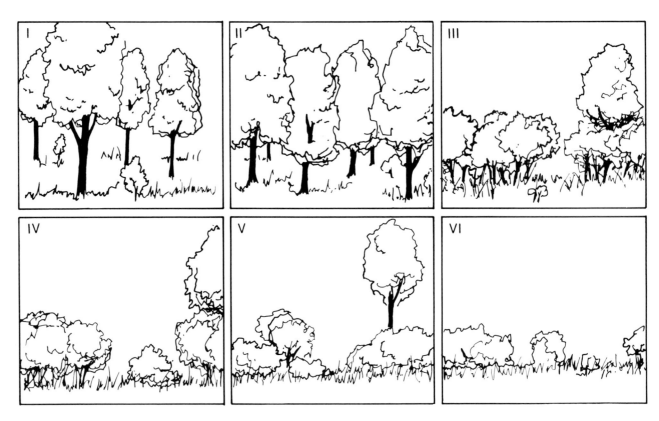

Figure 9. Examples of vertical configurations for the vegetation structural types defined (Figure 11) in the lower Colorado River Valley. Type I is open gallery forest; type II is closed gallery forest; type III is scrub thicket; type IV is scrub thicket with patches of bushes; type V is mostly shrubs and bushes with scattered scrubby thickets; type VI is bushes, shrubs, and grasses.

Heterogeneity in Tree Counts. The mean number of trees of a particular species can also vary considerably among patches. For example, the mean number of salt cedar per salt cedar thicket with patches of shrubs was 163 trees, with a very large standard deviation (105; Table 6). This could be expected in a very patchy habitat. Some patches will have more trees than others, which makes them patchy. However, habitats classified as honey mesquite-woodland had very few tree species present other than honey mesquite; salt cedar thickets had only one species present other than salt cedar (Table 6). Thus, while salt cedar is virtually the only tree present in salt cedar habitats, the trees within such habitats may be tall and relatively homogeneously distributed (type I) or scrubby and patchily distributed (type IV), with patches of shrubs intermingled among the salt cedar.

Within-habitat counts can also vary through highly localized edaphic features. For example, the soil moisture level in an old oxbow that is intersected by the transect may have a few individual tree species not found elsewhere on the transect.

Local heterogeneity in soil layering and structure can cause heterogeneity in plant structure. The distribution of soil types within a floodplain is typically heterogeneous. A highly localized, dense clay soil type could cause a very local concentration of soil electrolytes. Vegetation growing in such soil often attains less stature and biomass (Anderson and Ohmart 1982) and, therefore, vertical differentiation is simpler than for adjacent vegetation. Such variation may be so frequent that it is not feasible or desirable to delineate it within otherwise relatively homogeneous stands.

Another source of variation includes scattered individual trees that were once more widely distributed. In our study area, cottonwood and willow trees, often occurring as widely scattered individuals or as small clumps (66 × 66 ft [20 × 20 m]) of trees, are relics of gradually disappearing habitat (Ohmart et al. 1977).

Fire, another cause of within-stand heterogeneity, in varying degrees and at various times, has affected nearly every stand of vegetation along the lower Colorado River. When a stand is burned, not all parts of it burn with equal intensity; some corners or clumps remain intact. Parts of a stand may burn more than once, so at any given time not all parts

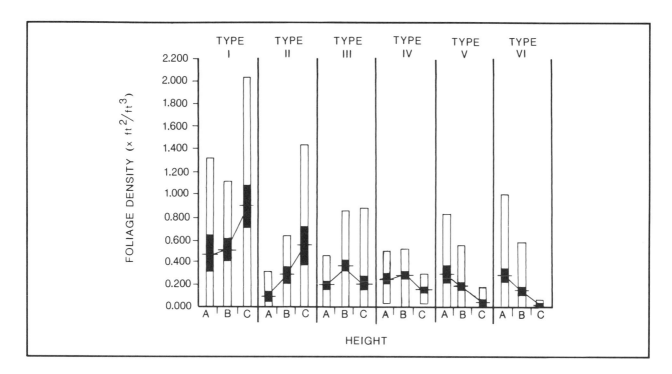

Figure 10. Variation in foliage density between subplots within all structural types at each of three vertical levels. The proportional distribution clearly differentiates the vegetation types, but foliage density does not. Horizontal lines represent mean values; large rectangles represent ± 1 standard deviation; small rectangles represent ± 2 standard errors. A = 0-2 ft (0.0-0.6 m); B = 2-15 ft (0.6-4.5 m); C = ≥ 15 ft (≥ 4.5 m).

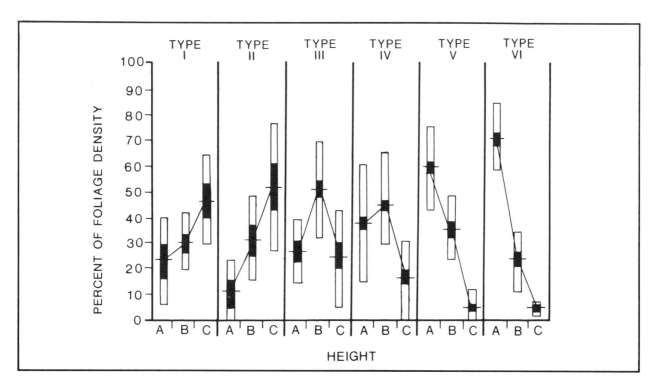

Figure 11. Proportional distribution of vegetation in three vertical layers among subplots within various stands of vegetation, generally classified as one vertical structural type (I-VI). Horizontal lines represent mean values; large rectangles represent ± 1 standard deviation; small rectangles represent ± 2 standard errors. A = 0-2 ft (0.0-0.6 m); B = 2-15 ft (0.6-4.5 m); C > 15 ft (4.5 m).

are at precisely the same stage of post-fire recovery. Even when burned evenly, not all parts of a stand redevelop at precisely the same rate. Thus, at some level of analysis, considerable heterogeneity could be found within any fundamentally homogeneous stand.

Although such delineation of plant species heterogeneity may be important for understanding some aspects of the distribution of vegetation or wildlife using the vegetation, it may be beyond the scope of study. Such delineation could require more time and money than is available. Such small parcels typically range from 2.5 a. (1 ha) to about 12.5 a. (5 ha). Areas smaller than 25 a. (10 ha) could not be accurately plotted on map scales of 1:9,449 cm. Availability of funding and consideration of the desired scale are factors that must be considered when deciding how much edaphic variation should be delimited.

Table 6. Average number of trees (± 1 SD) per subplot in each of 23 recognized riparian habitat types along the lower Colorado River.

Vegetation Type	N	Number of Trees Per Subplots 150 × 15 m (492 × 50 ft)											Percent of Subplots with No Trees of Dominant Species
		Salt Cedar		Cottonwood		Willow		Screwbean Mesquite		Honey Mesquite		
		$\bar{x}$	SD	$\bar{x}$	SD	$\bar{x}$	SD	$\bar{x}$	SD	$\bar{x}$	SD	
Salt cedar												
I	18	95	20	0	0	0	0	0	0	2	20	0
II	8	47	19	0	0	0	0	0	0	0	0	0
III	28	74	25	0	0	0	0	7	13	0	0	0
IV	32	163	105	0	0	0	0	0	0	0	0	0
V	109	133	146	0	0	0	0	1	3	0	0	1
VI	20	31	50	0	0	0	0	0	0	0	0	0
Salt cedar-cottonwood/willow												
I	18	52	13	59	27	87	23	0	0	0	0	0–0
II	10	129	46	38	22	49	34	0	0	0	0	0–0
III	62	130	147	19	44	54	66	13	23	6	7	0–6
IV	52	38	53	0	0	29	17	7	15	0	0	3–8
V	30	44	49	0	0	17	21	0	0	0	0	0–0
VI	22	19	32	1	1	1	26	0	0	0	0	0–50
Salt cedar-screwbean mesquite												
II	10	63	24	2	4	1	1	96	17	0	0	0–0
III	40	49	43	0	0	0	0	18	15	0	0	0–8
IV	78	60	58	0	0	4	25	39	31	0	0	1–6
V	84	45	39	0	0	0	0	44	62	0	0	0–8
VI	18	45	55	0	0	0	0	6	6	0	0	0–22
Salt cedar-honey mesquite												
IV	38	41	53	0	0	0	0	0	0	35	68	2–6
Honey mesquite												
III	24	0	0	0	0	0	0	1*		93	50	0
IV	122	0	0	0	0	0	0	0	0	31	42	1
V	56	0	0	0	0	0	0	0	0	12	7	2
VI	52	0	0	0	0	0	0	1*		9	7	2

*Standard deviation not calculated where $\bar{x} < 1$.

NOTE: N = number of subplots.

Intrahabitat Heterogeneity among Patches. The 169 yd (150 m) subplots along transects traversing stands of a given structural type will reveal much of the heterogeneity within a habitat. This heterogeneity reflects differences between subplots (patches) in vertical foliage distribution and foliage density. If the manager decides that a patch is any 5 a. (2 ha) area, the classification system and any subsequent wildlife use analyses will be entirely unsuitable for any stand less than 5 a. (2 ha). The system becomes more suitable as stand size approaches 25 a. (10 ha; larger sample of patches). For example, within vegetation classified as scrub habitat with patches of shrubs, vertical configuration in the various subplots more frequently resembles this habitat type (Table 7) than any other habitat type. However, in the strictest sense, it is not appropriate to give structural type designations to patches constituting a certain structural type. Structural types were defined on the basis of transects with similar average vertical foliage distributions. The foliage distributions were determined on the basis of measurements taken in subplots. That it is wrong to classify subplots (or any area 25 a. [10 ha]) can be seen from the following analogy.

Suppose that all books in six private libraries were measured and mean heights were found to be 8.7, 9.1, 9.4, 9.8, 10.2, and 10.6 in. (22, 23, 24, 25, 26, and 27 cm) for collections I through VI, respectively. It would be improper to conclude from examining the books in collection IV that those books < 9.4 in.(< 24 cm) in height came from collections I, II, or III, or that all books > 9.8 in. (> 26 cm) in height came from collections V and VI. Desirable as it might be to know the origin of the books in collection IV, such a determination simply cannot be made from the evidence presented.

We present the data in Table 7 merely to emphasize that (1) there is heterogeneity between subplots and (2) it is not valid to obtain foliage measurements for a 5 a. (2 ha) plot and then be able

to determine its vegetation type. This would be analogous to having a book 10 in. (26.2 cm) in height and concluding that it came from collection V. It really could have come from any of the collections. Desirable as it may be to classify a 5 a. (2 ha) stand and assess the wildlife use associated with it, such a determination is not possible with the data presented. This must be compatible with the objectives of the study. A classification at a smaller scale will lead inexorably to a proliferation of vegetation types recognized. This will be incompatible with the objective of emphasizing elements of similarity between stands rather than differences. More importantly, we have learned that classification at a smaller scale can lead to a cloudy or erroneous picture of how wildlife uses vegetation.

Cloudiness begins to appear at a scale of about 50 a. (20 ha; Anderson and Ohmart, unpubl. data), and an opaqueness emerges from analyses at a scale of about 5 a. (2 ha; Rosenberg 1980; Engel-Wilson 1982; Anderson and Ohmart, unpubl. ms), i.e., only weak wildlife use patterns are discernible at a scale of < 50 a. (< 20 ha), and either wrong impressions or no impression emerges at a scale of < 10 a. (< 2 ha). Investigators working in other habitats have reported similar findings (Wiens 1981; Wiens and Rotenberry 1981a, b).

Some of our conclusions about wildlife use of riparian vegetation along the lower Colorado River at the vegetation (habitat) type scale have been experimentally tested and confirmed (Meents et al. 1982; Anderson and Ohmart, in press-a). Other tests are in progress. It is critical to clearly define the purpose for conducting a study and to decide on the appropriate scale. A classification made for one purpose will probably fail when used for other than the intended purpose.

Our discussion thus far has centered on heterogeneity within habitats. Next, we consider the differences among a group of habitats.

Table 7. Subplots of six recognized structural types.

Structural Type		Subplots	Percent of Subplots of Structural Type					
		Number	I	II	III	IV	V	VI
I	Open gallery	36	38	31	9	9	13	0
II	Closed gallery	30	0	63	20	17	0	0
III	Scrub thickets	154	6	9	66	11	9	0
IV	Scrub thickets with patchy shrubs	366	1	4	23	38	19	15
V	Shrubs-scrub thickets	291	0	0	8	4	59	30
VI	Shrubs, annuals, grasses with scattered trees	279	0	0	0	8	18	75

NOTE: Variation in vertical configuration among subplots within each structural type is indicated by the following data. See text for discussion of tautology in this type of analysis.

ANALYZING HETEROGENEITY AMONG HABITATS

Although many of the differences between two habitats may be obvious to the observer (a patchy salt cedar-scrub thicket is obviously different in many ways from a cottonwood-willow gallery forest), the differences need to be quantified. Although one may adequately describe the differences between two habitats, such a description may require several pages and cannot be readily used in statistical treatments. Therefore, differences must be expressed quantitatively. Among the community attributes measured, several may be intercorrelated, i.e., as the value for one increases, the value for another also increases. When colinearity exists between variables, determining the extent to which either variable is associated with wildlife will not be possible without additional experimentation or without data from some area where these variables are not confounded. In such situations, a species or group of species could be significantly associated with both variables. In reality, one of the variables may be attracting the species and the other one may not.

Such situations are probably inevitable with any relatively large data set, and little can be done, except to recognize that some constellations of community attributes are positively associated with particular species or groups of species. Only carefully designed experiments will divulge which attributes among the constellation are really attracting wildlife. Analysis of a data set can be greatly simplified, however, if a constellation of intercorrelated variables can be quickly recognized and treated as a single variable.

Principal component analysis (PCA) is a statistical tool that combines intercorrelated variables into new derived variables. We have used the technique extensively; details are given elsewhere (Anderson and Ohmart 1984b). The derived variables can usually be readily interpreted, and they can be treated as independent variables in subsequent analyses. Each habitat receives a score from roughly -3 to $+3$ on each derived variable. In our study, PCA yielded four derived variables. The first included foliage density and diversity measures above the lowest layer and FHD. Wildlife associated with such a derived variable is most abundant in habitats with dense foliage that is horizontally and vertically diverse. Managing wildlife associated with this derived variable involves creating dense and diverse areas.

The second derived variable was bipolar, i.e., the number of honey mesquite per unit area was associated positively with this component, and the number of salt cedar was associated negatively. Species associated with this derived variable were positively associated with honey mesquite but negatively with salt cedar. Negative associations indicated a positive association with salt cedar, but no association or a negative one with honey mesquite. Management, in the first instance, might involve planting honey mesquite trees. The other two principal components were interpreted in similar ways.

PCA can be used to compress a large and complex set of measurements (vegetation community attributes) into a small set of derived variables that can be used as independent variables. Associations between wildlife and the attributes of the habitats can be determined by using the wildlife populations associated with various habitats in conjunction with the score of that habitat for each of the derived variables. Techniques such as analysis of variance, simple linear correlation, and multiple regression are appropriate for quantifying the extent of such associations.

Cluster analyses can be used to group transects with similar vertical configurations. These clusters can be further subdivided according to the numerically dominant vegetation present. By recognizing relatively few vertical configurations (stress similarities rather than differences, for example, 6) and relatively few subdivisions by dominant vegetation (again, 6), one can define up to 36 different habitats, all of which differ from one another by vertical configuration, dominant vegetation, or both. Recognizing relatively few vertical configurations (3 to 9) and having relatively few different dominant vegetation types (3 to 9) are aids to the memory. Most people can keep five or six definitions in mind. Thus, when looking at a stand of vegetation, the manager needs to answer only two questions to classify the stand:

(1) What is the vertical configuration of the vegetation, i.e., is it four-layered, three-layered, etc.?

(2) What plant species appear to be numerically dominant in the stand?

Thus, in a short time, with a classification scheme such as the one described here, the manager can acquire enough general information about the stand to describe it in detail in terms of the classification system. This augments communication and may be useful in making management decisions when such decisions need to be made quickly.

DETERMINING WILDLIFE-HABITAT ASSOCIATIONS

One can look for relationships between a given species and the vegetation attributes. Conceivably, every species in the habitats studied could be involved in such analyses. This information is often useful when the manager has collected information on a single species that is of particular management interest. For example, the Yuma clapper rail (*Rallus longirostris yumanensis*), which is on the endangered species list, is of great interest to biologists along the Colorado River. We found (Anderson and Ohmart 1985) that in spring, the Yuma clapper rail was linearly associated with the first principal component of an analysis of marsh habitat attributes. The marsh habitats were analyzed according to the method described above. The habitat breadth of various species can be used to identify habitat specialists or those species with narrow habitat breadths. The data in Tables 8 and 9 identify Bell's vireo (*Vireo bellii*), summer tanager (*Piranga rubra*), and yellow-billed cuckoo (*Coccyzus americanus*) as habitat specialists and cottonwood-willow woodlands as their "preferred" habitats (Meents et al. 1984).

Variables such as bird species diversity (BSD) and species richness may also be related to the derived variables. We found significant relationships during most seasons for BSD and species richness using various multivariate techniques (Rice et al. 1983). Densities of birds in various species groups, such as permanent resident insectivores, may also be related to the derived variables during one or more seasons.

Here we add a cautionary note. Analyses should be conducted over several seasons and years. We have found that analyses over just one season or over several seasons for only 1 or 2 years can lead to egregious errors in assessing habitat importance to wildlife (Rice et al. 1980, 1983, 1984).

Quite frequently, multiple linear regression is used as an analytical tool. However, not all meaningful relationships between wildlife and habitat attributes would be linear, i.e., as the amount of the habitat variable increased, the wildlife community attribute would increase or decrease. For example, we found that curvilinear relationships accounted for a significant amount of the variance for 19 common species of riparian birds.

We quantified deer use of habitats by finding deer use areas (foraging, resting, fawning, etc.) and analyzing the vegetation in plots 99 × 99 ft (30 × 30 m). These were subdivided into four subplots. Vegetation measurements and tree counts were taken within these subplots in the manner described above. In addition, measurements were taken in a series of randomly selected plots. Attributes of the vegetation in the deer use plots were then compared statistically with the randomly selected control plots (Haywood et al. 1984).

Pinyon-juniper/sagebrush association showing deer feeding area next to cover or resting areas.

Table 8. Average densities (birds/40 ha [100 a.]) of summer bird species in riparian communities of the lower Colorado River Valley.

Bird Species	Cottonwood/Willow						Screwbean Mesquite					Salt Cedar						Honey Mesquite				AR[1]	SH[2]
	I	II	III	IV	V	VI	II	III	IV	V	VI	I	II	III	IV	V	VI	III	IV	V	VI	VI	IV
Resident																							
Abert towhee	46	110	56	34	39	25	18	26	24	16	9	30	38	39	21	17	19	36	47	9	12	20	24
Black-tailed gnatcatcher	0	0	7	7	2	2	3	8	18	14	7	7	4	5	4	7	2	12	15	10	11	4	13
Crissal thrasher	0	2	9	8	5	6	3	5	9	7	8	1	7	7	4	4	3	12	7	7	6	4	8
Cactus wren	2	1	9	3	1	7	4	4	3	3	3	1	7	2	1	1	2	13	8	6	8	2	0
Gambel's quail	1	2	11	20	27	16	31	11	32	18	34	36	27	22	17	27	27	26	38	45	45	24	22
Gila woodpecker	35	16	8	4	3	3	2	0	0	1	1	36	27	22	17	27	27	8	1	1	0	0	0
Ladder-backed woodpecker	26	31	21	13	5	4	15	5	6	3	10	3	5	3	2	1	4	13	6	5	6	1	4
Mourning dove	21	236	146	80	67	27	436	145	102	28	47	79	129	112	84	35	129	147	109	44	55	11	78
Verdin	9	34	21	21	12	18	17	40	33	26	20	14	15	12	9	10	12	31	26	20	22	12	23
Nonresident																							
Ash-throated flycatcher	5	11	17	12	12	9	20	13	12	7	19	6	8	6	6	3	10	24	16	10	9	4	11
Blue grosbeak	4	14	16	12	19	13	4	7	10	8	6	8	13	23	11	6	7	2	2	0	0	8	9
Bell's vireo	0	0	3	3	0	0	5	0	0	1	0	0	0	0	0	0	0	1	0	0	0	0	0
Lucy warbler	1	28	15	17	15	5	16	17	19	19	16	43	44	8	13	5	5	46	24	13	14	2	26
Northern oriole	30	19	29	20	9	15	13	7	13	6	5	6	15	12	6	2	6	29	11	3	6	2	10
Summer tanager	17	10	8	2	0	0	0	0	0	0	0	13	0	1	0	0	0	0	0	0	0	2	0
Brown-crested flycatcher	20	18	10	3	4	1	16	6	2	1	5	2	0	1	0	0	1	5	0	0	0	0	0
White-winged dove	46	93	65	34	24	25	376	75	46	12	22	47	276	99	106	13	20	130	26	9	9	7	41
Yellow-billed cuckoo	9	5	5	1	1	0	2	0	1	0	0	0	0	1	0	1	0	3	0	0	0	0	0

[1] AR = arrowweed.
[2] SH = salt cedar-honey mesquite mix.

Table 9. Habitat breadth of summer bird species in riparian communities of the lower Colorado River Valley.

Bird Species	Habitat Breadth*	Percent of Maximum Habitat Breadth
Resident		
Abert towhee	1.28	0.94
Black-tailed gnatcatcher	1.28	0.94
Crissal thrasher	1.30	0.96
Cactus wren	1.20	0.88
Gambel's quail	1.30	0.96
Gila woodpecker	0.95	0.70
Ladder-backed woodpecker	1.20	0.88
Mourning dove	1.23	0.90
Verdin	1.32	0.97
Nonresident		
Ash-throated flycatcher	1.31	0.96
Blue grosbeak	1.33	0.98
Bell's vireo	0.62	0.46
Lucy warbler	1.26	0.93
Northern oriole	1.26	0.93
Summer tanager	0.66	0.49
Brown-crested flycatcher	0.98	0.72
White-winged dove	1.12	0.82
Yellow-billed cuckoo	0.86	0.63

*Habitat breadth calculated using the equation:

$$HB = -\overset{n}{\Sigma} p_i \log_{10} p_i$$

where p_i = the proportion of a species' population occurring in community.

Habitat Breadth Mean = 1.137
Standard Deviation = 0.226

We studied lizard use of the landscape over a heterogeneous 75 a. (30 ha) area by scattering plots measuring 10 × 10 ft (3 × 3 m). These were subdivided into 1 × 1 yd (m) subplots. Attributes of the vegetation were then determined by the methods described above. The nature of the substrate (sand, hardpan, etc.) was also noted. These plots were visited daily at the time of peak lizard activity; the number of each species detected was recorded. The characteristics of the landscape could then be associated with greatest numbers of detections of various lizard species (Anderson and Ohmart 1982). Data obtained from can traps were used to corroborate or refute observational data.

Rodent association with various habitats was determined using multiple regression analysis where relative densities of each rodent species were the dependent variables and the vegetation factor scores for each habitat (determined from PCA) were the independent variables. Curvilinear relationships were also considered (Anderson and Ohmart 1984a).

Finally, we determined the impact of clearing vegetation from areas by first obtaining the vegetation attributes of control and experimental areas (those to be cleared) before clearing. The impact of clearing, according to different patterns and amounts, was determined for each vegetation attribute separately (FHD, foliage density, etc.). The controls were used to indicate the extent of change when no clearing was done. We also noted the change in principal component factor scores for each of the habitats affected. Bird and rodent numbers were obtained before and after clearing in experimental and control areas in order to assess impacts on wildlife in various habitats (Anderson and Ohmart, in press-a).

LITERATURE CITED

ANDERSON, B.W. and R.D. OHMART. 1978. Phainopepla utilization of honey mesquite forests in the Colorado River Valley. Condor 80:334-338.

—— and ——. 1982. Revegetation for wildlife enhancement along the lower Colorado River. Final Rep. to U.S. Dep. Inter., Bur. Reclamation, Lower Colorado Region, Boulder City, NV.

—— and ——. 1984a. A vegetation management study for enhancement of wildlife along the lower Colorado River. Final Rep. to U.S. Dep. Inter., Bur. Reclamation, Lower Colorado Region, Boulder City, NV.

—— and ——. 1984b. Vegetation community type maps: Lower Colorado River. U.S. Dep. Inter., Bur. Reclamation, Lower Colorado Region, Boulder City, NV.

—— and ——. 1985. Habitat use by clapper rails in the lower Colorado River Valley. Condor 87:116-126.

—— and ——. In press-a. Evaluation of the impact of vegetation removal. Final Rep. to U.S. Dep. Inter., Bur. Reclamation, Lower Colorado Region, Boulder City, NV.

—— and ——. In press-b. Riparian vegetation as a mitigating process in stream and river restoration *in* Gore, J.A., ed. The Restoration of Rivers and Streams. Butterworth Publ., Stoneham, MA.

—— and W.C. HUNTER. 1983. Quantifying variables for classifying desert riparian vegetation. Pages 34-44 *in* Moir, W.H. and E.L. Hendzel, tech. coords. Proc. Workshop on Southwestern Habitat Types. U.S. Dep. Agric., For. Serv., Albuquerque, NM.

CODY, M.L. 1974. Competition and the structure of bird communities. Monogr. Population Biol. 7, Princeton Univ. Press, Princeton, NJ.

CONINE, K. 1982. Avian use of honey mesquite, interior and agricultural edge habitat in the lower Colorado River. M.S. Thesis, Arizona State Univ. Tempe.

DAUBENMIRE, R. 1968. Plant communities: A textbook of plant synecology. Harper and Row, Publishers. New York, NY. 300pp.

ENGEL-WILSON, R.W. 1982. Comparison of bird communities in salt cedar and honey mesquite along the lower Colorado, Verde, and Gila rivers. M.S. Thesis, Arizona State Univ., Dep. Zoology, Tempe.

GREEN, R.H. 1979. Sampling design and statistical methods for environmental biologists. John Wiley & Sons, New York, NY.

HAYWOOD, R.J., B.W. ANDERSON, and R.D. OHMART. 1984. Habitat use by four radio-collared mule deer along the lower Colorado River. U.S. Dep. Inter., Bur. Reclamation, Lower Colorado Region, Boulder City, NV.

HORN, H.S. 1966. Measurement of "overlap" in comparative ecological studies. Am. Nat. 100:419-424.

KUCHLER, A.W. 1967. Vegetation mapping. Ronald Press, New York, NY.

MACARTHUR, R.H. and J.W. MACARTHUR. 1961. On bird species diversity. Ecology 42:594-598.

MEENTS, J.K., B.W. ANDERSON, and R.D. OHMART. 1982. Vegetation relationships and food of sage sparrows wintering in honey mesquite habitats. Wilson Bull. 94:129-138.

——, ——, and ——. 1984. Sensitivity of riparian birds to habitat loss. Pages 619-625 *in* Warner, R.E. and K.M. Hendrix, eds. California Riparian Systems: Ecology, Conservation, and Productive Management. Univ. California, Berkeley.

MUELLER-DOMBOIS, D. and H. ELLENBERG. 1974. Aims and methods of vegetation ecology. John Wiley and Sons, New York, NY. 547pp.

OHMART, R.D., W.O. DEASON, and C. BURKE. 1977. A riparian case history: The Colorado River. Pages 35-47 *in* Johnson, R.R. and D.A. Jones, tech. coords. Importance, Preservation, and Management of Riparian Habitats: A Symposium. U.S. Dep. Agric., For. Serv. Gen. Tech. Rep. RM-43.

PLATTS, W.S. 1981. Stream and inventory garbage in—reliable analysis out: Only in fairy tales. Pages 75-85 *in* Armantrout, N.B., ed. Acquisition and Utilization of Aquatic Inventory Information. Western Div., Amer. Fish. Soc.

——, W.F. MEGAHAM, and G.W. MARSHALL. 1983. Methods for evaluating stream, riparian, and biotic conditions. U.S. Dep. Agric., For. Serv. Gen. Tech. Rep. 138.

RICE, J., B.W. ANDERSON, and R.D. OHMART. 1980. Seasonal habitat selection by birds in the lower Colorado River Valley. Ecology 61:1402-1411.

——, ——, and ——. 1983. Habitat selection attributes of an avian community: A discriminant investigation. Ecol. Monogr. 53:263-290.

——, ——, and ——. 1984. Comparison of the importance of different habitat attributes to avian community organization. J. Wildl. Manage. 48:895-911.

ROSENBERG, K.V. 1980. Breeding bird community organization in a desert riparian forest. M.S. Thesis, Arizona State Univ., Dep. Zoology, Tempe.

SHANNON, C.E. and W. WEAVER. 1949. The mathematical theory of communication. Univ. Illinois Press, Urbana. 125pp.

U.S. DEPARTMENT OF THE INTERIOR, BUREAU OF LAND MANAGEMENT. 1985. Rangeland Monitoring—Trend Studies. U.S. Dep. Inter., Bur. of Land Manage. Technical Reference 4400-4. 130pp.

WHITTAKER, R.H. 1975. Communities and systems, 2nd edition. MacMillan and Co. New York, NY.

WIENS, J.A. 1981. Scale problems in avian censusing. Pages 513-521 *in* Ralph, C.J. and J.M. Scott, eds. Estimating Numbers of Terrestrial Birds. Studies in Avian Biology.

—— and J.T. ROTENBERRY. 1981a. Censusing and the evaluation of avian habitat occupancy. Pages 522-532 *in* Ralph, C.J. and J.M. Scott, eds. Estimating Numbers of Terrestrial Birds. Studies in Avian Biology.

—— and ——. 1981b. Habitat associations and community structure of birds in shrub-steppe environments. Ecol. Monogr. 51:21-41.

32

MACRO-INVERTEBRATES

Fred Mangum

U.S. Forest Service
Aquatic Laboratory
Brigham Young University
Provo, UT 84602

Editor's Note: Macroinvertebrate surveys are one of the more specialized habitat analysis techniques. Macroinvertebrate analyses could, in theory, be used on any type of habitat; in practice, however, the technique is used primarily for stream habitat. In aquatic habitats, macroinvertebrate analyses have proven to be good indicators of habitat condition and water quality. In the future, such analyses may be used for other purposes, such as analyzing suitability of marshes for waterfowl.

INTRODUCTION

Macroinvertebrates are those invertebrates that can be detected with the unaided eye. Although macroinvertebrates are an important habitat component for many terrestrial vertebrates, such as insectivorous birds, terrestrial macroinvertebrates are rarely sampled as part of terrestrial habitat inventory and monitoring programs.

On the other hand, macroinvertebrates in the aquatic environment provide a link in the food chain between microscopic, multicelled organisms and fish populations. They are essential to the growth and production of fish and, because of their strict habitat requirements, are very useful indicators of aquatic habitat changes. The number, size, and species of aquatic invertebrates are important to fisheries habitat, as they are the primary food source for most salmonids and warm-water fish. Aquatic invertebrates include insects, such as mayflies, stoneflies, caddisflies, and diptera (two-winged flies); crustaceans, such as crayfish and shrimp; mollusks, such as snails and clams; and fresh-water earthworms.

Macroinvertebrate data and many other types of scientific information should be considered by land managers in the decisionmaking process. Inventory data covering physical, chemical, and biological water quality and aquatic habitat factors can be analyzed and interpreted in a manner that can be understood by interdisciplinary team members and planners. Current environmental disturbances should be identified as well as potential problems that could develop if new management activities adversely affect a stream. When linked to other factors, macroinvertebrate data can assist the decisionmaker in assessing impacts to stream ecosystems from land management activities.

Positive or negative effects from almost everything that occurs in a drainage show up in streams and affect the macroinvertebrate community composition. The community composition can reveal the health of an ecosystem, provide a warning system, or show the relative intensity of pollution problems. Macroinvertebrate analysis often identifies types of pollution, which is valuable information for conscientious land managers. To make use of all available physical and biological water quality and aquatic habitat data, there must be full coordination among specialists and management.

Data about macroinvertebrates are site-specific. Aquatic ecosystems cannot be managed on the basis of average values over large diverse areas. Particularly for grazing prescriptions, time and space considerations within a watershed must be considered in the planning process if high standards of aquatic habitat and water quality are to be maintained.

The U.S. Bureau of Land Management (BLM) and the U.S. Forest Service have used macroinvertebrate data to assess habitat quality and nutrients available for resident and anadromous fisheries. Effects from livestock grazing, dam building, mining, timber harvest, rotenone projects, instream improvement structures and exclosures, and sanitary facilities in campgrounds can be measured.

This chapter describes procedures for sampling aquatic macroinvertebrates and analyzing resulting data. These procedures are primarily used for stream surveys; however, parts of the procedure may be used for lake, pond, and reservoir surveys.

MACROINVERTEBRATE SURVEYS FOR STREAMS

Procedure

Surveys of macroinvertebrates consist of distinct phases: field sampling, laboratory analysis, and data analysis. The field biologist usually does the field sampling and sends samples to an aquatic laboratory for analysis. Field sampling methods are described here as well as data analysis and interpretation since many of the latter techniques are specific to aquatic macroinvertebrates.

Sampling Design. When designing a stream survey for macroinvertebrates, consult the aquatic specialists responsible for habitat management. This will ensure that the data and information generated will be useful in answering pertinent management questions.

A minimum of three stratified, random aquatic macroinvertebrate samples should be taken at each station, as described in the techniques section. A station is defined as a stream reach up to 30 m (100 ft) long. The samples generally provide desired community representation and data that can be statistically analyzed. Four samples may be needed for some streams, depending on the statistical reliability desired.

The macroinvertebrate community can reveal the quality of habitat components essential to aquatic fauna, such as water quality, substrate composition, riparian habitat quality, ecosystem stability, and past history.

Criteria for sampling station selection, duration, and frequency differ depending on the basis of inventory or monitoring emphasis. For example, if an action plan was developed to evaluate a new grazing prescription and an exclosure, three stations should be established—above, within, and below the proposed exclosure area. The "above" station should be within 50 yards of the exclosure; the "within" station, on the lower end of the exclosure; and the "below" station, with gradient and other natural physical characteristics similar to the "within" station, generally within 1.6 km (1 mi.) of the exclosure. Spring, summer, and fall samples should be taken before installing the exclosure; sampling on those dates should be repeated for 3 to 5 years following exclosure installation.

When inventorying physical, chemical, and biological parameters, I recommend establishing a minimum base period of 3 years to show effects of natural extremes in physical and water chemistry influences on an ecosystem, and a minimum frequency of three dates annually—spring, summer, and late fall. Additional samples may be taken to cover projected heavy-use periods.

For monitoring or surveillance of the effects of a management activity, a minimum of 1 year is necessary, but up to 3 or 5 years can be required depending on the activity or pollution source being monitored. The location and number of sampling stations depend on the management activity being monitored and its duration or projected commencement. Monitoring requires a minimum of two stations—one above (a control) and one below the activity monitored. A third station downstream helps define downstream impacts or recovery.

To more specifically locate a source of stream stress, stations can be added within the management area initially or upon detection of stress conditions. Point or nonpoint pollution sources may be monitored. To show the quality of the habitat and the water as it leaves public land, management plans for some streams may be adequately served by a single station. Control stations should be placed in a riffle, if possible, between 45 and 180 m (50 and 200 yd) above the upper boundaries of the suspected pollution sources.

Experimental stations should include at least one station below the lower boundaries of the suspected source. Stations may be placed in two categories depending on their projected use: (1) long-term (permanent) stations established on the main stream or major tributary in each drainage to monitor long-term projects or continuing land-use activities that, by their nature, could cause on-site or downstream, accumulated impacts or stress or (2) short-term (temporary) stations established to monitor projects such as timber harvest, prescribed burns, insect spray projects, or others having impacts over a definite time period. All such monitoring should include predisturbance (before), operation (during), and post-operation (after) sampling.

Substrate Sampled. Samples are taken in riffle areas with streambed substrate of gravel or rubble. A majority of the species occurring in the stream's aquatic macroinvertebrate community will be found there. Replicate samples should be taken within a 100-foot stretch of a stream, with each sample being taken in locations where velocity and depth are as similar as possible.

Equipment. Equipment needed for macroinvertebrate sampling is listed below:

- Modified Surber Net
- 250-micron sieve
- Three plastic bottles per station with strip of masking tape attached for identification purposes
- Preserving solution
- Hip boots
- Saturated saltwater solution
- Two aluminum bread pans
- Waterproof gloves
- Laundry pen (waterproof marker)

Field Sampling.

Modified Surber Net Samples. The modified Surber square-foot sample net (Figure 1) has proven to have a correlation coefficient equal to or better than other currently used sampling devices. I recommend using a 280-micron mesh, nylon net when sampling all macroinvertebrates. Three steps should be followed when using this modification.

1. The foot-square Surber frame is placed over the gravel-rubble substrate in the stream with the net downstream. As the rocks within the frame are hand scrubbed, macroinvertebrates are carried into the net by the flowing water. The substrate underlying the gravel-rubble is also stirred by hand to a depth of 7 to 10 cm (3 to 4 in.), if possible.

2. After allowing the water to drain from the net, the net is inverted into an aluminum pan containing a saturated saltwater solution. As the saltwater is poured into a second pan, the organic materials thus floated are caught in a 250-micron mesh sieve. The saltwater is then poured back into the first pan, the contents are again vigorously stirred, and the floating materials and specimens are poured for a second time through the sample sieve. The sample may require sieving two or three times.

3. The sample in the sieve is then washed from the sieve pan into the sample bottle with an alcohol solution. The alcohol solution is mixed at a ratio

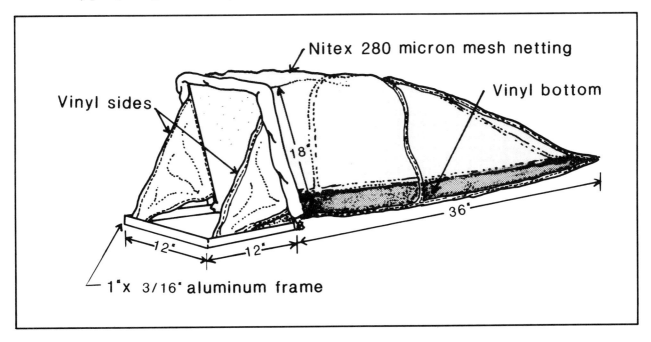

Figure 1. Modified Surber sampler.

of 1 cup of 10% formalin to 3.8 L (1 gal.) of 70% ethanol. Enough alcohol should be added to the sample bottle to cover the sample. Caddisflies in their cases must be handpicked from the pan and added to the sample.

Artificial Substrate Basket Samples. The use of artificial substrate sampling baskets is also recommended by the U.S. Environmental Protection Agency because of their comparatively low coefficient of variation in collection of macroinvertebrate individuals and taxa (see Figure 2).

The following methods are recommended for basket sampling:

1. *Placement.* The baskets, filled with two layers of baseball-sized rubble gathered from the immediate stream area, are worked down into the substrate in a riffle area among rocks of nearly the same size, if possible. The rocks may be collected along the bank of the stream or in the stream and placed in the basket. If the rocks are gathered from the stream substrate, they should be scrubbed clean to remove any existing insects. For statistical purposes, three baskets are placed at each station. Each station should not exceed a 100-foot distance between the upstream and downstream baskets.

2. *Retrieval.* After a 1-month (not to exceed 33 days) colonization period, samples are collected from the baskets. The baskets should be approached from their downstream side, the Surber net placed over the basket, and the basket pulled into the net. With one hand on the basket and the other holding the net, both are pulled from the stream in an upstream motion. The rocks from the baskets are placed in a bucket half filled with water. The Surber net is inverted and washed in the bucket of water, and the rocks are individually scrubbed with a brush. After scrubbing, the rocks are placed back into the basket that is then repositioned into the stream. The basket should be covered with water and camouflaged, if possible, to avoid vandalism. The water and sample in the bucket are poured into a 250-micron mesh sieve to remove the water. If a lot of debris and sand are present, the sample can be placed in a saturated saltwater solution that will float all organisms out of the sand and gravel. The sample is washed into the sample bottle from the sieve with alcohol. Alcohol is added to the bottle until it just covers the sample.

Supporting Data. Several types of supporting data are commonly collected with macroinvertebrate samples. Water chemistry and physical habitat data are integrated into the elevation to bring the total

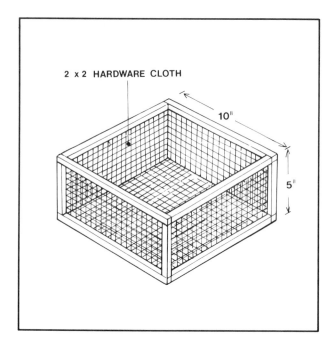

Figure 2. Artificial substrate basket.

biological analysis into perspective for the biologist and land manager. In particular, data on alkalinity, sulfates, gradient, and substrate composition are necessary for calculating a Biotic Condition Index (BCI). The following data are commonly collected with macroinvertebrate data:

1. *Specific Conductivity.* Specific conductivity, measured as umhos/cm at 25°C (77°F), is particularly important for streams with high alkalinity and hardness.

2. *Alkalinity.* Alkalinity, measured as HCO_3 concentration in mg/1, is closely linked to stream productivity and is necessary to determine the BCI. Alkalinity correlates with community density, diversity, and biomass, and also affects the primary production in a stream.

3. *Water Temperature.* Temperature is a limiting factor on certain sites.

4. *Nitrate Nitrogen.* Nitrate nitrogen, measured as mg/1, may indicate organic enrichment.

5. *Orthophosphate.* Orthophosphate, measured as mg/1, may indicate organic enrichment.

6. *Sulfate.* Sulfate, measured as mg/1, may indicate sources of accretion flows. It is a factor affecting

community composition and is necessary to determine the BCI. An increase in sulfate generally indicates a deterioration of natural water quality. Many poor quality waters in the western U.S. have high sulfate levels.

7. *pH.* High or low pH also limits biological productivity.

8. *Gradient.* Gradient, measured as a percent, is related to a stream's ability to maintain substrate quality. It affects community composition and is used in BCI analyses because of its positive correlation with macroinvertebrate community diversity.

9. *Elevation.* Elevation is used to define ranges for aquatic species.

10. *Substrate Composition.* Substrate composition, measured as the relative composition (ranking) of streambed boulder, rubble, gravel, and sand-silt materials, is necessary to determine the BCI. Rubble substrates are preferred by the greatest number of species because they provide a greater diversity of microhabitat than smaller substrates.

11. *Streamside Vegetation.* Streamside vegetation, measured as the relative dominance (rank) of grass, shrubs, brush, deciduous trees, and evergreen trees present on streambank riparian areas, affects stream stability and nutrient sources.

12. *Flow Rates.* Mean summer and mean low-flow rates, measured in ft^3/sec, significantly affect macroinvertebrate community structure. Methods for measuring each of these variables are described in Chapters 28 and 30.

Analysis

Laboratory Analysis. Normally samples are sent to regional laboratories for processing and analysis. Samples should be properly labeled with agency, administrative unit location, stream, station, and date.

Laboratory personnel analyze these data. These analyses are described below since the field biologists are probably familiar with how they are derived and interpreted even if they do not analyze the raw data.

Sample Analysis. Analyses are based on several factors such as the—

- Diversity and taxa index (DAT);
- Biomass of the macroinvertebrates per sample;
- Numbers of organisms per species;
- Species and trophic balance in the community;
- Abundance and degree of dominance among indicator species; and
- Tolerances of species in the community, as indicated by the community tolerance quotient (CTQ).

The BCI suggests a management strategy that integrates biological, chemical, and physical factors present in and adjacent to the stream's environment.

Analysis Elements (Major). The following three major analysis elements will be found on data sheets included in reports, along with scales indicating the significance of these data values:

1. *BCI.* The BCI measures a stream against its own potential and not that of other streams. The BCI is based on mean community tolerance, composed of the tolerances of individual taxa or species found in the community, which varies in response to intensity of perturbations in the ecosystem.

The BCI is calculated as follows:

a. Determine

(1) Gradient Percentage

(2) Relative Substrate Dominance given a ranking from 1 through 4
Boulder > 30 cm (over 12 in.)
Rubble   7.5-30   cm (3-12 in.)
Gravel   0.3-7.5   cm (1/8-2.99 in.)
Sand-silt < 0.3 cm ($<$ 1/8 in.)

(3) Total Alkalinity (mg/1)

(4) Sulfate (mg/1)

b. Determine, using the above information and the key in Table 1, the predicted community tolerance quotient (CTQ_p) for the reach on the study stream.

c. List, using at least three or four macroinvertebrate samples at a station, the taxa and their associated tolerance quotients (TQ) (Table 2).

d. Add the TQ values and divide by the number of taxa to get the actual community tolerance quotient

$$\frac{\Sigma TQs}{n} = CTQ_a$$

e. Determine the BCI $= \dfrac{CTQ_p}{CTQ_a} \times 100$

The scale of BCI values listed below can be used as indexes or values to determine the health of a stream ecosystem for which a defined management strategy can be based for each stream reach.

Scale	BCI
Excellent	Above 90
Good	75-90
Fair	Below 75
Poor	Below 75

The BCI is—

- Sensitive to all types of environmental stress;

- Applicable to various types of streams;

- Capable of giving a linear assessment from unstressed to highly stressed conditions;

- Independent of sample size, providing the sample contains a representative assemblage of species;

- Based on data readily available or easily acquired; and

- Capable of meshing with and supporting existing stream habitat or water quality management programs.

2. *Dominance and Taxa Diversity Index (DAT).* This index combines a measure of species dominance in the community with the number of species present. Many other indexes measure one or the other of these aspects.

Table 1. A key giving predicted community tolerance quotients (CTQ_p's) for various combinations of gradient (%), substrates, total alkalinity (mg/1 $CaCO_3$), and sulfate (mg/1 SO_4) for any given stream (from U.S. Department of Agriculture, Forest Service 1981).

Combinations	Go to Key No.	CTQ_p
1. Stream gradient 0.1–1.2	2	
1.3–3.0	15	
>3.0	28	
2. Substrate mostly boulder & rubble	3	
Gravel & rubble	7	
Sand & boulder, rubble, or gravel	11	
3. Total alkalinity 0–199	4	
200–300	5	
>300	6	
4. Sulfate 0–149		51
150–300		71
>300		90
5. Sulfate 0–149		53
150–300		71
>300		90
6. Sulfate 0–149		90
150–300		96
>300		108
7. Total alkalinity 0–199	8	
200–300	9	
>300	10	
8. Sulfate 0–149		53
150–300		85
>300		103

Table 1. A key giving predicted community tolerance quotients (CTQ$_p$ s) for various combinations of gradient (%), substrates, total alkalinity (mg/1 CaCO$_3$), and sulfate (mg/1 SO$_4$) for any given stream (continued).

Combinations	Go to Key No.	CTQ$_p$
9. Sulfate 0–149		55
150–300		86
>300		103
10. Sulfate 0–149		89
150–300		97
>300		108
11. Total alkalinity 0–199		12
200–300		13
>300		14
12. Sulfate 0–149		60
150–300		90
>300		108
13. Sulfate 0–149		60
150–300		90
>300		108
14. Sulfate 0–149		90
150–300		99
>300		108
15. Substrate mostly boulder & rubble	16	
Gravel & rubble	20	
Sand & boulder, rubble, or gravel	24	
16. Total alkalinity 0–199	17	
200–300	18	
>300	19	
17. Sulfate 0–149		50
150–300		65
>300		90
18. Sulfate 0–149		50
150–300		65
>300		90
19. Sulfate 0–199		90
150–300		96
>300		108
20. Total alkalinity 0–199	21	
200–300	22	
>300	230	
21. Sulfate 0–149		50
150–300		80
>300		103
22. Sulfate 0–149		55
150–300		80
>300		108
23. Sulfate 0–149		80
200–300		96
>300		108
24. Total alkalinity 0–199	25	
200–300	26	
>300	27	

Table 1. A key giving predicted community tolerance quotients (CTQ$_p$'s) for various combinations of gradient (%), substrates, total alkalinity (mg/1 CaCO$_3$), and sulfate (mg/1 SO$_4$) for any given stream (concluded).

Combinations	Go to Key No.	CTQ$_p$
25. Sulfate 0–149		66
150–300		88
>300		108
26. Sulfate 0–149		65
150–300		88
>300		108
27. Sulfate 0–149		85
150–300		93
>300		108
28. Substrate mostly boulder & rubble	29	
Gravel & rubble	33	
Sand & boulder, rubble, or gravel	37	
29. Total alkalinity 0–199	30	
200–300	31	
>300	32	
30. Sulfate 0–149		50
150–300		62
>300		100
31. Sulfate 0–149		50
150–300		62
>300		108
32. Sulfate 0–149		85
150–300		90
>300		108
33. Total alkalinity 0–199	34	
200–300	35	
>300	36	
34. Sulfate 0–149		50
150–300		77
>300		108
35. Sulfate 0–149		50
150–300		77
>300		108
36. Sulfate 0–149		90
150–300		99
>300		108
37. Total alkalinity 0–199	25	
200–300	26	
>300	27	
38. Sulfate 0–149		80
150–300		100
>300		108
39. Sulfate 0–149		80
150–300		100
>300		108
40. Sulfate 0–149		100
150–300		108
>300		108

Table 2. Tolerance quotients (TQs) of aquatic macroinvertebrates based on tolerance to alkalinity, sulfate, and sedimentation including low stream gradients (from U.S. Department of Agriculture, Forest Service 1981).

Taxa	TQ
Family Tipulidae	72
Antocha monticola	24
Dicranota sp.	24
Hexatoma sp.	36
Holorusia grandis	72
Helobia sp.	36
Tipula sp.	36
Family Psychodidae	36
Maruina sp.	36
Psychoda sp.	36
Pericoma sp.	36
Family Blephariceridae	2
Bibiocephala grandis	2
Agathon sp.	2
Family Deuterophlebiidae	4
Deuterophlebia coloradensis	4
Family Culicidae	108
Aedes sp.	108
Culex sp.	108
Anopheles sp.	108
Mansonia sp.	108
Psorophora sp.	108
Culiseta sp.	108
Family Dixidae	108
Dixa sp.	108
Family Simuliidae	108
Family Chironomidae	108
Family Ceratopogonidae	108
Family Stratiomyidae	108
Euparyphus sp.	108
Family Tabanidae	108
Tabanus sp.	108
Family Rhagionidae	24
Atherix pachypus	24
Family Dolichopodidae	108
Family Empididae	108
Hemerodromia sp.	108
Family Ephydrinae	108
Ephydra sp.	108
Family Muscidae	108
Limnophora sp.	108
Family Syrphidae	108
Chrysogaster sp.	108
Tubifera sp.	108
Helophilus sp.	108
Family Dytiscidae	72
Derovatellus sp.	72
Laccophilus sp.	72
Bidessus sp.	72
Agabus sp.	72
Hygrotus sp.	72
Hydroporous sp.	72
Oreodytes sp.	72
Illybius sp.	72
Rhantus sp.	72
Dytiscus sp.	72
Acilius sp.	72
Cybister sp.	72
Deronectes sp.	72

Taxa	TQ
Family Dytiscidae (continued)	
Thermonectes sp.	72
Coptotomus sp.	72
Family Hydrophilidae	72
Helophorus sp.	72
Hydrochara sp.	72
Berosus sp.	72
Enochrus sp.	72
Hydrophilus sp.	72
Tropisternus sp.	72
Hydrobius sp.	72
Paracymus sp.	72
Crenitus sp.	72
Ametor sp.	72
Helochares sp.	72
Laccobius sp.	72
Enochrus sp.	72
Cymbiodyta sp.	72
Family Elmidae	108
Zaitzevia sp.	
Narpus sp.	
Stenelmis sp.	
Dubiraphia sp.	
Optioservus sp.	108
Heterlimnius sp.	
Elmis sp.	
Simsonia sp.	
Microcylloepus sp.	
Lara sp.	
Family Gyrinidae	108
Gyrinus sp.	108
Family Amphizoidae	24
Amphizoa sp.	24
Family Hydraenidae	72
Order Diptera	
Family Hydroptilidae	
Leucotrichia sp.	108
Alisotrichia sp.	108
Mayatrichia sp.	108
Family Limnephilidae	108
Limnephilus sp.	108
Dicosmoecus sp.	24
Hesperophylax sp.	108
Oligophlebodes sp.	24
Apatania sp.	18
Amphicosmoecus sp.	18
Neothremma sp.	8
Lenarchus sp.	18
Chyranda sp.	18
Psychoglypha sp.	24
Ecclisomyia sp.	24
Homophylax sp.	18
Allocosmoecus sp.	18
Asynarchus sp.	108
Clistoronia sp.	108
Grammotaulius sp.	108
Imania sp.	48
Neophylax sp.	24
Onocosmoecus sp.	18
Pycnopsyche sp.	72

Table 2. Tolerance quotients (TQs) of aquatic macroinvertebrates based on tolerance to alkalinity, sulfate, and sedimentation including low stream gradients (continued).

Taxa	TQ	Taxa	TQ
Family Leptoceridae	54	Family Hydropsychidae	108
Oecetis sp.	54	*Hydropsyche* sp.	108
Leptocella sp.	54	*Cheumatopsyche* sp.	108
Triaenodes sp.	54	*Arctopsyche* sp.	18
Mystacides sp.	54	*Smicridea* sp.	72
Ceraclea sp.	54	*Diplectrona* sp.	48
Family Lepidostomatidae	18	*Macronema* sp.	48
Lepidostoma sp.	18	*Parapsyche* sp.	6
Family Brachycentridae	24	Family Hydroptilidae	108
Brachycentrus sp.	24	*Hydroptila* sp.	108
Micrasema sp.	24	*Agralyea* sp.	108
Oligoplectrum sp.	24	*Ochrotrichia* sp.	108
Amiocentrus sp.	24	*Stactobiella* sp.	108
Family Helicopsychidae	18	*Neotrichia* sp.	108
Helicopsyche borealis	18	*Ithytrichia* sp.	108
Family Polycentropodidae	72	*Oxyethira* sp.	108
Polycentropus sp.	72	Order Ephemeroptera	
Nyctiophylax sp.	72	Family Gerridae	72
Family Sericostomatidae	72	*Gerris* sp.	72
Gumaga sp.	72	*Rheumatobates* sp.	72
Order Coleoptera		Family Naucoridae	72
Family Haliplidae	54	*Ambrysus mormon*	72
Brychius sp.	54	*Pelocoris* sp.	72
Haliplus sp.	54	Family Notonectidae	108
Peltodytes sp.	54	*Notonecta* sp.	108
Family Periodidae		*Buenoa* sp.	108
Pictetiella expansa	18	Family Veliidae	72
Diura knowltoni	24	*Microvelia americana*	72
Isoperla sp.	48	*Rhagovelia distincta*	72
I. ebria	24	Family Mesoveliidae	72
I. fulva	48	*Mesovelia* sp.	72
I. mormona	48	Family Macroveliidae	72
I. quinquepunctata	48	*Macrovelia* sp.	72
Family Chloroperlidae	24	Order Plecoptera	
Family Perlidae	24	Family Nemouridae	36
Acroneuria abnormis	6	*Amphinemura*	6
Claassenia sabulosa	6	*Malenka*	36
Hesperoperla pacifica	18	*Prostoia besametsa*	24
Perlesta placida	24	*Podmosta*	12
Doroneuria theodora	18	*Zapada*	16
Order Trichoptera		*Nemoura*	24
Family Rhyacophilidae	18	Family Capniidae	32
Rhyacophila sp.	18	*Capnia*	32
Atopsyche sp.	18	*Eucapnopsis*	18
Himalopsyche sp.	18	*Isocapnia*	24
Family Glossosomatidae	32	*Mesocapnia frisoni*	32
Glossosoma sp.	24	*Utacapnia*	18
Anagapetus sp.	24	Family Taeniopterygidae	48
Protoptila sp.	32	*Taenionema*	48
Culoptila sp.	32	*Doddsia*	24
Family Philopotamidae	24	*Oemopteryx*	48
Chimarra sp.	24	Family Leuctridae	18
Dolophilodes (*sortosa*)	24	*Paraleuctra* sp.	18
Wormaldia sp.	24	*Perlomyia* sp.	18
Family Psychomyiidae	108	Family Pteronarcyidae	24
Polycentropus sp.	108	*Pteronarcella badia*	24
Nyctiophylax sp.	108	*Pteronarcys californica*	18
Psychomyia sp.	108	*P. princeps*	24
Tinodes sp.	108	Family Perlodidae	48

Table 2. Tolerance quotients (TQs) of aquatic macroinvertebrates based on tolerance to alkalinity, sulfate, and sedimentation including low stream gradients (concluded).

Taxa	TQ	Taxa	TQ
Family Perlodidae (continued)		**Family Ephemerellidae (continued)**	
Megarcys signata	24	*E. inermis*	48
Skwala parallela	18	*E. infrequens*	48
Cultus aestivalis	12	*E. spinifera*	24
Isogenoides sp.	24	Family Ephemeridae	36
I. elongatus	24	*Ephemera simulans*	36
I. zionensis	24	*Hexagenia limbata*	36
Kogotus modestus	18	Phylum Coelenterata	108
Order Megaloptera	72	Class Hydrozoa	108
Family Sialidae	72	Phylum Aschelminthes	108
Sialis sp.	72	Class Nematoda	108
Family Corydalidae	72	Phylum Mollusca	108
Corydalus cognata	72	Class Gastropoda	108
Order Lepidoptera	72	Family Lymnaidae	108
Family Pyralidae	72	*Lymnaea* sp.	108
Paragyractis kearfottalis	72	Family Physidae	108
Order Ephemeroptera	72	*Physa* sp.	108
Family Siphlonuridae	72	Family Planorbidae	108
Ameletus sp.	48	Phylum Annelida	108
Siphlonurus occidentalis	72	Class Hirudinea	108
Isonychia	48	Class Oligochaeta	108
Family Baetidae	72	Family Tubificidae	108
Baetis sp.	72	*Tubifex* sp.	108
Callibaetis sp.	72	Family Lumbricidae	108
Pseudocloeon sp.	72	*Lumbricus aquaticus*	108
Centroptilum sp.	36	Phylum Platyhelminthes	
Dactylobaetis sp.	36	Class Turbellaria	108
Paracloeodes sp.	72	Order Tricladida	108
Family Oligoneuriidae	36	Phylum Arthropoda	
Lachlania saskatchewanensis	36	Class Arachnida	
Homoeoneuria sp.	36	Suborder Hydracarina	108
Family Heptageniidae	48	Class Crustacea	108
Heptagenia sp.	48	Order Isopoda	108
Stenonema sp.	48	Family Asellidae	108
Cinygmula sp.	21	*Asellus* sp.	108
Rhithrogena sp.	21	Order Amphipoda	108
Epeorus sp.	21	Family Talitridae	108
Anepeorus sp.	48	*Hyalella azteca*	108
Family Leptophlebiidae	36	Family Gammaridae	108
Paraleptophlebia sp.	24	*Gammarus lacustris*	108
Leptophlebia sp.	24	Order Decapoda	108
Choroterpes sp.	36	Family Astacidae	108
Traverella sp.	36	*Pacifastacus gambeli*	108
Family Tricorythidae	108	*Cambarus laevis*	108
Tricorythodes sp.	108	Order Cladocera	108
Leptohyphes sp.	72	*Daphnia* sp.	108
Family Ephemerellidae	48	Order Copepoda	108
Ephemerella sp.	48	Order Ostracoda	108
E. grandis	24	Class Insecta	108
E. doddsi	48	Order Collembola	108
E. coloradensis	18	Family Poduridae	108
E. tibialis	24	*Podura aquatica*	108
		Family Entomobryidae	108

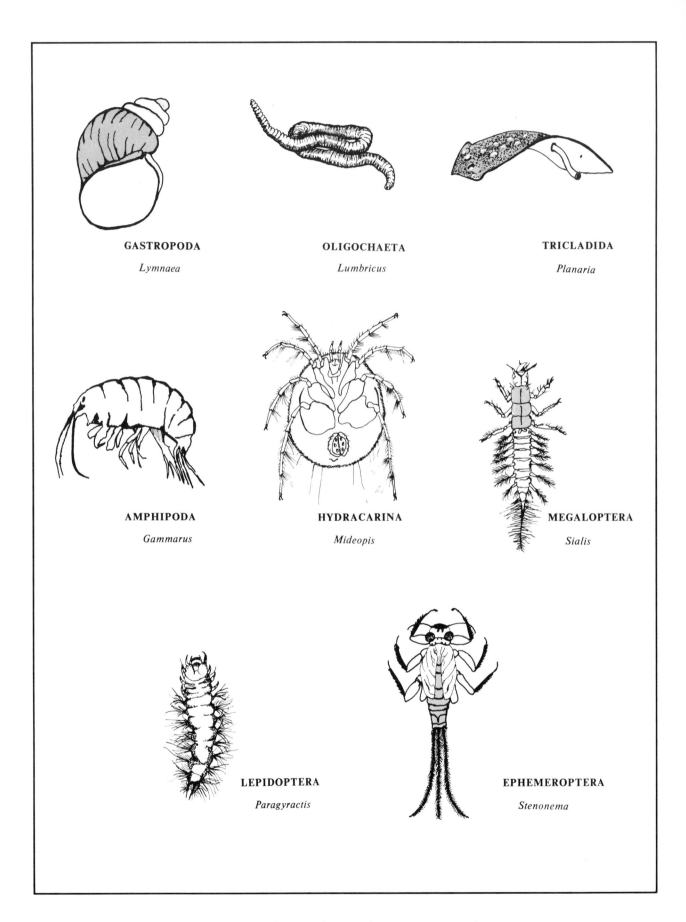

GASTROPODA

Lymnaea

OLIGOCHAETA

Lumbricus

TRICLADIDA

Planaria

AMPHIPODA

Gammarus

HYDRACARINA

Mideopis

MEGALOPTERA

Sialis

LEPIDOPTERA

Paragyractis

EPHEMEROPTERA

Stenonema

Figure 3. Common aquatic macroinvertebrate orders used in ecosystem analysis.

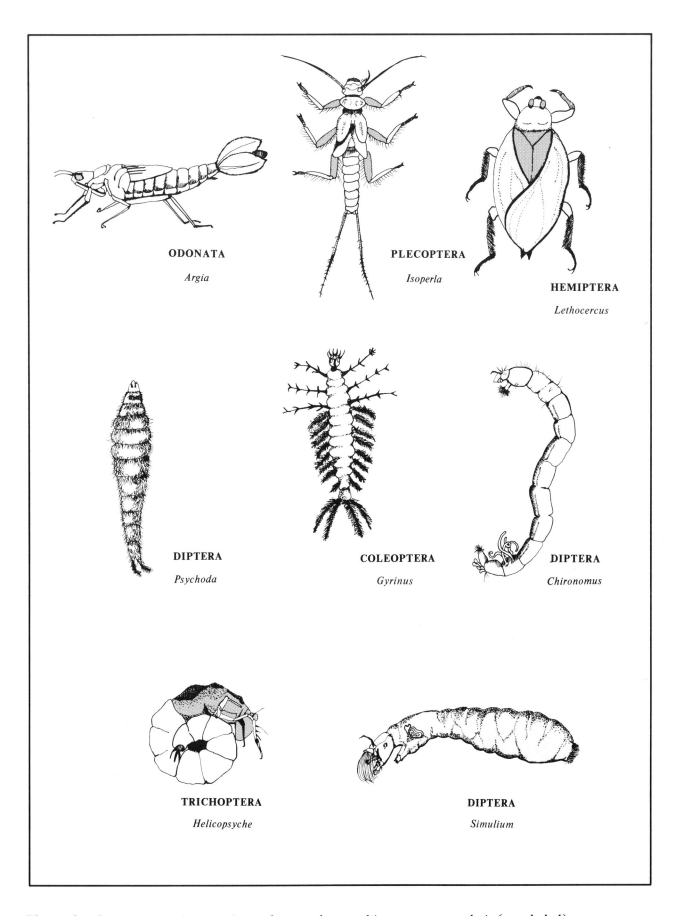

ODONATA

Argia

PLECOPTERA

Isoperla

HEMIPTERA

Lethocercus

DIPTERA

Psychoda

COLEOPTERA

Gyrinus

DIPTERA

Chironomus

TRICHOPTERA

Helicopsyche

DIPTERA

Simulium

Figure 3. Common aquatic macroinvertebrate orders used in ecosystem analysis (concluded).

The procedure for determining DAT is as follows: the dominance part of the index is determined by placing a sample of aquatic insects in a petri dish with lines marked on the bottom. Each species of insects viewed through a dissecting microscope can be identified if the dish is moved in a snake-like fashion so the same organisms are not viewed twice. Each organism and series can be counted. A series is recorded each time a sighted species is different from the previous one. If the sample has a sufficient number of organisms, 300 to 400 should be observed to determine the diversity index value. The number of series (s) is divided by the number of organisms (o) to determine the dominance value (Dom. = s/o), which will be a fraction between 0 and 1. The number of taxa in the sample is multiplied by this dominance value to obtain the DAT Diversity Index (Dom. × Taxa = DAT).

DAT Scale	Stream Value
18-26	Excellent
11-17	Good
6-10	Fair
0-5	Poor

3. *Standing Crop.* The dry weight of the organisms is determined for each sample. Small aluminum pans are predried for 8 to 24 hours and are weighed to the nearest tenth of a milligram on a Mettler balance. The samples placed in these pans are dried at a temperature of 65°C (149°F) for 8 to 24 hours; then the pan and its contents are weighed. This is important in indicating whether a stream is reaching its potential and shows the stream's potential for supporting a resident fishery. Figure 3 shows some of the more common aquatic insects used in aquatic ecosystem analysis.

Analysis Elements (Minor). The following summary analyses are helpful in evaluating aquatic ecosystems:

1. *Total Number of Species.* Total number of species is an indication of macroinvertebrate community diversity. It often gives an initial indication of the stability of the environment or of the community within the environment.

2. *Mean Number of Organisms Per Taxa Per Square Meter.* This value is an indication of the stability of the community, habitat, and water quality. Taxa may be transient individuals or resident populations that may indicate whether or not conditions are favorable.

3. *Standard Error of the Mean.* This is a measure of similarity in samples which indicates when enough samples have been taken to obtain the desired reliability. According to the U.S. Environmental Protection Agency standards (Weber 1973; Green 1979), this value should not be under 20%; on most streams, this can be achieved with three samples. Some streams require four or five samples. This value shows when the mean is within 80% confidence limits.

4. *Coefficient of Variation.* Coefficient of variation is a value that indicates variability in samples, independent of the number of samples. It evaluates the sampling technique and effectiveness of the sample equipment. The U.S. Environmental Protection Agency has set the standard at under 50% for acceptable reliability.

5. *Standard Deviation.* Standard deviation measures sample variation and indicates whether sampling techniques and number of samples are sufficient to effectively show community structure.

DISCUSSION

Macroinvertebrate data, when combined with data on aquatic features and water quality, can be useful to land managers in managing aquatic resources and surrounding areas. Positive or negative effects from almost every activity that occurs in a drainage are eventually reflected in the macroinvertebrate community composition of the streams that drain it. This community composition can reveal the health of the ecosystem, provide a warning system, or reflect the relative intensity of pollution problems. Macroinvertebrate analysis often can identify the type(s) of pollution, making it a valuable tool for conscientious land managers.

Macroinvertebrate data are site-specific and average values for large diverse areas should not be used for decisions. Time and space considerations are very important in maintaining high standards of aquatic habitat and water quality, particularly in formulating grazing prescriptions. Monitoring plans for such prescriptions need to incorporate the same considerations of time and space.

Finally, the biologist and manager should be cautioned against relying on macroinvertebrate data alone. Macroinvertebrate data should be used in conjunction with other types of data to provide sound information on the health of aquatic-riparian ecosystems.

LITERATURE CITED

GREEN, R.H. 1979. Sampling design and statistical methods for environmental biologists. John Wiley & Sons. 251pp.

U.S. DEPARTMENT OF AGRICULTURE, FOREST SERVICE. 1981. Aquatic habitat surveys handbook FSH 2609.23 for the General Aquatic Wildlife System. U.S. Dep. Agric., For. Serv. Region 4. Ogden, UT. 257pp. (Draft).

WEBER, C. 1973. Biological field and laboratory methods for measuring the quality of surface waters and effluents. EPA. 670/4-73-001.

V SPECIAL STUDIES

33

RADIO-TELEMETRY

Paul L. Hegdal[1]

U.S. Fish and Wildlife Service
Denver Wildlife Research Center
Building 16, Denver Federal Center
Denver, CO 80225

Bruce A. Colvin

Department of Biological Sciences
Bowling Green State University
Bowling Green, OH 43403

Editor's Note: Within the past 25 years, wildlife research has moved from subjective field observations to highly complex, objective measurements of animal behavior. The objective measurements, in many cases, are accomplished by use of radiotelemetry. This chapter provides an overview of current state-of-the-art uses of radiotelemetry in locating habitats used by subject animals.

While the urge to use new "gadgets" to learn about animals is understandable, today's biologists should conform to conventional responsibilities toward experimental design and project planning. "Does the end justify the means?" This chapter, therefore, also identifies current processes and equipment needed to plan and execute a telemetry program useful in habitat management, but recognizes the field is continuously expanding.

INTRODUCTION

The development and implementation of radiotelemetry in wildlife research has tremendously broadened the opportunity to examine components of species' natural history and ecology. Since its introduction into wildlife research approximately 25 years ago (Marshall and Kupa 1963; Mech 1983), radiotelemetry use has vastly increased, especially in recent years with the increasing attractiveness of "high-tech" approaches to research, their usefulness and availability.

Today, examples of radiotelemetry research are commonly found in literature. Radiotelemetry hardware, techniques, and uses are continuously being improved and evaluated. The number and diversity of species being studied with radiotelemetry also are continuing to grow and include mammals (Marshall et al. 1962; Mech 1977; Madison 1978; Barrett 1984), birds (Nicholls and Warner 1972; Cochran 1975), reptiles (Carr 1965; Schubauer 1981; Osgood 1970; Kenward et al. 1982), amphibians (Jansen 1982), fish (Winter et al. 1978), and even crabs (Wolcott 1980) and crayfish (Covich 1977). Habitats where these studies have been undertaken range from the polar circle (Kolz et al. 1980) to temperate regions (Verts 1963; Imboden 1975), tropical regions (Bruggers et al. 1983), and oceans (Garshelis and Garshelis 1984).

There are several possible reasons why radiotelemetry may be implemented as part of a wildlife research or management scheme. Accessibility of the species often is a principal reason. Physical characteristics of a species' habitat, such as rough terrain or dense vegetation, may limit the opportunity to seek

[1] Current affiliation: Denver Wildlife Research Center, APHIS/USDA Building 16, Denver Federal Center, Denver, CO 80225.

and observe a species. Also, a species may be nocturnal, highly secretive, difficult to trap repeatedly, capable of wide-ranging movements, or even subterranean or aquatic in its habits.

A second advantage of radiotelemetry is that data can take a continuous form rather than the discrete form which occurs for example, through trapping and marking. Once an operating radio transmitter is attached to an animal, that particular animal can potentially be located continuously either day or night. Radiotelemetry also provides the opportunity to remotely follow or census wildlife. Once instrumented, the specific animal can be identified and observed in a non-disruptive manner and, thus, a more accurate depiction of the species' movements, habitat use, and ecology may be acquired.

In contrast, when traps are used to locate an animal, one must assume that a trap is available to capture the animal at a particular location and time and that the animal will enter the trap. Traps (or observers) are typically placed at preconceived (subjective) locations where animals might range, and thus movement data generated from trapping (or direct observation) may be strongly biased. Additionally, trapping often takes on a day or night censusing form, depending on the activity periods characteristic of the species, thus adding to the discrete and limited nature of observations that can be made. Continuous observations also can be made by direct observation; however, without radiotelemetry, locating target animals, distinguishing individuals, and monitoring the activities of many isolated individuals may be far more difficult.

The purpose of this chapter is to discuss radiotelemetry techniques; types of available equipment; and applications for determining movement, migration, and habitat use by wildlife. In addition, we describe potential problems, limitations, and costs.

RADIO-TRACKING EQUIPMENT

Radio tracking should be considered as no more than a technique for extending the range of one's observational powers. Even the simplest equipment requires a significant financial investment. A simple system for tracking about 10 animals with hand-carried receivers and antennas will cost $3,000 to $4,000 (1986 values).

Many improvements have been made since the initial successful studies in the early 1960s, such as more efficient transmitters; better encapsulating materials; lighter, more energy-efficient batteries; solar units; and more efficient, easy-to-use receivers. In addition, all components and complete systems now are commercially available from several sources (Table 1).

Table 1. Possible sources of supply for radio-tracking equipment.[1]

Advanced Telemetry Systems, Inc.
23859 Northeast Highway 65
Bethel, MN 55005
(612) 434-5040

AVM Instrument Company
6575 Trinity Court
Dublin, CA 94566
(415) 829-5030

Cedar Creek Bioelectronics Laboratory
University of Minnesota
Bethel, MN 55005
(612) 434-7361

CompuCap
8437 Yates Avenue North
Brooklyn Park, MN 55443
(612) 424-2373

Custom Electronics
2009 Silver Court West
Urbana, IL 61801
(217) 344-3460

Custom Telemetry and Consulting
185 Longview Drive
Athens, GA 30605
(404) 548-1024

L. L. Electronics
Box 247
Mahomet, IL 53405
(217) 586-2132

Ocean Applied Research Corp.
10447 Roselle Street
San Diego, CA 92121
(619) 453-4013

Smith-Root, Inc.
14014 Northeast Salmon Creek Avenue
Vancouver, WA 98665
(206) 573-0202

Stuart Enterprises
Box 310, 124 Cornish Court
Grass Valley, CA 95945
(916) 273-9188

Telemetry Systems, Inc.
Box 187
Mequon, WI 53092
(414) 241-8335

Telonics
932 East Impala Avenue
Mesa, AZ 85204-6699
(602) 892-4444

Table 1. Possible sources of supply for radio-tracking equipment (concluded).[1]

Wildlife Materials, Inc.
R.R. 1, Grant City Road
Carbondale, IL 62901
(618) 549-6330

[1]Use of companies on this list does not imply Federal Government endorsement.

There are basically two components in a radio-tracking system: a transmitting system and a receiving system. The transmitting system consists of the transmitter which is attached to an animal by an appropriate method such as a radio collar on big game animals, patagial transmitters on birds, and implanted transmitters in fish or snakes. The receiving system consists of a receiver, a receiving antenna, and either an operator or recorder.

Patagial transmitter attached to a hen pheasant.

Transmitters

The specific type of transmitter chosen will depend on size, morphology, and behavior of the animal under study; possible attachment methods; transmitter availability and cost; necessary transmission range; habitat where used; and the particular data to be collected.

Almost any animal that weighs over 15 g (0.5 oz) can be equipped with a radio transmitter and monitored for at least a short time. Obviously, the larger the animal, the larger the transmitter package can be. Transmitters are available commercially ranging from slightly over a gram (0.03 oz) to several kilograms. The actual transmitter *per se* does not vary much in weight but the power source, packaging material, and attachment material can add substantially to the weight. Weight considerations for the animal usually become important only for the smaller (< 1 kg [< 2.2 lb]) species. This can be the most critical consideration with very small animals (< 20 g [< 0.7 oz]) and especially birds. Generally, the transmitter should be no more than 5% of body weight. The Banding Office of the U.S. Fish and Wildlife Service recommends no more than 3% of body weight for transmitters used on birds. Cochran (1980) stated that many species seem to tolerate a package that is 4% of their body weight and appear to behave normally not too long after such a package has been attached. He also added that there is nothing "magic" about 4%. However, there may be some species that cannot be radio-equipped with these transmitter-weights, or even lighter transmitters, without having significant behavioral or physical effects as a result of instrumentation.

Ordinarily, each transmitter used in a particular study area is on a unique frequency (or channel); therefore, to tune in each animal, the operator merely turns a dial or activates switches on a radio receiver to the appropriate frequency (or channel).

Radio frequency management in the U.S. is based on the Communications Act of 1934. This legislation divided frequency spectrum users into two groups (federal and non-federal). The National Telecommunications and Information Administration (NTIA) controls the federal portions of the spectrum, while the Federal Communication Commission (FCC) controls the non-federal portions of the spectrum for use by state and local governments as well as the private sector. Since segments of the spectrum are shared by federal and non-federal users, operations are mutually coordinated by the Interdepartmental Radio Advisory Committee (IRAC). Each Federal Government agency and the FCC are represented on the IRAC to address spectrum management issues. The IRAC, through NTIA, has authority to approve, disapprove, and cancel any federal radio-frequency assignment. In effect, IRAC is the licensing authority for federal users while the FCC licenses non-federal users.

Two portions of the spectrum have been set aside for wildlife telemetry use (40.16 to 40.20 MHz and 216 to 220 MHz); however, these frequencies have not been widely used by wildlife researchers or managers. Radio-frequency spectrum managers are becoming increasingly concerned about unlicensed operations and the violations of rules and regulations pertaining to radio communications. By law, telemetry users must operate within the rules and regulations because any interference occurring between authorized and unauthorized uses will cause unauthorized use to shut down, resulting in costly losses of time and effort expended on studies. One must have authorization to use a particular frequency before any transmitters can be placed on free-ranging animals. For further guidance and information, see Kolz (1983).

Most transmitters use mercury or lithium batteries to power the transmitter; however, solar-powered units, some with rechargeable batteries, also are available (Cochran 1980). Battery choice must be tempered by the amount of additional weight the animal can carry and the length of time the animal needs to be tracked. If the transmitter is retrievable or the animal recapturable, transmitters can be reused and their longevity extended by changing batteries.

Most simply, activating a transmitter includes soldering a final connection and then potting (covering) that connection with an appropriate quick-setting potting material (i.e., dental acrylic, epoxy patch, or silicone rubber); others are activated by cutting a wire that allows completion of a circuit. Additionally, with some transmitters, placing or removing a magnet near an imbedded switch turns the transmitter on or off. A magnet system is preferred as it does not require any soldering or potting by the user and is more likely to be completely sealed from moisture. Normally transmitters are activated only shortly before attachment to an animal. However, some users routinely turn transmitters on for a few days prior to attachment to assure proper operations. The loss of a few days of battery life may be critical only for small, short-lived transmitters.

Most transmitter antennas are some sort of tuned whip. The most efficient antenna lengths are in quarters of wave lengths of a particular frequency (such as ¼, ½, or whole wave). Except for the high frequencies, most wildlife transmitter antennas cannot be that long (a full wave length at 164 MHz = 1.82 m) and, therefore, are tuned with a coil to whatever length can be tolerated on the animal. Whip antennas are more efficient than loop antennas. However, in some applications, the loop antenna serves as an integral part of the attachment collar.

There are a variety of methods for attaching transmitters to animals, and before any transmitters are attached to any species, one should review available literature on the species, try the attachments, and act on the results of those endeavors. Neck collars are the most common radio-attachment method for terrestrial mammals (Cochran 1980). Harness, ear tag, and implanted transmitters have been used on some mammals that are difficult to collar (Mech 1983). For birds, harness, tail-clip, poncho, glued-on, leg-band, and patagial transmitters have been successfully employed (Bray and Corner 1972; Fitzner and Fitzner 1977; Amstrup 1980; Bruggers et al. 1981). Implantable or ingestible transmitters are useful where external attachment is impractical, such

as with fish or snakes (Osgood 1970). Tethers have proven useful for sea turtles and manatees (Timko and Kolz 1982).

A number of factors need to be considered when designing or specifying the type of collar, harness, or other attachment to be used. Shape, width, contouring, durability, flexibility, smoothness next to the animal, size adjustability, compactness, cryptic design, internal or external antenna, and ease of attachment all can be important (Cochran 1980). Sharp edges and points should be avoided or at least placed where there will be minimal irritation from contact or pressure. Without at least considering these factors, routine behaviors such as running, flying, feeding, mating, or even resting may be adversely affected. If necessary, one may have to test various attachments on some species where methods

Radio-collared opossum.

Radio-collared coyote.

and designs have not been evaluated by others. Ideally, the transmitter will be on the animal only as long as needed to collect the desired data. Some transmitters are designed to fall off after some predetermined time; however, there have been some problems with premature transmitter loss. With a well-designed attachment, many animals have not had significant problems carrying the transmitter for life. We have had transmitters on owls for over 5 years with no apparent problems.

Transmitters for remote locations generally cost between $100 and $250 each. A variety of special-purpose transmitters have been developed for detecting movement or mortality (Kolz 1975); measuring heart rate, respiration rate, temperature, and blood pressure, as well as conducting electrocardiograms and encephalograms (Amlaner 1978); firing darts on command for recapture (Mech et al. 1984); and some specific behaviors such as frequency of urination. However, these transmitters and receivers are more expensive than transmitters for remote locations.

Receivers

A variety of receivers are available, ranging from $700 for the simpler receivers to about $2,000 for some of the newer, wider band models with programmable automatic switching functions, often referred to as "scanners." However, paying more money for a receiver will not guarantee a more sensitive receiver. Most can be tuned to equal "state of the art" sensitivity (± 150 db)—even the $700 versions.

When planning purchases of telemetry equipment, at least one extra receiver should be acquired for the project as a backup. There is nothing more frustrating than having radio-equipped animals and no working receivers to track them. Extra batteries should always be available for receivers and any other equipment used in conjunction with them.

Most receivers have a—

(1) power switch, often with a position for internal or external power;

(2) channel selector (for digital frequency display models, this may be dials or switches for changing the displayed frequency);

(3) fine-tuning frequency dial (on non-digital models);

(4) gain (volume) dial;

(5) sweep switch that allows automatic sweep within a channel or between preset exact frequencies; and

(6) switches for setting frequencies to be searched.

Most receivers also have a variety of input and output plugs for antennas, headphones, external power, meters, pulse-interval counters, recorders, and other attachments.

Earphones are not necessary in many tracking situations. The inexpensive models ($20 or less) are adequate in most cases for hand or vehicle tracking. However, for tracking in aircraft in windy or noisy conditions, earphones are necessary, and it is worth the extra money to get the best—$100 to $200 each. (Long-continued use of earphones at high audio levels has resulted in diminished hearing abilities among some research biologists.)

Antennas

Almost any piece of metal connected to the antenna plug of a receiver will enhance the signal, but properly tuned and tested antennas should be used for maximum efficiency. The yagi antenna is the most commonly used antenna for radiotelemetry studies. A good, single hand-held yagi antenna costs $50 to $100. As frequency increases, wave length decreases and the size of antennas also decreases. Yagi antennas are too large to be very practical for hand-held or vehicle-mounting at the lower (30 to 50 MHz) frequencies but can readily be used on vehicles or hand-held at the higher (over 150 MHz) frequencies.

Antennas can be mounted on towers, vehicles, or aircraft. Two (or more) yagi antennas can be combined in such a manner (called stacking) to increase their range and directional ability. In dual array systems, antennas can provide a bearing accuracy of 1 to 2°. Often, permanent tracking stations consisting of a few strategically placed antenna towers or masts mounted on the highest hills in the study area will yield adequate signals. These towers can be similar to the large, automatically rotating system described by Nicholls and Warner (1972) or relatively simple structures with a coaxial cable left dangling near the base (Merson et al. 1982).

Permanent or temporary tower antennas can work well for sedentary animals; however, the accuracy of radio locations deteriorates near the base line of the antennas (because the angle of intercept nears zero). If additional towers or mobile tracking stations can be employed, this problem can be overcome.

Radio-tracking vehicles (mobile tracking stations) can be equipped with roof-mounted, dual yagi antenna systems. Bray et al. (1975) described a removable cartop antenna system. However, for most studies using mobile tracking stations, we strongly recommend vehicles equipped with a through-the-roof antenna system similar to that described by Hegdal and Gatz (1978). These antennas are rotated from inside the vehicles, and radio bearings are indicated on a 360°, 25-cm (10-in.) protractor by a pointer attached to the antenna mast. The pointer is aligned to the null of the dual yagi antennas. Coaxial cables from the dual yagis are attached to a null-peak switchbox (available from commercial suppliers), which allows switching from in-phase (for maximum signal strength) to out-of-phase (for precise bearings) operation. Additionally, radio communication, a plotting table, auxiliary batteries, and extra lighting installed in the vehicles will expedite tracking studies. Figure 1 shows an inexpensive method for equipping vehicles with a roof-mounted, dual-beam antenna system. If properly balanced, antennas can be rotated easily and animals can be tracked while the vehicle is moving as fast as 55 mph.

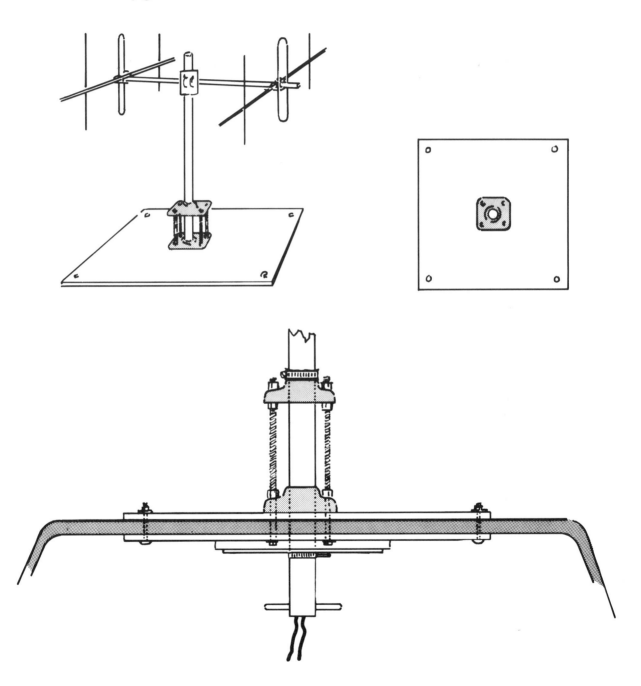

Figure 1. A roof-mounted, dual yagi, radio-tracking system.

On aircraft, antennas are usually mounted on wing struts (with certified antenna mounts) in a "side-looking" fashion, perpendicular to the fuselage (Gilmer et al. 1981). Care also must be taken to ensure that coaxial cables are properly secured with tape, not crimped, and that they and the rest of the telemetry equipment do not interfere with the pilot's operation of the aircraft.

Too often, new (and experienced) radio-trackers do not periodically test and check their antenna system. They may have an extremely sensitive receiver matched to a poorly tuned antenna and therefore have (unknowingly) a very inefficient receiving system.

Coaxial cables are used to connect antennas or other equipment, such as recorders, to receivers. This is a shielded cable (a center wire conductor surrounded by the ground wire). Care must be taken to avoid sharp bends, twisting, and flattening or pinching; distortion of the cable shape can drastically affect or eliminate signal reception.

A radio-tracking vehicle at a marked tracking station.

Other Equipment

Pulse interval counters are available for about $400 and can be used in conjunction with several receivers. These devices measure the time between consecutive, pulsed radio signals and usually display that value in thousandths of a second. They are especially helpful for identifying pulse rates (animals) when there is more than one transmitter operating on the same frequency (or channel). Recorders can be used in conjunction with automatic switching (scanning) receivers to record presence or absence of radio-equipped animals over time at sites such as dens or nests (Gilmer et al. 1971; Harrington and Mech 1982; Mech 1983). However, as with automatic tracking systems, one must have a good strong signal for most of the recorders and counters to work properly. The human ear can detect signals from the receiver better than any of the available auxiliary equipment.

Satellite radiotelemetry also has been used successfully on a few wildlife species (Kuechle et al. 1979; Timko and Kolz 1982). However, transmitters and receiving equipment are more specialized and considerably more expensive than those we have described, and it is beyond the scope of this chapter to fully discuss these aspects of radiotelemetry.

Advice

We strongly recommend that the telemetry user depend on electronic specialists for constructing and servicing transmitters, receivers, and other specialized equipment. However, the biologist must have a general knowledge of radio signal propagation; factors that affect it; and some skills and equipment for servicing, checking, and repairing parts of the telemetry system. Users should be able to charge power sources for receivers and other equipment; change batteries in some transmitters (some must be returned to the manufacturer); replace coaxial cables and antenna elements; turn transmitters on and off; check power sources, telemetry, and antenna systems for shorts and open circuits; and recognize that such problems exist. Minimal support equipment should include a volt-ohmmeter; battery tester; supply of miscellaneous wire connectors and terminals; soldering gun; solder; wire strippers; and various-sized screwdrivers, pliers, and adjustable wrenches.

DATA SAMPLING

The planning stages of a radiotelemetry study must include decisions on specific use or need of the technology, equipment, personnel availability, and cost. Just as important, however, are decisions on how data will be collected, analyzed, and interpreted. The recording of a single data point in the field can be a simple procedure; however, deciding the value or use of hundreds or thousands of coordinates may not be and should not be left until the field work is complete.

Locating an animal either on a monthly, weekly, daily, hourly, or minute-by-minute basis all may be possible depending on the available hardware, personnel, and funding. However, while a large number of radio-equipped animals can be located continuously, rarely is that done. The specific form and frequency of sampling should be particularly relevant to the specific questions that are being addressed with radiotelemetry use. It may be appropriate to simply monitor general movements or continued survivorship; thus, the sampling scheme may be extensive or random and the radio-tracking results may be presented in a rather descriptive form. In contrast, when evaluating habitat selection or rates of movement, for example, the sampling scheme may have a highly intensive or systematic style with data recorded in more of a quantitative manner (e.g., effort- or time-specific). In the latter case, animals may be located at specific and independent time intervals or continuously tracked within discrete and independent time periods.

Sampling scheme decisions also may be affected by the species being studied. Animals that are capable of wide-range movement or frequent habitat change may have to be located more often to avoid loss of contact than those that are largely sedentary. The length and timing of daily activity cycles of animals, for example, nocturnal versus diurnal, also will affect the length and timing of radio-tracking efforts; the sampling scheme for any given individual may have to be compromised considerably depending on how many other animals are simultaneously radio-equipped. Additionally, more frequent sampling may be needed if the hardware being used includes short transmission-reception range or a limited battery or radio attachment life.

A sampling scheme to evaluate the importance of specific habitat types might be based on the total time an animal spends in each habitat, the number of locations that are randomly or systematically recorded in each habitat type or, in contrast, the number of times an animal enters each habitat from alternative habitats. The time that an animal spends in a particular habitat may not be equated necessarily to the value of that habitat to the species; frequent, but short visits to other habitat types may indicate a greater resource value. In addition, when sampling for home ranges, Smith et al. (1981) stated that it is important to define a large portion of the area over a relatively short observation period. This is because home ranges are really time-specific, meaning they potentially can change with season, habitat, or the animal's reproductive state. Thus, intensive sampling efforts in a specific time period

may be necessary when accurately defining a home range.

One additional concern related to sampling is movements recorded immediately following animal instrumentation and release. Such movements should be considered biased (rather than exemplary) because of the disruption created by trapping and handling. Therefore, although tracking an animal immediately following release (e.g., 1 day) may be appropriate, there should be a degree of independence used in the initial observation of habitat or home range analyses.

FIELD-TRACKING

Field-tracking first dictates that one must become an expert in capturing live, uninjured animals of the desired species, which can become a major effort in itself for some species. Secondly, we strongly recommend that those new to radio-tracking and those not using it for 2 to 3 years visit and obtain training from a state-of-the-art ongoing project. Novice radio-trackers, especially, will encounter many pitfalls and these may be avoided by such help. Also, there are new developments annually that may be useful in any radiotelemetry project.

Triangulation is the basic principle in most radio-tracking. It can be accomplished by taking bearings from two locations; the animal is assumed to be near the point where the bearings cross (the location or "fix"). Ideally, bearings should cross at about a 90° angle and be taken simultaneously by two radio communication observers and as close to the animal as possible. As the angle of interception becomes more acute and the distance from the animal to the observers increases, the locations become less accurate and the error polygon increases. For a more thorough discussion of error polygon and means of estimating radio-location errors, see Mech (1983), Lee et al. (1985), and Saltz and Alkon (1985). Considerable experience in the field is necessary to become skilled at rapidly selecting tracking locations for accurate bearings.

When learning to radio-track, one should first practice locating an activated transmitter hidden by someone else. Repetition of this "game" can most readily acquaint anyone with radio-tracking techniques and the sensitivity and capability of the equipment.

Hand Tracking

In its simplest form, field radio-tracking is done by carrying the receiver and hand-held antenna and "homing in" (walking out) on the radio-equipped animal. Proper "homing" procedures involve determining the approximate direction of the transmitter, tuning in the signal, reducing gain to minimal level, again reducing gain to minimal level, and moving in the direction of the signal. While moving toward the signal, the antenna should be waved in an approximate 120° arc, back and forth, continuing to reduce gain to a minimal level. When gain cannot be reduced further, it indicates the transmitter is nearby. If the animal has not been observed or the transmitter found, it can be located by removing the antenna, turning the gain up so it barely can be heard and, depending on signal strength, determining the location by moving the receiver toward the strongest signal. A small "locator" loop antenna also is useful for radio-tracking at close range. These locator loops are especially useful when digging transmitters from underground burrows.

"Homing" procedures have some obvious drawbacks. For example, the animal may not be observed by the biologist before it has been "pushed" or flushed from roosting, foraging, or loafing areas, and the location recorded may not reflect the habitat utilized prior to the investigator's disturbance. Care must be used to avoid these false locations and artificial or stimulated movements caused by the investigator. Some animals (such as big game, raptors, or animals that are nocturnal) are difficult to observe or approach without disturbing them. This tracking method may be relatively useless for determining movements of nocturnal animals during activity periods, but may (with care) readily be employed to determine specific daytime roosting, denning, or bedding areas during periods of inactivity. When radio-tracking large numbers of animals, hand-held equipment becomes inefficient as it may take several hours to locate some animals by "walking them out." This is especially true in inaccessible areas or in areas of dense vegetation.

With some small, relatively immobile and fossorial species (such as rodents, small birds, and reptiles), virtually all radio-tracking may be done with hand-held equipment. Hand-held tracking will always be necessary to locate and recover dead animals, animals that must be recaptured, or transmitters that have fallen off the carrier animal.

Recovery of lost transmitters or dead animals can be difficult, sometimes requiring considerable digging, use of heavy excavating equipment, or explosives. For example, black-tailed prairie dogs were recovered in South Dakota at depths of 2.5 to 3 m (8.25 to 10 ft—deepest 4.3 m [14 ft]). Also, one cannot assume that radio-equipped animals always will be in normal habitat or locations expected for that species. Finding an animal is often based on what a species is "supposed to do" rather than what it may actually do. Birds, rodents, or most any species can be taken by predators as well as legally or illegally by humans. Animals and their transmitters have been recovered in raptor nests, burrows, under

buildings, in car trunks, freezers in homes, and many other unusual locations where the animal being tracked would not be expected to venture.

Paul Hegdal

Biologist tracking using a hand-held yagi.

Vehicle Tracking

Mobile tracking stations (vehicles) allow one to reduce the antenna-to-animal distance and take advantage of topography in the area for better tracking points. Vehicle tracking can only be done if there are reasonable access routes within the study area. Mobile tracking stations (two or more), equipped with the described antenna systems, radio communication equipment, auxiliary batteries, extra lighting, and plotting tables, allow investigators to quickly search areas and follow fast-moving animals such as migrating birds in daylight or darkness. During activity, it may be especially important to obtain simultaneous bearings. Since many animals can move rapidly, false interception points may be recorded if there is a time lag between bearings. Most dual-beam antenna systems mounted on a vehicle require a minimum clearance of about 3 m (10 ft). If the study area contains wooded areas with low-hanging branches, it may be necessary to trim several kilometers of road for adequate clearance of the tracking vehicle. In areas where this is not practical, a single yagi should be mounted in a horizontal plane. This will lower clearance requirements and still give fairly reasonable bearings, provided the distance from the tracking vehicle to the animal is short when bearings are taken.

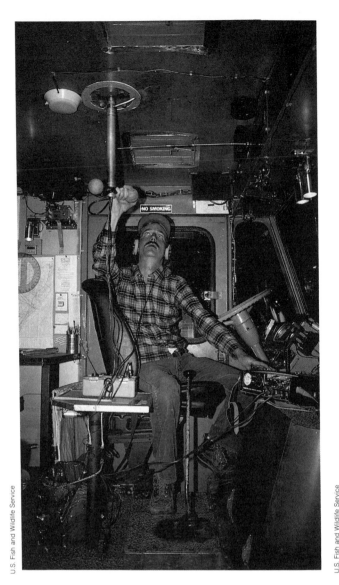

Turning directional yagi antenna from inside the tracking van.

Recording signals on plotter system.

Aerial Tracking

Usually, aerial tracking starts with searching the area for the animal's last known location, increasing altitude to 3,000 m (9,900 ft), and searching in an enlarging circle or flying swaths (20- to 50-km [12.4- to 31-mi.] wide) for complete coverage of the areas (Gilmer et al. 1981). In heavily populated areas near cities, there may be too much radio interference to fly at higher altitudes (over 500 to 1,000 m [310 to 620 ft]). Once a signal is detected, aerial tracking simply can become "homing," similar to "walking out" a radio-equipped animal (reducing gain and lowering altitude as the source of the signal).

The use of aircraft is especially important in large or inaccessible areas and with wide-ranging or migrating species. Additionally, aerial searches for missing or lost animals are usually much more efficient than ground searches. The additional height provided by aircraft greatly increases reception range. For example, our vehicle tracking system has a range of about 3 to 4 km (1.8 to 2.5 mi.) with a 7 g (0.24 oz) transmitter on a bird, while with aircraft, a 35-km (21.7-mi.) receiving range can be achieved.

The first step in aerial tracking is consulting with a certified aircraft mechanic to make sure that the antenna mounting system is certified by the Federal Aviation Administration (FAA). The biologist should be familiar with areas to be searched and review the flight, search area, and procedures with the pilot before the flight. Exact tracking procedures depend on terrain and habitat, as well as the mobility of the species being followed. Experience of the observer and pilot also can influence the efficiency of aerial tracking (Hoskinson 1976).

Yagi antenna mounting system on aircraft.

Data Recording

Radio locations need to be plotted initially on maps of an appropriate scale (U.S. Geological Survey 1:24,000) or aerial photographs (for many species, a 1:7,920-scale seems best [1 km = 12.7 cm, 1 mi = 8 in.]). A clearly defined grid coordinate system should be superimposed on the maps or photos, using acetate (5 mil thickness works well) overlays. Permanent ink felt pens should be used for marking the grid and any other permanent features, while temporary markers are best for plotting on the acetate. Our experience has indicated that black, red, green, blue, and purple are excellent colors to use. After the locations are recorded on data sheets, the temporary markings can be wiped off the acetate with a damp cloth. Our experience has shown that the Universal Transverse Mercator System (UTM; U.S. Department of the Army 1958) is ideal for most radiotelemetry studies. UTM coordinates are noted on U.S. Geological Survey maps and can be transferred to aerial photographs to create the grid coordinate system. Data then can be digitally recorded to the nearest km (0.62 mi.), 0.1 km (0.06 mi.), or even 0.001 km (0.006 mi.) as appropriate for the species. Additionally, the coordinates can be entered directly into a computer terminal for data analysis.

Figure 2 illustrates tracking forms used for recording radiotelemetry data. Observations are sequentially noted and include date, time, location, and any pertinent behavioral or habitat descriptions. Time is recorded as 0000 to 2400 hrs to prevent any possibility of errors. UTM coordinates include numerical and directional values, for example, 2760N, 824E, as explained by the U.S. Department of the Army (1958).

Problems

Radio interference can, in some locations, create difficulties. Bearings should be taken from natural high points in the area. Power lines, fences, and large buildings should be avoided since they can "bounce" radio signals and readily produce false and highly confusing bearings.

The number of biological studies using radiotelemetry has been increasing each year. For example, in 1985, over 20,000 transmitters were placed on wildlife species in the U.S. and a considerable portion of these were not authorized. In addition, some of the unauthorized frequencies being used are in the range of police or other users who are emitting very strong signals (compared to most wildlife transmitters) that can drastically interfere with anyone trying to track wildlife on these frequencies. These facts stress the importance of having the proper clearances for use of particular radio frequencies and the need to coordinate activities with telemetry users in the same area. This point becomes critical when tracking migrating birds. While tracking owls and hawks, problems have been encountered with other researchers using unauthorized transmitters on black bear. Obviously, one could be dangerously surprised "walking out" a bear while thinking it was an eastern screech owl.

Figure 2. Radio-tracking data forms.

No matter how well individuals or equipment perform, contact with some transmitters could be lost. To help locate these missing animals, aerial tracking may be necessary. In addition, receiving equipment should be left on at all times (tuned to the appropriate missing frequencies) while traveling in vehicles; missing animals are often located when least expected (frequently near their known home range). A bent transmitter antenna; the orientation of an animal's body and, thus, antenna orientation; or location of an animal in a low or structurally secluded area (such as underground) may drastically reduce reception range and thus cause the animal to essentially "disappear." Some transmitters will come off animals (or be taken off by them) and, depending where they end up, can be difficult to locate. Unfortunately, some lost transmitters are never located and no biological conclusions can be made in most of these situations.

DATA ANALYZING

Radio-tracking data may be reported in several different ways. Initial description of results usually includes the length of time that the animal carried an operating transmitter, fate of the radio-equipped individual (i.e., mortality, lost contact, dead battery), the number of data points recorded, and possibly the number of tracking periods or days. These data are helpful in relating the kind and number of observations made to the amount of tracking time and effort spent.

Enumeration data, reported in either descriptive or tabular form, include the frequency at which various events occurred or when observations were made—for example, the number of times that various types of mortality were documented or the frequency that animals were located at each type of roost or habitat type. Statistical comparisons then can be made between the frequency of habitat use and the availability of those same habitats within the range of the animal, resulting in determining habitat preferences (Johnson 1980).

Measurement data might include rates of movement (e.g., km/h), rates of habitat interception (e.g., number of locations per habitat type per hour), time spent in each habitat type (e.g., number of hours or percentage of total tracking time), distances between nest sites and foraging areas, and home range size. Home range size may be calculated several different ways. The recommended method is reviewing home range analysis techniques before deciding on any one method (Jennrich and Turner 1969; Dunn and Gipson 1977; Dixon and Chapman 1980; MacDonald et al. 1980; Anderson 1982; Hackett and Trevor-Deutsch 1982). However, most often radiotelemetry home ranges have been described as some form of a minimum area or convex polygon created by en-

compassing the recorded outermost points (see Barrett 1984; Garshelis and Garshelis 1984). Also, computer programs can be used to calculate home range size (Ford and Krumme 1979; Anderson 1982).

Presentation of radiotelemetry data in graphic form is common practice and may offer a reader a perceptive view of movements. To prepare a figure showing radiotelemetry results, tracing paper can be placed over a grid pattern of UTM coordinates marked to scale, and UTM coordinates recorded in the field can then be plotted on tracing paper. Various landmarks or habitat types can be added appropriately to emphasize relationships between locations, movement distances, and environmental features. The completed art work then can be reproduced photographically. Computer-assisted graphics also can be generated.

When diagramming radiotelemetry data, one should consider showing only those data that illustrate a particular point, rather than trying to present all or much of the data since that may not be necessary and can result in a confusing illustration. Movement data presented in graphic form may only exemplify the movement observed during any one tracking period.

Maps showing tracking data may show specific routes or sites where events such as initial capture, migration, nesting, or mortality occurred (Figure 3). Other types of graphics can include "scatter" diagrams that show the range of locations and centers of activity (Figure 4). Also, computer graphics can be particularly effective in relating centers of activity or utilization distributions (Tarter and Kronmal 1976; Anderson 1982), especially if the graphics are in three-dimensional form (Figure 5). Range overlap among conspecifics, or predator range versus that of prey, can be diagrammed and home range sizes presented clearly (Figure 6). Continuous movement patterns can illustrate the rate and directionality of movement (Figure 7), and the same radio-tracking data imposed on habitat types can show distinctly the relationships between movement patterns and particular habitat types (Figure 8). Active videographic techniques allow viewing distribution and movements of many animals in a continual, spatial, and temporal dispersion (White 1979).

Once locations are tabulated or graphically plotted, a critical aspect of a radiotelemetry study must follow, that is, interpreting the findings and answering why an animal was at a particular place at a particular time. Sanderson (1966) made an important point when he stated that researchers must shift their emphasis from concern over the movements of animals to the reasons for the movements. Sanderson (1966) continued by stating that movement patterns are established and regulated by the density of the

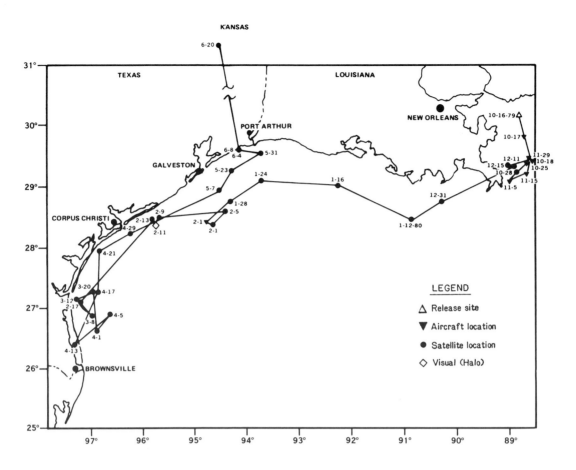

Figure 3. Movement of a loggerhead turtle radio-tracked from October 16, 1979 to June 8, 1980 in the Gulf of Mexico (from Timko and Kolz 1982).

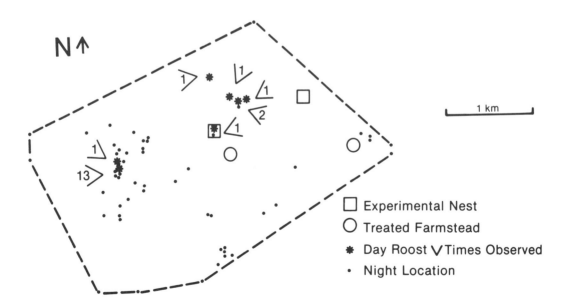

Figure 4. Range, night locations, and daytime roost sites recorded for a female common barn owl with young, 3-10 weeks old, in southwest New Jersey. The owl was radio-tracked randomly from June 2 to July 29, 1982. Dashed lines encompass outermost locations recorded (approximately 977 ha [2,250 a.]; from Colvin 1984).

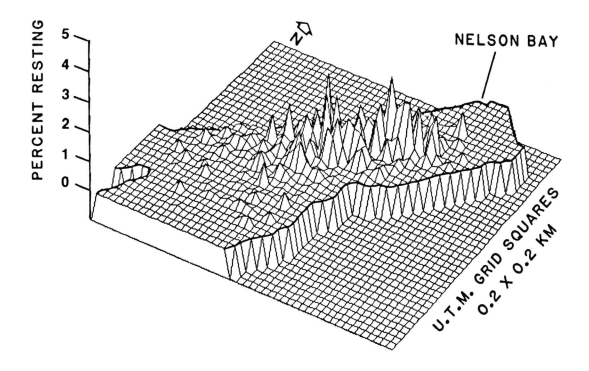

Figure 5. Distribution of resting locations (N = 1,163) of radio-tagged sea otters in Nelson Bay, a male area in Prince William Sound, Alaska, 1979-1981. Preferred rest area was near the center of the Bay (from Garshelis and Garshelis 1984).

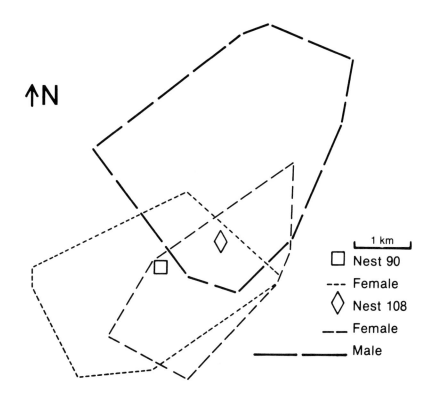

Figure 6. Home range overlap of three adult, common barn owls, radio-tracked in southwest New Jersey, June-July 1982 (from Colvin 1984).

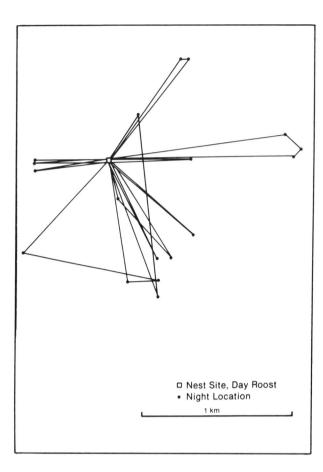

Figure 7. Pattern showing rate of movement of an adult, common male barn-owl between its nest site (3 young, 7.5 weeks old) and foraging habitats in southwest New Jersey. The owl was radio-tracked continuously 2043-2253 h on 12 August and 2107-2330 h on 13 August 1982 (total tracking time = 4 h, 33 min) (from Colvin 1984).

□ Nest Site, Day Roost
• Night Location

1 km

DISCUSSION

Although there are many positive reasons for incorporating radiotelemetry as part of a research effort, a researcher should not first decide to use radiotelemetry and then seek reasons to justify its use. A researcher should first rigorously consider the specific questions being addressed or investigated and decide whether those questions can be answered without radiotelemetry. Whether radiotelemetry is truly needed too often becomes a subjective procedure because of the attractiveness of radiotelemetry technology. Therefore, we strongly recommend that the objectives of the study, as well as the reasons for using radiotelemetry, be well-defined and associated costs and time be evaluated in relation to the type of data needed. Many other techniques for marking and studying the movements of animals are available and may be more appropriate. These include tattoos, brands, fur removal, aluminum or plastic tags or bands, neck collars, fluorescent bone marker, radioactive markers, microtaggents, and dyes (Day et al. 1980). Trap recapture or direct observation, in combination with one of the above marking techniques, may prove more appropriate than radiotelemetry given specific research designs, budgets, and personnel constraints.

To the novice, radiotelemetry may appear to be an efficient, simple, and exciting way to study wildlife. However, when considering initiation of a radiotelemetry project, even a researcher experienced in radiotelemetry is reminded of radiotelemetry's limitations and the time, cost, and technical problems that can be involved.

Radiotelemetry has been used in many specific ways in wildlife studies. Investigations of home range and general movement most commonly have been performed, and these studies actually are often the base process in the many types of wildlife research that may incorporate radiotelemetry. Home range analysis with radiotelemetry repeatedly has resulted in a much expanded view of species' home range and potential for movement than previously detected by trapping or direct observation (Taylor and Quy 1978). Basic studies of movement may focus on how movement patterns and home range size change as a function of sex and age, population density, seasons of the year, time of day, or available habitat types or habitat diversity (Mech et al. 1966; Trent and Rongstad 1974; Hemker et al. 1984).

Beyond the initial documentation of movement are important opportunities to investigate habitat use and habitat requirements and to find migration routes, wintering areas, nesting sites, and foraging areas (Marshall et al. 1962; Curtis and Braun 1983; Loft et al. 1984). Also, the positive or negative impact of various land management or land-use practices on wildlife may be discernible from radio-

species, food supply, reproductive activity, quality and physiographic arrangement of the habitat and, likely, many other factors. In other words, the total life-history strategy of a species (Stearns 1976) and both the biotic and abiotic components of its environment may have to be considered when interpreting the significance of a movement pattern or the habitat use disclosed by radiotelemetry. Therefore, background information on a species' natural history and ecology become critical in accurately interpreting movements. Additionally, detailed data on weather; availability of selected habitats or food resources; population density; and animal age, sex, and reproductive state all may be essential in evaluating movements and successfully completing the project. Certainly, radiotelemetry locations can be plotted and presented; however, the researcher who interprets the data in context with species' ecology will get the most out of the time, effort, and finances invested in radiotelemetry studies.

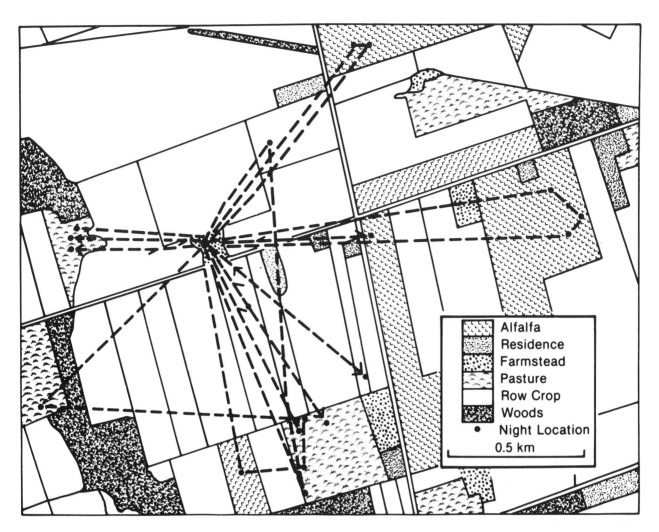

Figure 8. Movement pattern and habitats intercepted by an adult male common barn-owl with 3 young, 7.5 weeks old, in southwest New Jersey. The owl was continuously radio-tracked 2043-2253 h on 12 August and 2107-2330 h on 13 August 1982 (total tracking-time = 4 h, 33 min.) (from Colvin 1984).

equipped individuals that are subjected to a changing environment. When radio-tracking and habitat analysis are conducted in combination, a perceptive view of discrete habitat requirements and relationships between habitat and population maintenance may be achieved (Kohn and Mooty 1971; Jenkins and Starkey 1984; Pierce and Peek 1984; Riley and Dood 1984).

Examination of population dynamics, including age-specific survival rates and mortality factors, has been studied often with radiotelemetry (Stoddart 1970; Cook et al. 1971; Barrett 1984). A radio transmitter allows continued survivorship to be documented or, conversely, mortality to be documented essentially when it occurs. Thus, for example, a more accurate representation of the occurrence of various mortality factors in a population can be determined, compared to when radiotelemetry is not used, and emphasis is placed on those mortality factors that are

most easily identified (e.g., car collision). Predator-prey relationships also can be studied and provide additional insight into population dynamics (Mech 1967; Kolenosky 1972; Franzmann et al. 1980; Fuller and Keith 1980).

Radiotelemetry also provides great advantages in endangered species research because radio-equipping a single individual can potentially locate conspecifics in an efficient and non-disruptive manner (Mech 1977; Fagerstone et al. 1985). In addition, because endangered, rare, or threatened wildlife often have highly specific habitat requirements, these "micro" habitats may be more clearly and quickly identified with radiotelemetry and thus protected.

Other uses of radiotelemetry have included monitoring the status and movements of animals involved in translocations or reintroductions (Fritts et al. 1984). Also, population censusing has been conducted by determining the proportion of radio-equipped animals not observed in a direct count and adjusting the total population count upwards proportionately (Floyd et al. 1979). Additionally, vertebrate pest research often has included radiotelemetry in evaluation of movements of pest species, efficacy of wildlife control procedures on target species, and toxic hazards to non-target species (Taylor 1978; Fagerstone et al. 1981; Hegdal and Blaskiewicz 1984; Heisterberg et al. 1984). In a more specialized form, radiotelemetry has been used to investigate the physiological adaptation of free-ranging animals to their environment by remotely monitoring, for example, heart rate (Kanwisher et al. 1978; Follmann et al. 1982).

From a review of the literature, it may appear that uses of radiotelemetry are limited only by the creativity of researchers and available hardware. As the technology continues to improve, so will the opportunities to attempt new uses and to further address complex wildlife and ecological issues.

CONCLUSION

There are four major components of a radiotelemetry study:

(1) Justified use of the technology based on a specific research design;

(2) Consideration of hardware, personnel, cost, and sampling strategies;

(3) Implementation of field research and data collection; and

(4) Analysis and interpretation of data.

Each of the above components is equally important in the planning and success of a radiotelemetry study. Often, because of the specialization of these components and the time involved, a team approach is essential to adequately plan, conduct, and evaluate radiotelemetry studies. The experience of the "team" will strongly affect the efficiency, accuracy and, thus, the outcome of the project. In final form, discussion of radiotelemetry should be well-integrated with information on species biology and ecology to best understand and illustrate the role that movement, migration, and habitat use play in the life-history strategy of a species.

U.S. Fish and Wildlife Service

Radio-tagged mourning dove.

U.S. Fish and Wildlife Service

Barn owl instrumented with a transmitter and whip antenna.

LITERATURE CITED

AMLANER, C.J., Jr. 1978. Biotelemetry from free-ranging animals. Pages 205-228 *in* Stonehouse, B., ed. Animal Marking: Recognition Marking of Animals in Research. Macmillan and Company, London.

AMSTRUP, S.C. 1980. A radio-collar for game birds. J. Wildl. Manage. 44:214-217.

ANDERSON, D.J. 1982. The home range: A new nonparametric estimation technique. Ecology 63:103-112.

BARRETT, M.W. 1984. Movements, habitat use, and predation on pronghorn fawns in Alberta. J. Wildl. Manage. 48:542-550.

BRAY, O.E. and G.W. CORNER. 1972. A tail clip for attaching transmitters to birds. J. Wildl. Manage. 36:640-642.

————, R.E. JOHNSON, and A.L. KOLZ. 1975. A removable cartop antenna system for radio-tracking birds. Bird-banding 46:15-18.

BRUGGERS, R., J. ELLIS, J. SEDGWICK, and J. BOURASSA. 1981. A radio transmitter for monitoring the movements of small passerine birds. Proc. Int. Conf. Wildl. Biotelemetry 3:69-79.

————, M.M. JAEGER, and J.B. BOURASSA. 1983. The application of radiotelemetry for locating and controlling concentrations of red-billed quelea in Africa. Tropical Pest Manage. 29:27-32.

CARR, A. 1965. The navigation of the green turtle. Sci. Am. 212:79-86.

COCHRAN, W.W. 1975. Following a migrating peregrine from Wisconsin to Mexico. Hawk Chalk 14:28-37.

————. 1980. Wildlife telemetry. Pages 507-520 *in* Schemnitz, S.D., ed. Wildl. Manage. Techniques Manual. Wildl. Soc., Inc., Washington, DC.

COLVIN, B.A. 1984. Barn owl foraging behavior and secondary poisoning hazard from rodenticide use on farms. Ph.D. dissertation. Bowling Green State Univ., Bowling Green, OH. 326pp.

COOK, R.S., M.W. WHITE, D.O. TRAINER, and W.C. GLAZENER. 1971. Mortality of young white-tailed deer fawns in south Texas. J. Wildl. Manage. 35:47-56.

COVICH, A. 1977. Shapes of foraging areas used by radio-monitored crayfish. Am. Zoology 17:205 (Abstract).

CURTIS, P.D. and C.E. BRAUN. 1983. Radiotelemetry location of nesting band-tailed pigeons in Colorado. Wilson Bull. 95:464-466.

DAY, G.I., S.D. SCHEMNITZ, and R.D. TABER. 1980. Capturing and marking wild animals. Pages 61-68 *in* Schemnitz, S.D., ed. Wildl. Manage. Techniques Manual. Wildl. Soc., Inc., Washington, DC.

DIXON, K.R. and J.A. CHAPMAN. 1980. Harmonic mean measure of animal activity areas. Ecology 61:1040-1044.

DUNN, J.E. and P.S. GIPSON. 1977. Analysis of radiotelemetry data in studies of home range. Biometrics 33:85-101.

FAGERSTONE, K.A., D.E. BIGGINS, and T.M. CAMPBELL, III. 1985. Marking and tagging of black-footed ferrets (*Mustela nigripes*). Pages 10.1-10.10 *in* Anderson, S.H. and D.B. Inkley, eds. Proc. Black-footed Ferret Workshop, Sept. 18-19, Univ. Wyoming, Laramie.

————, G.H. MATSCHKE, and D. ELIAS. 1981. Radiotelemetry to evaluate effectiveness of a new fumigant cartridge for controlling ground squirrels. Proc. Int. Conf. on Wildl. Biotelemetry. Univ. Wyoming, Laramie. 3:20-25.

FITZNER, R.E. and J.N. FITZNER. 1977. A hot melt glue technique for attaching radio transmitter tail packages to raptorial birds. North Am. Bird Bander 2:56-57.

FLOYD, T.J., L.D. MECH, and M.E. NELSON. 1979. An improved method of censusing deer in deciduous-coniferous forests. J. Wildl. Manage. 43:258-261.

FOLLMANN, E.H., A.E. MANNING, and J.L. STUART. 1982. A long-range implantable heart rate transmitter for free-ranging animals. Biotelemetry Patient Monitoring 9:205-212.

FORD, R.G. and D.W. KRUMME. 1979. The analysis of space use patterns. J. Theoretical Biol. 76:125-155.

FRANZMANN, A.W., C.C. SCHWARTZ, and R.O. PETERSON. 1980. Moose calf mortality in summer on the Kenai Peninsula, Alaska. J. Wildl. Manage. 44:764-768.

FRITTS, S.H., W.J. PAUL, and L.D. MECH. 1984. Movements of translocated wolves in Minnesota. J. Wildl. Manage. 48:709-721.

FULLER, T.K. and L.B. KEITH. 1980. Wolf population dynamics and prey relationships in northeastern Alberta. J. Wildl. Manage. 44:583-602.

GARSHELIS, D.L. and J.A. GARSHELIS. 1984. Movements and management of sea otters in Alaska. J. Wildl. Manage. 48:665-678.

GILMER, D.S., L.M. COWARDIN, R.L. DUVAL, L.M. MECHLIN, C.W. SHAIFFER, and V.B. KUECHLE. 1981. Procedures for the use of aircraft in wildlife biotelemetry studies. U.S. Dep. Inter., Fish and Wildl. Serv. Resour. Publ. 140. 19pp.

————, V.B. KUECHLE, and I.J. BELL, Jr. 1971. A device for monitoring radio-marked animals. J. Wildl. Manage. 35:829-832.

HACKETT, D.F. and B. TREVOR-DEUTSCH. 1982. Radiotelemetric assessment of grid-trapping techniques in a study of the eastern chipmunk (*Tamias striatus L.*). Biotelemetry Patient Monitoring. 9:213-226.

HARRINGTON, F.H. and L.D. MECH. 1982. Patterns of homesite attendance in two Minnesota wolf packs. Pages 81-105 *in* Harrington, F.H. and P.C. Paquet, eds. Wolves of the World. Noyes, Park Ridge, NJ.

HEGDAL, P.L. and R.W. BLASKIEWICZ. 1984. Evaluation of the potential hazard to barn owls of Talon (*brodifacoum* bait) used to control rats and house mice. Environmental Toxicological Chemistry 3:167-179.

———— and T.A. GATZ. 1978. Technology of radio-tracking for various birds and mammals. Pages 204-206 *in* Symp. on Application of Remote Sensing Data to Wildlife Management. PECORA IV. Sioux Falls, SD.

HEISTERBERG, J.F., C.E. KNITTLE, O.E. BRAY, D.F. MOTT, and J.F. BESSER. 1984. Movements of radio-instrumented blackbirds and European starlings among winter roosts. J. Wildl. Manage. 48:203-211.

HEMKER, T.P., F.G. LINDZEY, and B.B. ACKERMAN. 1984. Population characteristics and movement patterns of cougars in southern Utah. J. Wildl. Manage. 48:1275-1284.

HOSKINSON, R.L. 1976. The effect of different pilots on aerial telemetry error. J. Wildl. Manage. 40:137-139.

IMBODEN, C. 1975. A brief radiotelemetry study on moreporks. Notornis 2:221-230.

JANSEN, D.K. 1982. A new potting material for radiotelemetry packages. Copeia 1982:189.

JENKINS, K.J. and E.E. STARKEY. 1984. Habitat use by Roosevelt elk in unmanaged forests of the Hoh Valley, Washington. J. Wildl. Manage. 48:642-646.

JENNRICH, R.I. and F.B. TURNER. 1969. Measurement of non-circular home range. J. Theoretical Biol. 22:227-237.

JOHNSON, D.H. 1980. The comparison of usage and availability measurements for evaluating resource preference. Ecology 61:65-71.

KANWISHER, J.W., T.C. WILLIAMS, J.M. TEAL, and K.O. LAWSON, Jr. 1978. Radiotelemetry of heart rates from free-ranging gulls. Auk 95:288-293.

KENWARD, R.E., G.J. HIRONS, and F. ZIESEMER. 1982. Devices for telemetering the behavior of free-living birds. Pages 127-129 in Cheesman, C.L. and R.B. Mitson, eds. Telemetric Studies of Vertebrates. Zoological Soc. London Symp. 49.

KEUCHLE, V.B., D.P. DEMASTER, and D.B. SINIFF. 1979. State of the art of and needs of the earth platform. Proc. Int. Symp. Remote Sensing Environment 13:505-518.

KOHN, B.E. and J.J. MOOTY. 1971. Summer habitat of white-tailed deer in north-central Minnesota. J. Wildl. Manage. 35:476-487.

KOLENOSKY, G.B. 1972. Wolf predation on wintering deer in east-central Ontario. J. Wildl. Manage. 36:357-369.

KOLZ, A.L. 1975. Mortality-sensing wildlife transmitters. Int. ISA Biomedical Sci. Instrument Symp. 12:57-60.

———, J.W. LENTFER, and H.G. FALLEK. 1980. Satellite radio-tracking of polar bears instrumented in Alaska. Pages 743-752 in Amlaner, C.J., Jr. and D.W. MacDonald, eds. A Handbook on Biotelemetry and Radio-Tracking. Pergamon Press, Oxford.

LEE, J.E., G.C. WHITE, R.A. GARROTT, R.M. BARTMANN, and A.W. ALLDREDGE. 1985. Accessing accuracy of a radiotelemetry system for estimating animal locations. J. Wildl. Manage. 49:658-663.

LOFT, E.R., J.W. MENKE, and T.S. BURTON. 1984. Seasonal movements and summer habitats of female black-tailed deer. J. Wildl. Manage. 48:1317-1325.

MACDONALD, D.W., F.G. BALL, and N.G. HOUGH. 1980. The evaluation of home range size and configuration using radio-tracking data. Pages 405-424 in Amlaner, C.J., Jr. and D.W. MacDonald, eds. A Handbook on Biotelemetry and Radio-Tracking. Pergamon Press, Oxford.

MADISON, D.M. 1978. Movement indicators of reproductive events among female meadow voles as revealed by radiotelemetry. J. Mammal. 59:835-843.

MARSHALL, W.H., G.W. GULLION, AND R.G. SCHWAB. 1962. Early summer activities of porcupines as determined by radio-positioning techniques. J. Wildl. Manage. 26(1):75-79.

——— and J.J. KUPA. 1963. Development and use of radio-telemetry techniques for ruffed grouse studies. Trans. North Am. Wildl. Nat. Resour. Conf. 28:443-456.

MECH, L.D. 1967. Telemetry as a technique in the study of predation. J. Wildl. Manage. 31:492-496.

———. 1977. Productivity, mortality, and population trend in wolves from northeastern Minnesota. J. Mammal. 58:559-574.

———. 1983. Handbook of animal radio-tracking. Univ. Minnesota Press, Minneapolis. 107pp.

———, R.C. CHAPMAN, W.W. COCHRAN, L. SIMMONS, and U.S. SEAL. 1984. A radio-triggered anesthetic-dart collar for recapturing free-ranging mammals. Wildl. Soc. Bull. 12:69-74.

———, K.L. HEEZEN, and D.B. SINIFF. 1966. Onset and cessation of activity in cottontail rabbits and snowshoe hares in relation to sunset and sunrise. Animal Behavior 14:410-413.

MERSON, M.H., R.E. BYERS, and L.D. LETA. 1982. A portable antenna base for fixed-station, radio-tracking. Wildl. Soc. Bull. 10:44-45.

NICHOLLS, T.H. and D.W. WARNER. 1972. Barred owl habitat use as determined by radiotelemetry. J. Wildl. Manage. 36:213-224.

OSGOOD, D.W. 1970. Thermoregulation in water snakes studied by telemetry. Copeia 1970:568-571.

PIERCE, J.D. and J.M. PEEK. 1984. Moose habitat use and selection patterns in north-central Idaho. J. Wildl. Manage. 48:1335-1343.

RILEY, S.J. and A.R. DOOD. 1984. Summer movements, home range, habitat use, and behavior of mule deer fawns. J. Wildl. Manage. 48:1302-1310.

SALTZ, D. and P.U. ALKON. 1985. A simple computer-aided method for estimating radio-location error. J. Wildl. Manage. 49:664-668.

SANDERSON, G.C. 1966. The study of mammal movements—a review. J. Wildl. Manage. 30:215-235.

SCHUBAUER, J.P. 1981. A reliable radiotelemetry tracking system suitable for studies of Chelonians. J. Herpetology 15:117-120.

SMITH, G.J., J.R. CARY, and O.J. RONGSTAD. 1981. Sampling strategies for radio-tracking coyotes. Wildl. Soc. Bull. 9:88-93.

STEARNS, S.C. 1976. Life-history tactics: A review of the ideas. Quarterly Review Biol. 51:1-45.

STODDART, L.C. 1970. A telemetric method for detecting jackrabbit mortality. J. Wildl. Manage. 34:501-507.

TARTER, M.E. and R.A. KRONMAL. 1976. An introduction to the implementation and theory of nonparametric density estimation. Am. Statistician 30:105-112.

TAYLOR, K.D. 1978. Range of movement and activity of common rats (Rattus norvegicus) on agricultural land. J. Applied Ecol. 15:663-677.

——— and R.J. QUY. 1978. Long-distance movements of a common rat (Rattus norvegicus) revealed by radio-tracking. Mammalia 42:63-71.

TIMKO, R.E. and A.L. KOLZ. 1982. Satellite sea turtle tracking. Marine Fish. Review 44:19-24.

TRENT, T.T. and O.J. RONGSTAD. 1974. Home range and survival of cottontail rabbits in southwestern Wisconsin. J. Wildl. Manage. 38:459-472.

U.S. DEPARTMENT OF THE ARMY. 1958. Universal Transverse Mercator Grid. Technical Manual TM 5-241-8. U.S. Govt. Printing Office 1969-390-947/404. 66pp.

VERTS, B.J. 1963. Equipment and techniques for radio-tracking striped skunks. J. Wildl. Manage. 27:325-339.

WHITE, G.C. 1979. Computer-generated movies to display biotelemetry data. Proc. Int. Conf. Wildl. Biotelemetry 2:210-214.

WINTER, J.D., V.B. KUECHLE, D.B. SINIFF, and J.R. TESTER. 1978. Equipment and methods for radio-tracking freshwater fish. Misc. Rep. 152. Agric. Experiment Station, Univ. Minnesota.

WOLCOTT, T.G. 1980. Optical and radio optical techniques for tracking nocturnal animals. Pages 333-338 in Amlaner, C.J., Jr. and D.W. MacDonald, eds. A Handbook on Biotelemetry and Radio-Tracking. Pergamon Press, Oxford.

34

FOOD HABITS

Allen Y. Cooperrider

U.S. Bureau of Land Management
Service Center
Denver, CO 80225

"Food is the burning question in animal society, and the whole structure and activities of the community are dependent upon questions of food supply."

—Charles Elton, from *Animal Ecology*

Editor's Note: An adequate food supply is one of the most basic habitat requirements of all species. Therefore, some understanding of food habits is a prerequisite to evaluating habitat and providing good habitat management. Similarly, forage utilization is an important factor in habitat monitoring. The two closely related topics are discussed in this chapter, emphasizing herbivore food habits and vegetation utilization.

INTRODUCTION

Measuring food habits and forage utilization may appear to be rather specialized monitoring techniques; however, such information is frequently required in monitoring studies, particularly when working with herbivores. These animals are capable of destroying, damaging, or altering their habitat through overgrazing or overbrowsing. Such impacts may affect not only the species itself but many others as well. Similarly, the species responsible for the damage may be either a wild or domestic ungulate, or combinations of one or more of these. On public lands of western North America, where many species of wild and domestic ungulates coexist on ranges being managed for multiple uses, information on forage utilization and food habits can be quite valuable.

Furthermore, the need for an understanding of food habits of species other than ungulates will probably increase. Twenty years ago, Gullion (1966) suggested the importance of understanding food habits of game birds. Today, biologists are charged with managing hundreds of vertebrate species, of which the majority of food habits are largely unknown.

In this chapter, I describe methods for measuring food habits and forage utilization, discuss problems associated with such measurements, and present and evaluate methods of analyzing such data. This chapter emphasizes techniques for herbivores since these are more commonly required in monitoring studies by management biologists. Techniques for omnivores and carnivores are covered briefly and reference is made to publications with more detailed information on this subject. Similarly, techniques for measuring forage utilization will be described in less detail than those for food habits since utilization techniques are well-described in numerous, readily available publications.

In the literature on subjects such as food habits, forage selection, preference, and utilization have been used quite loosely and even interchangeably. More seriously, this has often resulted in biologists confusing concepts and stating erroneous conclusions. In particular, workers have confused food habits or diet with forage preference. To avoid further confusion, I therefore begin with brief definitions of each of these measurements.

Food habits or diets refer to the actual foods that are eaten by one or more animals of the same species during a given season or time period within a defined geographic area. Thus, food habits are characteristic of an animal species, but only for a given time and place; extrapolation of food habit data to other times and regions, without supplementary data, is frequently misleading. Food habits are typically expressed as percentages of the overall diet, which consists of each individual food item (plant or animal species or species group; Figure 1); this is the most useful and easily interpretable measure. The percentages may be by weight or volume depending on the technique. Usually the two are pretty well correlated; however, food habits are also sometimes reported as a frequency (percentage of samples containing each food item) or, more rarely, as the weight of each food item in the daily (or seasonal) diet.

Forage utilization refers to the amount of vegetation (or food supply) removed by foraging animals from a defined area of land during a defined period. Utilization measurements are rarely made except on plant forages, although the same principles apply. They are thus attributes of the land, vegetation, or food supply and not of an animal or species of animal. Utilization measurements are usually expressed as the percentage of the available forage or annual forage production removed during a given season or year (Figure 2). They may be broken down by plant species or group and the percentage may be by weight or volume.

Forage utilization may also be expressed in a variety of other ways such as the percentage of plants or twigs that are grazed or browsed, or the height of grazed down plants. In practice, this utilization may be attributed to one species of animal or to several. When several species of large herbivores occupy the same range at the same time, determining the relative amount used by each animal could be difficult or even impossible.

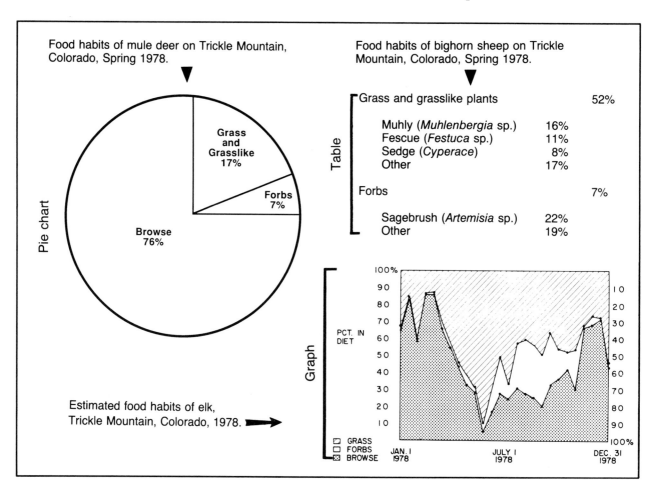

Figure 1. Food habits refer to the percentage of each forage species, items, or classes in the diet for a given period and location. These habits may be depicted in a pie chart, table, or graph.

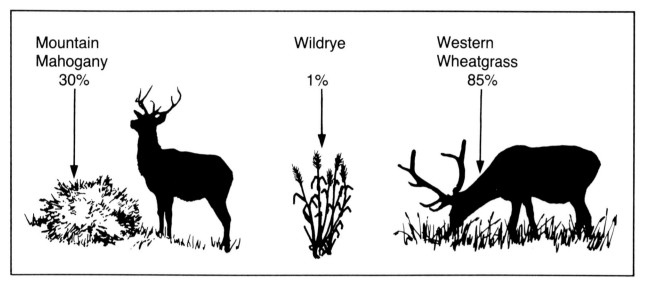

| Mountain Mahogany 30% | Wildrye 1% | Western Wheatgrass 85% |

Figure 2. Forage utilization refers to the percentage of annual production used by one or more animals.

The total amount of forage produced on an area during a given year or season is called forage production. This production may be used synonymously with availability or corrected for forage physically or seasonally unavailable to animals for various reasons. Measurement of forage production and availability are not described in this book in any detail because they are covered elsewhere (U.S. Department of the Interior, Bureau of Land Management 1984). However, they have been introduced here to clarify the concept of forage.

In contrast, forage preference is the relative degree to which animals select one forage species over another. It is thus an attribute of an animal or species. However, to quantify this variable, both food supply and food habits need to be measured. The simplest measurement of forage preference is the percentage ratio of a given food item in the diet to the entire food supply (available forage) that is present (Table 1). Clearly, both measurements must occur at the same time and in the same geographical area. (Food items with preference values greater than 1 are preferred.) The important concept to remember is that food habits are not synonymous with forage preference even though they are often treated the same in much of the older wildlife and range management literature. Put simply, forage preference is what an animal likes to eat; food habits are what it actually eats. For further discussion on this see Petrides (1975).

MEASUREMENT OF FORAGE UTILIZATION

Two basic procedures are available for determining forage utilization: (1) difference methods and (2) grazed-plant methods. Since many variations on these techniques have been developed and used, no single technique can be prescribed as "best."

Rather, the investigator will have to determine the most appropriate and efficient method for the problem at hand.

Difference Methods

Difference methods require estimating the amount of forage or herbage produced with and without grazing. The difference then is used to estimate the amount used. Estimates can be obtained in two different ways: single plots, before and after grazing, and paired plots, one grazed the other not.

In the before-and-after approach, the amount of forage is estimated or measured on an area before and after a grazing period or season. Any acceptable technique for measuring or estimating forage production can be used; however, variances in the estimates of differences can be reduced substantially by using permanent or marked plots for both measurements. In this case, the first (before) measurement cannot be made by using a removal method such as clipping. To reduce variances in utilization estimates, yet still use clipping methods, many workers have used paired plots. Using this method, a series of paired plots are selected that appear to be similar in species composition and total forage. One plot is then selected randomly for clipping prior to grazing; the other is clipped at the end of the season.

In the paired plot approach, cages or other exclosures are used to estimate ungrazed forage. Before the grazing season or period, paired plots with similar species composition and total forage production are selected, and one or the other plot is randomly chosen to be caged or excluded from grazing. At the end of the grazing period, the amount of forage on

Table 1. Forage production, food habits, and forage preference of bighorn sheep on Trickle Mountain, Colorado, 1978 (from Bailey and Cooperrider 1982).

Vegetation	Percent of Forage Production	Percent in Diet of Bighorn Sheep	Preference Index for Bighorn Sheep
GRASS			
Arizona fescue (*Festuca arizonica*)	12	7	0.58
Blue grama (*Boutelova gracilis*)	15	4	0.26
Muhly (*Muhlenbergia* sp.)	11	10	0.91
Sedge (*Cyperaceal*)	4	5	1.25
Other	11	12	0.92
FORBS	41	6	0.15
BROWSE			
Rabbitbrush (*Chrysothamnus* sp.)	3	*	<0.01
Sagebrush (*Artemisia* sp.)	1	25	25.00
Saltbrush (*Atriplex* sp.)	*	11	>100.00
True Mountain Mahogany (*Cercocarpus* sp.)	*	6	>100.00
Other	2	14	7.00

Note: The preference index is calculated by dividing percent in diet by percent of forage production.   * = trace

both the ungrazed and grazed plot are measured or estimated through clipping or other appropriate methods.

Both types of difference methods have problems and pitfalls. Obtaining good estimates of forage production is time-consuming and expensive. If measurements have to be made twice, then the costs in time and money increase. Furthermore, forage production estimates will yield even less precision. Forage production estimates are rarely better than within ± 10%. Therefore, difference methods should not be used unless utilization is expected to be high (50% or more). Difference methods thus may be good for determining high rates of utilization (50% to 100%), or for determining if utilization is high or not. These methods, however, are not particularly good for determining small differences in utilization, for example, distinguishing between 40% and 50% utilization.

Grazed-Plant Methods

Grazed-plant methods are used for both herbaceous plants and woody plants, but plants are examined only at the end of the grazing season. These methods fall into three general categories:

(1) frequency methods,

(2) height or length conversion methods, and

(3) form-class or ocular estimates.

Frequency methods require the biologist to count a number of plants to determine how many have been grazed or not. Previously developed regression tables can then be used to convert the percentage of grazed plants to percentage of utilization (Cook and Stubbendieck 1986). Alternatively, the average weight of grazed portions can be determined and used to calculate utilization (U.S. Department of the Interior, Bureau of Land Management 1984:21). This technique can also be used with browse species by counting the number of unbrowsed and browsed leaders.

Height or length conversion methods require the biologist to determine the average height that herbaceous species have been grazed or the average remaining leader-length for browse species. These measurements are then converted into percentage of

Measuring browse plant leader-length.

utilization through previously developed tables or regression equations (Cook and Stubbendieck 1986; U.S. Department of the Interior, Bureau of Land Management 1984).

Form-class or ocular measurements are used primarily with browse species. They are subjective, requiring judgments about the degree of past or current browsing of individual browse plants based on their shapes. These judgments are then used to infer the degree of utilization.

Problems with Utilization Techniques

Techniques for determining forage utilization are not precise, even though many methods are relatively time-consuming and expensive. Furthermore, the accuracy of most methods is limited because of factors such as regrowth of grazed plants, loss of forage from factors other than grazing, and many other causes. For a discussion of some of these factors see Martin (1970), Cook and Stubbendieck (1986), and Pieper (1978).

Because of the high variances, many biologists prefer utilization measurements of only a few plant species known to be key forages. Good estimates on a few key species are usually preferable to poor estimates on many, particularly if the key species are chosen carefully and judiciously. See U.S. Department of the Interior, Bureau of Land Management (1984) for a discussion on choice of key species.

In general, utilization measurements may be useful in answering general questions such as "Are perennial grasses being overused on summer ranges?"; "Is bitterbrush being used heavily in the fall by mule deer (*Odocoileus hemionus*)?"; or "Are the elk (*Cervus elaphus*) using grass or browse on the winter range?" They are not, however, very useful in determining slight variations in levels of utilization. Furthermore, some questions such as the last one above can be answered more easily and cheaply by food habit studies rather than utilization studies. The biologist must determine on a case-by-case basis which type of study and particular method will be most appropriate and efficient in terms of time and money.

MEASUREMENT OF FOOD HABITS

This section concentrates on techniques applicable to estimating herbivore diets. However, parallel techniques for carnivores are mentioned as appropriate.

Food habits of wild animals can be determined through three basic methods:

(1) direct or indirect observation of the animal,

(2) stomach or rumen analysis, and

(3) fecal analysis.

Direct or Indirect Observation

Direct observation of animals has been used with varying success for many years to estimate diets of free-ranging or tame animals (Neff 1974; Wallmo et al. 1973; Riney 1982). Feeding on individual food items is quantified as "bite counts" or "feeding minutes," resulting in data which are then converted, with or without correction factors, to percentage in the diet. It requires equipment no more complicated than binoculars (or spotting scopes) and a field notebook. This method can be extremely time-consuming, however, particularly if animals are difficult to locate or difficult to approach without flushing them. The technique works best with diurnal or crepuscular animals that occupy relatively open habitat because biologists can approach them close enough to observe their feeding habits without causing them to leave. Few animals meet all these criteria, although the technique has been successful with animals like bighorn sheep (*Ovis* sp.) and in National Parks and other areas where animals become accustomed to the near presence of human observers.

Because of the difficulty in locating and observing animals, some biologists have preferred to work with tame, semi-tame, or constrained animals. Typically, these animals are raised in captivity so they are accustomed to humans. To determine food habits, the animals are taken to an area and allowed to forage. The biologist then stays near the animal and observes what it eats. There are two potential problems with using tame animals: differences between tame and wild animals and cost.

Food habits of tame animals may be different from those of wild animals due to (1) previous dietary experience; (2) nutritional status immediately before a foraging trial (e.g., if the animal has a full stomach or has been starved before the trial); and (3) choice of a feeding site/foraging area by the captors rather than the animal. Some believe these differences can be overcome. However, use of tame animals remains an expensive method for measuring food habits and will probably be too expensive in most management (as opposed to research) situations.

The precision and accuracy of data from direct observation of animals have been questioned by some biologists. However, some believe that direct observation is not only adequate for management but is adequate for measuring food habits and establishing a standard to measure the accuracy of alternative techniques (Gill et al. 1983).

An alternative method of animal observation is the "feeding site" examination. This technique is similar in many ways to the utilization methods previously described, except the measurement obtained is food habits rather than forage utilization. Basically, animals are located in the field; then the exact location where the animal has been feeding is examined and the plants or twigs grazed are tallied. The number of plants of each species that have been grazed is then converted into a percentage to provide an estimate of the food habits of the animal. Such feeding can be relatively easy to observe in some situations, such as when animals are pawing through fresh snow to eat plants. This can also be done while trailing animals. At other times, accurately determining what the animal has eaten can be extremely difficult, if not impossible. Like other observation methods, feeding site examinations can be very time-consuming.

Direct observation or feeding-site observations are used primarily with herbivores. However, Riney (1982:132) suggests that direct observation is also easy with larger carnivores. In North America, large carnivores are rarely found in high enough densities such that direct observation would be feasible. Similar problems arise with smaller mammals as well as most bird, reptile, and amphibian species. A notable exception is diurnal raptors at nest sites. In this case, forages brought to nest sites by parent birds can be observed relatively easily and recorded, providing an estimate of food habits during the important nesting season.

Stomach or Rumen Analyses

Stomach or rumen analyses have frequently been used to determine food habits. The technique has been used on virtually every major group of vertebrates ranging from songbirds and small rodents to moose and elephants. Stomach or rumen samples are taken from animals that have been killed, or obtained in other ways; the contents are then analyzed in the field or sent to a laboratory for later analysis. Medin (1970) and Korschgen (1980) describe the basic technique in detail, including preservation of materials and identification of food items. Food habits can then be determined and quantified by (1) tabulating numbers of each food item, (2) tabulating frequency of occurrence of food items, (3) measuring volume, or (4) measuring weight.

Microscopic techniques, including the microhistological technique of Sparks and Malechek (1968) and the microscope-point technique of Heady and Van Dyne (1965) have also been used, primarily with herbivores.

Stomach samples create major problems in that they normally require shooting or otherwise sacrificing animals. In addition to being time-consuming, shooting animals for the sole purpose of studying their food habits is rarely warranted, at least with the larger or more economically important animals or with any rare or endangered species.

Recently, fistula techniques have been developed to remove forage samples from the rumen or esophagus of captive ungulates without killing them. This allows multiple samples to be taken from the same animal. These techniques were developed primarily by range and animal scientists working with livestock, but have been used successfully with only a few species of wildlife. Although the technique is useful in research, the time and money required to raise and keep fistulated animals prohibit this technique from being used to obtain information for routine land and wildlife management.

Fecal Analysis

Fecal analysis has been used more for estimating range herbivore food habits in the past 10 years than any other procedure (Holechek et al. 1982a). This happened in spite of the fact that the accuracy of the technique has been seriously questioned. The procedure is similar to stomach analyses except that a fecal sample rather than a stomach sample is collected.

In the laboratory, microscopic techniques are normally used to sample herbivores, whereas macroscopic techniques are used for carnivores. The techniques for identifying food items in the laboratory are the same ones used for stomach samples and, therefore, have the same advantages and disadvantages in terms of time, cost, precision, and accuracy. Typically, the management biologist need not learn how to perform the laboratory analyses, since nonprofit regional laboratories will perform the analyses at cost. As with many types of specialized laboratory techniques, it is usually more efficient for the management biologist to pay for such work than to try to do it independently.

Cooperrider et al. (1982) describe field procedures for herbivores, and Korschgen (1980) describes the macroscopic techniques for carnivores as well as herbivores.

Even though the fecal analysis technique for use with herbivores has been criticized (see Holechek et al. 1982a; Gill et al. 1983), the technique has some important advantages. Holechek et al. (1982a) list the following seven advantages:

- It does not interfere with the normal habits of animals.

- It permits practically unlimited sampling.

- It places no restriction on animal movement.

- It has particular value where animals range over mixed communities.

- It is the only feasible procedure to use when studying secretive and/or endangered species.

- It can be used to compare the diets of two or more animals at the same time.

- Actual sampling requires very little equipment.

In addition to these important considerations, Cooperrider et al. (1982) suggest that the technique is relatively cost-effective and is a practical technique for management biologists working in government agencies.

Holechek et al. (1982a), reviewing the many criticisms of the technique to that date, compiled a similar list of disadvantages of the fecal analysis technique for herbivores and concluded that inaccuracy is the greatest overall limitation. More recently, Gill et al. (1983) reiterated this criticism and suggested that the technique be critically evaluated.

Fecal analysis techniques are commonly used with carnivores, both large and small. Such use has generated far less criticism and controversy, although the accuracy of such procedures is not well known either. Before discussing accuracy, I will discuss the nature of diets of wild animals since this has an important bearing on both accuracy and precision, as well as the way such data are used.

VARIABILITY IN FOOD HABITS OF WILD ANIMALS

A common misconception of novice biologists and lay persons is that food habits of wild animals are rigid or fixed. Statements like "mule deer eat bitterbrush in winter" or "elk are grass-eaters" are quite common. Many similar statements can be found in scientific literature. Such statements tend to oversimplify the real situation.

Most vertebrate animals are opportunistic in their feeding habits and are capable of eating and surviving on a wide variety of foods. This is in contrast to insects, for example, many of which have become adapted to feeding on only one or a few closely related plant or animal species.

Animals have limitations imposed by the structure of their digestive tracts and their ability to locate, capture, or ingest adequate quantities of certain foods. Coyotes cannot survive on dry grass, and horses do not thrive by eating crickets. Nevertheless, a herbivore such as Rocky Mountain mule deer has been reported in 99 separate studies to eat over 700 different plant species (Kufeld et al. 1973).

Given the opportunistic nature of most vertebrates, particularly of most North American herbivores, and the diversity of habitats and environmental conditions that these animals are exposed to over their geographic ranges, it is not surprising that food habits vary greatly in time and space. Cooperrider et al. (1980), for example, have demonstrated that food habits of one bighorn sheep herd vary significantly between seasons, sites, and years. Differences between regions are likely to be even greater. Although these sorts of phenomena have not been analyzed explicitly for many carnivores, the diversity of the food habits data reported suggests that the same is true for many of these species. Food habits of animals are not an attribute of a species, but rather a species in a given locality during a specific time. Extrapolation of food habit data to other populations, localities, or times may be very misleading.

On the other hand, vertebrate feeding is far from random. Overwhelming data suggest that animals of the same species have similar if not identical preferences for food items. Thus forage preference as opposed to food habits, to a certain extent, is an attribute of an animal species. The prime determinants of food habits, what the animal actually eats, are forage availability and forage preference.

Forage availability is quite different from site to site; and changes over time from removal, phenology, weather, and other factors account for much of the variation in food habits. Given that forage preference is an attribute of an animal species and that it together with forage availability are the prime determinant of food habits, two important conclusions can be drawn. First, if forage preferences and forage availability are known or estimated, a biologist should be able to predict, albeit very crudely, food habits for a given site or range. Second, if food habits for a species are known for an area, then food habits should be the same in areas with similar forage availability. Both types of inferences require some initial estimation of food habits, however.

ACCURACY AND PRECISION OF FOOD HABIT MEASUREMENTS

The question of accuracy and precision of food habit techniques continues to be argued, yet few investigators give the subject enough priority or expend much effort in testing the techniques. However, in fairness, testing the accuracy of a technique is extremely difficult without having a "standard" technique that all investigators agree is both accurate and precise and from which other techniques can be evaluated. Even the obvious solution of feeding animals by hand can introduce biases, in addition to being costly and time-consuming. Therefore, there are few conclusions about accuracy and precision of given techniques that all biologists will agree upon. The reader who wants or needs to pursue the subject further is encouraged to investigate the literature. Holechek et al. (1982a, 1984) provide a good review of techniques for herbivores.

All three techniques (observation, stomach or rumen analysis, and fecal analysis) have limited accuracy. Direct observations can be deceptive because the number of "bites" or the time spent feeding on a given plant relative to the total bites or time may not be directly proportional to the percentage by weight of a species that is ingested. Problems with tame animals have already been discussed. For further discussion see Wallmo et al. (1973) and Wallmo and Neff (1970).

Stomach and fecal analyses have limited accuracy for basically the same reasons. The items counted or sampled from stomachs or feces may not reflect the proportion by weight in the diet. In all three cases, correction factors have been developed to adjust these figures. The development and use of these correction factors, however, continues to be more of an art than a science since they are frequently not written down, recorded, or reported in the literature. Thus it is difficult to replicate results.

Technical error, of course, is always a concern and can be a problem with any of these techniques. Field biologists have tried to at least check technical or other types of errors with stomach and fecal analyses by sending in replicate samples, i.e., two samples drawn from the same stomach, rumen, pellet group, etc. This is a good recommended practice; however, the biologist should be cautious about interpreting such information when it is returned. Many biologists have sent replicate samples to a laboratory and, after receiving results that were not "the same," have rejected the technique.

Determining if results are "the same" requires knowledge of the normal variation among samples. Whenever sampling from a "population" (in the statistical sense), results are expected to be different. Most food habit techniques, including microhistological, involve some sort of sampling; two analyses of the same sample should not be expected to be exactly the same. Depending on the precision of the technique and sampling error, results may be quite different. There are statistical procedures to determine the probability that two samples are really "different" providing one has estimates of variance or can obtain them. In summary, a basis for determining whether replicate samples are "the same" or "not the same" should be established before a technique is rejected or accepted, based upon such evidence.

The problem of accuracy will remain until sufficient studies are devoted to quantifying the problem. In the meantime, biologists must judge subjectively or intuitively if accuracy of a technique is within reasonable limits. Management biologists must also judge if the technique will be accepted or if the results will be deemed credible by the managers, agencies, courts, etc., that will be using, reviewing, or making decisions based on such information. The accuracy of the fecal analysis technique for herbivores has been criticized more than others, yet many of the most vocal critics have continued to use it and publish papers based on its use. As mentioned earlier, it is also the most widely used method, and results from such analyses have stood up in court hearings.

Knowledge of the precision of most techniques is also quite limited, although it is easier to quantify and evaluate. The subject is complicated by considerations of the level of precision needed. More specifically, the basic sampling unit is usually one stomach sample, one pellet group, or one day or session of bite counts. All of these more or less estimate the diet of an animal for 1 or 2 days. This daily diet can usually be estimated with good precision; however, the "daily diet" of one animal is not usually of much interest to management.

An animal's diet may change drastically from day to day, drainage to drainage, animal to animal, etc. Therefore, what is usually of interest is the seasonal or monthly food habits of a herd or some other logical grouping of individuals. Reasonable precision in estimating this can usually be obtained if the biologist can obtain enough samples. With fecal samples, this is usually not a problem, but with techniques that require killing or fistulating animals, it may be difficult or even impossible. Dearden et al. (1975), Cooperrider et al. (1982), and Holechek and Vavra (1983) discuss precision of microhistological and fistula estimates of herbivore food habits.

In deciding if accuracy and precision are within acceptable limits, the biologist must keep clearly in mind the reason data are being collected and the purpose of these data. Precision and accuracy required or feasible for management generally are not as stringent as those required for research. Similarly, precision and accuracy required to obtain preliminary insight into range utilization and foraging dynamics may be much less than for a statistically sound monitoring program. For example, a few fecal samples of deer and elk may be collected and analyzed to select plant species for intensive monitoring of utilization on winter range. Insight gained from limited, slightly inaccurate data may be quite helpful in focusing a monitoring project on relevant problems.

USE AND INTERPRETATION OF FOOD HABITS AND FORAGE UTILIZATION DATA

Because food habits or forage utilization data are rarely useful by themselves, the ways such data are used (and misused) in monitoring programs and in influencing management decisions are discussed below.

Forage utilization data are principally used to determine whether key plant species are being overused. If such a determination is made and more than one major herbivore is present on the range, then further study will be required to determine relative use by various species. This can be done with food habit studies or, if the animals are present at different times or seasons, it can be done with more detailed utilization studies.

In some cases, biologists attempt to use utilization measurements to make inferences about food habits. This procedure can be awkward and inaccurate for several reasons, even where only one principal herbivore is present on the range (Martin 1970; Cook and Stoddart 1953). For example, annual forbs may constitute a significant portion of the herbivores' diet, but if the forbs have already dried up and disappeared at the time utilization studies are conducted, such studies will not detect them and inferences about food habits will be inaccurate. If food habits need to be determined, a technique for measuring food habits should be chosen.

Food habits data have two principal uses: (1) determination of the adequacy of the habitat to supply food of sufficient quality and (2) analysis of competition for forage between two or more sympatric species.

Biologists cannot determine the adequacy of the forage supply from knowledge of food habits alone. They must know something about the nutritional

quality of the forage and the nutritional requirements of the animal. In some cases, subjective knowledge may be adequate. For example, if winter food habits indicate bighorn sheep are eating primarily winterfat and fringed sagebrush, and these are both known to be good nutritious winter forages, then the biologist can reasonably infer that the diet is adequate. In other cases, measurements of nutritional content of the plants may have to be obtained. The whole area of nutritional analysis is beyond the scope of this chapter; for herbivores, a reader interested in pursuing the subject is referred to several good books and publications on the subject reviewed and listed in Zarn (1981) and Holechek et al. (1982b).

Whether a diet is good or adequate does not mean that range conditions are good. Animals could be receiving an adequate diet while severely overusing many plant species on the range. To determine this, the biologist needs information on animal densities, forage production, or forage utilization.

Similarly, food habit data alone are not adequate to determine competition for forage. Forage competition refers to common use of forage by two or more animal species, and dual use of forages that are limiting factors for one or more of the animal species. Food habits of sympatric species are commonly compared by investigating dietary overlap or similarity. Dietary overlap is quantified using similarity indexes such as shown in Table 2. High dietary overlap is often used as evidence of severe competition for forage, and similarly low overlap is used to suggest absence of forage competition. These inferences may be unwarranted depending on additional data.

High overlap in forage use in a noncompetitive situation can occur on a range with an abundance of forage preferred by two species. Conversely, low overlap with severe competition can occur where one animal species uses preferred and limited forages in an area before a second animal species arrives. This situation, sequential competition, can occur when cattle occupy a range in summer that is used by wild ungulates in winter. If the cattle remove the preferred, presumably highest quality, forage for the wild ungulates, overlap in food habits can be low while competition for forage, extreme.

Both of these uses of food habit data point to the value of understanding forage preference. A biologist can, without great risk, infer that forage preference is well-correlated with nutritional value. Those species that are preferred generally contain the highest levels of basic nutrients such as digestible energy or digestible protein. If an animal is primarily eating forages that are known to be highly preferred by that species, a biologist may infer that the diet is good. Similarly, if two animal species are present on the

Table 2. Dietary overlap between bighorn sheep and cattle, Trickle Mountain, Colorado, 1978 (from Bailey and Cooperrider 1982).

Vegetation	Percent of Forage in Cattle Diet	Percent of Forage in Bighorn Sheep Diet	Dietary Overlap
GRASSES AND GRASSLIKE PLANTS			
Fescue (*Festuca* sp.)	17	7	7
Muhly (*Muhlenbergia* sp.)	14	10	10
Sedge (*Cyperaceal*)	16	5	5
Wheatgrass (*Agropyron* sp.)	21	0	0
Other	19	11	11
FORBS	4	6	4
BROWSE			
Sagebrush (*Artemisia* sp.)	2	25	2
Saltbrush (*Atriplex* sp.)	0	11	0
Other	7	14	7

Note: Dietary overlap determined by taking the lesser of the two figures in each row as circled; total dietary overlap is 46%.

same range and are using large quantities of a forage item that is in short supply and that is a preferred forage for at least one animal species, then a biologist may infer that forage competition is taking place. A thorough determination that the species are really competing requires more information, particularly evidence that populations of one or the other species are limited by availability of the preferred forage species.

Determination of forage preference requires information on both food habits and forage availability. This information is used in a variety of ways to calculate preference indexes—the simplest of which, and the only one with a straightforward interpretation, is the ratio of a given forage in the diet to the ratio of that same forage in the habitat. Other preference indexes include information on such factors as frequency on the range and frequency in the diet, an interpretation that is unclear at best (Chamrad 1979; Krueger 1972). For a thorough review of forage preference of ungulates, see Skiles (1984).

Food habits, as described earlier, can be considered to be primarily a function of forage preference and forage availability. Spatial arrangement of forage is of course important, but is difficult to quantify. All forage availability techniques, therefore, treat available forage as if it is equally available. Nevertheless, if forage preferences are known, then a biologist should be able to predict, albeit very crudely, the food habits of an animal species in that area. Many biologists are capable of doing this, through knowledge of forage preference and forage availability gained by experience and undocumented observations. However, attempts to use forage preference indexes and forage availability information in quantitative models to predict actual diets have not been very successful, at least with herbivores (Loehle and Rittenhouse 1982). Hopefully, future work in this area will result in preference indexes and quantitative models that will allow the biologist to predict diets. Developing more powerful and useful predictive models will probably depend on development of methods to quantify the spatial arrangement of forage in a way that can be measured simply and efficiently, yet is still useful for prediction. Until such models are available, biologists will need to continue to measure food habits directly.

SUMMARY

Measurement of forage utilization and food habits and the use of such data in monitoring programs are often required. However, forage selection and utilization by wild animals is a complex process, and most measurement techniques have limited accuracy and precision. In addition, many techniques require time, money, and equipment that are generally not available in some agencies or cannot be justified by the problems being addressed. Nevertheless, measurements of food habits and forage requirements will continue to be needed for special situations. Biologists should carefully choose appropriate techniques, considering the type of data needed, the precision and accuracy required, the acceptability of these data to those who must use it, and the relative cost in terms of money and personnel.

LITERATURE CITED

CHAMRAD, A.D. 1979. Preference ratings aid in food habit evaluations and interpretations. Pages 273-276 *in* Proc. First Welder Wildl. Foundation Symp.

COOK, C.W. AND L.A. STODDART. 1953. The quandary of utilization and preference. J. Range Manage. 6:329-335.

———— AND J. STUBBENDIECK. 1986. Methods of measuring herbage and browse utilization. Pages 120-121 *in* Cook, C.W. and J. Stubbendieck, eds. Range Research: Basic Problems and Techniques. Soc. Range Manage., Denver, CO. 317pp.

COOPERRIDER, A.Y., J.A. BAILEY, AND R.M. HANSEN. 1982. Cost efficient methods of estimating ungulate food habits by fecal analysis. Pages 399-406 *in* Arid Land Resource Inventories: Developing Cost-Efficient Methods. U.S. Dep. Agric., For. Serv. Gen. Tech. Rep. WO-28. 620pp.

————, S.A. MCCOLLOUGH, AND J.A. BAILEY. 1980. Variation in bighorn sheep food habits as measured by fecal analysis. Pages 29-41 *in* Proc. Biennial Symp. Northern Wild Sheep and Goat Council, Salmon, ID. 668pp.

DEARDEN, B.L., R.E. PEGAU, AND R.M. HANSEN. 1975. Precision of microhistological estimates of ruminant food habits. J. Wildl. Manage. 39:402-407.

GILL, R.B., L.H. CARPENTER, R.M. BARTMANN, D.L. BAKER, AND G.G. SCHOONVELD. 1983. Fecal analysis to estimate mule deer diets. J. Wildl. Manage. 47:902-915.

GULLION, G.W. 1966. A viewpoint concerning the significance of studies of game bird food habits. Condor 68:372-376.

HEADY, H.F. AND G.M. VAN DYNE. 1965. Prediction of weight composition from point samples on clipped herbage. J. Range Manage. 18:144-149.

HOLECHEK, J.L. AND M. VAVRA. 1983. Fistula sample numbers required to determine cattle diets on forest and grassland ranges. J. Range Manage. 36:323-326.

————, ————, AND R.D. PIEPER. 1982a. Botanical composition determination of range herbivore diets: A review. J. Range Manage. 35:309-315.

————, ————, AND ————. 1982b. Methods for determining the nutritive quality of range ruminant diets: A review. J. An. Sci. 54:363-376.

————, ————, AND ————. 1984. Methods for determining the botanical composition, similarity and overlap of range herbivore diets. Pages 425-471 *in* Developing Strategies for Rangeland Management. Westview Press, Boulder, CO. 2022pp.

KORSCHGEN, L.J. 1980. Procedures for food-habits analyses. Pages 113-127 *in* Schemnitz, S.D., ed. Wildl.

Manage. Techniques Manual, 4th Ed., The Wildl. Soc., Washington, DC. 686pp.

KRUEGER, W.C. 1972. Evaluating animal forage preference. J. Range Manage. 25:471-475.

KUFELD, R.C., O.C. WALLMO, AND C. FEDDEMA. 1973. Foods of the Rocky Mountain mule deer. U.S. Dep. Agric., For. Serv., Res. Pap. RM-111. 31pp.

LOEHLE, C. AND L.R. RITTENHOUSE. 1982. An analysis of forage preference indices. J. Range Manage. 35:316-319.

MARTIN, S.C. 1970. Relating vegetation measurements to forage consumption by animals. Pages 93-100 *in* Range and Wildlife Habitat Evaluation—A Research Symposium. U.S. Dep. Agric., For. Serv., Misc. Publ. 1147. 220pp.

MEDIN, D.E. 1970. Stomach content analyses: Collections from wild herbivores and birds. Pages 133-145 *in* Range and Wildlife Habitat Evaluation—A Research Symposium. U.S. Dep. Agric., For. Serv., Misc. Publ. 1147. 220pp.

NEFF, D.J. 1974. Forage preferences of trained mule deer on the Beaver Creek watershed. Arizona Game and Fish Dep., Spec. Rep. 4. 61pp.

PETRIDES, G.A. 1975. Principal foods versus preferred foods and their relations to stocking rate and range condition. Biol. Conserv. 7:161-169.

PIEPER, R.D. 1978. Methods for measuring utilization. Pages 123-147 *in* R.D. Pieper, ed. Measurement Techniques for Herbaceous and Shrubby Vegetation. Dep. Animal and Range Science, New Mexico State Univ., Las Cruces. 147pp.

RINEY, T. 1982. Study and management of large mammals. John Wiley and Sons, New York, NY. 552pp.

SKILES, J.W. 1984. A review of animal preference. Pages 153-213 *in* Developing Strategies for Rangeland Management. Westview Press, Boulder, CO. 2022pp.

SPARKS, D.R. AND J.C. MALECHEK. 1968. Estimating percentage dry weight in diets using a microscopic technique. J. Range Manage. 21:264-265.

U.S. DEPARTMENT OF THE INTERIOR, BUREAU OF LAND MANAGEMENT. 1984. Rangeland Monitoring—Utilization studies. U.S. Dep. Inter., Bur. Land Manage., Tech. Ref. 4400-3. 105pp.

WALLMO, O.C., R.B. GILL, L.H. CARPENTER, AND D.W. REICHERT. 1973. Accuracy of field estimates of deer food habits. J. Wildl. Manage. 37:556-562.

———— AND D.J. NEFF. 1970. Direct observation of tamed deer to measure their consumption of natural forage. Pages 105-109 *in* Range and Wildlife Habitat Evaluation—A Research Symposium. U.S. Dep. Agric., For. Serv., Misc. Publ. 1147. 220pp.

ZARN, M. 1981. Wild ungulate forage requirements—A review. U.S. Dep. Inter., Bur. Land Manage. 103pp.

35

WEATHER AND CLIMATE

James A. Bailey

Department of Fishery and Wildlife Biology
Colorado State University
Fort Collins, CO 80523

"Climate plays an important part in determining the average numbers of species, and periodical seasons of extreme drought or cold I believe to be the most effective of all checks."

——Charles Darwin, from *The Origin of the Species*

"Climate is what we expect, weather is what we get."

——Robert Heinlein

Editor's Note: Weather is an extremely important factor to consider in inventories or monitoring studies. In the western U.S., extreme fluctuations in weather are quite normal. Weather affects wildlife directly and indirectly: it can alter population size or cause changes in animal behavior that will bias study results.

This chapter identifies weather factors and describes how they are used to enhance the precision of studies and promote early detection of trends in wildlife populations and habitats.

INTRODUCTION

Weather affects wild animals directly by causing mortality, or by influencing behavior and physiology in ways that influence reproduction or mortality. Weather also affects wildlife indirectly by altering the production or availability of habitat resources and by influencing competitors, predators, and disease organisms. Consequently, much year-to-year variation in wildlife abundance and in the productivity or condition of wildlife and wildlife habitat is due to stochastic (random) variation in weather.

In addition, weather may affect the observability or activity of wildlife and thus may affect data obtained for wildlife monitoring. The objective of monitoring is to detect trends of improvement or decline in wildlife or in wildlife habitat. However, the stochastic direct and indirect effects of weather on wildlife, and the stochastic effects of weather on monitoring data, will reduce precision of the monitoring system and may delay detection of directional trends in wildlife populations or in habitat.

The objectives of this chapter are to describe some effects of weather on wildlife and on monitoring data, and to promote the use of weather data as a covariant in analyzing wildlife-monitoring data. Use of covariant analysis can enhance precision and early detection of directional trends in wildlife populations and habitats.

WEATHER AND WILDLIFE

Direct and Indirect Effects of Weather on Wildlife

A variety of direct and indirect impacts of weather on wild vertebrates has been reported (Table 1). The smaller species, in particular, may die from acute exposure to severe weather. Mortality of larger species during severe weather may result from a combination of direct exposure of the animals or indirect effects on the availability of habitat resources. Drought or severe runoff events may drastically alter current velocity, turbidity, and amount of

Table 1. Some reported effects of weather upon wildlife and on wildlife-monitoring data.

	Mammals	Birds	Amphibians, Reptiles	Fish
I. Direct effects:				
2 1. Acute mortality	Jacobs and Dixon 1981	Yocum 1950 Jones 1952 Smith 1960 Jehl and Hussell 1966 Stout and Cornwell 1976 Graber and Graber 1979 Stout and Cornwell 1976 Graber and Graber 1979		Larimore 1959 Jojhn 1964 Tramer 1977 Matthews and Styron 1981
2. Exposure with habitat loss	Martinka 1967 Meslow and Keith 1971 Connolly 1981			Nehring and Anderson 1984
3. Effects on reproduction	Wight and Conaway 1961 Picton 1984	Hammond and Johnson 1984		Starrett 1951 Gagnark and Bakkala 1960 John 1963 Crecco and Savoy 1984
4. Effects on habitat selection	Lovaas 1958 Richens 1967	Graber and Graber 1979		
5. Effects on movement patterns	Gilbert et al. 1970 Bruns 1977	Rutherford 1970	Obert 1976	Stehr and Branson 1938 Starrett 1951 Rinne 1975 May et al. 1976 Ottaway and Clark 1981
II. Indirect effects:				
1. Upon habitat	Smoliak 1956 Gallizioli 1965 Shaw 1965 Beatley 1969, 1976 Day 1971 Shiflet and Dietz 1974 Turkowski and Vahle 1977 Nixon et al. 1980 Stephenson and Brown 1980 Mueggler 1983	Gullion 1960 Francis 1970 Brown and Smith 1980	Hoddenbach and Turner 1968 Turner et al. 1969, 1976 Medica et al. 1975 Whitford and Creusere 1977	
2. Upon competition or disease	Longhurst and Douglas 1953	Vaught et al. 1967 Graber and Graber 1979		

Table 1. Some reported effects of weather upon wildlife and on wildlife-monitoring data (concluded).

	Mammals	Birds	Amphibians, Reptiles	Fish
III. Effects on monitoring data:				
1. Changed location affects duration	Lovaas 1958 Gilbert et al. 1970	Diem and Lu 1960 Rutherford 1970 Graber and Graber 1979 Best 1981	Obert 1976	
2. Persistence or detectability of sign	Wallmo et al. 1962	Emlen and DeJong 1981		
3. Activity and detectability of animals	Newman 1959 Morse and Balser 1961 Progulske and Duerre 1964 LeResche and Rausche 1974	Gullion 1966 Robel et al. 1969 Brown 1971 LaPerriere and Haugen 1972 Porter 1973 Morrison and Slack 1977 Shields 1979 Conner and Dickson 1980 Bock and Root 1981 Dawson 1981 Robbins 1971	Lillywhite 1982	
4. Trap results	Bailey 1969 Phillips et al. 1972	Raveling 1966	Vogt and Hine 1982	Kirkland 1962 May et al. 1976 Hubert and Schmitt 1982 a b
5. Observer diligence		Bock and Root 1981 Dawson 1981		

suitable fish habitat in streams and rivers, often causing acute mortality or downstream transport of fish. Weather may affect animal behavior in ways that influence reproduction, habitat selection, or movement patterns and distribution. Effects of weather on animal condition may persist for several months after a weather event (Clutton-Brock and Albon 1983).

Impacts of weather on the production or availability of habitat resources, especially forage, have been described. In arid areas, great variation in precipitation, and consequently in the quality and abundance of forage, has been correlated with reproductive success of mammals, birds, and reptiles. Weather may also influence wildlife indirectly by altering competition or by influencing exposure to disease.

The direct and indirect effects of weather on wildlife tend to be more acute (capable of quick effect) and severe for small animals than for large animals, and for populations living near the edges of their geographic ranges (Siivonen 1956; Birch 1958; Graber and Graber 1979).

Len Carpenter

Winter-stressed mule deer (when the ears are collapsed, the animal cannot be saved).

Effects of Weather on Wildlife Data

Numerous reports exist on weather conditions influencing the results of wildlife monitoring activities (Table 1). Weather may influence the concentration of wildlife and thus the probability that animals will be detected and counted. Weather may alter the locations of animals among habitats or among regions of the geographic range. Consequently, animals may move into habitats where they are less detectable or into habitats or regions away from the areas being monitored.

Weather factors have modified the persistence of wildlife sign and the transmission of sounds used in census methods. Activity patterns of animals have been altered in ways that influence detection and observability (Figure 1). Success of trapping animals and even sex-age structures of trapped samples of animals may be determined by weather. Wildlife observers may become less diligent during poor weather.

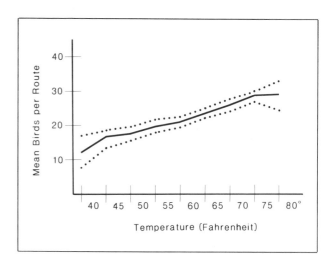

Figure 1. Effect of air temperature 1/2 hour before sunrise on numbers of cardinals (*Cardinalis cardinalis*) counted on standard breeding-bird survey routes. Dashed lines indicate 95% confidence limits for data in each 5°-interval set (after Robbins 1981).

WEATHER AND WILDLIFE MONITORING

Wildlife monitoring produces time-series data. These data provide information on trends in population size, density, or distribution; in population quality; or in habitat condition (Hocutt and Stauffer 1980; Worf 1980). Trends are usually measured over several years. Whereas the objective of wildlife monitoring is to detect persisting trends in wildlife or habitats, weather causes temporary changes in wildlife or habitats, or temporary bias in the monitoring data, that vary stochastically (improvement or decline) from year to year.

These temporary effects of weather may obscure long-term trends, especially if a biologist hopes to detect trends from a relatively short time-series of wildlife or habitat data. For example, 1 or 2 years of favorable weather may enhance a wildlife population even though the long-term trend in habitat condition or population is downward. Consequent delay in detecting the downward trend may result in several years' delay in developing a management response.

In response to these sources of bias, ornithologists have stressed a need to schedule bird surveys so that data are collected only during suitable weather. However, this option is not available in all wildlife monitoring. A few authors (Robel et al. 1969; Best 1981; Dawson 1981) have suggested that "adjustment factors" might be developed to account for weather bias. This approach is proposed in this chapter.

This problem can be diminished if effects of one or a few important weather factors on wildlife can be determined and measured during the early years of monitoring. Once the wildlife-weather relationships have been quantified, the temporary effects of weather can be isolated from long-term trends in time-series data. For example, although the indicated trend in wildlife or habitat condition for the most recent year or two may not be downward, the recent conditions may be poor when compared with only those previous years having similar weather conditions.

In the same manner, positive responses of wildlife or habitat to management programs can be detected more quickly if year-to-year effects of variable weather can be identified.

Selecting the Key Weather Factor

There are no rules to follow in selecting key weather factors for use in data analysis. Seven suggestions are--

(1) Use local or regional **"conventional wisdom."**
(2) Consider those weather factors known to affect production or availability of **limiting habitat resources** .
(3) Remember that autumn populations of species with high **biotic potentials** may be determined primarily by spring and summer weather affecting reproductive success, rather than by winter weather affecting overwinter survival and spring-breeding densities.
(4) Consider weather factors known to **bias** the distribution or observability of animals and therefore the accuracy of the monitoring system.
(5) Consider the amount of **seasonal precipitation** in arid areas as a key factor.
(6) Consider depth, persistence, and quality of **snow** in northern and alpine areas as key factors.
(7) Note that plants often respond to **cumulative** weather effects, whereas small wildlife at the edges of their geographic ranges are most apt to be directly affected by **acute** weather phenomena.

Key factors will vary among species, regions, and even sites (Mueggler 1971, 1983), and among monitoring systems. Selecting the key factor will be a local decision.

Conventional Wisdom. Much local and regional "conventional wisdom" exists regarding effects of weather on many species of wildlife. These widely accepted but often unquantified impacts of weather on wildlife are frequently used to determine the timing of yearly wildlife studies so as to gather data under similar weather conditions each year. When these attempts to standardize weather conditions fail, the assumed weather effects are used to subjectively interpret the resulting trends in wildlife data. For example, in northern regions, population indices based on "trend counts" of ungulates along fixed routes (aerial or ground counts) are often obtained during that part of each winter when snow is deepest and most widespread. When this strategy is successful, animals are presumed to be equally concentrated

and therefore equally distributed for being counted each year. When the strategy fails, as in a winter without much snow, trends in the counts are usually presumed to be due largely to the weather effect and are therefore ignored. Thus, failure to quantify the weather effect results in complete loss of 1 year's data.

Limiting Habitat Resources. Each vertebrate species has its own set of habitat requirements, and habitat resources vary temporally and geographically. Consequently, there is much taxonomic, temporal, and geographic variation in which habitat resources limit wildlife populations. However, if the limiting resources are known for a local population, then—by definition—the performance of the population (e.g., abundance, reproductive success, or survival) will be correlated with variation in the limiting resources. Furthermore, population performance may be correlated with weather factors that influence the production or availability of the limiting resources. These weather factors, perhaps precipitation influencing forage production or snow depth determining forage availability, may then be used in analyzing trends of population performance.

Biotic Potential. Species with high biotic potentials, such as small game or songbirds, have high rates of population turnover. In a favorable season of reproduction, these species may produce large autumn populations, regardless of variation in spring-breeding abundance (Steen 1944). A biologist monitoring autumn populations may use weather factors affecting the breeding season and reproductive success in analyzing trends in the population. However, weather factors that determine overwinter survival and spring-breeding density will not be useful when spring-breeding density is not well correlated with autumn abundance.

Bias. Weather will influence the distribution, habitat selection, movement patterns, and activity of wildlife, and consequently may influence the results of monitoring efforts. Effects of snow conditions on trend counts of ungulates are described above. Numerous studies have shown effects of weather on results of bird surveys (Table 1), despite the fact that these surveys are usually conducted within a narrow range of weather conditions. Weather may be known to affect observability of animals, or even sex-age classes of animals, and thus may affect measures of abundance or of population composition. Such weather factors are likely candidates for use in analyses.

Seasonal Precipitation. Several studies have shown wildlife data to be correlated with seasonal precipitation, especially in arid areas (Shaw 1965; Gallizioli 1965; Day 1971; Medica et al. 1975; Turner et al. 1976; Whitford and Creusere 1977; Brown and Smith 1980) where primary production is stimulated by thresholds of soil moisture and temperature (Beatley 1974). Most authors have used total precipitation for 6 or more months preceding the wildlife survey as a weather factor in data analysis.

Snow. In northern or alpine areas, snow depths, quality, and persistence have been correlated with wildlife data (Severinghaus 1947; Loveless 1967; Gilbert et al. 1970; Bartman and Steinert 1981; Adams and Bailey 1982). When information on daily snow depths is available, a good measure of snow impacts on animals and on habitat is the total number of winter days with more than a critical depth of snow on the ground. Critical snow depths for deer have been determined to be 38-50 cm (15-20 in.), about the height of a deer's brisket (Severinghaus 1947; Bartman and Steinert 1981). Similar depths may be estimated for other ungulates. However, for non-ungulates, and for study areas with modest snow accumulation, this criterion may not discriminate among years very well. (There may be very few days with >38 cm [15 in.] of snow on the ground in any year; yet there may be considerable important variation among years in persistence of snow depth <38 cm [15 in.].). In these situations, the mean snow depth for all winter days is an arbitrary criterion that will discriminate among years.

Cumulative vs. Acute Effects. When monitoring production of a habitat resource, such as forage, or a wildlife variable closely dependent on production of a habitat resource, consider selecting a key weather factor based on cumulative weather effects. For example, forage production may depend upon cumulative rainfall over 2-to-several months before and during the growing season (Fisher 1924). Negative effects of early-season weather upon forage production may be completely overridden by positive late-season effects. Consequently, forage production would not be correlated with weather data for a certain month, but may be correlated with cumulative weather data for 2 or more months.

In contrast, when monitoring a wildlife population that is expected to be directly affected by weather during a short period, the key weather factor correlated with population data is apt to be (1) attainment of a threshold of weather severity at any time during a long season, or (2) weather during a short season when the animals are especially vulnerable each year. The wildlife involved are apt to be small-bodied species, and populations near the edges of their geographic ranges (Graber and Graber 1979). For example, a severe period any time during the winter may acutely depress populations of small

Len Carpenter photos

Snow depths greater than 18 inches (45.7 cm) hamper mule deer and pronghorn movements.

birds, and a mild late-winter period cannot compensate once birds have died.

In this respect, large wild mammals are intermediate between plant and small wildlife. Large mammals draw upon substantial body reserves during severe weather and are less subject to acute effects of weather than are small wildlife. Population data for large mammals are often correlated with weather data based on cumulative effects.

Local Verification of Key Weather Factors

Selection of a key weather factor for use in analyzing wildlife monitoring data should be based upon a demonstrated correlation between the weather factor and the local wildlife or habitat data. One may assume that correlations based on conventional wisdom, on assumptions about limiting habitat resources, or on results from other areas will be correctly applicable to a new monitoring project. But this assumption should be tested with local time-series data before assuming there is much confidence in the results.

When a time series of wildlife data is available, it is tempting to assess numerous weather conditions for possible correlations with the wildlife data. Very many intercorrelated weather parameters can be generated from weather records. For instance, snow can be represented by several measurements relating to thresholds, persistence, and constancy, and each of these measurements can be tabulated for several separate as well as overlapping periods each winter. Correlations of each of these resulting parameters with the monitoring data can be assessed easily with computers. Some, often several, "statistically significant" correlations usually are found. Some of these may represent real direct or indirect relationships between weather and wildlife. Other correlations are probably due only to chance, since statistical significance is usually based on an error rate (probability of rejecting the hypothesis of no correlation when it is true) that applies separately to each weather parameter.

Can future wildlife monitoring data be evaluated by using any of these correlated weather parameters as covariants? Meslow and Keith (1971) discussed some aspects of this problem. If there is a biologically plausible hypothesis regarding a correlation between weather and the wildlife data, if the hypothesis is developed before any correlation in the data is evaluated subjectively or statistically, if only a few weather measurements are used to represent the weather parameter, and if a conservative (small) error rate is used, there should be little risk in accepting the correlation as a basis for evaluating future monitoring data. Otherwise, any strong correlations between a weather parameter and the monitoring

data should be viewed as a new hypothesis to be tested (1) for biological plausibility and (2) with several years of new data, before the indicated relationship is used in assessing the results of monitoring.

COVARIANT ANALYSIS

In the examples below, linear correlation and regression are used to estimate relationships between wildlife characteristics and weather factors. In reality, relationships such as these may be curvilinear, and abrupt thresholds may exist. With suitable statistical methods, non-linear relations between weather and wildlife may be used in covariance analysis of monitoring data. However, detection and verification of non-linear relationships will usually require abundant and precise estimates of both variables, and these are not common in wildlife monitoring. Consequently, most analyses will involve linear methods.

Example 1—Browse Utilization and Snow Depth

During the 1960s, the Montana Fish and Game Department measured winter utilization of serviceberry (*Amelanchier alnifolia*) browse by white-tailed deer (*Odocoileus virginianus*) in the Goat Creek drainage of the Swan Valley. Utilization was measured on several marked plants at the end of each winter. Presumably, browse utilization was being monitored as an index to the relative balance between numbers of deer and the availability of browse. A trend toward higher levels of utilization would indicate either increasing numbers of deer or a declining availability of browse and might require a management response. The purpose here, however, is only to address the problem of promptly detecting significant trends in levels of utilization when those levels fluctuate up and down each year (Figure 2). These data are extracted from Hildebrand (1971).

In 1965, 74% of serviceberry twigs on the transect had been browsed—the highest level of utilization in 6 years (Figure 2). But had a significant change in utilization occurred?

In the North, wintering white-tailed deer are very sensitive to snow conditions and tend to concentrate especially in conifer stands, as snow becomes deep. Browse transects were typically placed in these areas of concentration, often called "key areas." Consequently, among-years variation in utilization of browse on key areas often represented variation in concentration of deer caused by annual variation of snow conditions.

The number of days with >48 cm (19 in.) of snow on the ground each winter, recorded at the nearby Seeley Lake Ranger Station, was significantly correlated with percentage utilization of serviceberry for the years 1960-64 (Figure 3). Based on the regression for those years, the expected utilization of serviceberry in 1965, when there had been 69 days with >48 cm (19 in.) of snow on the ground, was 52.5 ± 12.3% (95% conf. limits). The observed utilization was 74%. Considering the regression from 1960 to 1964, the probability of this 74% utilization being due only to sampling error was <0.03. (I have calculated probabilities using untransformed utilization data, justified for 1960-64 when percentages were near 50.) This was strong evidence that something had changed in the balance between deer numbers and browse resources at Goat Creek. As it turned out, 1965 was the first of several years that exhibited comparatively high levels of utilization at Goat Creek (Figure 3).

In 1965, a biologist monitoring browse utilization in the Swan Valley may have considered 74% utilization on serviceberry as a signal for a closer look at conditions in the Valley. Certainly in 1966, when utilization was 78%, with only 25 days of deep snow, the biologist should have been convinced that something was amiss; and use of data on snow depths as a covariant in analyzing a time-series of browse-utilization data would have enhanced prompt detection of the change.

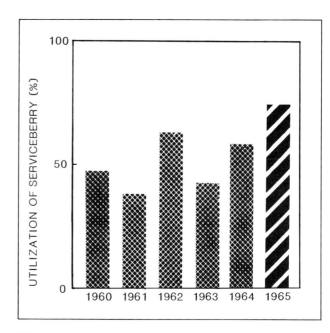

Figure 2. Utilization of serviceberry browse by white-tailed deer on the Goat Creek transect, Swan Valley, Montana (Data from Hildebrand 1971).

Furthermore, use of this covariant analysis of monitoring data would have enhanced detection of an impact of land-use practices on a wildlife population. Clear-cutting had begun on private lands in the Swan Valley in 1955. Winter range was being eliminated, concentrating deer on smaller amounts of range (Hildebrand 1971).

Example 2—Age Ratios and Snow Depth

Mountain goats (*Oreamnos americanus*) were introduced to the Sawatch Range, Colorado, in 1948 and onto Sheep Mountain in that range in 1950 (Adams and Bailey 1982). Age ratios of the Sheep Mountain herd have been observed as an index to monitor reproductive success since 1966. Age ratios varied greatly among years. Bailey and Johnson (1977) noted that these ratios for 1966-74 were correlated with the depth of snow each previous May at a high-elevation location observed by the U.S. Soil Conservation Service (Figure 4). It is biologically plausible that depth and persistence of snow on winter ranges will increase demands upon nanny goats and decrease forage availability, and that these impacts during late gestation might influence reproductive success, especially survival of neonates.

Tagged branch of browse plant.

The Sheep Mountain population of mountain goats grew steadily during 1965-74. Most rapid growth apparently occurred after 1970 (Adams and Bailey 1982). Based on concepts of density-dependence, especially with introduced ungulates (Caughley 1970), a decline in reproductive success (reproduction + neonatal survival) was expected. A

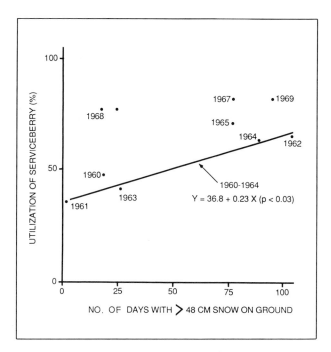

Figure 3. Use of snow-depth at Seeley Lake, Montana, as a covariant in analysis of browse-utilization data. A significant change in the relationship began in 1965.

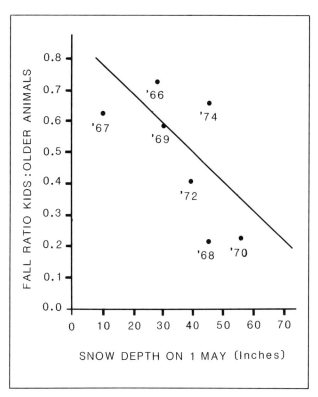

Figure 4. Relationship between 1 May snow depth from the previous winter at Monarch Pass and kid:older animal ratios from fall aerial surveys of mountain goats on Sheep Mountain and vicinity (Bailey and Johnson 1977).

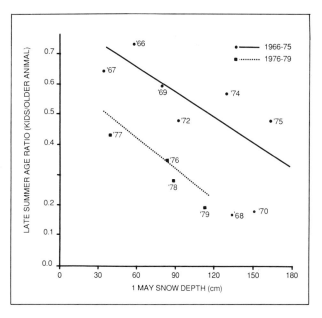

Figure 5. Relationship between 1 May snow depth from the previous winter at Monarch Pass and kid:older animal ratios of mountain goats on Sheep Mountain-Gladstone Ridge. Sawatch Range, Colorado, 1966-79 (Adams and Bailey 1982).

decline in age ratios was first suggested in 1976, and age ratios for 1976-79 were significantly different from age ratios for 1966-75 (Figure 5; Adams and Bailey 1982). To test this hypothesis, an "artificial variable" representing the two time periods was used in a multiple-regression analysis ($X = 0$ for 1966-75; $X = 1$ for 1976-79). At a mean snow depth of 97 cm (39 in.) for the 14 years, age ratios had declined by 47% in 1976-79 compared with 1966-75.

Note that the lowest age ratios had occurred in 1968 and 1970, before the decline indicated above. But 1968 and 1970 were very severe winters. It is only after using a weather variable in covariant analysis, so that winters of similar severity may be compared, that the decline in age ratios becomes obvious.

OBTAINING WEATHER DATA

Existing Records

Finklin (1983) described the sources of climatic data available to wildland managers. I have abstracted his suggestions.

Year-round weather data are published by the U.S. Weather Bureau and its successor agencies including the National Oceanic and Atmospheric

Administration (Hatch 1983). These data are available in many major libraries or from the National Climatic Center, Federal Building, Asheville, NC 28801. Information from local stations may be found in monthly and annual "Climatological Data" summaries for each state. Each station provides daily precipitation and maximum and minimum temperatures. Some stations also record evaporation, soil temperatures, monthly windspeed, relative humidity, sunshine, snowfall, and snow depth.

Fire-weather observations, maintained by the U.S. Forest Service, provide an additional data base, but for the fire season only. These include afternoon temperature, relative humidity, wind, daily precipitation, and daily maximum and minimum temperatures. Such data are archived on tapes at the National Fire Weather Data Library, Fort Collins, CO, and are available via access to the USDA computer at the Fort Collins Computer Center. (See Finklin 1983 for additional sources.)

Snow survey data for 11 western states are available from the USDA Soil Conservation Service, Portland, OR 97209 or from state offices of the Soil Conservation Service. Periodically, state or regional data are compiled into a Summary of Snow Survey Measurements.

Stream flow records, especially for major rivers, may be obtained from state or regional offices of the U.S. Geological Survey. These are compiled for states or for major watersheds within states and are in some libraries. Records include historic average rates, extreme rates, and daily rates.

See Finklin (1983) for other, minor sources of weather data.

Solar-powered weather station.

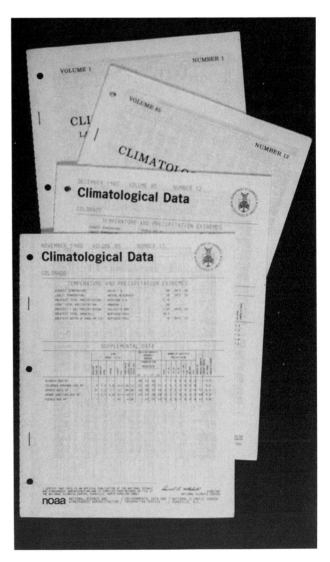

Climatological data summaries.

Obtaining Local Data

It may be desirable to monitor one or a few weather variables on a study area as part of the monitoring program. This would occur if existing weather stations are not nearby of if they do not adequately represent the study area because of differences in elevation, aspect, habitat, or topography. Also, key weather factors may not be recorded at the nearby cooperating Weather Bureau station. (For example, not all stations maintain records of snow depths.) Descriptions of commonly used weather instruments, of weather stations, and of weather data collection and analysis are available from Day and Sternes (1970) and Critchfield (1974).

Wildlife biologists have developed a few special instruments for measuring impacts of weather on animals. Although deep snow may hinder movements of large mammals, snow quality—in particular, crusting—may diminish or exacerbate problems of moving in snow, depending on the density and location of crusts in the snowpack. Hepburn (1978) described a penetrometer for measuring the effective depth of snow for large mammals when the snowpack is crusted. Energy demands of wintering big game may depend, in part, on the combined effects of temperature, wind, and radiation exchange with the environment (Moen 1968, 1973). Verme (1968) has described a simple device for measuring these combined effects upon energy demands.

LITERATURE CITED

ADAMS, L.G. and J.A. BAILEY. 1982. Population dynamics of mountain goats in the Sawatch Range, Colorado. J. Wildl. Manage. 46:1003-1009.

BAILEY, J.A. 1969. Trap responses of wild cottontails. J. Wildl. Manage. 33:48-58.

—— and B.K. JOHNSON. 1977. Status of introduced mountain goats in the Sawatch Range of Colorado. Pages 54-63 in Samuel, W. and W.G. Macgregor, eds. Proc. First Int. Mountain Goat Symp. Kalispell, MT.

BARTMANN, R.M. and S.F. STEINERT. 1981. Distribution and movements of mule deer in the White River Drainage, Colorado. Colorado Div. Wildl. Spec. Rept. 51. 12pp.

BEATLEY, J.C. 1969. Dependence of desert rodents on winter annuals and precipitation. Ecology 50:721-724.

——. 1974. Phenological events and their environmental triggers in Mohave desert ecosystems. Ecology 55:856-863.

——. 1976. Rainfall and fluctuating plant populations in relation to distributions and numbers of desert rodents in southern Nevada. Oecologia 24:21-42.

BEST, L.B. 1981. Seasonal changes in detection of individual bird species. Studies in Avian Biology 6:252-261.

BIRCH, L.C. 1958. The role of weather in determining the distribution and abundance of animals. Cold Spring Harbor Symposia in Quantitative Biology 22:203-215.

BROWN, D.E. and R.H. SMITH. 1980. Winter-spring precipitation and population levels of blue grouse in Arizona. Wildl. Soc. Bull. 8:136-141.

BROWN, W.H. 1971. Winter population trends in the red-shouldered hawk. Am. Birds 25:813-817.

BRUNS, E.H. 1977. Winter behavior of pronghorns in relation to habitat. J. Wildl. Manage. 41:560-571.

CAUGHLEY, G. 1970. Eruption of ungulate populations, with emphasis on Himalayan thar in New Zealand. Ecology 51:53-72.

CLUTTON-BROCK, T.H. and S.D. ALBON. 1983. Climatic variation and body weight of red deer. J. Wildl. Manage. 47:1197-1201.

CONNER, R.N. and J.G. DICKSON. 1980. Strip transect sampling and analysis for avian habitat studies. Wildl. Soc. Bull. 8:4-10.

CONNOLLY, G.E. 1981. Limiting factors and population regulation. Chapter 7 in Wallmo, O.C., ed. Mule and Black-tailed Deer of North America. Univ. of Nebraska Press, Lincoln.

CRECCO, V.A. and T.F. SAVOY. 1984. Effects of fluctuations in hydrographic conditions on year-class strength of American shad (Alosa sapidissima) in the Connecticut River. Can. J. Fish. Aquatic Sci. 41:1216-1223.

CRITCHFIELD, H.J. 1974. General climatology (3rd Edition). Prentice-Hall, Inc. 446pp.

DAWSON, D.G. 1981. Counting birds for a relative measure (index) of density. Studies in Avian Biology 6:12-16.

DAY, G.I. 1971. Wildlife research in Arizona, 1970-71. Pages 153-157 in Wildlife Research in Arizona. Arizona Game and Fish Dept. Phoenix.

DAY, J.A. and G.L. STERNES. 1970. Climate and Weather. Addison-Wesley Publ. Co. Reading, MA. 407pp.

DIEM, K.L. and K.H. LU. 1960. Factors influencing waterfowl censuses in the Parklands, Alberta, Canada. J. Wildl. Manage. 24:113-133.

EMLEN, J.T. and M.J. DEJONG. 1981. The application of song detection threshold distance to census operations. Studies in Avian Biology 6:346-352.

FINKLIN, A.I. 1983. Summarizing weather and climatic data—a guide for wildland managers. U.S. Dep. Agric., For. Serv. Gen. Tech. Rep. INT-148. 43pp.

FISHER, R.A. 1924. The influence of rainfall on the yield of wheat at Rothamsted. Royal Soc. London Phil. Trans., Series B. 213:89-142.

FRANCIS, W.J. 1970. The influence of weather on population fluctuations in California quail. J. Wildl. Manage. 34:249-266.

GAGNARK, H.A. and R.G. BAKKALA. 1960. A comparative study of unstable and stable (artificial channel) spawning streams for incubating king salmon at Mill Creek. California Fish and Game 46:151-164.

GALLIZIOLI, S. 1965. Quail research in Arizona. Arizona Game and Fish Dep., Phoenix. 12pp.

GILBERT, P.F., O.C. WALLMO, and R.B. GILL. 1970. Effect of snow depth on mule deer in Middle Park, Colorado. J. Wildl. Manage. 34:15-23.

GRABER, J.W. and R.R. GRABER. 1979. Severe winter weather and bird populations in southern Illinois. Wilson Bull. 91:88-103.

GULLION, G.W. 1960. The ecology of Gambel's quail in Nevada and the arid southwest. Ecology 41:518-536.

——. 1966. The use of drumming behavior in ruffed grouse population studies. J. Wildl. Manage. 30:717-729.

HAMMOND, M.C. and D.H. JOHNSON. 1984. Effects of weather on breeding ducks in North Dakota. U.S. Dep. Inter., Fish and Wildl. Serv. Tech. Rep. 1. 17pp.

HATCH, W.L. 1983. Selective guide to climatic data sources. Key to Meteorological Records Documentation No. 4.11. National Oceanic, Atmospheric Admin. Asheville, NC. 338pp.

HEPBURN, R.L. 1978. A snow penetration gauge for studies of white-tailed deer and other northern mammals. J. Wildl. Manage. 42:663-667.

HILDEBRAND, P.R. 1971. Biology of white-tailed deer on winter ranges in the Swan Valley, Montana. M.S. Thesis, Univ. Montana. Missoula. 91pp.

HOCUTT, C.H. and J.R. STAUFFER, JR., eds. 1980. Biological monitoring of fish. Lexington Books. Lexington, KY. 416pp.

HODDENBACH, G.A. and F.B. TURNER. 1968. Clutch size of the lizard Uta stansburiana in southern Nevada. Amer. Midl. Nat. 80:262-265.

HUBERT, W.A. and D.N. SCHMITT. 1982a. Factors influencing catches of drifted trammel nets in a pool of the Upper Mississippi River. Proc. Iowa Acad. Sci. 89:153-154.

—— and ——. 1982b. Factors influencing hoop net catches in channel habitats of Pool 9, Upper Mississippi River. Proc. Iowa Acad. Sci. 89:84-88.

JACOBS, D. and K.R. DIXON. 1981. Breeding-season precipitation and the harvest of cottontails. J. Wildl. Manage. 45:1011-1014.

JEHL, J. and D. HUSSELL. 1966. Effects of weather on reproductive success of birds at Churchill, Manitoba. Arctic 19:185-191.

JOHN, K.R. 1963. The effect of torrential rains on the reproductive cycle of Rhinichthys osculus in the Chiricahua Mountains, Arizona. Copeia 2:286-291.

——. 1964. Survival of fish in intermittent streams of the Chiricahua Mountains, Arizona. Ecology 45:112-119.

JONES, G. 1952. Hail damage to wildlife in southwest Oklahoma. Wilson Bull. 64:166-167.

KIRKLAND, L. 1962. A tagging experiment on spotted and largemouth bass using an electric shocker and the Petersen disc tag. Proc. Southeast. Assoc. Game and Fish Comm. 16:424-432.

LA PERRIERE, A.J. and A.O. HAUGEN. 1972. Some factors influencing calling activity of wild mourning doves. J. Wildl. Manage. 36:1193-1199.

LARIMORE, R.W. 1959. Destruction and re-establishment of stream fish and invertebrates affected by drought. Trans. Am. Fish. Soc. 88:261-285.

LE RESCHE, R.E. and R.A. RAUSCH. 1974. Accuracy and precision of aerial moose censusing. J. Wildl. Manage. 38:175-182.

LILLYWHITE, H.B. 1982. Tracking as an aid in ecological studies of snakes. Pages 181-191 in Scott, N.J., Jr., ed. Herpetological Communities. U.S. Dep. Inter., Fish and Wildl. Serv. Wildl. Res. Rep. 13.

LONGHURST, W.M. and J.R. DOUGLAS. 1953. Parasite interrelationships of domestic sheep and Columbian black-tailed deer. Trans. North Am. Wildl. Nat. Resour. Conf. 18:168-188.

LOVAAS, A.L. 1958. Mule deer food habits and range use, Little Belt Mountains, Montana. J. Wildl. Manage. 22:275-283.

LOVELESS, C.M. 1967. Ecological characteristics of a mule deer winter range. Colorado Div. Game, Fish and Parks. Tech. Publ. 20. Denver, CO. 124pp.

MARTINKA, C.J. 1967. Mortality of northern Montana pronghorns in a severe winter. J. Wildl. Manage. 31:159-164.

MATTHEWS, W.J. and J.T. STYRON, JR. 1981. Tolerance of headwater vs. mainstream fishes for abrupt physico-chemical changes. Am. Midl. Nat. 105:149-158.

MAY, N., L. TRENT, and P.J. PRISTAS. 1976. Relation of fish catches in gill nets to frontal periods. Fishery Bull. 74:449-453.

MEDICA, P.A., R.B. BURY and F.B. TURNER. 1975. Growth of the desert tortoise (Gopherus agassizi) in Nevada. Copeia 4:639-643.

MESLOW, E.C. and L.B. KEITH. 1971. A correlation analysis of weather versus snowshoe hare population parameters. J. Wildl. Manage. 35:1-15.

MOEN, A.N. 1968. Surface temperatures and radiant heat loss from white-tailed deer. J. Wildl. Manage. 32:38–344.

————. 1973. Wildlife Ecology. W.H. Freeman and Co. San Francisco, CA. 458pp.

MORRISON, M.L. and R.D. SLACK. 1977. Population trends and status of the Olivaceous Cormorant. Am. Birds 31:954-959.

MORSE, M.A. and D.S. BALSER. 1961. Fox calling as a hunting technique. J. Wildl. Manage. 25:148-154.

MUEGGLER, W.F. 1971. Weather variations on a mountain grassland in southwestern Montana. U.S. Dep. Agric., For. Serv. Res. Pap. INT-99. 25pp.

————. 1983. Variation in production and seasonal development of mountain grasslands in western Montana. U.S. Dep. Agric., For. Serv. Res. Pap. INT-316. 16pp.

NEHRING, R.B. and R. ANDERSON. 1984. Recruitment and survival of young-of-the-year brown trout (Salmo trutta L.) in the South Fork of the Rio Grande River versus parent spawner density, stream discharge and fry habitat. Proc. Colorado-Wyoming Chapt. Am. Fish. Soc. 19:35-43.

NEWMAN, D.E. 1959. Factors influencing the winter roadside count of cottontails. J. Wildl. Manage. 23:290-294.

NIXON, C.M., M.W. McCLAIN, and L.P. HANSEN. 1980. Six years of hickory seed yields in southwestern Ohio. J. Wildl. Manage. 44:534-539.

OBERT, H. 1976. Some effects of external factors upon the reproductive behavior of the grass frog, Rana temporaria. Oecologia. 24:43-55.

OTTAWAY, E.M. and A. CLARK. 1981. A preliminary investigation into the vulnerability of young trout (Salmo trutta L.) and Atlantic salmon (Salmo salar L.) to downstream displacement by high water velocities. J. Fish. Biol. 19:135-145.

PHILLIPS, R.L., R.O. ANDREWS, G.L. STORM, and R.A. BISHOP. 1972. Dispersal and mortality of red foxes. J. Wildl. Manage. 36:237-248.

PICTON, H.D. 1984. Climate and the prediction of reproduction of three ungulate species. J. Applied Ecol. 21:869-879.

PORTER, D.K. 1973. Accuracy in censusing breeding passerines on the shortgrass prairie. M.S. Thesis, Colorado State Univ. Ft. Collins. 107pp.

PROGULSKE, D.R. and D.C. DUERRE. 1964. Factors influencing spotlighting counts of deer. J. Wildl. Manage. 28:27-34.

RAVELING, D.G. 1966. Factors affecting age ratios of samples of Canada geese caught with cannon nets. J. Wildl. Manage. 30:682-691.

RICHENS, V.B. 1967. Characteristics of mule deer herds and their range in northeastern Utah. J. Wildl. Manage. 31:651-666.

RINNE, J.N. 1975. Changes in minnow populations in a small desert stream resulting from naturally and artificially induced factors. Southwest. Nat. 20:185-195.

ROBBINS, C.S. 1981. Bird activity levels related to weather. Studies in Avian Biology 6:301-310.

ROBEL, R.J., D.J. DICK, and G.F. KRAUSE. 1969. Regression coefficients used to adjust bobwhite quail whistle count data. J. Wildl. Manage. 33:662-668.

RUTHERFORD, W.H. 1970. The Canada geese of southeastern Colorado. Colorado Div. Game, Fish and Parks. Tech. Publ. 26. 65pp.

SEVERINGHAUS, C.W. 1947. Relationships of weather to winter mortality and population levels among deer in the Adirondack region of New York. Cong. 12:212-223.

SHAW, H. 1965. Investigations of factors influencing deer populations. Pages 125-143 in Wildlife Research in Arizona, 1964. Arizona Game and Fish Dep. Phoenix.

SHIELDS, W.M. 1979. Avian census techniques: an analytical review. Pages 23-51 in Dickson, J.G., R.N. Conner, R.R. Fleet, J.C. Kroll, and J.A. Jackson, eds. The Role of Insectivorous Birds in Forest Ecosystems. Academic Press. New York, NY.

SHIFLET, T.N. and H.E. DIETZ. 1974. Relationship between precipitation and annual rangeland herbage production on southeastern Kansas. J. Range Manage. 27:272-276.

SIIVONEN, L. 1956. The correlation between the fluctuations of partridge and European hare populations and the climatic conditions of winters in southwest Finland during the last thirty years. Papers on Game Res., Finnish Game Foundation 17:1-30.

SMITH, A. 1960. Hail: great destroyer of wildlife. Audubon Mag. 62:170-171, 189.

SMOLIAK, S. 1956. Influence of climatic conditions on forage production of shortgrass rangeland. J. Range Manage. 9:89-91.

STARRET, W.C. 1951. Some factors affecting the abundance of minnows in the Des Moines River, Iowa. Ecology 32:13-27.

STEEN, M.O. 1944. The significance of population turnover in upland game management. Trans. North Am. Wildl. Conf. 9:331-335.

STEHR, W.C. and J.W. BRANSON. 1938. An ecological study of an intermittent stream. Ecology 19:294-310.

STEPHENSON, R.L. and D.E. BROWN. 1980. Snow cover as a factor influencing mortality of Abert's squirrels. J. Wildl. Manage. 44:951-955.

STOUT, I.J. and G.W. CORNWELL. 1976. Nonhunting mortality of fledged North American waterfowl. J. Wildl. Manage. 40:681-693.

TRAMER, E.J. 1977. Catastrophic mortality of stream fishes trapped in shrinking pools. Am. Midl. Nat. 97:469-478.

TURKOWSKI, F.J. and J.R. VAHLE. 1977. Desert rodent abundance in southern Arizona in relation to rainfall. U.S. Dep. Agric., For. Serv. Res. Note RM-346. 4pp.

TURNER, F.B., P.A. MEDICA, J.R. LANNON, JR., and G.A. HODDENBACH. 1969. A demographic analysis of fenced populations of the whiptail lizard, *Cnemidophorus tigris*, in southern Nevada. Southwest. Nat. 14:189-202.

——, ——, and B.W. KOWALEWSKY. 1976. Energy utilization by a desert lizard (*Uta stansburiana*). US/IBP Desert Biome Monogr. 1. 57pp.

VAUGHT, R.W., H.C. MCDOUGLE, and H. H. BURGESS. 1967. Fowl cholera in waterfowl at Squaw Creek National Wildlife Refuge, Missouri. J. Wildl. Manage. 31:248-253.

VERME, L.J. 1968. An index of winter weather severity for northern deer. J. Wildl. Manage. 32:566-574.

VOGT, R.C. and R.L. HINE. 1982. Evaluation of techniques for assessment of amphibian and reptile populations in Wisconsin. Pages 201-217 *in* Scott, N.J., Jr., ed. Herpetological Communities. U.S. Dep. Inter., Fish and Wildl. Serv. Wildl. Res. Rep. 13

WALLMO, O.C., A.W. JACKSON, T.L. HAILEY, and R.L. CARLISLE. 1962. Influence of rain on the count of deer pellet groups. J. Wildl. Manage. 26:50-55.

WHITFORD, W.G. and F.M. CREUSERE. 1977. Seasonal and yearly fluctuations in Chihuahuan Desert lizard communities. Herpetologica 33:54-65.

WIGHT, H.M. and C.H. CONAWAY. 1961. Weather influences on the onset of breeding in Missouri cottontails. J. Wildl. Manage. 25:87-89.

WORF, D.L., ed. 1980. Biological monitoring for environmental effects. Lexington Books, Lexington, KY. 227 pp.

YOCUM, C.F. 1950. Weather and its effect on hatching of waterfowl in eastern Washington. Trans. North Am. Wildl. Nat. Resour. Conf. 15:309-319.

VI ANALYSIS AND PRESENTATION

I. T & E Species
  • bald eagles
  • black footed ferrets
II. Critical Habitats
  • Riparian
  •
  •

Shirley McCulloch 1987

36

DATA MANAGEMENT

Larry Peterson[1] **and Iris Matney**

U.S. Bureau of Land Management
Service Center
Denver, CO 80225

"A frequent predicament of field workers is to accumulate so many notes that time is lacking to analyze them, or to have notes string out over such a long period that the earlier ones are lost or hard to segregate by the time a sufficient volume are at hand to warrant a conclusion."

—Aldo Leopold, *Game Management* (1948)

Editor's Note: The field of data management is rapidly growing and changing. Computers are already widely used in business and science and are used increasingly in resource management. Furthermore, computers are no longer merely number crunchers; data processing now also includes image processing and word processing. While data management technology is quite sophisticated, its application is becoming more and more user friendly. This chapter provides an overview of the processes involved in data management, but the reader will have to keep up with specifics. A major obstacle to the new user of modern computer systems is the jargon associated with it. This chapter introduces many of the terms and concepts used in the field, so that the biologist can communicate with the data-processing specialist when necessary.

INTRODUCTION

Aldo Leopold (1948) warned biologists about problems of data management. This same problem exists today. By using computers, wildlife biologists can devote their attention to the collection of data and their time to the interpretation and analysis of information. They can provide options or recommendations to management while a computer performs the tasks of adding, subtracting, sorting, and other data manipulations. The computer is an important tool in the management of our natural resources.

Data processing for the wildlife biologist can mean very simple or complex procedures. It can mean dealing with a whole new group of people who have their own jargon and who may not be familiar with the biologist's needs or activities. This chapter discusses some of the most elemental concepts of data management. We have suggested some basic references at the end of the chapter to expand on the topics presented here.

The data processing field is now frequently called information management. It is relatively new and has been developing rapidly. The first large-scale electronic digital computer was built in 1946. It contained 18,000 vacuum tubes and was programmed by connecting various wires between units of the computer and setting up 6,000 switches so the program would run (Shelly and Cashman 1980:2.3). By today's standards, this computer was big, slow, unreliable, and difficult to program.

By 1954, the transistor brought about the second generation of computers which were faster, smaller, and less expensive. In 1964, third generation computers using Solid Logic Technology (SLT) began to appear.

[1]Current Address: Tekton Software, Inc., 1495 Canyon Blvd., Suite 100, P.O. Box 7300, Boulder, CO 80306.

The minicomputer and the new era of integrated electronics began with the use of silicon chips. Small processing units have brought the computer into many small businesses, homes, and schools. In fact, some colleges require incoming students to have microcomputers. It is a rare individual, even a wildlife biologist, who has not been affected in some way by a computer. The Internal Revenue Service, utility companies, grocery stores, payroll departments, and organizations—all use computers.

A relatively new development in computer technology, of particular interest to wildlife biologists and resource managers, is the use of Geographic Information Systems (GISs). A GIS consists of software and hardware for performing spatial analyses. Thus, the operations that biologists do on maps, such as calculating areas, amount of edge, distance from waters, etc., can now be automated. This technology is not discussed in detail in this chapter; however, the principles described apply equally well to such systems as to the traditional systems that process alphanumeric data. For further information on GISs, see de Steiguer and Giles (1981), Steenhof (1982), and Mayer (1984).

A common problem in thinking about data management is to consider data only as numerical data, and computers or automated systems as only "number crunchers" or systems for dealing with numerical data. Spatial data or maps analyzed by GISs are as much data as text processed on word processors. Unfortunately, the technologies for automating such data have developed separately in many cases, such that they must be used independently. However, the future trend is to develop integrated software and hardware so the user can easily use all three types of data in one system, just as biologists now use maps, tables, and written reports. The following discussion

---

MICROPROCESSORS AND MICROCOMPUTERS

A **microprocessor** is a one-chip central processing unit (CPU). That is, all of the components necessary to perform the CPU functions are contained on one silicon chip. The small, relatively inexpensive microprocessors are used in a variety of products, including hand-held calculators, vending machines, and microwave ovens.

A microprocessor together with additional chips containing circuitry for timing, temporary storage, and interfaces for input and output devices forms a **microcomputer.** First used in industrial automation, the microcomputer has moved into a diverse environment ranging from business and banking to transportation and manufacturing. Most personal and home computers are microcomputers. A microcomputer will be able to fill many of a biologist's computing needs. However, complex programs or large amounts of data may require larger computers to process the data efficiently.

MINICOMPUTERS

Minicomputer is a term which was first used to describe a machine that was smaller and less expensive than mainframe computers typically manufactured at the time. Since that time, the range in size, ability, and cost of computers has increased so much that the term has lost its original significance. Although the term is still used, its meaning varies greatly. A machine called a minicomputer by some users may be referred to as a small computer by others. Similarly, some people may call a microcomputer a minicomputer. The usual distinction between a "micro" and a "mini" is whether or not the processing unit is on one chip or many.

MAINFRAME COMPUTERS

Full-scale computers, termed **mainframe computers,** are capable of processing large amounts of data at very fast speeds with access to billions of characters of data. Depending on the amount of processing done at one location, several operators working in shifts may be required. Also, an alternate power supply and adequate air conditioning are generally required.

GEOGRAPHIC INFORMATION SYSTEM (GIS)

A Geographic Information System (GIS) stores, displays, retrieves, and analyzes spatial data. It is similar to other automated information systems except that it handles spatial data instead of just words and numbers. Since spatial data can be associated with specific geographic locations, the system can model or simulate land uses and resource values. Many different systems are available either as public domain software (not copyrighted) or as proprietary systems (copyrighted and sold under license) that must be purchased. MOSS (Map Overlay Statistical System) is a public domain system that is used by the U.S. Bureau of Land Management and several other agencies. ARC/INFO, on the other hand, is a proprietary system, available only under license from the manufacturer.

of data management applies to all types of data even though the examples given deal mostly with alphanumeric data.

A computer consists of a group of devices that process data without intervention by people at every step. The machinery that makes up the computer system is called hardware. Software or programming is merely a set of instructions telling the machine what to do.

Computers can do only a limited number of things. Programs must be written to tell them exactly what to do and when to do it. Computers do these functions quickly and reliably and are especially good for repetitive tasks, such as—

(1) Mathematical tasks, including addition, subtraction, multiplication, and division;

(2) Logical operations, which may include comparing two values to determine whether one is larger or smaller than the other; and

(3) Input/output operations, such as accepting data for processing or outputting data in a printed report.

A wildlife biologist does these same tasks. There is nothing a computer can do with data that cannot be done by hand. But a computer does calculations and comparisons much faster than wildlife biologists. In fact, all the data processing and computational work done by computers in the world today can no longer be done by hand: about 400 billion people would be needed to tackle this workload (Shelly and Cashman 1980:2.1).

The computer is as available as trucks, aerial photos, or helicopters, and it makes people more efficient. One does not need to know how to manufac-

---

WORD PROCESSING

One of the major uses of microcomputers by many businesses is word processing. Systems range from the editing typewriter to communicating word processors that provide file transfer or electronic mail capability. Some systems also have the ability through other software to perform some data processing applications such as payroll and accounting.

HARDWARE, SOFTWARE, AND FIRMWARE

Computer functions are often discussed in terms of **hardware** and **software.** Hardware is a term used for the physical components of the system. Input devices, output devices, main storage, and auxiliary storage devices are all part of the computer hardware. Software is the collection of programs (groups of written instructions) that tell the computer what to do. Each computer system has an operating system (program) to manage scheduling, input, computing, and output of the application programs it processes. An application program performs a specific task such as producing a wildlife inventory report or moving wildlife inventory data to storage. Programs that perform common procedures such as sort routines are called **utility programs.** These are "packaged" programs that perform functions common to many organizations such as accounting, statistics, and modeling.

With the extensive advancement in computer hardware and software, the distinction between the two is not always easy to define. Therefore, the term **firmware** is used to refer to a combination of hardware and software used to control the operations of a computer. Firmware instructions (microcode) are used to control some of the permanently wired circuits (called hardwired circuits).

COMPUTER SYSTEM

A computer system consists of input/output units, a processing unit, and secondary storage devices. Data are entered into input units such as card readers, magnetic tape drives, or key-entry terminals. Input units convert data to a form understandable to the computer. The data are then processed by a **Central Processing Unit (CPU).** The results of this processing are known as output. Output may be in a form understandable to people, such as printed reports, or it may remain in a form, readable only by computers, for input to another computer, such as data stored on tape. Output is made available to people through printers, magnetic tape drives, or terminals.

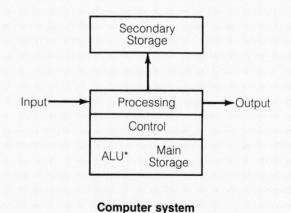

Computer system

Arithmetic/logic unit*

ture computers or to be a programmer any more than one needs to know how to repair a transmission or fly a helicopter to use those tools. Other specialists are available to assist with these tasks. It is important, however, to recognize computer capabilities and limitations.

Modern biologists often have computers or terminals on their desks or in an adjoining room. To benefit from these, the biologists need to learn how to turn them on, use program applications, and execute certain commands.

Many computer programs are being designed to be "user friendly." Knowing complicated programming languages is no longer necessary. In many instances, specific steps are outlined in user guides.

The computer is part of a technology that is becoming as important to the wildlife biologist as other common tools in the natural resource field. The wildlifer can use computers to assist in analyzing large volumes of data and make better decisions regarding wildlife habitats. Many wildlife management organizations already use computers to process wildlife species or habitat data. To get the information required, biologists must decide—

- what data to collect;
- how much data to collect;
- how to store and maintain the data;
- how to process the data.

An understanding of computers will affect these decisions.

Information processing remains a rapidly developing field, whether it be hardware, laser printers,

COMPONENTS

A computer consists of five **components:**

(1) Input units

(2) Main storage

(3) Arithmetic/logic unit (ALU)

(4) Control unit

(5) Output units

Input units are used to enter data into the computer. Data are usually entered through a keyboard, optical scanner, or other device. They are transferred to computer memory for processing and may then be stored on media such as magnetic tape or disk.

The ALU and control unit make up the **central processing unit (CPU).** These are the electronic components that cause processing to occur by interpreting instructions, performing calculations, moving data around in main computer storage, and controlling input/output operations.

The control unit directs and coordinates the entire computer system. This includes the entry and removal of data from main storage. The control unit may coordinate such activities as rewinding a tape reel or routing data from main storage to the ALU.

The ALU performs arithmetic and logic operations on data. The arithmetic circuitry performs calculations and related functions such as rounding. The logic circuitry performs logical operations such as comparing two sets of characters or testing a number to see if it is positive, negative, or zero.

Main storage (also called memory or internal storage) is frequently considered a part of the CPU. It is somewhat like an electronic filing cabinet with addressable locations. Each location is capable of holding data or instructions. This allows for certain locations in main storage to be used in specific ways, such as for calculation and instruction interpretation. When main storage is not considered part of the CPU, it is referred to as one of the secondary or auxiliary kinds of storage available.

Output units are used to obtain information in various forms. Some types of output are produced as printed reports or microfiche. Output is also displayed on video screen terminals.

DATA PROCESSING CYCLE

The **data processing cycle** consists of inputting, processing, and outputting data, which transforms data into information that is organized and usable.

The **input step** identifies the data to be processed and the instructions to be used for processing. During processing, data may be checked for completeness and accuracy. If they are not valid, the output will have no value. This is the basis for the term "garbage in— garbage out." Therefore, at this step, it is important to validate the data entered so the user can make necessary corrections before other processing is completed.

During the **processing step,** manipulations or computations will be performed according to instructions. For example, State codes could be expanded from an input abbreviation (NV) to output a full name (Ne-

computers small enough to fit in a hand, or better software programs. Few people know what the future holds, but if history is any indication, significant new developments will continue and will affect how people will do their work.

Because data management is a rapidly changing field, we have kept this chapter very general; users should keep up with the latest references or ask computer experts for the most up-to-date information. Not every wildlifer needs to be a statistician or programmer, but he or she should become familiar enough to converse with statisticians and data processing personnel to know when more highly trained assistance in these fields is needed.

This chapter presents some factors to consider when working with data processing or information management. We have tried to keep the main text as free from undefined jargon as possible. Many special topics and concepts are described in sidebars, and special terms are defined in the glossary. We have not discussed particular program or machine operations, as these are best covered in detailed manuals or user guides—and any discussion would soon become outdated.

USING THE COMPUTER

Accurate, timely information is vital in making decisions. Computers are often used to process data into the information required. Computers are helpful when—

(1) A large volume of data is to be processed;

(2) Complex comparisons are involved;

---

vada), or a code for an animal species (ODHE) will be output as mule deer. An example of a computation would be the accumulation of each animal species in each State.

The **output step** provides the processed information. During the data processing cycle, the data are organized so they will be meaningful to those who receive them. Because decisionmaking occurs in many areas and at many levels, one person's information may be another person's data.

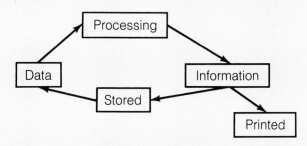

Data processing cycle

To illustrate the processing of data, consider a hypothetical study a wildlife biologist might conduct to determine the number of mule deer, elk, and desert bighorn sheep tagged for a special study in several States. Our example contains only 10 records so the relationship between input and output will be easier to see. We used the following codes for the input data: NV for Nevada, NM for New Mexico, and UT for Utah. The animal species codes are ODHE for mule deer,

CEEL for elk, and OVCAME for desert bighorn sheep. The data are as follows:

NV	ODHE
UT	CEEL
NV	ODHE
NV	CEEL
NM	CEEL
NM	OVCAME
UT	OVCAME
NV	ODHE
UT	CEEL
UT	OVCAME

Only after the above data were processed would they become useful information. The output might appear as follows:

Number of Vertebrate Species Tagged by State
as of 1/1/84

State	Species	Number
Nevada	Mule Deer	3
	Elk	1
New Mexico	Elk	1
	Desert Bighorn Sheep	1
Utah	Elk	2
	Desert Bighorn Sheep	2

Notice that the total for all species is 10, which is the same as the number of records input.

(3) Calculations need to be performed;

(4) Reordering (resequencing) is required.

Any time data are processed, the following series of functions must be performed, regardless of whether the process is performed manually or automatically:

(1) Define required data elements,

(2) Identify data sources,

(3) Develop a collection process,

(4) Define where data are to be processed,

(5) Define programming requirements,

(6) Define data entry procedures,

(7) Define input procedures,

(8) Identify processing requirements,

(9) Define output procedures.

When data are processed by a computer, these functions can be performed by a systems analyst, programmer analyst, or wildlife biologist. These functions are discussed further in the following paragraphs.

Define Required Data Elements

To identify data required for input, the biologist should identify and analyze each item on the output document. One way is to list each item, then analyze it to determine if the data are read in, calculated, or generated. Figure 1 provides an example of an output document. The data elements requiring analysis are numbered 1 through 7.

DATA REPRESENTATION

Data must be in a form recognizable to the computer to be accepted by a data processing system. Symbols are used to represent data. The symbols on this page are recognizable by people. They represent a language. Electronic signals are the symbols used in computer language. When people communicate with a computer, they must use special devices to translate people-language into machine-language.

Data going into a computer are recorded in various ways, depending on the type of input device being used. They can be recorded as punched holes on input media such as cards, magnetic spots on magnetic tape and disk, characters and lines on paper documents, and so on. Not all data are recorded on an intermediate input media such as cards, magnetic tape, or disk. On some terminals, they may go directly to main storage with no input medium.

When data are entered through an input device, such as a card reader or a terminal, the device translates each character of input into a series of electronic signals. A signal, called a **bit,** is in one of two states—on or off, just like a light bulb. When individual signals are grouped together as a set of signals, they are called a **byte.** Each byte represents an addressable location in the computer's main storage. When data have been transferred to a location in main storage, they can be located and used in calculations or manipulations as necessary.

A character also is represented by one byte. Each character has a different set of bits. One character is different from another according to the bits which are on or off within its set. The combination of bits and the number of bits used to represent a character make up a code. Because codes used by computers vary, a code set is used to convert data from one form of representation to another. Codes that represent alphabetic, numeric, and special characters form a code set. Examples of commonly used code sets are **Extended Binary Coded Decimal Interchange Code (EBCDIC), American Standard Code for Information Interchange (ASCII), and Binary Coded Decimal (BCD).**

Codes are also used to indicate the end of data. The computer accepts all these signals and stores them in main storage. They can then be referenced and manipulated within the processing unit. When processing is completed, the electronic signals can be converted back into characters readable by people through output devices. Because of the similarity between the input and output functions, some devices are designed to perform both functions.

The above discussion refers to code sets used for character representation and should not be confused with coding of computer programs.

DATA STRUCTURES

The data used during the execution of a program are contained in a **data structure** known as a file. Data must be organized in such a way that they can be identified and located during the execution of a program. The smallest data structure is a character (byte). A group of characters is a **data element;** a group of data elements is a **record;** and a group of records is referred

Stream Name	River Mile (Start)	River Mile (End)	Segment Length (mi)	Mean Riparian Width (ft)	Riparian Acreage
North Creek	7.2	9.4	2.2	20	11.1
South Creek	0.0	5.0	5.0	35	42.4
East Creek	4.1	4.3	0.2	40	1.9
West Creek	3.7	4.7	1.0	25	6.1
TOTALS			8.4		61.5

Figure 1. Sample output document.

to as a **file.** For example, a person's name, consisting of a specific number of characters, could represent a data element. When several data elements containing information about the person are collected, a record is formed. The data elements in the record could contain the State codes and species codes. Several records with different data create a file. A file may be located on any media such as cards, tape, or disk.

Each field within a record contains the same number of characters as the corresponding field on another record. Because a space is a valid character, some fields may contain more spaces than others. For example, if a field contains 10 characters, the data "ABCD" would use 4 characters and 6 spaces to complete the field.

MAIN STORAGE CAPACITY

A computer's **main storage capacity** determines the amount of data and instructions that can be held in the system at any one time. The more main storage available, the faster storage and retrieval of data can occur. Although it would be desirable to have as much main storage as possible, it is expensive, and cost is often a limiting factor.

Computer storage is measured in **K**s; one K represents 1,024 bytes (characters). Computer main storage sizes range from as little as 4K on a microcomputer to as large as 16,000K (16 million bytes) on a large computer. One million bytes is called a **megabyte.**

APPLICATION PROGRAMS

Application programs perform specific user functions such as payroll, wildlife inventory, or material sales. Many programming languages are available. Three of the most commonly used are **COBOL (Common Business Oriented Language), FORTRAN (Formula Translator),** and **BASIC (Beginner's All-Purpose Symbolic Instruction Code).** These languages make essential and difficult computer programming tasks easier.

The sequence of instructions that make up the program is read into the computer's main storage. The instructions are processed in sequential order and the results produced. Once the program has begun to process, it will continue, without any human intervention, until completed. The instructions will be processed exactly as the program indicated.

PACKAGED PROGRAMS

An application program may be a generalized, pre-written program that performs a function requested by the user. This type of program, known as a **packaged program,** is increasingly available to the user. Many such programs are available for business and scientific functions. They usually contain alternatives that users may select for their particular situation. Sometimes these programs require modifications to meet the users' specific requirements. The cost for a packaged program is often less than having a specific program written. Consideration must be given to the computer system the program will be executed on.

Identify Data Sources

An analysis of the data elements indicates that data elements 1, 2, 3, and 5 are read in from a file. Data element 4 is calculated by subtracting data element 2 from data element 3. Data element 6 is calculated by converting data element 4 to feet, calculating the area, and converting the results to acres. Data element 7 is an accumulation of the indicated data elements.

The source of the data to be read in must be identified. The data may be in a form ready for input to the computer, such as a file located on disk or magnetic tape. The data may be located on source documents, such as field observation forms, but the data must be converted for input to the computer. If the data are not readily available, arrangements must be made to collect them.

Develop a Collection Process

A method for collecting data must be established. A special form may need to be designed for this purpose. Careful consideration should be given to the design of data entry forms.

Define Where Data are to be Processed

When data are to be processed manually, arrangements must be made as to where they will be processed and who will do the processing. If a computer is to process the data, arrangements must be made with the computer facility for processing. Because of the various sizes and capabilities of computers, it is important to know that the computer to be used is capable of processing the job. Where the computer is located will determine the method used in making the input data available.

READERS

Readers perform the input function in the data processing cycle. They read data into the computer's main storage where it will be available for processing. The devices discussed here are only capable of reading data. Punched cards were once the most important medium for data entry. In some locations they are still used despite their disadvantages of slow input, susceptibility to operator error, and machine malfunctions. Because of their disadvantages, cards are being replaced as an input media by direct entry to an electronic storage medium.

Another type of reader is the paper-tape reader. This device senses data as holes punched in paper tape. Another reader, the magnetic-ink character reader, translates magnetic-ink characters into electronic signals. It is widely used by the banking industry. Optical-character-recognition devices are often used to scan or read special marks, bars, letters, numbers, and characters from special printed documents which are then converted to electronic signals for computer processing.

To transfer graphics, drawings or images such as a map to the computer, a **digitizer** is used. A **cursor** or some other reading mechanism that can be passed over the surface converts the image to digital data. These data can then be displayed on a **cathode ray tube (CRT)** screen or processed by a computer system.

INPUT CONSIDERATIONS

Input data are often preprocessed or edited to ensure their validity. Because a process for updating ac-

counts receivable will have different edit requirements than a wildlife inventory update, there will be different edit criteria for each. However, the following are general considerations that are usually included in an edit:

(1) Tests to ensure numeric data are numbers and alpha data are characters.

(2) Tests for reasonableness of the data. For example, the months in a year should not exceed 12 or be less than 0.

(3) Range tests to see if data, such as acreage and herd numbers, fall within a range of acceptable values.

(4) Checklists of acceptable values to see if data are valid, such as correct species codes.

(5) Tests for data consistency. The data entered may be valid by themselves, but invalid in relation to other data entered. For example, when a wildlife inventory record has an entry for a hypothetical occurrence and a verified occurrence, only one may be entered. An entry for both, or blanks for both, indicates error.

(6) Checks for transcription and transposition errors. These errors usually occur when the data are being key-entered.

The instructions performed during edit processing are included in a computer program. When input data are processed, each record is checked using the instruction in the program. Any invalid data are identified so that they may be corrected. The process may be repeated as many times as necessary to obtain valid data.

Define Programming Requirements

Each processing step must be performed specifically and in the correct sequence. Because a computer can only perform calculations, comparisons, and data movements, all steps must consist of these types of instructions. The computer will process these instructions in sequential order. For example, if data are to be calculated, they must be read in before the calculation instruction is processed.

Programming is not as simple as it first appears, since every instruction has to be given to the computer. However, once these instructions have been prepared by a programmer and stored on storage media, the user needs only to issue a few commands and the instructions will be executed. Programs to do these calculations may already be available in some agencies or elsewhere. Furthermore, many software packages for common tasks are available, particularly for microcomputers. These include **spreadsheet** and **data base management** software. Such software requires simple commands to set up and perform tasks, but does not require knowledge of a programming language. Many biologists use such software without assistance from a computer programmer or specialist.

Define Data Entry Procedures

The data to be processed must be prepared for input. Data may need to be transferred to a data entry form if it is not on a document that can be directly used for data entry. If a form is required, the person filling out the form and the method of entering the data to be used should be identified.

Define Input Procedures

Data must be converted to a form usable by the

METHODS OF PROCESSING

One of several tasks performed by the computer when processing data is to interpret instructions. Another is to set up a connection to the input or output devices indicated in the instructions. The total tasks required to process a given set of data are known as a **job.**

Two basic processing methods are used by a computer system: **batch processing** and **interactive processing.** In batch processing, data are collected into groups (batches) and stored before being processed. Batch jobs are scheduled and prioritized by the computer operators or the computer's operating system, depending on the installation. They may be deferred to complete the processing when computer workloads are lower.

In interactive processing, data are entered directly into the computer and processed immediately. The user interacts with the program while it is processing, providing input and receiving output on a terminal.

OUTPUT CONSIDERATIONS

A printed report is one of the main types of output. It may be produced on various output devices and media. Printers can produce reports on a variety of forms or on microfiche. There are three major categories of reports: **detail reports, summary reports, and exception reports.**

Detail reports imply that each input record is read to determine if it will be printed on the report. A summary report provides a summary of the input data. It is usually used by management for making decisions.

Exception reports contain information determined to be an "exception" or other than normal. They are produced when specific information is needed. Their advantage is that they save time and money. Large reports that required many hours to produce and are printed on many pages do not have to be produced when the required information can be produced in a few minutes on a few sheets of paper.

INQUIRY

Output from interactive processing is usually obtained by **inquiry.** An inquiry is a request from the terminal operator to a computer system for information. This method provides the user with the most current information in the shortest period of time. Often a printed copy of the information on the terminal screen can be obtained. Usually the screen will prompt the user for entries and provide status information. Inquiry systems are usually designed for a wide variety of users and are easy to use. A well-designed inquiry system will provide prompts to guide the user. It will acknowledge all the user's entries and respond almost immediately. A wildlife biologist might use this type of system to determine the number and type of species in a certain location. This information can be requested and received from the computer system by the user without the need for a specific program to be written. Often programs have already been written and are available to assist the user in manipulating or extracting information from their data.

computer. Various input methods are available to accomplish this. The amount of data, the media the data are on, and the organization of the data (fields, records) are factors that should be considered. If input is directly through a terminal, computer access procedures must be established.

Identify Processing Requirements

The manipulations that must be performed to convert the data to information must be identified. All functions must be specified precisely and the sequence in which they are to be performed must be identified exactly. These are the instructions that will be followed during the execution of the program.

Define Output Procedures

The method of distributing the output and the type of output must be identified. Output may be in several forms. Due consideration should be given to the types available. Future use of the output should also be considered.

SYSTEM LIFE CYCLE

Just as computer technology has evolved from vacuum tubes to semiconductor chips, so have methods for developing systems. The first computer applications, such as payroll, were relatively simple. Problems in developing systems began to appear when applications such as wildlife were put on computers. These systems had a wide variety of data and complex relationships. System failures and lack of structure prompted managers to emphasize control of the development process. During the 1970s, computer specialists increasingly employed the sys-

PRINTERS AND PLOTTERS

Printers convert electronic signals received from the computer system's processor to letters and words on paper (hard copy) that can be understood. Nearly every computer system has a printer; many have several. Because printing requirements vary from user to user, many things must be considered when selecting and installing a printer. Some considerations are the volume of printing, the number of multiple copies required, the use of special forms, and the print quality required.

One way to classify printers is by the manner in which they print information. Serial printers print one character at a time; line printers print one line of information at a time; and page printers print a complete page of information at a time. Most computer sheets (11 x 14 in.) contain 66 horizontal lines printed 6 lines per inch with 132 characters in each line.

Another way to classify printers is by the way information is printed. When the printing elements are pressed (impacted) against the paper, the method is known as impact printing. Nonimpact printers use thermal (heat), chemical, electrical, or optical techniques to form images.

The way a printer forms characters is another method of classification. A solid character is like the characters used by a typewriter. Dot-matrix characters are formed with a series of dots. Impact printers use solid or dot-matrix characters. Nonimpact printers use only dot-matrix techniques.

Plotters are output devices that convert numerical information to graphic form. The output is produced by the plotter through use of pens or pencils or by electrostatic means. Many types of statistical information can be graphically illustrated by using a plotter.

MAGNETIC TAPE

Magnetic tape units are used for both input and output. They are capable of reading and writing on magnetic tape. They can read the equivalent of 300,000 punch cards a minute.

The typical magnetic tape reel contains 2,400 ft of 0.5-in., oxide-coated mylar tape. Data are recorded on the tape as magnetized spots in parallel channels or tracks along the length of the tape. The density or number of characters that can be written on a tape varies from 800 bytes per inch (**bpi**) to 6,250 bpi. The equivalent of 1.5 million fully punched cards can be stored on one reel of tape.

Magnetic tapes provide a compact, relatively inexpensive media for retaining data. They require protection from dust, humidity, and temperature fluctuation. To assure that data stored on a tape remain readable, they should be transferred (copied) to another tape once a year. It is not always necessary to use a new tape. The data on a tape can be erased, making it possible for the tape to be reused many times.

tem life cycle as a methodology for system development. It is still widely used today.

Although it has been developed for large-scale application, the principles and processes are applicable to any system. A wildlife biologist, setting up a system for storing and retrieving data on annual waterfowl, counts on the office microcomputer and follows the same basic procedure.

The evolution of an automated objective, such as wildlife inventory, from an initial idea to the required output, consists of several phases. These phases (which may be referred to by different terminology) consist of initiation, development, and operation.

During the initiation phase, the general requirements for meeting the objective are established.

The feasibility and cost of automating are documented; necessary approvals are obtained and justifications prepared; alternative processing procedures are identified; and requests for computing resources are made.

The development phase consists of definition, design, programming, and testing. During the development phase, the user's requirements are defined. From these requirements, specifications are prepared, the system is designed, and programs are written and tested, or appropriate software is located or purchased and tested. Documentation is prepared and user and operator guides provided as necessary. Testing results are reviewed by the user to assure the results are adequate. All deficiencies are identified and corrected. When the results produced meet the requirements, the development phase is complete.

MAGNETIC DISK AND DISKETTE

Magnetic disks and **diskettes** are often referred to as **hard disks** and **floppy disks.** The distinction refers to the flexibility of the material from which they are made. In this section, we refer to hard disks as disks and floppy disks as diskettes or flexible disks.

Magnetic disk units that read and write on magnetic disks are called **disk drives.** A magnetic disk is a thin metal platter coated on both sides with a metal oxide. Data are recorded as magnetized spots placed in circles on the surface of the disk. These circular recording positions are called tracks. Even though the tracks in the center of a disk are smaller, they contain the same amount of data as the outside tracks. The number of tracks on one surface of a disk varies from less than 100 on microcomputers to over 800 on large mainframes. The two recording surfaces of a disk have a storage capacity ranging from 2 million to about 20 million characters, depending on the number of characters written on each track. When several disks are combined on a common hub, they are known as a **disk pack.**

There are three categories of disk drives: (1) fixed, (2) removable, and (3) sealed. A fixed disk drive contains non-removable disks. These units provide large amounts of quickly accessible storage. A removable disk drive requires a disk or a disk pack to be mounted on the drive's vertical shaft before the data on the disk can be accessed. The need to increase data reliability resulted in the development of a sealed cartridge known as a Winchester disk. The cartridge contains the disks and other components used in reading and writing on the disks.

Another type of disk drive reads and writes on diskettes (floppy disks). A floppy disk is sealed in a square, plastic jacket. The most common sizes are 8 inches, 5 1/4 inches, and 3 inches. Since the slits in the jacket expose the recording surface, users should be careful not to touch the exposed area; this could damage the recording surface. Diskettes provide convenient, low-cost data-recording media that are easy to handle and can be reused.

Devices capable of storing large amounts of data on media such as magnetic tapes and disks are known as mass storage devices. Other types of mass storage devices capable of performing both input and output functions include magnetic drum and data cartridge. These types of storage are used by large computer systems because of their efficient intermediate storage capabilities.

ACCESS METHODS

There are two methods of accessing data: **sequential** and **direct.** In sequential access, data are read and written in a sequential order. To access data located at the end, all data preceding it must be read. The accessing procedure always starts at the beginning of the data.

In direct access, also called **random access,** data may be written to or read from any location on the medium. Data at the end of a project can be directly accessed. That is, none of the preceding data would be accessed. Devices capable of accessing data directly are called **direct-access storage devices.**

The operation phase includes maintenance, evaluation, and modifications, if required.

The limitations of the system life cycle have sometimes resulted in a backlog of applications to be placed on computers. Complex systems require a year or more to reach full production if this procedure is followed. Many organizations use structured analysis and design techniques and very high-level languages to reduce the time required to develop a system. Using these techniques, a skeleton system can be developed to the point of user involvement within a short period of time. Only a few months may then be required to bring the system to full production. The use of these techniques will grow in the future. The time involved to develop a system depends on its complexity. Such considerations as identifying data elements, defining codes to be used, and designing procedures for inputting data may be more involved for a complex system than a simple one.

SUMMARY

This chapter is not an in-depth discussion on any of the subjects mentioned. Additional information can be obtained from a number of good publications, such as those listed in the Literature Cited section at the end of this chapter. Another good source of information is through computer courses offered at most colleges and universities. For information on particular applications, many organizations have individuals who provide training and assistance.

Computers are sophisticated tools that require various amounts of training in their use. The information they provide is a very valuable resource. As with other resources, information must be man-

TERMINALS

Entering data directly into a computer's main storage is possible from a **terminal.** Receiving output (information) from a computer system is also possible at a terminal. A terminal may be a single device, two or three connected devices, or a computer system that sometimes acts like a terminal.

One of the most commonly used terminal devices is the **cathode ray tube (CRT).** It consists of a television-like screen and a typewriter-like keyboard. Data are entered through the keyboard by the terminal operator. Output information is presented in display form on the screen.

Another popular terminal device is the printer terminal. This device creates hard copy output instead of displaying the output information on a screen. It may or may not have a keyboard for data entry. When it is used only for receiving data, it is called a **receive-only (RO) terminal.**

Terminals that do nothing more than pass data back and forth are known as **dumb terminals.** A terminal that can perform limited processing functions, such as editing data before sending it to the computer, is known as an **intelligent terminal.** In addition to a keyboard and display screen (or printer), an intelligent terminal has a processor, main storage, and input/output interfaces. The processor circuitry may be a microprocessor.

Data may be entered and sent to a location(s) remote from the central computer site, if desired. Through **remote job entry (RJE),** data to be processed is entered directly into the computer via a remote terminal. Processing occurs on the central computer and output is sent back to one or more remote terminals.

DATA COMMUNICATIONS

The transmission of data from one location to another is known as **data communication.** When the transmission is over a long distance by means of telephone or telegraph lines, microwave, or radio, it is referred to as **telecommunications. Teleprocessing,** on the other hand, is an activity that involves both data processing and telecommunications.

A system in which data are collected from one or more points of origin, transmitted to a central location, and processed to produce results that are distributed to one or more points of use is known as a teleprocessing system.

The device used to convert electronic signals to a form for transmission over telephone lines is a modulator-demodulator, usually called a **modem.** It may be a separate unit or part of a communication control unit. Both the receiving end and the sending end of the line require a modem to convert signals. A special type of modem is known as an **acoustic coupler,** which uses a standard office telephone and does not require special wiring.

Data are transmitted over data communication channels (also called data lines or data links). There are several types of data communication channels, including (1) standard telephone lines, (2) coaxial cable, (3) microwave transmission, (4) satellite communications, and (5) fiber optics. The costs of these vary; standard telephone lines are the least expensive.

aged. Computers are one of the tools that can be used to manage information and other resources more effectively and efficiently.

Changes have taken place rapidly over the past few years and that trend is expected to continue. The real accomplishments of today may be only commonplace tomorrow. We believe the future holds great promise for the use of data processing by biologists. Exact applications of this technology are hard to predict, however. The use of hand-held data terminals, graphics, video text, laser printing, and fiber optics are just getting started. Many may be commonplace in the future. Sophisticated communications technology will soon allow electronic messaging and networking to be part of our lives. If

recent trends continue, hardware prices will decrease, speed of computations will increase, size will decrease, and computers will become more "user friendly."

Data processing for financial and administrative activities is simple and widespread compared with programming for wildlife and other natural resource fields. It is often difficult to explain all of the resource interactions to the programmer who is developing a particular application. However, biologists should not allow these complexities to intimidate them. Remember, the computer is just a tool. It is a powerful tool which can collect, store, and analyze data to expand knowledge about the resources we manage and make better wildlife management decisions.

Another factor affecting cost is line speed. Data are transmitted in bits per second (bps). A low-speed device transmits 40 to 300 bps. Although these devices usually transmit over telegraph communication lines, standard telephone lines used for voice communication (called "voice-grade" lines) can be used (with special modems) for full-duplex transmission at speeds up to 2,400 bps. For speeds of 4,800 bps and above, special communications are always required.

OPERATING SYSTEM

Each computer has an **operating system** that consists of a collection of software to supervise its operations. The operating system is usually provided by the computer manufacturer. Usually changes cannot be made to it by the local computer staff. When enhancements are made by the manufacturer, a copy is provided to the user. Operating systems vary from computer to computer even among those of one manufacturer. They are closely designed to the architecture of the computer hardware.

Functions of the operating system include supervising the execution of programs, directing input/output devices, and loading data into main storage. Most operating systems have programs that sort and merge data and transfer data from one media to another.

Operating systems are often identified by acronyms. For example, **Disk Operating System (DOS)** is a commonly used system for microcomputers.

TIME SHARING

Time sharing is a method whereby a computer is shared by several users for different purposes at the same time. While in time sharing, a user may interact

with a program while it is processing, submit processing to be performed later, or issue commands to determine the status of processing. Users appear to be served simultaneously due to rapid electronic speeds, although service is actually sequential.

DATA BASE

The term **data base,** in a generic sense, refers to all data elements that will be created, used, or manipulated by an automated data system. It does not imply any particular organization or structure of the data, nor that a **data base management system (DBMS)** will be used. The definition of and the procedures for using a data base may vary because of the different structures and organizations.

The updating process for a data base provides for changing the data for only one data element rather than a data element in several files. The value of the data element will be the same on the output from each program.

A data dictionary or **data element dictionary** is a tool that lists all data elements, their definitions, how and where they are used, and who is responsible for them. The dictionary helps standardize definitions of each data element. It is up to user departments to ensure that the data they need are truly represented in an organization's data base.

A major task for many organizations is deciding the data bases they need, the best locations, the data that should be stored in them, and the organization of the data.

LITERATURE CITED

BOHL, M. 1980. Information processing. Sci. Res. Associates, Inc., Chicago, IL. 492pp.

————. 1981. An end-user's guide to data base. Prentice-Hall, Inc., Englewood Cliffs, NJ. 144pp.

DE STEIGUER, J.W. and R.H. GILES, Jr. 1981. Introduction to computerized land-information systems. J. Forestry 79:734-737.

LEOPOLD, A. 1948. Game management. Charles Scribner's Sons. New York, NY. 481pp.

MAYER, K.E. 1984. A review of selected remote sensing and computer technologies applied to wildlife habitat inventories. California Fish and Game 70:102-112.

SHELLY, G.B. and T.J. CASHMAN. 1980. Introducton to computers and data processing. Anaheim Publishing Company, Fullerton, CA. 337pp.

SIEGERT, P.P. 1972. Systems and general management—a rationale. Am. Manage. Assoc. 181pp.

STEENHOF, K. 1982. Use of an automated geographic information system by the Snake River Birds of Prey Research Project. Computer-Environment Urban System 7:245-251.

STRACKBEIN, R. and D.B. STRACKBEIN. 1983. Computers and data processing simplified and self-taught. ARCO Publishing, Inc., NY. 94pp.

WINKLER, C. 1983. The computer careers handbook. ARCO Publishing, Inc., NY. 142pp.

37

STATISTICAL ANALYSIS

William H. West

U.S. Bureau of Land Management
Service Center
Denver, CO 80225

"Quantification as such has no merit except insofar
as it helps to solve problems."

—P.B. Medawar, *Advice to a Young Scientist*

*Editor's Note: A book on inventory and monitoring
of wildlife habitat would not be complete without
a discussion of statistics. Statistics are the basic
tool that biologists must use for analyzing quantitative data. Although many specialized techniques
have been developed for analyzing habitat data, in
many cases the traditional statistics are adequate.
One chapter cannot, of course, substitute for adequate basic training in statistics. It does, however,
describe the use of traditional statistics as well
as some of the new techniques such as multivariate
analysis to evaluate habitat.*

INTRODUCTION

Statistics should be a standard tool of the biologist working with inventory or monitoring. While
statistics are sometimes confusing and difficult to understand, they are procedures a resource manager
or biologist cannot afford to be without. Reliable
data are a must when managing natural resources in
today's society. However, we simply cannot afford to
measure every square inch of a resource! Statistical
inference allows the biologist to measure enough of
a site to make informed decisions based on data
representative of the area.

Statistics provide a way of describing wildlife
habitat as accurately as possible with the least
amount of cost. A biologist can describe a habitat
with a few factors and assign a level of confidence
about these factors. This provides the manager with
a good understanding of the problems faced and
allows a more knowledgeable decision to be made.
Finally, statistics provide a biologist with a means to
detect and test the results of management decisions.
Results that may be too small to be detected by visual inspection of a site or data can be displayed by
statistics, and variation from natural events, rather
than management actions, can be separated.

In all cases, statistics are merely a tool to be
used by a biologist or manager. Statistics do not
make decisions; they only provide managers with
information to make decisions. A manager or biologist who depends on statistics to make a decision
is abusing the use and intent of statistical analysis.
Only the manager can weigh all available data, determine the level of risk he or she is willing to accept,
and make a decision based on that information.

Statistics are tools, and there are special tools to
be used for special jobs. No one tool can be used
in all situations, and it is important to use the right
tool for the job at hand. A statistician can help select
and use the right tool and should be consulted before designing a study; after the study has started
is too late. Working with a statistician before data
are collected will help clarify questions, result in a
better study design, and save time and money.

Use of the right statistical tool can help support or refute the perceptions of a biologist. What a biologist sees, or thinks he or she sees, may not actually be occurring. Natural variation can cloud the situation and lead a biologist to a wrong conclusion. If the right statistical tool is used, confusion can be reduced or at least accounted for.

This chapter is not intended to teach statistics; the reader is assumed to have some basic knowledge. Rather, the chapter is intended to acquaint the reader with inventory and monitoring situations that require or are appropriate for statistical analysis and to supply the reader with statistical tools applicable to such situations. Basic statistical courses teach the equations, but seldom teach techniques of using them. The intent of this paper is to help teach how to use the equations.

TYPES OF STATISTICS

Generally statistics fall into two categories: descriptive and inferential. Descriptive statistics are used to describe a population or sample. In statistics a population is defined as the total items of interest that might occur (Box et al. 1978). The population is defined by a biologist before any testing is conducted. How a population is defined depends on the questions a biologist is interested in answering. If a biologist is interested in answering questions about the production of prairie falcons in Colorado, then the population would be defined as the number of falcon eyries in Colorado on a certain date. The numbers describing the population are the parameters of the population (e.g., the mean number of falcon eyries).

A description of the population is usually based on a sample from the population. The sample is always a subset of the population under study. The 125 falcon eyries surveyed during the summer of 1984 would be a sample of the population defined above. To help meet the assumptions made when using statistical analysis, the population sample is usually taken randomly. A random sample is one in which each member of the population has an equal and independent chance (probability) of being selected in any sample (Harnett 1982).

Inferential statistics, as the name implies, help a biologist infer or conclude something about a population, based on a sample. Inferential statistics allow analysis of the following:

(1) True population parameters (e.g., mean and standard deviation);

(2) Population differences;

(3) Association between two (or more) factors the biologist has measured;

(4) The effect on one factor from changes to other factors; and

(5) Whether a management action is having the desired effect.

Natural variation in populations and differences in samples taken make it difficult to determine differences or patterns just by looking at raw data. Inferential statistics help remove or account for the effects of natural and sampling differences, allowing a biologist to look more at the population without all the "noise."

STEPS TO USING STATISTICS

Use of statistics as a tool is most effective when there is a clear understanding of what is to be accomplished. Examining a data set without any clearly defined purpose to discover relationships or hypotheses is known as "data snooping." Data snooping is useful, but not the most efficient or effective means of examining data.

Green (1979) outlines 10 principles for designing a study. These principles are presented as a guide; not all situations may warrant using all 10 steps. A biologist must choose the applicable principles and use the concepts as guideposts.

(1) State the question concisely.

(2) Take replicate samples within each combination of time, location, and any other controlled variables.

(3) Take random samples. Putting samples in representative or typical places is not random sampling.

(4) Test whether a condition has an effect. Collect samples where the condition is present and where it is absent, but all else is the same.

(5) Do preliminary sampling to provide a basis for evaluating sampling design and statistical analysis.

(6) Verify that the sampling device or method is sampling the population thought to be sampled.

(7) Break large areas into relatively homogeneous subareas and allocate samples to each in proportion to the size of the subarea.

(8) Verify that sample unit size is appropriate to the size, densities, and spatial distribution of the organisms being sampled.

(9) Test data to determine if the error variation is homogeneous, normally distributed, and independent of the mean.

(10) Having chosen the best statistical method to test an hypothesis, stick with the result (Green 1979).

Of these principles, the most important are 1 and 10, although the others should not be ignored. Stating clearly the questions being asked will save many problems during the course of the study. Vague questions lead to vague answers, collection of unnecessary data, wasted time and money, bad conclusions, and use of inappropriate statistical tests. The importance of clear questions cannot be overstressed. A good question is the starting point or foundation of all good studies, and can lead to a good study design and proper selection and use of test statistics.

If the questions are properly asked, a biologist can avoid discarding these data because the results were incorrect or unexpected. A conclusion may be undesirable but the results will still be valid if the question was stated properly and the correct test chosen. Data and results should never be discarded on the basis that the results and conclusions were not what was wanted.

DESCRIPTIVE STATISTICS

Populations can be described in many different ways. The intent of any description is to convey an understanding of the population. A population (or a sample) can be described to a manager by merely listing all data in the population. For small data sets (<10 values), this may be a satisfactory method but listing becomes impractical when the number of values is large. Giving a manager a long list of numbers does not convey much information. It would be much more meaningful and easier to remember if only one or two values were listed to describe the population. The population mean and standard deviation, or sample average and standard deviation, supply information in a more manageable way.

Measures of Central Tendency

Descriptive statistics are used to convey more information in less space than listing all raw data. The first statistic used to describe a data set is some measure of the central tendency of these data. Three measures of central tendency are mode, median, and mean. The mode is a value in a data set (sample) that occurs most often; the median is a middle value that arranges data in ascending order; and the mean is a sum of all values divided by the total number of values (Harnett 1982).

EXAMPLE 1

A biologist has collected data on the number of sagebrush plants per square meter (square yard) on a single mesa top. A total of 20-meter-square plots were sampled and these following data were collected:

3, 9, 1, 5, 9, 0, 4, 7, 9, 5, 5, 1, 1, 6, 3, 8, 4, 4, 7, 5

The data value that occurs most often (mode) is 5. When these data are arranged in ascending order, the middle value of the data set (median) is also 5. The mean is 4.8 plants per m^2.

With continuous rather than discrete data, the mode is better calculated using groups or classes of data rather than each individual data set. If raw data are used, possibly only one value would occur for each measurement. By grouping these data, a more meaningful mode can be determined. However, the overall usefulness of the calculated mode depends on how the classes are constructed.

The mode and median are not used as often to describe a data set as the mean or average. However, there are situations when the mean of a data set does not make sense, as when working with nominal data (functional groups for vegetation classification, i.e., shrubs, half shrubs, grasses, etc.) or with ordinal data in which subjects are ranked, i.e., suitability of ecosystems for elk habitat (Krebs 1978). The mean of a population or the average of a sample can be thought of as the "point of balance of these data, analogous to the center of gravity" (Harnett 1982), and is the most commonly used statistical value.

Measures of Dispersion

The mean, mode, and median indicate the central tendency of these data but not how these data are grouped around the center. Measures of dispersion tell how these data are grouped or spread around the center. The range of these data is a measure of dispersion, indicating the difference between the high and low values. A common method of describing these data spreads is the standard deviation or the variance of these data. Each data set can be looked at for differences from the average. However, this method of describing these data has the same problem as discussed earlier; it conveys little meaning and is difficult to remember. A single summary value describing the spread of these data is much more satisfactory. However, simply summing the deviations conveys even less information than listing, since the sum of the deviations will always equal zero.

The average of all the squared deviations is the variance of these data. The square root of the variance is the standard deviation of these data. The standard deviation can be thought of as the typical deviation around the mean (Harnett 1982) and is more convenient to work with than the variance because it is in the same units as these original data.

EXAMPLE 2

Using these same data described in the previous example, the deviations of each plot value from the average of the entire sample (4.8 plants per m²) result in the following:

-1.8, 4.2, -3.8, 0.2, 4.2, -4.8, -0.8, 2.2, 4.2, 0.2, 0.2, -3.8, -3.8, 1.2, -1.8, 3.2, -0.8, -0.8, 2.2, 0.2

The sum of these deviations is zero. The sample variance is 7.9 and the standard deviation is 2.8.

Through repeated collection of continuous data, measurements tend to cluster around the mean measurement in a very predictable pattern. This pattern is the normal or bell-shaped distribution (see Figure 1). This distribution is described by two parameters: the mean (μ), describing the peak of the distribution, and the standard deviation (σ), describing the spread of these data around the mean.

This distribution has useful properties for dealing with continuous measurements. Approximately 68% of all data lies within plus or minus one standard deviation of the average, and 95% lies within plus or minus two standard deviations of the average. In the above example, 68% of all data lies between the values 2.0 and 7.6. The standard deviation and how it describes a sample will be important when testing a hypothesis or making inferences about the parent population.

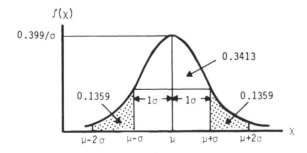

Figure 1. Normal distribution with mean and standard deviation.

Frequency Distributions

While the average and standard deviations are the most common methods of describing a data set, other descriptors are also useful in understanding these data. By grouping these data into equal intervals, dividing the number of observations in each interval by the total number of observations, and plotting the calculated frequencies, a frequency distribution can be derived. The shape of a frequency distribution helps explain data characteristics. Attributes of these data such as unimodal (one central peak), bimodal (two central peaks), or multimodal (many peaks) can be easily displayed with a frequency distribution. The shape of the distribution is very sensitive to the grouping of these data.

EXAMPLE 3

A biologist, working on the biological assumption that the size of a sagebrush plant crown is directly related to the age of the plant, collects average crown diameter (in centimeters) from 25 randomly selected plants from a specific vegetation type.

5, 5, 6, 7, 8, 8, 8, 9, 12, 12, 15, 16, 18, 18, 22, 24, 25, 25, 25, 26, 26, 27, 28, 29, 29

To attain the following frequency distribution, group these data into 2-cm intervals and divide the number in each class by the total number. The sum of the frequencies for all classes will be 1.

CLASS	NUMBER	FREQUENCY
4.50-6.49	(3)	0.12
6.50-8.49	(4)	0.16
8.50-10.49	(1)	0.04
10.50-12.49	(2)	0.08
12.50-14.49	(0)	0.00
14.50-16.49	(2)	0.08
16.50-18.49	(2)	0.08
18.50-20.49	(0)	0.00
20.50-22.49	(1)	0.04
22.50-24.49	(1)	0.04
24.50-26.49	(5)	0.20
26.50-28.49	(2)	0.08
28.50-30.49	(2)	0.08
TOTAL:	(25)	1.00

The frequency distribution shows two peaks (bimodal) in these data at 6.50 to 8.49 cm and again at 24.50 to 26.49 cm. The mean was calculated at 17.32 cm and the standard deviation at 8.68 cm (Figure 2).

The biologist would describe these data as having a mean diameter of 17.32 cm and a bimodal distribution with peaks at 6.50 to 8.49 cm and 24.50 to 26.49 cm. Based on the biological assumption made when these data were collected, the biologist would conclude the population has old and young plants, but few plants of medium age. This distribution may lead the biologist to ask why there was this type of distribution in age.

INFERENTIAL STATISTICS

Inferential statistics use information from a sample to infer something about the parent population or to test a theory or hypothesis about the population. The type of statistical test used will depend on the assumptions (statistical assumptions, rather than biological assumptions) made about the population.

Parametric statistics are used when the population can be assumed to have a known distribution. The normal or bell-shaped distribution is one that is familiar to the average user. Since standard deviation of the population is usually unknown, a t-distribution based on the sample is substituted for the normal distribution. The t-distribution is similar to the normal distribution (Huntsberger and Billingsley 1977); the exact shape of the distribution depends on the size of the sample taken. The larger the sample size, the closer the t-distribution will approach a normal distribution.

An assumption made about the sample is that the sample items have a normal distribution and are independent of each other. The selection of an item (or subject) to sample will not affect the distribution of other items in the sample (Box et al. 1978).

To ensure the assumptions are met, it is important a random sample from the population be used. Collecting data in representative or typical areas does not constitute a random sample (Green 1979). The largest sample that is economically feasible should be collected so sample distribution more

closely approximates the population distribution. A good discussion on the consequences of violating these assumptions when using ecological data can be found in Green (1979).

When no assumption can be made about the distribution of the population, nonparametric statistics are employed. Nonparametric statistics are used to test the assumption of a normal distribution and to conduct statistical tests without making assumptions about the form of the distribution. Collecting a random sample has more influence on the results of any statistical analysis than the assumption of a population with an unknown distribution (Box et al. 1978). Nonparametric statistics will be discussed after some of the common parametric statistics.

Confidence Intervals

The first parametric statistic deals with the inference of the true population mean, based on the sample average and standard deviation and desired level of probability. This type of statistic is known as the confidence interval and assumes normal distribution of population. The confidence interval, in effect, indicates the range of potential values of the population mean, given the level of error a biologist is willing to accept.

EXAMPLE 4
A biologist has defined a population as the standing crop (g/m^2) of a particular pasture during the week of July 4, 1983. Sixty plots, each 1 m^2, were sampled, and a sample average of 327 g/m^2 and sample standard deviation of 112 g/m^2 were calculated. Confidence intervals for the mean at an 80% confidence level and a 95% confidence level were calculated.
80% C.L. on the mean = 308 g/m^2 to 345 g/m^2 95% C.L. on the mean = 298 g/m^2 to 355 g/m^2
The biologist would conclude the population mean lies somewhere within the ranges calculated with the indicated probability.

The confidence level expresses the probability that a parameter falls within the indicated limits but, more importantly, the level of risk a biologist is willing to accept in coming to a wrong conclusion. When a biologist says he or she is 80% confident the mean is within the limits, what is actually being said is he or she is willing to accept a 20% chance of being wrong. A 95% confidence means a 5% chance of being wrong.

The smaller the acceptable risk of being wrong, the larger the limits. This concept becomes important when testing hypotheses using a high confidence level. The higher the confidence level, the more difficult to disprove or reject an hypothesis. It

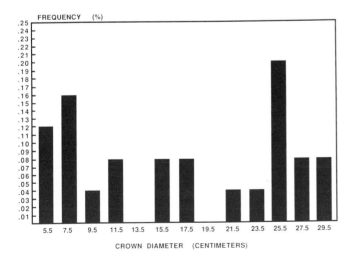

FREQUENCY DISTRIBUTION
SAGEBRUSH CROWN DIAMETER

Figure 2. Frequency distribution of sagebrush crown measurements.

must also be remembered there is a trade-off between the size of a sample and the confidence level desired. A statistic calculated from a small sample size with a high confidence level may not tell much about the population parameter being estimated.

EXAMPLE 5

The biologist decides to collect only four samples from the population (Example 4) and determines the sample average to be 327 g/m^2 and a sample standard deviation of 112 g/m^2. He or she is interested in taking little risk when estimating the population mean and desires a confidence level of 95% or 99%.

95% C.L. on the mean = 148 g/m^2 to 505 g/m^2
99% C.L. on the mean = −0.10 g/m^2 to 654 g/m^2

The biologist has high confidence the population mean is between the limits 0.0 g/m^2 and 654 g/m^2. However, because of the range of values, nothing more is known than when started. The small sample size coupled with the high confidence level have made the numbers meaningless.

Sample Size

To ensure the statistics will be meaningful for the desired confidence level and range of limits, an adequate sample size should be calculated. Before any sampling is done, a biologist must determine the level of risk, the maximum range of acceptable limits, and the funds available for sampling (Harnett 1982). With these conditions in mind, a biologist can then collect a few samples and determine the sample size needed to conform to the stated specifications, based on the preliminary samples. (See Example 6.)

When choosing an adequate sample size, set reasonable expectations for the results. Do not make the range of limits too small! Knowing population values with a very small range and high confidence level may be desirable, but collecting these data may be too expensive. In Example 6, if the biologist had set a range of 10 g/m^2 with a 99% confidence level, a total of 5,300 samples would have to be collected. Additionally, because the adequate sample is based on a preliminary sample, the adequate sample size should be recalculated periodically throughout the sampling period to determine if any changes in the adequate sample size have occurred from changes in the sample mean or standard deviation.

There is a balance between meaningful results and the cost of sampling. It is important to strive for the most meaningful results within the constraints of time and money. If the commitment of resources is not going to be made to obtain meaningful results, then it is better to not sample at all, or to reduce the population size to fit within the monetary con-

straints. Do not reduce the limits of the results below the level where they convey any information. Subjective, qualitative information gathered by a site visit, for example, may be better than quantitative information derived from an inadequate data set. No data are just as good as vague data and much less costly. Example 5 is a situation where the cost of data collection was minimal, but the information gathered was useless.

Hypothesis Formulation

The next area of inferential statistics involves testing of ideas or concepts. Essential to this process is the formulation of hypotheses. Two hypotheses are always formed about the ideas being tested. The null hypothesis (H_o) is assumed to be correct until proven false by the test. The alternate hypothesis (H_a) is assumed to be correct in the event the null hypothesis is proven false. The null hypothesis and alternate hypothesis are complementary.

Green (1979) cited some general rules for formulating null hypotheses. First, the null hypothesis should be the simplest one possible and yet describe the concept being tested. If the hypothesis is complex, the question asked is too broad. Second, the null hypothesis must be falsifiable; the data collected must be able to disprove the concept (no amount of data can ever prove a concept). Finally, the null hypothesis should have the fewest number of unknown explanatory factors. If the concept tested has many unknown factors affecting the result, conclusions will be difficult to form.

EXAMPLE 6

Before sampling the population described in Example 4, the biologist decides to determine an adequate sample size before completing the sample. The decision has been made to accept a 10% chance of error with a maximum range in the limits of 50 g/m^2. After collecting 10 samples, a sample average of 327 g/m^2 and sample standard deviation of 112 g/m^2 are calculated.

Solving the equation:

$$n = \frac{(2ts)^2}{w^2}$$

Where: t = the t-variable for the sample at the stated level of error.
s = the standard deviation of the sample.
w = the width of the desired confidence interval.

Based on the preliminary sample, the biologist determines that 67 samples must be collected to meet the desired specifications. An additional 57 samples are then collected.

Hypothesis formulation relates directly to the questions a biologist is asking. If good questions are asked, the formulation of hypotheses will be easier than if poorly formed or vague questions are asked. The formulation of hypotheses should be made when the questions are asked. This helps determine what data should be collected and what tests conducted to falsify the null hypothesis and answer the questions.

Included in the formulation of the null hypothesis should be the probability level at which the null hypothesis will be rejected in favor of the alternate hypothesis. The alternate hypotheses should also indicate if all the chance for error is to be placed in one tail or both tails of the probability distribution of the sample. The chance for error can be placed in one tail if there is reason to believe there is no chance of the error occurring in the opposite direction. When testing the hypothesis that standing crop on a salt flat is zero, there is no need to test if the standing crop is less than zero. Any chance of error is placed on the side of standing crop being greater than zero.

t-Test

The most common statistic employed to test a hypothesis or compare the means of two samples (populations) is the t-test. The test assumes the population has a normal distribution and the sample has a t-distribution.

EXAMPLE 7

A biologist has identified two sagebrush flats on either side of a small canyon (site A and site B). Both sites are influenced by the same weather patterns and are on the same soil formations. The biologist wants to know whether the sites are the same and can be managed as such. The biologist also wants to know if site B has enough standing crop (at least 1,120 g/m^2) to support the deer herd using the site.

The two populations are defined as the total standing crop (g/m^2) at sites A and B on the first week in August. The following specific questions and hypothesis are formulated:

(1) Is the mean standing crop of population A the same as population B?

H_o: Mean A = Mean B
H_a: Mean A ≠ Mean B

EXAMPLE 7 (concluded)

(2) Is the mean standing crop of population B at least equal to the minimum standing crop needed (1,120 g/m^2) to support the deer herd using the site?

H_o: Mean B = 1,120 g/m^2
H_a: Mean B = 1,120 g/m^2

The biologist is willing to accept a 10% chance of error of estimating the mean incorrectly, with a range of 60 g/m^2. For the first question, the chance of error will be distributed between both tails of the t-distribution. For the second question, the probability will be placed entirely in the lower portion of the t-distribution since the biologist is only interested in a value less than 1,120 g/m^2.

Ten preliminary samples were collected at both sites. For site A, the preliminary sample had an average of 973 g/m^2 and standard deviation of 68 g/m^2; from this information an adequate sample size of 17 plots was calculated. For site B, with a sample average of 1,010 g/m^2 and standard deviation of 107 g/m^2, an adequate sample size of 43 was determined. From the adequate sample sizes, the final average of site A is 985 g/m^2 with a standard deviation of 70 g/m^2; the final average for site B is 1,022 g/m^2 with a standard deviation of 116 g/m^2.

From these sample data, a t-test statistic of -1.22 for Question 1 was calculated. Comparing this value to a table value (1.671) for the t-distribution of these sample data, the biologist found the chance of error was not greater than the stated rejection level. Since the biologist did not reject the null hypothesis (H_o), he or she concluded the two populations were the same, or the two samples were from the same population.

For Question 2, a t-test statistic of -5.5 was calculated and compared to a table value of 1.303 for the t-distribution for these sample data. The calculated t-test statistic was found to exceed the permissible error level (10%). The null hypothesis (H_o) was then rejected and the alternate hypothesis (H_a) accepted. The biologist concluded the standing crop at site B was not sufficient to supply the minimum needs of the deer herd at 1,120 g/m^2.

Analysis of Variance

The t-test is useful when comparing two samples or when comparing a sample to some hypothesized value. However, when more than two samples (populations) are compared, an Analysis of Variance (ANOVA) table is used. The ANOVA table accounts for the variation of different factors of many populations simultaneously and is very useful when comparing the effectiveness of different management treatments. The table can separate variation between treatments and within treatments so a biologist can more directly evaluate the response of the site to the management actions. The ANOVA table provides information for the calculation of statistics, such as the F-statistic, that can be used to compare populations or test hypotheses.

Construction of an ANOVA table is flexible and can be built to account for environmental conditions and the experimental design used. By careful experimental design, a biologist can remove (account for) some of the variability in these data and examine only the factors of interest. A good experimental design is the key to using an ANOVA table, and a statistician should be consulted at the very beginning of the test to ensure the design is adequate. Major factors affecting the experimental design are the biological and environmental conditions present. A biologist must have a good understanding of these factors when the statistician is consulted. Differences in soils, climate, or species being studied might all prompt changes in the design of the experiment and must be considered prior to starting the study.

EXAMPLE 8

Two herbicide dealers want a biologist to use their products in a proposed spraying of tamarix plants to reduce plant cover. Both herbicides are applied to the soil and are absorbed through the plant roots. Before buying either product, the biologist wishes to determine which of the two sprays is more effective.

A small hillside is used in a test of the two sprays. The biologist notes a difference in the soil type, depth, and available moisture at the bottom, middle, and top of the slope; all other environmental factors (to the best of the biologist's knowledge) are the same. Because of these differences, the biologist feels these changes must be accounted for in the experimental design. The design is, therefore, blocked (partitioned) based on the position of each test plot on the slope. One-ha plots (selected at random) at the top, middle, and bottom of the slope are sprayed with Herbicide A; the other similar plots are sprayed with Herbicide B. Control plots of untreated tamarix are also located at each position on the slope to compare with the treated plots.

The population the biologist is interested in is defined as the cm^2 of ground covered by the aerial portions of the tamarix plants per square meter of ground area, 1 month after spraying has occurred. The following specific questions are to be answered by the study:

(1) Is there any difference in the effectiveness of the three herbicides?

H_o: Mean A = Mean B = Mean C
H_a: At least two means are not equal

Where: Mean A = the plots treated with Herbicide A.

EXAMPLE 8 (continued)

Mean B = the plots treated with Herbicide B.

Mean C = the untreated plots.

(2) Is there any difference in the cover of tamarix at each position on the slope after treatment?

H_o: Mean L = Mean M = Mean T
H_a: At least two means are not equal

Where: Mean L = the plots at the lower level of the slope.

Mean M = the plots in the middle of the slope.

Mean T = the plots near the top of the slope.

The biologist determined a 10% chance of error is acceptable and set a 90% confidence level for the test. One month after spraying the following results were obtained:

		TREATMENT		
		A	B	C
	T	37	38	36
SLOPE	M	88	76	81
	L	51	42	47

The following ANOVA table was constructed from these data:

SOURCE OF VARIATION	DF*	SUM OF SQUARES	MEAN SQUARE	F STATISTIC
Block (position on slope)	2	3,313.56	1,656.78	139.71
Treatment (herbicide)	2	67.56	33.78	2.83
Residual	4	47.78	11.94	
TOTAL:	8	3,428.90	N/A	N/A

*DF: Degrees of Freedom

Comparing the F-statistic for treatments calculated from these data (2.83) to the table value (4.32) for the F-distribution, the null hypothesis (H_o) for the first question cannot be rejected.

The biologist would thus conclude that neither treatment is effective in reducing the cover of tamarix plants, since treatment with Herbicide A or B did not significantly reduce the tamarix cover below that of the untreated plots. The ANOVA table does not tell the biologist why the herbicides are ineffective, only that there is no difference in the tamarix cover of the plots. If the biologist had found significant differences in the treatments, he or she could then go on to test and examine which treatments were different.

For the blocks (position on slope) the calculated value (139.71) exceeds the table value (4.32) and the null hypothesis (H$_o$) is rejected. Thus, the biologist would conclude that there are significant differences in cover of tamarix at different positions on the slope. The conclusion would also be reached that the decision to block the experiment on the basis of the position of the plot on the slope was appropriate, as significant differences were found in the tamarix cover on the bottom, middle, and top of the slope.

In addition to determining differences between treatments, the ANOVA table can also evaluate interactions of treatments when applying two or more treatments to plots in combination. This use of the ANOVA table enables a biologist to examine each kind of treatment individually and in combination to determine differences and interactions of the treatments.

If in Example 8 the biologist had also been interested in the effect the type of application (aerial versus hand application) had on the effectiveness of the herbicides, the experimental design could be altered to examine these interactions. The experimental design would be the same as described except each herbicide treatment would have been applied manually and aerially. The biologist would be able to answer the same questions as before, but would also be able to answer the following questions:

(1) Is there a difference in the effectiveness of the mode of application?

(2) Is there any interaction between the mode of application and type of herbicide used?

Regression Analysis

Another situation often encountered is the need to predict the changes in one factor as other factors change. This type of situation is handled statistically by the use of regression analysis, using either simple linear regression (one dependent variable and one independent variable) or multiple linear regression (one dependent variable and many independent variables). Regression analysis uses associations between the dependent and independent variables to construct an equation describing the dependent variable based on the independent variables. From this equation, the biologist can predict what the dependent variable will be as the independent variables change. Another application of the equation is to permit a biologist to predict a variable too expensive or difficult to measure directly (dependent variable) from variables less costly to measure (independent variables).

Closely associated with regression analysis is correlation analysis. While regression analysis describes how one factor will change as other factors change, correlation analysis determines the degree of association between the factors.

The biologist has noted an apparent association between the density of sagebrush plants and the density of sage grouse in a certain mountain basin. Based on this association, the biologist wishes to predict the number of sage grouse per square kilometer from the number of sagebrush plants per hectare, and has collected the following sets of data:

SET	SAGEBRUSH PLANTS/ha	SAGE GROUSE/km^2
1	200	21
2	600	29
3	500	30
4	100	12
5	700	32
6	700	27
7	100	17
8	500	32
9	900	37
10	200	18
11	300	25

Based on these data the biologist calculates the regression equation:

$$Y = 0.0255 \, X + 14.32 \qquad r = 0.91$$

Where: Y = the number of sage grouse per square kilometer.

X = the number of sagebrush plants per hectare.

r = the correlation coefficient of the two variables.

The biologist then asks what the population density of sage grouse will be if sagebrush density is reduced to 300 plants per hectare. Replacing the X in the regression equation, the biologist estimates there will be 22 sage grouse per square kilometer at a plant density of 300 plants per ha. The biologist goes on to ask for the range of estimates in the sage grouse density if he or she was willing to accept only a 10% chance of error, and constructs a 90% confidence interval around the estimate.

90% C.I.: 22 sage grouse ± 6.37 sage grouse

The correlation coefficient given in the previous example is a measure of the degree of association between the independent and dependent variables. A correlation coefficient (r) approaching 1 indicates a high positive association between the two variables; as one variable increases, the other variable also increases. A correlation coefficient of -1 indicates a high negative association, where one variable increases as the other decreases. The closer the r value is to 1 or -1, the stronger the association; the closer to zero, the weaker the association.

The correlation coefficient is only an indication of how the two variables will change in association with each other. It does not indicate a cause-and-effect relationship although there may be one. In Example 9, the high r value of 0.91 does not necessarily mean the change in sagebrush density is causing a change in sage grouse density.

Even though two variables have a high correlation, one variable will not necessarily be a good predictor of the other. The two variables may be changing in association with each other, but the amount of change is so small the predication equation does not provide any information. This situation can be discovered by testing to see if the slope of the regression line is significantly greater than zero.

The lack of significance in Example 10 may be due more to the small sample size than a true lack of slope in these data. A larger sample size could indicate a slope significantly different from zero. However, this example is typical of the sample sizes many biologists use or must use.

The example and descriptions of uses of simple linear regression given here can be expanded to more than one independent variable by the use of multiple linear regression. Multiple regression can be useful in choosing which independent variables of many can be useful in predication, by testing the coefficients of each variable to see whether they are greater than zero (as done in Example 10).

Nonparametric Statistics

Many of the statistics discussed so far have been based on the assumption that the populations, from which the samples come, have a normal or some other distribution. This assumption may not always be the case (as in Example 3) or a biologist may not be willing to make the assumption. In such situations, a distribution-free or nonparametric test can be used, analogous to the parametric tests already presented. It is also possible to transform these data so the assumptions for parametric tests can be made; however, this is a topic that will not be discussed here.

Mann-Whitney U Test. The Mann-Whitney U test is used in situations appropriate for a t-test, but only

---

EXAMPLE 10

For the last 9 years, the biologist has been measuring the ambient temperature on April 1 and the peak standing crop (g/m^2) on July 1, in a certain mountain valley, hoping the temperature may be used to predict the standing crop.

YEAR	TEMP(°C)	STANDING CROP(g/m^2)
1	11	500
2	12	520
3	12	519
4	13	530
5	14	535
6	14	537
7	9	492
8	11	498
9	5	480

The following regression line is calculated from these data:

$$Y = 6.71X + 437.05 \qquad r = 0.92$$

The high correlation coefficient of the equation (0.92) suggests there is a strong positive association between the two variables. The biologist wants to test whether the temperature is a good predictor of standing crop. To do this he or she asks the question and formulates the hypothesis:

Is the data slope of the temperature line significantly different from zero?

$$H_o: B = 0$$
$$H_a: B \neq 0$$

Where: B = the slope of the regression line.

The biologist determines that only a 2% chance of error is acceptable. A t-test statistic is calculated for the slope of the line at 2.44. It is then compared to a table value of the t-distribution of these data of 2.998. The test statistic is not beyond the level of error set for the test; therefore, the null hypothesis cannot be rejected. The biologist would conclude the slope of the regression line is not significantly different from zero, and the ambient temperature on April 1 is not a good predictor of standing crop on July 1, despite the high correlation between the two variables.

---

where no assumption of a normal distribution is made and samples are from independent populations (Harnett 1982). (See Example 11.)

Contingency Table. Another nonparametric procedure is the use of the Chi-Square statistic to test the independence of two or more classifications made on the same site or subject by using a contingency table. Data used in this test are the frequency of classification combinations given to the study subject. The question asked is "Is one classification of a site independent of another classification of the same site or does one classification tend to occur consistently with another classification?"

portance as a tool of the ecologist. The intent of this section is to merely introduce the reader to these procedures and to describe general areas where these techniques could be applied.

EXAMPLE 11

A biologist has encountered a similar situation as described in Example 7, but is unwilling or unable to make the assumption that the population has a normal distribution. Again, the biologist wants to know if the two samples are from the same population and, thus, forms hypotheses to test the relationship at a 5% chance of error.

H_o: Population A = Population B
H_a: Population A $\neq$ Population B

Ten random samples are located in each site and standing crop data (g/m^2) are collected from each site:

SITE A	SITE B
900	1,065
1,201	843
857	912
1,013	1,104
923	1,292
951	1,312
1,173	742
1,021	961
914	1,093
777	776

A Mann-Whitney U test statistic is calculated from these data at 46 and compared with a table value of 78 (Snedecor and Cochran 1967). The calculated value exceeds the acceptable error established for the test (the calculated value is less than the table value), and the null hypothesis is rejected. The biologist would conclude the two samples are not from the same population.

EXAMPLE 12

A specialist has identified 22 separate mountain valleys that can be grazed by either cattle or elk. By an arbitrary system, each valley has been classified as good, fair, and poor elk range and as good, fair, and poor cattle range. The specialist is interested in determining if the two classifications are independent of each other, or if good elk range also tends to be good cattle range. To answer the question at the 5% level of rejection, the hypotheses are formed:

H_o: The classifications are independent.
H_a: The classifications are dependent.

Each valley classification is arranged in a contingency table.

	ELK		
	Good	2/2.64	3/1.2	1/2.16
CATTLE Fair	4/4.84	2/2.2	5/3.96
Poor	5/3.52	0/1.6	3/2.88
	Good	Fair	Poor

Where the values in the table are read as—

OBSERVED FREQUENCY/EXPECTED FREQUENCY

From these data, the calculated Chi-Square statistic is 6.14, which compared with the table value (9.49) is not beyond the level of rejection established for the test. The null hypothesis cannot be rejected, and the specialist would conclude the two classifications are independent of each other. Good elk range is not always good cattle range.

MULTIVARIATE ANALYSIS

All the analyses dealt with so far have used only one variable at a time, e.g., standing crop, crown diameter, plants per unit area. This type of analysis is known as univariate analysis. Unfortunately, most habitats and habitat relationships cannot be adequately described by only one variable, but require the use of many variables. Descriptions using more than one variable are the area of statistics known as multivariate analysis. This area of statistical analysis is receiving greater emphasis from the ecological community (Johnson 1981), despite the complexity of calculation and difficulty of interpretation. However, as the availability of computer programs expands and as biologists become more familiar with these techniques, this area of statistics will attain greater im-

Although not a true multivariate analysis, the first technique that comes to mind is multiple regression. Touched on briefly before, this analysis permits a biologist to predict a variable of interest (dependent) from many other variables (independent). The technique can be used to predict a variable too costly to measure directly from less costly variables; to predict changes in a variable based on changes in other variables; or when using stepwise multiple regression, to select those independent variables that account for the most variability in the dependent variable. A common use in habitat analysis is to predict animal abundance (dependent variable) from a set of habitat attributes (independent variables).

Discriminant Analysis

Discriminant function analysis is used to separate observations into groups (Johnson 1981). When a number of groups or sites have been defined on the basis of certain ecological factors, discriminating between the different sites is sometimes difficult because of overlapping distributions of ecological factors used to describe the sites. A biologist cannot clearly assign a site to one group or another because the site could have attributes of both groups.

Based on the variables used to describe the original groups, discriminant analysis creates new distributions (hybrid distributions of the original variables) that result in greater separation or discrimination between the defined groups (Webster and Burrough 1974). The hybrid distributions make it easier to assign a site to one group or another because of greater definition between the groups. This is potentially one of the most useful multivariate techniques, especially in the area of habitat classification.

The discriminant analysis is a transformation of the original factors for each site into a single value (score) distribution for each site, with more distinction between the sites. The biologist calculates the discriminant score for each new site, plots the new score on the distributions of the defined sites, and determines which site the new location more closely approximates. (See Example 13.)

Principal Component Analysis

The principal component analysis is a multivariate technique used to combine "measurements of similar nature into a fewer number that may be more stable" (Johnson 1981). The process selects a few important variables out of many, by taking a set of similar observations (measurements) and combining them into a single variable. For example, measurements of tree height, diameter, age, and stand density may all be combined into a single variable. The first new component constructed from these original data will account for the largest possible variability of these original data, and each additional component constructed will account for the largest possible amount of the remaining variability left after construction of previous components. (See Example 14.)

Principal component analysis is useful in identifying which groups of measurements will account for the greatest variability in these data. If several soil, climate, and vegetation measurements are collected for a site, principal component analysis will identify which group (soil, climate, or vegetation) accounts for the greatest variability in these data. Because all these data are included in the analysis, some combinations of measurements could be difficult to interpret. Tree measurements and soil measurements could be combined into a single principal component making it difficult to interpret exactly what the principal component is telling a biologist.

Canonical Correlation

Very similar to the principal component analysis is the canonical correlation analysis. The difference is that canonical correlation analysis uses two separate sets of measurements and derives a linear combination of each data set such that the correlation between the two derived values (components) is

---

EXAMPLE 13

A biologist defines two habitat types on the basis of these available data and on past experience. To define the types, the biologist relied on the percentage of shrub cover, annual precipitation, and the annual forage production. When examining new locations, the biologist had difficulty placing new locations into one of the two habitat types. One factor (e.g., forage production) may place the location in one type, whereas the other factors (e.g., percentage shrub cover and annual precipitation) would place the same location in a different type. To help differentiate the new locations into the two habitat types, the biologist performed a discriminant analysis on the two previously defined types and obtained a discriminant equation:

$$D = aX + bY + cZ + C$$

Where:
- X = the standardized shrub cover.
- a = the standardized discriminant coefficient for shrub cover.
- Y = the standardized annual precipitation.
- b = the standardized discriminant coefficient for precipitation.
- Z = the standardized annual forage production.
- c = the standardized discriminant coefficient for forage production.
- C = the constant for the discriminant equation.
- D = the discriminant score.

A mean discriminant score was calculated for each of the two known habitat types. As each new site was encountered, a discriminant score was calculated and compared to the means of the two known groups (habitat sites). Each new site was then classified into one of the two known habitat types, based on which of the known discriminant groups had the highest probability of containing the discriminant value from the new site.

EXAMPLE 14

In the previous example (Example 13), the biologist decided not to limit these data to the three sets described and instead decided to use 19 climatic variables (data from Newnham 1968):

NUMBER	VARIABLE	
1	Latitude	
2	Elevation, feet	
3	Average daily max. temp. (°F),	Winter
4		Spring
5		Summer
6		Fall
7	Average daily min. temp. (°F),	Winter
8		Spring
9		Summer
10		Fall
11	Average daily mean temp. (°F),	Winter
12		Spring
13		Summer
14		Fall
15	Average precipitation (inches),	Winter
16		Spring
17		Summer
18		Fall
19	Average frost-free period, days	

After computation, three components are derived that account for 92.2% of the variation of these data.

COMPONENT

VARIABLE	1	2	3
	COEFFICIENTS		
1	−0.63	−0.50	1.00
2	−0.85	0.10	−0.67
3	0.97	0.10	−0.41
4	0.02	1.00	−0.18
5	−0.11	0.99	−0.29
6	0.94	0.13	−0.45
7	1.00	−0.02	−0.10
8	0.90	0.35	0.50
9	0.84	0.31	0.75
10	0.99	−0.05	−0.01
11	1.00	0.02	−0.22
12	0.57	0.85	0.17
13	0.38	0.94	0.22
14	0.99	0.03	−0.19
15	0.72	−0.67	−0.23
16	0.59	−0.73	−0.26
17	0.40	−0.86	0.06
18	0.71	−0.70	−0.10
19	0.93	0.01	0.05
PERCENT OF VARIATION	57.4	29.4	5.4

Once each coefficient was determined for each variable, the biologist multiplied each by its coefficient and summed the products to arrive at the value for each principal component. The three components would then be used in the discriminant analysis as described in Example 13.

maximized (Warwick 1975). A second canonical correlation (component) is then constructed from the remaining variability of these original data so the highest correlation is achieved between the next two components.

Whereas the principal component analysis derives values from a single set of data to account for the greatest variation in these data, the canonical correlation analysis derives values from two sets of measurements to attain the highest correlation between the two data sets. If one data set contained vegetation measurements and a second contained abiotic measurements, canonical correlation analysis would identify which of the abiotic measurements is most highly associated (correlated) with the vegetation measurements.

EXAMPLE 15

A biologist has collected data on relative humidity (V1), precipitation (V2), wind speed (V3), and climatic temperatures (V4). Data have also been collected on vegetation cover (V5), frequency (V6), production (V7), and standing crop (V8). The biologist is curious how the two data sets (V1 through V4 and V5 through V8) relate to each other.

The canonical analysis selects the V1 and V2 values from the first set, and V7 and V8 from the second set to be used in the first canonical variant (CANVAR1). Since the biologist is only interested in the effects of climate on vegetation, only the coefficients for these climate data are presented.

CANVAR1 = −0.527(V1) −0.463(V2)

The V3 and V4 values from the first set and the V5 and V6 values from the second set are selected for the second canonical variant (CANVAR2).

CANVAR2 = 0.542(V3) − 0.635(V4)

The first canonical variant has a correlation of 0.889, indicating that these data in the first canonical variant (V1, V2, V7, V8) share 79% (the square of the correlation) of the variance of these data. The second variant has a correlation of 0.824 and shares 68% of the variance.

After conducting canonical correlation, the biologist found precipitation-humidity data and production-standing crop data had the highest correlation, followed by wind speed, temperature, and cover-frequency data.

As with principal component analysis, a biologist runs the risk of obtaining combinations of data that are hard to interpret. This example was constructed in such a way as to present the clearest interpretation; however, this type of clarity will seldom be present in most ecological situations.

TIME-SERIES ANALYSIS

Ecologists have long recognized that ecological systems experience a cyclic behavior over time. The use of time-series analysis allows a biologist to describe how a variable changes through time and to predict how the variable will change in the future. The time frame used with this analysis can be any unit the biologist wishes: seconds, minutes, hours, years, or other measures of time (Chatfield 1980). In most statistical analysis, all measurements are assumed independent; in time-series analysis, observations taken over time are often not independent and an observation may be influenced by past occurrences.

Time-series analysis has three major uses in the field of ecology. First, it can be used to describe the type of variation occurring (seasonal, cyclic, trend, or irregular fluctuations). Second, the observed variation in one time series can be used to explain the observed variation in another time series (e.g., the variation in forage production has the same time series pattern as the variation in deer productivity). Third, time series can be used to predict a variable at some future time.

EXAMPLE 16

A biologist has collected 20 years of data on rabbit population densities in a certain mountain valley. By plotting these raw data, the biologist can see a cyclical pattern in the densities; however, due to the "noise" in these data, the pattern is unclear. After performing time-series analysis, the biologist develops a logistic curve to describe these data:

$$Xt = \frac{A}{(1 + B \exp[-Ct])}$$

Where: A, B, and C = parameters and t = time.

Upon examining the equation and the plot of the equation, the biologist can clearly see the cycles in these data, an overall trend (up or down) to these data, and whether the amplitude of the cycles is increasing or decreasing.

The equation also allows the biologist to predict the density of rabbits at some future time. By comparing the time series for the rabbits to time series for factors affecting rabbit density (e.g., coyote density), the biologist may also be able to explain the pattern of the rabbit time series by the pattern of the time series of other factors.

The use of time-series analysis holds great promise in the area of habitat management. However, it is a complicated procedure that requires the help of a statistician, and large data sets are needed to adequately determine the pattern of fluctuations. As with multivariate analysis, the advent of computer programs will make the use of time-series analysis more available to the biologist.

OPTIMAL ESTIMATION

Better techniques for estimating resource measurements are beginning to appear in the natural resources field. These techniques provide the biologist with an estimation of the number of samples that must be made and how often (e.g., every 5 years) samples must be taken to maintain a predefined level of variance in these data (Jameson 1985). These techniques hold great promise for the efficient planning of monitoring studies over the long term and can be applied either to univariate or multivariate conditions.

The process utilizes Bayesian statistics to determine when the process variance becomes unacceptable, based on actual sample variation and estimated change in the variance over time. The change in the variance over time may be made by either assuming a constant change or by simulating the changes based on the conditions present, using a simulation model.

As time passes, the variance of the process will increase until the variance surpasses the maximum tolerable level set by the biologist or manager (Figure 3). To return the variance to a tolerable level, a sample must be taken to reduce the overall variance of the process.

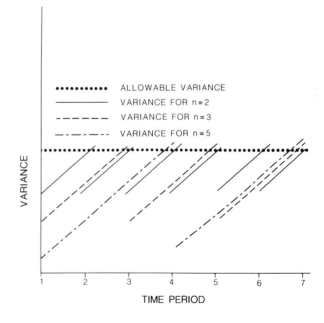

Figure 3. Changes in process variance over time for three levels of sampling (Jameson 1985).

The biologist has the option of collecting a few samples at short time intervals or collecting many samples over longer time intervals. By applying cost estimates for the sampling process, the biologist can evaluate the sampling scheme (few samples—short time frame; many samples—long time frame) that is most economical.

CONCLUSION

Statistics are an important and powerful resource tool. The techniques can be used to describe habitats, to test ideas and concepts, to evaluate management alternatives and decisions, and to predict changes. While they are a powerful tool, statistics are only a tool and are not capable of making decisions. Statistics only aid the resource biologist in the decision process.

To be properly employed and not abused, statistics must be considered from the very beginning of any data collection or impact study effort. As part of conceptualizing a project, statistics can help to clarify the questions being asked, avoid the collection of unnecessary data, and reduce the collection of meaningless data. When used as intended, statistics can provide the biologist with meaningful and useful information.

LITERATURE CITED

BOX, G.E.P., W.G. HUNTER, and J.S. HUNTER. 1978. Statistics for experimenters—An introduction to design, data analysis, and model building. John Wiley & Sons, New York, NY. 653pp.

CHATFIELD, C. 1980. The analysis of time series: An introduction. Chapman and Hill, London. 268pp.

GREEN, R.H. 1979. Sampling design and statistical methods for environmental biologists. John Wiley & Sons, New York, NY. 257pp.

HARNETT, D.L. 1982. Statistical methods, 3rd ed. Addison-Wesley Publ. Co., Reading, MA. 730pp.

HUNTSBERGER, D.V. and P. BILLINGSLEY. 1977. Elements of statistical inference, 4th ed. Allyn and Bacon, Inc., Boston, MA. 385pp.

JAMESON, D.A. 1985. Sampling intensity for monitoring of environmental systems. Applied Mathematics and Computation. Elsevier Sci. Publ. Co., Inc., New York, NY.

JOHNSON, D.H. 1981. The use and misuse of statistics in wildlife habitat studies. Pages 11-19 *in* Capen, D.E., ed. The Use of Multivariate Statistics in Studies of Wildlife Habitat. U.S. Dep. Agric., For. Serv. Gen. Tech. Rep. RM-87. 249pp.

KREBS, C.J. 1978. Ecology—the experimental analysis of distribution and abundance, 2nd ed. Harper & Row, New York, NY. 678pp.

NEWNHAM, R.M. 1968. A classification of climate by principal component analysis and its relationship to tree species distribution. Forest Science 14:254-264.

SNEDECOR, G. and W.G. COCHRAN. 1967. Statistical methods, 6th ed. Iowa State University Press, Ames. 593pp.

WARWICK, P.V. 1975. Canonical correlation analysis: Subprogram CANCORR. Pages 515-527 *in* Nie, N.H., C.H. Hull, J.G. Jenkins, K. Steinbrenner, and D.H. Bent, eds. Statistical Package for the Social Sciences (SPSS), 2nd ed. McGraw-Hill, New York, NY. 675pp.

WEBSTER, R. and P.A. BURROUGH. 1974. Multiple discriminant analysis in soil survey. J. Soil Science 25:120-134.

38

HABITAT EVALUATION SYSTEMS

Allen Y. Cooperrider

U.S. Bureau of Land Management
Service Center
Denver, CO 80225

"'What Is Game Range?' When the game manager asks himself whether a given piece of land is suitable for a given species of game, he must realize that he is asking no simple question, but rather he is facing one of the great enigmas of animate nature. An answer good enough for practical purposes is usually easy to get by the simple process of noting whether the species is there and ready, or whether it occurs as 'similar' range nearby. But let him not be cocksure about what is 'similar,' for this involves the deeper questions of why a species occurs in one place and not in another, which is probably the same as why it persists at all. No living man can answer that question fully in even one single instance."

—Aldo Leopold, *Game Management*

Editor's Note: Habitat evaluation systems are the tools for analyzing wildlife habitat, and the habitat model is the basic building block for such systems. Therefore, use of such models and systems is basic to the habitat inventory and monitoring process. Biologists should be familiar with existing techniques in this area. Most of the major concept and system developments have occurred in the past 15 years and the methodology is likely to continue to develop rapidly. This chapter provides an introduction to habitat evaluation systems and models, their history, construction, and use in the inventory and monitoring process, as well as an overview of current models and systems.

INTRODUCTION

Unorganized data are of little value to the biologist or manager. Data need to be organized, integrated, and summarized into useful information. The biologist can then use such information to make inferences about relative conditions of habitats and predictions about future conditions under alternative management practices. Statistical analysis, as discussed in the previous chapter, is one means of analyzing data.

In this chapter, I discuss methods specifically designed for organizing and analyzing wildlife habitat data. I do not discuss in detail models and systems designed for analyzing a single species (e.g., a system for analyzing mule deer habitat) or a particular type of habitat (e.g., a system for analyzing riparian habitat). Rather, I focus on models and systems that can be used for many different species (e.g., habitat suitability index [HSI] models) or many different types of habitats or communities (the system to be used determines the data to collect). The reverse process, in which a biologist collects data and then searches for a system that can use the data, is inefficient and should be avoided.

The habitat model, a correlation between habitat components and some attribute of animal population(s), is central to any habitat evaluation system, although it may not be labeled as such. Therefore, much of this chapter focuses on habitat models which are the basic building blocks of any such system.

In this chapter, I—

(1) Review the historic development of habitat evaluation systems and models;

(2) Discuss the elements and types of habitat models;

(3) Describe the procedure a biologist should follow to develop or modify a model for use in habitat evaluation;

(4) Discuss the relationship between habitat evaluation systems and models and the habitat inventory and monitoring cycle; and

(5) Review models and systems currently available or in use.

DEVELOPMENT OF HABITAT INVENTORY, MONITORING, AND EVALUATION SYSTEMS

Inventory and monitoring of wildlife habitat has been conducted in the U.S. for over 50 years, although such efforts were rarely described by those names. Aldo Leopold, in his classic work on *Game Management,* published in 1933, described methods for "game range evaluation" that are essentially habitat inventory and monitoring techniques. Such evaluations were mostly limited to practices such as browse condition and trend surveys for white-tailed deer (*Odocoileus virginianus*) winter ranges.

Although more and better techniques were developed, until about 1970 most habitat surveys consisted of measuring a few habitat components for a particular game species. Methods were not available for either analyzing habitat for nongame species or analyzing the capability of a habitat to support a wildlife community (as opposed to a single species).

At the same time, zoologists, naturalists, and other biologists were acquiring a large body of knowledge on the distribution of vertebrates and the habitats used by most vertebrates in North America. Habitat observations were typically made incidentally by biologists who were studying a particular species or surveying a region for wildlife. Few biologists made any effort to systematicaliy collect or synthesize such information. Until about 1970, the best summaries of such species-habitat relationships were the popular field guides such as Peterson's *Field Guide to Western Birds.*

These guides provided simple "verbal models" of habitats used by individual species. For example, the American dipper (*Cinclus mexicanus*) is characterized as using habitat described as "Fast-flowing streams in or near mountains. Lower levels in winter." (Peterson 1969).

Beginning in the late 1960s, interest in habitat evaluation increased dramatically in the U.S. The public became (1) more aware of the value and importance of all wildlife, not just the huntable or economically important species, and (2) more concerned about the impact of human actions on wildlife habitat. This concern was eventually expressed in a series of federal legislative mandates that were used by agencies to manage habitat for all wildlife species and to publicly address and mitigate, where possible, the impact of management actions on wildlife resources.

This mandate required new systems and approaches to habitat inventory and monitoring. Wildlife biologists were thus faced with new problems and challenges.

The first major challenge for biologists was dealing with all species or at least all vertebrate species. Wildlife biologists were not trained or experienced in working with most nongame species. On the other hand, zoologists were not accustomed to collecting the types of data that were relevant to management. Neither group was experienced in working with an entire vertebrate community. Habitat requirements for many species were not known, and techniques for measuring habitats or populations of many species groups were primitive. Costs for measuring habitats and populations of all species were prohibitive, yet systems for setting priorities for field work did not exist.

The second major challenge was to make predictions about impacts from human activities. Biologists had always made such predictions, but they tended to be informal and based on experience and subjective interpretation of limited data. Legislation such as the National Environmental Policy Act (NEPA) required impact predictions to be based on data that were systematically collected and analyzed, and that such predictions be formally presented and open to public scrutiny in environmental assessment reports (EARs), environmental impact statements (EISs), and other decision documents.

More recently the need for systems to valuate wildlife resources has emerged. Economic analysis of wildlife resources is still primitive, but economic values can be quite important in influencing management systems. Such economic analyses require input on the wildlife population responses to management actions.

At the same time new demands were being made of biologists, new technology became available. Of particular importance were the new developments in remote sensing and computer technology.

Remote sensing has been used by wildlife biologists for many years, primarily aerial photography for cover mapping and radiotelemetry for tracking animal movements. However, the development of these technologies, particularly in the past 15 years, has allowed biologists to collect better data, more efficiently than in the past.

Newly developed computer hardware and software have probably been the most important new technologies for the biologist concerned with wildlife habitat inventory and monitoring. Two factors of computer technology have been particularly valuable: (1) the capability of efficiently storing and retrieving large amounts of data and (2) the ability to rapidly manipulate numbers and images.

The storage capability of computers has allowed large amounts of inventory and monitoring data to be efficiently stored and retrieved. This has relieved much of the burden of handling large volumes of data and lessened the errors associated with transcribing data by hand.

The data manipulation capability of computers has allowed not only rapid generation of summary statistics, but also more sophisticated approaches such as multivariate analyses. Such analyses would not be practical without the aid of modern computers. Similarly, many of the models developed for integrating data would not be practical without both the storage and data manipulation capabilities.

HABITAT MODELS

The habitat model forms the basis for all habitat inventory, management, and monitoring. It is thus the general underlying principle of habitat management.

A habitat model is a method of using a set of habitat components or attributes to predict some attribute of a wildlife population or populations (Figure 1). All habitat models are designed for this purpose. Habitat models are complex because of the almost limitless habitat components and attributes that can be used (Table 1), the diversity of population attributes that can be predicted (Table 2), and the complicated relationships between them.

Habitat models have always been used by biologists; the previous example of the American dipper using habitat consisting of "fast-flowing streams in or near mountains" is a simple, verbal model. If we

define "fast-flowing" and "near" in terms of meters (feet)/seconds and kilometers (miles) respectively, then we would have a simple, quantitative model.

To understand and categorize a habitat model, one needs only to identify the habitat components being used as predictors, the population attribute being predicted, and the type of function being used to relate one to the other. In the following discussion I describe each of these.

Model Components—Habitat Attributes

The habitat attributes listed in Table 1 form the basic predictors of terrestrial habitat models. They are analogous to the independent variables in a regression equation. They are discussed in more detail below to help explain the concept of a habitat model.

Geographic Location. The single most important predictor of occurrence is probably geographic location. Most wildlife species are quite restricted in geographic distribution; therefore, geographic location, together with knowledge of a species distribution, is adequate to predict species potentially present in an area. However, wildlife species are rarely present continuously within their geographic ranges, and complete delineations of all sites used by a species are usually not available. Furthermore, location is of little help in predicting more sophisticated attributes of a wildlife population, such as relative abundance or density. Therefore, geographic location in habitat models is usually used implicitly in models as a boundary condition, i.e., animals outside their known geographic range are assumed to be absent. More accurate prediction of presence and more detailed predictions about population attributes obviously require more detailed information on habitat components present.

Vegetation. Beyond geographic location, vegetation is probably the next most important habitat component. Almost all habitat models use vegetation in predicting animal population attributes. In the simplest models, the presence and absence of animal species are simply associated with a vegetation type such as pinon-juniper (*Pinus-Juniperus* sp.) or sagebrush (*Artemisia* sp.) grassland. More complex models consider structural components of the vegetation (e.g., tree density, shrub density, etc.) or more detail on plant species composition (e.g., percentage cover of big sagebrush [*A. tridentata*], density of antelope bitterbrush [*Purshia tridentata*]).

The relative importance of vegetation structure (physiognomy), as opposed to plant species composition (floristics) in determining suitability of habitat

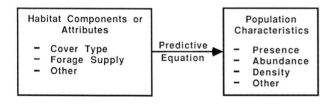

Figure 1. Basic components of a habitat model.

Table 1. Habitat components and attributes useful in predicting presence, abundance, or density of vertebrates.*

<table>
<tr><td valign="top">

Geographic location

Vegetation—Live
  Vegetation type
    Species composition (floristics)
    Presence
    Abundance
    Density
    Cover
    Frequency
    Biomass
    Diversity
  Vegetation structure (physiognomy)
    Presence
    Abundance
    Density
    Cover
    Frequency
    Biomass
    Diversity

Vegetation—Dead
    Litter or mulch
    Dead and down woody material
    Persistent
    Non-persistent
    Snags

Physical features
  Landform types
    Alluvial fan
    Rock pediment
    Other
  Landform attributes
    Slope
    Aspect
    Elevation
  Soils
  Edaphic habitats
  Geomorphic habitat features
    Cliffs
    Caves
    Talus
    Lava flows
    Sand dunes
    Other

</td><td valign="top">

Animal-made habitat features
    Beaver dams
    Dens
    Nest cavities

Man-made features
    Roads
    Bridges
    Buildings
    Other

Water
  Presence
    Attributes
      Depth
      Flow (velocity)
      Temperature
      Chemistry (DO, pH, turbidity, TDS, etc.)
      Substrate

Food supply
    Vegetation
    Animal prey base (vertebrates)
    Macroinvertebrates
    Other
Presence, absence, or abundance of competitors
Presence, absence, or abundance of predators
Presence, absence, or abundance of parasites or diseases
Presence, absence, or degree of human disturbance
    Noise
    Human activity
    Traffic
    Other
Presence, absence, or intensity of hunting or harvesting

Weather and climate

Historical occurrence

</td></tr>
</table>

*The *spatial* and *temporal* arrangements of tne attributes and components are also an important determinant of animal abundance.

for wildlife species, is a subject of continuing debate. Biologists, such as Short (1983, 1984) and Short and Burnham (1982), have proposed using habitat models primarily based on structural characteristics, whereas some researchers provide evidence that species composition is more important. The management biologist does not need to be concerned with the controversy. Some wildlife species greatly depend on particular plant species (e.g., sage grouse [*Centrocercus urophasianus*] on sagebrush, ruffed grouse [*Bonasa umbellus*] on quaking aspen [*Populus tremuloides*]). The biologist working with such

species is well-advised to pay attention to species composition. On the other hand, habitat layers or other structural components, as proposed by Short (1984), can provide a good initial prediction of animal species presence or absence. Chapter 31 in this book describes how both types of measurements can be taken and used to make predictions about animal populations.

Vegetation has been measured in many ways for many purposes, resulting in literally thousands of measurement techniques being described in the literature. For this reason, the chapter on vegetation (Chapter 31) does not attempt to cover all possible techniques. Rather, it presents an example of how vegetation variables can be used to predict species occurrence and abundance.

Wildlife biologists often collect large amounts of vegetation data without a clear idea of how they are going to use such data. Habitat models are the mechanism for using vegetation data to make predictions about animal populations. The biologist should, therefore, have a model in mind before collecting vegetation data. The same caveat applies to all other types of habitat variables, but is emphasized here since so much time, effort, and money continue to be expended in collecting vegetation data that are not used.

Table 2. Animal population characteristics predicted by habitat relationships models.

Single Species Characteristics
Presence or absence
Probability of occurrence
Abundance or density
Relative abundance or density index
Carrying-capacity index
Biomass
Geographic distribution
Mortality or natality
Animal condition
Population dynamics
Multiple-Species Characteristics
Species richness
Species diversity
Biomass
Guilds or life-forms
Community suitability index

Dead Vegetation. Various types of dead vegetation, such as snags, litter, and downed logs, are becoming increasingly more important to wildlife biologists. As a result, measures of these components are being used increasingly in habitat models. However, few formal systems for quantifying such components are available, and in many cases the biologist must devise *ad hoc* measurement systems. These habitat variables are described in more detail in Chapter 27, Terrestrial Physical Features.

Physical Features. Physical features are important habitat components in both aquatic and terrestrial systems. Because of their importance, two chapters in this book have been devoted to describing systems for measuring them (Chapter 27, Terrestrial Physical Features, and Chapter 28, Aquatic Physical Features). In addition, because of its central import-

ance, an entire chapter has been devoted to the subject of soils (Chapter 26).

Water. Many terrestrial wildlife species require free water. Therefore, presence of free water is an important habitat component for these species. This may be expressed as a distance from free water, as a density of springs, or as many other factors. The properties of the water are generally not important. With amphibious and aquatic species, however, properties of water such as turbidity, temperature, and pH become important. Therefore, measurements of theses properties are described in a separate chapter (Chapter 30, Water Quality). In addition, two other chapters deal with water-related variables. Chapter 29, Hydrological Properties, deals with dynamic water variables such as flow rates that are important for many wildlife and fish species; Chapter 32, Macroinvertebrates, focuses on using measurements of macroinvertebrates as indicators of water quality and other habitat deterioration.

Food Supply. Food is such an important factor determining presence, absence, or abundance of wildlife species that it is usually incorporated into habitat models, either implicitly or explicitly. When animal species are simply associated with a vegetation or cover type, or with a habitat layer within a vegetation type, the model assumes the vegetation type provides an adequate food supply. At the other extreme, food supply may be so important to some species that actual measurements or estimates of the food supply must be made. Schroeder (1984), for example, describes a winter model for black brant (*Branta bernicla*) that uses two habitat variables, one of which is the percentage of cover of the forage eelgrass (*Zostera marina*). In the case of predatory animals, the density or abundance of prey species may be the important habitat variable. Use of food supply as a habitat variable is probably best developed for large herbivores such as elk (*Cervus elaphus*) and deer. With these animals, some habitat models (frequently called carrying-capacity models) predict the number of animals that can be supported on a range by using food supply as a factor. Some of these models not only require data on weight of individual plant species present by season, but also data on the nutritional content of various plant species or species groups. Such models are discussed in more detail in Chapter 25, Ungulates.

Presence, Absence, or Abundance of Competitors. The presence of competitors is rarely considered formally in habitat models. Yet, the phenomena of competition is recognized by many biologists as an important factor affecting distribution or abundance of animal species. There is, of course, much disagreement among biologists about the importance of competition and the mechanism by which competition occurs. Similarly, many biologists do not consider presence of a competitor as a "habitat component." However, in the context of habitat models, predators may be treated as habitat components just like any other. For example, many species of cavity-nesting songbirds are adversely affected by the presence of starlings (*Sturnus vulgaris*). Removal of starlings can improve the habitat for many of these species and allow them to become more abundant. Therefore, habitat models for such species must consider the influence of the presence or abundance of starlings in the habitat.

Presence, Absence, or Abundance of Predators.
Like competitors, predators are not usually considered in formal quantitative habitat models, but are often discussed in verbal or written models. As with competition, biologists disagree about the role and mechanism of predation in limiting animal populations. In any case, if a biologist believes that a predator is or could limit a population, presence or abundance of the predator should be measured and included as a habitat factor in the model. Human hunting, which may be considered a special case of predation, is discussed below.

Presence, Absence, or Abundance of Parasites or Diseases.
Like the previous two "habitat components," parasites or diseases are rarely considered in formal models. However, the role of parasites or disease in limiting animal populations is well-documented in many specific cases. As with competition and predation, an impact to a wildlife population from parasites or disease is often correlated with, if not caused by, a change in physical habitat conditions. In the case of disease, however, very little study has been done on correlating disease impacts with changes in habitat.

Presence, Absence, or Degree of Human Disturbance.
Disturbance includes a wide variety of factors other than physical or vegetative features of the environment, such as noise, highway construction, drilling, etc. In many cases, these are very important factors affecting abundance of vertebrates. In fact, they are frequently factors that biologists are asked to quantify in analyses such as EISs and EARs. Yet very few, formally published habitat models include disturbance as an explicit habitat component. Some models do consider disturbance as an implicit factor, however. For example, Schroeder (1984) developed an HSI model for black brant in which roosting cover was one of the habitat variables. Human disturbance has also been identified as an important factor limiting black brant populations. Therefore, in the model, roosting cover is defined as the "percent of shoreline ... that contains sandy areas that are isolated from human disturbance" (Schroeder 1984). Thus disturbance is considered as either present or absent.

A more challenging problem is determining the effects of a given degree of disturbance on a wildlife population. Few, if any, formal models have even attempted to do this. Yet, such information is needed for biologists to evaluate the impacts to wildlife from the myriad human activities occurring in wildlife habitats. I would expect that in future years biologists will be developing and using more models that incorporate disturbance as a habitat factor.

Presence, Absence, or Intensity of Hunting or Harvesting.
Like other factors above, hunting is not generally considered a habitat factor. However, in the context of habitat models, it is useful to consider it such, since it obviously can limit animal populations. Its impact is also greatly interdependent on physical and vegetative factors, such as the amount or quality of cover. If hunting pressure is limiting wildlife populations, then habitat models that only consider physical or vegetative habitat components will be poor predictors of population responses to habitat management or disturbance. Therefore, in developing and using habitat models, biologists must first consider if hunting is limiting the population. If hunting is not a factor, which is the case with virtually all nongame species and many game species in this country, the biologist may safely omit it from further consideration. However, if it is or appears to be a factor, the biologist must take it into account. Analyzing impacts of habitat alteration on wildlife populations has little value when physical or vegetative habitat factors are not limiting.

Weather and Climate.
Weather is the state of the atmosphere at a given time; climate refers to the characteristics of the atmospheric conditions of a region. Or, as one wag described it, "climate is what you expect; weather is what you get." Whereas climate is relatively predictable, weather is not, and weather strongly influences many wildlife populations. Furthermore, as Bailey (1984) pointed out, even though the biologist or manager has no control over the weather, when devasting impacts occur to wildlife populations from severe weather conditions, the manager may be blamed, "for there is no satisfaction in blaming the weather." Therefore, in inventory and monitoring, biologists must incorporate weather measurements or considerations into their study design whenever dealing with populations that are heavily influenced by weather. Because of the importance of weather and climate in determining animal abundance, an entire chapter in this book (Chapter 35, Weather and Climate) has been devoted to the subject. Weather is not included explicitly in most formal habitat models; however, it is generally recognized as a concomitant influence that affects animal abundance in many ways and, under extreme conditions, may override the importance of all habitat variables.

Historical Occurrence. Historical occurrence is not generally thought of as a habitat component, yet it can be an important characteristic of habitat. If an animal species has been recorded as occurring on an area within historic times, then such information is excellent evidence that the species can or does occur there as long as the physical habitat has not been drastically altered. Of course, the shorter the time since that occurrence has been verified, the more probable it is that the species persists there. Even when a species is known to have been extirpated, historical occurrence is important information when considering such things as reintroductions. Introduction of animals, such as peregrine falcons (*Falco peregrinus*) and bighorn sheep (*Ovis canadensis*) into areas that were not historic habitats, has rarely been successful.

Model Components—Population Attributes

As with the habitat components of a habitat model, many population attributes can be predicted (Table 2). These may be either characteristics of a single species population, multiple species populations, or community characteristics, such as species richness. However, unlike with habitat components, most of these models can only predict one population or community attribute. In other words, several habitat components may be used as predictors, but only one population attribute is normally predicted.

Most models have been developed to predict attributes of single species. In fact, most wildlife research and management has been single-species oriented. Furthermore, even many multiple species models, such as those for species richness, are developed from a set of single-species models.

Presence or Absence. The presence or absence of a species is the simplest sort of population attribute that can be predicted. However, for many purposes, such a determination is adequate information for the majority of wildlife species.

Probability of Occurrence. Probability of occurrence considers presence or absence as a probability rather than as an absolute. Since models produce predictions rather than absolute truths, uncertainty is always associated with their predictions; use of models that predict occurrence probability are more realistic because they attempt to quantify the uncertainty associated with the predictions. For example, a biologist may need to predict if an area is used by prairie falcons for nesting. Yet time is not available to make an absolute determination since the analysis must be made in winter and the proposed impact will occur during the next breeding season. Using a model that has probability of occurrence as an output, a biologist can predict, based on habitat components, that "the probability of the site being

occupied by prairie falcons is 90%." Models for probability can be used for other purposes, such as predicting the probability that a population of a certain density occurs. The most common use of probability measures of animal populations as predicted outputs is in "pattern recognition (PATREC) models," discussed in more detail later in this chapter.

Abundance or Density. Abundance here refers to the number of animals in a population, whereas density refers to the number of animals per unit area. Abundance or density is quite difficult to predict. Thus, very few models attempt to actually predict such attributes. In most situations, biologists neither can nor need to make such precise estimates.

Relative Abundance or Density Index. Abundance or density indexes are values that correlate with abundance or density, but for which the quantitative relationship between the two is unknown. For example, an area with a mule deer (*O. hemionus*) index of 0.5 may be expected to have twice as many deer as an area with an index of 0.25. However, the relationship between the index and the actual number of deer is unknown. If, for example, an index of 0.5 was known to correspond with a density of 30 deer per square mile, then it would not be a density index, but rather a predictor of density. Abundance or density indexes in habitat models (predicted density indexes), like the measured abundance or density indexes described in Chapter 2, Data Types, are most useful for comparisons. A biologist can compare different areas or the same area during different years or under varying habitat impacts.

Carrying Capacity. Carrying capacity is considered by range managers to be the number of animals an area can support. It is, thus, a property of the land and the condition of the habitat, but is expressed in terms of numbers or density of animals. The actual number of animals present may be lower than the carrying capacity. Carrying capacity is unaffected, for example, by weather, hunting, or other decimating factors that are not habitat related. Although the term has generated much controversy and discussion (Bailey 1984:279-303), it remains a useful working concept that allows a biologist to quantify the value of habitat without considering short-term fluctuations in animal numbers from weather, hunting, or predation. Carrying capacity has been used as an output in many models (models developed for ungulates in which carrying capacity is assumed to be primarily a function of forage supply).

Carrying-Capacity Index. Carrying-capacity indexes are similar to density indexes except, like with carrying-capacity estimates, they are strictly a function of habitat. The most common carrying-capacity indexes are the habitat suitability indexes used in the U.S. Fish and Wildlife Service HSI models (Schamberger et al. 1982). These models use an index that varies from 0 to 1, with 1 being some maximum carrying capacity, and 0 indicating unsuitable habitat.

Biomass. Biomass is rarely used in habitat models since it is usually not of interest to managers, at least with terrestrial species. However, it is often used in ecological models designed for understanding ecosystem processes. Nonetheless, some management models do exist, particularly in fisheries. For example, Binns (1979) describes a model that uses nine stream habitat variables to predict the standing crop of trout.

Geographic Distribution. Geographic distribution is basically an extension of presence or absence. In presence and absence models, the biologist merely predicts whether a species will be present on a given site. By using habitat attributes at a series of sites, one can predict the geographic area that a wildlife species can be expected to occupy. One may also note that "geographic location" and "historic distribution" are also described as a model input. Thus, according to the description of models provided here, historic distribution can be used, for example, to predict geographic distribution. This may seem to be rather trivial. However, this is, in fact, a rather commonly used model, even though it is rarely identified as such. The implicit model, used by most biologists as historical records of a species in an area, is the best predictor of future occurrence, and the more recent the historical observation, the greater the predictive power. However, as discussed under historical occurrence, past observation is not a perfect predictor; conditions often change, resulting in local extirpations, and the biologist needs to be alert to such situations.

Mortality or Natality. Some models predict the mortality or natality rather than a population density. Mortality is usually expressed in terms like number, density, or abundance of animals killed over winter. Similarly, natality is usually expressed as some measure of productivity, such as young fledged per nest, or as some ratio of young to old animals, such as fawns per doe. When used, both types of measurements are considered useful indicators of the "health" of the species population.

Animal Condition. Animal condition, expressed in such terms as weight, kidney fat indexes, etc., is also used as a model output and, like productivity, is considered a surrogate measure of the "health" of the population.

Population Dynamics. In some cases, biologists may be more interested in predicting the dynamics of a population rather than a static or fixed popula-tion level. All populations fluctuate in numbers and, in some cases, the frequency and amplitude of such fluctuations may be of more interest than the "average" population size. Although numerous population dynamics models are available, most do not use any physical or vegetative habitat features to predict population responses. They use weather, hunting pressure or, in some cases, predation. Thus they are not commonly considered habitat models.

Very few models attempt to predict changes in wildlife populations over time as a result of changes in habitat factors, although a few are available (Cooperrider and Bailey 1984; Cooperrider and Behrend 1980). Models with dynamic outputs (expressed as changes over time) require at least one dynamic input (changes independently of the model). Such inputs are said to "drive" the model. In most dynamic or simulation models, weather is the dynamic input; however, other inputs can be used. The model of Cooperrider and Bailey (1984), for example, can use forage production to drive the model.

Model Components—Multiple Population or Community Characteristics

Characteristics of several populations are the plural counterparts of the population characteristics just described. They are predicted from similar habitat attributes. However, instead of making inferences about only one species, some inference is made about (1) several taxonomically related species in an area (e.g., songbirds, ungulates); (2) several species that use similar habitat components (e.g., cavity-nesting birds); or (3) all species in a habitat.

Species Richness. Species richness is the number of species present in an area. It is the plural counterpart of presence or absence. Models that predict species richness are usually composed of a series of individual species presence and absence models, i.e., the models usually not only predict the number of species, but also the specific species.

Species Diversity. Diversity or species diversity refers to not only the number of species but also their relative abundance in an area. Species diversity is rarely used directly as an output from habitat models, at least the type of habitat models used in land management. This is not surprising, since a model to predict species diversity must predict not only presence or absence but also density or relative abundance of each species present. Some models, however, are based on the premise that diversity of vegetation structure is correlated with species diversity as measured by some species diversity index. (See Chapter 2 for a discussion of diversity indexes.) These models predict an index of species diversity without explicitly predicting the species and their relative abundance.

Biomass. Biomass of all species, or all species within a defined species group such as small mammals, fishes, or ungulates, is sometimes used as a model output. As with individual species biomass, it is used most commonly with fish.

Guilds or Life-Forms. Guilds and life-forms are both groups of species that use similar habitat components for feeding, breeding, or other biological functions. Several systems have been devised that use guilds or life-forms as outputs, as described in the next section. The advantage to the biologist is that he or she can deal with 10 or 20 guilds, rather than 400 or 500 vertebrate species in an area. Predictions can be made and verified in terms of impacts on whole guilds rather than on individual species. Life-forms, as discussed later in the chapter, may be considered a special case of guilds.

Community Suitability Index. In some cases, a rating of the relative value of a community to support a wildlife community is the output from a model. Such indexes are either implicitly or explicitly thought to be correlated with a population measurement, such as species richness or species diversity. For example, Short (1984) describes a model for generating a suitability index for a habitat based on the layers of habitat present. It is further based on the assumption that structurally more complex habitats have more wildlife guilds and greater species richness.

Model Components—Correlation Functions

The precision, accuracy, and usefulness of habitat models depend on the selection of the appropriate habitat components for use. Equally important, however, is the process of linking these variables together in a meaningful way so the best prediction can be made. A thorough description and set of guidelines on model development and construction is beyond the scope of this publication. However, a few critical concepts and principles are discussed under the Developing Habitat Models section, following. For a more thorough treatment of model building, see the U.S. Fish and Wildlife Service **Ecological Services Manual** on "Standards for the Development of Habitat Suitability Index Models (HSI)" (U.S. Department of the Interior, Fish and Wildlife Service 1981), which contains a good introduction to the subject. That discussion focuses on one particular type of model; however, the procedures can generally be applied to other classes of models.

DEVELOPING HABITAT MODELS

The following basic steps can be used in developing a model:

(1) Determine model objectives;

(2) Select and quantify habitat variables;

(3) Determine the correlation or prediction function;

(4) Document and verify the model.

These steps correspond roughly to the phases of construction described in the U.S. Department of the Interior, Fish and Wildlife Service **Ecological Services Manual** (1981).

Determining Model Objectives

Model objectives should be based on the objectives of the inventory and monitoring effort, as described in more detail in Chapter 1, Inventory and Monitoring Process. The process includes determining the desired output (e.g., species density, relative density, species richness) as well as the geographic area, seasons, and other factors the model should predict.

Selecting and Quantifying Habitat Variables

Determining habitat variables that should be incorporated into a model is critical. A biologist should use the least number possible, since habitat measurements are expensive to obtain. These variables should be the "limiting factors" as described in basic ecology texts (Odum 1969) or surrogates for them.

The concept of a surrogate variable is important in model construction. A surrogate variable is one that closely relates to a habitat variable of interest but which, for one reason or another, is easier to measure or verify. For example, a Lewis' woodpecker (*Melanerpes lewis*) is reported to need forests having tree canopy closures less than 75% and does best in areas with 0 to 30% closure (Sousa 1983). However, within the range of 0 to 75% canopy closures, the basal area of trees highly correlates with canopy closure in many areas. Furthermore, basal area is usually easier to measure than canopy closure or may be available from sources such as timber inventories. Therefore, the biologist may prefer to substitute basal area as a surrogate for canopy closure.

If a model is being used to predict the impacts of a particular management action, then at least some of the habitat variables selected should be those affected by the management action in some predictable way.

The habitat variables then must be carefully defined. To convert a conceptual or verbal model into a written or even quantitative model generally requires carefully defining the variables. For example, basic habitat factors required by bighorn sheep for survival have been described as food, water, and escape terrain (Hansen 1980). Escape terrain has been further described by various authors as open, steep, rocky, and rugged terrain. The biologist must define or quantify the terms if the model is to be used by other biologists or if habitat measurements are to be repeated. "Open" can be defined as the percentage of canopy cover of trees and shrubs or as some measure of visual obstruction. Similarly, "steep" can be defined as percentage of slope. The evolution of models from concepts to quantitative descriptions requires carefully defined and eventually quantified terms (Figure 2).

Determining the Correlation or Prediction Function

Once habitat variables have been selected, defined, and quantified, the biologist must determine the relative importance of each to the others. In the simplest case, a biologist can determine that all variables are equally important; these variables can then be added to provide a simple additive model (Figure 3a). On the other hand, some habitat factors may be considered more important than others. For example, the biologist may decide that food supply is twice as important as escape terrain. By attaching a number to the variable, the biologist can weigh the model so the index produced is influenced more by food supply than other variables, resulting in a weighted additive model (Figure 3b).

The relationship between variables may be much more complicated, however, and the biologist should try to model it. For example, the additive

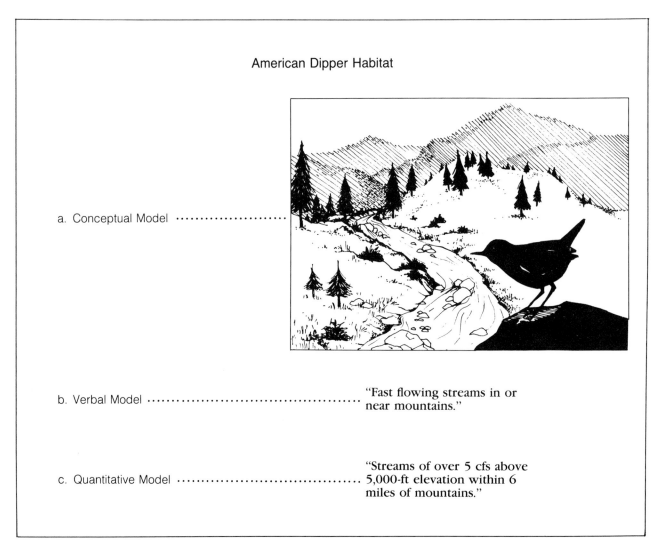

Figure 2. Progression of models from conceptual to quantitative.

relationship shown for desert bighorn sheep in Figure 3a may not be realistic. A habitat could have no water at all and yet have other important components. The index value derived would still be 0.66 for equation (a) or 0.75 for equation (b), which are both fairly high ratings. Yet such habitats do not support bighorn sheep. For these reasons, a multiplicative or limiting factor model (Figures 3c and 3d) may be more appropriate. With such a model, if any attribute has a suitability rating of 0, the overall index will become 0.

Habitat components can be combined in unlimited ways using various weighting factors and mathematical functions. Similarly, seasonal or functional requirements can be combined to form compound models. For example, summer habitat requirements can be combined with winter habitat requirements, or feeding habitat requirements with breeding habitat requirements.

One of the most difficult problems of combining habitat attributes is taking into account spatial arrangement of habitat components. Biologists know that interspersion and juxtaposition of habitat features can be very important to animals. However, quantifying these relationships in a meaningful way is difficult. The use of geographic information systems (GISs) to analyze these relationships may assist greatly in the future.

Numerous statistical and numerical techniques can assist in determining both the form of the function and the appropriate weighting. Techniques such as linear regression, multivariate analysis, or least-squares curve fitting may all be useful when data are available. However, in many cases, the biologist must rely on literature, expert opinion, and existing sources of information, rather than raw data.

Documenting and Verifying the Model

Documenting a model is important. In many cases, models are developed by using a group of species experts. Even though every function or assumption of the model is not backed up by extensive research, a model that represents an expert consensus is easy to defend. If the model is being constructed for some sort of impact analysis, then getting interested parties to design or evaluate the model(s) can be most helpful in obtaining project impact concensus. Documentation is also important when made available to other biologists with similar problems.

A model, once constructed, is basically no more than an untested or working hypothesis. Ideally, all models would be thoroughly tested and refined before use. In practice, most decisions need to be made with incomplete information. However, monitoring can be used to verify models, as discussed in the next section.

Type of Model

a. Simple Additive Model ···· $HSI = \dfrac{V_1 + V_2 + V_3}{3}$

b. Weighted Additive Model ········ $HSI = \dfrac{2V_1 + V_2 + V_3}{4}$

c. Multiplicative Model ······ $HSI = (V_1 \times V_2 \times V_3)^{1/3}$

d. Limiting Factor Model ····· $HSI = Min\,(V_1, V_2, V_3)$

All four models calculate a habitat suitability index (HSI) from 0 to 1 for desert bighorn sheep based on three habitat factors—a forage index (V_1), an escape terrain index (V_2), and a water availability index (V_3); the latter indexes also range from 0 to 1.

Figure 3. Types of quantitative models.

Without water, other important habitat components for desert bighorn sheep are not sufficient.

THE HABITAT INVENTORY AND MONITORING CYCLE AND HABITAT MODELS

The habitat inventory and monitoring cycle has been explained in detail in Chapter 2. It is reviewed here to clarify the central role of the habitat model in both the cycle and the habitat evaluation systems. For further discussion of the roles of models in monitoring, see Salwasser et al. (1983), Cole and Smith (1983), and O'Neil and Schamberger (1983).

The habitat inventory and monitoring cycle may be viewed as consisting of five steps:

(1) Scoping,

(2) Data collection and analysis,

(3) Prediction,

(4) Decision/action, and

(5) Monitoring (Figure 4).

These steps correspond roughly to the stages outlined in Chapter 1, but emphasize model development, use, or refinement. Habitat models and evaluation systems are used in all steps, but most importantly in step 3, where they are the basic tools for predictions. Similarly, monitoring verifies predictions and can also be used to refine model(s).

Scoping

The driving force for a monitoring program is a "problem" or a proposed action of some sort. This may be a very small action, such as a new fence, or a major action, such as a power plant. It may be a very loosely defined issue, such as a "need to reverse habitat deterioration which is causing perceived decline of deer in an area," or it may be a very specific proposal with specified alternatives. It may also be a wildlife problem, such as the deer decline, or an activity, such as a coal lease that is expected to adversely affect the wildlife resource. A typical problem is generally the need to know the resources present on an area for land-use planning, etc. This is the driving force for a basic inventory. All these problems, big and small, well-defined or vague, should result in the same procedure. An important principle is that the magnitude and intensity of the data collection and analysis should correlate with the perceived impact of the problem.

The next step is to clearly define the problem. This will generally require some assessment of the wildlife resources (animals or habitat) present, which are likely to be affected. This assessment frequently is based on some rapid examination or analysis of available data. A critical initial decision is to

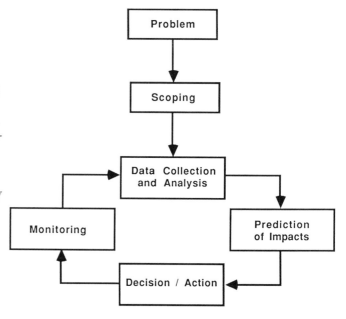

Figure 4. The habitat inventory and monitoring cycle.

determine the geographical area of concern and "bound the study area." This process of taking a vague problem or proposed action, clarifying it, and making an initial assessment of potential resource impacts is commonly termed "scoping."

Scoping may significantly alter the direction of a project. By identifying actions particularly detrimental to wildlife at an early stage, a biologist may be able to direct planners to less detrimental alternatives. This effort may result in much greater benefits to wildlife resources than a thorough analysis at a later stage of an action.

At this stage, the biologist uses habitat models, possibly very vaguely defined conceptually or qualitatively. For example, the biologist may know that forage supply is a limiting habitat factor for a bighorn sheep population. Therefore, he or she can generally predict that a proposal to expand a grazing lease into a critical summer bighorn range will be detrimental to the bighorn. On the other hand, the biologist may only have a very vague idea of how detrimental the impact will be.

If the decision is made to further consider the proposal, then the biologist must plan the data needed. At this point, more quantitative habitat models should be developed. In the bighorn example discussed above, the biologist might need to locate or develop a model that related forage supply to numbers of bighorn. Forage supply would then be defined more specifically and quantitatively as, for example, total pounds of grasses and perennial forbs on summer range. This habitat variable (and possibly others identified in the model) would then be the ones for which the biologist would need to gather data. Depending on the situation, the biologist might also need to collect data on the bighorn sheep population, such as numbers, movements, or lamb survival.

Data Collection and Analysis

Data collection and analysis may suggest refinement of a preliminary model. For example, after intensive field work, the biologist may determine that water supply is also limiting. The biologist then may need to modify the model to incorporate water as a habitat factor, and additional data on number of waters, supplies, etc. may need to be collected.

Prediction

The next step is to use data to predict the effect of alternative management actions. This step requires using a model since the data collected must be used to predict a future state. The models may be simple or complex. Returning to the previous example, the biologist might use the model to predict that expanding the grazing lease would remove 50% of the available forage, reducing the bighorn population by 30%. In this case, the biologist has used a quantitative carrying-capacity model. In other situations, a biologists may be forced to use a simple conceptual model. The trend, however, is to use more formal and quantitative models, since these allow more precision and can be clearly documented.

In the past, biologists have concentrated on predicting biological consequences of actions. Recently, biologists and economists have been asked to go one step further and assess economic consequences of these actions. This also requires using models to attach values to wildlife resources with and without the action.

Decision/Action

The next step is the familiar one of choosing an alternative and taking some action. Except in the case of a wildlife-related action (such as a habitat improvement project), the biologist usually has a minor role in this process. The manager must weigh potential impacts to other resources; economics; and other social, political, and legal factors. However, the model becomes the basic tool for summarizing the collected data and making predictions. The model becomes the tool of the manager, even though the latter may be primarily concerned with the model outputs. The model has, in effect, synthesized the assumptions about limiting habitat factors and their effects on wildlife populations.

Monitoring

Once an action has been taken, a biologist needs to monitor the biological effects of the action. This monitoring can serve two purposes. The biologist can determine empirically whether the impact to wildlife resources is as predicted or within tolerable limits. If the action is not achieving the desired goal or if the impacts are outside tolerable limits, then the manager may be able to stop or modify the action being taken. The biologist can also determine the quality of the model in predicting impacts and modify it as necessary.

Many biologists have advocated adding monitoring as a key element in a resource management program and termed it, among other things, "adaptive environmental assessment" (Holling 1978), "adaptive management" (Barrett and Salwasser 1982), "cyclic incrementalism," or more simply "muddling through" (Bailey 1982) or "common sense management" (Barrett and Salwasser 1982). These approaches vary in details, but are all based on the following assumptions:

(1) Many features of biological systems (such as weather) are unpredictable;

(2) The tools for both measuring biological resources and predicting future states are crude and the time, money, and personnel for such efforts are limited; and

(3) Continuing selective remeasurement (monitoring) can be effective in both correcting or improving management actions and also refining the predictive tools.

The need to monitor may seem obvious; however, the list of projects and programs that have failed because monitoring was not included (or was given the lowest priority) is long and growing fast.

Monitoring without an underlying model may be useful in determining whether management objectives are being met, but it is unlikely to lead to a better understanding of the system being managed.

Clearly, the five steps of the habitat and monitoring cycle are similar and sometimes overlap. Scoping, for instance, is a form of low-level or "quick-and-dirty" inventory and prediction phase. Although monitoring may involve similar data collection, it is done in the inventory phase and for different purposes.

In the next sections, I describe the systems, models, and other programs that can be used when performing one or more of the tasks identified in this section.

CURRENT HABITAT MODELS AND EVALUATION SYSTEMS

Models, as considered here, are any formal method for correlating habitat variables with population attributes, whether they are for single species or for multiple species or communities, regardless of the purpose for which they were designed and used.

Simple Correlation Models

Single-species models range from very simple correlations to rather elaborate correlations of species presence with many habitat factors. In the simplest case, presence of a species is simply associated with presence of a vegetation type. More elaborate variations take into consideration other habitat features within that habitat type and other animal population attributes. These include season of use; successional stage of vegetation; special habitat requirements; biological functions for which they are used (breeding, feeding, resting [cover], special); relative importance or value of the habitat feature (critical, optimum, acceptable, marginal, etc.); and, in some cases, some qualitative measure of relative density or abundance (abundant, common, rare, etc.). The approach is exemplified in the models developed and reported by Verner and Boss (1980; Figure 5).

Habitat Suitability Index (HSI) Models

HSI models have been developed by the U.S. Fish and Wildlife Service and others for use in their Habitat Evaluation Procedures (HEP; U.S. Department of the Interior, Fish and Wildlife Service 1981). In developing the HSI models, the biologist uses existing data, literature, and expert opinion to develop an equation or algorithm to use a small number of selected habitat variables in predicting the suitability of habitat for a wildlife species. Suitability is indicated by an index ranging from 0 to 1, with 0 indicating unsuitable habitat and 1, optimal habitat. For

example, habitat suitability for the marten (*Martes americana*) is a function of four variables:

(1) Percentage of tree canopy closure,

(2) Percentage of overstory canopy containing fir or spruce,

(3) Successional stage of stand, and

(4) Percentage of ground surface covered by downfall over 3 in. in diameter (Allen 1982; Figure 6).

Since habitat suitability cannot be directly measured, validation of HSI models is difficult if not impossible. HSI models are usually developed for a single species; however, sometimes they are developed for a group of species or guilds, such as dabbling ducks, which respond similarly to the same set of habitat variables. Approximately 300 HSI models are in some stage of development in North America, of which, about half are for aquatic species.

Pattern Recognition (PATREC) Models

PATREC models are similar to HSI models in that they use a set of habitat variables to predict the expected capability of the habitat to support an animal species. They differ from HSI models in that they use a formal statistical procedure to predict habitat capability, expressed as a probability. Usually the probability is of a certain population density or classes of animals. For example, Williams et al. (1977) describe a PATREC model for pronghorn antelope that predicts the probability that a habitat with a given set of characteristics will support a high or low density antelope population. By providing definitions for high density and low density, the model can also be used to calculate an expected population density. PATREC models are generally developed from field data; however, they can use data from expert opinion.

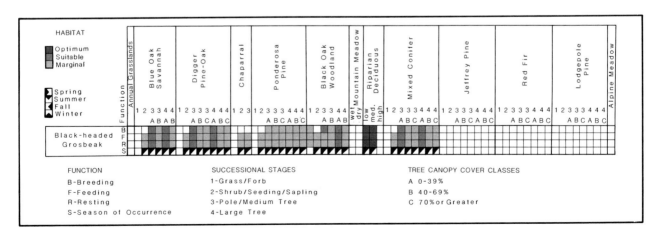

Figure 5. An elaborate correlation model (from Verner and Boss 1980).

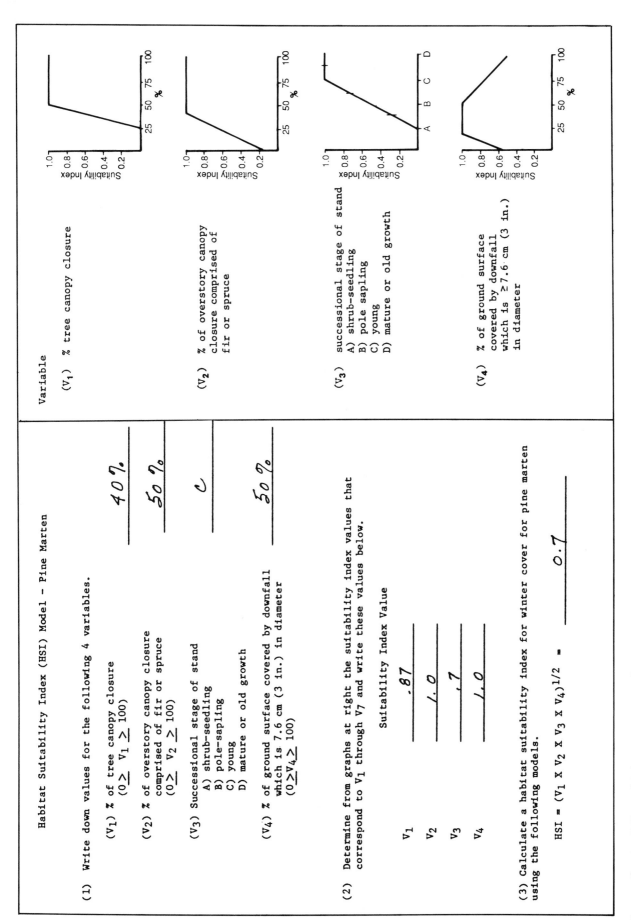

Habitat Suitability Index (HSI) Model – Pine Marten

(1) Write down values for the following 4 variables.

(V₁) % of tree canopy closure
(0 ≥ V₁ ≥ 100)   _40%._

(V₂) % of overstory canopy closure
comprised of fir or spruce
(0 ≥ V₂ ≥ 100)   _50%_

(V₃) Successional stage of stand
A) shrub-seedling
B) pole-sapling
C) young
D) mature or old growth   _C_

(V₄) % of ground surface covered by downfall
which is 7.6 cm (3 in.) in diameter
(0 ≥ V₄ ≥ 100)   _50%_

(2) Determine from graphs at right the suitability index values that
correspond to V₁ through V₇ and write these values below.

Suitability Index Value

V₁   _.87_

V₂   _1.0_

V₃   _.7_

V₄   _1.0_

(3) Calculate a habitat suitability index for winter cover for pine marten
using the following models.

HSI = (V₁ × V₂ × V₃ × V₄)^(1/2) =   _0.7_

Variable

(V₁) % tree canopy closure

(V₂) % of overstory canopy
closure comprised of
fir or spruce

(V₃) successional stage of stand
A) shrub-seedling
B) pole sapling
C) young
D) mature or old growth

(V₄) % of ground surface
covered by downfall
which is ≥7.6 cm (3 in.)
in diameter

Figure 6. An HSI model for pine marten (modified from Allen 1982).

Habitat Capability Models

Habitat capability models, as used here, are similar to HSI models, except the habitat variables are used to predict an animal density. Thus, these models could include the traditional carrying-capacity models used for many ungulates. Clearly, some PATREC models fall into this category when the population variable is some measure of population density. The U.S. Forest Service uses the term habitat capability models to include PATREC models and HSI models; however, the U.S. Forest Service converts the models so the output is some measure of population density.

Matrix Models

The simplest form of multi-species models is the species-habitat matrix, in which the presence of each species in a cover type is indicated by an X or other similar notation. Many variations on this approach exist. A relative density (e.g., H = high, M = medium, L = low) or abundance (e.g., A = abundant, C = common, U = unusual, R = rare, etc.) may be indicated. Similarly, the season of use (e.g., W = winter, Sp = Spring, etc.) or breeding status (e.g., B = breeds in habitat, N = does not breed in habitat) may be indicated. Such information is commonly provided by computer-based systems such as RUN-WILD (Patton 1979) and "Procedures" (U.S. Department of the Interior, Fish and Wildlife Service 1980a).

Such models have commonly been used in documents such as EISs to describe current wildlife resources that may be affected by a land-use decision; however, they are not particularly useful for predicting which species will actually be affected or how it will be affected. Such prediction requires that species presence or density be related to components of the habitat, such as vegetation structure or physical features. Several systems, including life-forms and guilding, do this to some extent.

The Life-Form Approach

The life-form approach was developed in Oregon by Thomas (1979), based on earlier work by Haapanen (1965) on birds in Finnish forests. Thomas and others expanded the concept to include all terrestrial vertebrates. A life-form is defined as "a group of wildlife species whose requirements for habitat are satisfied by similar successional stages within given plant communities" (Thomas 1979:480).

For the Blue Mountains of Oregon, Thomas (1979) aggregated over 300 vertebrate species into 16 life-forms (Figure 7). These life-forms were then correlated with successional stages of each plant community. Thus, if a biologist can predict the effect

of management on succession, the life-forms and species that will be present can also be predicted.

The life-form approach was developed for forest lands in response to timber management programs, intended to provide a forest manager with information on impacts to wildlife from management practices. A major impact of logging is to set back forest succession, and succession in forest lands is relatively predictable. This approach is more suited to forest lands than rangelands, where livestock grazing is often the principal commercial use and plant succession is less predictable. Thomas (1979) also recognized the need to supplement the life-form approach with consideration of special habitats (e.g., riparian zones); unique habitats (e.g., cliffs, caves); and separate models for featured species (e.g., mule deer and elk).

Guilding Approach

Use of a community guild model or "guilding" is similar to the life-form approach. A guild was originally defined as a "group of species that exploit the same class of environmental resources in a similar way" (Root 1967). Application of the guild concept appears to have many potential uses in wildlife management; however, the way guilds are defined and used varies greatly (Verner 1984). Short (1983, 1984) and Short and Burnham (1982) have developed formal procedures for applying the guild concept to wildlife habitat evaluation and have termed it the "community guild model." Development of the technique was supported in part by the U.S. Bureau of Land Management. The most recent version of the model is described here.

Guilds are defined according to the habitat layers a species uses for breeding and feeding. Species are then assigned to appropriate cells based on existing data and literature. For example, a species, such as the black-headed grosbeak that breeds in shrubs and feeds in trees, shrubs, and terrestrial (ground) surface (Short 1983:186), would be assigned to rows 8, 6, and 5 of column 7 in Figure 8. (In a life-form analysis, this bird would be assigned to life-form 11; Thomas 1979:323.)

Species occupying the same combination of cells are then lumped into guilds much as done with life-forms. Using such a model, a biologist can predict the guilds affecting various layers of habitat that will be lost or adversely affected by management actions.

Habitat Evaluation Procedures (HEP)

The HEP system was formally developed and used by the U.S. Fish and Wildlife Service and some other federal agencies, particularly the U.S. Bureau of Reclamation and the U.S. Army Corps of Engineers.

Life form	Reproduces	Feeds	No. of species[1]	Examples
1	in water	in water	1	bullfrog
2	in water	on the ground, in bushes, and/or in trees	9	long-toed salamander, western toad, Pacific treefrog
3	on the ground around water	on the ground, and in bushes, trees, and water	45	common garter snake, killdeer, western jumping mouse
4	in cliffs, caves, rimrock, and/or talus	on the ground or in the air	32	side-blotched lizard, common raven, pika
5	on the ground without specific water, cliff, rimrock, or talus association	on the ground	48	western fence lizard, dark-eyed junco, elk
6	on the ground	in bushes, trees, or the air	7	common nighthawk, Lincoln's sparrow, porcupine
7	in bushes	on the ground, in water, or the air	30	American robin, Swainson's thrush, chipping sparrow
8	in bushes	in trees, bushes, or the air	6	dusky flycatcher, yellow-breasted chat, American goldfinch
9	primarily in deciduous trees	in trees, bushes, or the air	4	cedar waxwing, northern oriole, house finch
10	primarily in conifers	in trees, bushes, or the air	14	golden-crowned kinglet, yellow-rumped warbler, red squirrel
11	in conifers or deciduous trees	in trees, in bushes, on the ground, or in the air	24	goshawk, evening grosbeak, hoary bat
12	on very thick branches	on the ground or in water	7	great blue heron, red-tailed hawk, great horned owl
13	in own hole excavated in tree	in trees, in bushes, on the ground, or in the air	13	common flicker, pileated woodpecker, red-breasted nuthatch
14	in a hole made by another species or in a natural hole	on the ground, in water, or the air	37	wood duck, American kestrel, northern flying squirrel
15	in a burrow underground	on the ground or under it	40	rubber boa, burrowing owl, Columbian ground squirrel
16	in a burrow underground	in the air or in the water	10	bank swallow, muskrat, river otter
		Total:	327	

[1]Species assignment to life form is based on predominant habitat-use patterns.

Figure 7. Life-forms for the Blue Mountains of Oregon (from Thomas et al. 1979).

	Temporary Water Sources	Bottom of Water Column	Water Column	Water Surface	Terrestrial Subsurface	Terrestrial Surface	Shrub Layer	Tree Bole	Tree Canopy	Breeds Elsewhere
10. Feeds Elsewhere										
9. Air										
8. Tree Canopy							●			
7. Tree Bole										
6. Shrub Layer							●			
5. Terrestrial Surface							●			
4. Terrestrial Subsurface										
3. Water Surface										
2. Water Column										
1. Bottom Water Column										
	1.	2.	3.	4.	5.	6.	7.	8.	9.	10.

Feeding Loci

Breeding Loci

Figure 8. Habitat layers used to define guilds for use in the community guild model (from Short 1983).

The basic building blocks of the system are the HSI models previously described. One or more HSI models are used to represent components of habitat potentially affected by a project. The index values are multiplied by the acres of habitat to produce "habitat units" present before and after the project. These habitat units are then used to determine equitable mitigation. An increase in habitat units from mitigation is calculated in the same way to produce the number of units before and after a mitigation action.

HEP is used mostly by the U.S. Fish and Wildlife Service and development agencies to analyze water projects that have legal requirements for equitable mitigation. It is used much less on projects that do not have these requirements.

An important feature and one of the major strengths of the HEP system is the emphasis on getting all interested parties together early in the evaluation to agree on the species and precise HSI models to be used in the analysis. This helps prevent later disagreement regarding the results of the evaluation.

In practice, HEP is used with very little follow-up monitoring.

The HEP system is thoroughly described by the U.S. Department of the Interior, Fish and Wildlife Service (1980b) with various applications discussed in Schamberger and Farmer (1978) and Urich and Graham (1983).

Wildlife and Fish Habitat Relationships (WFHR) System

The U.S. Forest Service has developed a system of habitat evaluation called the Wildlife and Fish Habitat Relationships (WFHR) system. This is not a formal system like HEP, but rather a set of standards and collection of evaluation tools to be used by agency biologists (Nelson and Salwasser 1982). Biologists may do evaluations by using the life-form approach or HSI, PATREC, or habitat capability models as appropriate (Sheppard et al. 1982). In addition, on some projects, the U.S. Forest Service makes use of dynamic simulation models such as DYNAST to predict forest succession after timber harvesting or other disturbance. Static models such as HSI models are then used to predict the wildlife species or abundance associated with future successional stages (Barrett and Salwasser 1982). The U.S. Forest Service also emphasizes and, thus, has developed methodology to analyze cumulative impacts (Salwasser et al. 1983) and viable populations (Salwasser and Samson 1985). Methodology for such analyses is still primitive but an important subject that will likely be used more and more in the future.

SUMMARY AND CONCLUSIONS

The field of habitat evaluation has advanced rapidly in the past 15 years. The concept of a habitat model as a basis for habitat evaluation has been developed and used in a variety of ways. Although such models provide prototypes for biologists, the biologist will need to specifically develop models for the area and project under consideration. Such model building is basically nothing more than a more formal and quantifiable approach to the conceptual and qualitative models that biologists have used in the past.

Habitat models are clearly an integral part of the inventory and monitoring process, although they may not be labeled as such. Although monitoring can be done without any sort of an explicit model, such monitoring is not likely to increase the understanding of wildlife resources being managed, nor lead in the long run to better management. Human disturbance factors are incorporated into very few models, yet they are among the most important impacts to wildlife. Future habitat models will need to be developed to incorporate these factors.

The U.S. Fish and Wildlife Service HEP procedures, by emphasizing the process of gaining concensus on models to be used in an analysis, have demonstrated a useful way to alleviate confrontation in the habitat evaluation process. Disagreements focus on analysis tools that are easier to evaluate objectively, rather than on analysis results. This approach promises to be useful in many situations, regardless of whether the biologist is using other formal aspects of HEP.

The U.S. Forest Service has developed and applied many new approaches. The linking of dynamic simulation models of succession with static habitat models, which the U.S. Forest Service pioneered, should be useful wherever succession is reasonably predictable. Similarly, the efforts of U.S. Forest Service personnel and collaborators to develop and use cumulative effects models and viable population analysis models are pioneering efforts that are both necessary and promising. Future habitat modeling will likely emphasize these two areas.

As with other areas of inventory and monitoring, use of habitat models and evaluation systems requires the biologist to use sound, professional judgment and to keep aware of current developments. The techniques will probably continue to develop rapidly, and the biologist cannot afford to be content with "cookbook" procedures or outdated technology.

LITERATURE CITED

ALLEN, A.W. 1982. Habitat suitability index models: Marten. U.S. Dep. Inter., Fish and Wildl. Serv. FWS/OBS-82-10.11. 9pp.

BAILEY, J.A. 1982. Implications of "muddling through" for wildlife management. Wildl. Soc. Bull. 10:363-369.

———. 1984. Principles of wildlife management. John Wiley and Sons, New York, NY. 373pp.

BARRETT, R.H. and H. SALWASSER. 1982. Adaptive management of timber and wildlife habitat using dynast and wildlife-habitat relationship models. Paper presented at Western Assoc. of Fish and Wildlife Agencies, Las Vegas, NV, July 21, 1982. 16pp. (mimeo)

BINNS, N.A. 1979. A habitat quality index for Wyoming trout streams. Wyoming Game and Fish Dep., Fish. Res. Rep. 2. 75pp.

COLE, C.A. and R.L. SMITH. 1983. Habitat suitability indices for monitoring wildlife populations. Trans. North Am. Wildl. and Nat. Resour. Conf. 48:367-375.

COOPERRIDER, A.Y. and J.A. BAILEY. 1984. A simulation approach to forage allocation. Pages 525-559 in Developing Strategies for Rangeland Management. Rep. prepared by the Committee on Developing Strategies for Rangeland Manage., Natl. Res. Council/Natl. Acad. Sciences, Westview Press, Boulder, CO. 2022pp.

——— and D.F. BEHREND. 1980. Simulation of the interaction of deer with northern forest vegetation. New York Fish and Game J. 27:142-155.

HAAPANEN, A. 1965. Bird fauna of the Finnish forests in relation to forest succession. I. Ann. Zool. Fenn. 3(3):153-196.

HANSEN, C.G. 1980. Habitat. Pages 64-79 in Monson, G. and L. Summer, eds. The Desert Bighorn. Univ. Arizona Press, Tucson.

HOLLING, C.S., ed. 1978. Adaptive environmental assessment and management. Vol. 3, International Series on Applied Systems Analysis. John Wiley and Sons, New York, NY. 377pp.

NELSON, R.D. and H. SALWASSER. 1982. The Forest Service wildlife and fish habitat relationships program. Trans. North Am. Wildl. and Nat. Resour. Conf. 47:174-183.

ODUM, E.P. 1969. Fundamentals of ecology. W.B. Saunders Company, Philadelphia, PA. 546pp.

O'NEIL, L.J. and M.L. SCHAMBERGER. 1983. Habitat models as a monitoring tool. Pages 424-427 in Bell, J.F. and T. Atterbury, eds. Renewable Resource Inventories for Monitoring Changes and Trends. SAF83-14, Oregon State Univ., Corvallis.

PATTON, D.R. 1979. RUNWILD II: A storage and retrieval system for wildlife data. Trans. North Am. Wildl. and Nat. Resour. Conf. 44:425-430.

PETERSON, R.T. 1969. A field guide to western birds: Field marks of all species found in North America west of the 100th Meridian, with a section on the birds of the Hawaiian Islands. 2nd ed. (revised and enlarged). Houghton Mifflin Co., Boston, MA. 336pp.

ROOT, R.B. 1967. The niche exploration pattern of the blue-gray gnatcatcher. Ecol. Monogr. 37:317-350.

SALWASSER, H., C.K. HAMILTON, W.B. KROHN, J.F. LIPSCOMB, and C.H. THOMAS. 1983. Monitoring wildlife and fish: Mandates and their implications. Trans. North Am. Wildl. and Nat. Resour. Conf. 48:297-307.

——— and F.B. SAMSON. 1985. Cumulative effects analysis: An advance in wildlife planning and management. Trans. North Am. Wildl. and Nat. Resour. Conf. 50:313-321.

SCHAMBERGER, M.A. and A.H. FARMER. 1978. The habitat evaluation procedures: Their application in project planning and impact evaluation. Trans. North Am. Wildl. and Nat. Resour. Conf. 43:274-283.

———, ———, and J.W. TERRELL. 1982. Habitat suitability index models: Introduction. U.S. Dep. Inter., Fish and Wildl. Serv. FWS/OBS-82-10. 2pp.

SCHROEDER, R.L. 1984. Habitat suitability index models: Black brant. U.S. Dep. Inter., Fish and Wildl. Serv. FWS/OBS-82/10.63. 11pp.

SHEPPARD, J.L., D.L. WILLS, and J.L. SIMONSON. 1982. Project applications of the Forest Service Rocky Mountain Region wildlife and fish habitat relationships system. Trans. North Am. Wildl. and Nat. Resour. Conf. 47:128-141.

SHORT, H.L. 1983. Wildlife guilds in Arizona desert habitats. U.S. Dep. Inter., Bur. Land Manage., Tech. Note 362. 258pp.

———. 1984. Habitat suitability index models: The Arizona guild and layers of habitat models. U.S. Dep. Inter., Fish and Wildl. Serv. FWS/OBS-82/10.70. 37pp.

——— and K.P. BURNHAM. 1982. Techniques for structuring wildlife guilds to evaluate impacts on wildlife communities. U.S. Dep. Inter., Spec. Sci. Rep.—Wildl. 244. 34pp.

SOUSA, P.J. 1983. Habitat suitability index models: Lewis' woodpecker. U.S. Dep. Inter., Fish and Wildl. Serv. FWS/OBS-82/10.32. 14pp.

THOMAS, J.W., ed. 1979. Wildlife habitats in managed forests—the Blue Mountains of Oregon and Washington. U.S. Dep. Agric., For. Serv., Agric. Handbook 553. 511pp.

URICH, D.L. and J.P. GRAHAM. 1983. Applying habitat evaluation procedures (HEP) to wildlife area planning in Missouri. Wildl. Soc. Bull. 11:215-222.

U.S. DEPARTMENT OF THE INTERIOR, FISH and WILDLIFE SERVICE. 1980a. An evaluation of "A procedure for describing fish and wildlife in Pennsylvania." U.S. Dep. Inter., Fish and Wildl. Serv. FWS/OBS-79/19-A. 15pp.

———. 1980b. Habitat evaluation procedures (HEPs) 102 ESM. U.S. Dep. Inter., Fish and Wildl. Serv. (unnumbered)

———. 1981. Standards for the development of habitat suitability index models. 103 ESM. U.S. Dep. Inter., Fish and Wildl. Serv. (unnumbered)

VERNER, J. 1984. The guild concept applied to management of bird populations. Environmental Manage. 8(1):1-13.

——— and A.S. BOSS, eds. 1980. California wildlife and their habitats: Western Sierra Nevada. U.S. Dep. Agric., For. Serv., Gen. Tech. Rep. PSW-37. 439pp.

WILLIAMS, G.L., K.R. RUSSELL, and W.K. SEITZ. 1978. Pattern recognition as a tool in the ecological analysis of habitat. Pages 521-531 in Marmelstein, A., ed. Classification, Inventory and Analysis of Fish and Wildlife Habitat. U.S. Dep. Inter., Fish and Wildl. Serv. FWS/OBS-78/76. 604pp.

39

EVALUATION AND INTERPRETATION

Allen Y. Cooperrider

U.S. Bureau of Land Management
Service Center
Denver, CO 80225

"Statistical analysis is not a substitute for thinking."

—Alan Speigel, *Speigel's Laws of Management*

Editor's Note: The best data sets and most elegant quantitative analyses will not likely affect management unless they are interpreted and evaluated for those who make the decisions. This process requires the biologist to creatively bring together information from various sources. These sources include not only data collection and statistical analyses of them, but also field observations, experience from other areas or projects, and opinions from others knowledgeable about the subject or area. Few biologists are effective in influencing decisions, unless they have mastered the art of evaluation and interpretation. This chapter discusses the process and some factors a biologist should consider at this stage of an inventory or monitoring effort.

INTRODUCTION

Interpretation and evaluation of data are critical steps in the inventory and monitoring process. At this stage, the biologist must explain what all the data, information, and analyses mean. This is not a formal process; if it were, it would be included with other analytical methods. Since the process is essentially subjective, very little has been written about it. Why, then, include a chapter on such a nebulous subject? Because biologists often do a poor job of interpretation and evaluation or tend to skip this step.

Biologists frequently present a manager with lists of species present in habitats, correlation coefficients, t-tests, or other test statistics and expect a manager to understand how these relate to the land management decisions to be made. The manager does not understand; therefore, the biologists are not performing their jobs as thoroughly and professionally as they could. A biologist is tasked with explaining the meaning of data; suggesting implications from the findings; cautioning about known or potential weakness in the data; and explaining the significance of the anticipated resource impacts. The biologist who fails to do this has not completed the job and is not fully using the information. Collecting and analyzing data are frequently expensive, and the biologist should not waste information derived from such data.

The art of interpretation and evaluation cannot be taught, any more than one can be taught to think or to use good judgment. The aims of this chapter are more modest. In it, I explain what interpretation and evaluation are and list some of the many possible aspects that must be considered during the process. Biologists hoping to improve their abilities to interpret and evaluate may find some useful guidance. However, the process cannot be reduced to a cookbook procedure.

Interpretation and evaluation is thus one of the most important and challenging tasks of the professional, yet one which is frequently done poorly and with very little guidance. The reasons biologists struggle with these tasks usually relate to their training and background. Many wildlife biologists are thoroughly trained in the scientific methods and have experience in research. This scientific training is quite valuable and important. However, it tends to make biologists cautious. Scientists are taught to—

(1) Collect data carefully and systematically,

(2) Concentrate on what the data demonstrates conclusively,

(3) Avoid predicting trends, and

(4) Leave out value considerations.

A management biologist should also collect data carefully and systematically. However, the management biologist must operate quite differently with the other three factors since these are opposite from what a biologist is asked to do in interpretation and evaluation. Typically a manager wants predictions about the future. Rarely does a biologist have enough data to predict in a scientific way what will happen on an area; instead he or she has many diverse sources of data and information upon which to base some future states. This is needed and wanted by management to make an informed decision. A scientist can afford to wait for conclusive results; a resource manager cannot.

Similarly, biological scientists do not deal much with values other than "scientific value" and that elusive "ecological value;" most biologists are taught that consideration of values is the domain of philosophy, economics, sociology, psychology, or religion. Yet, a management biologist must constantly deal with values. Biologists are paid to manage wildlife and wildlife habitat because people place some value on those resources. But, those values are quite diverse. A professional biologist must be aware of these values and explain them to the manager.

Ideally, a scientific manager would have "hard" data and conclusive evidence on which to base all of his or her decisions. In real life, in resource management as well as in agriculture, business, economics, politics, and other fields, decisions are made on "soft" data. A decisionmaker may have good data on one decision factor and only an opinion or limited data on other factors. A manager would be foolish to make decisions based only on factors for which good data were available, if he or she knew other factors were also important.

INTERPRETATION

To interpret has been defined as "to explain or tell the meaning of: present in understandable terms" (Merriam-Webster 1983). Once data are collected, organized, put on the computer, processed and massaged in a variety of ways, and the results printed, the information needs to be explained. Casual observations while out in the field and talks with other people in the field; specialists in other disciplines; and other biologists familiar with the area or the problem being addressed, are other sources of information. The experience of the biologist with similar problems or areas is also a source of information. All these sources can be used to explain to the public, the manager, or the decisionmaker what the data mean. They can also be used to predict a future with or without a proposed action. Some of the following questions should be considered.

What do the data mean? A biologist may have been studying the behavior and foraging habits of elk (*Cervus elaphus*) to determine if expansion of a grazing lease into its summer range will adversely affect the herd. The biologist has measured elk and cattle use in a series of adjacent pastures. After analyzing the data, he or she may have concluded with the aid of a statistician that "use of pastures by elk is significantly and negatively correlated with use by cattle ($R^2 = 0.99$)." More obscurely, "Spearman's rank correlation coefficient between elk use days and cattle use days is -0.94." These statements need to be translated into a language understood by the natural resource manager, i.e., "elk are avoiding areas used by cattle." (The pure logician, blissfully ignorant of western cattle operations, could of course argue that cattle are avoiding elk, but managers are not too interested in this type of argument.)

What is the cause? Biologists and managers must be concerned with causes. Knowing that something happens is useful, but knowing why is even more useful. Considering the previous example, the manager may want to know why elk avoid areas used by cattle. One possibility is that elk simply prefer different types of pastures than those normally used by livestock operators for cattle grazing. However, the biologist may have observed that elk use pastures until cattle move onto them, after which they avoid them. This is useful information in interpreting data, even though it has not been collected with a well-designed study. The biologist may believe from his or her observations that elk avoid pastures because forage conditions are much worse after cattle have been "highgrading" current forage production. Furthermore, the biologist may be able to cite studies in similar situations that indicate such avoidance is due to forage conditions. Thus information from a variety of sources has been used to explain the observed phenomena.

A common problem in determining causality is that the results observed are due to some unexpected but obvious cause, other than the one a biologist was trying to isolate. Weather is often such a factor. For example, a biologist may have been monitoring changes in vegetation cover in two similar streams: one grazed by cattle; the other ungrazed. During the fifth year, a 100-year storm occurs in the drainage of the ungrazed stream, causing severe flooding and scouring of the entire streambed. The data after 5 years would suggest that grazing improves the condition of the streamside vegetation, whereas just the opposite is true. A biologist would be foolish, not to mention unprofessional, to mechanically interpret the data without recognizing the more obvious, but largely undocumented, causes. In Chapter 35, Weather and Climate, ways of dealing with variations caused by weather are described. These methods will help in most cases, but exceptions will occur. Record events, such as the 100-year storm, the record low frost, the wettest spring on record, are occurring somewhere in the world every day.

What are the expected impacts of the proposed management? This is, of course, the reason data have been collected and the crucial question to be answered. Consider the previous example again. If elk avoid areas used by cattle because forage conditions have been degraded, what are the expected

impacts of expanding grazing leases? Initially, one may expect that the expansion will change the pattern of elk use on the area. This may be a concern to either livestock or wildlife management. Certain types of livestock management, such as rest rotation systems, may be doomed to fail because elk will concentrate in the pastures that are supposed to be "rested." Or, such management may force elk to move to other areas where they may be more vulnerable to poaching or where they may damage agricultural crops.

The biologist is thus interpreting and extrapolating the data that have been collected to make inferences that are useful in making management decisions. In following this process, he or she must also be evaluating the adequacy of the information. This leads to another series of questions.

How good are the data? A biologist rarely can collect the quantity or quality of data required for risk-free conclusions. For one thing, budgets for such efforts are usually rather limited. Furthermore, well-designed studies for evaluating year-to-year variation typically take 3 to 5 years of data collection; yet, managers cannot wait 5 years to make decisions. Thus, the best study designs can rarely be used, even if a biologist or agency could afford them.

Even the data collected are often inadequate or questionable. Erroneous data are collected by inexperienced, trained, or unmotivated technicians. Equipment fails or malfunctions occur resulting in data gaps or data of questionable accuracy. Weather, travel difficulties, or budget problems prevent certain data from being collected. Management actions or "acts of God" destroy or invalidate study sites or plots. The list goes on, but these are normal working conditions for the field biologist and should not be confused with problems caused by poor study design. The latter can be prevented; the former cannot. An experienced biologist can lessen these problems by planning for contingencies, training personnel thoroughly, carefully testing equipment, and taking other precautions. The problems can never entirely be prevented, however.

This explains why most data are "soft." Hopefully, the data obtained are better than having no data at all. However, the biologist must determine the quality of the data and convey this information to others who use or make decisions based on such data. Consider the previous elk and cattle example. If the technician who collected the habitat-use data could not distinguish elk from cattle tracks, one may not want to stake his or her reputation on the study results.

Study design may also cause problems. Designing studies requires making a series of reasonable assumptions so certain statistical procedures can be used. Typically, assumptions that seemed reasonable at the beginning of a study may become very questionable after more is learned about the habitat or population being studied. For example, one may assume that a drainage contains a discrete herd of mule deer (*Odocoileus hemionus*) but, after a field study, discovers two separate subherds: one that is resident year-round and the other migratory and found on the area only in winter. A study designed to determine the amount of forage to be allocated for deer might produce misleading results if based on the former assumption.

Thus, the biologist may have only poor data, for reasons beyond his or her control. Nevertheless, the manager should be informed of the reliability of the data. Poor data can cause enough problems, and problems should not be compounded by pretending the data are good.

Are the data adequate? I have alluded to the fact that biologists rarely consider data adequate; yet, most of the time, they must live with such data. Sometimes, however, collecting more data is both necessary and feasible. The biologist is responsible for advising the manager of such contingencies. As with initial planning decisions, such mid-course decisions must be made by weighing the time and costs involved against other priority projects.

To this point, I have talked about the quality of the data, the meaning of the data, and predicted impacts. A closely related question is "What is the significance of such impacts?" Put another way, "What values will be enhanced or destroyed or are at risk?" This leads to the subject of evaluation.

EVALUATION

Evaluation is the process of determining the value of something. Used here, evaluation is the process of determining the value of the wildlife resources.

After data have been carefully collected, analyzed, and interpreted, the value of the wildlife resources that may be affected needs to be explained. When questions such as "Who cares if the elk herd decreases by 50%?" or "What is 300 acres of riparian habitat worth?" are being asked, the biologist needs to place a value on the resource or at least explain the resource values.

Wildlife biologists have traditionally concentrated on enhancing or ensuring the production or conservation of wildlife resources in the best manner possible. The criteria they use are primarily biological or ecological and include factors such as "ecological diversity" or "ecosystem stability" (Krutilla

1974). Most wildlife biologists place high value on wildlife and have not felt a need to seriously examine wildlife values (Bailey 1984). Furthermore, many biologists dislike the concept of placing monetary values on wildlife, believing the real values of wildlife are aesthetic, biological and, most importantly, unmeasurable. However, if biologists argue a case for wildlife resources against actions that destroy wildlife habitat, they must be thoroughly familiar with all wildlife values and some valuation methods (Steinhoff 1971).

Economists have traditionally placed monetary values on economically commercial resources (those resources that can be bought and sold) so the resources can be analyzed. Amenity resources (aesthetic, ecological, and other non-commercial resources), however, are more difficult to place values on and, therefore, more difficult to analyze formally (Krutilla 1974). Since many wildlife values fall in the amenity category, economic analysis of wildlife values is still in its infancy. However, the field is developing rapidly and is of such importance that a chapter on the subject is included in this book. Whereas in this chapter I discuss some types of wildlife values for the biologist to consider subjectively, Chapter 40, Economic Analysis, presents the state-of-the-art for formal quantitative analysis methods. For further reading on wildlife values, I recommend Bailey (1984:34-50), King (1966), Steinhoff (1971), Shaw and Zube (1980), or Kellert (1980a, b).

King (1966) comprehensively categorized wildlife values. He divided these values, which have subsequently been used by several other authors, into seven categories:

(1) Commercial;

(2) Recreational;

(3) Biotic;

(4) Scientific, philosophical, and educational;

(5) Aesthetic;

(6) Social; and

(7) Negative.

Of these values, only the commercial value can be easily translated into dollars for conventional economic analyses. Techniques for valuation of recreation are available and more are under development (Sorg and Loomis 1985). Numbers 3 through 6 are, for the most part, unquantifiable and will remain that way for a long time, at least in terms of placing a dollar value on them. Negative values can occur in all categories. Damage to orchards by elk is relatively easy to translate into dollar values; on the other hand, the negative value of Canada goose droppings on putting greens is harder to quantify.

Values, however, can be looked at and measured in different ways. Kellert (1980a) measured and described wildlife values in terms of 10 attitudes toward animals (Table 1). Some of these, such as the ecologistic and scientistic attitudes, correspond neatly with King's values, whereas others, moralistic and dominionistic, do not have any obvious counterparts. Kellert (1980a) surveyed American public attitudes toward animals and more specifically wildlife (Table 2) as one measure of values. The attitudes are, of course, much more complex than can be represented in a few simple tables, but biologists need to be aware of public attitudes (values). Many biologists, who were trained and spent years in the profession when wildlife management was primarily game management, were slow to recognize changing public attitudes toward wildlife and the changes

they wanted from wildlife managers. U.S. Bureau of Land Management biologists, for example, differ significantly from the general public in the same tests (Peyton and Langenau 1985). They score significantly lower on utilitarian and negativistic scales and higher on ecological, scientistic, dominionistic, and naturalistic scales. Biologists must be aware of not only their own values but also those of the general public and be able to articulate these values. This is a difficult, sensitive, but necessary task, for which there are no easy solutions or cookbook approaches. Kellert (1980) summarized the importance of the task:

"The wildlife management field appears to be confronted by a major change in the public it serves, with many new and atypical groups becoming appropriate recipients of professional attention. This expanded constituency must inevitably constitute a threat as much as a challenge to a field that has historically defined itself in far narrower terms. Nevertheless, the challenge represents a rare change, and it would be a disservice to the profession, let alone to an

Table 1. Classification of attitudes toward animals (from Kellert 1980a).

Attitude	Description
Naturalistic	The primary characteristic is a strong interest and affection for outdoors and wildlife. Observation and personal involvement with wildlife are the keys to the naturalistic interest in the outdoors. Animals provide the context and meaning for active participation in natural settings.
Ecologistic	Directed at a conceptual understanding of the interrelationships of species in the context of ecosystems, with major concern for dependencies between animals and their natural habitats. Wild animals are valued less as sources of affection or amusement, and more as devices for comprehending the broader functionings of natural systems.
Humanistic	Emphasizes feelings of strong affection and attachment to individual animals, typically pets. The animal is the recipient of feelings and emotional projections somewhat analogous to those expressed toward other people.
Moralistic	Concern for the ethically appropriate humane treatment of animals. A basic moralistic principle is the fundamental similarity of all animals, each endowed with equivalent rights to existence.
Aesthetic	Emphasizes the attractiveness or symbolic significance of animals.
Scientistic	Concern for the biological and physical characteristics of animals. Wildlife are primarily interesting as problem-solving objects, not as sources of companionship or wilderness recreation.
Utilitarian	The relevance of animals is largely derived from their usefulness to people. Animals should serve some human purpose and, thus, be functional as sources of personal gain. Animals are desirable insofar as they facilitate some type of tangible advantage or reward.
Dominionistic	Satisfactions derived from the mastery and control of animals, typically in a sporting context (e.g., rodeos, trophy hunting, bullfighting). Animals provide opportunities for expressions of prowess, skill, strength, and masculinity.
Negativistic	Active dislike or fear of animals. This domain includes neutralism—a more passively oriented avoidance of animals for reasons of indifference.
Neutralistic	Primary orientation is a passive avoidance of animals caused by indifference.

Table 2. American attitudes toward wildlife (from Kellert 1980b).

Attitude	Estimated % of American Population Strongly Oriented Toward the Attitude*	Common Behavioral Expressions	Most Related Values/Benefits
Naturalistic	10	Outdoor wildlife-related recreation; back-country use, nature birding, and nature hunting.	Outdoor recreation
Ecologistic	7	Conservation support, activism and membership, ecological study.	Ecological
Humanistic	35	Pets, wildlife tourism, casual zoo visitation.	Companionship, affection
Moralistic	20	Animal welfare support/membership, kindness to animals.	Ethical, existence
Aesthetic	15	Nature appreciation, art, wildlife tourism.	Aesthetic
Scientistic	1	Scientific study/hobbies, collecting.	Scientific
Utilitarian	20	Consumption of furs, raising meat, bounties, meat hunting.	Consumptive, utilitarian
Dominionistic	3	Animal spectator sports, trophy hunting.	Sporting
Negativistic	2	Cruelty, overt fear behavior.	Little or negative
Neutralistic	35	Avoidance of animal behavior.	Little or negative

*Totals more than 100% since persons can be strongly oriented toward more than one attitude.

American public and wildlife resource in need, if the professional reaction was more to avoid an alien reality than a creative and bold response to an evolutionary opportunity."

Clearly the days of simply managing ducks for duck hunters and deer for deer hunters are gone. The biologist must consider and explain wildlife values to managers and others when presenting information from inventory and monitoring studies.

SUMMARY

Interpretation and evaluation are an important part of the inventory and monitoring process. Biologists must explain to the manager and others what the information means. Explanation, at this stage, should be based on all sources of information, not merely on a narrow statistical conclusion. Biologists must also explain the values of the wildlife resources under consideration. To do this, biologists should be aware of the values the public places on wildlife resources, since these may differ significantly from their personal values.

LITERATURE CITED

BAILEY, J.A. 1984. Principles of wildlife management. John Wiley and Sons, New York, NY. 373pp.

KELLERT, S.R. 1980a. Americans' attitudes and knowledge of animals. Trans. North Am. Wildl. Nat. Resour. Conf. 45:111-124.

————. 1980b. Contemporary values of wildlife in American society. Pages 31-60 *in* Shaw, W.W. and E.H. Zube, eds. Wildlife Values. Center for Assessment of Noncommodity Natural Resource Values, School of Renewable Natural Resources, Univ. Arizona, Institutional Series Rep. 1. Tucson. 117pp.

KING, R.T. 1966. Wildlife and man. New York Conservationist 20:8-11.

KRUTILLA, J.V. 1974. Methods for estimating the value of wildlife resources. Pages 125-136 *in* Bailey, J.A., W. Elder, and T.D. McKinney, eds. Readings in Wildlife Conservation. The Wildlife Society, Washington, DC. 722pp.

MERRIAM-WEBSTER, A. 1983. Webster's ninth new Collegiate dictionary. Merriam-Webster Inc., Publishers, Springfield, MA.

PEYTON, R.B. and E.E. LANGENAU, Jr. 1985. A comparison of attitudes held by BLM biologists and the general public towards animals. Wildl. Soc. Bull. 13:117-120.

SHAW, W.W. and E.H. ZUBE, eds. 1980. Wildlife values. Center for Assessment of Noncommodity Natural Resource Values, School of Renewable Natural Resources, Univ. Arizona, Institutional Series. Rep. 1. Tucson. 117pp.

SORG, C.F. and J. LOOMIS. 1985. An introduction to wildlife valuation techniques. Wildl. Soc. Bull. 13:38-46.

STEINHOFF, H.W. 1971. Communicating complete wildlife values of Kenai. Trans. North Am. Wildl. and Nat. Resour. Conf. 36:428-438.

40

ECONOMIC ANALYSIS

John B. Loomis[1]

U.S. Fish and Wildlife Service
Western Energy and Land Use Team
Creekside One Building
2627 Redwing Road
Fort Collins, CO 80526-2899

Editor's Note: Many biologists are just beginning to recognize the need for economic analyses of wildlife values. In many cases the economic evaluation of the effects of a project will affect decisions more than the biological evaluation. Biologists need to be aware of bio-economic techniques and theory so that they can plan biological assessments to provide economists and managers with the information they need on economic values of wildlife.

INTRODUCTION

Several new federal directives requiring evaluation of the dollar benefits of wildlife have increased the need for biologists and economists to understand the available bio-economic techniques. Improved techniques for valuation of amenity (non-marketed natural resources), such as wildlife, have largely displaced older, more subjective (and often erroneous) approaches. Any reader unfamiliar with the major advances in the economics of non-marketed natural resources will be pleasantly surprised with improvements made since the 1970s.

The purposes of this chapter are to describe concepts and measurement of economic values of wildlife, to provide an overview of bio-economic analysis techniques, and to discuss some of the issues and common misconceptions about economic analyses of wildlife values. More detailed information on actual bio-economic analysis techniques can be found in the appendix.

Most federal agencies are required to translate the biological effects of their actions into economic values. For example, the U.S. Bureau of Land Management's (BLM's) Final Rangeland Improvement Policy (U.S. Department of the Interior, Bureau of Land Management 1982) indicates that willingness to pay values for wildlife need to be developed so they can be used in rangeland investment (SageRam) programs that rank alternative livestock management actions. The U.S. Forest Service planning procedures require estimates of present net value of all resources having an established market value or an assigned value (U.S. Department of Agriculture, Forest Service 1982). Within these resources, wildlife recreation has a dollar value set by the Chief of the U.S. Forest Service; this value is initially developed from existing research on the economic value of wildlife recreation. The present net value (in dollar terms) has become one of the U.S. Forest Service's key criteria in comparing planning alternatives and in determining what represents maximum net public benefits (Peterson 1983).

[1]Current Address: Division of Environmental Studies, University of California at Davis, Davis, CA 95616.

WILDLIFE VALUES AND THE PUBLIC TRUST DOCTRINE

Much confusion exists about the economic value of wildlife. In this section, the types of wildlife values and their relationship to the public trust doctrine are discussed.

Economic value is often confused with financial value. For a good or service to have economic value, it must meet the following two criteria:

(1) It must provide some consumers satisfaction or enjoyment, and

(2) The good or service must be scarce in the sense that consumers want more than is available at no cost.

Wildlife certainly meets both of these criteria.

Economic values include commercial, recreational, option, existence, and bequest values (Figure 1). Besides the economic values of on-site recreation (both consumptive and non-consumptive) and commercial uses of wildlife, there are many off-site user values. These include option, existence, and bequest value. Option value refers to an individual's willingness to pay to maintain wildlife recreation opportunities. Option value can be thought of as an insurance premium people would pay to ensure wildlife recreation opportunities in the future. Existence value is the economic benefit received from simply knowing wildlife exists. Bequest value is the willingness to pay for providing wildlife resources to future generations.

The first pitfall one faces in identifying and quantifying wildlife values concerns the difference between economic values and financial values. Financial values are defined as actual revenue or sales received by firms or public agencies (i.e., cash changing hands). Financial values ignore social benefits or costs that cannot be captured as revenue by firms. At best, financial values are a subset of economic values (see Figure 1) and, at worst, may be a serious distortion.

The disparity between economic and financial values for wildlife is confusing to resource managers and local officials accustomed to dealing only with marketed resources such as coal or timber. For these resources, it is customary to assume the economic and financial values of additional units of outputs are almost synonymous.

Financial values (sales revenue, profit) are useful in answering questions about profitability of guide services or retail outlets for recreational equipment. Financial feasibility of business is often important to county and state officials from the standpoint of job creation or property taxes. These legitimate concerns have little to do with the economic value of wildlife, however.

In the U.S., laws assign ownership of the nation's wildlife resources to the state or federal government. The governments thus have the responsibility to manage these resources as trustees for the benefit of the public. Public ownership implicitly recognizes that inefficient resource allocation would result without cooperative intervention. The public agent is expected to incorporate all benefits and costs into decisions and not merely the financial costs and returns seen by private firms. This is called the Public Trust Doctrine.

The Public Trust Doctrine recognizes that all benefits and costs of wildlife to people are not captured in the commodity values of private markets. Therefore, the public agencies are responsible for protecting the interests of birders, hunters, and citizens who enjoy knowing wildlife exists.

Although public agencies are charged with protecting all wildlife values, current methodology for quantifying such values is often limited to recreational and commercial values.

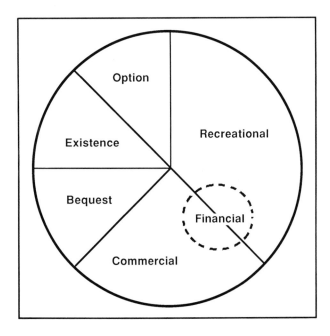

Figure 1.   Economic values of wildlife.

MEASUREMENT OF ECONOMIC VALUES OF WILDLIFE

As discussed earlier, the economic values of wildlife and wildlife recreation differ from financial values. Even in determining economic values of wildlife, some confusion still exists. Before techniques for measuring economic value are discussed, it is necessary to have an operational definition of just what needs to be measured.

In the marketplace framework of supply and demand, the supply curve defines the quantities of a good that producers are willing to market in return for various payments. A supply curve has a positive slope because, at a higher price per unit, producers are willing to supply more goods. The demand curve is generated by the quantities of a good that consumers are willing to buy when faced with various prices. Higher prices will lead to a lower quantity demand, causing a negatively sloped demand curve. The intersection of the supply and demand curves indicates equilibrium—which is reached at a price where the quantity that producers are willing to supply equals the quantity consumers are willing to buy (Figure 2).

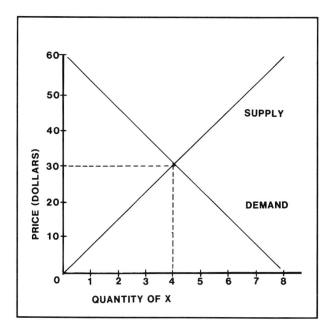

Figure 2. Supply and demand for good X.

In the hypothetical example in Figure 2, equilibrium is reached at a price of $30 and supply of good X equals demand. The demand curve shows that a consumer is willing and able to pay $60 for the first unit of good X. When faced with a price of $30, a consumer surplus of $30 results on the first unit. Alternatively, consider the situation where X is free. In this case, eight units of X would be demanded and the entire area under the demand curve would be a measure of consumer surplus with no revenue collected. From this hypothetical example, one can see that the price charged is a measure of expenditures or financial value while the difference between what the individual is willing to pay and expenditures is a measure of net benefits (consumer surplus or net willingness to pay).

Although the same concepts of supply and demand and consumer surplus apply to all goods whether they are marketed or not (as wildlife), empirical estimation may be difficult for unmarketed goods. Supply of a species is regulated by wildlife managers and the carrying capacity of the land. When carrying capacity has not been reached, the management costs of supplying various quantities of a species can be used to generate a supply curve. Estimating a demand curve is less straightforward. In the case of a market good, a demand curve is generated by monitoring purchasing behavior of individuals at various prices and mapping a demand curve. However, in the case of wildlife-related recreation, a demand curve cannot be derived easily because wildlife ordinarily is considered a publicly owned good that one does not have to pay to hunt or view. Hunting and fishing licenses are not market-determined prices but administratively determined fees. As a result, prices cannot be associated with various quantities, and a demand curve cannot be plotted directly.

For wildlife values, the demand curve is used as a basis for estimating consumers' (or in this situation, recreationists') willingness to pay for increases in wildlife recreation opportunities. (Harberger 1971; Sassone and Schaffer 1978). A hypothetical demand curve (Figure 3) shows the number of trips a recreationist would take at different travel costs. The total area under the curve is the gross willingness to pay. The net willingness to pay is the area above the actual cost but below the demand curve.

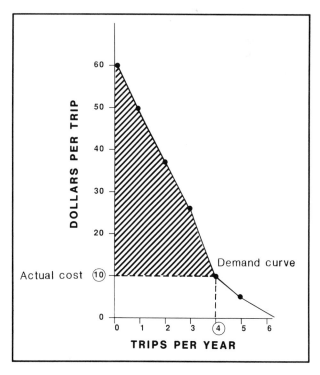

Figure 3. Hypothetical demand curve for wildlife recreation.

If the actual cost was $10 then the shaded area in Figure 3 is the net willingness to pay which is $105. The gross willingness to pay would be $105 plus the $40 (4 trips x $10 per trip) which comes to $145.

Economists term consumers' net willingness to pay as "consumer surplus." Consumer surplus represents the consumers' additional willingness to pay for the opportunity to hunt or fish at some site. It is a net or additional willingness to pay because it is added to current expenditures.

Consumer surplus sometimes stands as a conceptual "stumbling block" for those involved in economic valuation. Consumer surplus is often not seen as a real or tangible economic benefit because it represents money that has not actually been collected by a business or government agency. If individuals could be feasibly charged a price equal to their maximum willingness to pay for each unit, the estimate of consumer surplus could be verified. Such pricing schemes exist, but the government does not use them to capture the full willingness to pay for each unit (the consumer surplus) as revenue.

Several methods are used to derive demand curves indirectly and provide measures of net willingness to pay. Those most often used include the travel cost method and the contingent value method.

Travel Cost Method (TCM)

This approach was developed by Clawson (1959) to empirically estimate recreation benefits. The method is based on the belief that travel cost can be used as a proxy for price in deriving a demand curve for a recreation site. The first step of zonal TCM analysis involves dividing the area around the site into zones or counties of origin of recreationists. One assumes that the costs from a particular zone to a recreation site are the same for all individuals in that zone. Based on origin data, a visitation rate (trips per capita) is calculated for each zone. Regression analysis can be used to estimate a function for visitation rates based on travel cost and socioeconomic data. Such a regression line is shown in Figure 4.

The different travel costs for making a trip from each of four origins (counties) surrounding a site are plotted against the number of trips per capita from each county to the site. These different combinations of travel cost and trips per capita represent price-quantity points that trace a demand curve. From this demand curve, the consumer surplus or net willingness to pay for recreation at a particular site can be calculated by taking the area under the demand curve but above the travel cost for each zone of origin. For details on use of the technique, see Rosenthal et al. (1984).

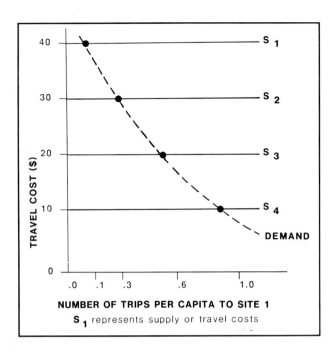

Figure 4. Regression of travel costs versus number of visits per capita.

The TCM requires data on wildlife recreationists' travel cost to or distance from a recreation site. If surveys providing travel cost (or distance) and city or county of residence are available, they should be used. However, one advantage of the TCM is that existing information from hunting licenses, game tags, or even license plates can be used to determine the wildlife recreationist's city or county of residence. If one knows the county or city of residence, the round-trip distance to the fishing or hunting site can be calculated from maps. The distance can be converted to a travel cost by using the government publication "Cost of Owning and Operating a Motor Vehicle" (U.S. Department of Transportation 1985).

The information on visits needs to be grouped by county so the trips per capita can be calculated by dividing trips by county population. This becomes a dependent variable in the regression analysis used to statistically estimate the demand curve. Thus, it is generally important to know the county or city (or zip code) of wildlife users. Knowing the number of wildlife recreationists per vehicle and number of days per trip is also useful.

Data sources are often available for calculating travel costs. For example, several data sources exist for big game hunting. State wildlife management agencies often record the zip code or city of residence from hunting licenses or post-season harvest surveys for the general big game seasons. Wildlife agencies also record the herd unit from which an animal is harvested. These provide the two basic types of data for TCM: location of residence and herd unit.

Matching these two together allows calculation of round-trip distance and estimation of round-trip travel costs. For details on these procedures see Loomis (1982).

In many states, license plate numbers are keyed to county of residence. By simply visiting the recreation site of interest and recording license plate numbers (in some States, the county name is even printed on the plate), one can get an approximate idea of the origin of wildlife recreationists. This is useful in collecting data on nonconsumptive users of wildlife, such as birding or photography.

The TCM can be used to measure the economic value of nonconsumptive wildlife recreation such as birdwatching or wildlife photography. Data on distance traveled can be obtained on site at areas where a significant amount of nonconsumptive use of wildlife takes place.

A useful characteristic of TCM is that it can be used for valuation and use estimation simultaneously. A simple single site TCM demand curve can be used to estimate hunter demand over time. This is done by multiplying each county's current trip per capita rate times future county population.

Thus, if a demand estimate is needed for the year 1990 for example, all one must do is—

(1) Use the equation to estimate current trips per capita at the current travel cost for each county, and

(2) Multiply this current trip per capita by each county's forecasted population in 1990.

When using a regional TCM that includes a quality variable such as harvest, one can even estimate a future visit rate per capita that varies with future harvest. To get a future demand estimate, the analyst would multiply each county's future trip per capita figure by each county's future population.

The strengths and weaknesses of TCM as a tool for estimating benefits of recreation are described by Dwyer et al. (1977) and Rosenthal et al. (1984).

Contingent Value Method (CVM)

The Contingent Value Method (CVM) is also known as the "Direct Method" or "Bidding Method." Unlike the familiar market situation where people alter consumption in response to price changes, bidding involves asking individuals to respond to changes in hypothetical prices for an unmarketable good. The term "contingent valuation" stems from asking individuals how their behavior would change,

contingent on a new hypothetical situation. Thus individual users are asked to provide data to estimate their net willingness to pay (consumer surplus).

Estimation (distinguished from application) requires administration of a carefully constructed survey. The U.S. Water Resources Council (1979) and Dwyer et al. (1977) provide good reviews of the steps in survey design and implementation. Although wildlife biologists at the field level will rarely construct such a survey, they should understand how the method works and what the information means.

The CVM relies on mail and personal or telephone interviews. The interview begins with an introduction and a full explanation of the purpose. The introduction is often aided by the use of maps, graphs, or photographs in an attempt to define the good being valued. Next, participants are asked (1) how much they would be willing to pay to achieve an improved situation, (2) how much compensation they would require to accept a reduction from their current situation, or (3) how much they would be willing to pay for current circumstances. Depending on how the questions are phrased, the resulting bids represent either a willingness-to-pay or willingness-to-sell measure of consumer surplus (see Brookshire et al. 1980).

The iterative bid procedure may be necessary to obtain a complete measure of maximum willingness to pay. In this process, a recreationist reacts to a starting bid and is successively asked if he or she would pay higher incremental amounts until a negative response is obtained. The last positive response is considered the measure of maximum willingness to pay. The bidding process forces individuals to analyze their preferences more fully, providing a more accurate measure of consumer surplus.

Values of trout fishing and deer hunting in 11 western states derived with CVM are shown in Table 1. These dollar values per day resulted from an iterative bidding sequence performed in a personal survey and represent net willingness to pay over and above current costs (in 1980 dollars).

Other sources of CVM derived values include articles appearing in such journals as *Land Economics, American Journal of Agricultural Economics, Western Journal of Agricultural Economics,* and *Journal of Leisure Research.* Ph.D dissertations and Masters theses prepared in the economics department of the University of Wyoming, University of New Mexico, Utah State University, and University of Washington often empirically estimate dollar values for wildlife recreation in western states by using the CVM. The *Transactions of the North American Wildlife Conference* often contains economic values derived by CVM.

Table 1. Value (net willingness to pay) for trout fishing and deer hunting (U.S. Department of the Interior, Fish and Wildlife Service and U.S. Department of Commerce, Bureau of Census 1982).[1]

	Dollars per Day of Trout Fishing		Dollars per Day of Deer Hunting	
	Value[2]	Mean[3]	Value[2]	Mean[3]
Arizona	19.54	±4.19	32.50	±4.95
California	20.53	±2.08	37.35	±7.87
Colorado	16.16	±1.95	23.49	±4.18
Idaho	12.93	±0.93	28.77	±2.63
Montana	16.47	±1.88	25.42	±2.43
Nevada	12.35	±1.48	29.02	±3.92
New Mexico	15.70	±1.46	29.11	±2.60
Oregon	13.49	±1.82	21.44	±3.06
Utah	12.57	±1.17	25.72	±2.69
Washington	14.03	±2.54	24.18	±4.26
Wyoming	16.87	±1.54	36.26	±3.26

[1]Values derived using Contingent Value Method; iterative bidding was used.
[2]Values are expressed in 1980 dollars.
[3]Dollars are expressed as mean, plus or minus standard error.

Experience with CVM indicates that it can reliably measure values if the survey is carefully constructed and carried out. However, studies generally indicate that CVM estimates of net willingness to pay are conservative estimates of value (Bishop and Heberlein 1979; Brookshire et al. 1982). This conclusion is based on comparisons of actual market data to the Contingent Valuation bids.

The CVM is particularly well-suited for estimating the value of nonconsumptive wildlife recreation as well as option, existence, and bequest values.

Persons having little or no experience with CVM should seek assistance from experienced users of the method. Data from studies that employed the method may also be useful, since they are expressed in units, such as dollars per hunter day.

Advantages of Valuation Methodologies

Two techniques for measuring the net willingness to pay for wildlife recreation have been discussed—Travel Cost Method and Contingent Value Method. Each method has its strengths and weaknesses in valuing wildlife recreation. TCM has two advantages:

(1) It has the capability to use existing data from hunter applications, licenses, or other sources for statistically estimating a demand curve for the activity at a particular site.

(2) It can be used for both a benefit estimate and use projection (demand projection) over time from the same model framework.

The advantage of CVM is its ability to look directly at the dollar value of improvements in harvest or quality of recreation (for example, the increase in value for higher success rates or for trophy animals).

There are several advantages to empirical techniques such as the TCM and CVM. One advantage is that these methods provide objective measures of the benefits of wildlife recreation as revealed by the recreationists themselves. This is a significant improvement over the subjective methods whereby specialists assign the value based on the benefits they think the recreationists receive.

Another advantage of TCM or CVM is that confidence intervals around the benefit estimates can be displayed to give the decisionmaker some indication of the precision of the benefit estimate. In this way, sensitivity analysis can be performed and determinations made as to whether more precise estimates of wildlife values are critical to ranking of alternatives.

BIOLOGICAL-RECREATIONAL-ECONOMIC RELATIONSHIPS: OVERVIEW

Many methods of predicting bio-economic response require estimating how a change in management will cause change in population numbers and thus in recreation (hunter or angler) days. Values from CVM can then be used to attach a dollar amount to a recreation day. Five procedures for bio-economic analysis are listed below:

(1) "Hunter Day Short Form" developed by the U.S. Bureau of Land Management's Moab District Office (U.S. Department of the Interior, Bureau of Land Management 1983). This procedure has been developed for big game hunting only.

(2) Suislaw National Forest's Salmonoid Fisheries Model (Kunkel and Janik 1976).

(3) "Biological Response Approach" developed by the U.S. Bureau of Land Management, Oregon State Office (U.S. Department of the Interior, Bureau of Land Management 1979).

(4) "Short Form for Bio-economic Evaluations of Wildlife in Washington State" (Oliver et al. 1975).

(5) "Human Use and Economic Evaluation" (HUEE) system (U.S. Department of the Interior, Fish and Wildlife Service 1980a).

These procedures are described here briefly; two, Hunter Day Short Form and HUEE, are documented in more detail in Appendixes I and II.

All of these procedures share certain similarities (Figure 5). In particular, all five approaches require that harvest (or population) figures be known or estimable (Figure 5).

In the State of Washington's "Bio-Economic Short Form" (Oliver et al. 1975) and the U.S. Forest Service's anadromous fish model (Kunkel and Janik 1976), biological effects must be estimated in terms of effects on populations. If population simulation models are available, the linkage of resource decisions to populations may be possible.

Although HUEE analysis (U.S. Department of the Interior, Fish and Wildlife Service 1980a) and the

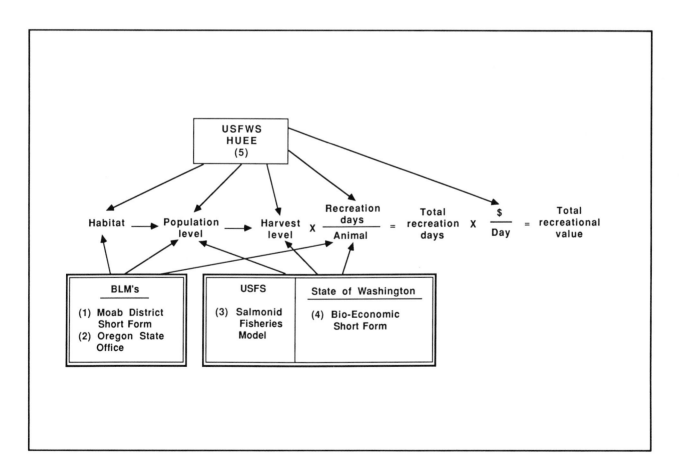

Figure 5. Overview of bio-economic approaches.

Oregon Biological Response approach (U.S. Department of the Interior, Bureau of Land Management 1979) can model the biological impacts in terms of population or harvest, both have the capability to convert changes in habitat variables (e.g., food, cover, reproduction) into changes in carrying capacity. Changes in carrying capacity can often be converted to changes in population or harvest. Since changes in habitat variables due to management actions are often easier to predict, this habitat-based evaluation may be useful in evaluating Habitat Management Plans (HMPs) or Allotment Management Plans (AMPs).

The next step required in all five approaches is the estimation of wildlife recreation use levels associated with a given number of animals (or fish) available for harvest. Typically, this involves multiplying hunter days or angler days per animal harvested by the change in animals available for harvest.

Once the change in days of wildlife recreation is known, these days are often multiplied by an average dollar value per day. This yields an estimate of the economic effects of the change in wildlife recreation associated with some original biological change, not the total economic effects to society as a whole. It does not include option, bequest, or existence values. These values can be quantified, but at a cost that often makes it impractical for routine analyses of HMPs, AMPs, etc.

The five methods provide a range of analysis techniques varying from simple to complex. Thus it cannot be said that one approach is better than the other, only that one approach may be more cost-effective for screening possible allotment management plans (AMPs) or habitat management plans (HMPs), whereas another, better suited for in-depth analysis of the remaining (after screening) candidate AMPs or HMPs.

One bit of inventory data is common to all of these basic approaches: determining the wildlife recreationists' days dependent on or produced from the wildlife unit under study. This concern is important because very few animals may actually be harvested in the area under study. For migratory animals, big game animals, and fish species, each piece of habitat contributes something to producing a harvestable animal. For such migratory animals, determining the equivalent number of animals dependent on a habitat area can be fairly complex. A step-by-step procedure for doing this is shown in Table 2.

Table 2. A step-by-step procedure for calculating equivalent number of animals harvested that are dependent on a habitat area.

Section 1—Animals harvested in the study area.	
Enter animals harvested in study area	_____ line 1
Multiply line 1 by the percentage that are year-round residents	_____ line 2 _____ line 3 (answer)
Number of animals harvested on site that are migrants; subtract line 3 from line 1	_____ line 4
Multiply line 4 by the dependency of these migrant animals on the study area	_____ line 5 _____ line 6 (answer)
Subtotal of animals harvested on study area; add lines 3 and 6	_____ line 7

Section II—Animals harvested outside the study area but dependent on the study area.	
Enter animals harvested in state wildlife management area or herd unit adjacent to or surrounding study area	_____ line 1
Enter percentage of these animals that spend time on the study area but are harvested elsewhere	_____ line 2
Multiply the percentage in line 2 by line 1 and enter on line 3	_____ line 3
Multiply line 3 by the importance of the study area's habitat to the species (can use time in study area)	_____ line 4 _____ line 5 (answer)

Section III—The total equivalent number of animals harvested that are dependent on the study area is found by adding line 7 from Section I and line 5 from Section II. _____ Total

The first step is to determine the number of animals of a particular species that are harvested in the study area. This can often be determined by looking at state wildlife management agencies' harvest data. The population or harvest in the wildlife management unit may need to be prorated to one or more specific allotments. Although an acre-per-acre proration is the simplest, use of information on population concentration will allow a more accurate proration. Details of the Moab District Short Form and HUEE procedures are described in Appendixes I and II, with additional references provided there.

DISCUSSION

Wildlife biologists and managers are often confused about the economic value of wildlife because they generally do not have enough knowledge of basic economic concepts. This is aggravated by a common failure to identify and separate different policy questions that require different kinds of dollar value-related answers. The information required by questions of national economic efficiency, for example, are different from that needed to address concerns about local economic impact.

Three issues cause confusion:

(1) The distinction between economic efficiency values and expenditures;

(2) The relationship of price to consumer surplus; and

(3) The difference between net benefits and resource quality.

These are discussed here; more detail on the subject can be found in Loomis et al. (1984).

Economic Efficiency Values Versus Expenditures

Many of the questions posed by federal and state wildlife programs involve determining whether the economic gain from some investment, such as fish ladders or habitat developments, exceeds the costs of such developments. A similar question is asked when evaluating National Forest plans or the cost-effectiveness of mitigation plans. To determine whether the benefits exceed the cost of some resource action, the willingness to pay (consumer and producer surplus) of project gainers needs to be compared with the willingness to pay of the losers (Dwyer et al. 1977; U.S. Water Resources Council 1979, 1983; Walsh 1986). When the willingness-to-pay values of project gainers exceed willingness-to-pay values of losers, the present net value is positive or the benefit-cost ratio is greater than 1. This

means the efficiency of resource use has been increased by reallocating resources from lower value uses to higher value uses, which is economically efficient.

The Resources Planning Act (RPA), National Forest Management Act (NFMA), BLM's Rangeland Investment Policy, and the U.S. Water Resources Council Principles and Guidelines all require resource valuation in terms of net economic surplus to the consumers or producers. This net surplus is the value remaining after all costs have been paid, and is the net willingness to pay. This net economic value is not measured by the actual expenditures or costs of the consumer. Expenditure information is useful for certain kinds of policy decisions requiring knowledge of community dependency, as opposed to net benefit and economic efficiency. It is also useful for analyzing economic impacts where the purpose is to expose the distribution of costs and benefits.

Use of actual expenditure information to measure wildlife benefits for efficiency-related decisions is incorrect and misleading. The price actually paid is an expenditure or cost incurred by the purchaser. This price or expenditure is received as sales revenue or wages by the provider of the good to the purchaser.

Costs are defined as benefits foregone. The more it costs society to harvest a certain number of trees, the less the net gain to society. That is, the more one gives up to get something, the less net benefit there is to having it. A timber sale will often require building several miles of expensive road which will result in thousands of dollars of expenditures. However, if the value of trees is less than the expenditures, there has been a net loss to society. Expenditures in excess of economic benefits means the cost of what was given up exceeded the benefits of what was received.

An example of beneficial treatment wildlife gets when the net benefits (gross benefits minus expenditures) of agricultural development are compared with habitat preservation can be seen in a paper on the Birds of Prey Conservation Area in southern Idaho (Hyde et al. 1982). Hyde et al. evaluated a trade-off between agricultural development and preservation of the prey base. The net benefits of agricultural development were very low because of the high costs needed for farmers to cultivate the land and pump water from the Snake River. If one judged the economic benefits on an expenditures basis, the inefficient agricultural development would look valuable. However, given high costs, there are the low net benefits of agriculture. Hence, the opportunity cost of maintaining the prey base for the Birds of Prey Conservation Area was low and the net benefits were greater for the habitat preservation option.

There are legitimate uses of expenditure information, particularly measuring the local income and employment effects of a management action. Like the process of economic growth itself, changes in resource allocations will displace some job skills (and workers having only those job skills) and create demands for workers with different job skills. The National Environmental Policy Act and local public officials often require federal agencies to display the types of workers and industries that will be positively or negatively affected by resource actions taken on public lands.

Price Versus Consumer Surplus

Another obstacle to correct wildlife valuation is the common allegation that market prices and consumers' surplus cannot be compared. This problem stems from confusion about underlying concepts and failure to separate different questions requiring different answers. The correct measure of gross value to the consumer is the amount of monies the consumer is willing to pay for the goods in question. Net value to the consumer is this sum minus the expenditures required to obtain it, i.e., consumers' surplus.

The technical relationship between price and consumers' surplus is shown in Figure 6. Again, the demand curve is the measurement of consumers' valuation (Harberger 1971). The actual shape of the demand function will depend on the nature of the market and the context of the question. In Figure 6, a downward-sloping function represents the entire market or industry. For the good in question, let the current quantity being exchanged be 100 units at a price of $10. The gross value of one additional unit in this market area is $10. This is the consumers' gross willingness to pay for that unit. The price or cost to the consumer is also $10, so the net willingness to pay is zero. The marginal unit has no consumer surplus.

If the quantity supplied is increased from 100 units to 150 units, the old price of $10 cannot be used as the consumers' gross willingness to pay for the 50 additional units. The gross willingness to pay for these 50 additional units is the area under the demand curve between 100 and 150 units, in this instance, about $375. At the new level of consumption, the 150 units can all be purchased for $5 each. The gross willingness to pay for the last unit consumed is thus the market price of $5 and the net willingness to pay for this last unit is zero.

The willingness to pay for the other 49 added units is greater than $5, however, as shown by the downward slope of the demand curve, and thus generates consumers' surplus. For example, the 100th unit consumed could have been sold for $10, but it has been sold for $5. The net willingness to pay

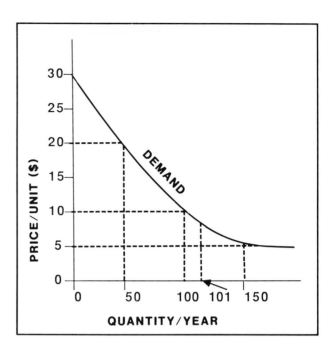

Figure 6. Relationship between price and consumer surplus.

enjoyed by the consumer for this unit is thus $5 in the form of consumers' surplus. The additional consumer surplus associated with the increase of 50 units is the triangular area below the demand curve between 100 and 150 units and above the price of $5, or about $125. When the added consumer surplus from the decline in price from $10 to $5 on the original 100 units is added to the $125, the total increase in consumer surplus is $625. This is the net economic benefit of the change whether the units are bicycles, trees, or hunter days. The differences arise because some questions ask for net willingness to pay at the margin (e.g., a small change from 100 to 101), and some questions ask for net willingness to pay for non-marginal changes (e.g., a very large change from 100 to 150). In any case, if there is surplus created by a quantity change, it should be measured and counted.

Hunting and fishing often take place in small or localized markets. Most hunters and anglers visit areas within 200 miles of their homes. Removing fishing opportunities at one major cold-water stream or lake could make a substantial change in the price (i.e., travel cost) of fishing opportunities. In such a situation, there will be significant consumer surplus associated with eliminating or adding an opportunity. On the other hand, imagine a place in Minnesota where there are hundreds of identical uncongested lakes, each no more than a mile from another. The loss of one lake would have no measurable effect on the price faced by an angler and hence no loss in consumer surplus.

Net Benefits Versus Resource Quality

Another source of confusion relates to differences in the value of resources of different quality. The gross willingness to pay for steelhead fishing, for example, is generally higher than for trout fishing. However, because steelhead fishing opportunities are often available only at a few remote rivers, travel costs for steelhead fishing tend to be higher than for trout fishing. The combined effect is that net willingness to pay for steelhead fishing may be lower than that for trout fishing. In these situations, lower net benefit flows from the higher quality resource because the higher price offsets the quality difference. On the other hand, introduction of a new steelhead site that requires travel costs similar to those at trout fishing sites will produce more net benefit than a new or existing trout site.

A parallel situation exists for timber. For example, walnut trees are much more valuable than pine trees, but a remote stand of walnut trees in an inaccessible location will have a lower bid price than a stand of pine trees near a mill. In this example, the higher quality trees are worth less because of higher harvest costs.

SUMMARY AND CONCLUSIONS

As is evident from this chapter, several bio-economic analysis systems provide the capability to translate the benefits of habitat improvements into dollar terms. Besides fulfilling legal requirements to make such conversions, the benefits can be compared to the costs of making a given habitat improvement.

Because the traditional valuation techniques only measure recreation, recreation benefits cannot appropriately be interpreted as the total value of animals or their habitat. Rather, net benefits (present net worth or internal rate of return) provide information about the willingness to pay of recreationists for the proposed habitat improvements. If the recreation benefits alone exceed the cost, the project will usually increase national economic well-being. If the benefits are less than the cost, the decisionmaker must ask whether the project substantially increases intangible economic efficiency benefits (option, existence, bequest values for a wildlife species of high public interest) or substantially improves equity. Thus, the internal rate of return or benefit-cost ratio does not by itself make the decision to implement or not implement a management action. The internal rate of return or benefit-cost ratios tell the decisionmaker and the public taxpayer what the economic efficiency of such investments are.

There may be other legitimate social objectives that outweigh economic efficiency in determining whether the investment is to be made. These other objectives should be documented in the decision process regardless of what the economic efficiency analysis shows. In this way, bio-economic analysis and economic analysis in general contribute to improved and informed decisions rather than binding the decisionmaker's hands.

LITERATURE CITED

ALLEN, A. and M. ARMBRUSTER. 1982. Preliminary evaluation of a habitat suitability for the pronghorn in McKenzie, J. ed., Proc. l0th Pronghorn Antelope Workshop.

BISHOP, R. and T. HEBERLEIN. 1979. Measuring values of extra market goods: Are indirect measures biased? Am. J. Agric. Economics 61(5):926-930.

BROOKSHIRE, D., A. RANDALL, and J. STOLL. 1980. Valuing increments and decrements in natural resource service flows. Am. J. Agric. Economics 63(3):165-177.

————, M. THAYER, W. SCHULZE, and R. D'ARGE. 1982. Valuing public goods: A comparison of survey and hedonic approaches. Am. Economic Review 72:165-177.

BROWN, W., C. SORHUS, B. CHOU-YANG, and J. RICHARDS. 1983. Using individual observations to estimate recreation demand functions: A caution. Am. J. Agric. Economics 65(1):155-157.

CLAWSON, M. 1959. Methods of measuring the demand for and value of outdoor recreation. Resources for the Future. Washington, DC.

DWYER, J., J. KELLY, and M. BOWES. 1977. Improved procedures for valuation of the contribution of recreation to national economic development. Res. Rep. 128, Water Resources Center, Univ. Illinois at Urbana.

HARBERGER, A. 1971. Three basic postulates for applied welfare economics: An interpretive essay. J. Economic Literature 9(3):785-797.

HYDE, W., A. DICKERMAN, and D. STONE. 1982. Development versus preservation in the Snake River Birds of Prey Conservation Area. Am. J. Agric. Economics 64:756-760.

JUST, R., D. HUETH, and A. SCHMITZ. 1982. Applied welfare economics and public policy. Prentice Hall, Englewood Cliffs, NJ.

KRUTILLA, J.V. 1967. Conservation reconsidered. Am. Economic Review 47:777-786.

KUNKEL, C. and P. JANIK. 1976. An economic evaluation of salmonid fisheries attributable to Suislaw National Forest. Suislaw National Forest, Corvallis, OR.

LOOMIS, J. 1982. Use of travel cost models for evaluating lottery-rationed recreation: Application to big game hunting. J. Leisure Res. 14(2):117-124.

———— and R. OLSON. 1981. Recreational and commercial activities involving wildlife potentially affected by the Lower Gunnison River Project. U.S. Dep. Inter., Fish and Wildl. Serv., Fort Collins, CO. (unpubl. rep.)

————, G. PETERSON, and S. SORG. 1984. A field guide to wildlife economic analysis. Trans. North Am. Wildl. Nat. Resour. Conf. 49:315-324.

MATULICK, S., J. HANSON, I. LINES, and A. FARMER. 1982. HEP as a planning tool: An application to waterfowl enhancement. Sci. Pap. 6163, Agric. Res. Center, College of Agriculture, Washington State University. Pullman.

MISHAN, E. 1976. Cost-benefit analysis. Praeger Publishers, New York, NY.

OLIVER, W., C. YOUNG, and D. ELDRED. 1975. A short form for bio-economic evaluations of wildlife in Washington State. Bull. 7. Washington Game Dep. Olympia.

PETERSON, M. 1983. Response to Assistant Secretary Crowel regarding land and resource management planning. U.S. Dep. Agric., For. Serv. Memorandum dated May 17, 1983.

ROSENTHAL, D., J. LOOMIS, and G. PETERSON. 1984. The travel cost model: Concepts and applications. U.S. Dep. Agric., For. Serv. Gen Tech. Rep. RM-l09. Fort Collins, CO.

SASSONE, P. and W. SCHAFFER. 1978. Cost-benefit analysis: A handbook. Academic Press, New York, NY.

U.S. DEPARTMENT OF AGRICULTURE, FOREST SERVICE. 1982. National Forest System land and resource management planning *in* Federal Register, September 30, 1982, Vol. 47(190):43,026-43,052.

U.S. DEPARTMENT OF THE INTERIOR, BUREAU OF LAND MANAGEMENT. 1979. Biological response approach. U.S. Dep. Inter., Bur. Land Manage., Oregon State Office. (unpubl. rep.).

————. 1982. Final rangeland improvement policy. Instruction Memorandum 83-27. October 15, 1982.

————. 1983. Rangeland investment analysis Bull. UT-060-83-B6, Moab District Office, UT.

U.S. DEPARTMENT OF THE INTERIOR, FISH and WILDLIFE SERVICE. 1980a. Human use and economic evaluation (HUEE). U.S. Dep. Inter., Fish and Wildl. Serv., Div. Ecol. Serv. Manual l04: Washington, DC.

————. 1980b. Habitat evaluation procedures (HEP). U.S. Dep. Inter., Fish and Wildl. Serv., Div. Ecol. Serv. Manual l02. Washington, DC.

————. 1981. Standards for the development of habitat suitability index models. U.S. Dep. Inter., Fish and Wildl. Serv., Div. Ecol. Serv. Manual 103. Washington, DC.

———— and U.S. DEPARTMENT OF COMMERCE, BUREAU OF CENSUS. 1982. 1980 National survey of fishing, hunting, and wildlife associated recreation. U.S. Govt. Printing Office. Washington, DC. 156pp.

U.S. DEPARTMENT OF TRANSPORTATION. 1985. Cost of owning and operating a motor vehicle. Federal Highway Administration. Washington, DC.

U.S. WATER RESOURCES COUNCIL. 1979. Procedures for evaluation of national economic development (NED) benefits and costs in water resources planning in Federal Register, Vol. 44 (242) Final Rule. December 14, 1979.

————. 1983. Economic and environmental principles and guidelines for water and related land resources implementation studies. March 10, 1983. U.S. Govt. Printing Office. Washington, DC.

WALSH. 1986. Recreation economic decisions. Dep. Agric. and Resour. Economics. Colo. State Univ., Fort Collins.

APPENDIX I. <u>BLM Moab District Hunter Day Short Form</u>

The BLM Moab District Hunter Day Short Form (U.S. Department of the Interior, Bureau of Land Management 1983) was developed to allow for a systematic but rapid evaluation of the change in big game hunter days associated with changes in livestock use levels. The first page of the form provides a simple word model of the changes in life requisites or habitat components in relation to habitat suitability for a particular big game species (Figure A-I-1). The word model keys in on the critical factors likely to be affected by changes in livestock uses.

The current model structure provides some information on limiting habitat factors but the importance of that limiting factor is not explicitly recognized. That is, the model structure assumes that lack of water can be offset by greater cover, space, or forage. This assumption may be tenuous at times, and the information on the limiting factor can be helpful to biologists in designing habitat improvements. If water is the limiting factor, then guzzlers would provide the biggest payoff, not more cover. This basic model could easily be modified to make the limiting factor concept explicit. Techniques for incorporating limiting factor concepts into indexes are described in "Standards for the Development of Habitat Suitability Index Models" (U.S. Department of the Interior, Fish and Wildlife Service 1981).

The second page of the Moab District Short Form requires calculating hunter days from population and application of the index factor (Figure A-I-1). The hunter day/population estimates provided at the top of the table are for southeastern Utah. These numbers may seem counter-intuitive because they combine percentage of harvestable population and days needed to harvest one animal.

The biologist must estimate the existing population level. In addition, for habitat improvement projects, the prior stable or potential population must be estimated. If such estimates are available, this approach is probably preferable. However, existing population data and potential population estimates (prior stable) may not be available. In these cases, harvest estimates must be obtained. State wildlife management agencies generally have existing harvest data. Estimating potential harvest is no more difficult than estimating potential population, given optimum habitat conditions. In addition, using harvest allows use of hunter days per animal harvested, a number that is also more readily available. A Hunter Day Short Form for use with harvest data is also available (Figure A-I-2). Page 1 of the form is identical to that shown on Figure A-I-1, but the calculations on page 2 are based on hunter days per harvest rather than hunter days per population. Detailed instructions for using the Moab District Hunter Day Short Form can be found in BLM's Moab District Bulletin UT-060-83-86 (U.S. Department of the Interior, Bureau of Land Management 1983).

In summary, the Hunter Day Short Form provides a very easy to use and yet systematic approach for evaluating biological-economic effects for big game animals. By using some of the modifications suggested in this paper, the short form analysis can be upgraded when sufficient data exist on the importance of one habitat type as a limiting factor. The form can be modified to use harvest data when population data are unavailable. The basic advantages of the Moab District Hunter Day Short Form approach are minimal data requirements and speedy analysis. It is a very useful approach when one has dozens of areas to evaluate in a short time.

Figure A-I-1. Rangeland investment analysis—based on population.

Appendix A. Bio-Economic Analysis of Wildlife

Table A-2. Rangeland investment analysis - based on population.

_____ Hunter Day Estimates without investment package
___X___ Hunter Day Estimates with investment package
_____ of _____ Habitat changes through time

Allotment **#1**   Alternative **I**
Wildlife Species **DEER**   Wildlife Biologist **JIM SMITH**

Category	Rank	Criteria	Points Change 1	Points Change 2
Forage Competition	3	Forage consumption conflicts totally or nearly eliminated.		
	1,2	Forage consumption conflicts reduced.	2	
	0	No change.		
	-1,-2	Forage consumption conflicts increased.		
	-3	Forage consumption conflicts become a major problem.		
Forage	3	Key browse, forb, and grass species increase in vigor and trend by more than 30 percent.	3	
	1,2	Either/or browse, forbs, and grass increase in vigor and trend by less than 30 percent.		
	0	No change.		
	-1,-2	Either/or browse, forbs, and grass decrease in vigor and trend by less than 30 percent.		
	-3	Key browse, forb, and grass species decrease in vigor and trend by more than 30 percent.		
Cover	1,2,3	Cover availability increases.	1	
	0	No change.		
	-1,-2,-3	Cover availability decreases.		
Water	1,2,3	Water availability increases.	2	
	0	No change.		
	-1,-2,-3	Water availability decreases.		
Space	1,2,3	Spatial conflicts decreases.	2	
	0	No Change.		
	-1,-2,-3	Spatial conflicts increases.		
		Total Points	10	

Total Points / (number of categories considered x 3) = Adjustment Factor

10 / (**5** x 3) = | **.67** | Adjustment Factor Change 1

_____ / (_____ x 3) = | _____ | Adjustment Factor Change 2

Figure A-I-1. Rangeland investment analysis—based on population (concluded).

Appendix A.   Bio-Economic Analysis of Wildlife

Table A-2.   Continued.

```
┌─────────────────────────────────────────────────┐
│  Hunter Day / population (HD/pop) estimates      │
│                                                   │
│      Deer                   2.0 HD/pop            │
│      Elk                    4.0 HD/pop            │
│      Antelope               0.2 HD/pop            │
│      Desert Bighorn Sheep   0.2 HD/pop            │
└─────────────────────────────────────────────────┘
```

Base Year: ___100___   Existing Population

                                  x ___2.0___   HD/pop

                                  ___200___   HD

_____ months on allotment ÷ 12 = x ___.25___   Length of stay adjustment

                          ┌──────────────┐
                          │   50   │ Base year HD input
                          └──────────────┘

Habitat Worsening   Change 1   Change 2
                                                        Base Year HD
                        x _____   x _____   Adjustment factor
                                                        HD Loss
                        + _____   + _____   Base Year HD

                        ┌────────┐   ┌────────┐
                        │   │   │   │   HD Input
                        └────────┘   └────────┘

                        ┌────────┐   ┌────────┐
                        │   │   │   │   Years to Change
                        └────────┘   └────────┘

Habitat Improvement

   __200__ Prior Stable for General Area

 - __100__ Existing Pop =   100   Potential Change
                        x __.67__   x _____   Adjustment Factor
                           67   Population Change
                        x __2__   x _____   HD / pop
                          134 HD   HD
   Months on
 - Allotment ÷ 12 =   x __.25__   x _____   Time Adjustment
                          33 HD   HD Change
                        + 50 HD   + _____   Base Year HD

                        ┌────────┐   ┌────────┐
                        │ 88   │   │   │   HD Input
                        └────────┘   └────────┘

                        ┌────────┐   ┌────────┐
                        │ 20   │   │   │   Years to Change
                        └────────┘   └────────┘
```
```

Figure A-I-2. Rangeland investment analysis—based on harvest.

Appendix A. Bio-Economic Analysis of Wildlife

Table A-3. Rangeland investment analysis - based on harvest.

_____ Hunter Day Estimates without investment package
__X__ Hunter Day Estimates with investment package
  of _____ Habitat changes through time

Allotment _____|_____
Wildlife Species ___DEER___

Alternative _____|_____
Wildlife Biologist _JIM SMITH_

Category	Rank	Criteria	Points Change 1	Points Change 2
Forage Competition	3	Forage consumption conflicts totally or nearly eliminated.		
	1,2	Forage consumption conflicts reduced.	2	
	0	No change.		
	-1,-2	Forage consumption conflicts increased.		
	-3	Forage consumption conflicts become a major problem.		
Forage	3	Key browse, forb, and grass species increase in vigor and trend by more than 30 percent.	3	
	1,2	Either/or browse, forbs, and grass increase in vigor and trend by less than 30 percent.		
	0	No change.		
	-1,-2	Either/or browse, forbs, and grass decrease in vigor and trend by less than 30 percent.		
	-3	Key browse, forb, and grass species decrease in vigor and trend by more than 30 percent.		
Cover	1,2,3	Cover availability increases.	1	
	0	No change.		
	-1,-2,-3	Cover availability decreases.		
Water	1,2,3	Water availability increases.	2	
	0	No change.		
	-1,-2,-3	Water availability decreases.		
Space	1,2,3	Spatial conflicts decreases.	2	
	0	No Change.		
	-1,-2,-3	Spatial conflicts increases.		
		Total Points	10	

Total Points / (number of categories considered x 3) = Adjustment Factor

__10__ / (__5__ x 3) = |__.67__| Adjustment Factor Change 1

_____ / (_____ x 3) = |_____| Adjustment Factor Change 2

Figure A-I-2. Rangeland investment analysis—based on harvest (concluded).

Appendix A. Bio-Economic Analysis of Wildlife

Table A-3. Continued.

> Hunter Days/harvest (HD/harvest) estimates
> for Utah
> | | |
> |---|---|
> | Deer | 8.0 HD/harvest |
> | Elk | 11.3 HD/harvest |
> | Antelope | 3.0 HD/harvest |
> | Desert Bighorn Sheep | 13.0 HD/harvest |
>
> from Utah Big Game Harvest Book

Base Year:

_____ **25**   Existing Harvest (or avg. of 3 years)

x _____ **8**   HD/harvest

_____ **200**   HD

3 _ months on allotment ÷ 12 = x _____ **.25**   Length of stay adjustment

| **50** | Base year HD input |

Habitat Worsening   Change 1   Change 2

	Change 1	Change 2	
	x _____	x _____	Base Year HD / Adjustment factor
			HD Loss
	+ _____	+ _____	Base Year HD
	[_____]	[_____]	HD Input
	[_____]	[_____]	Years to Change

Habitat Improvement

_____ **50** Prior Stable or Potential Long Run Harvest

- _____ **25** Existing Harvest = **25**

x _____ **.67**   x _____   Potential Change / Adjustment Factor
_____ **16.75**   Population Change

x _____ **8**   x _____   HD/harvest
_____ **134**   HD

3 Months on
_ Allotment ÷ 12 =   x _____ **.25**   x _____   Time Adjustment
_____ **33**   HD Change

+ _____ **50**   + _____   Base Year HD

| **88** | [_____] | HD Input |
| **20** | [_____] | Years to Change |

APPENDIX II. Human Use and Economic Evaluation (HUEE) System

The Human Use and Economic Evaluation (HUEE) system was developed by the U.S. Fish and Wildlife Service Western Energy and Land Use Team (WELUT). Human Use and Economic Evaluation (HUEE) procedures provide means for determining both the extent of human uses of wildlife and the dollar values of these uses. These procedures were developed and are intended for use with the Habitat Evaluation Procedures (HEP). The HEP and HUEE together with the Habitat Suitability Index (HSI) models (U.S. Department of the Interior, Fish and Wildlife Service 1980a, 1980b, 1981) provide a complete set of procedures for field staff to use in making both biological and economic assessments of wildlife resources.

HUEE procedures can be used in conjunction with HEP or with just population or harvest data. In addition, HUEE is compatible with the Travel Cost Method (TCM) and Contingent Value Method (CVM) valuation. HUEE can also use unit day values when the added costs of TCM or CVM cannot be justified.

The HUEE procedures are designed for use by field staff, principally biologists, assigned to evaluate the impacts of resource development projects. These procedures may be applied in field studies without the assistance of economists or recreation planners. However, to apply advanced methods such as the TCM or CVM, the assistance of a specialist, such as an economist or recreation planner is recommended (U.S. Department of the Interior, Fish and Wildlife Service 1980a).

HUEE provides a way to evaluate both the effects on supply of hunter days and effects on the demand for hunter days (Figure A-II-1). The term "potential use" in Figure A-II-1 refers to the amount of use people wish to make of the wildlife resource. The term "sustainable use" is the amount of use days that can be provided by the habitat. "Planned use" is the lesser of the sustainable and potential use. Thus, HUEE is general enough to account for both situations where demand exceeds supply at the current license cost and also where supply of animals exceeds the demand for hunting. Figure A-II-2 shows how supply and demand over time are related to HUEE's concepts of sustainable use, potential use, and planned use. In this example, the initial factor determining hunter days is human demand. By year 20, demand has risen and supply fallen such that hunter days demanded and supplied are equal. After year 20, demand (at current permit fees) exceeds supply so that lottery rationing or shorter seasons are likely to keep hunter pressure in line with available populations.

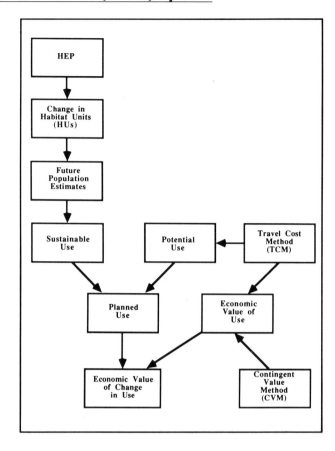

Figure A-II-1. Human use and economic evaluation (HUEE) system.

Figure A-II-3 illustrates a negative impact to a species' population from a project. Loss of habitat generally does not change the demand or potential use by humans but rather adversely affects the ecosystem's capability to support days of hunting or fishing. Thus, the effects are modeled as a reduction in sustainable use. Alternatively, enhancement of habitat suitability by management can increase sustainable use.

This conceptual framework is fairly complete, but to be useful, it must be easy to translate into practice. The two factors influencing the actual amount of wildlife recreation that can be realized are potential use and sustainable use.

Potential use can be estimated in several ways. A biologist can do a time series regression of past hunter/angler day levels in that management unit. This equation can then be used to forecast future wildlife recreation demand, assuming current trends continue. It is important to remember that these forecasted levels of demand will not be translated into actual use unless the wildlife habitat can support such levels of use.

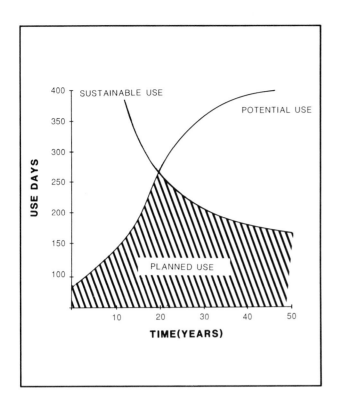

Figure A-II-2. Relationships between sustainable use, potential use, and planned use.

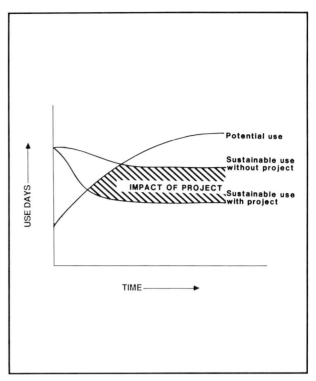

Figure A-II-3. Negative economic impact of a project from reduction in sustainable use.

An alternative and better way to forecast future use is to use TCM. This technique estimates the economic benefits per day and allows use of forecasting methods in valuing wildlife use.

Once the number of wildlife recreation days demanded (potential use) are known, one needs to develop the amount of use the wildlife habitat can support or supply on a sustainable basis (sustainable use). The steps in calculating sustainable use are shown in Figure A-II-4. The end result of these calculations are (1) sustainable use days of fishing or hunting or (2) nonconsumptive use days associated with a given alternative plan.

Each species or group of species (e.g., waterfowl, upland game birds, etc.) must be calculated separately. The calculation can begin at Point 1 (Habitat Units [HUs]), Point 3 (animal population size), or Point 5 (harvest). The starting point is the biologist's decision and is generally constrained by the data available on HUs, population size, or harvest. If an HSI model for the species being evaluated is available along with either current population or current harvest, it is fairly easy to estimate future use days.

If suitable HSI models are not available, then the future population size or harvest rate with and without the project must be estimated by some other method in order to estimate future use days.

HUs are the basic units of analysis in the U.S. Fish and Wildlife Service HEP. HEP and the use of HSI models are described in other chapters in this book and in U.S. Department of the Interior, Fish and Wildlife Service (1980b, 1981). An HSI is a number from 0 to 1 that serves as an index to the quality of the habitat in an area for a given species. An index of 1 represents "optimal" habitat and an index of 0 represents totally unsuitable habitat. For terrestrial species, HUs are the product of the HSI and the acreage for a given site.

HSI × Acreage = Habitat Units

example: 0.60 × 1,000 acres = 600 habitat units.

Animal numbers are calculated as the product of HUs and number of animals per habitat unit (productivity per HU in Figure A-II-4). This calculation assumes that animal population size is linearly correlated with both habitat suitability (as measured by the HSI) and acreage. If both values (HUs and animals per HU) are available then the calculation is straightforward.

Typically the latter figure (animals per HU) must be estimated or calculated from other data. If current populations are known, the animals per HU can be calculated by dividing current population (or the average population for the last 3-5 years) by current HUs. This yields animals per HU that can

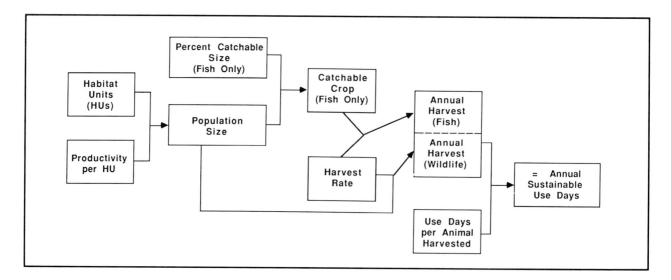

Figure A-II-4. Steps for calculating sustainable use.

then be multiplied by HUs in future target years to calculate estimated animal numbers under alternative management.

Next, harvest must be calculated. For terrestrial species, the population size is multiplied by a sustainable or allowable harvest rate. This is a harvest rate that can be sustained without detriment to the population. For fish, the calculation involves the additional steps of calculating percentage of population of catchable size from which a catchable crop is calculated.

The next step is to estimate hunter or angler days per harvest so that sustainable use days can be calculated. Hunter days per harvest can be calculated from data on success rates and number of days in the field. Otherwise, it must be estimated or extrapolated from other areas. A decrease in the number of animals available for harvest could cause success rates to drop, but use days would remain the same. That is, the same number of hunters continue to hunt even though they must hunt more days for each animal harvested. If this is an accurate descrip-

tion of hunter behavior in the study area, then HUEE can reflect this. This constant level of lower and lower quality hunter days will be reflected as a drop in economic benefits because as harvest per day decreases, benefits per day generally decrease. Thus, one advantage of HUEE over other systems is its ability to estimate changes in economic values even if the number of days hunted or fished remains unchanged.

The sustainable use days are then compared to potential use and the lessor of potential use and sustainable use is recorded as "Planned Use" (Figure A-II-2). The planned use is then multiplied by value per day to obtain the economic value of such recreation. Beyond this point, HUEE provides a format and step-by-step procedure and accounting system for projecting these values into the future and making various types of corrections and adjustments.

More information on the details of HUEE can be found in the U.S. Fish and Wildlife Service Manual (U.S. Department of the Interior, Fish and Wildlife Service 1980a).

41

WRITTEN COMMUNICATIONS

Donald Zimmerman

Department of Technical Journalism
Colorado State University
Ft. Collins, CO 80521

"The greatest problem in communication is the illusion that it has been achieved."

——George Bernard Shaw

Editor's Note: No inventory or monitoring study is complete until results are communicated to the people who need to see them. Many of us allot little time to writing reports or making verbal presentations—but these activities are vital if management and the public are to understand our work and make better natural resource decisions.

This chapter provides methods to identify and accomplish your objectives for written communications. The chapter on verbal presentations does the same for oral communications, because speaking to groups is just as important in getting your message across.

INTRODUCTION

Once you finish your data analysis and interpretation, you will write the needed memos, letters, reports, and other documents. You must write. It is part of your job.

"I MUST WRITE?"

Good writing becomes important for two reasons. First, writing that communicates a project's results may be as important as the study itself. If you do not communicate your study's results in writing so others understand the findings and know the needed actions and management decisions, the resource may not be managed properly. By writing, you document and explain the action needed.

Second, good writing becomes important for you because your career depends on it. If you do not communicate with your peers, supervisors, and administrators, they will not know your abilities and skills. Successful resource managers communicate through writing and they become known for making themselves understood. Good writing advances your career.

When you think about writing, what ideas emerge? Why do you write? What do you want to accomplish? Do you think about your readers? Do you plan ahead or do you wait until the last minute to write?

There is more to consider: What constitutes writing? How do you organize your thinking? Do you outline? Do you rewrite? Do you find writing difficult or easy? Do you avoid writing?

Before I discuss writing further, consider how others judge your writing. They judge your writing on its content, its appearance, and its communication effectiveness. The content centers on how well you carried out your professional problem solving. This book will help you improve your content. Appearance centers on style, mechanics, spelling, typing, layout, and printing. Later, I suggest style manuals and guides and techniques for checking your writing's appearance. Communication effectiveness centers on your objectives—do you want to inform, instruct, or persuade your readers? Will your readers understand the points you are making? Will your readers agree with you? Will your readers accurately perceive your content?

Consciously or not, many professionals ask themselves such questions as they write. By asking yourself such questions, you will begin thinking about your writing and answering the questions that will help you communicate more effectively.

To achieve your objectives, your writing must be clear and concise. Therefore, I suggest a writing strategy and include ways to improve your writing's objectives.

In this chapter I present a 12-step writing process for preparing longer reports:

1. Thinking and planning
2. Organizing your writing
3. Preparing illustrations
4. Drafting the manuscript
5. Writing abstracts and executive summaries
6. Revising and self-editing
7. Editing for style and grammar errors
8. Correcting spelling errors
9. Editing illustrations—tables and figures
10. Having the manuscript retyped
11. Copyediting the manuscript
12. Seeking peer reviews.

As you read through the chapter, remember that some documents do not have illustrations and others do not require peer reviews. Furthermore, no two professionals write in exactly the same way. Some individuals may combine steps whereas others may break the identified steps into several activities. From the 12-step writing process, adopt and adapt techniques to improve your writing process.

I close the chapter with a brief discussion of printing, the Information Age, and computers' impacts on writing and communication.

A WRITING STRATEGY

Thinking and Planning

Writing begins when you start thinking about what you will write, your illustrations, and your content. Effective writing requires thinking ahead—weeks, months, or years for larger projects. When you begin thinking about writing, ask: Who are my readers? What do I want to communicate to my readers? What is the appropriate written format? How long will my writing take?

"Who Are My Readers?"
As a biologist, you have diverse readers. Think about who reads your writing. Reader-oriented writing may change information levels, behaviors, and possibly attitudes. But too often we fail to keep our readers clearly in mind. Within the Bureau of Land Management and other government agencies you have two major groups of internal readers: (1) technical readers—i.e., fellow scientists, and (2) managers—i.e., the decisionmakers.

Depending on the content of your writing, you will have different external readers: (1) biologists and managers from other agencies; (2) judges, lawyers, congressmen, and senators; and (3) the general public—including special interest and advocacy groups.

Consider the functions of your writing. Most technical and scientific writing informs, instructs, persuades, and documents. Informing requires attracting the reader's attention, having the message accepted, having it interpreted, and having it stored for later use (Schramm and Roberts 1972). Instructing requires the same steps as informing, plus the reader must do something with the message—i.e., practice or use the information provided (Schramm and Roberts 1972). Persuading requires convincing the readers of your position; it requires that readers yield to your viewpoint. Documenting provides a permanent record. Most technical reports, notes, journal articles, memos, and letters document a project, a finding, or a decision.

Think about the outcomes you want from your writing. Do you only want readers to understand? Or do you want readers to agree with you? Do you want the readers to accurately perceive your facts? Communication may improve understanding, but decrease agreement. Your readers may accurately perceive your facts and your recommendations, but they may not agree with you.

When you write for managers, keep in mind that they like to have several options and the implications of each option clearly spelled out. If a manager decides on option C, what are the likely consequences of that decision? What impact will option C have on the resources? What impact will option C have on the agency?

WRITING "SHOULD" BEGIN WITH THINKING...

Consider wild burros. From a management viewpoint, too many burros may destroy a range or reduce its carrying capacity for livestock and wildlife. So you recommend reducing burro numbers. From a budgetary standpoint, shooting them may be the least expensive control technique. But such a recommendation would soon cause an uproar. Groups will clearly understand your recommendation, but many will not agree with you.

When you think of your readers, think about how they will use the information you provide. Will the information be for decisionmaking? If so, what kinds of decisions will your readers be making? How will your readers use the information? What information will you need to provide so your readers make a decision based on sound management principles? What facts must you provide? How should you organize those facts?

How do your readers read what you write? Communication research consistently shows that most people read only what interests them or they read only what they think will be of value to them. Readers are selective. And your readers will not read everything that you write. To find out how people read what you write, produce a document and distribute it. Then ask the people what they read. Ask them what they learned. Their answers will help you tailor your subsequent writing to their needs.

When people read a document, they do not retain all the information. Too often what they retain and recall are only the points and information that reinforce their viewpoints.

Beyond how readers read, consider their frames of reference—the sum of their background, education, and experience. Too often we assume our readers see the world as we do. We assume our readers understand the terms we use. We assume they comprehend what we are saying. Often they do not. At best, the commonality of the frames of reference of a writer and reader remain imperfect, incomplete, and partial.

"What Information Do You Communicate?"
With your readers in mind, what content will you present? How much information should you present? What information will you leave out? Will leaving out some information create problems later? What information can you include? Will including some information create problems?

"What is the Appropriate Format?"
Keeping selectivity in mind, choose the appropriate format to quickly give readers the key information. Table 1 identifies readers and selects formats and then suggests lengths and purposes. Whenever possible, be succinct. Use Table 1 as a general guide.

Table 1. Summary of target audiences, type documents, suggested maximum lengths, and purpose.

Target audience	Type document	Maximum length (pages)	Purpose
Subordinate biologist	Memo Letter Manual Guidelines Procedures	1 1 Varies Varies Varies	Inform/Instruct Inform/Instruct Inform/Instruct Inform/Instruct Inform/Instruct
Other biologists (General)	Technical notes Technical reports Journal articles	5 5 Varies	Inform/Document Inform/Document Inform/Document
General public	Letters Short report	2 5	Inform Inform
Advocacy groups or individuals	Letter Short report Technical report EIS Executive summary of above	2 5 5 100 5	Document/Inform Document/Inform Document/Inform Document/Inform Document/Inform
Supervisory biologists Supervisory Staff (i.e., Chief of Resources)	Short report Technical report Memo Short report Technical report EIS EAR	5 5 1–2 5 Varies 100 100	Inform Inform Inform/Persuade Document Document Document Document
Line manager	Memo Short report or Executive summary of EIS or Technical report	1–2 with back-up reports 5 5	Inform/Persuade Inform/Persuade Inform/Persuade
Congressional inquiry (Usually public through Congressman)	Memo with accompanying reports, etc. as documented	2	Inform/Document
Court Judge	Affidavit Deposition	Varies	Inform/Document (Persuade)

The more you know about your readers, the more you can target and tailor your writing and communicate more effectively.

"How Long Will Writing Take?"

When you begin writing, you need to know how many hours, days, or weeks it will take you to write memos, letters, reports, and other documents. So keep records. And when you plan a project, budget enough time for completing the project's writing tasks.

You may find incremental writing useful. Incremental writing involves writing parts of a manuscript as a project progresses. Often, you can write sections of a report early in a project and use them in later manuscripts. Such an approach allows you to produce a final report in less time at the project's end. Avoid, if possible, putting off writing until the project's end. By beginning your writing early, you will have time for rewriting which will produce a better manuscript.

Organizing Your Writing

Too often writers turn to an old report, an old memo, or other manuscripts as a guide for organizing their writing. Before you do, ask yourself if regulations, policies, or publication guidances require that you use a specific organization. If so, follow it. If allowed, add a memo, letter, abstract, or executive

summary giving the key points your readers should know. By doing so, you will help busy readers recall the essential points if they do not have time to read the entire report.

Make sure your manuscripts communicate. Too often manuscripts tell about rather than tell. Consider the memo and comments in Figure 1.

For longer papers, you will find outlining makes your writing easier. Outlining serves as a map to guide your writing. Outlining saves you time—making changes on an outline takes less time than rewriting a manuscript. An outline helps you see your organization more clearly than a manuscript's narrative.

Professionals use different approaches to outlining. In one of the few studies of outlining practices, McKee (1975) studied technical writers in the Society for Technical Communication. Of the 80 writers who responded to McKee's survey, 60% used outlines consisting of words or words and phrases. Another 30% used outlines consisting of words, phrases, and sentences. Only 5% used the traditional sentence outline, and 5% used no outline.

Chandler (1978) wrote that ready-made outlines cheat you and your readers. He stated that ready-made outlines hamper communication because the authors who use them bury their main points and force readers to read hundreds of words to learn the main points. Instead of the ready-made outline, Chandler recommended letting the contents and the points you want your readers to know dictate how you organize your manuscripts.

Some professionals summarize their main points before they begin their outlines. Professor James A. Bailey of Colorado State University says he writes his conclusions in one to five short sentences. Then he lets those sentences guide his outlining.

Bailey also cautions against letting the order of data analysis dictate your organization. How you analyze data may have no relation to the data's order of importance and the conclusions you draw from the data. So let the importance of the points dictate the data's organization and order of presentation.

Other writers begin by making a rough outline of their major points and repeatedly expand the outline. Gradually, an outline emerges that the authors use as a guide for drafting their manuscripts.

I used such an approach in outlining this chapter. I prepared seven versions before a 23-page typed working outline emerged. After letting the outline rest, I discussed it with an editor and other professionals. Next I incorporated selected points from the first 13 pages into the last 10 pages. These changes

Original Memo	Comments/Questions
FROM: District Biologist	
SUBJECT: Interim Preliminary Report Barstow-Las Vegas Motorcycle Race on wildlife habitats	Why not say interim report or preliminary report? Do you really need both words?
The initial investigation was completed in October 1974 and the follow-up investigation was completed in October 1975. The investigation was the most interesting I have undertaken and it should provide us with practical information for assessing potential damages from future motorcycle races and related off-terrain vehicle use.	Why take the whole sentence to add the dates? Include them with the subject line. Why was the investigation the most interesting that you undertook? What's the point of the memo? The State Biologist doesn't have time to wade through a lengthy, general narrative. Of what practical value should the data be? How will the data help the agency assess future data? Provide specifics.
There were two study sites chosen in the vicinity of the start of the Barstow-Las Vegas Race. Study Sites I and II contained two different habitat types. Both pre and post race sites were evaluated.	What were the sites? What specific vegetation sites/habitat types were studied? Why? Do you mean that you had two or four study sites? You're unclear. What's your experimental design? What's the methodology? Provide specifics.
On Study Sites I and II the pre-race capture success was low. The trapping success rates after the race were even lower. A marked reduction in trapping success occurred on the area.	What do you mean low? Provide specifics. What does even lower mean? Provide specifics. What's a marked reduction? What are the limitations on the data?
The effects of the race on the habitat types varied and the agency can draw specific conclusions from the pre and post-race data for subsequent races.	How did the effects vary? Be specific. What conclusions should you draw?
Most data were of great practical use and some were quite interesting. . . and show how motorcycles and off-terrain vehicles may have an impact on vegetation types in the deserts.	What are the practical values of the data? What implications do the data and your interpretations have for subsequent management? Should you hedge with "may have an impact" or should you be specific and identify the impact?
It was good that we were able to complete the project as it provided excellent information for management decisions and assessing impacts on the desert environment.	Why good? What does good mean? What does "excellent information" mean?
I think "atta bodys" should go to Dave Smith and Kim Vandermiden, area biologists who helped with the project on their own time and at their own expense. They helped collect the very valuable and important information for us.	Should the State Biologist send a letter of thanks? Or take other action? Be specific. Reorganize the memo so you tell the State Biologist in the first paragraph the impacts of the race on the habitat types and the management implications. Provide alternatives; be specific.

Figure 1. Memo that "tells about" more than it "tells."

gave a tighter focus on developing a writing strategy and minimizing the discussion of research on professional writing. I then added more marginal notes. Figure 2 shows one page that I used to guide my drafting the manuscript.

So, what guidelines emerge from the foregoing discussion? First, use some form of an outline. The exact form does not matter as long as it helps you write. You may find a detailed approach helpful or you may find a few key words and phrases enough to guide your writing. Second, let your outline rest before revising it. Time helps give you a critical perspective and will help you improve the manuscript's organization. Third, when you revise, evaluate your logic. Do you need to delete points, add points, or rearrange points to build your rationale and logic?

Preparing Illustrations

Ideally, plan your illustrations—tables, photographs, graphs, and line art—when you begin the project. You may encounter problems if you wait until the project's end to shoot photographs and have your line art prepared. Most illustrations benefit from early planning in the project. At the latest, prepare the tables and graphs after you have outlined the manuscript.

Most style manuals and guides divide illustrations into tables and figures. Any illustration that is not a table is a figure. Although tables normally present numbers, they can present short narratives. Figures include graphs, line art, photographs, and listings.

Good illustrations save writing, support the narrative, and show essential points that are difficult to present in the narrative. Illustrations help you communicate your key points clearly and succinctly. And a good illustration may eliminate hundreds or thousands of words.

What kinds of illustrations should you use? Tables work best for presenting statistics, data, and complex information. Graphs—line graphs, bar graphs, and circle graphs—may give specific information, but more often they give a general impression and show trends. Newspapers and popular magazines use greatly simplified graphs and tables. Line art (drawings) serve well for many readers, but line art must be oriented for readers. Will your readers understand the line art? Maps, for example, provide useful, detailed information, but they need a north arrow, legend, and scale. Without such information, readers unfamiliar with an area will have trouble locating the site. Photographs provide an image of real animals, objects, vegetation, or an area, and often convey concepts more effectively than tables (Figure 3). Photographs work well for most readers, but

some readers may not see what you want them to see. So provide information in the legend or caption.

Before preparing any illustrations, study the publication's style for illustrations. If you have no style manual or guide, follow the current Journal of Wildlife Management style and CBE Style Manual (CBE Style Manual Committee 1983).

Tips on Preparing Tables. A standard table format produces uniformity and makes data presentation more efficient and effective. Readers need not search for missing information and they will find table interpretation easier. Figure 4 shows the standard parts of the table as adapted from the CBE Style Manual. These parts also conform to the Journal of Wildlife Management's style.

A cursory review I did of BLM publications showed inconsistencies such as lack of a title above tables and inconsistent use of divider lines. Other problems involved cramming too much information into a table and reducing tables to a size that many readers could not easily read the numbers and words. When reducing, some photocopying machines blur letters and numbers.

Another common problem involves incorrectly using significant digits. Some authors use digits after the decimal when whole numbers would do. Thus, in a food habits study, reporting a particular food in 5.1% rather than 5% of the samples illustrates unnecessary detail and a level of precision that does not exist.

When tables will be printed from typed tables, use a sans-serif type face such as Letter Gothic or Orator (Figure 5). Sans serif faces have no cross strokes at the letter's end. Serif type such as Prestige Elite, Courier, and Modern has cross strokes at the letter's end. Such type faces make for easier reading of lengthy narratives but blur when reduced too small, and reading becomes difficult.

If possible, use upright or vertical format tables as Figure 4 illustrates. Avoid using tables that force the reader to turn the manuscript sideways to read the table and avoid reducing tables so small that readers have trouble deciphering the numbers, as in Figure 6. Many readers will not take the time and effort to turn a manuscript or decipher small printing.

Avoid multiple-page tables and tables with excessive columns. In most instances you can avoid the above-mentioned problems by breaking complex tables into two or more tables.

Tips on Figures. When preparing figures, put the titles below, not above the figures. Use a consistent format and style for titles and do not mix typed, typeset, and hand-lettered titles. For typed

Original outline too heavy on theory - Incorporate points into applied sections. *Lead?*

VI. A suggested approach to writing

    A. Thinking and Planning

    Provide adequate time for thinking and planning your communications.
Consider:

Desired outcome? Understanding? Agreement? Accuracy

    1. Who are my readers? *Readers' time limited* *Figure? Frame of reference*

    2. What is my content?

    3. What do I want to communicate to my readers? *Function - inform instruct persuade document*

    4. What is the appropriate format and organization for presenting
my information? *Biologists write under supervisors' signatures.*

    B. Developing a working outline
       ＊Organizing to help readers
    1. Your outline may be a mixture of sentences, phrases, clauses
and words. It's a working document and seldom will others see it.

    2. Outlining helps you see your thinking and putting your thinking
on paper helps most writers. *Content-style-readers*

    3. Letting an outline rest a few days or more helps you reconsider
your approach.

    4. Remember it's easier to revise an outline than it is to revise
an entire document.

    5. When you begin writing, keep your outline in mind, but don't
feel constrained by it. After having thought about it, an improved
organization may emerge.

    C. Prepare your tables and figures *-- Illustrative materials*

Delete? Incorporate into narrative

    1. Tables and figures should be based on your message and
reader's abilities to understand and interpret them. Anything
not a table is a figure. Figure XX provides guidelines for selecting
different kinds of tables and figures. *Functions -- clarify experiment/data reduces writing*
    INSERT FIGURE XX ABOUT HERE

    2. By planning illustrations early, illustrators, artists and
photographers can meet the publication's deadlines.

    Type illustration -- content - audience - function

Figure 2. Sample page of working outline developed for this chapter.

Figure X. Recovery of Ramsey Creek following stream corridor fencing in 1974.

Table XX. Comparison of some vegetation and physical parameters of Ramsey Creek from 1974 to 1980 following stream corridor fencing and natural revegetation.[1]

	1974	1976	1978	1980
Vegetation				
Percent Cover				
Bare Soil	8	26	17	5
Litter	2	4	14	12
Grass	5	23	9	9
Forbs	12	15	22	8
Shrubs	–	30	35	30
Trees	–	2	23	36
Stems/Acre over 1" dbh	–	–	354	986
Physical Parameters				
Average stream width (m)	3.1	2.7	2.5	2.1
Average depth (m)	.09	.08	.21	.33
Streambank stability (% vegetation)	Poor (0–25)	Fair (26–50)	Good (51–75)	Excellent (75–100)
Streamside cover (rating) (dominant vegetation type)	Poor (Forbs)	Fair (Grass/Forbs)	Good (Shrubs)	Excellent (Shrubs/Trees)

1/ Simulated Data

Figure 3. Comparison of tables and photographs illustrating the habitat changes from 1976 to 1980

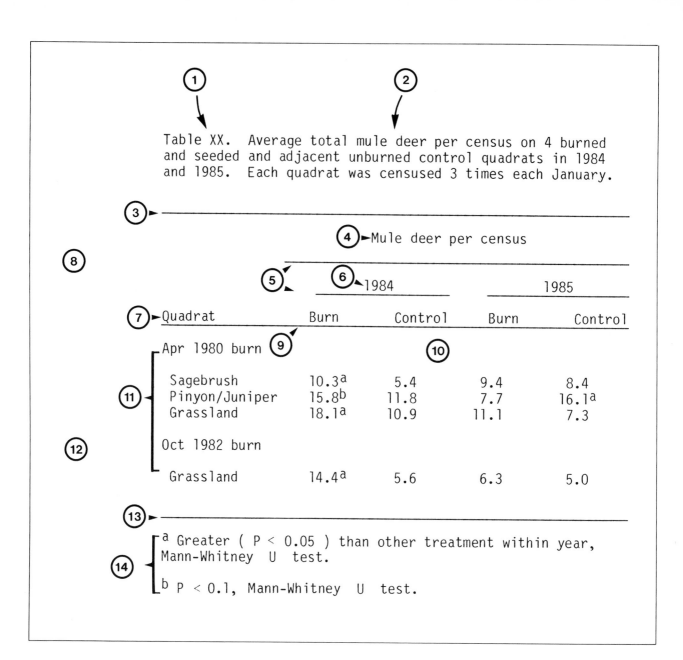

Figure 4. Parts of a typical table.

①table number　②table title or legend　③rule　④spanner head

⑤rules　⑥sub-spanner heads with rules　⑦stub head　⑧spanner

⑨rule　⑩field　⑪subheadings　⑫stub　⑬rule　⑭footnotes

Serif Type Faces	Sans-serif Type Faces
Prestige Elite	Letter Gothic
Courier	Presentor Orator

Figure 5. Typical type faces illustrating serif and sans-serif type faces.

publications, type all titles and insert them after the figures have been reduced to fit the page. Make sure the type remains legible and easy to read. Make the titles complete so the figure can stand alone by including such information as the location of the study and the plant or animal species studied.

Have graphs and artwork drawn larger than, but proportional to the final page size. When drawing figures, do not use too much information or too many lines and clutter the figure. But provide enough information so the figure is not confusing. For example, adding a regression formula helps clarify your data in a line graph.

When you submit figures for a publication, mark the top. When you check the galleys or proofs of the article, make sure the figure was not inserted upside down or backwards. (Don't laugh—it happens much to the embarrassment of authors and editors.) If someone else inserts the figures, make sure they have inserted them correctly.

If you need photographs to illustrate a manuscript, shoot black and white negatives during the project. Even if you foresee no need for photographs, shoot them anyway. And when you have the prints prepared, request glossy black and white prints. For a detailed discussion of illustrations, see Allen (1977) and CBE Style Manual Committee (1983).

Drafting the Manuscript

To draft your manuscript, use your outline and illustrations as guides and put your thoughts on paper quickly. Do not become a slave to your outline—you may develop ideas that will improve your organization, your content, or your points. If so, use them. When you write your first draft, do not worry about spelling, style, and grammar—correct them later.

As you work through your outline, use tables, figures, and other illustrations to reduce the length of your narrative. Discuss their important points. Point out what you think the data and information mean. Place illustrations in the text right after their first mention in the narrative. So provide instructions for inserting the illustrations into the text. Insert a line such as

`Insert Figure XX about here`

to tell the word processing operator, typist, or printer where to insert the illustration in the copy to be printed or reproduced.

Today, many professional writers compose directly on typewriters or word processors. Recent advances in computers suggest that more and more professionals from all fields will soon be using computers with word-processing capabilities. But for now, many biologists do not have access to a computer with word-processing capabilities or even a typewriter for their personal use. So they must write longhand with pencil and paper.

Draft your manuscript and then have it typed double spaced with 1- or 1-1/2-inch margins on all sides. Type on only one side of the paper. Once you have a typed copy, make a photocopy for revising and editing. Store the original in a safe place as you may need it later.

Writing Abstracts and Executive Summaries

When preparing lengthy documents, include either an abstract or an executive summary. Often an abstract is the only part of your writing that busy managers, supervisors, and biologists will read. Professionals seldom read an entire report, article, or document, but they do read the abstracts and executive summaries. Furthermore, the abstract or executive summary will often be separated from the report and circulated to different readers. Therefore, your abstract or executive summary must stand alone and

TABLE 1-19
LIVESTOCK REDUCTION/MAXIMIZING WILD HORSE AND BURRO ALTERNATIVE - ESTIMATED FUTURE PRODUCTION AND USE, YEAR 1991 and 2024 (AUMs)
PARADISE-DENIO RESOURCE AREA

Allotment a/	Available Vegetation b/ Big Game	Available Vegetation b/ Livestock or Wild Horse c/	Estimated Future Available Production Through Range Improvements - Year 1991 d/ Water Developments	Land Treatments	Estimated Available Vegetation c/	Estimated Future Available Production Through Management - Year 2024 Improvement Through Mgt. Systems e/	Improvement Through Reduction in Grazing Intensity f/	Areas Potentially Suited for Production that will Improve Through Mgt. g/	Estimated Available Vegetation h/ Big Game	Estimated Available Vegetation h/ Livestock or Wild Horses c/	Estimated Use - Year 1991 Livestock	Estimated Use - Year 1991 Wild Horse	Estimated Use - Year 2024 Livestock	Wild Horse	Big Game Mule Deer	Big Game Antelope	Big Game Bighorn Sheep	Balance Big Game
Proposed Allotment Management Plans																		
Abel Creek	121	971	0	1,791	2,762	0	204	17	152	2,983	2,762	0	2,983	0	152	0	0	0
Alder Creek	2,436	3,897	0	0	3,897	0	818	0	2,947	4,715	3,453	444	0	4,715	1,725	392	319	511
Andorno	14	200	0	1,343	1,543	0	42	2	17	1,587	1,543	0	1,587	0	2	0	12	3
Bloody Run -	235	954	0	1,023	1,977	48	200	243	296	2,468	1,977	0	2,468	0	195	0	0	101
Asa Moore	30	38	0	413	451	2	8	48	38	509	451	0	509	0	30	0	0	8
Total	(265)	(992)	(0)	(1,436)	(2,428)	(50)	(208)	(291)	(334)	(2,977)	(2,428)	(0)	(2,977)	(0)	(225)	(0)	(0)	(109)
Buffalo -	21	242	0	567	809	0	51	13	26	873	809	0	873	0	26	0	0	0
Antelope	94	268	0	568	836	0	57	0	119	893	836	0	893	0	75	0	2	42
Total	(115)	(510)	(0)	(1,135)	(1,645)	(0)	(108)	(13)	(145)	(1,766)	(1,645)	(0)	(1,766)	(0)	(101)	(0)	(2)	(42)
Crowley Creek	82	2,743	0	771	3,514	0	576	0	99	4,090	3,514	0	4,090	0	58	24	0	17
Double H	494	1,208	0	3,217	4,425	60	254	79	623	4,818	4,425	0	4,818	0	0	22	65	536
Dyke Hot	137	757	0	288	1,045	38	159	1	173	1,243	1,045	0	1,243	0	96	0	0	77
Eden Valley -	174	1,255	0	1,066	2,321	63	264	58	219	2,706	2,321	0	2,706	0	219	0	0	0
Scott Spring	119	795	0	1,920	2,715	40	0	0	125	2,755	2,715	0	2,755	0	125	0	0	0
Golconda Butte	0	288	0	751	1,039	14	60	169	0	1,282	1,039	0	1,282	0	0	0	0	0
Total	(293)	(2,338)	0	(3,737)	(6,075)	(117)	(324)	(227)	(344)	(6,743)	(6,075)	(0)	(6,743)	(0)	(344)	(0)	(0)	(0)
Flat Creek	57	2,262	0	2,057	4,319	0	475	39	72	4,833	4,319	0	4,833	0	72	0	0	0
Fort McDermitt -	23	1,344	0	903	2,247	67	282	5	29	2,601	2,247	0	2,601	0	16	0	0	13
Cordero	2	83	0	0	83	4	18	18	2	123	83	0	123	0	0	0	0	2
Total	(25)	(1,427)	(0)	(903)	(2,330)	(71)	(300)	(23)	(31)	(2,724)	(2,330)	(0)	(2,724)	(0)	(16)	(0)	(0)	(15)
Fort Scott	41	233	0	0	233	0	49	0	52	282	233	0	282	0	52	0	0	0
Hanson Creek	29	43	0	63	106	0	9	0	37	115	106	0	115	0	37	0	0	0
Happy Creek -	300	1,672	0	1,021	2,693	84	351	505	378	3,633	2,693	0	3,633	0	262	0	38	78
Deer Creek	85	14	0	0	14	0	3	0	107	17	0	14	0	17	34	0	58	15
Total	(385)	(1,686)	(0)	(1,021)	(2,707)	(84)	(354)	(505)	(485)	(3,650)	(2,693)	(14)	(3,633)	(17)	(296)	(0)	(96)	(93)
Horse Creek -	663	1,124	0	171	1,295	56	236	33	835	1,620	1,295	0	1,620	0	643	55	98	39
Little Horse Creek	94	56	0	0	56	3	12	73	119	144	56	0	144	0	77	0	33	9
Total	(757)	(1,180)	(0)	(171)	(1,351)	(59)	(248)	(106)	(954)	(1,764)	(1,351)	(0)	(1,764)	(0)	(720)	(55)	(131)	(48)
Humboldt Valley -	1,190	3,127	7	637	3,771	156	657	107	1,499	4,691	3,771	0	4,691	0	300	0	0	1,199
Sand Dunes	90	2,304	48	2,260	4,612	115	484	81	113	5,292	4,612	0	5,292	0	90	0	0	23
Sand Pass	64	1,016	0	407	1,423	51	213	324	81	2,011	1,423	0	2,011	0	60	0	0	21
Total	(1,344)	(6,447)	(55)	(3,304)	(9,806)	(322)	(1,354)	(512)	(1,693)	(11,994)	(9,806)	(0)	(11,994)	(0)	(450)	(0)	(0)	(1,243)
Jackson Mountains - j/	866	2,192	0	0	2,192	0	460	0	1,048	2,652	0	2,192	0	2,652	448	72	346	182
Desert Valley	114	167	0	40	207	0	35	0	144	242	207	0	242	0	73	0	34	37
Blue Mtn.	23	3,608	0	0	3,608	181	758	198	29	4,745	3,608	0	4,745	0	29	0	0	0
Total	(1,003)	(5,967)	(0)	(40)	(6,007)	(181)	(1,253)	(198)	(1,264)	(7,639)	(3,815)	(2,192)	(4,987)	(2,652)	(550)	(72)	(380)	(219)
Jordan Meadows	290	4,074	0	1,933	6,007	0	856	33	351	6,896	6,007	0	6,896	0	170	120	0	61
Kings River	1,305	2,998	0	3,548	6,546	0	630	161	1,597	7,337	6,546	0	7,337	0	1,360	72	109	38
Little Owyhee (summer)	434	7,998	0	4,506	12,504	0	1,680	0	525	14,184	12,504	0	14,184	0	175	187	72	91
Mullinix	27	120	0	0	120	6	25	3	34	154	120	0	154	0	34	0	0	0
Osgood -	480	1,699	0	1,600	3,299	85	357	83	605	3,824	3,299	0	3,824	0	330	0	0	275
Iron Point	0	223	0	0	223	11	47	242	0	523	223	0	523	0	0	0	0	0
Total	(480)	(1,922)	(0)	(1,600)	(3,522)	(96)	(404)	(325)	(605)	(4,347)	(3,522)	(0)	(4,347)	(0)	(330)	(0)	(0)	(275)
Pine Forest	1,099	2,363	0	2,280	4,643	118	496	825	1,385	6,082	4,643	0	6,082	0	1,158	108	72	47
Rebel Creek	93	894	0	0	894	0	188	0	112	1,082	894	0	1,082	0	100	0	10	2
Singus	47	103	0	34	137	0	22	2	59	161	137	0	161	0	59	0	0	0
Solid Silver	18	112	0	0	112	0	24	0	23	136	112	0	136	0	23	0	0	0
U.C.	152	6,049	0	2,660	8,709	0	0	0	152	8,709	8,709	0	8,709	0	130	0	22	0
Wilder-Bilk	1,747	9,476	0	2,894	12,370	0	1,990	242	2,114	14,602	12,370	0	14,602	0	1,418	236	93	367
William Stock	206	2,440	0	640	3,080	0	512	0	249	3,592	3,080	0	3,592	0	170	36	0	43
Willow Creek	3	984	0	344	1,328	0	206	0	4	1,534	1,328	0	1,534	0	4	0	0	0
No Allotment Management Plans																		
Bullhead	295	0	0	0	0	0	0	227	357	227	0	0	0	227	105	0	190	62
Daveytown -	45	1,817	0	0	1,817	0	0	0	45	1,817	1,685	132	65	1,752	45	0	0	0
Sod House	0	190	0	0	190	0	40	11	0	241	190	0	241	0	0	0	0	0
Total	(45)	(2,007)	(0)	(0)	(2,007)	(0)	(40)	(11)	(45)	(2,058)	(190)	(132)	(306)	(1,752)	(45)	(0)	(0)	(0)
Gallagher Flat	0	148	0	0	148	0	31	0	0	179	148	0	179	0	0	0	0	0
McDermitt Creek	11	0	0	0	0	0	11	0	13	11	0	0	11	0	13	0	0	0
Upper Quinn River -	17	198	0	0	198	0	42	0	21	240	198	0	240	0	0	0	0	21
Lower Quinn River	0	187	0	0	187	0	39	0	0	226	187	0	226	0	0	0	0	0
Total	(17)	(385)	0	0	(385)	(0)	(81)	(0)	(21)	(466)	(385)	(0)	(466)	(0)	(0)	(0)	(0)	(21)

Figure 6. Reducing tables impairs the legibility and makes them difficult to read. Turning tables sideways on the pages discourages reading.

contain the essential information your readers need to know.

Abstracts and executive summaries should tell rather than tell about (see Figure 1). Simply provide the necessary specifics and come to your points quickly. Usually, abstracts are for narrowly-focused, specific research projects; executive summaries are for more broad-based, diverse investigations.

Your abstracts should contain brief statements on the research question or purpose, methodology, and conclusions. With tight writing, you can condense an abstract to one, two, or three sentences. But normally your abstracts will run between 25 and 200 words, depending upon the agency's or publication's guidelines. Do not cite literature, refer to tables or figures in the report, or include tables or figures in the abstract.

Executive summaries may run up to 1,000 words, and they explain the project in more depth than an abstract. Furthermore, executive summaries are usually prepared for administrators and less technical readers. Therefore, translate jargon and define technical terms to be sure your readers understand your points.

Keep your writing succinct and provide only enough detail to support your points. Keep in mind that most readers will not read your full report. Thus, the executive summary must be a tight presentation of the key points. And, like writing the abstract, do not include citations, illustrations, figures, or tables.

Finally, most professionals find writing the abstracts and executive summaries easy after they have written the complete report. Conclusions, headings, and major titles often provide guidelines for developing abstracts and executive summaries.

Revising and Self-editing

Clear writing comes from clear thinking and rewriting. Rewriting entails self-editing—a way of revising your writing. By rewriting you can sharpen your narrative and make your points succinctly. Some professionals rewrite their manuscripts two, three, four, or more times before they have a copy for others to critique.

Self-editing helps you tighten your writing. Too often we write long, complex, involved sentences. Most readers find short sentences easier to understand than long sentences. As a rule sentences should average about 20 words, but avoid short, choppy sentences. Vary sentence length. Avoid sentences with excessive prepositional phrases; edit sentences with long, complex, involved clauses; and

avoid sentences with greatly separated subjects and verbs.

To practice self-editing, plan to make several trips through your typed manuscript to achieve the following goals:

1. Correct obvious typing and spelling errors.
2. Correct errors in content.
3. Correct organizational and logic problems.
4. Eliminate wordiness.

To illustrate self-editing, assume you have drafted the introduction to a BLM Technical Note as in Figure 7. How can it be improved? I pose questions about its content and readers, and then I suggest how you might tighten the copy. By applying self-editing to your writing, you will clarify your points.

Correct Typing and Spelling Errors. Begin by quickly reading through your typed manuscript and correcting obvious typographical and spelling errors. Correct the errors by using standard copyediting symbols as illustrated in Figure 8. The copyediting symbols show standard changes for retyping or typesetting the manuscript as galleys—the printed copy. When copyediting, use a soft-lead pencil. Changes made with hard-lead pencils are hard to read and difficult to erase.

Check for Content Errors. Read through your manuscript again looking for errors in content. Have you accurately presented the data? Have any typographical errors changed any meanings? Are you using the correct terms? Have you used the terms in the correct context? Have you presented anything or used an approach that will raise questions about your problem-solving skills? If so, have you explained why? Critically review your manuscript as if it were written by another author.

Errors easily creep in if you are not extremely cautious and careful. Thus, the author who writes

"During the study we collected 12 fish species in 1960, 15 in 1965, 17 in 1970, 18 in 1975, and 20 in 1980. The 116% decrease can be attributed to..."

Here the author should have written, "The 116% increase in species can be attributed to..." Although strikingly apparent, such errors can creep in when writers become too close to their writing. To reduce the chances of such errors slipping into your writing, put it aside for days or better yet a week or two before you review it. Then carefully check for errors. And then have another professional check your manuscript.

Original	Comments	Suggested rewrite
In compliance with the National Environmental Policy Act (NEPA) of 1970, the Bureau of Land Management (BLM) is required by law to address the resources and impacts of land use on national public lands in the form of Environmental Impact Statements (EISs).	**Is the first paragraph needed? Don't the readers know about the NEPA and EISs? If so, delete the paragraph. If not, tighten it.**	To comply with the National Environmental Policy Act (NEPA) of 1970, the Bureau of Land Management (BLM) must file Environmental Impact Statements (EISs) for uses of national public lands.
Extensive wildlife inventories were first implemented on public lands following the October 1973 lawsuit filed in the Federal District Court of the District of Columbia by the Natural Resources Defense Council and other conservation groups. It was successfully argued that evaluation of livestock grazing on public lands, first filed by the BLM with the Council on Environmental Quality was too general in content to properly address localized impacts, and therefore, did not comply with NEPA.	**Is it necessary to say the BLM implemented the inventories? What did the suit change? Should it be that specific? Should other conservation groups be mentioned? Who successfully argued? The Defense Council? Other groups? Can the sentence be recast in active voice?**	The BLM implemented (began?) extensive inventories . . . The plaintiffs successfully argued that the initial BLM inventories did not adequately address the impacts of local grazing and did not comply with NEPA.
It is estimated that 310 stream miles and over 11,800 acres of riparian woodland are administered by the BLM in Arizona. In an effort to comply with the court, it became the purpose of this study to provide aquatic habitat and water quality information to the Phoenix District Office of the Bureau of Land Management. These baseline data are to serve as an information source to be utilized in the management plans for terrestrial and aquatic resources on public lands.	**Why be so wordy? Recast into active voice for a tight sentence.** **Here's another wordy sentence. Can it be tightened? Can the "Bureau of Land Management" be abbreviated?** **Again, can the point be made more quickly? Is "on public lands" necessary? BLM doesn't handle other lands, does it? Did the suit focus on only public lands?**	The BLM administers about 310 stream miles and over 11,800 acres of riparian woodland in Arizona. To comply with the court, this study provided aquatic habitat and water quality information to the BLM's Phoenix District Office. The baseline data provide information for developing management plans for terrestrial and aquatic resources.

Figure 7. Introduction to a Technical Note with comments and suggestions for rewriting.

Meaning	Example
Delete	It has zones of high and . . .
Circle means to spell out	(26) trees were sampled
Circle means to abbreviate	The (Bureau of Land Management) . . .
For capitals, underline three times	The department of the interior . . .
Draw a slanted line through a letter to change to lower case	The Agency policy includes . . .
Delete letter and close-up using normal spacing	Its numbers were reduxced.
Delete letters and use normal spacing between words	. . . butxx occursg in fewer numbers.
Underline to have words set in italics	Dipodomys merriami
Begin a new paragraph	Eight species were snap trapped.
Center copy	] Introduction [
Set or type flush left	References [
Set or type flush right	] Totals
Insert missing words	The highest for Ord's kangaroo rat . .
Insert missing letter	. . . nothern grasshopper mouse . . .
Transpose words	Eight species were |trapped|snap.
Transpose letters	Eight speçies . . .
Separate run-on words	Eight species were trapped.
Insert period	Eight species were trapped
Insert comma	Additionally the white-footed mouse . .
Insert hyphen	. . . the white=footed mouse . . .
Let original copy stand	Simple monotypic vegetation types . . .
Close up copy	Arizona Upland was further divided into three standard habitat sites based on gradient. They included desertscrub
For grossly misspelled words, mark out and write above	Its numbers were reduced.

Figure 8. Selected copyediting marks for revised typed manuscripts.

On the basis of your expertise in wildlife, do you see any errors of logic in your approach? Did you follow acceptable and logical ways of solving the problem? Do your data support your conclusions? Do you limit your conclusions? In what ways might your content be criticized? Have you adequately supported your position? What weak points in logic, problem solving, and methodologies become apparent upon reading? Can you correct the weaknesses? As weaknesses become apparent, consider the potential criticism. Should you revise? You may find yourself revising sentences, paragraphs, or whole sections.

Check Your Organization. Read through your manuscript again. Have you adequately considered the reading habits of your readers? Do you give your readers an overview of what is to come? Will your organization help your readers understand your content? Do you progress logically from point one to point two to point three? Should you make some points later in your manuscript? Should some points be made earlier? Have you adequately defined and explained points when you introduce them? Does your organization raise any questions about your logic?

Eliminate Wordiness. Your writing will benefit by cutting wordiness. With a heavy edit, you will improve your writing's clarity and conciseness. When you write tightly, your thinking comes through clearly and you will increase your reader's understanding.

To cut wordiness, eliminate unneeded words, phrases, clauses, sentences, and paragraphs. When possible, replace a clause with a phrase, and a phrase with a word. Question your words. Can you say what you want more effectively? Can you make your points in fewer words? Do you need that word? That phrase? That clause? What can you eliminate?

Developing your self-editing skills requires recognizing wordy constructions and knowing how to improve them. To improve your writing:

1. Use active voice.
2. Use pronouns.
3. Replace small, weak verbs.
4. Eliminate unnecessary clauses.
5. Eliminate unnecessary phrases.
6. Omit needless words.
7. Replace vague, general, and abstract terms.
8. Avoid jargon and acronyms.

Use Active Voice Active voice makes clear who did what. It tells the reader who carried out the action. Compare the active voice with passive voice constructions:

Active: The division manager cancelled the project.

Passive: The project was cancelled.

Passive: The project was cancelled by the division manager.

In the first sentence we know who did what. In the second sentence, we do not know who cancelled the project. In the third sentence, we finally learn who did what, but late in the sentence. The active voice quickly tells your reader who carried out the action. Use the active voice for shorter sentences.

You can recognize whether a sentence is active or passive by asking, "Did the subject carry out the action?" If not, you have a passive construction. You can recognize passive constructions by looking for is, was, were, and other to be verb forms. In the two passive constructions above, was signals the passive voice. In some sentences, a prepositional phrase beginning with by signals the passive construction.

When should you use the passive construction? The CBE Style Manual (CBE Style Manual Committee 1983) suggests the use of passive voice when the agent of the action is irrelevant and when something or someone other than the agent is more important. Consider:

The National Environmental Policy Act was passed in 1970.

Here the passage of the act was more important than who passed it. In other words, as illustrated below, what you want to emphasize dictates whether you use the active or passive voice:

Many technical reports are prepared by consultants.

Consultants prepare many technical reports.

Use Pronouns. Correctly used, pronouns provide a succinct way of making your points. The CBE Style Manual (CBE Style Manual Committee 1983) endorses "I discovered..." rather than "It was discovered..." and calls the second example the "passive of modesty." Avoid such passive voice constructions when your name or the agency's name goes on the manuscript. By using personal pronouns you write in active voice and you make it clear who did what or who recommended an action.

Replace Small, Weak Verbs. Many writers build their sentences around small verbs: is, are, was, were, and related forms. Sometimes writers use trapped verbs as shown in Figure 9.

Noun	Verb Form
refusal	refuse
promulgation	promulgate
assignment	assign
reliance	rely
verification	verify
happening	happen
occurrence	occur
participation	participate
disclosure	disclose

Figure 9. Common nouns representing trapped verbs. Adapted from and used by permission of Felker et al. (1982).

To find trapped verbs, look for words ending in: -al, -tion, -ence, and -ure (Felker et al. 1982) or look for nouns near such verb forms as effected, obtained, performed, produced, required, carried out, implemented, accomplished, occurred (Brandner et al. 1974).

Consider "The area is a typical representation of ..." versus "The area represents..." or "Excessive eutrophication of aquatic ecosystems by livestock defecation results in pollution and bacterial contamination..." versus "Livestock defecation pollutes and produces excessive eutrophication of aquatic ecosystems and contaminates them with bacteria..."

Compare "I have made general recommendations for maintaining and improving each group of reptile and amphibian" versus "I recommend ways of maintaining and improving each reptile group." And consider "It was the purpose of this study to supplement previous work completed for the Bill Williams drainage (Kepner 1979) in addition to describing the aquatic resources of the Hassayampa River drainage." versus "Our study supplements the work of Kepner (1979) on the Bill Williams drainage and describes the aquatic resources of the Hassayampa River drainage."

Eliminate Unneeded Clauses. Long, complex sentences often reflect loose, rambling writing. Most readers find long sentences difficult to follow. Can the following sentences be written more succinctly?

> It is the opinion of field personnel in the South Dakota Department of Game, Fish, and Parks that one of the primary factors influencing population levels of big game and turkeys in the southern Black Hills is a limited water supply.

How can we tighten the sentence? Consider the first clause, "It is the opinion of..." Why not replace the clause with "believe." Thus

> "Field personnel in the South Dakota Department of Game, Fish, and Parks believe..."

Looking further, let's replace "... that one of the primary factors influencing..." with "... restricts..." Recasting the sentence gives

> "Field personnel in the South Dakota Department of Game, Fish, and Parks believe that a limited water supply restricts the population levels of big game animals and turkeys in the southern Black Hills."

I have trimmed 10 words, nearly 25%, from the original 41-word sentence. Later, when I discuss vague, general, and abstract words, I show how to tighten the passage by being specific.

Eliminate Unneeded Phrases. Too many prepositional phrases in a sentence clutter your writing. Often you can strike out unneeded prepositional phrases. Look with suspicion on prepositional phrases ending sentences. Are they really needed? Do they repeat a point made earlier? If so, eliminate them. Consider

> "We tagged 25 mule deer in this study." versus "We tagged 25 mule deer."

Change prepositional phrases to modifiers. Consider

> "The evaluation report of the BLM..." versus "The BLM evaluation report..."

or

> "The population level of big game and turkeys..." versus "The big game and turkey population levels..."

Or replace prepositional phrases with possessives. Consider "The report of the division biologist..." versus "The division biologist's report..."

Or change prepositional phrases to adverbs. Consider

"The rattlesnake crawled in a slow manner across..." versus "The rattlesnake crawled slowly across..."

Omit Needless Words. Look for words you can omit. Crossing them out often improves sentences. Consider

in order to	to
in the same general area	in the same area
brown in color	brown

Figure 10, from the CBE Style Manual (CBE Style Manual Committee 1983), lists succinct words and phrases to replace wordy constructions.

Replace Vague, General, and Abstract Words. The example of eliminating unnecessary clauses referred to "field personnel." What did the writer mean? Biologists? Technicians? Game protectors? Conservation officers? Replacing "field personnel" with "biologists" leaves no doubt who believed what:

"Biologists in the South Dakota Department of Game, Fish and Parks believe that a limited water supply restricts the levels of big game animals and turkeys in the southern Black Hills."

Specifying the big game animals—deer and bear—would further clarify the point.

If you use vague, general, and abstract terms, you leave the interpretation to the reader, and the reader usually has a different frame of reference. Therefore, replace abstract words with concrete words. Replace vague words with specific terms. Replace general words with precise words.

Figure 11 lists examples. If you do not agree, your interpretation provides even stronger evidence for using specific, precise, concrete terms.

Avoid Jargon and Acronyms. Although you understand the jargon of your speciality, your readers may not. Thus, "Palustrine wetlands" may convey a precise meaning to a waterfowl ecologist, but other biologists may call such areas "marshes" or "swamps." Furthermore, your readers may not define the terms as you do. If you use jargon, define your terms. As you reread your manuscript, ask yourself if your readers know the terms you use. If they know the terms, do they define the terms as you do?

Acronyms create problems. One natural resource agency hires CIA agents—not the Central Intelligence Agency type, but conservation information

assistants. Your varied readers may not know or understand acronyms you use. If you use acronyms, define them following their first mention such as "...Habitat Management Plan (HMP)..."

Some readers will not be familiar with the BLM or other Government agencies. In addition, many readers will not know your specialized field and the acronyms you know so well.

Editing for Style and Grammar Errors

Read through your document checking for grammar and style errors. Keep in mind that different agencies and publications have different style rules. For most technical manuscripts, follow the current Journal of Wildlife Management style. To answer specific questions, see the current CBE Style Manual (CBE Style Manual Committee 1983), the Chicago Manual of Style (University of Chicago Press 1983), or the U.S. Government Printing Office Style Manual (U.S. Government Printing Office 1984).

If you are preparing publications for general audiences, check with the publication's editor to learn the publication's style. Many newspapers and magazines follow the Associated Press Stylebook (Angione 1977) or their own style manuals.

Periodically, style rules change and agencies and publications issue new style manuals. If your style manuals are more than 5 years old, check to see if new editions have been issued.

Correcting Spelling Errors

Read through your manuscript checking for spelling errors. When in doubt, look up the word. If you cannot find the spelling in a desk dictionary, use an unabridged dictionary. The Journal of Wildlife Management and CBE Style Manual instruct authors to follow Webster's Third International Dictionary, unabridged (Gove 1966). Other style manuals and publications may follow other unabridged dictionaries. As a matter of style, dictionaries do spell some words differently. Be especially careful with hyphenated words. Because the language changes, publishers issue new editions of unabridged dictionaries, so your office may need to buy a new unabridged dictionary.

Editing Illustrations—Tables and Figures

Make one trip through your manuscript checking tables and figures. Make sure they are numbered sequentially through the manuscript. Tables have one sequential numbering and the figures have another sequential numbering. Make sure your narrative's table and figure references are correct and

Wordy	Concise
in the vicinity of	near
in view of the fact that	because
it is often the case	often
it is possible that the cause is	the cause may be
it is this that	this
it would thus appear that	apparently
large numbers of	many
lenticular in character	lenticular
masses are of large sizes	masses are large
necessitates the inclusion of	needs, requires
of such hardness that	so hard that
on the basis of	from, by, because
oval in shape, oval-shaped	oval
plants exhibited good growth	plants grew well
prior to (in time)	before
serves the function of being	is
subsequent to	after
the fish in question	this fish
the tests have not as yet	the tests have not
the treatment having been performed	after treatment
there can be little doubt that this is	this probably is
throughout the entire area	throughout the area
throughout the whole of the experiment	throughout the experiment
two equal halves	halves
a number of	few, many, several
an innumerable number of tiny veins	innumerable tiny veins
as far as our own observations are concerned, they show	we observed
ascertain the location of	find
at the present moment, at this point in time	now
bright green in color	bright green
by means of	by, with
(We) conducted inoculation experiments on	inoculated
due to the fact that	because
during the time that	while
fewer in number	fewer
for the purpose of examining	to examine
for the reason that	because, since
from the standpoint of	according to
goes under the name of	is called
if conditions are such that	if
in all cases	always, invariably
in order to	to
in the course of	during
in the event that	if
in the near future	soon

Figure 10. Replace wordy constructions with concise terms. From CBE Style Manual (CBE Style Manual Committee 1983) with permission.

Vague, General, Abstract Terms	Specific, Concrete, Precise Terms
small pond	a 4-hectare pond
a few hens in the flock	five hens in the flock
many grass species	10 grass species
steep terrain	60° slopes
low biomass	10 kilograms
a hot day	40° C with 95% humidity
strong winds	55-miles-per-hour winds
several days	six days
considerable disparity in monthly precipitation	precipitation ranged from 0 to 20 cm monthly
diminutive in size	less than 8 mm
significant	$P < 0.05$
often used	daily, weekly, monthly
mildly acidic	report pH level

Figure 11. Suggestions for replacing vague, general, and abstract terms with specific, concrete, and precise terms.

where you want them inserted is clearly marked. Be sure the insertions follow their first mention in the manuscript.

Carefully check the tables and figures for content, style, spelling, and typographical errors. Numbers are easily transposed, so recheck every number in every table and figure in the final draft. Make sure your calculations are correct. Check row and column entries because they are easily inverted and transposed. Make sure no information has been deleted.

Having the Manuscript Retyped

Once you have made the changes you want, have your manuscript retyped. When you work with typists and word processing operators, provide the publication's layout and format guidelines. They give instructions for setting margins, beginning the first page, numbering pages, and placing information on later pages. Some publication guidelines may call for not breaking sentences and paragraphs between pages.

If your manuscript was originally entered on a word processor, check with the operator on how to mark changes. Some operators want changes marked in brightly colored felt-tip pens to speed up their work. If you delete or add matter, find out how the operator wants you to do so. Follow the operator's instructions or you will slow their work of correcting the manuscript.

Copyediting the Manuscript

After retyping the manuscript or revising it on the word processor, carefully copyedit it. Look for spelling, grammar, and style errors. Check to make sure that nothing has been deleted or added. Because you have worked closely with your manuscript, you may have difficulty spotting errors. You will read things in and you will read things out. By being familiar with the manuscript, you may overlook errors and details. To overcome that problem, have a competent peer, secretary, or editor check your manuscript. But also read the manuscript yourself.

Reading a manuscript aloud and slowly checking works well for some authors. Others read their manuscripts into a tape recorder and play the tape back. As the tape plays, they check spelling, grammar, and style. If you find errors, correct them with the standard copyediting symbols.

Depending on the editor's guidelines, you may submit a manuscript with a few copyediting marks, or you may be required to submit a clean copy. Manuscripts on word processors are easily changed. But carefully copyedit the revised pages again; errors may creep in. Likewise, when you have a page retyped, check for new errors that may have been made in retyping.

Seeking Peer Reviews

Most manuscripts benefit from competent peer

reviews. The number of reviews you seek depends upon your manuscript's length, the content, and the manuscript's importance to the resource and the agency. The more important the content, the more reviews your manuscript will need. Sometimes you will need only three or four reviews and in other instances you may need more.

When you seek peer reviews, you are asking for other professionals to view your manuscript from their perspectives. No two reviewers will have exactly the same comments. Some comments will be superficial; others will provide detailed, constructive criticism. Some reviewers will agree with you; others will not.

When you read the reviews, keep in mind that some reviewers' comments will be extremely helpful and fair; others will not. When you receive a superficial, uncritical review, seek another review. When you receive a highly critical, harsh review, consider the reviewer's comments carefully. Some reviewers may disagree with you or be threatened by your conclusions. Such reviewers may be unfair and bring irrelevant objections. So weigh each reviewer's comments carefully, but do not be intimidated by their comments.

Keep in mind your agency's internal review policy. Such policies prevent erroneous statements occurring in agency documents. If your agency has a review policy, follow it.

In some instances, you will find yourself having to make changes reviewers suggest before your manuscript is approved for publication. Your editor, and perhaps your supervisor, will provide helpful guidelines.

As you rewrite and revise, work carefully. Incorporate the needed revisions and carefully copyedit your manuscript for errors. Check every number in every table again. Remember changes made now are easier to make and less costly and time-consuming than changes made after the final typing or typesetting the manuscript.

PRINTING, COMPUTERS, AND MANUSCRIPTS

Much of the time, your manuscripts will be printed in their typewritten form. But occasionally, a manuscript may be typeset and you may see it through the printing process. Before you do, learn the basic steps in the printing process and when and where to make changes. The CBE Style Manual (CBE Style Manual Committee 1983) contains three excellent chapters on printing and publishing. Other helpful references include Turnbill and Baird (1980) and Hill and Cochran (1979).

The rapid advances of computers in the printing industry in the 1970s and 1980s and personal computers in the 1980s ushered in the Information Age. Software packages enable word processing on most personal computers. Other software packages check spelling, grammar, and style. And computers can be linked to phototypesetters.

You may find yourself more involved with printing than you envision. Preparing manuscripts for typesetting will soon require entering specific commands on your personal computer. You will need to enter such information as the type face, size, spacing, column width, and other typesetting specifications. At this point you can call your printer and transmit the manuscript by telephone to the phototypesetter.

The Information Age will change how we produce documents. The equipment on which we work may change, but many of the steps will remain the same. Equipment and software will make some tasks easier, but you will still be writing and checking your work. The Information Age will encourage the proliferation of manuscripts, reports, and other documents. Therefore, it will become more and more important to target your communications to specific readers and to write clearly and concisely.

LITERATURE CITED

ALLEN, A. 1977. Steps toward better scientific illustrations. Allen Press. Lawrence, KS. 64pp.

ANGIONE, E., ed. 1977. The Associated Press stylebook and libel manual. The Associated Press. 50 Rockefeller Plaza. New York, NY 10020. 276pp.

BRANDNER, L.O., A. BIDWELL, and I. TEARE. 1974. Let logic guide your writing. Contribution 136, Vice-President for Agriculture Office, and 1431, Department of Agronomy, Agricultural Experiment Station, Kansas State University. Also published in September-October 1974, J. of Soil and Water Cons. 29(5):235-238.

CBE STYLE MANUAL COMMITTEE. 1983. CBE style manual: a guide for authors, editors, and publishers in the biological sciences. 5th edition, revised and expanded. Council of Biology Editors. Bethesda, MD. 324pp.

CHANDLER, H.E. 1978. The "how to write what" book. American Society for Metals. Metals Park, OH. 92pp.

FELKER, D.B., F. PICKERING, V.R. CHARROW, V.M. HOLLAND, and J.C. REDISH. 1982. Guidelines for document designers. American Institutes for Research. 1055 Thomas Jefferson St. NW, Washington, DC 20007. 117pp.

GOVE, P.B., ed. 1966. Webster's third new international dictionary, unabridged. G & C Merriam Co., Springfield, MA. 2662pp.

HILL, M. and W. COCHRAN. 1979. Into print: a practical guide to writing, illustrating and publishing. William Kaufman, Inc. One First Street, Los Altos, CA 94022. 175pp.

McKEE, B. 1975. Types of outlines used by technical writers. J. Eng. Teaching Techniques. 17:30-36.

SCHRAMM, W. and D.F. ROBERTS. 1972. The process and effects of mass communication. Revised edition. Univ. of Illinois Press. Urbana. 997pp.

TURNBILL, A.T. and R.N. BAIRD. 1980. The graphics of communication. 4th ed. Holt, Rinehart, Winston. New York, NY. 398pp.

UNIVERSITY OF CHICAGO PRESS. 1983. The Chicago style manual. 13th edition. Univ. of Chicago Press. 738pp.

U.S. GOVERNMENT PRINTING OFFICE. 1984. The U.S. Government Printing Office style manual. Revised edition. Superintendent of Documents. U.S. Government Printing Office, Washington, D.C. 479pp.

APPENDIX.

Suggestions for a Professional Library

From time to time, you will have questions about writing, mechanics, spelling, and style. Professional writers and editors regularly have questions too. To answer their questions, they turn to their office library of books on writing, data presentation, illustrations, printing, grammar, style, and usage. Below are suggested publications for your office library.

Books on Writing

CHANDLER, H. 1978. The "how to write what" book. American Society of Metals, Metals Park, OH 44073. 92pp.

ROMAN, K. and J. RAPHAELSON. 1981. Writing that works. Harper and Row. New York, NY. 105pp.

ZINSSER, W. 1983. Writing with a word processor. Harper and Row. New York, NY. 117pp.

———. 1980. On writing well. Harper and Row. New York, NY. 187pp.

Style Guides

ANGIONE, H., ed. 1977. The Associated Press style book and libel manual. The Associated Press. 50 Rockefeller Plaza. New York, NY 10020. 276pp.

CBE STYLE MANUAL COMMITTEE. 1983. CBE style manual: a guide for authors, editors and publishers in the biological sciences. 5th edition, revised and expanded. Council of Biology Editors, Inc. Bethesda, MD. 324pp.

UNIVERSITY OF CHICAGO PRESS. 1983. The Chicago style manual. 13th edition. University of Chicago Press. Chicago. 738pp.

U.S. GOVERNMENT PRINTING OFFICE. 1984. GPO style manual. Revised edition. U.S. Government Printing Office. Washington, DC. 479pp.

Data Presentation and Illustrations

ALLEN, A. 1977. Steps toward better scientific illustrations. Allen Press, Inc. Lawrence, KS. 64pp.

ENRICK, N.L. 1980. Handbook of effective graphic and tabular communication. Robert E. Krieger Publishing Company. Huntington, NY. 214pp.

REYNOLDS, L. and D. SIMMONDS. 1982. Presentation of data in science. Martinus Nijhoff Publishers. The Hague and Boston. 209pp.

Printing

HILL, M. and W. COCHRAN. 1979. Into print: a practical guide to writing, illustrating, and publishing. William Kaufman, Inc. One First Street, Los Altos, CA. 94022. 175pp.

TURNBILL, A.T. and R.N. BAIRD. 1980. The graphics of communication. Fourth Edition. Holt, Rinehart, and Winston. New York, NY. 398pp.

Grammar, Style, and Usage References

BERNSTEIN, T.M. 1978. The careful writer: a guide to modern usage. Atheneum. New York, NY. 487pp.

———. 1971. Miss Thistlebottom's hobgoblins. Farrar, Straus, and Giroux. New York, NY. 260pp.

CREWS, F. 1979. The Random House guide. Random House. New York, NY. 434pp.

O'HAYRE, J.O. No Date. Gobbledygook has gotta go. Superintendent of Documents. U.S. Government Printing Office. Washington, DC. 20402. 112pp.

STRUNK, W. and E.B. WHITE. 1979. The elements of style. Third edition. MacMillan Publ. Co. Inc. New York, NY. 85pp.

42

VERBAL PRESENTATIONS

Eugene Decker

Department of Fishery and Wildlife Biology
Colorado State University
Fort Collins, CO 80521

"Silence is the virtue of fools."

——Francis Bacon

Editor's Note: Communication should not end with a written report. Unfortunately, many of us avoid speaking to groups of people. We must overcome this tendency if wildlife is to be adequately represented in multiple-use decisions and allocations.

Proper planning, practice, and advance work will greatly improve the presentations you give, while increasing understanding and acceptance of your results.

INTRODUCTION

Communication has been defined as "the process of informing and being informed; it implies understanding." In other words, if there is no understanding, there is no communication. Personal presentations are often the best means to inform an audience, as they provide a better opportunity to communicate than do written communications.

A speaker usually receives immediate reaction from the audience and can appropriately respond. In addition to directly answering questions, the speaker can respond to comments, facial expressions, attention levels, gestures, and other signals from the audience during the presentation. Such responses can quickly clarify points not understood by the audience.

Another advantage of personal presentations is that a good speaker can convey credibility, sincerity, concern, and emotion. This personal factor can be most effective in getting a message across to a general public audience.

A verbal presentation of a management plan by a member or members of the resource staff may often determine the acceptance of the plan by other staff, administrators, or special interest groups. In fact, the success or failure of many months of effort by team members may well focus on a single presentation.

Unfortunately, I have seen such team efforts frustrated by presentations that were poorly prepared and communicated. It is no wonder that dull, highly technical, jargon-filled presentations illustrated with unreadable visuals result in nonacceptance of management plans. This chapter is intended to assist personnel in preparing and delivering effective personal presentations which I hope will result in sound resource management.

SPEAKER CREDIBILITY

Several factors affect your image as a speaker to

the audience, some even before the talk begins. Your appearance and behavior at a meeting before the talk, support and endorsement by members of the group, and a concise introduction by the host stating your qualifications, all help establish you as a professional.

Several factors during your talk can also affect your credibility. First, knowledge of the subject matter is of utmost importance. Due to constant exposure to media, Americans are a sophisticated audience and can easily spot a phoney. A speaker should not try to discuss subjects or answer questions beyond his or her expertise.

The second factor is trust, especially with special interest groups. An introduction by a host who endorses you will help establish confidence in the audience. Also, you should not avoid a controversial issue, especially if you know your audience is already aware of it. If there are other sides to an issue, be sure to acknowledge them before individuals in the audience bring them up; admit earlier mistakes, never try to hide them.

Dynamism is the third factor. Expressing interest, concern, and enthusiasm in a well-delivered presentation can greatly increase your effectiveness. However, if the first two factors, knowledge and trust, are weak, then it will make little difference how dynamic you are. But, if your qualifications and trust are sound, an energetic, interesting delivery will greatly enhance your acceptance by the audience.

BARRIERS TO COMMUNICATION

A number of problems can interfere with your audience's understanding of your messages. Below are several common ones:

1. Use of jargon is a major problem with many professionals. Jargon, bureaucratic buzz words, in-terms, and acronyms (HEP, HMP, NEPA, AUM, etc.) are used to save time when communicating with colleagues, but are usually unknown to the general public. Use of such terms causes confusion and often loss of attention by an audience.

2. Technical terms, scientific names, and other formal terminology are part of a professional's vocabulary, but these terms are not commonly used by the general public. Avoid these terms if possible, but if you have to use one, be sure to define it. As an example, the term "forb" is regularly used by agency personnel, but it should be defined for the general public.

3. Another problem is use of words that convey different meanings to different people. Such words as ecosystem, carrying capacity, environment, ecology, conservation, habitat, and wilderness have broad meanings. Another confusing term often used is resources. I heard an agency person tell an audience that "... we have difficulties managing your resources as Congress did not give us the financial resources for the resources necessary to do the job." You can imagine the audience reaction!

4. The environment of the meeting site can cause problems. The audience will not give you its full attention if the room temperature is uncomfortable, the air stuffy due to poor circulation, if there are distracting materials on the walls or blackboard, disturbing noises, or the chairs are positioned awkwardly in reference to the speaker or screen. You should correct as many of these problems as possible before the audience arrives.

5. The audience condition is also an important factor. You will have problems maintaining audience attention if people have been seated too long without a break, if you have run into the coffee break or lunch hour, if you are the last speaker of a 4-hour series, or if it is very late in the afternoon or evening. Be aware of these situations and try to correct and adjust by shortening your talk, giving them a break, or trying to be more dynamic and interesting.

6. The cultural, social, and educational aspects of your audience must also be considered. You should be aware of their history, experiences, education, and values in order for you to effectively convey your message to them. It is important that your presentation relate to some aspect of their lives to be clearly understood. An urban audience (service club, naturalist group, etc.) may have problems relating to issues of economic survival of ranchers whereas a rural audience may not understand an integrated management plan to meet increasing outdoor recreation needs by city residents.

PREPARING FOR THE PRESENTATION

I offer the following suggestions to assist you in preparing for personal presentations, particularly slide talks, to special interest groups and the general public. They will be covered in four stages: **planning, preparation, presentation,** and **evaluation.** Presentations to agency staff and management level personnel are discussed later.

Planning

Once you have been asked or assigned to give a presentation you should consider the following:

1. Decide on the purpose of your presentation and write it in a clear, concise statement (for example, "to inform the Red Rock Livestock Association of wildlife improvements," or "to explain results of management alternatives on the antelope herd," etc.). This will help give direction to your subsequent efforts. In general, your purpose will be to produce a change in your audience. This may be one, or a combination, of the following: (1) awareness, (2) knowledge, (3) attitude about a situation, or (4) behavior, i.e., support or action related to a situation.

2. Prepare an audience analysis. Determine as much as possible about your audience before the meeting. Such things as education levels, exposure to previous speakers, age and sex composition, previous experiences, stands on similar issues, their leaders, numbers of persons usually present, and contact with other staff persons. Your analysis should give a good picture of your audience from which you can tailor your presentation.

3. Complete a preliminary rough outline as soon as possible. This is helpful as a reminder of needed facts, graphics, and other visual aids that can be useful to your talk.

4. Make a list of the visual aids and equipment you will need. Color slides are especially useful in describing field situations (before/after treatments, contrasts, impacts, etc.), but may not be appropriate for other occasions where factual information only is to be offered. For these presentations, overhead transparencies or a flip chart alone may be appropriate.

   Handouts are useful for many occasions. A concise outline of information may be helpful to guide an audience through a complex process. Do not provide lengthy written materials during a presentation, as some people will read it and not listen to you. Such materials should usually be given at the end of the program.

5. Be sure to put the date of the presentation on your calendar and allow time for preparation and travel. If it is a major presentation, do not schedule too much for that date, as a speaker who has worked all day, driven 2 hours, and rushed to a meeting will be tired, harried, and usually a less effective speaker. Your presentation should be the top priority item for that day.

Refer to Appendix I, Checklist for slide show presentations, to help you with planning for your programs.

Preparation

Now that your planning is underway, you are ready to move on.

1. Develop a final outline. I suggest an outline that includes major items for your introduction, main content, and conclusion. The introduction to your talk should relate the audience to your topic. The introduction should also tell the audience what you will be covering and why (this relates to your purpose statement in the planning phase). You may also wish to tell the audience more about yourself, your qualifications, and experience related to your topic. A good introduction in your presentation will increase the audience reception to you and your ideas.

   Some speakers use 5- x 7-inch cards for their outlines with just one or two brief statements on each. (Be sure to number the cards to keep them in order.) These cards can be helpful when planning a slide show. Use one card for each slide and put the number of the slide and a simple sketch of the photo on the card with the statement. You can lay these cards out on a table (or on a frame "story board") to help you organize your presentation. In this way you can visualize the whole presentation and add, remove, or rearrange as needed.

   Other speakers find an outline typed on one or two sheets to be effective. Type in caps and triple space for ease in reading. Use red underlining to emphasize important material.

   You should include a conclusion in your outline as it is usually a good idea to summarize your talk. You may then wish to state what actions may be taken by the audience or where additional information may be obtained. Be sure to have a meaningful closing.

   The outline is recommended instead of a verbatim script so that you can quickly refer to the outline and then talk directly to the audience. Few persons can read a script well and maintain eye contact.

2. Prepare a brief biographic sketch of yourself for the host to use in introducing you. This should be a short, one-page statement of your education and experience. (I find that typing in all caps and triple spacing makes it easier to read.) A good introduction by the host is important, as the audience must know who you are and that you are qualified to justify their attention.

3. Prepare appropriate and effective visual aids (see Visual Aids Section following). Also, practice using them with the equipment that you will use at the talk.

"How many slides should I use?" I believe there is no firm rule as your subject and schedule will usually control the situation. However, too many slides rapidly changed can provide an unpleasant overkill. Likewise, it is not a good idea to spend too much time on one slide. In the latter situation, use two or three similar slides to provide some variety when a discussion is necessary. Good planning and rehearsing can reduce this problem so that you have a clear and concise presentation.

4. Now that you are prepared, take time to rehearse. A small cassette recorder will provide a good tape for your rehearsal. Review it for timing, organization, technical terms, jargon, and verbal distractions. Based on this review, revise your outline and try again. You will be pleased at the improvement.

Some offices have portable TV equipment. If you can borrow equipment, tape yourself and then review it on a monitor (TV set). This can be a great learning experience—"to see yourself as others see you."

If you are scheduled for a major presentation involving a potentially controversial subject, I suggest an additional rehearsal. Have several competent colleagues serve as an audience for you and act as members of various interest groups at the discussion period after your talk. Make your presentation to them and then have a "no holds barred" question and answer session. Because they have probably been exposed to these situations, they will be able to ask many slanted and embarrassing questions. This type of rehearsal will give you a chance to answer them, then review how effectively you replied. Such an activity can help you respond better to the real audiences, as you will have been able to anticipate some of the comments. The participating staff can also help you with suggestions for appropriate replies.

Always run through your slides before the meeting to be sure that they are right side up, not backwards, and that you have the appropriate slides in the cartridge. I also suggest carrying the slides with you; do not put them in your baggage if you are flying or give them to someone else to bring.

Fred forgot to rehearse.
The audience forgot Fred.

5. I mentioned earlier that you should have prepared an outline for your presentation. This will be most useful in your rehearsal and for your introduction and closing, but the written outline of your major points will be difficult to follow in a darkened room. With ample rehearsing, you should be familiar enough with your subject material that the slides serve as your outline and

you will not need to refer to any written material. However, there is usually enough light reflecting from the screen onto a correctly placed podium so that you will often be able to refer to some of your notes if necessary. A podium light is usually available, but the light reflecting from your note paper and hitting the bottom of your face may give an unpleasant appearance.

6. On the day of your presentation, be sure to check out the equipment before you leave your office. **Arrive early** and check the facilities, i.e., seating, podium, heating, ventilation, and lighting. Make adjustments before the audience arrives. Also, set up visual aids and audio equipment and test them before the meeting starts. Position your podium at the front of the room so that you do not block the audience's view of the screen. Do not speak from the projector; stay front and center near the screen.

If you are using a slide or overhead projector, make sure there is an extra bulb and practice changing the bulb. If a bulb burns out during the program, request the lights on and take a 5-minute break. This will give you an opportunity to change the bulb quickly, and get organized so that the show can continue smoothly. It is quite awkward to change a bulb when you do not know how and have to have the audience help you. Also, never grab the bulb with bare fingers as the only thing the audience will remember is the smell of burning flesh and what you said when you grabbed it.

7. Be sure to tie down the cords from the projector, both power and control cords, to the stand or table leg before continuing on to the outlet or podium. This prevents people from tripping over the cords or pulling the projector off the table.

8. When setting up the equipment before the meeting, be sure to have your slide image fill the screen and keep it as high as possible. If you have a number of vertical slides, you must adjust your image for the verticals which means that your horizontals will be lower on the screen. However, if you have just a few verticals, you can usually position the verticals with part of the top cut off in order to have the horizontals as high and wide on the screen as possible.

9. Practice with the microphone before the audience arrives. Have someone stand in the back of the room to advise you on the correct volume

level. Adjust the microphone for your height and practice so that you know the correct distance from "mouth to mike" for best sound.

Presentation

1. Check your appearance. As mentioned previously, the impression you give to an audience depends a great deal on your appearance, particularly before the talk begins. A professional should dress as a professional, which means that you should be neatly groomed and appropriately dressed. It is not what the audience thinks you are, it is what you convey to the audience of what you think of yourself. You should convey the impression that you are a professional and that you know you are. The too casual approach can turn an audience off.

If at all possible, try to take it easy, leave your office early and plan to get to the meeting site well ahead of time. If appropriate, freshen up and rest in a motel before the meeting in order to arrive more relaxed and less harried.

2. Give the introduction with the lights on before going to the slides. This is important as the audience can become acquainted with you, your gestures, and expressions before the lights go off. Provide a verbal transition to your slides as a clue to the persons you have appointed to operate the projector and the lights ("Now with some slides, I would like to show you . . ." or "May I have the projector, please . . ."). The correct sequence is for the projector to go on and then the lights off. This prevents having the audience in total darkness with the projector operator scrambling to find the switch.

Likewise, it is important to have a transitional sentence at the end as a clue to the light operator to turn the lights on and then the projector off ("That's my last slide, but I would like to discuss further . . ." or "May we have the lights . . ."). Also, it is advisable to have a meaningful closing, as described previously, after the slides, and with the lights on.

3. Change the slides yourself. Be sure to have an extension cord so that the control can be at the podium where you are. It is very awkward to give verbal or sound clues (stamping the floor, snapping your fingers, etc.) to the projector operator. However, it is advisable to have the projector operator do the fine focusing of the slides on the screen as you will be too close to the screen to know whether or not they are in sharp focus.

4. Meet your host and give him or her your biographic sketch. Whenever possible, have your host introduce you to others and talk with them before your talk if you are at a new place with a new audience. This is helpful when you get in front of the group and find that there are a few friendly faces in the audience. The audience will also appreciate the fact that you took time to talk with some of their group. One of the worst things that you can do is to arrive at a presentation, sit in a back corner, and not be involved with the group until you are introduced. Such actions convey the impression that you care little about them and are there just to do a job.

5. Maintain eye contact with the audience. Refer to your notes, then return to the audience. Try to look at everyone during each minute or two. This is hard for some, but practice will help. Eye contact is an important factor in personal presentation, as it makes the presentation personal. The audience wants to understand what you are telling them and not have something read to them. Only by talking to an audience can you reflect your interests, concern, and credibility.

Do not talk to the screen as this ruins projection of your voice for the people in the back of the room. Look at the screen, make sure you are talking about the right thing, and turn back to the audience to continue your presentation. One way to break talking to the screen is to point your feet toward the audience, not the screen.

6. When using a pointer, stand to the side of the screen and lightly touch the screen. This prevents confusion for the audience as to what you are pointing at. If you stand away from the screen, the audience can see the pointer plus the pointer shadow on the screen which may be indicating different things.

7. Avoid distracting mannerisms. You should have picked up on some of these during your rehearsals with the tape recorder. Such things and repetitious terms ("and uh . . . , and . . . , you know, this is a slide, this is a typical . . .") can be most distracting, especially when the audience starts counting them. Excessive or unnatural movements, hands in pockets, playing with keys or pointers, scratching, pacing, can also distract an audience from your message.

8. Maintain enthusiasm. If you come across with a "don't give a damn" attitude, the audience will respond in the same way. Monotones or very fast delivery can also turn them off. You need not be a Johnny Carson to be effective, but you should convey your interest and sincerity by a lively delivery. The audience will respond likewise. An increase in volume or an occasional pause to emphasize a point are often good techniques.

9. Watch the audience and be responsive to them. They will convey messages to you by gestures, expressions, comments, etc., and you will know when they do not understand a term or are not following your train of thought. If heads start nodding and some fall asleep, you know you have lost them.

The use of humor can release tension and provide a relief during a serious or technical program. However, the humor should be appropriate, low-key, and not distracting. There is no place for the unrelated, lengthy, or off-color joke.

10. Keep on schedule. Your rehearsal should have given you an idea of the length of your talk and you should stay within the allotted time schedule. This is especially important if you are one of a series of speakers with assigned time periods. Some speakers put their watches beside their outline on the podium to remind them of the time. Others have the host provide an inobtrusive signal, i.e., turn over a sheet of paper with "2 Minutes" written on it when you have that time left.

11. Instruct your projector operator to turn the projector completely off with the last slide. Most projectors give off a buzzing sound which is distracting to the audience. Also, there is little difference in the life of your bulb whether the fan is left on or off.

12. It is usually a good idea to have agreed beforehand that the host will direct the discussion session. The host should not let one or two persons dominate and should dismiss inappropriate or unrelated comments. This protects you and permits you to stay on the subject. Avoid arguing as some persons try to bait the speaker. Do not drag the discussion session on unnecessarily, and stop while the group is still attentive, not when they start drifting away.

Evaluation

Evaluation is necessary for self-improvement and to determine if you have achieved your purpose. Most of this can be informal. You should know if you got your message across to the audience by their attentiveness and overall reactions, comments, and questions.

It is also advisable to write a "memo to the files" on your presentation as soon as possible. Include the subject, purpose, date, place, audience analysis, reaction, performance by the host and other staff members, the quality of the visual aids, and suggestions for improvements. These will provide reminders when preparing for the next presentation and may be helpful to other staff members who will be contacting the same audience later.

You may also consider placing a small cassette recorder near the podium during your talk so that you can review it later and make comments on the memo, if necessary.

If you know someone in the audience who could objectively review your presentation, you might consider asking them to do so.

IN-HOUSE PRESENTATION TO SMALL GROUPS

A situation often faced by resource professionals is explaining their ideas to personnel of other disciplines or to high-level managers, administrators, and other decision makers. Unless these people can understand your views on impacts of various alternatives, value of a management practice, or the uniqueness of a special habitat, your input will have little meaningful value. Also, you must be effective as this may be the only chance you will have to make your case.

The basic principles discussed previously for general public audiences apply also for presentations of this type, but there are some modifications that should be considered. A good general rule is "the smaller the audience, the less formal the presentation." However, this does not mean that you should not be as prepared or organized. With small groups, (even a single person may be your "audience") you need to be more conversational, and you must provide opportunity for appropriate audience participation. This can be done with ample pauses which encourage comments, and with direct questions. These enable good two-way communications during a presentation and are effective for many situations.

Visual aids are as helpful for these situations as for larger audiences. However, color slides may not be appropriate, especially if you only have a 20-minute appointment with the district manager or with personnel who know the area and program well. In these situations, a neatly prepared series of overhead transparencies or pages on a portable flip chart may be suitable to support your presentation.

Whenever possible, try to give your presentation in a small room other than an office where you can arrange the seating for the expected group size and set up your visual aid equipment before the scheduled time. This is especially relevant if your audience is high-level management. Their offices are usually busy with telephones and other interruptions that greatly detract from your message.

VISUAL AIDS

Appropriate and properly-prepared visual aids can greatly increase the effectiveness of your presentation. As the term implies, these provide visual assistance for the audience in understanding your verbal message.

There are five types of visual aids:

1. **Actual objects** are the best and should be used when appropriate. When discussing big game foods, bring along some clippings of mountain mahogany, bitterbrush, aspen, etc.; when talking about sex and aging of wildlife, take along some deer jaws or grouse wings; or, show them the specialized equipment used in gaining information about your project, such as telemetry gear, ear tags, big game collars, immobilizing darts, and live traps.

2. **Models** can be used when the actual object is too large to bring or too small for the audience to see. A miniature deer trap that really works would be a good example.

3. **Static graphics** are maps, charts, and diagrams that may be shown to the group or hung on the wall. Unless these are specially prepared, they generally are not effective, as they are too complex or the printing is too small. Static graphics are generally good to have available for the audience to view after your presentation. They should not be displayed at the front of the room during the talk as they can be distracting.

4. **Active graphics** are graphics that progressively disclose items you are discussing. Examples are flip charts, hook and loop (velcro) boards, flannel boards, or a chalkboard. These can be effective in outlining major points for the audience or a sequence of events or elements of a program.

5. **Projected visuals** include slides, overheads, television, and movies.

Although you may use several types of visual aids in your presentation, the following rules should be followed in planning and preparing graphics for presenting facts and figures:

1. **Boldness.** The elements (numbers of words) must be seen by the audience to be understood. How many of you have heard a speaker say, "I know you can't see this, but..." or have strained your eyes trying to read visuals at a professional conference or staff meeting?

   For elements to be easily read by the audience, they must be 1-1/2 inches high for small rooms (up to 30 feet), 2 to 2-1/2 inches for medium rooms (up to 60 feet), and 3 inches or larger for distances up to 100 feet. It is important to be able to read the visual from the podium. Move to the back of the room and see if you can see it from there. However, if you see that the letters are only 1/2 inch high on the screen, you will know that most of the audience can never see them.

2. **Simplicity.** Because you want your audience to recognize the elements immediately, use simple block letters or numbers as script; fancy lettering delays recognition.

   Presentation of complex data is confusing. You can greatly facilitate understanding by rounding off, condensing, and abbreviating material. For example, on a visual the reader has difficulty comparing

ANNUAL DEER HARVEST IN MONTANA
1960–1980

| Beaver County | 5,260.79 |
| Mineral County | 2,596.89 |

but when shown as

MONTANA DEER HARVEST

| Beaver County | 5300 |
| Mineral County | 2600 |

the reader can immediately see that one is twice as large. Because you are explaining the graphic, you do not have to include everything on the visual as you would in a publication. The graphic should illustrate your main point.

Also, because you are generally trying to have your audience understand concepts (projections, trends, comparisons, etc.), there may be no need to present precise data. The use of decimal points is seldom necessary and often conveys an impression of precision that seldom exists in natural resources. I suggest rounding off to the nearest 10, 100, 1000, etc., as appropriate for fast comprehension. Also, avoid complex, cluttered graphics. It is better to have several graphics with a few items than to jam them all onto one.

3. **Color.** Use of color should be considered for several reasons. Correct use of color can attract attention and present a more pleasant visual. However, be aware of contrast as the elements must stand out from the background if they are to be easily read. Use dark colors against bright ones such as yellows, tans, golds, and light blues and greens.

Preparing Graphics

Overhead Transparencies. Overheads are suitable for many presentations. The advantages are that they can be used with the room lights on. The speaker can easily maintain eye contact with the audience as a transparency can be read correctly on the projector. Overheads are especially appropriate for smaller meetings (in-house management) where you may wish to encourage discussion during the presentation.

A disadvantage is that in most rooms the speaker blocks the view of the screen for some of the audience while at the projector. This can be avoided by moving to the side of the screen once the overhead has been positioned correctly. Items can be identified on the screen with a pointer.

Material for overheads can be easily made from black elements on a white sheet of standard sized paper (8 1/2 x 11 inches). The sheet is then run through the office copy machine using a transparent sheet instead of paper for the copy.

Standard type in office typewriters does not provide suitable size elements as the letters and numbers are too small to be seen when projected. However, the IBM "orator" type is large enough for making transparencies for use in a small room. When preparing overheads using the "orator" type, place two sheets of paper in the typewriter for better strike, use all caps, leave a space between each letter to prevent bleeding, and use triple spacing between lines.

The best transparencies are made from letters that are 3/16 inch high or larger. This produces the correct size image on the screen when projected. These can be made from dry transfer (press-on) letters, from a lettering machine (many offices now have them), from type prepared by a commercial print shop, or made with a hand-lettering stencil set. The best size type is 24-point (a printer's term for size), but 18- or 20-point is also acceptable.

Make a rough layout sketch of your overhead. Use this to position your printing on a white sheet of paper. I use a light table with a lined sheet under the white paper to keep spacing uniform and parallel. With prepared type, you can cut and paste the items as the edges will not show on the transparency when copied. You can add lines with a good inking or felt-tip pen. Color can be added to these black and white transparencies (underlining, etc.) with bright colored felt-tip pens.

Suitable graphs, charts, and diagrammatic maps can be made by using these colored felt-tip pens. Be sure the pens are made for transparencies or you will have a smeary mess. Rough out your artwork in pencil, then place a clear transparency over it and draw in with the colored pens.

Another method for diagrammatic maps and some charts is to do the lettering, numbers, and any lines (roads, streams, x/y axes of graphs, etc.) in black on a white sheet of paper and make the transparency on the copy machine. Then, add color to this transparency with the colored pens. Different habitat types can be cross-hatched in various colors, or several colored lines can be used on a line graph.

More sophisticated materials can be made with the help of an experienced graphic artist. The new generation computers have programs that can prepare high quality artwork on printers. However, remember to keep it simple and be sure the elements are large enough to be seen when projected.

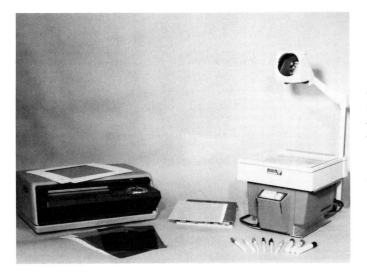

Equipment and materials used in making an overhead presentation. Left, a thermofax machine that transfers printed material onto transparencies. Center, transparencies that can be reproduced in a copying machine. Right, felt-tip markers for writing on acetate film, and an overhead projector.

35mm Slides. Color slides are appropriate visual aids for many presentations as much field work can easily be photographed with a 35 mm camera. Slides can be used to show contrasts, seasonal differences, relationships, or impacts; explain management practices and research techniques; and describe a species or management area. Because slides are so useful in public presentations, I consider the 35 mm single lens reflex camera an important part of every biologist's personal and professional equipment. High quality equipment is now reasonably priced, and I suggest you own your own and know how to use it.

it makes your presentation "first person," not an abstract "third person."

Effective slides showing changes from pioneer days can be made from old black and white photos usually available from the local historical society. Photograph them with color slide film.

Use only sharp, correctly exposed slides and keep them clean. Dust can be removed with a camel-hair brush or a blower. Smears should be removed with film cleaner.

As you plan a slide presentation, try to include variety whenever possible. A presentation on deer or sage grouse management when using only slides of deer or sage grouse and preferred habitats can be visually boring. I suggest including photos of other animals in the habitat: birds, small mammals, snakes, etc. A few good wildflowers are almost always well received when describing plants in the habitat in addition to the main food or cover items. Also, try for variety in lens angle. When describing a habitat, start with a wide angle scenic or panoramic, then go to a slide with a normal lens, move on to a smaller area, and maybe even closer to a plant community or a few key plants.

Include people in your photos when appropriate and yourself, if possible. You in a photo can improve your credibility and should be supported by verbal descriptions of your involvement. This is effective as

In addition to pictorial slides, suitable graphic slides can help clarify items in your presentation. You can prepare suitable artwork easily and photograph it to make good graphic slides. One method is to use an 8-1/2- x 11-inch or 9- x 12-inch sheet (this is about the proportion of the 35 mm slide) of colored paper as background for the artwork. I find light colored art paper in earth tones (golds, oranges, tans, and greens) to be good. Printing can be added by using 24-point (or 20) dry transfer letters and 1/8-inch matte press-on tapes in various colors for lines. These tapes are the right proportion in relation to the letters for lines or bars in graphs. The tape is also available as contour tape that can be used for making curved lines. The paper, letters, and tapes are available in graphic art or drafting supply stores.

Make a rough pencil layout of your design before starting on the colored paper. Use the edge of a thin sheet of white paper as a line for placing letters, not a penciled line. The pencil line, when erased, will photograph a smudged line. A piece of masking tape will lift off mistakes with the dry transfer letters when lightly touched to the letter. Keep all important material in at least 1-1/4 inches from each edge to permit easy camera adjustment when photographing the artwork.

Effective diagrammatic maps can be made by using different colors of paper to show various ownerships, habitat types, seasonal ranges, etc. These are usually better than showing a slide of a part of a complex topographical sheet. Pie charts are also effective graphics as they show comparisons much better than numbers on a chart.

A typewriter can be used for making acceptable slide graphics if the material is kept within a 3- x 5-inch space on a 4- x 6-inch area of a light colored sheet. You must come in close and photograph the 4- x 6-inch space when using typed letters in order for the printing to be large enough when projected. This is the reason you cannot photograph a page with a chart or table directly from a publication to make a slide. The elements will be too small. Take the material from the publication, simplify, condense, round off, and abbreviate to make a new graphic, as described above.

You can do your own photography of artwork to make your slides. A copy stand is handy, but you can use a tripod and shoot material held with masking tape to a wall or on a drawing board. Natural light works, but flash or flood lamps can be useful. Practice shooting at various exposures to get the best results. Unless you have a lot of graphics to shoot, it may be cheaper to have a commercial photographer shoot them for you.

CONCLUSION

This chapter is intended to help you with effective verbal presentations regardless of the audience, i.e., peers, administrators, advisory groups, or special interest publics.

A professional is one who knows his subject area, is experienced, and can communicate ideas well to other professionals and lay people. Unfortunately, training in communications receives minor emphasis in university preparation. This situation is being improved somewhat by in-service training in some states and by communications workshops offered annually by the Arizona Chapter and the Western Section of the Wildlife Society.

In addition to these possibilities, I suggest you consider joining the local Toastmasters Club. This group meets weekly for the sole purpose of improving members' communication skills. If there is not one near you, start a club in your locality. Contact Toastmasters Club International, P.O. Box 10400, Santa Ana, CA 92711.

The only way to become a good speaker is through practice behind the podium. Toastmasters provides such an opportunity. You might also consider attending speech classes offered at the local university, junior college, or through adult education programs. In addition to practicing, you will also receive objective critiques which can be most useful.

Good communication is essential in modern natural resource management. As professionals, your challenge is to obtain an understanding of complex wildlife/habitat interrelationships and communicate this understanding to people whose support you need for your management program. I hope you will accept this challenge.

APPENDIX I.

Checklist for slide show presentations.

A. Planning
1. Prepare statement of purpose.
2. Analyze audience—education, number, experience, etc.
3. Outline presentation.
4. List visual aids and related equipment needs.
5. Clear calendar of conflicts, confirm date.

B. Preparation
1. Prepare final outline.
2. Write biographic sketch for host.
3. Prepare appropriate graphics.
4. Check slides for relevance, quality, timeliness, dirt, etc.
5. Check out equipment:
   - projector (extra bulb)
   - projector stand
   - screen
   - extension cords—control, power
   - pointer
   - lens cleaning kit—brush, lens cleaner, tissue
6. Rehearse—check timing, order of slides. Use tape recorder.
7. Arrive early on day of presentation:
   - check facilities—heat, ventilation, seating
   - position projector and screen, tie down cords
   - focus and position first slide
   - adjust PA system and microphone
   - locate light switches
   - minimize distracting light

C. Presentation
1. Check appearance, grooming, etc.
2. Meet host—give biographic sketch, mix with group.
3. Appoint projector and light-switch assistants.
4. Give introduction with lights on.
5. Begin slides. (Transition: projector on, then lights off.)
6. Give meaningful closing with lights on. (Transition from slides: lights on, then projector off—no fan.)
7. Keep on schedule.
8. Have host handle discussion period.

D. Evaluation
Write memo to files—include information and slides needed, response, personnel performance.

APPENDIX II.

Suggested Readings.

Of the many publications on public speaking and visual aids, I suggest several that are excellent:

Making Effective Slides for Meetings; Fisher, H.L., Leaflet 21119, Cooperative Extension, U.S. Dep. Agric., University of California, Berkeley, CA 94720

The following are selections from many fine publications available from Eastman Kodak Company, 343 State Street, Rochester, NY 14650:

Presenting Yourself (S-60)
Effective Lecture Slides (S-22)
Legibility—Artwork to Screen (S-24)
Planning and Producing Slide Programs (S-30)
Slides with a Purpose (VI-15)

GLOSSARY

This glossary was prepared by using definitions provided by the authors or from the following dictionaries:

The Dictionary of the Biological Sciences. Peter Gray. Van Nostrand Reinhold Company. New York, NY. 1967 edition.
A Dictionary of Ecology, Evolution, and Systematics. R.J. Lincoln, G.A. Boxshall, and P.F. Clark. Cambridge University Press. London.
McGraw-Hill Dictionary of the Life Sciences. McGraw-Hill Book Company. New York, NY. 1974 edition.
The Random House College Dictionary, 1st ed. Random House, Inc. New York, NY. 1975 edition.
Resource Conservation Glossary, 3rd ed. Soil Conservation Society of America. Ankeny, IA. 1982 edition.
Webster's New Collegiate Dictionary. G&C Merriam Company. Springfield, MA. 1979 edition.
Webster's Third New International Dictionary (unabridged). G&C Merriam Company. Springfield, MA. 1966 edition.

ABIOTIC   devoid of life; non-living.

ABLATION   the removal of a surface layer, as of ice by melting or evaporation.

ABNEY LEVEL   a surveying clinometer consisting of a short telescope, bubble tube, and graduated vertical arc used especially for measuring tree heights.

ACCURACY   relates to the freedom from bias.

AGL (ABOVE GROUND LEVEL)   used to define heights that certain aerial censuses should be flown.

ALBEDO   a measure of surface reflectivity, that fraction of incident electromagnetic radiation that is reflected by a body or surface, usually expressed as a percentage.

ALKALI   a substance having marked basic properties in contrast to acid properties; a substance with a pH above 7.

ALKALINITY   the quality or state of being alkaline (having a pH balance above 7).

ALTRICIAL   helpless and naked when hatched, as young pigeons are (compare to precocial).

ARBOREAL   living in or adapted for living in trees.

AREAL   any particular extent of space or surface, as a geographical region.

ASYNCHRONY   lack of synchronism.

AUFEIS   German term for sheets of ice formed by the freezing of overflow water.

AUM (ANIMAL UNIT MONTH)   the quantity of forage required by one mature cow (1,000 lbs.) or the equivalent for one month.

AUTOECOLOGICAL   the study of the individual, or members of a species collectively, in relation to environmental conditions.

AUTOTROPH   an organism capable of synthesizing organic nutrients directly from simple inorganic substances such as carbon dioxide and inorganic nitrogen.

BENEFITS FOREGONE   the benefits that would have come from options not chosen when a choice between options has to be made.

BENTHIC   pertaining to or living on the bottom or at the greatest depths of a large body of water.

BEQUEST VALUE   the amount an individual would be willing to spend to ensure that a resource would be present in the future for future generations.

BIOGEOGRAPHY the biological study of the geographical distribution of plants and animals.

BIOMASS the total amount of living material, plants and/or animals, above and below the ground in a particular habitat or area.

BIOTIC pertaining to life or living organisms, caused or produced by or comprising living organisms.

BOGS a plant community that develops and grows in areas with permanently waterlogged peat substrates; also known as moor or quagmire.

BOREAL pertaining to cool or cold temperate regions of the northern hemisphere, the northern coniferous zone and taiga.

CARNIVOROUS flesh eating.

CHEMOCLINE the transition in a meromictic lake between the mixolimnion layer (at the top) and the monimolimnion layer (at the bottom).

CHIONOPHILES animals that thrive in snow-covered habitats.

CHIONOPHOBES animals intolerant of snow-covered habitats.

CIENEGAS an area where the water table is at or near the surface of the ground; standing water occurs in depressions in the area, and it is covered with grass or sometimes with heavy vegetation.

CLASSIFICATION the act or method of distributing portions of land and their attendant biotic/abiotic attributes into groups or divisions wherein each portion within a group has similar or identical characteristics; also, naming systematically.

CLINOMETER any of various instruments for measuring angles of elevation or inclination.

COAXIAL CABLE a transmission line that consists of a tube of electrically conducting material surrounding a central conductor held in place by insulators and that is used to transmit telegraph, telephone, and television signals of high frequency.

COLD-WATER FISH fish that can stand temperatures ranging from 33 degrees Fahrenheit to 70 degrees Fahrenheit.

COLINEARITY having corresponding parts arranged in the same linear order.

CONDUCTIVITY a measure of the ability of a material to conduct an electrical charge; the reciprocal of resistivity.

CONSPECIFIC of the same species.

COOL-WATER FISH fish that can stand temperatures ranging from 33 degrees Fahrenheit to 75 degrees Fahrenheit.

CORM an underground stem, such as that of the gladiolus, similar to a bulb but without scales.

CREPUSCULAR active in twilight, at dawn or dusk.

CRYOPEDOGENIC caused by or associated with permanently frozen ground or intensive frost action.

CURSORIAL adapted for running.

DEMAND CURVE a curve that shows the amount demanded at each price level.

DENDROGRAM a branching diagrammatic representation of the interrelations of a group of items sharing some common factors (as of natural groups connected by a common ancestral form).

DEPILATORY a liquid or cream used to remove unwanted hair from the body.

DETRITIVORES organisms that feed on fragmented particulate organic matter (detritus).

DETRITUS fragmented particulate organic matter derived from the decomposition of plant and animal remains, organic debris; accumulated in sand, water, or on mud or soil.

DIATOMS any of numerous microscopic, unicellular (single-celled), marine or freshwater algae having siliceous cell walls.

DIMICTIC used to describe a lake having two seasonal overturn periods of free circulation, with accompanying description of the thermocline.

DIURNAL pertaining to those organisms that are active during daytime.

DO (DISSOLVED OXYGEN) refers to the amount of dissolved oxygen in water.

DOMINANCE TYPE species, that by their activity, behavior, or number have considerable influence or control upon the conditions of existence of associated species; a species that controls its habitat and food web.

DRUMMING to make a succession of strokes or vibrations that produce sounds like drumbeats by beating the wings, like a male grouse.

DYSTROPHIC pertaining to an environment that does not supply adequate nutrition.

ECHOLOCATION the perception of objects using high frequency sound waves, used by some animals for navigation and orientation within the environment.

ECOLOGICAL SITES areas of land described by polygons on a map or photograph that have potential for producing similar potential vegetation, developed from the ecological site system of the U.S. Soil Conservation Service.

ECOTONE a transition line or strip of vegetation between two communities, having characteristics of both kinds of neighboring vegetation as well as characteristics of its own.

ECTOTHERMIC poikilothermic, having a body temperature determined primarily by the temperature of the environment; cold-blooded.

EDAPHIC of or pertaining to soil, especially as it affects living organisms.

EMERGENT PLANTS (aquatic) an aquatic plant having most of its vegetative parts above water.

EPHEMERAL (1) relating to a stream or a portion of a stream that flows only in direct response to precipitation and receives little or no water from springs or no long-continued supply from snow or other sources, and its channel is at all times above the water table; (2) lasting for only a day; short-lived or transient.

EPILIMNION a freshwater zone of relatively warm water in which mixing occurs as a result of wind action and connection currents.

ESTIVATE (a variant of **AESTIVATE**) to pass the summer, especially in a state of dormancy.

ESTUARINE of, relating to, or formed in an estuary (water passage) where the tide meets a river current.

EULITTORAL a subdivision of the benthic division of the littoral zone of the marine environment.

EURY- a prefix meaning wide.

EUTROPHIC rich in nutrients, characterized by abundant plankton and high turbidity.

EUTROPHIC LAKES lakes that are rich in nutrients and organic materials, therefore, highly productive for plant growth. These lakes are often shallow and seasonally deficient in oxygen in the hypolimnion.

EUTROPHICATION a means of aging of lakes whereby aquatic plants are abundant and waters are deficient in oxygen. The process is usually accelerated by enrichment of waters with surface runoff containing nitrogen and phosphorus.

EXISTENCE VALUE the amount of money an individual would be willing to spend to know a resource presently exists and would continue to exist.

FACULTATIVE contingent; assuming a particular role or model of life but not restricted to that condition. Used of organisms having the facility to live, or living, under atypical conditions.

FECUND capable of producing offspring; fertile, productive.

FELL-FIELD a type of tundra ecosystem having sparse, dwarfed vegetation and flat, very stony soil.

FENS a peaty, moist tract, usually derived from the aging or drainage of a swamp.

FISTULA an abnormal passage leading from an abscess or hollow organ to the body surface or from one hollow organ to another. Sometimes done surgically to enable scientists to examine stomach contents.

FLORISTICS the plant life of a given region, habitat, or geological stratum.

FOSSORIAL adapted for or used in burrowing or digging.

GALLINACEOUS belonging or pertaining to the Order Galliformes, comprising the grouse, pheasants, turkeys, partridges, domestic fowls, etc.

GEOMORPHIC of or pertaining to the figure of the earth or the forms of its surface. Of or like the earth, its shape or surface configuration.

GEOMORPHOLOGY a science that deals with the land and submarine relief features of the earth's surface and seeks a genetic interpretation of them.

GLEY a bluish-gray or olive-gray sticky layer of clay formed under the surface of certain waterlogged soils.

GREGARIOUS tending to aggregate actively into groups or clusters.

GUILD a group of species having similar ecological resource requirements and foraging strategies and therefore having similar roles in the community.

HARD WATER water containing dissolved salts of calcium and magnesium, especially water containing more than 85.5 parts per million of calcium carbonate.

HEP (HABITAT EVALUATION PROCEDURES) a planning and evaluation technique which focuses on the habitat requirements of fish and wildlife species. It is a standardized procedure for conducting habitat evaluations in the field developed and used by the U.S. Fish and Wildlife Service.

HERBIVORE an animal that feeds on plants.

HERBIVOROUS (HERBIVORY) feeding on plants; phytophagous.

HERPETOFAUNA animals that are either amphibians or reptiles.

HETEROGENEITY differing in kind; having unlike qualities, possessed of different characteristics.

HETEROTROPHIC obtaining nourishment from exogenous organic material. Used of organisms unable to synthesize organic compounds from inorganic substrates.

HETEROTROPHS an organism that obtains nourishment from the ingestion and breakdown of organic matter.

HETEROZYGOSITY having two different alleles at a given locus of a chromosome pair.

HIBERNACULA   the domicile in which an animal hibernates or overwinters; winter quarters.

HOLARCTIC   of or designating the zoogeographic region that includes the northern areas of the earth and is divided into Nearctic and Palearctic regions.

HOME RANGE   the area, usually around the domicile, over which an animal normally travels in search of food.

HOMEOTHERMIC   maintains a relatively constant and warm body temperature that is independent of environmental temperatures; warm-blooded.

HORIZON   a layer of soil or soil material approximately parallel to the land surface and differing from adjacent, genetically related layers in physical, chemical, and biological properties or characteristics.

HQI (HABITAT QUALITY INDEX)   this index relates habitat quality to fish biomass in streams. (Refer to Binns, N.A. 1979. A habitat quality index for Wyoming trout streams. Fishery Res. Rep. Monogr. Series 2. Wyoming Game and Fish Dep. Cheyenne. 75pp.)

HSI (HABITAT SUITABILITY INDEX) MODEL   a specific type of habitat model used by the U.S. Fish and Wildlife Service in its Habitat Evaluation Procedures (HEPs). A set of habitat variables are used to predict an index from 0 to 1 of habitat suitability for a species.

HYDRIC SOILS   soils that are characterized by or thriving in an abundance of moisture.

HYDROGEN IONS   the positively charged ion of hydrogen, H+, formed by removal of the electron from atomic hydrogen.

HYDROLOGIC   relating to the science dealing with the properties, distribution, and circulation of water on the surface of the land, in the soil and underlying rocks, and in the atmosphere.

HYDROMETEOROLOGY   the study of ensembles of liquid in the atmosphere—rain, drizzle, snow, sleet.

HYDROPERIODS   the control of vegetative processes in plants by periodic dryness; seasonal hydroperiodism.

HYDROPHYTE   (1) a plant that grows in a moist habitat; (2) a plant requiring large amounts of water for growth.

HYPOLIMNION   the cold bottom water zone below the thermocline in a lake.

INFRALITTORAL   the depth zone of a lake permanently covered with rooted or adnate macroscopic vegetation, often divided into upper (with emergent vegetation), middle (with floating vegetation), and lower zones (with submerged vegetation).

INTERFACE   the ability of computing devices or programs to communicate information from one system to another.

KROTOVINAS (also **CROTOVINAS**)   a former animal burrow in one soil horizon that has been filled with organic matter or material from another horizon.

LACUSTRINE   of, relating to, or growing in lakes.

LAMINAR FLOW   streamline flow in a viscous fluid near a solid boundary (compare to turbulent flow).

LANDSAT IMAGE   photographic images from satellites, observing earth resources. A satellite program that developed the Earth Resources Technology Satellite–1 (ERTS–1), which is now called LANDSAT 1.

LAVA TUBES   a tubular-like extrusion of lava.

LEK   an assembly area for communal courtship displays.

LENTIC   pertaining to static, calm, or slow-moving aquatic habitats.

LIMNETIC of, pertaining to, or inhabiting the pelagic region of a body of fresh water.

LIMNOLOGICAL relating to lakes, ponds, and other standing waters and their associated biota.

LINCOLN INDEX an estimate of population size obtained after release and recapture of marked animals; the estimated population size ($\hat{N}$) is calculated from the number of marked animals released (M), the number captured in a sample (n) after release, and the number of marked individuals in sample (m) using the formula:

$$\hat{N} = \frac{nM}{m}$$

This is also known as Lincoln/Peterson index or Peterson estimator.

LINEAR COMPREHENSIVE MANAGEMENT to measure all components of habitats and populations and know all limiting factors (have comprehensive, quantitative, and continuous knowledge of the system they manage).

LITTORAL of or pertaining to the biogeographic zone between the high- and low-water marks.

LOCI (plural of **LOCUS**) (1) the position that a gene occupies on a chromosome; (2) the set or configuration of all points satisfying specified geometric conditions.

LOTIC pertaining to fast-running water habitats, such as rivers and streams.

MACROINVERTEBRATES large or exceptionally prominent animals that lack a spinal column.

MACROPHYTES a large macroscopic plant, used especially of aquatic forms such as kelp.

MARGIN the change that would occur with the addition or subtraction of one unit.

MARINE pertaining to the sea.

MARSH a periodically wet or continually flooded area where the surface is not deeply submerged, covered dominantly with sedges, cattails, rushes, or other hydrophytic plants.

MAST the fruit of the oak and beech or other forest trees, used as food by hogs, birds, and other animals.

MEROMICTIC used of a lake that is permanently stratified due to the presence of a density gradient resulting from chemical stratification.

MESIC having a moderate rainfall.

MESOTROPHIC having intermediate levels of primary productivity, pertaining to waters having intermediate levels of the minerals required by green plants.

METALIMNION the zone of steep temperature gradient (thermocline) between the epilimnion and the hypolimnion in a lake.

MICROCOMPUTER a compact and inexpensive computer relatively limited in capability and capacity, consisting of a microprocessor and other components of a computer.

MICROHABITAT the smallest unit of a habitat, like in a clump of grass or a space between rocks.

MICROPROCESSOR a miniaturized integrated circuit that performs all of the functions of a central processing unit.

MOBBING a collective attack, by a group of animals, on a predator that is too large or aggressive to be repelled by individual effort.

MOLLUSCS any invertebrate of the Phylum Mollusca comprising the chitons, snails, bivalves, squids, octopuses, etc., typically having a calcareous shell of one, two, or more pieces that wholly or partly enclose the soft, unsegmented body.

MONOCULTURE raising crops of a single species year after year on the same land.

MONOMICTIC used of a lake having a single period of free circulation or overturn per year, with consequent disruption of the thermocline; may be either cold monomictic or warm monomictic.

MORAINIC of, pertaining to, forming, or formed by a moraine (an accumulation of earth and stones carried and finally deposited by a glacier).

MOSAIC an assemblage of overlapping aerial photographs whose edges have been matched to form a continuous photographic representation of an area.

NALED a short-lived insecticide of relatively low toxicity to warm-blooded animals that is used especially to control crop pests and mosquitos.

NEONATES newborn, recently hatched.

NEOTROPICS a zoogeographical region comprising South America, West Indies, and Central America, south of the Mexican border.

NONPERSISTENT an item that is not persistent, does not exist for a longer than usual time or continuously.

OBLIGATE essential, necessary, unable to exist in any other state, mode, or relationship.

OLIGOTROPHIC of a lake, lacking plant nutrients and usually containing plentiful amounts of dissolved oxygen without marked stratification.

OMNIVORE an animal that feeds on a mixed diet of plant and animal material.

OMNIVOROUS feeding on a mixed diet of plant and animal material; pantophagous.

OPTION VALUE the option demand is that demand from individuals who are not now consumers or are not now consuming as much as they anticipate consuming, and who therefore would be willing to pay to perpetuate the availability of the commodity. The option value is the amount an individual is willing to pay.

OXBOW a bend in a river that resembles the U-shaped frame forming a collar about an ox's neck and supporting the yoke.

PALUSTRINE living or thriving in a marshy environment; being or made up of marsh.

PELAGIC (1) pertaining to water of the open portion of a lake; (2) pertaining to water of the open portion of an ocean, above the abyssal zone and beyond the outer limits of the littoral zone.

PERCOLATION the downward movement of water through the soil.

PERIGLACIAL applies to an area bordering the edge of an ice-sheet, to the climate of that area, to physical processes involving freeze-thaw activity and to their results.

PERMAFROST permanently frozen subsoil.

PERMUTATIONS the act of altering a given set of objects in a group.

PERSISTENT refusing to give up or let go; lasting past maturity without falling off, like certain leaves or flowers.

PERTURBATIONS the state or condition of being perturbed; agitation.

PETERSON ESTIMATOR see Lincoln Index.

pH a numerical measure of acidity or hydrogen ion activity. Neutral is pH 7. All pH values below 7 are acid, and all above 7 are alkaline.

PHENOLOGICAL the relationship between climate and periodic biological phenomena such as bird migration or plant flowering.

PHENOLOGY the study of the temporal aspects of recurrent natural phenomena and their relationships to weather and climate.

PHREATOPHYTES a plant that absorbs water from the permanent water table.

PHYSIOGNOMY the characteristic features or appearance of a plant community.

PHYTOPLANKTON unattached microscopic plants of plankton, subject to movement by wave or current action.

PIEDMONT a district lying along or near the foot of a mountain range.

PINGO a low hill or mound forced up by hydrostatic pressure in an area underlain by permafrost.

PIONEERING an animal or plant species that establishes itself in a previously barren environment.

PIXEL derived from picture element; the smallest unit on the ground that can be detected by a multispectral scanner. For the LANDSAT MMS, the pixels are located on the ground on 57×79 meter centers.

PLANKTON suspended, floating, or weakly swimming microscopic plants and animals in the water that provide a basis for the aquatic food chain.

PLAYA the sandy, salty, or mud-caked flat floor of a desert basin having interior drainage, usually occupied by a shallow lake during or after prolonged, heavy rains.

POINT-CENTER QUADRAT a method of plotless sampling of vegetation in which lines are erected at right angles from the sampling point to produce four quarters in each, from which a measure is taken of the distance from the sampling point to the nearest neighbor.

PRECISION relates to the repeatability of a result.

PRECOCIAL of or characterizing birds that are covered with down and capable of moving about when first hatched.

PROFILE BOARD a scaled board that when photographed behind vegetation displays the physiognomy of a plant or group of plants. Sequential photographs can be used to display vegetation changes.

PROFUNDAL pertaining to the deep zone of a lake below the level of effective light penetration, and hence of vegetation.

QUADRATS a small plot or sample area, frequently 1 square meter or 1 milacre in size.

RAIN SHADOW an area of light rainfall situated on the lee side of a range of mountains or hills.

REDD the spawning ground or nest of various fishes.

REDOX POTENTIAL reduction potential; a measure of the tendency of a given system to act as an oxidizing (electron acceptor) or reducing (electron donor) agent.

RELEVES a random sample of vegetation.

RELICT a remnant or fragment of a flora that remains from a former period when it was more widely distributed.

RESPIRE CUTANEOUSLY to breathe in and out (inhale and exhale) through the skin.

REVETMENT a facing of masonry or the like, especially for protecting an embankment.

RIPARIAN HABITAT   relating to or living or located on the bank of a natural watercourse (like a river) or sometimes of a lake or a tidewater.

RIVERINE   pertaining to a river.

ROSETTES   any structure or marking resembling a rose.

ROTENONE   a white, crystalline, water-insoluble, poisonous heterocyclic compound obtained from derris root; used in certain insecticides.

ROTIFER   any of various minute, multicellular aquatic organisms of the Phylum Rotifera, having at the anterior end a wheel-like ring of cilia.

SALINITY   the concentration of dissolved solids or salt in water.

SALMONID   any of a Family Salmonidae of elongate soft-finned fishes that have the last vertebrae upturned.

SAPROPEL   used of organisms inhabiting mud, rich in decaying organic matter.

SAVANNA   the tropical and subtropical grassland biome, transitional in character between grassland or desert and rain forest, typically having drought-resistant vegetation dominated by grasses with scattered tall trees.

SCANNER   any of various electronic or optical devices by which images or recorded information are sensed for subsequent modification, integration, or transmission.

SERAL   pertaining to a succession of plant communities in a given habitat leading to a particular climax association; a stage in a community succession.

SERES   the entire sequence of ecological communities successfully occupying an area.

SERPENTINE PARENT MATERIAL   a soil parent material derived mainly from serpentine rock and dominated by serpentine minerals such as antigorite, chrysolite, fibrolite, and talc.

SOFT WATER   water containing little or no dissolved salts of calcium or magnesium, especially water containing less than 85.5 parts per million of calcium carbonate.

SOIL CONSISTENCE   the feel of the soil and ease with which a lump can be crushed by the fingers. Terms commonly used to describe soil consistence are loose, friable, firm, plastic, sticky, hard, soft, or cemented.

SOIL ERODIBILITY FACTOR (K)   a measure of the susceptibility of soil particles to detachment and transport by rainfall and runoff. The K factor is used in the Universal Soil Loss Equation.

SOIL STRUCTURE   the combination or arrangement of primary soil particles into secondary particles, units, or peds.

SPATIALLY   the pattern of distribution of organisms in space.

SPECIES RICHNESS   the absolute number of species in an assemblage or community.

SPECIFIC CONDUCTANCE   the quality of living matter responsible for the transmission of and progressive reaction to stimuli within the living system.

STATISTICAL TYPE II ERROR   when a true alternative hypothesis is rejected.

STENO-   a prefix meaning narrow.

STOCHASTIC   pertaining to randomness.

STRATA   (1) the divisions/groups into which homogeneous polygons that describe a mapped land area are placed so that all portions or polygons within a division appear to have similar or identical attributes; (2) divisions of a classification system.

STRATIFICATION to become layered, like layers of water temperature in a body of water.

STRIP TRANSECT a method of sampling that entails walking a predetermined line, counting the animals observed, and recording the distances at which they are seen or flushed. The average of the flushing distance is calculated and used to determine strip width.

SUBMERGENTS pertaining to a plant or plant structure growing entirely underwater.

SUBNIVEAN situated or occurring under the snow.

SUBSTRATE (1) (biology) the base of substance upon which an organism is growing; (2) (hydrology) the bottom material of a waterway.

SWAMPS areas saturated with water throughout much of the year but with the surface of the soil usually not deeply submerged.

SYMPATRIC used of populations, species, or taxa occurring together in the same geographical area. The populations may occupy the same habitat (biotic sympatry) or different habitats (neighboring sympatry) within the same geographical area.

SYNCHRONY a synchronous occurrence, movement, or arrangement (occurring at the same time).

SYNECOLOGICAL a subdivision of ecology that deals with the study of groups of organisms associated as a unit.

TAIGA northern coniferous forest biome. The ecosystem adjacent to the arctic tundra, but used with varying scope to include only the arctic timberline ecotone through to the entire subarctic north temperate forest.

TALUS fragments of rock and other soil material accumulated by gravity at the foot of cliffs or steep slopes.

TDS (TOTAL DISSOLVED SOLIDS) dissolved solids are anhydrous residues of the dissolved substances in water.

THERMOCLINE a horizontal temperature discontinuity layer in a lake in which the temperature falls by at least 1 degree Celsius per meter depth; thermal layer.

THERMOREGULATE a mechanism by which mammals and birds attempt to balance heat gain and heat loss in order to maintain a constant body temperature when exposed to variations in cooling power of the external medium.

THERMOREGULATION the maintenance or regulation of temperature; the maintenance of a particular temperature of the living body.

TRAMMEL NET a vertically set fishing net of three layers, consisting of a finely meshed net between two nets of coarse mesh.

TRANSDUCER a device that is activated by power from one system and supplies power in another form to a second system.

TURBIDITY (1) the cloudy condition caused by suspended solids in a liquid; (2) a measurement of the suspended solids in a liquid.

TYPING the act of delineating homogeneous areas of land and their attendant vegetation cover on aerial photographs or maps.

ULTRASONIC pertaining to acoustic frequencies above the range audible to the human ear, or above approximately 20,000 cycles per second.

UNGULATE an animal having hooves.

USLE (UNIVERSAL SOIL LOSS EQUATION) an equation used to design water erosion control systems: $A = RKLSPC$ wherein A is average annual soil loss in tons per acre per year; R is the rainfall factor; K is the soil erodibility factor; L is the length of slope; S is the percent slope; P is the conservation practice factor; and C is the cropping and management factor.

UTM (UNIVERSAL TRANSVERSE MERCATOR) a land data geographic referencing system that is based on a series of 60 zones worldwide, each covering 6 degrees of longitude in a north-south strip.

WARM-WATER FISH fish that can stand temperatures ranging from 33 degrees Fahrenheit to 80 degrees Fahrenheit.

WEG (WIND ERODIBILITY GROUP) a soil erodibility grouping for soils based on the stability of soil aggregates against breakdown by tillage and abrasion from wind erosion. The WEG is used in the wind erosion equation to estimate soil loss due to wind.

WEIR a small dam in a river or stream or a fence, as of brush, set in a stream, channel, etc. for catching fish.

YAGI ANTENNA a highly directional and selective shortwave antenna consisting of a horizontal conductor of one or two dipoles connected to the receiver and a set of nearly equal insulated dipoles parallel to and on a level with the horizontal conductor.

ZOOPLANKTON unattached microscopic animals of plankton having minimal capability for locomotion.

INDEX

450, 475, 482, 491, 538, 583, 584, 649, 655, 686, 691, 770, 797

Hand capture, 504

Hand tracking, 686

Handling techniques, 504, 505

Hegdal, Paul L., 679

Hiders, 527

Horizonation, 568

Horizontal diversity, 647-649

Horizontal vegetation structure, 138, 139, 268, 271

Hydrologic soil group, 575, 581

Hydrology of lakes, 623

Hypothesis formulation, 746, 747

Impacts on desert habitats, 142

Impoundments, 185, 191, 218, 223, 224, 239, 240, 251, 261, 372, 385

Indicator species, 22, 78, 79, 85-88, 288, 307, 311, 439, 665

Indirect effects, 124, 711, 712, 713

Indirect observation, 703

Inferential statistics, 66, 742, 745, 746

Instream flow needs, 227, 605

Integrated mapping, 64

International bird census, 300, 310

Interpretation, 1, 2, 5, 6, 21, 62, 65, 85, 99, 103, 107, 165, 222, 232, 274, 304, 313, 343, 344, 355, 494, 514, 554, 575, 585, 589, 601, 616, 623, 628, 662, 696, 707, 709, 727, 751, 753, 758, 777, 778, 782, 805, 811, 822

Jaccard's similarity coefficient, 21

Jackrabbits, 453, 454, 455, 465, 467, 468, 470, 471, 472, 473, 478, 479

Jones, K. Bruce, 1, 11, 123, 267

Jumping mice, 433

Kangaroo mice, 432

Kangaroo rats, 104, 136, 137, 432, 572, 582

Kerr, Richard M., 49

Key species approach, 523, 524

King strip census, 422

Kochert, Michael, 313

Laboratory analysis, 662, 665

LaBounty, James, 237

Landforms, 491, 588, 589, 590, 591, 592, 600, 601

Landsat imagery, 158, 160, 166

Landsat images, 62, 540

Late nesters, 380, 390, 391

Lava flows, 80, 592, 593, 594, 760

Lemmings, 432, 433, 451

Length of fish, 262, 264

Lent, Peter C., 149, 519

Lentic habitats, 134, 135

Levels of data needed, 1, 4, 11

Levels of inventory, 243

Life-form approach, 79, 772, 775

Life stages, 258, 261, 263, 360, 607

Life zones of a lake, 241

Lincoln estimator (see Lincoln index)

Lincoln index, 19, 306, 398, 436, 437, 444, 446, 448, 449, 450, 467, 490

Line transect, 24, 219, 302, 310, 326-328, 345, 356, 358, 366, 368, 444, 451, 473, 558

Linear correlation, 656, 717

Linear density transects, 362, 363

Linear regression, 657, 749, 750, 767

Literature searching, 29, 31, 33, 38

Litter, 22-24, 65, 80, 101, 115, 116, 130-132, 138, 141, 178, 182, 267-269, 271, 276, 283, 288, 441, 443, 470, 472, 478, 582, 584, 588, 594-596, 760, 761

Litter and mulch, 595, 596

Livestock grazing, 2, 4, 142, 143, 171, 173, 180, 185-190, 195, 197-199, 234, 426, 534, 595, 605, 662, 772

Logging and roads, 192

Logs, 22, 80-82, 118, 124, 131, 132, 135, 138, 182, 183, 187, 205, 231, 267-269, 274, 275, 276, 281, 432, 437, 440, 443, 484, 486, 503, 596, 597, 609, 761

Loomis, John, 785

Lotic water, 134

Macroinvertebrates, 46, 197, 202, 216-218, 221, 227, 229-231, 258, 607, 611, 661-663, 665, 669-671, 761

Mangum, Fred, 661

Man-made structures, 132, 140, 141, 326, 392, 417, 419, 433, 485, 500, 502, 514, 588, 596, 598-600

Mann-Whitney U-Test, 304, 750, 751

Manning equation, 622

Mapping variables, 578

Mark and recapture, 15, 19, 20, 264, 281, 306, 436, 437, 444, 446, 449, 463, 467, 530, 536, 559

Marked plot strip transect, 355, 362

Marking techniques, 285, 289, 507, 694

Marmots, 153, 432, 437, 587

Marsh succession, 215

Masked bobwhite, 99, 146, 411, 418, 426, 428

Matney, Iris, 727

Matrix models, 772

Maximum effort monitoring, 245

Maximum level inventory, 244

Mearn's quail, 410, 417, 418, 426

Measurement of evaporation, 615

Measurement of precipitation, 615

Measurement of snow, 615

Measures of central tendency, 743

Measures of dispersion, 743

Mergansers, 207, 221, 376-379

Minimum effort inventory, 243

Minimum effort monitoring, 245

Mining, 2, 7, 21, 143, 190, 234, 241, 309, 345-347, 580, 599, 611, 614, 633, 637, 638, 662

Mist-netting, 499, 504, 508, 512, 514

Mojave Desert, 28, 125, 127, 130, 275, 289, 471

Moles, 431, 440, 591, 636

Monitoring, 1, 2, 4-9, 11, 12, 14, 15, 17-19, 24-27, 29, 30, 32, 33, 49, 54, 61, 62, 67, 73, 74, 77-80, 84-91, 96-99, 123, 124, 131, 138, 141, 142, 144, 145, 152, 153, 158-161, 163, 164, 166, 201, 202, 217, 218, 222, 225, 231, 233, 237, 243, 245, 251-253, 257, 265, 266, 268, 275, 286, 288, 289, 291, 292, 295, 296, 304, 305, 306, 307, 311, 313, 314, 315, 328, 330, 331, 339, 342-344, 348, 351, 356, 363, 369, 371, 379, 387, 390, 391, 394, 395, 401, 402, 407, 430, 434, 436, 437, 438, 439, 442, 443, 444, 447, 448, 450, 453, 476, 491, 497, 508, 516, 517, 519, 534, 538, 543, 544, 548, 550, 551, 554, 559, 585, 595, 598, 600, 601, 610-613, 628, 632, 634, 637, 638, 639, 660-663, 674, 681, 695-697, 699, 707, 709, 710, 711-718, 721, 722, 724, 741, 742, 754, 756-759, 762, 765, 767-769, 775, 776, 777, 779, 782, 787, 805

Monitoring methods for lakes, 243, 252, 253

Monitoring studies, 1, 2, 4, 7, 9, 12, 19, 27, 29, 33, 54, 62, 73, 123, 124, 144, 145, 245, 265, 268, 387, 430, 442, 443, 450, 497, 699, 711, 754, 782

Mourning dove, 113, 411, 421, 423, 426, 427, 658, 659

Multivariate analysis, 28, 89, 90, 147, 311, 562, 741, 751, 754, 767

Muskrats, 204, 206, 207, 218-221, 223, 429, 431, 435, 436, 445, 446, 451, 452, 484, 576